⊙ Harden's

Best UK Restaurants

2023

ESTABLISHED 1991

INDEPENDENT AND UNBIASED REVIEWS OF 3,000 RESTAURANTS

'It will tell you what Diners actually like as opposed to mere Restaurant Critics'
Richard Vines, Restaurant Critic, Koffmann & Vines

Put us in your client's pocket!

Branded gift books and editions for iPhone

call to discuss the options on 020 7839 4763.

Follow Harden's on Instagram and Twitter @hardensbites

© **Harden's Limited 2022**

ISBN 978-1-9160761-5-0

British Library Cataloguing-in-Publication data: a catalogue record for this book is available from the British Library.

Printed in Britain by Short Run Press, Exeter

Assistant editors: Bruce Millar, Antonia Russell
Design: paulsmithdesign.com

Harden's Limited
MissionWorks, 41 Iffley Road, London W6 0PB

Would restaurateurs (and PRs) please address communications to 'Editorial' at the above address, or ideally by email to: editorial@hardens.com The contents of this book are believed correct at the time of printing. Nevertheless, the publisher can accept no responsibility for errors or changes in or omissions from the details given.

◎ Harden's 100

The UK's 100 Best Restaurants for 2023, as dictated by Harden's annual survey of diners

1	Andrew Fairlie, Auchterarder	26	Hambleton Hall, Hambleton
2	Evelyn's Table, London W1	27	The Forest Side, Grasmere
3	Waterside Inn, Bray	28	LPM, London W1
4	Endo at The Rotunda, London W12	29	Paul Ainsworth at No6, Padstow
5	The Kitchin, Edinburgh	30	Joro, Sheffield
6	Core by Clare Smyth, London W11	31	The Little Chartroom, Edinburgh
7	Adam Reid at The French, Manchester	32	SOLA, London W1
8	L'Enclume, Cartmel	33	The Art School, Liverpool
9	Maru, London W1	34	Anglo, London EC1
10	Pine, East Wallhouses	35	Morston Hall, Morston
11	Da Terra, London E2	36	A Wong, London SW1
12	The Five Fields, London SW3	37	Ynyshir Restaurant and Rooms, Eglwys Fach
13	Sorrel, Dorking	38	Meadowsweet, Holt
14	Restaurant Martin Wishart, Edinburgh	39	The Ledbury, London W11
15	Hjem, Wall	40	Nobu, London W1
16	Belmond Le Manoir aux Quat' Saisons, Great Milton	41	Roots, York
17	Adam's, Birmingham	42	Alchemilla, Nottingham
18	PLU, London NW8	43	House of Tides, Newcastle upon Tyne
19	The Araki, London W1	44	Outlaw's New Road, Port Isaac
20	Muse, London SW1	45	Aulis at L'Enclume, Cartmel
21	Lumière, Cheltenham	46	The Latymer, Bagshot
22	Estiatorio Milos, London SW1	47	Club Gascon, London EC1
23	The Little Fish Market, Brighton	48	ChefsTable at TRUEfoods, Melmerby
24	Lympstone Manor, Exmouth	49	Oxeye, London SW11
25	Kitchen Table, London W1	50	Cail Bruich, Glasgow

"AT GUSBOURNE WE EMBRACE TRADITION
BUT READILY CHALLENGE CONVENTION,
EVEN TO MAKE WHAT MIGHT SEEM LIKE
VERY SMALL DIFFERENCES TO THE
FINISHED WINE. ATTENTION TO DETAIL
IS OFTEN THE DIFFERENCE BETWEEN
GREAT AND EXCEPTIONAL."

CHARLIE HOLLAND
WINEMAKER

GUSBOURNE.COM

◎ Harden's 100

The UK's 100 Best Restaurants for 2023, as dictated by Harden's annual survey of diners

51	Roketsu, London W1
52	Cornerstone, London E9
53	Chez Bruce, London SW17
54	SY23, Aberystwyth
55	Trinity, London SW4
56	Aulis London, London W1
57	Robin Wylde, Lyme Regis
58	Bibendum, London SW3
59	The Clove Club, London EC1
60	Opheem, Birmingham
61	Bohemia, The Club Hotel & Spa, Jersey
62	Restaurant Twenty Two, Cambridge
63	Outlaw's Fish Kitchen, Port Isaac
64	The Angel, Hetton
65	The Black Swan, Oldstead
66	Frog by Adam Handling, London WC2
67	Umu, London W1
68	Unalome by Graeme Cheevers, Glasgow
69	Le Gavroche, London W1
70	The Sportsman, Seasalter
71	Pied à Terre, London W1
72	Ekstedt at The Yard, London SW1
73	Mana, Manchester
74	The Sea, The Sea, London E8
75	Midsummer House, Cambridge

76	The Peat Inn, Cupar
77	Moor Hall, Aughton
78	The Whitebrook, Whitebrook
79	Old Stamp House, Ambleside
80	The Moorcock Inn, Sowerby Bridge
81	Lyle's, London E1
82	Sollip, London SE1
83	Imperial Treasure, London SW1
84	Gidleigh Park, Chagford
85	Behind, London E8
86	Elderflower, Lymington
87	Wilson's, Bristol
88	BiBi, London W1
89	Amaya, London SW1
90	The Olive Tree, Bath
91	The Ritz, London W1
92	The Wilderness, Birmingham
93	Sketch, London W1
94	Quilon, London SW1
95	Kol, London W1
96	The Fat Duck, Bray
97	Myrtle, London SW10
98	The Small Holding, Goudhurst
99	The Cellar, Anstruther
100	Fraiche, Oxton

www.exmoorcaviar.com   info@exmoorcaviar.co.uk   tel.: 08454 349 587
563-565 Battersea Park Road London SW11 3 BL, U.K.

 @londonfinefoods   @londonfinefoods   @londonfinefoods

CONTENTS

Lyle's, London

Cambium, Brockenhurst

The Barbary, London

7

RATINGS & PRICES

Ratings

Our rating system does not tell you as most guides do that expensive restaurants are often better than cheap ones! What we do is compare each restaurant's performance as judged by the average ratings awarded by reporters in the survey with other similarly-priced restaurants. This approach has the advantage that it helps you find whatever your budget for any particular meal where you will get the best 'bang for your buck'.

The following qualities are assessed:

F	—	Food
S	—	Service
A	—	Ambience

The rating indicates that, **in comparison with other restaurants in the same price-bracket**, performance is…

5	—	Exceptional
4	—	Very good
3	—	Good
2	—	Average
1	—	Poor

Prices

The price shown for each restaurant is the cost for one (1) person of an average three-course dinner with half a bottle of house wine and coffee, any cover charge, service and VAT. Lunch is often cheaper. With BYO restaurants, we have assumed that two people share a £7 bottle of off-licence wine.

Small print

Telephone number – including area code.

Map reference – shown immediately after the telephone number.

Full postcodes – for non-group restaurants, the first entry in the 'small print' at the end of each listing, so you can set your sat-nav.

Website and Instagram – shown in the small print, where applicable.

Last orders time – listed after the website (if applicable); Sunday may be up to 90 minutes earlier.

Opening hours – unless otherwise stated, restaurants are open for lunch and dinner seven days a week.

Credit and debit cards – unless otherwise stated, Mastercard, Visa, Amex and Maestro are accepted.

Dress – where appropriate, the management's preferences concerning patrons' dress are given.

Sustainability – if a restaurant or group has a star rating from the Sustainable Restaurants Association, this is shown.

YOUR CONTRIBUTION

Celebrating our 32nd year!

This guide is based on our annual poll of what 'ordinary' diners-out think of London's restaurants. The first such survey was in 1991 with a few over 100 people taking part. This year, the total number of reporters in our combined London/UK survey, conducted mainly online, numbered 3,000, and, between them, they contributed 30,000 individual reports. Last year, some aspects of the guide needed amendment in order to allow for the effects of the Covid pandemic: for example, presenting two years of openings in a single edition. As far as possible this year, the format and content have been arranged on the same basis as all previous years, on the presumption and hope that where we are now is the longanticipated 'new normal'.

How intelligent is AI?

At a time when the credibility of online reviews and influencer posts are under ongoing scrutiny, there is an ever-greater need for trusted sources such as the Harden's annual national diners' poll. In particular, the active curation by humans that we provide. For – while obviously folks can attempt to stuff the Harden's ballot too – our high degree of editorial oversight, plus our historical data about both the restaurants and those commenting, makes it much harder to cheat. In this way Harden's can socially source restaurant feedback, but – vitally – curate it carefully. It is this careful curation that provides extra 'value-added' for diners.

How we determine the ratings

In general, ratings are arrived at statistically. We create a ranking akin to football leagues, with the most expensive restaurants in the top league and the cheaper ones in lower ones. Any restaurant's ranking within its own particular league determines its ratings.

How we write the reviews

The tone of each review and the ratings are guided by the ranking of the restaurant concerned, derived as described above. At the margin, we may also pay regard to the balance of positive votes (such as for 'favourite restaurant') against negative ones (such as for 'most overpriced'). To explain why an entry has been rated as it has, we extract snippets from user comments ("enclosed in double quotes"). On the most well-known restaurants, we receive over a hundred reports, and a short summary cannot do individual justice to all of them. What we seek to do – without any regard to our own personal opinions – is to illustrate key themes in the collective feedback.

How do we find our reporters?

Anyone can take part. Register now at www.hardens.com if you have not already done so! In fact, we find that once people have taken part, they often continue to do so.

Consequently, many people who complete the survey have done so before. With high repeat-participation, the endresult is really more the product of a very large and everevolving panel, or jury, than a random 'poll'.

Emerging from two years in which the pandemic kept them closed for long periods and caused untold disruption, restaurants barely had time to take a breath before they were hit by a whirlwind of price rises and staffing issues that threaten to be even more damaging.

Soaring energy costs, sky-rocketing food inflation, combined with a dearth of people ready, willing, or able to take up the tens of thousands of vacancies, has seen many restaurants reluctantly forced to reduce opening hours or mothball sites as well as rethink menus.

Just as they demonstrated incredible creativity, resilience, and innovation to keep serving us (when permitted) through Covid, our favourite places for eating out are, for the most part, putting those attributes to good use again. Even more hearteningly, many have spotted that we've really hit the perfect nexus between what's good for business and the planet.

How can diners spot those restaurants that are taking action to tackle climate change while simultaneously protect their profits?

With energy prices up as much as 400% and the UK experiencing record temperatures (another tangible reminder of the climate crisis), more restaurants are switching to induction hobs, providing a cleaner, more efficient cooking process as well as a cooler kitchen.

Shorter menus, featuring whole, local and seasonal ingredients, many with more veg-based dishes are becoming the norm, as chefs and restaurants look to reduce their food costs and minimise waste, while also taking account of smaller kitchen teams. The scarcity of vegetable oil, caused by the war in Ukraine means you're likely to notice some restaurants eschewing the deep frier – creating a third additional beneficiary – your health.

The real mark of a restaurant that's taking real steps to serve up meals designed to help you use the power of your appetite wisely is one boasting Food Made Good stars – awarded to those that complete the Sustainable Restaurant Association's Rating and that reach the requisite scores. From January 2022, the Green Claims Code has provided us all with a citizens' charter to challenge spurious sustainability claims. A valid rating from the SRA, is the best way for a restaurant to demonstrate that it's not just talking the sustainability talk.

Knowing what sustainable food really looks and tastes like doesn't come naturally to all. Throughout 2023, encouraged by the SRA, many restaurants will be highlighting their One Planet Plate – as part of the continuing campaign to point out the most sustainable dishes on the menu so you can vote with your fork for a better food future.

Look out for those restaurants serving a One Planet Plate, (www.oneplanetplate.org) and search in the guide for those with an SRA Food Made Good Sustainability Rating, either One, Two or Three Stars, achieved by proving they are taking action on these ten key things:

- Support Global Farmers
- Value Natural Resources
- Treat People Fairly
- Feed Children Well
- Celebrate Local
- Source Fish Responsibly
- Serve More Veg & Better Meat
- Reduce Reuse Recycle
- Waste no Food
- Support the Community

www.foodmadegood.org
Twitter: @the_SRA
Instagram: @foodmadegood

www.oneplanetplate.org
@oneplanetplateglobal

Barrafina, London

SURVEY MOST MENTIONED

RANKED BY THE NUMBER OF REPORTERS' VOTES

These are the restaurants which were most frequently mentioned by reporters. (Last year's position is given in brackets.)

1 J Sheekey (4)	22 The Cinnamon Club (10)
2 Scott's (2)	23 La Poule au Pot (27)
3 Chez Bruce (3)	24 Medlar (20)
4 The Wolseley (6)	25 Trinity (33)
5 Core by Clare Smyth (1)	26 Gordon Ramsay (29)
6 Clos Maggiore (17)	27 Murano (36)
7 The River Café (7)	28 Pied à Terre (21)
8= The Delaunay (31)	29 Hélène Darroze,
8= Brasserie Zédel (9)	The Connaught Hotel (39)
10 Le Gavroche (5)	30 Sams Riverside (14)
11 Noble Rot (11)	31= Gauthier Soho (12)
12= A Wong (12)	31= Wiltons (-)
12= Andrew Edmunds (26)	31= Elystan Street (24)
14 Gymkhana (16)	34= Sabor (-)
15 Bocca di Lupo (18)	34= Lorne (-)
16 La Trompette (8)	36 Kiln (-)
17 The Five Fields (19)	37= Galvin La Chapelle (23)
18 The Ivy (28)	37= Mere (32)
19 Bentley's (22)	39= St John Smithfield (-)
20= The Ritz (25)	39= Parsons (-)
20= Noble Rot Soho (-)	

J Sheekey

SURVEY NOMINATIONS

Top gastronomic experience

1   Core by Clare Smyth (1)
2   Chez Bruce (3)
3   The Five Fields (5)
4   Le Gavroche (2)
5   Frog by Adam Handling (-)
6   La Trompette (4)
7   The Ritz (-)
8   The Ledbury (-)
9   The Anglesea Arms (-)
10   Medlar (-)

Favourite

1   Chez Bruce (1)
2   The Wolseley (4)
3   The River Café (6)
4   Core by Clare Smyth (3)
5   Le Gavroche (-)
6   Frog by Adam Handling (-)
7   The Delaunay (-)
8   La Trompette (2)
9   Pied à Terre (-)
10   Sams Riverside (-)

Best for romance

1   Clos Maggiore (1)
2   La Poule au Pot (2)
3   Andrew Edmunds (3)
4   The Ritz (9)
5   Sessions Arts Club (-)
6   Chez Bruce (10)
7   Core by Clare Smyth (-)
8   Scott's (-)
9   Le Gavroche (4)
10   The Five Fields (6)

Best bar/pub food

1   Harwood Arms (1)
2   Canton Arms (4)
3   The Anchor & Hope (2)
4   The Anglesea Arms (10)
5   The Wigmore, The Langham (-)
6   The Red Lion & Sun (7)
7   Bull & Last (3)
8   The Eagle (5)
9   The Camberwell Arms (-)
10   The Cadogan Arms (-)

Best for business

1   The Wolseley (1)
2   The Delaunay (3)
3   Hawksmoor (2)
4   Coq d'Argent (9)
5   Scott's (6)
6   The Ivy (-)
7   Wiltons (-)
8   Cabotte (-)
9   Goodman (-)
10   The Dining Room, The Goring Hotel (8)

Best breakfast/ brunch

1   The Wolseley (1)
2   Dishoom (2)
3   Côte (3)
4   The Delaunay (4)
5   Granger & Co (5)
6   The Ivy Cafés, Grills & Brasseries (9)
7   Caravan (7)
8   Megan's (6)
9   Fischer's (-)
10   The Breakfast Club (8)

Most disappointing cooking

1   Oxo Tower (Restaurant) (1)
2   The Ivy (-)
3   Gordon Ramsay (2)
4   Holborn Dining Room (-)
5   Rick Stein (8)
6   German Gymnasium (-)
7   Scott's (-)
8   Hélène Darroze, The Connaught Hotel (5)
9   Gauthier Soho (-)
10   Murano (-)

Most overpriced restaurant

1   The River Café (1)
2   Sexy Fish (2)
3   Hélène Darroze, The Connaught Hotel (9)
4   Oxo Tower (Restaurant) (6)
5   Gordon Ramsay (5)
6   Hakkasan (-)
7   Nusr-Et Steakhouse (-)
8   Hawksmoor (-)
9   Sushisamba (-)
10   Scott's (-)

SURVEY HIGHEST RATINGS

FOOD	SERVICE	AMBIENCE	OVERALL

£130+

FOOD	SERVICE	AMBIENCE	OVERALL
1 Evelyn's Table	1 Endo at The Rotunda	1 Pied à Terre	1 Endo at The Rotunda
2 Endo at The Rotunda	2 Core by Clare Smyth	2 Endo at The Rotunda	2 Core by Clare Smyth
3 Core by Clare Smyth	3 Pied à Terre	3 The Ledbury	3 Pied à Terre
4 Maru	4 The Ledbury	4 Da Terra	4 Da Terra
5 Estiatorio Milos	5 The Five Fields	5 Core by Clare Smyth	5 The Ledbury

£100–£129

FOOD	SERVICE	AMBIENCE	OVERALL
1 SOLA	1 LPM	1 The Ritz	1 The Ritz
2 LPM	2 Ekstedt at The Yard	2 Petersham Nurseries	2 LPM
3 A Wong	3 The Ritz	3 The Chiltern Firehouse	3 Ekstedt at The Yard
4 Nobu, Como Met'	4 Chez Bruce	4 Zuma	4 Chez Bruce
5 Dinings	5 Hide Ground	5 Ekstedt at The Yard	5 Kol

£75–£99

FOOD	SERVICE	AMBIENCE	OVERALL
1 Cornerstone	1 Sale e Pepe	1 Rules	1 Sale e Pepe
2 Benares	2 Noizé	2 Sale e Pepe	2 Benares
3 Lyle's	3 Charlie's at Brown's	3 Sams Riverside	3 Charlie's at Brown's
4 Amaya	4 Margot	4 Cambio de Tercio	4 Cornerstone
5 Myrtle	5 Villa Di Geggiano	5 Clos Maggiore	5 Sams Riverside

£55–£74

FOOD	SERVICE	AMBIENCE	OVERALL
1 Jin Kichi	1 Behind	1 Circolo Popolare	1 The Sea, The Sea
2 Behind	2 The Sea, The Sea	2 Sessions Arts Club	2 Behind
3 Sabor	3 Hereford Road	3 La Poule au Pot	3 Sabor
4 The Sea, The Sea	4 Babur	4 The Sea, The Sea	4 The Anglesea Arms
5 Babur	5 Bombay Palace	5 Oslo Court	5 Sessions Arts Club

£54 or less

FOOD	SERVICE	AMBIENCE	OVERALL
1 Dastaan	1 The Wet Fish Café	1 Mercato Metropolitano	1 Supawan
2 Kiln	2 Sumi	2 Ciao Bella	2 Black Dog Beer House
3 Supawan	3 Black Dog Beer House	3 Bar Italia	3 Ciao Bella
4 Farang	4 Yard Sale Pizza	4 Brasserie Zédel	4 Potli
5 Lahore Kebab House	5 Paradise Hampstead	5 Smokestak	5 Kiln

SURVEY BEST BY CUISINE

These are the restaurants which received the best average food ratings (excluding establishments with a small or notably local following).

Where the most common types of cuisine are concerned, we present the results in two price-brackets. For less common cuisines, we list the top three, regardless of price.

British, Modern

£75 and over		Under £75	
1	Evelyn's Table	1	Behind
2	Core by Clare Smyth	2	The Plimsoll
3	The Five Fields	3	The Camberwell Arms
4	Da Terra	4	The Anglesea Arms
5	Kitchen Table	5	The Jones Family

French

£75 and over		Under £75	
1	LPM	1	Les 2 Garcons
2	Pied à Terre	2	Casse-Croute
3	Club Gascon	3	Le Vacherin
4	Bibendum	4	Oslo Court
5	Sollip	5	Blanchette

Italian/Mediterranean

£75 and over		Under £75	
1	Theo Randall	1	Manteca
2	Luca	2	Popolo
3	Caractère	3	Vasco & Piero's
4	Murano	4	Bocca di Lupo
5	Norma	5	Anima e Cuore

Indian & Pakistani

£75 and over		Under £75	
1	Amaya	1	Grand Trunk Road
2	BiBi	2	Dastaan
3	Gymkhana	3	Babur
4	Tamarind	4	Trishna
5	Kahani	5	Lahore Kebab House

Chinese

£75 and over		Under £75	
1	A Wong	1	Barshu
2	Imperial Treasure	2	Silk Road
3	Min Jiang	3	Mandarin Kitchen
4	Hunan	4	Four Seasons
5	Yauatcha	5	Singapore Garden

Japanese

£75 and over		Under £75	
1	Endo at Rotunda	1	Jin Kichi
2	Maru	2	Sushi Atelier
3	Nobu, Metropolitan Hotel	3	Tsunami
4	Dinings	4	Chisou
5	Umu	5	Sticks'n'Sushi

British, Traditional

1	The Ritz
2	Quality Chop House
3	The Game Bird

Vegetarian

1	The Gate
2	Mallow
3	Farmacy

Burgers, etc

1	The Plimsoll
2	Bleecker Burger
3	MEATLiquor

Pizza

1	50 Kalò di Ciro Salvo
2	Yard Sale Pizza
3	Homeslice

Fish & Chips

1	Olympus Fish
2	Toff's
3	Nautilus

Thai

1	Kiln
2	Supawan
3	Farang

Steaks & Grills

1	Quality Chop House
2	City Social
3	Lurra

Fish & Seafood

1	Estiatorio Milos
2	Cornerstone
3	Behind

Fusion

1	Da Terra
2	Sollip
3	Tsunami

Spanish

1	Sabor
2	Cambio de Tercio
3	Barrafina

Manteca, London

Evelyn's Table, London

Sabor, London

THE RESTAURANT SCENE

Muted post-Covid bounce-back

For the London restaurant scene, there has been no 'twang back' to high growth, post pandemic. Instead the outlook has been tame – but not disastrous – with net growth towards the bottom of the range considered normal since 2000.

There are 136 newcomers this year: the lowest level of openings since the 2012 edition (launched in calendar 2011). This figure is boosted by nine (9) restaurants that re-opened, having been marked as 'Temporarily Closed'. It falls right at the bottom of the range of 134-200 noted in all but two of the last twenty years.

Closures stand at 85. This is not a high level and suggests that the challenge faced by the restaurant scene is not yet (for all the awful headlines) a lack of custom.

Net growth (Openings minus Closures) was 51: an indifferent level by the yardstick of the last 31 years. It was well out of the range of the 100+ new openings recorded in 2014-2018, which now feels like a golden era.

Brexit is particularly hitting hospitality

Immediately post-pandemic, restaurateurs and their backers seemed to be betting that the 'new normal' would look fairly like the old one. That view is currently being revised down to the low end of that historic norm.

The Covid-induced shift to WFH looks ever-less like a brief passing phase. Lower office occupancy explains why more licensed premises in the City of London have closed than anywhere else in the country, with the number of such locations down by 14% since 2020.

Another headwind, of course, is the war in Ukraine and rising costs. That's certainly contributed to rising menu prices (see below), but the extent to which it's already causing folks to cut back on eating out is harder to discern.

And then, of course, there's the ongoing recruitment crisis in hospitality and Brexit's effects. Supporters of the vote's outcome are apt to point to staff shortages in hospitality across Europe (in France, for example). They explain the ongoing dire inability to recruit in London restaurants as a broader Covid-related labour market shift that's disadvantaged hospitality in all countries.

But, as recent Oxford University research shows, UK hospitality is notably hard-hit by Brexit, because Europeans have historically made up such a big chunk of its workforce.

When this guide began, before 1993's Maastricht Treaty, restaurateurs often bemoaned their inability to expand due to poor supply of good staff. Now this limitation is back with a vengeance. The consequences so far do not include better employment conditions for anyone, but do look set to add up to a less lively restaurant scene.

On the rise: the Middle East

After Modern British (26) openings, Italian cuisine was this year's favourite (with 18 debuts), beating Japanese cuisine, which was last year's runner up, into third place (with 9 openings). This year's most promising rising star cuisines were Middle Eastern (accounting for 8 openings).

In terms of location, Central London was unusually dominant, accounting for 57 arrivals. In the 'burbs, East London led the way (with 25 openings) just beating South London (with 23). West London registered a poor year (16), only just exceeding North London's rate of opening (15).

Dorothy… did you remember your wallet?

Was it just a dream? It seems like only a few ticks since a dinner costing over £100 per head was a talking point. Now, for anything that might pass as 'haute cuisine', a mere 'ton' per head seems suspiciously cheap. The situation all feels a little bewildering. How did we get here?

A perusal of the Harden's archive shows that it was the post-Brexit, 2017 edition (published in autumn 2016) in which we first introduced a £100+ top price band at the front of the book. At that time, there were 37 such entries, of which just one had a formula price over £150 per head.

Fast forward five years, and £100+ is – in this edition – for the first time the delimiter merely of our second highest price category. Our highest band is now set at £130+.

Now, there are 154 entries in the guide above the £100 level. And in a neat symmetry with the figures above, there are 37 restaurants with a formula price over £150 per head.

In fact there are 17 entries now over £200 per head and six above £250! It feels like everything is speeding up.

That's because it is! But London's ever-more pricey restaurant scene is not just a factor of price inflation as caused by staff shortages and rising food costs. It is also driven by the arrival in recent years of a higher proportion of openings focused at the very top end.

Restaurant price inflation

The average price of dinner for one at establishments listed in this guide is £69.28 (c.f. £64.14 last year). Prices have risen by an annualised rate of 8.1% in the past year. Having led inflation in recent times, this rate was slightly below CPI growth of 10.1% for the 12 months to July 2022. However, given how quickly prices are rising, this disparity is most probably just a reflection of the time lag between our research effort and publication. The rise is most marked amongst pricey restaurants (over £100 per head). In this group, the annualised growth is again higher than for restaurants generally, at 11.7% (up from 8.8%).

The Palomar, London

OPENINGS AND CLOSURES

The listings below relate to the period from Autumn 2021 to Autumn 2022. Most restaurants marked as "Temporarily closed" last year went on to close permanently. Where they have reopened, this is listed below as a (re) Opening. Only branches of small groups in the listings below contribute to the grand total figures.

† marked last year as temporarily closed.   * temporarily closed as we to go to press.

Openings (136)

Acme Fire Cult
Akub
Alex Dilling Café Royal
L'Amorosa †
Andina Spitalfields *(E1)*
Apricity
Aragawa
Ar tisans of Sardinia
Attimi
The Audley
The Aubrey
Le Bab *(SW9, SW11)*
Balady *(EC1)*
Bacchanalia
The Barbar y Next Door
Belvedere
Björn Frantzén at Harrods
Black Bear Burger *(EC1, E14)*
The Black Lamb
Boiler & Co
Bone Daddies *(SW15)*
Bossa
Bottle & Rye
La Brasseria *(W11)*
Bubala Soho *(W1)*
Bund †
Caia
The Campaner
Cantinetta Antinori
Caravan *(E14)*
Caravel
Cedric Grolet, The Berkeley
Cher Thai
Chick 'n' Sours *(E8)* †
Chotto Matte *(W1)*
Chucs *(NW8)*
Cicchetti Knightsbridge *(SW3)*
Cycene
Dai Chi
Danclair's
Dear Grace

Les 2 Garcons
Dipna Anand
Dragon Castle †
Ela & Dhani
Elis
Emilia's Crafted Pasta *(E14)*
Facing Heaven
Fatto Pizza & Beer KX *(N1)*
Firebird
Flat Iron, The Cut *(SE1)*
Forza Win
400 Rabbits *(SE17)*
Galvin Bar & Grill
Gazette *(SW17, EC4)*
Giulia
Goddard & Gibbs
Gopal's of Soho †
Granger & Co *(W1)*
Gunpowder Soho *(W1)*
Gura Gura
Hawksmoor *(E14)*
Haz *(WC2)*
Hithe & Seek
Holy Carrot
Isibani
Itaku
The Ivy in the Park *(E14)*
Jeru
Joia
The Jones Family Affair
Kanada-Ya *(W1)*
Kasa & Kin
Kerridge's Fish & Chips
Kilig
Ko ya Ko *(E8)*
Koyn
The Libertine
Lina Stores *(W1, EC4)*
Lino's
Lisboeta
Long Chim
The Lore of the Land †

M Restaurant *(E14)*
Maddox Tavern
Magenta
Manna †
Maria G's
Marugame Udon *(W1, SE10, E14)*
Masalchi
The Meat & Wine Co
Mayfair
MEATliquor *(WC1, SW4)*
Mildreds *(WC2)*
Miro Mayfair
Miscusi *(WC2, N1)*
Miznon London
Nessa
Noci
El Norte
Off the Hook
Other Naughty Piglet †
Ottolenghi *(SW1)*
Parrillan *(SE1)*
Pastan
Patty and Bun *(W11, W12, SW11)*
Le Petit Beefbar
The Pig's Head
Plaza Khao Gaeng
Popeyes
Porte Noire
Postbox
The Princess Royal
RAI
Rambutan
The Residency
Restaurant 1890
Restaurant St Barts
Revolve
Richoux *(W1)*
Riding House *(WC1)*
Riviera
Rock & Rose *(W4)*
Roji
Roti King *(SW8)*

The Rushmere
Sagar *(SW1)*
Salt Yard *(W12, SE1)*
Saltie Girl
Santa Maria *(N1)*
Sarap Filipino Bistro
The Seafood Bar
Shoryu Ramen *(W8)*
Sichuan Fry
Simpsons in the Strand †
Socca
Soffice London
Sparrow Italia
Speedboat Bar
St Martin's House
Stem & Glory
Straker's
Street Burger *(EC1)*
SUDU
The Tamil Prince
Tapas Brindisa *(SW11)*
Taqueria *(EC1)*
Taro *(SW1, N3, E17)*
temper Shoreditch
The Tent
Three Uncles *(SW9)*
Tofu Vegan *(NW11)*
28-50 Oxford Circus *(W1)*
Vinoteca Borough *(SE1)*
Yard Sale Pizza *(SE4)*
Zephyr
Zia Lucia *(N16)*

Closures (85)

Acre
Adams Café
Albertine
L'Artigiano
Bando Belly
Baozi Inn *(WC2)*
Bertie Blossoms
The Betterment
Boisdale of Bishopsgate
Bone Daddies *(W8)*
Boxcar Bar & Kitchen
Burger & Lobster *(EC1)*
Casacosta
Casita Andina *(W1)*
Ceviche Old St *(EC1)*
Chick 'n' Sours *(E1, W1)*
Chicken Shop & Dirty
  Burger *(SW19)*
The Clock N8
Colette *(SW10, SW19)*
Comptoir Gascon
Il Convivio
Corner Room
Darjeeling Express
Davies and Brook
Dip & Flip *(SW11, SW19)*
Dirty Burger *(SW8, E1)*
Dynamo *(SW17)*
Epic Pies
Firebrand *(EC1R)*
Flat Three
Flor
Gallipoli *(N1)*
The Gate *(NW8)*
The Good Plot
The Greenhouse
Hankies *(SW1, W2)*
Haz *(EC3)*
Hot May Pot Pot
Hot Stone *(W1)*
Kazan *(Café) (SW1)*
Kiraku
The Laughing Heart
Liv
M Bar & Grill
  Twickenham
Madame Pigg

Malabar
Malabar Junction
Mama's Jerk
Mãos
Michael Nadra *(W4)*
Molly's Café
Momo
Morso *(NW10)*
Nordic Bakery *(W1)*
The Oak SW11 *(SW11)*
On The Bab *(EC1)*
Ottolenghi *(EC1)*
Party Store Pizza *(SW4)*
Pastaio *(W12)*
Patri Ealing *(W5)*
Patty and Bun *(W11,
  EC3, E2)*
Peg
The Phoenix
Pino
Pizza Pilgrims *(W1)*
RAW *(W1)*
Relais de Venise *(W1)*
Roux at the Landau*
Sake No Hana
Salon Brixton
Shampers
Shoryu Ramen *(WC1)*
Showaken
Sidechick
Sri Suwoon
St Clair
Stockwell Continental
Sushi Tetsu
Sushiology by
  Atari-Ya *(W1)*
Talad
Taro *(EC4)*
Terroirs *(SE22)*
Tomahawk Steakhouse
Turul Project
28-50 *(WC2)*
Vinoteca *(W1)*
The White Onion
Wright Brothers *(EC2)*
Yming

The Petersham, London

Angelina, London

A CENA TW1 £60 333

418 RICHMOND ROAD
020 8288 0108   1–4A

A "wonderful, smart, family-run Italian with imaginative cooking" ("not pizza and pasta!") that's an "ideal neighbourhood restaurant" for those living near St Margaret's – "we've eaten here every three weeks since moving to the area almost a year ago, and there's a constantly changing menu with high-quality presentation and service". Top Tip – "the set-price lunch/early evening dinner is particularly good value". / TW1 2EB; www.acena.co.uk; @acenarestaurant; Tue-Sat 10 pm, Sun 2 pm; closed Tue-Thu L closed Sun D, closed Mon; booking max 6 may apply.

A WONG SW1 £112 553

70 WILTON RD   020 7828 8931   2–4B

"A next-level culinary adventure" – Andrew Wong's "unique interpretation" of his native cuisine "makes you rethink everything you thought you knew about Chinese cooking" and has elevated this relatively humble-looking establishment, near Victoria station, to a place of foodie pilgrimage. Run for decades by his parents (when it was called Kym's), the premises have been transformed over the last 10 years by their LSE-graduate son, to become Michelin's highest-rated Chinese restaurant outside China; and, "put very simply, there is no better Chinese restaurant in London". (A move to a new site has been mooted over the years, with no final announcement as yet). The "exquisite" dishes display an "unexpected degree of artistry" – in particular "the Five Movements tasting menu is absolutely incredible": "ruinously expensive but bizarrely feeling like exceptional value". ("The grated foie gras with pork and wind-dried sausage was a full-on work of genius; as was the crab claw with tomato and wasabi, which truly looked nothing like the description, but was so moreish it's untrue"). Somewhat more affordably, "the innovative Dim Sum is simply outstanding… if you can get in" ("the second star makes it even harder for long-time fans to book"). "And prices are up, up and away... but still it's worth it for such astonishing food". / SW1V 1DE; www.awong.co.uk; @awongSW1; Tue-Sat 10.30 pm; closed Sun & Mon; credit card required to book.

THE ABINGDON W8 £67 333

54 ABINGDON RD   020 7937 3339   6–2A

"A cut above the normal pub" – with its "stylish mix of bar area and secluded, more intimate booths", this smart venue on a Kensington backstreet has entertained well-heeled locals with a menu of elevated gastropub fare for a quarter of a century. / W8 6AP; www.theabingdon.co.uk; @theabingdon; Mon-Sat 10 pm, Sun 9 pm.

ACME FIRE CULT E8 £41

THE BOOTYARD, ABBOT STREET   NO TEL   14–1A

Vegetables are centre-stage at Andrew Clarke and Daniel Watkins's vibey Dalston BBQ, which – with its mostly outdoor set-up in a former car park, live-fire cooking, impressively bearded chef, and extensive microbrewery beer selection (40FT Brewery's Steve Ryan is a partner) – reads like a checklist of East London clichés. It opened in April 2022 too late to generate feedback in our annual diners' poll, but all the newspaper press critics are impressed, with The Evening Standard's Jimi Famurewa declaring: "It has the spirit, soul and craft of a serious restaurant, coupled with a vibrant, veg-heavy menu that feels like pyromaniacal Ottolenghi." / E8 3DP; www.acmefirecult.com/acme-at-40ft-brewery; @acmefirecult; Wed-Sat 9.30 pm, Sun 4 pm; closed Wed L closed Sun D, closed Mon & Tue.

ADDIE'S THAI CAFÉ SW5 £40 322

121 EARL'S COURT RD   020 7259 2620   6–2A

This "deservedly busy" Thai canteen has been an Earl's Court staple since the late 1990s, serving a cheap and tasty menu which is "all good, from the prawn crackers to som tum". / SW5 9RL; www.addiesthai.co.uk; @addiesthai.co.uk; Mon-Sun 10 pm; closed Mon & Tue, Sun L; no Amex.

AFGHAN KITCHEN N1 £33 322

35 ISLINGTON GRN   020 7359 8019   9–3D

This enduring little café on Islington Green has thrived for three decades on its "amazing" cheap curries (if certainly not its basic interior). / N1 8DU; @afghankitchenldn; Tue-Sat 11 pm; closed Sun & Mon; cash only; no booking.

AGLIO E OLIO SW10 £49 322

194 FULHAM RD   020 7351 0070   6–3B

This "family-run bustling Italian with a loyal clientele" near Chelsea & Westminster hospital is "the locals' favourite – I could eat here once a week". The food (especially the pasta) is "well above average" ("bring a hearty appetite as portions are generous") and prices "reasonable", but it does get "very hectic" to the point of being "too noisy in the evenings". / SW10 9PN; www.aglioeolio.co.uk; Mon-Sun 11 pm.

AKIRA AT JAPAN HOUSE W8 £86 332

101-111 KENSINGTON HIGH STREET
020 3971 4646   6–1A

"A revelation!" – the "pricey-but-good" first-floor restaurant (or better still "the private tatami mat dining room") at Kensington's Japan House cultural centre serves "food close to what you eat in Japan" alongside an extensive sake menu, and "everything is beautifully presented". "Quite apart from the food, the entire experience in the building and the Japanese welcome make a visit worthwhile". / W8 5SA; www.japanhouselondon.uk; @japanhouseldn; Tue-Sat 11 pm; closed Sun & Mon.

AKOKO W1 £147 444

21 BERNERS STREET
020 7323 0593   5–1A

"An incredibly special dining experience, like nowhere else in London" – Aji Akokomi has achieved something "totally unique, supremely atmospheric and slick" at his Fitzrovian homage to West Africa. The warm bronzed interior is all urban sophistication, but channels an earthy African energy with its impeccably chosen (and, for the most part, specially commissioned) décor and tableware. The open kitchen was on our visit predominantly staffed by Europeans and Asians, but they deliver "an exquisite and well thought-out" extended tasting menu, mixing Nigerian, Ghanaian and Senegalese culinary influences, and with an "on-point wine pairing" option. Head chef, Theo Clench (who won it a Michelin star) moved on in March 2022 just prior to our annual diners' poll – no public appointment of a successor has been made as yet. / W1W 3LJ; akoko.co.uk; @akokorestaurant; Tue-Sat 11 pm; closed Tue-Fri L, closed Sun & Mon.

AKUB W8

27 UXBRIDGE STREET   NO TEL   7–2B

Fadi Kattan crowd-funded nearly £1m to open this Palestinian newcomer in Notting Hill which – originally slated to debut in 2021 – is set to open in the second half of 2022. He opened his first restaurant (Fawda) in Bethlehem in 2016. Here, the focus will be specialities from that city as well as Jerusalem, Jericho, Gaza and Nablus, and the website promises 'hot bright salads of the Gaza coastline, deep stews from the rolling hills of Ramallah and foraged akub will feature alongside the locally sourced British ingredients'. / W8 7TQ;

AL DUCA SW1 £63 322

4-5 DUKE OF YORK ST
020 7839 3090 3–3D

This "conveniently placed old favourite", on
a St James's corner, serves "above-average
Italian" including "particularly good fish
cooking", backed up by an "intriguing wine list
with some unusual choices". Nobody would
accuse it of much in the way of pizzazz, but
even those who say it's "middle of the road and
time for a revamp" still rate it well all-round.
/ SW1Y 6LA; www.alduca-restaurant.co.uk;
@al_duca; Mon-Sat 11 pm; closed Sun.

AL MARE, JUMEIRAH CARLTON TOWER HOTEL SW1 £98 333

CADOGAN PL   020 7858 7250   6–1D

"I was very sad to see the Rib Room go…"
– this luxurious new Italian is a sequel to the
age-old traditional British venture that sat (in a
slightly different position) within the hotel for
60 years. And like its predecessor, it is certainly
"expensive". But while one or two reports write
it off as being "disappointing all-round", the
majority are more upbeat. It is a "beautiful
and well spaced room" with views of the
leafy square, and most diners feel that Marco
Calenzo's cooking, which puts an emphasis
on seafood, is "thankfully very good" or even
"exceptional". Top Tip – interesting option
of a 45-minute business lunch. / SW1 9PY;
www.jumeirah.com/en/stay/london/
the-carlton-tower; @jumeirahgroup; Mon & Tue
10.30 pm, Wed-Sat 10 pm, Sun 3.30 pm; closed
Sun D.

ALAIN DUCASSE AT THE DORCHESTER W1 £224 232

53 PARK LANE   020 7629 8866   3–3A

"It was a lovely meal, no doubt… but it was
nothing particularly memorable… far from
mind-blowing… certainly not worth 3 Michelin
stars… really quite overpriced": this has too
often been the story of this Mayfair dining
room, fêted from its 2010 debut by Michelin on
the strength of carrying the name of arguably
France's most famous chef. To be fair, this
luxurious chamber does also have its fans, for
whom executive chef Jean-Philippe Blondet's
menu is "simply the pinnacle of modern French
cooking" (with a wine list to match); and "a real
treat, from the moment you are greeted at the
entrance to the last second as you leave". But
this year, as every year, it is concerning just how
many reports say "it's just not up there with
the best…"; "…nice but very unremarkable".
/ W1K 1QA; www.alainducasse-dorchester.com;
@alainducasseatthedorchester; closed Mon-Sat &
Sun; Jacket required.

ALEX DILLING CAFÉ ROYAL W1

CAFÉ ROYAL, 68 REGENT STREET
020 7406 3333   4–2C

Since it closed its iconic Café Royal Grill
Room, this super-swanky five star by Piccadilly
Circus has lacked a flagship restaurant. …
till now, that is, when – in early September
2022 – they open this new 34-cover dining
room, overseen by the eponymous former chef
of Mayfair's now-defunct Greenhouse. The
website promises a 'modern take on traditional
French gastronomic cuisine' in a room
'overlooking the curvature of Regent Street'. /
W1W 4DY; www.hotelcaferoyal.com/alexdilling;
@hotelcaferoyal; Fri & Sat 8 pm, Sun 4 pm.

ALEXANDRIE W8 £74 333

38C KENSINGTON CHURCH STREET
020 7937 2244   6–1A

This "impressive Kensington gem" serves
"traditional Egyptian dishes with a sophisticated
French influence" – "hopefully it will find
more fans post-pandemic". Top Menu Tip
– "mehalabya (Egyptian milk pudding) is a
delicious way to end the meal". / W8 4BX;
@alexandrie_kensington; Wed-Sat 10 pm, Sun 9.30
pm; closed Wed-Fri L, closed Mon & Tue.

THE ALFRED TENNYSON PUB BELGRAVIA SW1 £75 223

10 MOTCOMB STREET
020 7730 6074   6–1D

This smartly kitted-out pub with a "nice
outdoor terrace" on a cobbled Belgravia street
has a "short, simple and well-executed menu",
providing "Sunday roast and fish 'n' chips of
quality". / SW1X 8LA; thealfredtennyson.co.uk;
@cubitthouse; Mon-Sat 10 pm, Sun 9.30 pm.

ALI BABA NW1 £32 322

32 IVOR PL   020 7723 5805   2–1A

"A family Egyptian with unique character" –
this unchanging venture (est 1970) occupies
a room behind a takeaway, near the top of
Baker Street. The affordable dishes are highly
authentic, as is the no-frills vibe. Unlicensed
so BYO. / NW1 6DA; alibabarestaurant.co.uk;
@alibabarestaurantlondon; Mon-Sun 10 pm; cash
only; booking online only.

ALLEGRA E20 £63 333

THE STRATFORD, 20-22 INTERNATIONAL
WAY   020 3973 0545   14–1D

With a chef (Patrick Powell) from the Chiltern
Firehouse and an interior by the design team
behind Copenhagen's Noma, this seventh-
floor venue near Westfield Stratford is a
"lovely slice of West End-type glamour in
East London". "Great food and wine, nice
outdoor terrace" complete a uniformly positive
picture. / E20 1GQ; www.allegra-restaurant.com;
@allegrarestaurant; Wed-Sat 10 pm; closed Wed &
Thu L, closed Mon & Tue & Sun.

Acme Fire Cult E8

THE ALMA SE19 £67 334

95 CHURCH ROAD   020 8768 1885   1–4D

"A step above normal pub grub": chef David
Yorkiston's kitchen produces a high standard
of cooking at this carefully modernised mid-
Victorian pub on Crystal Palace's hip 'Triangle'
– a "lovely building" with large windows, oodles
of outdoor space, and a lively atmosphere. "It's
a shame children under 10 can't go or we'd be
there all the time!" / SE19 2TA; thealmapub.com;
@TheAlmaCP; closed Mon-Sat & Sun; payment –
credit card only; booking online only.

ALOO TAMA SW1 £26 443

18 GREENCOAT PLACE
020 7834 9873   2–4C

"This cosy little restaurant behind Victoria
station serves tasty home-style Nepalese
cuisine". It's "well hidden, and surely
dependent on word of mouth" – which makes
it all the more impressive that it's "mostly full".
"So book to avoid disappointment" – they're
"welcoming and keen to help diners explore
the non-standard menu choices". They also
have a lunchtime food truck at the Merchant
Square market in Paddington. / SW1S 1PG;
www.alootama.com; @alootamaofficial; Tue-Sat 10
pm, Sun 9 pm; closed Tue-Sun L, closed Mon.

ALTER E1 £34 432

15 LEMAN STREET   NO TEL   10–2D

"An 'alter' I'm happy to worship at!" – Andy
Goodwin brings an innovative approach
to plant-based cuisine at this modern hotel
dining room, near Aldgate East. To the odd
sceptic, it's too "exhausting and suitable only
for hardcore vegans" ("lack of any protein
leaves sauces too soupy, and lots of pickles
leads to vinegary flavours"), but for fans (the
majority) it's "just incredible… tastes I've never
experienced before… beautifully presented…
a perfect balance of fresh vegetables served
with creativity, flair and passion!" / E1 8EN;
www.alterldn.com; @alter_ldn; Tue-Sat 10 pm;
closed Tue, Sat L, closed Sun & Mon.

AMAYA SW1 £89 [5][3][4]

HALKIN ARCADE, 19 MOTCOMB ST
020 7823 1166   6–1D

"Exploding any lingering prejudices about Indian food" – this "innovative and beautiful" operation (created in 2004 by Ranjit Mathrani, Namita Panjabi and Camellia Panjabi, who own Chutney Mary et al) "remains a favourite premium destination" for "Indian cuisine at its finest, with a great open kitchen". "It is pricey, but the food is exceptional, while service is fast and friendly". / SW1X 8JT; www.amaya.biz; @amaya.ldn; Tue-Sat 10.30 pm, Sun 10 pm; closed Mon.

AMAZONICO W1 £95 [3][3][4]

10 BERKELEY SQUARE
020 7404 5000   3–3B

"It's the full experience – live music, vibe, décor, cocktails, food – that makes for a magical evening", according to fans of this forested Brazilian-Japanese fusion haunt, in the heart of swanky Mayfair. On the downside, prices for its sushi and luxurious grills are "absurd", but even those finding the venue "faintly ridiculous and definitely pretentious" say "the décor is worth the price of admission and I couldn't help enjoying the ride!" / W1W 6EF; amazonicorestaurant.com/london; @amazonicolondon; Mon-Sat 1 am, Sun midnight.

THE AMERICAN BAR SW1 £75 [2][3][5]

THE STAFFORD, 16-18 SAINT JAMES'S PLACE   3–4C

"A quick lunchtime drink can turn into several hours of cocktails and delightful bites" at this St James's institution: "a bar full of Americana and with staff who put on a great show of mixology". The Med-inspired brasserie menu is arguably "limited" but suits the venue, which is a "very buzzy" and "efficiently run" space. / SW1S 1NJ; thestaffordlondon.com/the-american-bar; @americanbarlon; Sun-Wed midnight, Thu-Sat 1 am; booking lunch only.

AMETHYST W1 £193

6 SACKVILLE STREET
020 3034 3464   3–3D

Carlo Scotto, formerly of short-lived but excellent Xier (RIP), is the chef at this highly ambitious and heavily trailed Mayfair newcomer, which opened in May 2022 (too late for survey feedback) about nine months later than originally announced. It occupies a dramatic two-floor site near Green Park tube, where the main action surrounds a striking, zig-zag chef's table on the ground floor seating 20 around an amethyst and quartz centrepiece, in view of the open kitchen. The 12-course tasting menu (£150) incorporates Nordic, Japanese, French and Arabic influences and one early fan was The Times's Giles Coren, who – awarding it 27/30 – noted the meal's "delicacy and dedication to detail", with every dish "belaboured intensively at the pass by Mr Scotto". In the 'Wine Cellar' basement seating 16, there's also the option of a six-course

menu. / W1W 3DD; www.amethystdining.com; @amethystdining; Tue-Sat 11 pm.

L'AMOROSA W6 £63 [4][4][4]

278 KING ST   020 8563 0300   8–2B

Ex-Zafferano head chef, Andy Needham's "fab and friendly neighbourhood Italian" near Ravenscourt Park station reopened in spring 2022 after a catalogue of disasters (pandemic, floods, dodgy construction upstairs...) – much to the relief of its many fans. There's "always well-prepared food and a warm reception". Top Menu Tips – "lovely risottos and the ragu". / W6 0SP; www.lamorosa.co.uk; @#lamorosa; Thu-Sat 9.30 pm; closed Thu-Sat L, closed Mon-Wed & Sun.

AMPÉLI W1 £119 [3][4][3]

18 CHARLOTTE STREET
020 3355 5370   2–1C

Influenced by the modern wine-focused restaurants of Athens – photographer Jenny Pagnoni's Fitzrovia two-year-old specialises in Greek and Eastern Mediterranean dishes (many seared in the Josper oven). Feedback remains limited but is upbeat: "delicious food, marvellous service and a beautiful venue". / W1W 2LZ; www.ampeli.london; @ampeli.london; Tue-Sat 10 pm; closed Sun & Mon; payment – credit card only.

AMRUTHA SW18 £31 [4][5][2]

326 GARRATT LANE   020 8001 4628   11–2B

"Carefully prepared Indian-style vegan dishes" and "wonderfully friendly service" are behind the popularity of old school friends Arvin Suntaramoophy & Shyam Kotecha's Earlsfield crowd-pleaser. And the "as-much-as-you-can-eat ethos" and BYOB policy means it is "incredibly well-priced". Top Tip – if you're really hard up, they'll feed you in return for a couple of hours' work. / SW18 4EJ; www.amrutha.co.uk; @amruthauk; Tue-Sat 10 pm, Sun 9 pm; closed Tue-Fri L, closed Mon.

THE ANCHOR & HOPE SE1 £67 [3][3][3]

36 THE CUT   020 7928 9898   10–4A

"Still serving hearty gastropub food in a chilled-out way" – this "long-time favourite" near the Old Vic remains one of London's top foodie boozers thanks to its "ever-changing menu" of "innovative dishes with a nod to nose-to-tail dining". Its performance has been less consistent in recent years, though ("some options matched the reputation for robust, powerful flavours, but others in my party reported basic errors that we wouldn't expect at these prices"). / SE1 8LP; www.anchorandhopepub.co.uk; @anchorhopecut; Wed-Sat 9 pm, Sun 3.30 pm; closed Wed-Fri L closed Sun D, closed Mon & Tue; no Amex; no booking.

ANDANZA SE1 £51 [4][3][3]

66 WESTON STREET
020 7967 1972   10–4C

"Spectacular if slightly cramped tapas restaurant" that occupies a former bookies' in Bermondsey. "Staff are keen to talk about the menu and any of the dishes are brilliant". / SE1 3QJ; www.andanza.co.uk; @andanza.se1; Mon-Sun 11 pm; booking online only.

ANDINA SPITALFIELDS E1 £48 [2][1][3]

60-62 COMMERCIAL STREET
020 3141 6000   13–2C

Nowadays just in Spitalfields (with Soho, Shoreditch and Notting Hill branches opening and closing over the years), this Peruvian-inspired haunt received mixed reviews this year, linked with one or two incidents of "awful" service. Feedback on its Latino fare, which majors in ceviches and salads (but which is also accompanied by a selection of larger and mostly meaty 'classic dishes') is more consistent, though, and fans say it's "still a cracking place, even after relocating". / E1; www.cevichefamily.com/andina; @andinalondon; Mon & Tue, Sun 9.30 pm, Wed-Sat 10.30 pm.

ANDREW EDMUNDS W1 £69 [3][4][5]

46 LEXINGTON STREET
020 7437 5708   4–2C

"The kind of place to bring your lover" – this "perfect", "sweet" townhouse is an "old-favourite", whose "cosy, panelled and candle-lit" setting is perennially nominated as one of London's most romantic. Despite its "Dickensian" charm, it has an "idiosyncratic", even "groovy" vibe, inspired by its long-term independent owner, whose shop dealing in antiquarian prints is next door (and pre-dates the restaurant, which opened in 1985, by about a decade). From a slightly "limited" menu, the "robust and honest" cuisine "isn't going to win any innovation awards, but is very well-executed" and well-priced; and it moves with the times. The real attraction is the superb wines at non-greedy prices" selected by Edmunds ("not as broad a list as Noble Rot but much more affordable"), which helps fuel its "decadent and sexy" appeal. Service can be "hard pressed" but is "so friendly". Top Tip – the basement has its plus points, but the best seats are on the ground floor. / W1W 0LP; www.andrewedmunds.com; @andrew.edmunds; Mon-Sun 10.30 pm; no Amex; booking max 10 may apply.

ANGELINA E8 £61 [4][2][3]

56 DALSTON LANE   020 7241 1851   14–1A

Italian and Japanese cuisines are combined on multi-course 'kaiseki' (10-course) and 'omakase' (4-course) menus to intriguing effect at this ambitious haunt in Dalston. Its highly rated again by reporters this year, despite a couple of experiences where service went awry ("we received the same dish twice, which we did not refuse as it was enjoyable!") / E8 3AH; angelina.

london; @angelina.dalston; Mon-Fri 10 pm, Sat 10.30 pm, Sun 3.30 pm; closed Mon-Fri L closed Sun D; no shorts.

ANGIE'S LITTLE FOOD SHOP
W4   £48   2 4 2
114 CHISWICK HIGH ROAD
020 8994 3931   8–2A

This "rather sweet little café" in Chiswick from transplanted South African Angie Steele provides "very friendly and quick service for a light menu" of healthy-ish treats from breakfast to 5pm. / W4 1PU; www.angies.co.uk; @angieslondon; Tue-Fri 5 pm, Sat 10.30 pm; closed Tue-Fri D, closed Sun & Mon.

ANGLER, SOUTH PLACE
HOTEL EC2   £111   3 3 4
3 SOUTH PL   020 3215 1260   13–2A

"Perfectly executed fish" from a "varied and delicate" menu adds to the elevation of this 7th-floor D&D London perch, at the top of a hotel near Broadgate, where the "nice verandah" comes into its own in the summer months. Cooking of this quality is rare in the City, and even non expense-accounters will seek it out. This year's most critical report? – "probably worth its Michelin star, but pricey and the chef didn't take any gambles". / EC2M 2AF; www.anglerrestaurant.com; @angler_restaurant; Tue-Sat 9.15 pm; closed Sun & Mon; may need 8+ to book.

THE ANGLESEA ARMS
W6   £61   4 4 4
35 WINGATE RD   020 8749 1291   8–1B

"One of London's truly great gastropubs" – this characterful boozer occupies an attractive backstreet near Ravenscourt Park and has "friendly staff and a nice buzz". "The menu changes a lot but is always delicious", delivering "reliable unpretentious food at honest prices" that's of "more-than-pub quality", plus "a good selection of wines". / W6 0UR; www.angleseaarmspub.co.uk; @theangleseaarmsw6; Mon-Sat 11 pm, Sun 10.30 pm; closed Mon-Fri L; payment – credit card only; no booking.

ANGLO EC1   £101   5 4 2
30 ST CROSS STREET
020 7430 1503   10–1A

"A tiny spot with just over 20 covers and food to die for" – the focus is very much on the "very clever cooking at an affordable price point" at this "personal" Farringdon address, run by head chef Anthony Raffo and manager Marie Danzanvilliers. The food is "super-seasonal" ("sometimes foraged within a stone's throw of the restaurant"), "traditional techniques are revived with pickles and ferments" and the resulting dishes have "exceptional flavour combinations and contrasts". / EC1N 8UH; www.anglorestaurant.com; @anglorestaurant; Tue-Sat 8.30 pm; closed Tue-Thu L, closed Sun & Mon; booking max 6 may apply.

ANIMA E CUORE
NW1   £62   4 2 2
129 KENTISH TOWN RD
07590 427171   9–2B

"Behind an unprepossessing facade, on an equally unprepossessing part of not-quite-Camden, not-quite-Kentish Town, lie gastronomic delights from Italy" conjured up in a tiny kitchen by Moroccan-Italian Mustapha Mouflih, a chef who "combines high-quality ingredients with imagination". "Even if the ambience is somewhat chaotic and basic, at best, the cooking is wonderful" ("the ravioli, malfatti, tortellini and so on are of a freshness and stuffed with flavours you would otherwise have to get on a plane to find"). / NW1 8PB; www.animaecuore.co.uk; Tue-Sat 11 pm, Sun & Mon 8 pm.

ANJANAAS NW6   £33   3 2 2
57-59 WILLESDEN LANE
020 7624 1713   1–1B

The "delicious southern Indian dishes" at this Kilburn Keralan have "a fine subtlety in their flavours". "It has the feel of an unpretentious family-run business, where their hearts are in the cooking and service". / NW6 7RL; www.anjanaas.com; Mon, Wed & Thu 10.30 pm, Fri & Sat 11 pm, Sun 10 pm; closed Tue.

ANNIE'S W4   £60   3 3 4
162 THAMES RD   020 8994 9080   1–3A

A "great neighbourhood restaurant and brunch spot" – this cosy all-day operation in pretty Strand on the Green was the first from West London restaurateur Lorraine Angliss and has catered for 20 years to a local clientele looking for "reliable cooking" rather than gastronomic fireworks. (A branch in Barnes shut up shop a couple of years ago, blaming the closure of Hammersmith Bridge for reduced trade). / W4 3QS; www.anniesrestaurant.co.uk; @anniesrestaurant; Tue-Sat 10 pm, Sun 9 pm; closed Tue-Fri L, closed Mon.

THE ANTHOLOGIST
EC2   £53   2 2 3
58 GRESHAM ST   0845 468 0101   10–2C

A handy location, near the Guildhall, "buzzy" large interior and versatile menu of "decent (if unspectacular) food" mean it's worth remembering this "reliable option in the City", although it "can be incredibly busy". / EC2V 7BB; www.theanthologistbar.co.uk; @drakeandmorgan; Mon-Wed 11 pm, Thu & Fri midnight, Sun 5 pm; closed Sun D, closed Sat.

L'ANTICA PIZZERIA DA
MICHELE   £64   5 3 2
44 OLD COMPTON STREET, W1
020 7434 4563   5–2A
199 BAKER STREET, NW1
020 7935 6458   2–1A

The "outstanding pizzas" – "huge, delicious and authentically Neapolitan" – win top marks for the two London outposts of a Naples original dating back 150 years, which featured in Elizabeth Gilbert's global bestseller 'Eat Pray Love'. The toppings are "mostly traditional", with some "interesting combinations and extras". Don't be misled by the "plain exterior, which makes it look like all the cheap restaurants and snack places along Baker Street" – this branch and its Soho sibling are "very good indeed". / www.anticapizzeriadamichele.co.uk; anticapizzeriadamicheleuk.

ANTILLEAN SE1   £62   3 2 3
74 BLACKFRIARS RD
020 3011 4449   10–4A

"The lovely space that was Baltic (RIP)" – a former Georgian coachbuilding works south of Blackfriars Bridge – nowadays hosts chef-patron Michael Hanbury's yearling, which is billed as the capital's 'first pan-Caribbean restaurant'. The service has sometimes seemed "slightly confused", but the "original and very flavourful" food receives steady praise. / SE1; antillean.co.uk; @antilleanrestaurant; Tue-Sat 11 pm; closed Sun & Mon.

APPLEBEE'S FISH
SE1   £74   3 3 3
5 STONEY ST   020 7407 5777   10–4C

"Reliably good fish and seafood" make this straightforward operation "an attractive option at the edge of Borough Market". It's a flexible spot, which makes for an easy transition between indoor and al fresco eating. / SE1 9AA; www.applebeesfish.com; @applebeesfishlondon; Mon-Wed 10 pm, Thu-Sat 11.30 pm, Sun 6 pm; no Amex.

APRICITY W1   £84   2 4 3
68 DUKE STREET   020 8017 2780   3–2A

Former Tredwells chef, Chantelle Nicholson, has opened this Mayfair newcomer in April 2022, with a hyper-seasonal, low-waste ethos and prettily distressed, minimal décor. Initial reports in our diners' survey are mixed. All feedback suggests the (vegetable-heavy) menu "sounds so interesting", but what are "exceptional plant-based dishes" to some tastes arrive with "not a lot of flair or flavour" to others. (And press reviewers are also split: what is to The Guardian's Grace Dent "too good and truly delicious" to The Evening Standard's Jimi Famurewa "occasionally feels like it loses sight of fun and basic diner enjoyment"). / W1W 6JU; www.apricityrestaurant.com; @apricityrestaurant; Tue-Sat 9 pm; closed Sun & Mon.

APULIA EC1   £61   3 2 2
50 LONG LANE   020 7600 8107   10–2B

"Ideal if you're visiting the Barbican" – this "reliable, genuine, family-run Italian" opposite Smithfield market is a "very friendly little place". The "great pizza and pasta" and "very good Italian wine list" are "fairly priced" and represent "good VFM", especially for the area. / EC1A 9EJ; www.apuliarestaurant.co.uk; @apuliarestaurant; Mon-Fri 10.30 pm, Sat 10.45 pm, Sun 10.15 pm.

AQUA KYOTO W1 £92 `3``3``4`

240 REGENT ST (ENTRANCE 30 ARGYLL ST) 020 7478 0540 4–1A

With its outdoor rooftop terraces over central London near Regent Street, this Hong Kong-owned Japanese joint (a sibling of more famous Aqua Shard) makes a "romantic" location – "even a touch exotic" – to dine on "lovely food" which "looks as good as it tastes". "The rent must be pretty steep, presumably explaining why prices are very high too". / W1B 3BR; www.aqua-london.com; @aquakyotolondon; Sun-Thu 10 pm, Sat, Fri 10.15 pm.

AQUA SHARD SE1 £112 `2``2``3`

LEVEL 31, 31 ST THOMAS ST 020 3011 1256 10–4C

Near the top of the Shard, on its 31st floor, there's no doubt this is a stunning venue, most recommended for a special date or the "amazing afternoon tea". No-one says its modern British menu is disappointing, but there is a feeling that it's "very expensive" and the cynical verdict is that "you don't go for the food, you go for the toilets, which give you an unparalleled widescreen view of London". / SE1 9RY; www.aquashard.co.uk; @aquashard; Mon-Sun 10.15 pm; closed Sat & Sun L.

AQUAVIT SW1 £97 `2``3``2`

ST JAMES'S MARKET, 1 CARLTON ST 020 7024 9848 4–4D

The "outstanding Scandinavian" flavours created by Swedish chef Emma Bengtsson – a superstar in New York – are showcased at this stark, "very spacious" modern venue (lots of "high-quality wood and granite") in the St James's Market development behind Piccadilly Circus. It's never reproduced the excitement anything in London that it enjoys in Manhattan. Even critics acknowledge "it could be so good", but some items seem "absurdly expensive" and the room itself can seem icy in its beauty. / SW1Y 4QQ; www.aquavitrestaurants.com; @aquavitlondon; Tue-Thu 9 pm, Fri & Sat 10 pm; closed Sun & Mon; cash only.

ARABICA £58 `3``4``2`

7 LEWIS CUBITT WALK, N1 020 3747 4422 9–3C
3 ROCHESTER WALK, SE1 020 3011 5151 10–4C

"Excellent" Middle Eastern food – "lots of very tasty dishes, with the veggie plates taking the crown" – wins solid ratings for this former festival stall that has moved steadily upmarket over two decades, and now has a glass-fronted flagship at Borough Market, a restaurant in King's Cross and an outlet in Selfridges' food hall. For regulars, its revised menu inspires mixed feelings ("an improvement" to some, "a step back" for others). / www.arabicalondon.com; arabicalondon.

ARAGAWA W1

38 CLARGES ST 020 7493 3807 3–4C

Esteemed Tokyo steakhouse, Aragawa (est 1967, and actually predated by its Kobe branch) is set to open in late 2022 on the Mayfair site that for over 20 years as Miyama (long RIP) was an exemplar of traditional Japanese cuisine. Tokyo diners may pay over £400 per head for the best cuts… and that's before you go wild with the list of Premiers Grands Crus on the wine list. / W1.

THE ARAKI W1 £380 `5``4``3`

UNIT 4 12 NEW BURLINGTON ST 020 7287 2481 4–3A

Matsuhiro Araki returned to the Far East in 2019 (he had moved to London while his daughter went to uni in the UK) and left this nine-seat Mayfair venue (for which he gained three Michelin stars) in the hands of his apprentice – UK-born Marty Lau – who has run it along similar lines ever since. Of course, it's a second-mortgage job, but the sushi omakase menu here is very seldom rated anything less than "outstanding", and why Michelin now chooses to ignore a restaurant which satisfies such a high proportion of customers at one of London's top price points is baffling. One quibble – "it's £300 a person, but you still have to leave after your 2-hour sitting". / W1S 3BH; the-araki.co.uk; @arakisart; Tue-Sat 9 pm; closed Tue-Sat L, closed Sun & Mon; no Amex; no shorts.

ARCADE FOOD HALL WC1

103-105 NEW OXFORD STREET 020 7519 1202 5–1A

The food court in the landmark Centrepoint building by Tottenham Court Road station was relaunched by JKS Restaurants under a new, tightly curated format and with new outlets in early summer 2022, after two years of off-and-on trading during the pandemic. It now offers American, Middle Eastern, Indian, Nepali, Indonesian, Thai, Vietnamese, Japanese and Spanish food options, along with a jelly & ice cream bar and several booze outlets – with between them six negroni or five G&T options, among others. Everything is listed on one centralised menu, so you can mix and match without slogging around – and queuing up at – a succession of individual stalls. / WC1W 1DB; www.arcade-london.com; @arcadefoodhall; Tue-Sat 11 pm, Sun 5 pm; closed Sun D, closed Mon.

ARK FISH E18 £53 `3``3``2`

142 HERMON HILL 020 8989 5345 1–1D

With "fish fresh from Billingsgate" and enthusiastic family ownership, this substantial South Woodford chippy is a "good local standby" and "good value" meal rather than take-away. / E18 1QH; www.arkfishrestaurant.co.uk; @ark_fish_restaurant; Tue-Thu 9.45 pm, Fri & Sat 10.15 pm, Sun 8.45 pm; closed Mon; no Amex; no booking.

ARROS QD W1 £102 `2``2``2`

64 EASTCASTLE STREET 020 3883 3525 3–1D

"Good food, but not great value" is a common verdict on this Spanish venture north of Oxford Street – the London outpost of chef Quique Dacosta, whose Alicante restaurant has three Michelin stars. It certainly looks impressive, with an open kitchen dominated by a six-metre woodfired stove, at which choice cuts of meat and fish are grilled alongside a dozen rice dishes cooked in the pan. But while it is praised for its "perfect paella", it is also often cited as diners' "most overpriced meal of the year". / W1W 8NQ; www.arrosqd.com; @arrosqd; Tue-Sat 11 pm, Sun 3 pm; closed Sun D, closed Mon.

ARTISANS OF SARDINIA SW15 £65 `3``4``3`

16 LACY ROAD 020 8785 9962 11–2B

Massimo Masili's Sardinian showcase is a "very welcome new addition to the SW15 dining scene" thanks to its "excellent food and extremely friendly service". It can, though, seem "too expensive for what it is" – "Putney location, Mayfair prices!" / SW15 1NL; www.artisansofsardinia.com; @artisansofsardinia_putney; Tue-Sat 10.30 pm; closed Sun & Mon.

L'ARTISTA NW11 £51 `2``4``3`

917 FINCHLEY RD 020 8731 7501 1–1B

"Delicious Italian favourites", "efficient service with a smile" and a "great family vibe" is the formula that makes this Golders Green

BAO

institution so popular. "I remember bringing my girlfriends here when I was a teenager, so it's been serving pizza and pasta for a very long time!". "Don't worry about its location under the railway arches – the noise of the trains is drowned out by the noise of the customers". / NW11 7PE; www.lartistapizzeria.com; Mon-Sun midnight.

ARTUSI SE15 £51 433

161 BELLENDEN RD 020 3302 8200 **1–4D**

This tiny, hip Peckham local "delivers great food" from a short but impeccably prepared Italian menu. They look after their neighbourhood clientele well, with "home delivery kits a lifesaver during lockdown". The name checks Pellegrino Artusi, 19th-century don of Italian cuisine. / SE15 4DH; www.artusi.co.uk; @artusipeckham; Tue-Thu 9.30 pm, Fri & Sat 10 pm, Sun 4 pm; closed Tue L closed Sun D, closed Mon.

ASAKUSA NW1 £39 432

265 EVERSHOLT ST 020 7388 8533 **9–3C**

This "lovely little Japanese restaurant" near Mornington Crescent tube has no airs and graces, but provides "great food and atmosphere", with a menu that covers most of the classics of the cuisine, from sushi and sashimi to yakitori grills, hotpots and noodle dishes. / NW1 1BA; asakusa.has.restaurant; Mon-Sat 11.30 pm; closed Mon-Sat L, closed Sun.

ASSAGGI W2 £75 343

39 CHEPSTOW PL 020 7792 5501 **7–1B**

"Excellent Italian food and very personable service" have made this unusual venue, on the first floor of a Notting Hill pub, a place of more-than-local interest for more than 25 years. Admittedly it no longer generates anything like the gigantic buzz it once did, but diehard fans say "it's comforting that it survived the pandemic and the food's even better post-lockdown". / W2 4TS; www.assaggi.co.uk; @Assagginottinghill; Tue-Sat 10 pm; closed Sun & Mon; no Amex.

THE ATLAS SW6 £52 323

16 SEAGRAVE RD 020 7385 9129 **6–3A**

This "fab gastropub" with a "great menu" of Mediterranean-inspired scoff may not be quite worth a detour – but is certainly "a strong recommendation if you're in the area", close to West Brompton tube station. In business in its current incarnation for almost 25 years, it now has an "excellent terrace garden", making it even more attractive for Sunday lunch or warm summer evenings. / SW6 1RX; www.theatlaspub.co.uk; @theatlaspub; Mon-Sun 9.30 pm; closed Mon-Thu L.

ATTAWA E8 £20 332

6 KINGSLAND HIGH STREET 020 7254 1236 **14–1A**

This Dalston two-year-old from MasterChef: The Professionals 2019 semi-finalist Arbinder Dugal is a "very solid representative of the by-now-not-quite-so-new wave of modern Indian restaurants – probably the best in this part of town". Named after the owners' home village in the Punjab, it serves a short menu of tasty north Indian dishes. / E8 2JP; attawa.co.uk; @attawadalston; Tue-Sun 10 pm; closed Tue-Sun L, closed Mon.

ATTIMI N10 £48 333

THE BROADWAY 020 8444 8777 **1–1B**

This new Italian in Muswell Hill has an "interesting selection of tasty and well-presented small plates", with a "focus on quality and taste". The chic modern interior makes for a "nice buzzy atmosphere", and locals are encouraged to use it as a wine bar – there are more than 100 bottles in stock, most of them Italian. / N10 3SH; @attimi_restaurants_london; Tue-Fri 10.30 pm, Sat & Sun 10 pm; closed Tue-Fri L, closed Mon.

THE AUBREY SW1 £243 343

MANDARIN ORIENTAL, 66 KNIGHTSBRIDGE 020 7201 3899 **1–1D**

Billing itself somewhat misleadingly as an 'eccentric Japanese izakaya experience' (which would suggest it's down-to-earth... which it isn't), this luxurious space decked with Japanese prints is this Knightsbridge hotel's new incumbent for the basement space that was previously Bar Boulud (RIP). It is rated on limited feedback to date, but all of it enthusiastic. Top Tip – bargain set lunch menu featuring katsu sandos, plus cocktails. / SW1S 7LA; www.mandarinoriental.com/london/hyde-park/fine-dining/japanese-izakaya/the-aubrey; @mo_hydepark; Mon-Wed midnight, Thu-Sat 1 am; closed Sun.

THE AUDLEY W1

43 MOUNT STREET NO TEL **3–3A**

The first London project for Artfarm – behind The Fife Arms in Braemar and Somerset's Roth Bar & Grill, and now owner of Soho's Groucho Club – this fine Victorian boozer (built in 1888) in Mayfair is set to relaunch in autumn 2022. Set over five floors, it will comprise a street-level pub, first-floor dining room ('The Mount Street Restaurant') and upper-floor event spaces, all showcasing artworks created by Hauser & Wirth's roster of artists. / W1W 3AH; theaudleypublichouse.com; @Audleypublichouse; Mon-Sun 11 pm.

AUGUSTINE KITCHEN SW11 £58 443

63 BATTERSEA BRIDGE RD 020 7978 7085 **6–4C**

"Weekday set lunch is incredibly good value" and justifies the hop over to Franck Raymond's bistro, just south of Battersea Bridge, where the "excellent" Gallic food is inspired by the Alpine cuisine of his childhood, near Evian on Lake Geneva. / SW11 3AU; www.augustine-kitchen.co.uk; @augustinesw11; Tue-Sat 9 pm; closed Sun & Mon.

AULIS LONDON W1 £188 444

16A ST ANNE'S COURT 020 3948 9665 **4–1D**

"Charlie Taylor and his small team are brilliant hosts, striking the perfect balance of informality and professionalism to draw you into the intimate dinner-party style mood" at this tiny chef's table experience in a Soho alleyway, whose menu is, in part, a showcase for owner Simon Rogan's famous L'Enclume. "Don't come expecting linen table cloths and flunkies: you are dining in an extended kitchen, so it only works if you want the food to be the star. And it's truly stellar" – "strong classic flavour combinations inspired by seasonal produce". One niggle repeated a couple of times this year: "numerous dishes seemed simply ready to plate" which can detract from the experience ("I was disappointed that all we really saw was the final touches to the preparation, it was fun, but I missed the opportunity to learn more about the food, as you can at some chef's tables"). For the most part, though, few doubt that a meal here is anything other than "stunning". Despite awarding L'Enclume three Michelin stars, both these men bizarrely award no stars here. / W1W 0BF; aulis.london; @aulissimonrogan; Tue-Sat 11.30 pm; closed Tue-Thu L, closed Sun & Mon; no Amex.

AUTHENTIQUE EPICERIE & BAR NW5 £47 333

114-116 FORTESS ROAD 020 3609 6602 **9–2C**

"Like a French tapas bar", this Tufnell Park showcase celebrates the wines (700) and beers (75) of the French-speaking world, with themed dinners highlighting produce from 12 regions in rotation. "As the name suggests, food is secondary – decent, but basically an accompaniment to the outstanding selection of reasonably priced wines". / NW5 5HL; authentique-epicerie.com; @authentiquelondon; Tue-Sat 11 pm, Sun 8 pm; closed Mon.

AVANTI W4 £34 332

SOUTH PARADE 020 8994 9444 **8–2A**

This Mediterranean fusion spot on the edge of Bedford Park in Chiswick combines "excellent pizzas and tapas". The gazebo adds to the Med effect in good weather. / W4 1LD; avantichiswick.com; Mon-Sun 10 pm.

AVE MARIO WC2 £58 334

15 HENRIETTA STREET NO TEL **5–3C**

"Totally bonkers" and "Insta heaven" – the latest maximalist, Central Casting interpretation of Italian restaurant culture from the French group Big Mamma (who hit paydirt with Gloria and Circolo Populare) opened in Covent Garden in summer 2021. Despite being massive (with 295 covers over two floors and two terraces), and its cheesily cheeky menu ('Lettuce Pray' salad, 'Chocolate al Porno') it's not inspired a huge number of reports. Perhaps this was due to the pasting it received from the press ("Nonna's gone to

Iceland", said The Evening Standard's Jimi Famurewa) but our (quite limited) feedback includes no major complaints. / WC2W 8QG; www.bigmammagroup.com/en/trattorias/ave-mario; @bigmamma.uk; Sun-Wed 10.30 pm, Thu-Sat 10.45 pm.

L'AVENTURE NW8 £75 444

3 BLENHEIM TERRACE
020 7624 6232 9–3A

"Run by the owner for 41 years and I have been a customer for over 35 years and the quality has never varied!" – Catherine Parisot's "brilliant longstanding favourite" in St John's Wood "never fails to delight": in particular its cute interior and pretty location make it a top choice for a date. Under the "able guidance" of la patronne, it provides classic 'cuisine bourgeoise': "you always know what you are going to get as the menu never changes, but the food is always good". / NW8 0EH; www.laventure.co.uk; Mon-Sat 11 pm; closed Sat L, closed Sun.

THE AVENUE SW1 £71 333

7-9 ST JAMES'S STREET
020 7321 2111 3–4D

This cavernous modern brasserie (owned by D&D London) was something of a 1990s icon, but – despite a convenient St James's location – goes somewhat unsung nowadays. On limited feedback, though, all reports are upbeat, saying it's "a good spot for a business lunch", or that "Jose and his team know how to lay on a good brunch". / SW1A 1EE; www.avenue-restaurant.co.uk; @avenuestjames; Tue-Sat 9.30 pm, Sun 5 pm; closed Sun D, closed Mon.

AVIARY EC2 £101 234

10TH FLOOR, 22-25 FINSBURY SQUARE
020 3873 4060 13–2A

This hotel rooftop bar-restaurant overlooking Finsbury Square is a "gorgeous spot for lunch – quiet and with good views". Glass igloos are installed for winter, so it's a year-round operation. The modern corporate brasserie cooking attracts little notice, either favourable or otherwise. / EC2E 1DX; aviarylondon.com; @aviaryldn; Mon-Sun midnight.

AWESOME THAI SW13 £39 332

68 CHURCH RD 020 8563 7027 11–1A

This "great local Thai" in Barnes owes its enduring popularity to its efficient and "welcoming" family owners and its handy position in the centre of the more villagey bit of SW13 (directly opposite the Olympic Studios indie cinema). / SW13 0DQ; www.awesomethai.co.uk; Fri & Sat, Mon-Thu 10.30 pm, Sun 10 pm; closed Mon-Thu L.

BABABOOM SW11 £39 332

30 BATTERSEA RISE 07809 903181 11–2C

A tight menu of "delicious" Middle Eastern-inspired street food, especially kebabs, is found at this Battersea Rise venue and its 2022 spin-off in Westfield Stratford. Founder Eve Bugler, an ultra-marathon runner and erstwhile director of Nando's, launched the business in 2015 with backing from senior industry figures including former boss David Niven, Mark Selby of Wahaca and Peter Borg-Neal of Oakman Inns. / SW11 1EE; www.bababoom.london; @bababoomlondon; Thu-Sat 11 pm, Sun-Wed 10 pm.

BABUR SE23 £57 553

119 BROCKLEY RISE 020 8291 2400 1–4D

"The deft flavours of fine Indian dining" at this "Honor Oak stalwart" have induced discerning diners to "make the awkward trip" to SE23 for almost 40 years now. "The place maintains its standards" and has a credible claim on being "the best Indian in southeast London" thanks to its "exciting" dishes, "excellent" service and "elegant" interior. / SE23 1JP; www.babur.info; @baburrestaurant; Mon-Sun 11 pm; no shorts.

BACCHANALIA W1

BERKELEY SQUARE NO TEL 3–2B

Richard Caring has outlined plans for his most spectacular and decadent restaurant yet. This former Porsche garage in Berkeley Square will channel the atmosphere of Ancient Greece and Rome, alongside suitably Mediterranean-inspired cuisine and promises to make his glitzily glam Sexy Fish, a near-neighbour, look like a vicarage tea party. No opening date yet! / W1W 5AR; Tue-Sun 4 pm.

BACCO TW9 £71 332

39-41 KEW RD 020 8332 0348 1–4A

This "excellent local Italian" in the middle of Richmond offers "friendly service and attractive menu choices at reasonable prices". Pre-show options ensure that it's "good for the local theatres". / TW9 2NQ; www.bacco-restaurant.co.uk; Tue-Sat 10 pm; closed Sun & Mon; no shorts.

BAGERIET WC2 £20 422

24 ROSE ST 020 7240 0000 5–3C

"Fabulous Swedish cakes and good coffee" are the siren call to this tiny Scandi kafé in Covent Garden, if you can nab a seat – but "it's just so small you can't always get in". Top Tip – "the prinsesstårta is to die for". / WC2E 9EA; www.bageriet.co.uk; Tue-Fri 5.30 pm, Sat 6 pm; closed Tue-Sat D, closed Sun & Mon; no booking.

BALA BAYA SE1 £69 333

OLD UNION YARD ARCHES, 229 UNION STREET 020 8001 7015 10–4B

"The really tasty and innovative modern Israeli cuisine never fails to impress" at former Ottolenghi chef Eran Tibi's all-day venue in the "very hip setting" of a Southwark railway arch. "Every wine is from Israel – and ours were very good". / SE1 0LR; balabaya.co.uk; @bala_baya; Mon-Sat 11 pm, Sun 10 pm.

BALADY £31 421

750 FINCHLEY ROAD, NW11
020 8458 2064 1–1B
39-41 LEATHER LANE, EC1
020 8458 2064 10–1A

"Outstanding delicious falafels" – "some of the best in London" – are the star turn at this Jewish-Moroccan veggie spot in Temple Fortune. "Don't be put off by the strip lighting aesthetic, although there's possibly better ambience in the street outside". In the last couple of years the three Sabbo brothers have opened follow-ups in High Barnet (selling meat) and Clerkenwell's Leather Lane (and also in Lakewood, New Jersey!) /

BALTHAZAR WC2 £85 123

4 - 6 RUSSELL STREET
020 3301 1155 5–3D

"An excellent simulacrum of a Parisian brasserie" – this big, prominently situated Covent Garden fixture, just off the Piazza (created by English-born New Yorker, Keith McNally, but nowadays part of Caprice Holdings) provides "good vibes for Sunday brunch or a meal around a show". But even fans feel "the main draw is the buzzy atmosphere, not the unexciting food" and – especially when it becomes "too busy for its own good" – this is, for its critics, "the worst kind of hell", with food that's "absolutely average and poor value for the price". / WC2B 5HZ; www.balthazarlondon.com; @balthazarldn; Mon-Sat 10.30 pm, Sun 9.30 pm.

BANCONE £56 443

10 LOWER JAMES STREET, W1
020 3034 0820 4–3C
39 WILLIAM IV STREET, WC2
020 3034 8786 5–4C

"A perfect pre-theatre choice that's quick and classy" – these West End pasta-stops off Trafalgar Square and in Soho provide "excellent pasta, reasonable prices and a speedy turnaround". "Buzzy rather than comfortable (many tables only have stools), really keen nearly all Italian staff provide the (fairly) limited menu" – "fab fresh pasta" with "modern Italian flavours" that's "not complicated, but done with precision", all "at an amazing price". / www.bancone.co.uk.

BANG BANG ORIENTAL NW9 £48 322

399 EDGWARE ROAD NO TEL 1–1A

The "wonderful street-food vibes" justify a trip to Colindale to visit this enormous Oriental food court. "Quality varies greatly between the units", but if you make the right choices, you're bound to enjoy a "party for the mouth". / NW9 0AS; www.bangbangoriental.com; @bangbangoriental; Sun-Thu 9.30 pm, Fri & Sat 10 pm; no booking.

BANNERS N8 £57 2|3|3

21 PARK ROAD 020 8348 2930 1–1C

With an all-day menu that bounces happily from the Caribbean and Mexico to the Isle of Man and Thailand, Juliette Banner has provided up-beat service in Crouch End for more than 30 years. "A Banners breakfast is the perfect cure for a hangover" – and you can also earn one with the "great cocktails". The "authentic American-style burgers" must have attracted Bob Dylan, the bard of Americana, whose 1993 visit is commemorated with a plaque – you can even book the table he sat at! / N8 8TE; www.bannersrestaurant.com; @BannersN8; Sun-Thu 9.30 pm, Fri & Sat 10.30 pm; no Amex.

BAO £38 3|4|4

31 WINDMILL ST, W1 020 3011 1632 5–1A
53 LEXINGTON ST, W1 07769 627811 4–2C
4 PANCRAS SQUARE, N1 NO TEL 9–3C
13 STONEY STREET, SE1
020 3967 5407 10–4C
1 REDCHURCH STREET, E2 NO TEL 13–1B
NETIL MARKET, 13-23 WESTGATE STREET, E8 NO TEL 14–2B

"The best-ever bao buns: so light and fluffy with absolutely delicious fillings" again win raves for this five-strong chain, backed by JKS Restaurants (which plans a Battersea opening later in 2022). "Worth queuing for, although happily they now take bookings". Top Menu Tips – "very good Taiwan-style spicy beef noodles"; "the warm bao with horlicks ice-cream is the most unusual!" / baolondon.com; bao_london.

BAOZI INN £36 3|2|2

24 ROMILLY STREET, W1
020 7287 3266 5–3A
34-36 SOUTHWARK STREET, SE1
020 8037 5875 10–4C

"Authentic and tasty dumplings" and other northern Chinese street-food classics make any of Wei Shao's small group "a great standby for a quick and fun meal". Some prefer to stay longer ("our family goes for a Sunday feast") with the biggest range of dishes at the 120-cover flagship near Borough Market. There are also branches in Chinatown, Soho, and the Market Halls in Victoria and Oxford Street. / baoziinn.com.

BAR DES PRÉS W1 £116 3|4|4

16 ALBEMARLE STREET
020 3908 2000 3–3C

"Asia meets France" at this Mayfair yearling from French TV chef Cyril Lignac, named after his Paris restaurant in St Germain des Prés. "There's a large team of sushi chefs and the place has a lively, Parisian feel", with "French desserts, which are superb" – as they should be, given that Lignac trained as a pâtissier. It's no shock that the place is pricey, but fans say it's worth it: "absolutely top class, can't wait to return". / W1W 4HW; bardespres.

com; @bardespres; Mon-Sat 11 pm, Sun 10 pm; no trainers.

BAR DOURO SE1 £50 4|4|4

ARCH 35B, 85B SOUTHWARK BRIDGE RD 020 7378 0524 10–4B

"Really enjoyable Portuguese tapas" is served in this "lovely, light and airy space", tucked under a railway arch, near London Bridge. Founded by Max Graham, from the Churchills port dynasty, fans even say it's "reminiscent of early-years Barrafina". Top Tip – "the tiny clams". (Note: don't be put off by the queue outside – it may be for the pancake shop in front!). / SE1 0NQ; www.bardouro.co.uk; @bardouro; Tue-Sat 10 pm, Sun 9 pm; closed Tue-Thu L, closed Mon; booking max 4 may apply.

BAR ESTEBAN N8 £62 3|3|3

29 PARK RD 020 8340 3090 1–1C

This "cosy and vibey" tapas bar has a strong local following in Crouch End, and celebrates its tenth anniversary this year. 'Esteban', its founder, is in fact Glasgow-born record producer Stephen Lironi, a long-time fan of Spanish cuisine; chef Pablo Rodriguez is from Barcelona, while manager Naroa Ortega is from Bilbao. / N8 8TE; www.baresteban.com; @bar__esteban; Mon, Fri, Tue-Thu 10 pm, Sat 11 pm, Sun 9.30 pm; closed Mon, Fri L; booking max 8 may apply.

BAR ITALIA W1 £37 2|4|5

22 FRITH ST 020 7437 4520 5–2A

"Irresistible for its history and authenticity" (as well as for "espresso and pastries") – this 24-hour coffee bar defines Soho as the hub of London nightlife, as it has done ever since 1949, when the Polledri family – still the owners – opened it to serve what was then a thriving local Italian community. It's "still skanky – but great" for those who appreciate post-war interiors. / W1D 4RF; www.baritaliasoho.co.uk; @baritaliasoho; Mon-Sun 5 am; no booking.

THE BARBARY WC2 £76 4|3|4

16 NEAL'S YARD NO TEL 5–2C

"Everything's delicious beyond words", say fans of Layo and Zoe Paskin's "hugely fun" and stylish North African-inspired small-plates operation in Neal's Yard, younger sibling of the Palomar. With "excellent bar food at a counter", it makes the "best pre-theatre spot around". Top Tips – "the Jerusalem bagels and squid are stand-out items". / WC2H 9DP; www.thebarbary.co.uk; @barbarylondon; Tue-Sat 10 pm, Sun 9 pm; closed Tue, Wed L, closed Mon; no booking.

THE BARBARY NEXT DOOR WC2 £45 4|2|2

16A NEAL'S YARD AWAITING TEL 5–2C

On the minuscule Covent Garden site that was Jacob The Angel (RIP), this "cheek-by-jowl café" serves similar North African-inspired small plates to the neighbouring mothership.

"The bill for the admittedly good food racks up", though, and some feel it's "not good enough value, considering you can hear your fellow diners chewing and you're fighting for elbow room". / WC2W 9DP; thebarbarynextdoor. co.uk; @thebarbarynextdoor; Wed-Sat 10 pm, Sun 4 pm; closed Wed L closed Sun D, closed Mon & Tue.

LA BARCA SE1 £83 3|3|3

80-81 LOWER MARSH
020 7928 2226 10–4A

This "busy Italian", whose familiar ship has sailed behind Waterloo station for almost 50 years, has hosted countless pre- and post-theatre meals for audiences and cast from the Old Vic opposite. It's "unchanged for decades, but actually very appealing as a result". Though sometimes considered "expensive for what it is", fans say the cooking is "cracking". / SE1 7AB; www.labarca-ristorante.com; @labarca1976-gb; Mon-Sat 10.30 pm; closed Sat L, closed Sun; booking max 12 may apply.

BARRAFINA £70 5|4|4

26-27 DEAN STREET, W1
020 7813 8016 4–1D
10 ADELAIDE ST, WC2
020 7440 1456 5–4C
43 DRURY LANE, WC2
020 7440 1456 5–2D
COAL DROPS YARD, N1
0207 440 1486 9–3C
2 DIRTY LANE, SE1 NO TEL 10–4C

"Sights and smells of Spain sitting at the counter" provide "heaven on a stool" at the Hart Bros' faithful recreations of Barcelona's Cal Pep: still, after 15 years, one of the most-mentioned groups in our survey. The "extraordinary tapas is full of fresh ideas" – there's "always something new to try on the menu" (created by their chef/director Angel Zapata Martin) – and it "still deserves top marks, particularly the seafood (which is the only option nowadays at the WC2 'Mariscos' outlet). A meal is "not cheap" mind you (in fact, even fans can find prices "crazy") but the overall verdict? "Worth the queue, and the bill!" (In July 2022, they added a new, fifth branch to the group, in SE1's Borough Yards developments). / www.barrafina.co.uk.

BARSHU W1 £51 5|2|2

28 FRITH ST 020 7287 6688 5–3A

This "amazing Sichuan specialist" stands out from the competition with a "really interesting selection" of super-spicy options that are "a long, long way above and beyond the usual Chinatown fare". "The recently revamped menu is now even better than before" – "not the greatest ambience but my goodness the food is good" ("took a gourmet friend who declared that six of the seven dishes were exceptional… the seventh was just delicious!"). Top Tip – "if you have a dry wok dish and don't finish it, get a doggy bag". / W1D 5LF; www.barshurestaurant.co.uk; @barshurestaurant; Sun-Thu 10 pm, Fri & Sat 10.30 pm.

BASE FACE PIZZA
W6 £38 343

300 KING STREET   020 8617 1092   8–2B

Jazz music's loss was Hammersmith pizza-lovers' gain: professional bass-player Tim Thornton lost his living when live music was silenced under lockdown, so he turned to making "really delicious" pizzas. Now he has a "fantastic little pizza restaurant" on King Street that is "busy and full of locals" ("the best pizzas we've eaten in years – a real find!"). / W6; www.basefacepizza.com; @base.face.pizza; Tue-Sun 10 pm; closed Tue-Sun L, closed Mon.

BEAST W1 £121 222

3 CHAPEL PL   020 7495 1816   3–1B

A candle-lit temple to the atavistic delights of consuming quantities of ribeye steak and king crab that's "in fact very good, if grossly overpriced for what it is" ("£100 for a bit of crab!"). But spending big is arguably central to the 'Beast Experience' touted (tongue in cheek), on the website: 'the place will make an impression on your client or whomever, and everyone will remember the occasion'. / W1G 0BG; www.beastrestaurant.co.uk; @beast.restaurant; Mon-Sat 10.30 pm; closed Mon-Thu L, closed Sun; may need 7+ to book.

THE BEGGING BOWL
SE15 £54 443

168 BELLENDEN RD   020 7635 2627   1–4D

After 10 years, this "lively" Peckham neighbourhood Thai remains a "consistently terrific place" that "delivers great food that's as good as you get in Bangkok, but with a twist". Co-owner Jane Alty, who makes regular trips to Thailand to research recipes and ingredients, discovered the cuisine while working in the kitchen at David Thompson's Nahm (long RIP). / SE15 4BW; www.thebeggingbowl.co.uk; @the-begging-bowl; Tue-Sat 10 pm, Sun 4 pm; closed Tue-Thu L closed Sun D, closed Mon; booking online only.

BEHIND E8 £72 554

20 SIDWORTH STREET   NO TEL   14–2B

"Hackney's newest foodie hotspot doesn't disappoint" and "the passionate commitment of all involved shines through" at Andy Benyon's year-old 18-seater, near London Fields. "Very friendly chefs serve you personally" at a counter overlooking the kitchen "allowing a view of the preparation of each course (it's a bit like dining on the set of an episode of MasterChef: The Professionals)". The focus is on fish and seafood, and "a succession of elegantly prepared dishes bring complex flavours to some of the most sustainable species on the market", all adding up to a "superb" overall meal. Given its high quality, it's not an overpriced venue at all: "you get amazing value on top of an amazing experience!" / E8 3SD; www.behindrestaurant.co.uk; @behindrestaurant; Tue-Sat 11 pm; closed Sun & Mon; booking online only.

BELLAMY'S W1 £69 354

18-18A BRUTON PL   020 7491 2727   3–2B

"With its quietly thrumming ambience, well-spaced tables and unobtrusive service from staff used to looking after royalty", this "eternally discreet" brasserie hidden in a cute Mayfair mews is a long-established favourite for a blue-blooded, establishment crowd (and "perfect for doing business in"). Elegantly suited owner, Gavin Rankin, smoothly commands the space – "his team are wonderfully welcoming" and "all this is supported by classic French food, an excellent and keenly priced wine list, and a set lunch menu that's a bargain (ideal for when Finance put a cap on your entertaining budget)". Top Menu Tips – "Martinis, oysters and staples like steak tartare are prominent". / W1J 6LY; www.bellamysrestaurant.co.uk; @bellamysmayfair; Mon-Fri 10.30 pm, Sat 11.30 pm; closed Sat L, closed Sun; Jacket required.

BELLANGER N1 £59 223

9 ISLINGTON GRN   020 7226 2555   9–3D

Created by Jeremy King and Christopher Corbin, this smart brasserie on Islington Green is long on Belle Époque-style charm, and – thanks to "a menu that suits most moods and a warm welcome" – has, for many locals, become "a go-to for most occasions, particularly family lunch and brunch". Its cuisine (with some emphasis on its selection of tartes flambées) has always tended to be "fine if not particularly distinguished" but the experience is enhanced by "decent, unrushed service". Now part of Minor International's Wolseley Hospitality Group following its April 2022 takeover of Corbin & King: "I fear for it under its new ownership" is a common worry among regulars. / N1 2XH; www.bellanger.co.uk; @bellanger_n1; Tue-Sat 10 pm, Sun 9 pm; closed Mon.

BELVEDERE W8

OFF ABBOTSBURY RD IN HOLLAND PARK   020 7602 1238   8–1D

One of London's most stunning and prettily located venues – this 17th-century former ballroom in Holland Park itself is scheduled to reopen in the latter half of 2022 under the ownership of Ilya Demichev and George Bukhov-Weinstein, the Russians behind Chelsea's Wild Tavern and surf-and-turf specialists Goodman and Burger & Lobster. The menu is expected to be Italian-led and there will be room for 120 diners on two floors – each with its own bar. The venue has had various high-profile tenants, including Marco Pierre White, but has often slipped into complacency based on its location – let's hope they break that mould. / W8 6LU; www.belvedererestaurant.co.uk; @the-belvedere-restaurant-holland-park; Mon-Sat 11 pm, Sun 3.30 pm; closed Sun D.

BENARES W1 £95 444

12A BERKELEY SQUARE HOUSE, 020 7629 8886   3–3B

Sameer Taneja's "exceptional" cuisine continues to maintain the high standing of this well-known Berkeley Square destination.

Despite the odd "unexciting" report, most accounts are of "fabulous" meals from "a menu that's very spice-led and refined-tasting". Located on the first floor, its modern design "doesn't feel too 'posh Mayfair' in ambience terms", with meals here said to be "well-paced" and "refreshing". / W1J 6BS; www.benaresrestaurant.co.uk; @benaresofficial; Tue-Sat 10.30 pm; closed Sun & Mon; no trainers.

BENTLEY'S W1 £98 443

11-15 SWALLOW ST   020 7734 4756   4–4B

"A classic for oyster lovers!" – acclaimed Irish chef, Richard Corrigan, continues to be a superb steward of this 106-year-old veteran (established in 1916), cutely tucked away in a side street near Piccadilly Circus, which he has rebuilt over the years into one of the Top 40 destinations in our annual diners' poll. "For outstanding oysters or fish, you can't go wrong", with tips including "cracking fruits de mer" and "simply delicious fish stew". His "fabulous" and "professional" staff help create a "lovely" atmosphere, although the top 'craic' in the ground-floor bar is often tipped over the grander but more sedate upstairs restaurant. (Another excellent option, particularly in summer, is the superb heated outdoor terrace). On the downside, the pricing is somewhat "prohibitive of a frequent visit", but fans say "despite the expense, a meal here is an all-round package that is predictable in a good way". Top Menu Tips – "oh-so-tasty options from the specials board" and "ask for more soda bread!!" / W1B 4DG; www.bentleys.org; @bentleysoysterbar; Mon-Sat 9.30 pm, Sun 8 pm; booking max 8 may apply.

BERBER & Q £61 544

ARCH 338 ACTON MEWS, E8 020 7923 0829   14–2A
EXMOUTH MARKET, EC1 020 7837 1726   10–1A

"Smoky perfection!" – Josh Katz's "yummy and very moreish" Middle East-inspired grills in a vibey Haggerston railway arch and on Exmouth Market have won a massive reputation since he launched his take on 'live-fire cooking' in 2015; and the "buzzy, intimate atmosphere" of both locations is also a big winner. Top Menu Tip – "the flatbreads, chicken and cauliflower shawarma are standouts". /

BERENJAK W1 £64 444

27 ROMILLY STREET   020 3319 8120   5–2A

"I can't stress how addictive it is!" – Kian Samyani (backed by JKS Restaurants) channels his Iranian heritage at this "friendly" Soho charcoal grill (one of Dua Lipa's fave raves, apparently) to deliver "terrifically tasty kebabs grilled over the coals, with sourdough tandoori flat breads that are perfect for dunking in any of their truly moreish dips". And it's "fun to sit at the bar and watch the action", too. As of summer 2022, it's on the expansion trail, taking over the two-storey Borough Market site that was until recently Flor (RIP), to offer a wider menu incorporating larger dishes and an expanded wine list from the Eastern Med. / W1W 5AL; berenjaklondon.com;

@berenjaklondon; Tue-Sat 10 pm; closed Tue-Fri L closed Sat D, closed Sun & Mon.

BERMONDSEY LARDER
SE1   £52   4|4|3

153-157 TOWER BRIDGE ROAD
020 7378 6254   10–*4D*

With a "taster menu that's second to none", Robin and Sarah Gill's crack kitchen team have settled in well to their new home in a Bermondsey 'aparthotel'. They moved over from Clapham's The Dairy, which did not survive the pandemic, but a taste of the latter's "imaginative, skillful small-plate cooking" using carefully sourced seasonal ingredients is still available here. / SE1 3LW; www.thedairybermondsey.com; @bermondseylarder; Thu-Sat, Wed 10 pm, Sun 4 pm; closed Wed L closed Sun D, closed Mon & Tue.

THE BERNERS TAVERN
W1   £100   2|2|5

10 BERNERS STREET
020 7908 7979   3–*1D*

"Jason Atherton certainly knows how to tart up traditional British fare", according to fans of his "indulgent and delicious" cuisine within this "fabulous" space – a converted banking hall that's part of Marriott's glam, Ian Shrager-designed Edition hotel, north of Oxford Street. Ratings overall, though, are in middle territory, with harsher reports feeling it "rarely elevates above the level of a good gastropub". Top Menu Tip – "the mac 'n' cheese is simply the best". / W1T 3NP; @bernerstavern; Thu & Fri, Tue, Wed, Sat 9.45 pm; closed Tue, Wed, Sat L, closed Sun & Mon.

BEST MANGAL
£48   4|4|2

619 FULHAM RD, SW6
020 7610 0009   6–*4A*
104 NORTH END RD, W14
020 7610 1050   8–*2D*

A wide range of Anatolian grilled meat including "superb lamb doner made in-house, fresh every day", earns consistent high praise for these "welcoming" and "good value" venues in Fulham and West Kensington. / www.bestmangal.com.

BIBENDUM SW3   £196   4|3|4

81 FULHAM RD   **020 7589 1480**   6–*2C*

With its "light-filled setting and high ceilings", this "beautiful and iconic dining room" (converted in 1987 by the late Sir Terence Conran) on the first floor of South Kensington's landmark Michelin Building makes an "impressive" choice for either a business meal or a date, and is "best seen at lunchtime". Over the five years since Claude Bosi took over the stoves, he has started to make the venue his own, and many reports this year are of a "stupendous culinary experience" thanks to his "incredible" and "inventive" cuisine, matched with "an amazing cellar" and provided by "attentive but not over-pompous staff". The caveat is an obvious one – a meal here comes "at a cost…" / SW3 6RD; www.claudebosi;

@claudebosiatbibendum; Wed & Thu 9 pm, Fri & Sat 9.30 pm; closed Mon & Tue & Sun; booking max 12 may apply.

BIBENDUM OYSTER BAR
SW3   £85   4|3|4

MICHELIN HOUSE, 81 FULHAM ROAD
020 7581 5817   6–*2C*

"If you fancy oysters or other seafood, head for the Michelin Building" – one of London's few venues that truly deserve the adjective 'iconic' – where the "cheaper" alternative to Claude Bosi's grand restaurant upstairs is his "classic oyster bar (nice wines too)" in the elegant foyer of the building, in which "you can sit, nibble on light fare and watch the world go by". / SW3 6RD; www.bibendum.co.uk; @claudebosiatbibendum; Wed & Thu 9 pm, Fri & Sat 9.30 pm; closed Mon & Tue & Sun; no booking.

BIBI W1   £93   5|5|4

42 NORTH AUDLEY STREET
020 3780 7310   3–*2A*

"Absolute 'god tier level' from start to finish!" – JKS Restaurants have totally nailed it once again with this "novel" autumn 2021 newcomer, which inhabits the "tiny but convivial space" on the fringe of Mayfair that was formerly Truc Vert (RIP); and which has now become "a high-end homage to old-school curry houses, including flock wallpaper!". Chef Chet Sharma delivers "an amazing original riff on classic Indian flavours" with "a range of new and vibrant dishes" that are "truly memorable" and "an utter joy". Service is "impeccable and well informed" too and the press have utterly raved (Grace Dent called it "part genius and clearly part subversive"; Giles Coren awarded '11/10') – so, it's "a rare example of a restaurant where every broadsheet reviewer had got it exactly right!" / W1W 6ZR; www.bibirestaurants.com; @bibi_ldn; Tue-Sat 10 pm; closed Tue L, closed Sun & Mon.

BIBIMBAP SOHO
W1   £42   3|3|2

11 GREEK ST   **020 7287 3434**   5–*2A*

This Soho canteen is "one of the better Korean restaurants in town", serving "authentic" Korean fast food headed by the dish it takes its name from – hot rice with savoury toppings that you stir before eating. There's also a take-away option in the City. / W1D 4DJ; bibimbapsoho.co.uk; @bibimbapsoho; Sun-Fri 10 pm, Sat 10.30 pm; no Amex.

BIBO BY DANI GARCÍA
EC2   £79   2|2|3

MONDRIAN HOTEL, 45 CURTAIN ROAD
020 3146 4545   13–*1B*

Bibos in Madrid, Marbella, Cádiz and Doha have pre-dated this latest opening for celeb Andalusian chef Dani Garcia, within the newly opened Mondrian Shoreditch (on the site of Red Rooster, RIP). Perhaps because of the drubbings it's received from press reviewers, not very many reporters visited. One or two that did found it "all-round exceptional", but

others were "fairly underwhelmed, first by the lengthy explanation of the tapas, and then by the pretty pedestrian-for-the-money food". / EC2; www.sbe.com/restaurants/bibo/shoreditch; @bibo_shoreditch; Sun-Wed 10.30 pm, Thu-Sat 11.30 pm.

BIG EASY   £72   2|2|3

12 MAIDEN LN, WC2   **020 3728 4888**   5–*3D*
332-334 KING'S RD, SW3
020 7352 4071   6–*3C*
CROSSRAIL PL, E14   **020 3841 8844**   12–*1C*

"Big, bold and brassy, with lashings of tasty American food" – a meal in this BBQ and crabshack is "like having a holiday in the southern USA". And you don't have to battle through Heathrow to get there: a King's Road, Chelsea fixture for more than 30 years, it now has spin-offs in Covent Garden and Canary Wharf. "Our grandsons loved this place. We enjoyed it too, and the cocktails were nice". / www.bigeasy.co.uk.

BIG FERNAND
SW7   £28   4|4|2

39 THURLOE PLACE   **020 3031 8330**   6–*2C*

London outpost (in South Ken's 'Little France') of a Paris-based chain, with over 50 branches in France and the Arab World – this 'Maison du Hamburgé' is "not to be missed" for its "great value and utterly delicious burgers" (e.g. "with raclette! who knew?") / SW7 2HP; www.bigfernanduk.com; @bigfernand_uk; Sun-Thu 10.30 pm, Fri & Sat 11 pm.

BIG JO BAKERY
N7   £27   3|3|3

318-326 HORNSEY ROAD
020 3915 6760   9–*1D*

From the same hipster-favourite stable as Primeur and Westerns Laundry, this eat-in artisan bakery between Finsbury Park and Holloway serves a small, simple menu from the blackboard as well as pâtisserie and brunchish fare from breakfast onwards. Feedback is relatively limited, but one Hornsey reporter feels it's "worth crossing north London for". / N7 7HE; www.bigjobakery.com; @bigjobakery; Thu-Sat 11 pm, Sun-Wed 4 pm; closed Sun-Wed D.

THE BIRD IN HAND
W14   £53   4|4|4

88 MASBRO ROAD   **020 7371 2721**   8–*1C*

"Pizzas with an absolutely stunning crust – and excellent toppings as well" – win rave reviews for this pub conversion near Brook Green. It's a well-run operation, part of the Oak group of pizza-pubs, and everything on the menu is "fresh and well-sourced". / W14 0LR; www.thebirdinhandlondon.com; @thebirdw14; Tue-Sun 11 pm; closed Tue-Fri L, closed Mon; booking weekdays only.

BISTRO UNION
SW4   £60   342

40 ABBEVILLE RD   020 7042 6400   11–2D

"Great to have in the locale" – Adam Byatt
provides a "friendly neighbourhood spot" at this
"good 'Abbeville village' location" with "lovely
food, very nice service and a good atmosphere".
It's not of the calibre of his main HQ though
– "it's Trinity's little sister, but it's not clear
that's reflected in the cooking". / SW4 9NG;
www.bistrounion.co.uk; @bistrounionclapham;
closed Mon-Sat & Sun; booking max 8 may apply.

BJÖRN FRANTZÉN AT
HARRODS SW1

87-135 BROMPTON ROAD   NO TEL   6–1D

Harrods enticed Swedish superstar Björn
Frantzén to open his first London outlet as
the trump card in their beefed-up in-store
hospitality offering, with a scheduled late-2022
launch date. His self-named Stockholm flagship
is a regular on 'World's Best' lists and his
Singapore offshoot Zén is not far behind, which
indicates he's not bad at running multiple sites
globally. We look forward to feedback. / SW1S
7XL; www.harrods.com; Mon-Sun 8.30 pm.

BLACK BEAR
BURGER   £46   432

11-13 MARKET ROW, SW9
020 7737 3444   11–2D
MARKET HALLS CANARY WHARF, CANADA
SQUARE, E14   NO TEL   12–1C
BOXPARK SHOREDITCH, 2-10 BETHNAL
GREEN ROAD, E1   NO TEL   13–2B
17 EXMOUTH MARKET, EC1
020 7837 1039   10–1A

"The burgers are so juicy and tasty" – "just
the right combination of taste and juiciness"
– at this small group, which has continued to
expand from its Shoreditch's Boxpark origins
via a proper restaurant in Brixton Market Row
to new branches in Market Halls Cargo at
Canary Wharf and also the largest opening to
date: a 45-seater in Exmouth Market (formerly
a Dirty Burger). The brand only uses grass-fed,
dry-aged British beef. / blackbearburger.com;
black_bear_burger.

THE BLACK BOOK
W1   £53   344

23 FRITH STREET   020 7434 1724   5–2A

"A hidden gem in Soho" for œnophiles – this
"lovely, intimate basement" has a "great
selection of wines for the enthusiast", including
"old, rare and super-interesting bottles",
"from top producers at affordable prices".
Founded by master sommeliers Gearoid
Daveney and Xavier Rousset as the premises
for Trade, a private club for people working
in hospitality, it remains at its best as an
after-hours option. There's a "simple menu"
of charcuterie, well-made cheese toasties and
the like. Top Tip – "a dangerous joint to know
about as it's open till 3am on weekends!" (1am
midweek). / W1W 4RR; blackbooksoho.co.uk;
@theblackbooksoho; Tue, Wed 1 am, Thu-Sat 3
am; closed Tue-Sat L, closed Sun & Mon.

BLACK DOG BEER HOUSE
TW8   £54   443

17 ALBANY ROAD   020 8568 5688   1–3A

This "very well run" Brentford backstreet
boozer was created five years out of the
former Albany Arms by Pete Brew – clearly a
victim of nominative determinism, he has even
established an in-house nano-brewery, Fearless
Nomad. Fans say, "the food is as good as it gets
in a pub, and all the better for having a brilliant
selection of cask and keg ales to choose from".
/ TW8 0NF; www.blackdogbeerhouse.co.uk;
@blackdogbeerhouse; Mon, Wed-Sat 11 pm, Sun
10.30 pm; closed Tue.

THE BLACK LAMB
SW19   £60

67 HIGH STREET   020 8947 8278   11–2B

Wimbledon's White Onion (RIP) has gone
from the Village high street, to make way for
the Gladwin family's 6th London opening
in their Sussex-based business's field-to-
fork empire, a 'countryside-luxe' take on
British food, together with wines from the
family's 'Nutbourne' vineyard. An early
doors July 2022 review here by The Evening
Standard's Jimi Famurewa echoed the mixed
reports our survey sometimes throws up
regarding the Gladwin chain: he accused it
of being "afflicted by a kind of well-meaning
mediocrity", delivering a "playful spin on…
quintessentially British flavour combinations…
devoid of the requisite skilled execution". /
SW19 5EE; www.theblacksheep-restaurant.com;
@theblacksheep_resto; Wed-Fri 10.30 pm, Tue
10 pm, Sat 11.30 pm, Sun 8.30 pm; closed Tue L,
closed Mon.

BLACK RADISH
SW19   £81   453

28 RIDGWAY   020 8617 3960   11–2B

"The food is exceptional" from a monthly
changing menu at this three-year-old
independent in Wimbledon Village, owned
by "talented young chef" Toby Cartwright,
who is supported well by a "knowledgeable
front of house team". Most of the
restaurant's fan club are local, but they feel
it deserves wider recognition. / SW19 4QW;
www.blackradishsw19.com; @blackradishsw19;
Wed-Sat 11.30 pm; closed Wed-Fri L, closed Mon
& Tue & Sun.

BLACK SALT
SW14   £49   532

505 - 507 UPPER RICHMOND ROAD WEST
020 4548 3327   11–2A

"Oh, the lucky punters of East Sheen!" – this
suburban yearling is "more convenient than
Dastaan in Ewell" (its legendary elder sibling)
but has become a similar must-visit for those
serious about ticking off London's best Indians.
Manish Sharma's "very classy" cooking is
"some of the best ever" according to some
reports, with "very subtle spicing and very good
quality ingredients… amazing". "Bravo!" Top
Menu Tips – the lamb chops and chilli garlic
tiger prawns. / SW14 7DE; blacksaltsheen.com;
@blacksaltsheen; Tue-Thu 10 pm, Fri & Sat 10.30
pm, Sun 9 pm; closed Tue-Fri L, closed Mon.

BLACKLOCK   £51   343

24 GREAT WINDMILL ST, W1
020 3441 6996   4–3D
16A BEDFORD STREET, WC2
020 303 4139   5–3C
28 RIVINGTON STREET, EC2
AWAITING TEL   13–1B
13 PHILPOT LANE, EC3
020 7998 7676   10–3D

"You can't really go wrong with the plates
of meaty delicious chops" ("nothing delicate
or subtle just full flavours doing the meat full
justice") at these "no-frills but hearty" pit stops,
which provide a "vibrant" and "excellent-value"
option for an inexpensive meal out. "It's great
to be able to choose how many chops you want
to eat and the sides and sauces are the absolute
best". "They deliver an impressively consistent
performance", and "given that there is nowhere
to hide when the food is this simple, it's hats
off to the chefs here!" "Don't go for a quiet
night", though, as they "can be rather rowdy".
Top Tip – "the Monday night Butcher's Block
offer is super value, especially when teamed up
with £10 corkage to BYO". / theblacklock.com;
blacklockchops.

BLANCHETTE W1   £67   343

9 D'ARBLAY ST   020 7439 8100   4–1C

"A real gem in the heart of Soho", this little
slice of Belle Époque Paris serves small plates
of "proper bistro food in a proper bistro
setting" – "not fancy, but delicious". Founded
by three French brothers and named after their
mother, it celebrates its 10th anniversary this
year. / W1F 8DS; www.blanchettesoho.co.uk;
@blanchettelondon; Mon-Sat 11 pm; closed Sun.

BLANDFORD COMPTOIR
W1   £72   333

1 BLANDFORD STREET
020 7935 4626   2–1A

A visit to this "very focused" Marylebone wine
bar from sommelier Xavier Rousset is "an
exciting experience for wine lovers" – "the
breadth and array of Rhône vintages allow
for an exploration that's not possible anywhere
else". The "small plates" of bistro food tick
the boxes, but can seem "rather mundane" by
comparison. / W1U 3DA; blandford-comptoir.
co.uk; @blandfordcomptoir; Tue-Sat 11 pm; closed
Sun & Mon; no Amex.

BLEECKER
BURGER   £28   422

205 VICTORIA ST, SW1   NO TEL   2–4B
THE BALCONY, WESTFIELD WHITE CITY,
W12   020 3582 2930   1–3B
UNIT B PAVILION BUILDING, SPITALFIELDS
MKT, E1   07712 540501   13–2B
BLOOMBERG ARCADE, QUEEN VICTORIA
STREET, EC4   AWAITING TEL   10–3C

"The best burgers in town" – "the juiciest,
the most flavourful" – are a credible claim
for this quartet in Spitalfields, Victoria, the
City's Bloomberg Arcade and Westfield White

Benares W1

City, the highest-rated of the non-mainstream burger chains in our survey this year. New Yorker Zan Kaufman named them after the Greenwich Village street where she ate the burger that inspired her to quit her job as a corporate lawyer and start flipping patties on the back of a London truck, 11 years ago. / www.bleecker.co.uk; bleeckerburger.

BLEEDING HEART BISTRO EC1 £63 3 3 4

BLEEDING HEART YARD
0207 2428238   10–2A

"Overlooking the atmospheric and historic Bleeding Heart Yard", this "agreeable" if "slightly cramped", "old-school" bistro (with a splendid terrace in summer) is "well worth the venture outside the City perimeter" for finance-types, both for a "fun and not too formal" client lunch or a "so romantic" evening meal. "Dependable quality French-ish fare" completes the picture. / EC1N 8SJ; www.bleedingheart.co.uk; @bleedingheartyd; Mon-Fri 10.30 pm, Sat 10 pm; closed Sat L, closed Sun; booking max 12 may apply.

BLUE BOAR PUB SW1 £77 3 2 2

CONRAD LONDON ST JAMES, 22-28 BROADWAY   020 3301 1400   2–3C

This 'modern take on the British pub' with food by chef Sally Abé, formerly of the stellar Harwood Arms, is "part of the huge improvement of the City of Westminster's offering over the last few years". "The food is good, particularly the meat" – but calling it a 'pub' can feel like "a hopeless misnomer" ("it is a hotel restaurant with formal service – OK, no tablecloths – but waiters standing to attention") and at quiet times it can lack atmosphere. / SW1S 0BH; blueboarlondon.com; @blueboarpub; Mon-Sun 11 pm.

BLUEBIRD SW3 £96 2 1 4

350 KING'S ROAD   020 7559 1000   6–3C

This stylish conversion of a landmark 1920s Chelsea car showroom from the D&D London stable certainly looks the part, but it continues to generate amazingly little feedback in our annual diners' poll beyond the occasional complaint along the lines of: "service was appalling and the food not much better". / SW3 5UU; www.bluebird-restaurant.co.uk; @bluebirdchelsea; Mon-Wed, Fri, Thu, Sat 10.30 pm, Sun 9.30 pm.

BOB BOB RICARD £86 2 4 5

1 UPPER JAMES STREET, W1
020 3145 1000   4–2C
LEVEL 8, 122 LEADENHALL STREET, EC3
020 3145 1000   10–2D

"Always fun with the 'Press for Champagne' button!" – Leonid Shutov's decadently boothed joint sets an extravagant tone, ideal "for special occasions" and also "taking the awkwardness out of any business lunch or dinner". It's "not a cheap option, though, so you have to like the guest...". The luxurious food, including a selection of caviar, is "fair" – "stick with the classics (such as beef Wellington to die for) to avoid disappointment". Fortunately, the wine is "not overpriced" thanks to a £50 mark-up limit which favours the top of the list. In late 2021, Shutov relaunched the glitzy offshoot in the City's Cheesegrater, changing its name from Bob Bob Cité to Bob Bob Ricard City. Early reports say it's "got a lot to live up to, but it turns out the vibe amongst the banks, bling and skyscrapers of the Square Mile really works!". More spinoffs are planned, as in late summer 2022, the brand announced it has VC backing for national and international expansion.(Note: Bob Bob Ricard has raised funds for Ukraine and changed the spelling of chicken Kyiv following the Russian invasion). /

BOB'S LOBSTER SE1 £59 3 4 2

UNIT 71, ST THOMAS STREET
020 7407 7099   10–4C

"Very good lobster backed up by good chips" and "fast service" win fans for this American-style joint near Borough Market, also with a bright red-and-white VW campervan offshoot that parks at various locations through the summer. But the bill can be "toppy". / SE1 3QX; www.bobslobster.com; @bobs_lobster; Tue-Fri 11 pm, Sat 9 pm; closed Tue-Thu L, closed Sun & Mon.

BOBO SOCIAL SE17 £67 3 3 3

23 SAYER STREET   020 7636 9310   1–3C

One of the bright sparks near Elephant & Castle – this attractive haunt (with cocktail bar) majors in breakfast and brunch options, but also offers a small, eclectic selection of impactful bites (the Bobo Burger, truffle pasta, Thai curry, steak, fish 'n' chips…). We've rated it on limited feedback. / SE17 1FY; bobosocial.

com; @bobosocial; Mon-Sun 11.30 pm; payment – credit card only.

BOCCA DI LUPO W1 £66 4 3 3

12 ARCHER ST   020 7734 2223   4–3D

"Wildly popular for its diverse offering of small plates of terrific and original Italian regional cuisine": Jacob Kenedy's "relentlessly busy" ("cramped and noisy") West End venue is many reporters' first choice for a favourite London Italian. Aided by a convenient situation, just a short stroll from Piccadilly Circus and "well-located for the theatres" – it's become a regular feature in the list of Top-20 London restaurants in our annual diners' poll. The selection of carefully researched and sourced Italian 'tapas' are "reliably original and sometimes surprising"; and matched with a "hugely varied" Italian wine list. The food rating slipped a tad this year, though, due to gripes of some dishes "lacking their customary perfection" or "leaning towards being overpriced". "It's a fairly small, intimate venue with counter seating at the front, where you can watch the chefs cook, as well as some more relaxed and comfortable tables at the back" (most regulars feeling it's "best at the bar"). Top Tip – "superb negronis and stuffed olives and the risotto is always top notch". / W1D 7BB; www.boccadilupo.com; @bocca_di_lupo; Mon-Sat 11 pm, Sun 9.30 pm; booking max 10 may apply.

BOCCONCINO RESTAURANT W1 £107 2 2 2

19 BERKELEY ST   020 7499 4510   3–3C

"The glitz, the glamour, the bling" – this Mayfair outpost of Mikhail Gokhner's Moscow-based chain dishes up wood-fired pizza and Italian comfort food with mixed results: to critics it's extravagant pricing is far too OTT, but there is also the odd fan who "wanted to dislike it but was charmed". / W1J 8ED; www.bocconcinorestaurant.co.uk; @bocconcino_london; Mon-Sat 12.30 am, Sun 10.30 pm.

BOILER & CO SE1 £52 5 4 3

5 CANVEY STREET   020 7928 1554   10–4B

"Imaginative Caribbean fine dining is an unlikely find at any time – particularly considering the bland location of Anguilla-born Kerth Gumbs's Bankside newcomer, which opened in early 2022 amidst the anonymous glass-fronted offices behind Tate Modern. The Evening Standard's Jimi Famu thought his east Caribbean-inspired tasting menu to be "dumbfoundingly good… laser-honed… top end" cuisine, while one early reporter questions "is this a potential Michelin star at some stage". Definitely "worth trying". / SE1 9AN; boilerandco.com; @boilerandcompany; Tue-Thu 11 pm, Fri & Sat 1 am, Mon 5 pm, Sun 4 pm; closed Sun & Mon D.

BOISDALE OF BELGRAVIA
SW1 £85 223

15 ECCLESTON STREET
020 7730 6922 2–4B

"With its excellent exterior cigar terrace, range of whiskies and food usually with a Scottish twist – there's always a fun evening" (often buoyed by live jazz too) at Ranald Macdonald's Scottish-themed Belgravia stalwart, a short walk from Victoria station. Eldest son of the 24th chief and captain of Clanranald, his wine-trade background is evident in a strong list, while the selection of steaks and venison reveal him as an early champion of British ingredients. Critics say the food is only "average", but for a red-blooded business meeting it's tailor made for the purpose. / SW1W 9LX; www.boisdale.co.uk/belgravia; @boisdale_uk; Mon-Fri 1 am, Sat midnight, Sun 4 pm; closed Mon, Sat L closed Sun D.

BOISDALE OF CANARY
WHARF E14 £69 324

CABOT PLACE 020 7715 5818 12–1C

"If you want a reliable weekend meal and some, mmmm, smooth funktastic jazz", this Canary Wharf member of Ranald Macdonald's Caledonian-themed group often comes recommended thanks to its "great live music entertainment", "good-value set menus" and "decent roasts". During the week, its menu of oysters, Scottish beef and other fairly traditional fare is nominated for an "excellent business lunch". / E14 4QT; www.boisdale.co.uk/canary-wharf; @boisdale_restaurants; Tue, Wed 11 pm, Fri & Sat 2 am, Thu midnight, Sun 4.30 pm; closed Mon.

BOMBAY BRASSERIE
SW7 £88 333

COURTFIELD ROAD 020 7370 4040 6–2B

"Authentic flavours", "attractive surroundings" and "reasonable prices for what you get" win consistent solid ratings for this upmarket Indian veteran, now 40 years old and owned by the Taj Hotels group. / SW7 4QH; www.bombayb.co.uk; @bombaybrasseriesw7; closed Mon-Sat & Sun.

BOMBAY BUSTLE
W1 £73 544

29 MADDOX STREET 020 7290 4470 3–2C

"Noisy and aptly named bustle" – this "well-executed and brilliant concept" (sibling to Jamavar) is inspired by the street food of Mumbai: a "deeply impressive range of dishes" and results are "mind-blowing" – with just "the right balance of spices and herbs". / W1W 2PA; www.bombaybustle.com; @bombaybustle; Mon-Sat 10.30 pm, Sun 9.30 pm.

BOMBAY PALACE
W2 £62 543

50 CONNAUGHT ST 020 7723 8855 7–1D

"The name is very apt" for this "superb" and rather old-fashioned operation, "quietly tucked away behind Edgware Road". Now celebrating its 40th anniversary, it serves "consistently brilliant" and "authentic food, using traditional recipes", including an "imaginative selection of Indian street-food dishes". "It's not pretentious, and the service is good – never rushed. The makeover a couple of years back still looks attractive and helped modernise the venue". / W2 2AA; www.bombay-palace.co.uk; @bombaypalacelondon; Mon, Thu, Wed, Sun 9.30 pm, Fri & Sat 10.30 pm; closed Wed L, closed Tue.

BONE DADDIES £42 333

NOVA, VICTORIA ST, SW1 NO TEL 2–4B
30-31 PETER ST, W1 020 7287 8581 4–2D
46-48 JAMES ST, W1 020 3019 7140 3–1A
24 OLD JAMAICA ROAD, SE16
020 7231 3211 10–4D
22 PUTNEY HIGH ST, SW15
020 8246 4170 11–2B
THE BOWER, 211 OLD STREET, EC1
020 3019 6300 13–1A

This ten-year-old rock 'n' roll ramen concept is in expansion mode at the moment, having pushed into the southwestern suburbs with openings in Richmond and Putney in recent years, followed by High Street Ken and the former Eurostar terminal at Waterloo station in 2022. They "still do a very fine bowl of tonkotsu", and the classic rock soundtrack stays the same. / www.bonedaddies.com; bonedaddies.

BONOO NW2 £57 333

675 FINCHLEY ROAD 020 7794 8899 1–1B

A wide variety of unusual and tasty small plates is on the menu at this family-run Indian in Child's Hill, which scores consistently high ratings for its delicious cooking. / NW2 2JP; www.bonoo.co.uk; @bonoo.indian.tapas; Mon-Sun 10.30 pm; closed Mon-Sun L.

BOOKING OFFICE 1869, ST
PANCRAS RENAISSANCE
HOTEL NW1 £83 335

EUSTON ROAD 020 7841 3566 9–3C

During the pandemic, this fine space was given a lavish makeover and relaunched in late 2021, complete with eight 8-metre tall palm trees, striking pendant lights (made up of 267 brass leaves each), and a 22-metre long bar. The all-day menu created by chef Patrick Powell is a succession of luxurious bites (there's a raw bar, salads, fish finger sarnie, steak…), making this "an excellent place for a good-quality and fairly priced bar-type meal" as you make the most of the extensive cocktail menu. In summer months, the hotel also runs a substantial roof garden along the same theme. / NW1 2AR; www.booking-office.co.uk; @bookingoffice; Tue-Thu midnight, Fri & Sat 1 am, Mon 11 pm; closed Mon D, closed Sun.

BOOKS FOR COOKS
W11 £23 344

4 BLENHEIM CRESCENT
020 7221 1992 7–1A

"A hidden find" in Notting Hill's famous cookbook shop, where staff knock up a set lunch following recipes from one of the books in stock. ("Where can you have a 3-course lunch for £7?". "Not sure if I want too many people to know about this place – absurdly cheap no-choice menu, but one of the best meals I had all year. Can still taste it now. Please don't go!"). / W11 1NN; www.booksforcookslondon; @booksforcookslondon; Tue-Sat 6 pm; closed Sun & Mon.

BOQUERIA £51 332

192 ACRE LN, SW2 020 7733 4408 11–2D
278 QUEENSTOWN ROAD, SW8
020 7498 8427 11–1C

"Bright modern tapas with some old favourites" are on the menu at this "stylish" pair south of the river, named after the food market in Barcelona. "Consistently good cooking" and "reasonable prices" are the plus points, although they may "lack the extra zing of the very best places". / www.boqueriatapas.com; boqueria_london.

IL BORDELLO E1 £57 323

METROPOLITAN WHARF, 70 WAPPING
WALL 020 7481 9950 12–1A

"If you want a family Italian restaurant look no further", say fans of this trattoria and pizza favourite of two decades standing at the foot of a Wapping warehouse conversion: "supported by locals and always busy". / E1E 3SS; www.ilbordello.com; @ilbordellorestaurant; Mon-Sat 11 pm, Sun 10.30 pm; closed Mon L.

IL BORRO W1 £128 333

15 BERKELEY STREET
020 3988 7717 3–3C

The jury is still out on this ultra-high-end Italian following its lockdown-delayed 2021 opening in the Mayfair premises formerly occupied by Nobu Berkeley (RIP). It's a "lovely space" with a "great fit-out", and "the fish is fantastic" – so "all the ingredients are there and it could become really good once it has shaken down". On the debit side, it's "ridiculously overpriced" (which it needs to be to cover the rent, a local record). Owned by the Ferragamo fashion family, it's named after their Tuscan estate, whose produce and wine are on the menu. / W1W 8DY; ilborrotuscanbistro.co.uk; @tuscanbistrolondon; Mon-Wed midnight, Thu-Sat 1 am, Sun 07.

BOSSA W1

3 VERE STREET AWAITING TEL 3–1B

Launching beneath the Brazilian consulate in Marylebone in a former branch of Maroush – this late 2022 debut represents part of the ever-more thriving Latino scene in the capital. Brazilian chef Alberto Landgraf is of German and Japanese heritage and, back in the day, started working in hospitality in London (for Gordon Ramsay and Tom Aikens) to fund his studies as a physics graduate. Back home and bitten by the hospitality bug, he later went on to found Epice (in São Paolo) and Oteque (in Rio, and on the World's 50 Best list) before now returning to the capital promising 'contemporary Brazilian food and a very strong wine and cocktail list'. / W1W 0DG; Mon-Sun midnight.

BOTTLE & RYE SW9

GROUND FLOOR, 404-406 MARKET ROW NO TEL 11–2D

From Robin and Sarah Gill, this July 2022 newcomer in Brixton's Market Row is a little (28 covers) all-day venture, which invokes Parisian café culture as its inspiration. As the name hints, it's as much about drinking as it is about eating, with an imaginative small menu served alongside a list of ever-changing funky wines and cocktails. / SW9 8LD; www.bottleandrye.com; @bottleandrye; Mon-Wed 10 pm, Thu-Sat 10.30 pm.

BOUDIN BLANC
W1   £87 ③③④

5 TREBECK ST   020 7499 3292   3–4B

"Unquestionably French", this "fun and atmospheric bistro" is a "long-term favourite" in Mayfair's cute Shepherd Market. Top Tip – "arrive early – the brilliant specials are very popular and can run out". / W1J 7LT; www.boudinblanc.co.uk; @leboudinblanc; Tue-Sat 10.30 pm; closed Sat L, closed Sun & Mon.

BOULEVARD WC2   £57 ②③③

40 WELLINGTON ST   020 7240 2992   5–3D

This "old-fashioned" Gallic brasserie has served "wonderfully consistent French fayre" "right in the middle of Covent Garden" for more than 30 years. It's "great fun with very decent food for the price given the area", with a "cheap, cheerful and reliable" prix-fixe menu for pre- or post-theatre dining. / WC2E 7BD; www.boulevardbrasserie.co.uk; @boulevardbrasseriewc2; Mon & Tue, Sun 10 pm, Wed-Sat 11 pm.

THE BOUNDARY E2   £69

**2-4 BOUNDARY STREET
020 7729 1051   13–1B**

In May 2022 (too late for any survey feedback), this Shoreditch design hotel reopened its ground-floor bar/restaurant (fka The Albion Café) as an all-day brasserie. The 100-seat space, whose original hard-edged design was overseen by the late Sir Terence Conran, has been modified and somewhat cosied up (no longer with its own street entrance). Chef Robin Freeman also looks after the hotel's glam-looking refurbished rooftop bar and restaurant, while what was once Tatra in the basement is nowadays an event space. The rooftop looks set to become the place to be here. / E2 7DD; boundary.london; @boundaryldn; Mon-Sun 11 pm.

BOXCAR BAKER & DELI
W1   £10 ③③③

7A WYNDHAM PLACE   020 3006 7000   2–1A

"Great coffee and an always-buzzy vibe" make it worth remembering this attractive, all-day Marylebone deli/café, which serves a mix of patisserie, cakes, soups, salads and sarnies from breakfast onwards. / W1W 1PN; boxcar.co.uk; @boxcarbaker; Mon-Sun 5 pm; closed Mon-Sun D.

BRACKENBURY WINE ROOMS
W6   £55 ②③③

**111-115 HAMMERSMITH GROVE
020 3696 8240   8–1C**

A "fantastic wine list", including "interesting wines by the glass", is the strong suit at this Hammersmith hub, where verdicts on the "bistro cooking" range from "dependable, with good ingredients" to "OK but rather boring". Breakfast gets a thumbs-up – "fab baps" and "they remember how you like your coffee". / W6 0NQ; winerooms.london/brackenbury; @wine_rooms; Mon-Sat 11 pm, Sun 4 pm; closed Sun D.

BRADLEY'S NW3   £66 ②②②

25 WINCHESTER RD   020 7722 3457   9–2A

Simon Bradley has been cooking for well over 30 years at this stalwart venue, in a backstreet near Swiss Cottage tube station, whose smart interior is judged somewhere between "gloomy" and "pleasant". The "mostly good" (if occasionally "erratic") European cuisine and "nicely priced wine list" mean it's "well above the norm for the area", making it particularly "useful for a pre-Hampstead Theatre meal." / NW3 3NR; www.bradleysnw3.co.uk; @bradleysnw3; Wed-Sat, Tue 9 pm, Sun 2.30 pm; closed Tue L closed Sun D, closed Mon.

LA BRASSERIA   £86 ③③③

**42 MARYLEBONE HIGH STREET, W1
020 7486 3753   2–1A
290 WESTBOURNE GROVE, W11
020 7052 3564   7–2B**

"The quality and consistency of the dishes is first-class and service excellent" at the original location of this Italian duo ('La Brasseria Milanese'), which opened in Marylebone in May 2018. A second all-day offshoot opened in Notting Hill in autumn 2021. It's inspired little commentary as yet, but Tom Parker Bowles in The Daily Mail praised its "handsome" styling and a menu of "old-fashioned crowd pleasers and greatest hits". / https://www.labrasseria.com.

BRASSERIE
BLANC   £62 ②②②

**119 CHANCERY LANE, WC2
020 7405 0290   2–2D
GOLDHURST HOUSE, PARR'S WAY, W6
020 8237 5566   8–2C
9 BELVEDERE RD, SE1
020 7202 8470   2–3D
60 THREADNEEDLE ST, EC2
020 7710 9440   10–2C**

"A perfect location opposite the National Theatre and Festival Hall and good pre-theatre set-menu" win particular nominations for the SE1 branch of this well-known national group. Even some fans "wish there were more adventurous choices on the menu", but they still recommend the "French-influenced" brasserie cooking as "better quality than many rivals even if it is very much chain fare". The overall verdict, though, is that it's "just OK, especially

bearing in mind the prestigious name under which they trade". / www.brasserieblanc.com.

BRASSERIE OF LIGHT
W1   £77 ②②⑤

400 OXFORD STREET   020 3940 9600   3–1A

"Fabulous décor" is the main talking point at Richard Caring's brasserie for shoppers on the first floor of Selfridges, which is dominated by Damien Hirst's 24ft tall crystal-encrusted Pegasus (Caring has become the artist's leading British collector in recent years). The place is also "great for people-watching & a buzzy atmosphere – I love it". And the food? "OK, but nothing to shout about". / W1W 1AB; www.brasserie-of-light.co.uk; @brasserieoflight; Mon-Sat midnight, Sun 11 pm.

BRASSERIE ZÉDEL
W1   £49 ①④⑤

20 SHERWOOD ST   020 7734 4888   4–3C

"A unique feature in London's dining scene" – this "incredible subterranean cathedral of Art Deco glamour and French classic cuisine" was created 10 years ago by Corbin & King in homage to the brasseries of Paris. It occupies a "vast" and "absolutely stunning Art Deco basement" (Grade I listed with "gilding, marble columns and red velvet seating") and "what is so outstanding is to find a restaurant of this quality just a stone's throw from Piccadilly Circus". To be clear, the lengthy menu of brasserie staples "won't surprise you" – the catering has always been "OK" at best, and the food score this year was beyond humdrum. But next to the "white tablecloths and terrific old-world atmosphere and buzz"; plus "formally attired" service that's "efficient and charming"; then "the food is almost beside the point" and the availability of "some extremely cheap menus" underpins its "eyebrow-raisingly good value (so you can forgive it a lot)". With the management changes within The Wolseley Hospitality Group just prior to our annual diners' poll, many reporters feel "it's sad to see the founders no longer involved" and continue to worry – "will its distinctive qualities be lost?" Top Tip – "try to go later in the evening when the band is playing for an authentic French vibe. Also pop into the Bar Americain for a pre- or post-dinner cocktail." / W1F 7ED; www.brasseriezedel.com; @brasseriezedel; Mon-Sat 11 pm, Sun 10 pm.

BRAT E1   £87 ④③③

FIRST FLOOR, 4 REDCHURCH STREET   NO TEL 13–1B

"Sensational" cooking over an open fire in the corner of the room has won the highest culinary esteem (including from the Harden's London Restaurant Awards) for Tomos Parry's "unassuming" Shoreditch venue, which sits in a "functional and slightly industrial", first-floor dining room above 'Smoking Goat'. In particular, "the signature turbot is a must-try" ('Brat' is another name for turbot) and has become a checklist item for London foodie fashionistas. Its food rating slipped this year from the highest heights on a few reports of "great but slightly inconsistent" meals. For most of its many fans, though, a meal here is still "always wonderful". Top Menu Tips – aside from the turbot: "still superb bread and anchovy…", "soused mackerel in a piquant broth was divine…", "smoked potatoes are my Death Row dish…" / E1 6JJ; www.bratrestaurant.com; @bratrestaurant; Mon-Sun 9.45 pm.

BRAT AT CLIMPSON'S ARCH E8 £94 **433**
CLIMPSON'S ARCH, 374 HELMSLEY PLACE 020 7254 7199 14–2B

A "too-cool-for-school railway arch" and covered courtyard ("a great fun place on a sunny day") provides the "quirky" setting for Tomos Parry's "funky hang-out" in London Fields (a pandemic pop-up in 2020 that turned permanent). Staff are "casual but super-knowledgeable" and deliver "simple food cooked over fire" that's often "fabulous" ("that turbot… Wow!"). But, while most reporters have found it "hard to pick fault the few times we have visited", others feel it's "interesting and trendy, but at a hell of a price for a glorified pop-up" or say "I really wanted to like it but came away underwhelmed by the food and the plastic tent (prefer the original)". / E8 3SB; bratrestaurant.com/climpsons-arch; @bratrestaurant; Wed-Sat 10 pm, Sun 9 pm; closed Wed-Fri L, closed Mon & Tue; payment – credit card only.

BRAVI RAGAZZI SW16 £48 **422**
2A SUNNYHILL ROAD 020 8769 4966 11–2D

This ten-year-old pizzeria has a loyal following for its "exceptional" sourdough base and toppings. Neapolitan-born co-founder Andrea Asciuti has also launched a modernised take on his home city's cooking with 081 Pizzeria at Peckham Levels. / SW16 2UH; www.braviragazzipizzeria.co.uk; @braviragazzipizzeria; Mon-Thu 10.30 pm, Fri & Sat 11 pm, Sun 10 pm; closed Mon-Thu L.

BRAWN E2 £76
49 COLUMBIA ROAD 020 7729 5692 14–2A

This former icon of East End gastronomy is starting to look like a handy stop-off point near Columbia Road flower market, but not much more. The odd fan still hails its Med-inspired food and funky wine list as "exceptional all-round", but – as Ed Wilson and his team have diverted effort to Sargasso in Margate – interest seems to be on the wane here (and, given the surprising paucity of reports, we've left it un-rated this year). / E2 7RG; www.brawn.co; @brawn49; Tue-Sat, Mon 10.30 pm; closed Mon L, closed Sun.

BREAD STREET KITCHEN EC4 £82 **233**
10 BREAD STREET 020 3030 4050 10–2B

"As Gordon Ramsay chain restaurants go, the food is dependable enough" at this generously spaced modern brasserie, in a big mall next to St Paul's (but even those who agree it's "absolutely fine" may also consider it "very poor value"). "Despite being in EC4, the restaurant has a decent vibe", and it's tipped both for a business lunch and its "generous Sunday lunch". / EC4M 9AJ; www.gordonramsayrestaurants.com/bread-street-kitchen; @breadstkitchen; Mon-Wed midnight, Thu-Sat 1 am, Sun 10 pm.

BREAKFAST CLUB £42 **333**
BRANCHES THROUGHOUT LONDON

These "quirky, popular and lively venues" (nine in London; four more out of town) serve "British and American comfort foods" in "good portions" – think pancakes, full English fry-ups, French toast, plus cocktails later in the day. It's all "deeply unhealthy – but soooo delicious with good-quality ingredients". Top Tip – "benefits for over-65s" (in the shape of half-price dishes). / www.thebreakfastclubcafes.com; thebrekkyclub.

BRICIOLE W1 £64 **332**
20 HOMER ST 020 7723 0040 7–1D

"Real country-style cooking" can be found at this "good-value neighbourhood deli/trat" near Edgware Road station, serving "the sort of dishes you would find in many a small-town restaurant in Italy". Originally it was a spin-off from Latium (RIP) in Fitzrovia, which closed in 2018 after 14 years. Top Menu Tip – "black bean and pork stew, polenta, bitter turnip tops and perfectly stewed borlotti beans". / W1H 4NA; www.briciole.co.uk; @briciolerestaurant; Mon-Sat 10.30 pm, Sun 10.15 pm.

BRICK LANE BEIGEL BAKE E1 £9 **421**
159 BRICK LN 020 7729 0616 13–1C

"Unmatched in London", this remnant of the East End Jewish community is "always busy, and you can see why". Every week it produces up to 20,000 beigels (note the traditional European spelling), available 24/7 stuffed with "good portions of salt beef", lox, pickled herring and more. "A dire location, but I can't help going back on a regular basis, as I've done for nearly four decades". / E1 6SB; www.beigelbake.co.uk; @beigel_bake; Mon-Sun midnight; cash only; no booking.

BRIGADIERS EC2 £71 **544**
BLOOMBERG ARCADE, QUEEN VICTORIA STREET 020 3319 8140 10–3C

"One of the sheer tastiest places to eat in town" – JKS Restaurants' highly popular outpost in Bloomberg Arcade continues to inspire raves for its "delicious and different" Indian cuisine (very much "not your traditional curry house"). The large interior, with its many bars and TV screens, is more divisive: it's "awesome" for its core clientele, but "the ambience screams 'City Boys' (especially when there's on)". Top Menu Tip – "Indo-Chinese chilli paneer lettuce cups… so many tastes at the same time!" / EC2E; brigadierslondon.com; @brigadiersldn; Mon-Sat 10.45 pm; closed Sun.

BRIGHT E8 £84 **443**
NETIL HOUSE, 1 WESTGATE STREET 020 3095 9407 14–2B

"No name on outside" bespeaks the confidence of this hipster favourite in London Fields (from the same stable as P Franco and the recently defunct Peg) – a high-ceilinged, sparse space that lives up to its title (but can become "very noisy"). In the group's trademark style, it serves "a short menu of good small plates and selection of low-intervention wines, including by the glass". / E8 3RL; www.brightrestaurant.co.uk; @bright_restaurant; Wed & Thu 11.30 pm, Fri-Sun midnight; closed Wed & Thu L, closed Mon & Tue.

THE BRIGHT COURTYARD W1 £84 **322**
43-45 BAKER ST 020 7486 6998 2–1A

"Good food", including dim sum, makes this modern Chinese an "always dependable" option in Marylebone, although the setting – an office block near Portman Square – isn't an attraction in itself. / W1U 8EW; www.lifefashiongroup.com; @BrightCourtyard; Mon-Sat 10.30 pm, Sun 9.30 pm.

BRINKLEY'S SW10 £69 **223**
47 HOLLYWOOD RD 020 7351 1683 6–3B

The flagship of John Brinkley's wine-focused southwest London group attracts a well-heeled Chelsea set out for a good time. "You really shouldn't expect great food, let alone good value at this address" – but there's plenty of fun to be had here, and at spin-offs in Wandsworth Bridge Road and overlooking Wandsworth Common. / SW10 9HX; www.brinkleys.com; Mon-Sun 11 pm.

BRINKLEY'S KITCHEN SW17 £65 **223**
35 BELLEVUE RD 020 8672 5888 11–2C

This "always busy neighbourhood favourite" overlooking Wandsworth Common ticks the boxes as a "very handy local", with John Brinkley's trademark "keenly priced wine list" and "competent modern British food". / SW17 7EF; www.brinkleys.com; @brinkleyskitchen; Tue-Sat 11 pm, Sun 4 pm; closed Tue-Fri L closed Sun D, closed Mon.

THE BROADCASTER W12 £61 **333**
101 WOOD LANE 020 4549 7420 1–2B

Near the entrance to the former TV Centre (and Westfield's John Lewis), this striking-looking modern pub opened in October 2021, followed the following summer by its good-looking 'Aerial Roof Top' bar. It's not dissimilar to King's Cross's well-known Lighterman (same owners) and well-rated for its food – a contemporary brasserie menu that makes something of a feature of its selection of flatbreads. / W12 7FA; www.thebroadcaster.co.uk;

@thebroadcasterlondon; Tue-Fri 11.30 pm, Sat 12.30 am, Sun 7 pm; closed Mon.

BROOK HOUSE
SW6 £68 3|3|3

65 NEW KING'S ROAD
020 7371 5283 11–1B

Overlooking Eel Brook Common in Fulham, this "great (although rather pricey for a pub)" rustic-chic Fulham gastroboozer offers "fast service from attentive staff", and is the follow-up from former royal equerry Mark Dwyer and his partner Eamonn Manson, who sold their local trio the Sands End (Prince Harry's occasional watering hole), Cross Keys and Brown Cow for a reported £10m six years ago. / SW6 4SG; brookhousefulham.com; @brookhousefulham; Tue-Thu 11 pm, Fri & Sat midnight, Sun 5 pm; closed Tue L closed Sun D, closed Mon; payment – credit card only.

BROOKMILL SE8 £47 3|3|3

65 CRANBROOK ROAD
020 8333 0899 1–4D

The food is "always good" at this gentrified Victorian pub on a corner site near St John's station in Deptford, part of a well-run quartet of indie gastropubs in southeast London. It has a garden as well as smartly kitted-out guest rooms. / SE8 4EJ; www.thebrookmill.co.uk; @brookmillse8; Mon & Tue 11 pm; closed Mon & Tue L, closed Wed-Sat & Sun.

THE BROWN DOG
SW13 £58 3|2|3

28 CROSS STREET 020 8392 2200 11–1A

"Tucked away among the terraces of Barnes's cute 'Little Chelsea'", this "longstanding food pub" is these days rather more gastro than boozer, and attracts "local ladies who lunch with its tasty cooking". "Dogs, kids and menfolk are equally welcome" – the latter two more in evidence at the weekend. / SW13 0AP; www.thebrowndog.co.uk; @browndogbarnes; closed Mon-Sat & Sun.

BROWN'S HOTEL,
THE DRAWING ROOM
W1 £84 3|4|4

ALBEMARLE ST 020 7493 6020 3–3C

The "quiet and stylish" wooden-panelled Drawing Room has changed little since this Mayfair hotel was built in 1837, and makes a "lovely setting" for afternoon teas that have been enjoyed by Queen Victoria and Agatha Christie, among a roll-call of the great and the good of the past two centuries. Despite the pedigree, fans feel it's "not as stilted and pompous as some famous places", and offers a "much better and friendlier tea, with delicious homemade-style cakes and scones". / W1S 4BP; www.roccofortehotels.com/hotels-and-resorts/brown-s-hotel/dining/the-drawing-room; @Browns_Hotel; Mon-Sun 9 pm; no shorts.

BRUNSWICK HOUSE CAFÉ
SW8 £66 3|2|5

30 WANDSWORTH RD
020 7720 2926 11–1D

You "dine under chandeliers" in the "unique ambience" of a Georgian mansion at Vauxhall Cross which doubles as an architectural salvage emporium and restaurant with "an ever-developing, innovative menu". Chef Jackson Boxer has "turned things up a notch – the food is really very interesting again after a little dip in form over recent years" – while "the atmosphere remains fantastic: louche at lunchtime, party vibes in the evening". / SW8 2LG; www.brunswickhouse.london; @brunswick_house; Wed-Sat, Tue 09.45 pm, Sun 5 pm; closed Tue L closed Sun D, closed Mon.

TRATTORIA BRUTTO
EC1 £49 3|4|5

35-37 GREENHILL RENTS NO TEL 10–1A

"Very cool… very Tuscan… great negronis… it's like going on a mini-break!" – Russell Norman's "dark and sexily-down-to-earth" newcomer is "a fun riff on a Florentine trattoria theme (steak Florentine stars on the menu) from the founder of the late-lamented Polpo, and a very worthwhile addition to the Smithfield area". He's achieved "a superb homage" – it's "skilfully run with its own distinct personality", staff are "charming" and if it's "true that it's noisy, it's good noise: the sound of people enjoying themselves!". Practically nobody has a bad word to say about the "delightfully non-standard Italian food" either: "rustic dishes that are generally simple and well-executed". "I rarely return this many times, in such a short space of time, but this place has it all!" Top Menu Tip – "anchovy with sourdough is the perfect simple starter". / EC1E 6BN; msha.ke/brutto; @bru.tto; Tue-Sat 10.30 pm; closed Sun & Mon.

BUBALA £40 4|4|3

15 POLAND STREET, W1 NO TEL 4–1C
65 COMMERCIAL STREET, E1
020 7922 2111 13–2C

"Prepare to be blown away by the flavours at this tiny spot in Spitalfields" – its "absolutely brilliant vegetarian and vegan", Middle Eastern-inspired dishes "truly sing", delivering "a taste explosion" such that "carnivores will not miss the meat" ("the charred oyster mushroom skewers are stunning… thinking about the labneh, hummus and laffa bread makes me salivate!"). Having opened it in 2019, Marc Summers launched a 50-cover sibling in Soho in July 2022 on the former site of Vasco & Piero's Pavilion (see also), complete with open kitchen and counter-style dining. The chef is rising star Helen Graham. /

THE BULL N6 £63 3|3|3

13 NORTH HILL 020 8341 0510 9–1B

A big outside terrace adds further to the appeal of this attractive old Highgate pub, well-rated for its "reliable food and great beer". / N6 4AB;

thebullhighgate.co.uk; @bullhighgate; Mon-Sat 10 pm; closed Sun.

BULL & LAST
NW5 £74 3|3|3

168 HIGHGATE RD 020 7267 3641 9–1B

"Near the edge of Hampstead Heath", this mega-popular gastroboozer "lives up to the hype" and has "retained its pubby feel in spite of a major renovation", which added six bedrooms. At busy times it can be a bit "rowdy", but "the place balances great food with a pub atmosphere which adds to the flavour, and the staff are always 'on it'". / NW5 1QS; www.thebullandlast.co.uk; @thebullandlast; Mon-Thu 11 pm, Sat midnight, Sun 10.30 pm; closed Sat D, closed Fri.

BUN HOUSE WC2 £17 4|3|3

26-27 LISLE STREET 020 8017 9888 5–3A

"Top egg yolk buns" are a big draw at China-born architect Z He and chef Alex Peffly's well-known Chinatown pit stop, which provides an "excellent bustling ambience and wonderful heart-filling food". / WC2W 7BD; bun.house; @8unhouse; closed Mon-Sat & Sun; payment – credit card only; no booking.

BUND N2 £37 3|3|3

4-5 CHEAPSIDE, FORTIS GREEN
020 8365 2643 1–1B

This Pan-Asian two-year-old between Muswell Hill and East Finchley makes a "really great neighbourhood" spot, with its contemporary take on hit oriental dishes from Singapore via China to Korea and Japan. / N2 9HP; bundrestaurant.co.uk; @bundrestaurant; Tue-Sun 10 pm; closed Tue-Sun L, closed Mon.

BURGER & BEYOND
E1 £50 4|3|2

147 SHOREDITCH HIGH STREET
020 3848 8860 13–1B

A "cool spot" in Shoreditch that's the permanent home of a former truck selling some of the "best burgers in London" – "flavoursome, with great ingredients", most notably Yorkshire-bred beef which is dry-aged in Himalayan salt fridges. They also do chicken burgers, funky sides and boozy milkshakes. Spin-offs have opened in Soho and Borough Market, with delivery kitchens in Camden, Vauxhall and Acton. / E1 6JE; burgerandbeyond.co.uk; @burgerandbeyond; Mon-Thu 10 pm, Fri & Sat 11 pm, Sun 9.30 pm.

BURGER &
LOBSTER £72 3|3|3

HARVEY NICHOLS, KNIGHTSBRIDGE, SW1
020 7235 5000 6–1D
26 BINNEY STREET, W1
020 3637 5972 3–2A
29 CLARGES STREET, W1
020 7409 1699 3–4B
36 DEAN STREET, W1 020 7432 4800 5–2A
6 LITTLE PORTLAND STREET, W1
020 7907 7760 3–1C
18 HERTSMERE ROAD, E14

Cinnamon Kitchen EC2

020 3637 6709   12–1C
52 THREADNEEDLE STREET, EC2
020 7256 9755   10–2C
BOW BELLS HS, 1 BREAD ST, EC4
020 7248 1789   10–2B

"Does what it says on the tin", with "no delay making choices". This "simple, good and easy" surf-and-turf chain has grown to nine sites in the capital in 11 years – most with "sufficient space to eat and talk" (rare enough in fast-food joints). The formula is working around the world, too, with openings from New York to the Genting Highlands in Malaysia. "Love the way they give you plastic sheets to cover yourself from flying bits of lobster!" / www.burgerandlobster.com.

BUSABA   £48   322

BRANCHES THROUGHOUT LONDON

This "cheap 'n' cheerful" Thai-fusion group (founded in 1999) with its mix of pad thais, curries and other spicy bites maintains a decent fan base and achieved very steady ratings this year. Creator Alan Yau of Wagamama and Hakkasan fame has long since departed and the business has had a bumpy ride, settling down to nine London branches and offshoots in Oxford and Cardiff. / www.busaba.com; busabaeathai.

BUSTRONOME
WC2   £132   234

40B VICTORIA EMBANKMENT
020 3744 5554   5–4D

"A gourmet meal on a sightseeing bus in London" – might sound hellish but is surprisingly well-reviewed, including by some locals: "the food was tasty and it was a great experience!" / WC2W 6PB; @bustronomelondon; Mon-Sun 10 pm.

BUTLERS WHARF CHOP
HOUSE SE1   £82   223

36E SHAD THAMES   020 7403 3403   10–4D

"A great place for meat, nicely served" – this modern version of the traditional British chophouse is a business-friendly destination close to the City, from the D&D London stable. Its main attraction is a comfortable dining terrace above the river, with spectacular views of Tower Bridge. The restaurant was created by Sir Terence Conran as part of his 'Gastrodome' complex on the South Bank of the Thames, and has flown somewhat

under the radar for many years now. / SE1 2YE; www.chophouse-restaurant.co.uk; @butlerswharfchophouse; Mon-Fri 10 pm, Sat 4 pm, Sun 9 pm; closed Sun L closed Sat D.

BUVETTE W11   £67   223

9 BLENHEIM CRESCENT
020 7229 8398   7–1A

"Really loved discovering Buvette in Paris so was excited to see them opening in London… but while the food was good, the interior lacks the heart of its Paris neighbour" – this cute 'gastrothèque' in Notting Hill is part of an NYC-based group and hasn't made too many waves since it opened in 2020. The extensive drinks offering is a lot longer than its menu of brunch-friendly fare (Les Croques, Salades, Les Oeufs Vapeur) alongside one or two slightly more substantial options (e.g. Steak Tartare or Salmon Rillettes). / W11 1NN; ilovebuvette.com; eat-drink-london-location; @buvettelondon; Mon-Thu 10 pm, Fri midnight, Sat 11 pm, Sun 9 pm.

BYRON   £45   333

BRANCHES THROUGHOUT LONDON

Back from the brink? After a tumultuous couple of years, a CVA, sale, the closure of over half its branches, and new CEO, ratings have steadied at this well-known burger chain. It may only be "standard burger fayre", but most reports say it "ticks so many boxes". / www.byronhamburgers.com.

C&R CAFÉ W1   £35   322

3-4 RUPERT COURT   020 7434 1128   4–3D

"Cheap 'n' cheerful" Malaysian-Chinese diner on the edge of Chinatown that's built a strong fan-base over 25 years for its "excellent food that does not break the bank", combining classic regional dishes with more unusual family recipes. Top Tip – "exceptional Singapore laksa". / W1D 6DY; www.cnrcaferestaurant.com; @cnr.cafe.restaurant; Tue-Thu, Sun 10 pm, Fri & Sat 11 pm; closed Mon.

CABOTTE EC2   £77   354

48 GRESHAM ST   020 7600 1616   10–2C

"Flying slightly under the radar", this "superior City venue" is "a lovely find, right in the heart of the the Square Mile where it can be hard to encounter a good meal" ("clients are always pleased to visit it!"). "The front of house team

are so charming" and deliver "precise and tasty" Gallic cuisine. The major attraction here, though, is the "comprehensive wine list" – "one of the best wine selections in London: it's hard to find a better selection of Burgundy, but the other region lists are well represented", with "many rewards to be found, both on pricing and rare gems". / EC2E 7AY; www.cabotte.co.uk; @cabotte_; Mon-Fri 10 pm; closed Sat & Sun.

THE CADOGAN ARMS
SW3   £69   223

298 KING'S ROAD   020 3148 2630   6–3C

Since it was "gussied up" last year, this "beautiful and comfortable" old Chelsea pub (built in 1838) hasn't made waves, despite a PR push and a laundry list of influential backers (including the owners of JKS Restaurants and Kitchen Table's James Knappett). Its slick gastropub fare can be "excellent", but is not reliably so; service sometimes strikes an "entitled" note; and it can appear "sad to see an institutional Chelsea boozer become a self-conscious eatery". / SW3 5UG; thecadoganarms. london; @cadoganarmspublichouse; Mon-Thu 10 pm, Fri & Sat 10.30 pm, Sun 6 pm; closed Sun D.

CAFE CECILIA E8   £57   223

CANAL PLACE, 32 ANDREWS ROAD
0203 478 6726   14–2B

By the canal in Hackney, this August 2021 newcomer arrived with high expectations thanks to the CV of chef Max Rocha and was quickly blessed by The Guardian's Grace Dent, who felt that despite it's "homespun edge", it was "only just getting started on its path to being one of London most serious restaurants". Our feedback was more cautious: split between finding it "a really nice, friendly new favourite" and "not living up to the hype". / E8 4RL; www.cafececilia.com; @cafececilialondon; Wed & Thu, Sun 3 pm, Fri & Sat 8.30 pm; closed Mon & Tue.

CAFÉ DECO WC1   £53   322

43 STORE STREET   020 8091 2108   2–1C

"It can feel a little uncomfortable" and "canteen-like", but this converted greasy spoon in Bloomsbury (nowadays a 'bar, restaurant and wine shop') belies its looks by serving "imaginative seasonal cooking from a constantly changing menu reflecting the availability of ingredients". The involvement of chef Anna Tobias (who's worked with a host of star chefs) and the hip 40 Maltby Street team hasn't harmed its PR – our feedback is positive, but not quite at the level of raves from the likes of Grace Dent and Tom Parker Bowles. / WC1W 7DB; www.cafe-deco.co.uk; @cafe_deco_bloomsbury; Tue-Sat 9.30 pm; closed Sun & Mon; no Amex.

CAFÉ DU MARCHÉ
EC1   £59   345

22 CHARTERHOUSE SQ
020 7608 1609   10–1B

A "charming" old-style Gallic brasserie (est. 1986), with a "genuine French ambience, in an interesting setting tucked away on the edge of the City" near Smithfield Market. Its classic cuisine remains well-rated, and live jazz in the evenings adds to a special appeal that many find "romantic". / EC1M 6DX; www.cafedumarche.co.uk; @cafedumarche; Tue-Fri 10 pm, Sat 9.30 pm; closed Sat L, closed Sun & Mon.

CAFÉ IN THE CRYPT, ST MARTIN IN THE FIELDS
WC2 £34 2️⃣2️⃣4️⃣

DUNCANNON ST   020 7766 1158   2–2C

Tucked away in the crypt beneath St Martin-in-the-Fields, this "handy" self-service cafeteria occupies a "fantastic space which always feels welcoming" and its no-frills soups, salads and hot plates are just the job for a "quick bite and coffee/glass of wine" when you visit the National Gallery across the road. / WC2N 4JJ; stmartin-in-the-fields.org/cafe-in-the-crypt; @smartininthefields; Mon & Tue, Sun 5 pm, Thu-Sat 7.30 pm, Wed 3 pm; closed Sun-Wed D; no Amex; may need 5+ to book.

CAFÉ KITSUNÉ AT PANTECHNICON
SW1 £20 3️⃣3️⃣4️⃣

**19 MOTCOMB STREET
020 7034 5425   6–1D**

For a posh cup of coffee, the chichi, Japanese-inflected patisserie at the foot of this monumental Belgravia landmark (with mezzanine and foyer seating) has a number of fans – grab a brew, take the weight of your feet and nibble on a double-baked matcha croissant or lunchtime sando. / SW1S 8LB; www.pantechnicon.com; @_pantechnicon; Mon-Sun 7 pm; booking max 12 may apply.

CAFE MURANO £74 2️⃣2️⃣2️⃣

**33 ST JAMES'S ST, SW1
020 3371 5559   3–3C
36 TAVISTOCK ST, WC2
020 3371 5559   5–3D
PASTIFICIO, 34 TAVISTOCK STREET, WC2
020 3535 7884   5–3D
184 BERMONDSEY STREET, SE1
020 3985 1545   10–4D**

"A good choice for a light meal in the centre of own, with a broad menu of uncomplicated dishes to suit most people", and offering "a delicious and authentic taste of Italy" – that's how their large army of followers see Angela Hartnett's "buzzy" and "unpretentious" cafés, proclaiming them "a decent effort all in all". Major complaints are few, but ratings overall end up middling due to gripes of "tired" décor; or culinary results that are "OK but nothing special". Top Menu Tip – "the arancini are always worth a go". / www.cafemurano.co.uk; cafemurano.

CAFÉ SPICE NAMASTE
E16 £69 5️⃣4️⃣4️⃣

**1-2 LOWER DOCK WALK, ROYAL DOCK
020 7488 9242   12–1D**

"New venue, same great flavours and hospitality" – Cyrus and Parvin Todiwala score a major thumbs up for their new "Indian paradise", which, in early 2022, relocated from their age-old location (on the grungy fringes of the City) to this "new site in a fabulous spot on the Royal Docks, and right on the River Thames too, giving you amazing views back up the river past City Airport to Canary Wharf" (nearest DLR, Gallions Reach). The menu is in a new format too – focused more on small plates and designed for sharing – and delivers "Indian dishes often with a Portuguese twist that are excellent". A "genuine welcome" is also part of the attraction, and – having been greeted – a well-stocked cocktail bar is another new addition that will help you recover from the schlep to get there… / E16 2GT; www.cafespice.co.uk; @cafespicenamasteldn; Tue-Sat 10 pm; closed Tue L, closed Sun & Mon.

CAFFÈ CALDESI
W1 £73 3️⃣2️⃣2️⃣

**118 MARYLEBONE LN
020 7487 0754   2–1A**

"Wonderful pasta prepared on site" is the highlight at Tuscany-born chef Giancarlo Caldesi and wife Katie's long-running Marylebone headquarters (they also have a country venue in Bray and a cookery school). Fans reckon it's "always a treat to dine here – it's traditional Italian with attentive and authentic service". / W1U 2QF; www.caldesi.com; @caldesiinmarylebone; Mon-Sat 10.30 pm, Sun 4.30 pm; closed Sun D.

CAIA W10

46 GOLBORNE ROAD   07927 328076   7–1A

Opened in summer 2022 (too late for our annual diners' poll), this 60-seat Portobello 'Wine bar, music venue and open-fire restaurant' is founded by locals Rishabh Vir and Tim Lang; its features include a seasonally changing menu cooked on a custom-made grill in the open kitchen and a 12-seater wine room. / W10 5PR; caia.london; @caia.london; Tue-Thu midnight, Fri & Sat 1 am; closed Tue-Fri L, closed Sun & Mon.

CAKES AND BUBBLES
W1 £71 3️⃣4️⃣3️⃣

**HOTEL CAFE ROYAL, 70 REGENT STREET
020 7406 3310   4–4C**

"Extraordinary" and "visually stunning" – the desserts and cakes at this café on a prime site in Regent Street come sprinkled with Adrià family magic (patron Albert is the brother of Catalan genius Ferran Adrià, and worked as pastry chef at his world-beating restaurant El Bulli, RIP). However, even those who feel "the desserts are really exceptional" can also note that "they don't really deserve the price tags". Still, "once at least you should give it a try, especially with all London's Christmas lights aglow". / W1W 4DY; www.cakesandbubbles.co.uk; @cakesandbubbleslondon; Mon-Sun 10 pm.

CALICI NW3
£51 3️⃣2️⃣2️⃣

29 BELSIZE LANE   020 7435 9888   9–2A

This three-year-old neighbourhood Italian wins solid ratings for its modern cuisine and is a bright spark in Belsize Park's fairly dim culinary constellation. / NW3 5AS; @calici_restaurant; Tue-Thu, Sun 11 pm, Fri & Sat 11.30 pm; closed Tue-Thu L, closed Mon.

THE CAMBERWELL ARMS
SE5 £61 4️⃣4️⃣4️⃣

**65 CAMBERWELL CHURCH ST
020 7358 4364   1–3C**

"Feeling like a piece of hip Shoreditch dropped onto a random patch of Camberwell" – this "thriving" fixture is one of London's best-performing gastropubs in our annual diners' poll. "It's always busy and buzzing and deservedly popular, with friendly and efficient service even when it's super-busy." "Its innovative food, with a focus on sharing, is definitely not playing it safe" and "when it rocks, it really does: big umami blasts of good flavours, realised without fuss". Top Menu Tip – "Sunday lunch with the whole family is a real treat… the shared big joints are wonderful". / SE5 8TR; www.thecamberwellarms.co.uk; @thecamberwellarms; Wed-Sat, Tue 11 pm, Sun 5 pm; closed Tue L closed Sun D, closed Mon; payment – credit card only.

CAMBIO DE TERCIO
SW5 £81 5️⃣4️⃣4️⃣

**161-163 OLD BROMPTON RD
020 7244 8970   6–2B**

"Spanish food is all the rage now but this place has been thriving for years", say fans of Abel Lusa's "fun" but relatively unsung Hispanic in the Old Brompton Road, founded in 1995. "If you're into great Spanish food, this is possibly the best in London" – and it has a "terrific Spanish-only wine list". "Food, wine and service are simply first class", and "they never let you down". / SW5 0LJ; www.cambiodetercio.co.uk; @cambiodetercio; Tue-Sat 11.30 pm, Sun & Mon 11 pm.

CAMINO
£63 2️⃣3️⃣2️⃣

**3 VARNISHERS YD, REGENT QUARTER, N1
020 7841 7330   9–3C
2 CURTAIN ROAD, EC2
020 3948 5003   13–2B
15 MINCING LN, EC3
020 7841 7335   10–3D**

"Reasonable enough tapas, with all the standard dishes" help make this long-running Hispanic trio into "decent" value and also quite "fun" options. The original and best-known branch is "tucked away incredibly close to King's Cross station, which makes it very handy for a meet-up" (with Shoreditch and Monument also useful addresses). / www.camino.uk.com.

Cinnamon Bazaar WC2

THE CAMPANER SW1

1 GARRISON CLOSE, CHELSEA BARRACKS NO TEL 6–3D

In the rarefied quarters of the Candy Brothers' plutocratic Chelsea Barracks development, this autumn 2022 newcomer aims to be the first permanent occupant of the purpose-built space that has previously hosted two Ollie Dabbous pop-ups: The Chelsea Barracks Kitchen and Hideaway. José Parrado of Barcelona's ventures Martinez and Bar Canete is behind the project, whose name means bell ringer in Spanish. / SW1S 8BP; thecampaner.com; @thecampanerchelsea; Mon-Thu midnight, Fri & Sat 12.30 am.

CANTINETTA ANTINORI SW1

4 HARRIET STREET   NO TEL 6–1D

A new spin-off from a famous Florence-based international group (founded in the 1950s, whose HQ is the 15th-century Palazzo Antinori) – this Autumn 2022 newcomer is the brand's first UK venture. It occupies a three-storey site just off Sloane Street, from which it will offer all-day dining featuring Tuscan food and wine in a fairly old-school vein. The opening sounds like it's a project of serious intent, as evidenced by their 10-year lease. Cantinetta Antinori also has outlets in Zurich, Moscow, Vienna and Monaco. / SW1S 9JR; cantinetta-antinori.com/en.

CANTO CORVINO
E1   £77   223

21 ARTILLERY LANE
020 7655 0390   13–2B

By Spitalfieds, this modern Italian makes a feature of fairly straightforward dishes – pasta is a speciality as are grills from the Josper oven. Feedback this year was up-and-down, with some resistance to their current pricing. / E1 7HA; www.cantocorvino.co.uk; @cantocorvino; Mon-Sat 9 pm; closed Sat L, closed Sun.

CANTON ARMS
SW8   £52   334

177 SOUTH LAMBETH RD
020 7582 8710   11–1D

"Simply the best food you'll find in a proper boozer" – this sibling to SE1's Anchor & Hope narrowly beats its relation these days in votes as London's top gastropub (and is a respectable No. 2 on the list). "This isn't a restaurant masquerading as a pub, but the real thing, with atmosphere to match and a great selection of proper beers". "Decent, hearty gastropub fare with a European accent" is served from a "seasonal menu" delivering "big flavours"; and there's also "an interesting wine list, where natural wines are highlighted to avoid surprises". "If the service is a bit idiosyncratic, that's all part of the fun". / SW8 1XP; www.cantonarms.com; @thecantonarms; Tue-Sat 9.45 pm, Sun 3.45 pm; closed Tue, Wed L closed Sun D, closed Mon; no Amex; no booking.

CARACTÈRE W11   £111   454

209 WESTBOURNE PARK ROAD
020 8181 3850   7–1B

"Bringing the expertise and professionalism of Le Gavroche to a more local setting" – Emily Roux (daughter of Michel) and her husband Diego Ferrari's (former head chef at Le Gavroche) Notting Hill four-year-old has become one of London's more notable destinations. It's "an excellent combination of gastronomic dining in a relaxed and civilised interior with just the right balance of buzziness" that provides "understated luxury, but without an eye-watering price tag". The French/Italian menu "changes regularly to show off seasonal ingredients" – "slightly quirkily presented" and with "thoroughly enjoyable" results. And the experience is buoyed by "excellent attention to detail from arrival to departure" from its "skilled and friendly" staff. Top Tip – "divine" lunch menu, which is "brilliant value". / W11 1EA; www.caractererestaurant.com; @caractererestaurant; Mon-Sat 9 pm; closed Sun.

CARAFFINI SW1   £75   343

61-63 LOWER SLOANE ST
020 7259 0235   6–2D

"Just part of Chelsea's culinary 'furniture'!" – this "always enjoyable Italian stalwart" (est 1994), south of Sloane Square, is an "old favourite" for a dedicated silver-haired following, who've patronised it for many years. "The same friendly faces (albeit sometimes masked! in the Covid months)" provide "courteous and amiable service" of "reliable, traditional dishes" ("certainly not cheap but good quality"). / SW1W 8DH; www.caraffini.co.uk; @caraffinirestaurant; Mon-Sat 10.30 pm; closed Sun.

CARAVAGGIO EC3 £62   232

107-112 LEADENHALL ST
020 7626 6206   10–2D

"Somehow still relevant as a City lunch spot", this "reliable" Italian in a converted banking hall is "really a canteen for senior people at Lloyd's – but done in an excellent manner", with "well-executed fare, quickly delivered". The late, great Luciano Pavarotti declared it open in 1996. / EC3A 4DP; www.caravaggiorestaurant.co.uk; @caravaggio_ldn; Mon-Fri 10 pm; closed Sat & Sun.

CARAVAN   £59   222

YALDING HOUSE, 152 GREAT PORTLAND STREET, W1   020 3963 8500   2–1B
1 GRANARY SQ, N1   020 7101 7661   9–3C
METAL BOX FACTORY, GREAT GUILDFORD ST, SE1   020 7101 1190   10–4B
UNIT 2, REUTERS PLAZA, E14
020 3725 7600   12–1C
11-13 EXMOUTH MKT, EC1
020 7833 8115   10–1A
BLOOMBERG ARCADE, QUEEN VICTORIA ST, EC4   020 3957 5555   10–3C

"Delicious shakshuka with maxing smoky flavours" is typical of the "colourful and flavoursome" brunch-friendly dishes at this "very buzzy if not loud" chain, known for its "top coffee" (which they roast themselves), and whose best-known sites are the Exmouth Market original and large Granary Square branch. Recently, they also added an opening in Canary Wharf and a brew bar at their Caledonian Road roastery (not listed), with further 'measured expansion' planned. For the most part, they are still mostly seen as a "reliable" choice for an "interesting and healthy" breakfast: "not everything is a hit but for a casual lunch I am pretty happy". Top Tip – "when the sun is shining, it's worth waiting for an outside table" in N1. / www.caravanonexmouth.co.uk.

CARAVEL N1   £48   334

172 SHEPHERDESS WALK
020 7251 1155   14–2A

A real "find and well worth visiting" – this converted barge moored on the Regent's Canal near Angel has a tight modern Franco-Italian menu from Lorcan Spiteri, who trained under Jeremy Lee at Quo Vadis. With the Studio Kitchen next door, it is the first venture from Lorcan and his brother Fin, who were born to the job – dad is restaurateur John Spiteri (St John, Quo Vadis, Sessions Arts Club), mother Melanie Arnold co-founded Rochelle Canteen. / N1 7ED; thestudiokitchen.co.uk/the-boat; @caravel_restaurant; Thu-Sat 10.30 pm; closed Thu-Sat L, closed Mon-Wed & Sun.

CARMEL NW6   £81   544

LONSDALE ROAD   020 3848 2090   1–2B

"A great addition to Queen's Park" – this October 2021 newcomer from the team behind East London hipster favourite, Berber & Q, gives them another hit on the other side of town. "Everything about this place is spot-on": from the charming staff, to the "excellent atmosphere", to the "delicious and inventive Israeli-style cooking"… "it was one of those meals that I did not want to end". Quibbles? – "some might dislike the lack of tables with much privacy, or the trendy wine list full of options you have never heard of!" / NW6 6RR; www.carmelrestaurant.co.uk; @carmelrestaurantldn; Tue-Sat 11 pm; closed Sun & Mon; payment – credit card only.

CAROUSEL W1   £71   432

19-23 CHARLOTTE STREET
020 7487 5564   3–1C

Relocated from Marylebone to this new Fitzrovia site, sprawling across three knocked-together Georgian townhouses: "a great place where an amazing array of constantly changing residencies by superstar chefs from all corners of the globe, make it a unique place to be entertained", and one that's typically "good value" too. On the downside, the "acoustics of the new venue are underwhelming" for some reporters. (The rating is for the visiting chef programme – no-one really mentions their new permanent in-situ wine bar operation). / W1W 1RL; www.carousel-london.com; @Carousel_LDN; Tue-Sat midnight; closed Sun & Mon.

THE CARPENTER'S ARMS W6 £57 3 3 3

91 BLACK LION LN 020 8741 8386 8–2B

Cutely tucked away near Hammersmith's gracious St Peter's Square, this independent Victorian boozer is a superior local whose inviting menu is more 'gastro' than it is 'pub' (although it serves a fairly traditional Sunday lunch). The "delightful garden" makes it a special treat for a meal in the summer. / W6 9BG; www.carpentersarmsw6.co.uk; @thecarpentersarmsw6; Thu-Sat 9.30 pm, Wed 21.30 pm, Sun 6.30 pm; closed Mon & Tue; payment – credit card only.

CASA DO FRANGO £56 4 2 3

**32 SOUTHWARK STREET, SE1
020 3972 2323 10–4C
3 KING JOHN COURT, EC2
020 7654 3020 13–1B**

"Nando's eat your heart out", say fans of the "real" Portuguese peri-peri grilled chicken "and very tasty sides" at this "fun if busy, busy, busy" (to the point of being "overwhelming") duo near Borough Market and Shoreditch (of which the former is by far the most commented-on). It's backed by MJMK (who also run Kol, Lisbetoa et al) and a first central London branch seating 200 is set to open in 2022 in Mayfair's Heddon Street. / www.casadofrango.co.uk; casadofrango_london.

CASA FOFÓ E8 £75 5 4 3

**158 SANDRINGHAM ROAD
020 8062 2489 14–1B**

"Not prioritising form over substance" – Adolfo de Cecco's well-reputed three-year-old is "fairly un-smart for a foodie hotspot" but "cosy and romantic", especially in the "covered back garden, which is gorgeous as the sun sets (a very 'London' setting)". "Outstanding food is brilliantly and passionately served" from an "eclectic tasting menu" ("and they've lightened up since Grace Dent accused them of being too serious a couple of years ago!") / E8 2HS; www.casafofolondon.co.uk; @casafofolondon; Wed-Sun 9.30 pm; closed Wed-Fri L, closed Mon & Tue; no Amex.

CASA PASTÓR & PLAZA PASTÓR N1 £73 3 2 2

COAL DROPS YARD 020 7018 3335 9–3C

"Noisy!...but great margaritas" and some "very tasty" bites are the draw at the Hart Bros' Mexico City-style street food specialist in Coal Drops Yard. On the debit side, it can be "hard to feel truly relaxed in this mammoth space". See also El Pastor. / N1N 4AB; www.tacoselpastor.co.uk; @tacos_el_pastor; Tue-Sat 11 pm, Sun 8 pm; closed Tue-Thu L, closed Mon.

CASA TUA WC1 £48 4 2 3

**106 CROMER STREET
020 7833 1483 9–4C**

"The beef ragu is an absolute delight" – just one highlight among this "amazing fresh pasta" and other "beautiful" dishes at this "lovely neighbourhood spot in the backstreets of King's Cross": a simple corner café that's "a decent-value find in the area". / WC1W 8BZ; www.casatuacamden.com/kings-cross; @casatualondon; Mon-Sun 10 pm.

CASSE-CROUTE SE1 £69 4 4 4

**109 BERMONDSEY ST
020 7407 2140 10–4D**

"La vraie chose! A French restaurant staffed by French cooking staff and waiters who speak French amongst themselves" – "cramped, noisy, but still brilliant". With its "excellent" menu of Gallic classics, chalked up daily, you'd be happy to find this bistro in Bordeaux or Briançon – let alone Bermondsey. It's "great fun and great food" – a "cosy place where one can happily while away a whole evening". / SE1 3XB; www.cassecroute.co.uk; @cassecroute109; Mon-Sat 11 pm, Sun 5 pm; closed Sun D.

CAVITA W1 £97

**55 WIGMORE STREET
020 3928 1000 3–1A**

Originally slated for late 2019 (and following a pop-up at the Dorchester's glam rooftop), Adriana Cavita's May 2022 debut was worth waiting for by all accounts, although it arrived too late for our annual diners' poll. Occupying two dining spaces (one with views of the open kitchen), it is decked out in earthy tones and with a mass of hanging plants; while the menu incorporates a 'raw' seafood selection and street-food dishes, but with larger sharing plates as the main event. According to an early review by The Evening Standard's Jimi Famurewa it's "a scintillating, fully-formed reminder of exactly how it should be done" delivering a "knockout combination of abuela-level domestic generosity and top-tier chef's technique" that's "absolutely stormingly good". / W1W 1PU; www.cavitarestaurant.com; @cavita.restaurante; Tue-Sun 10.30 pm; closed Tue-Sun L, closed Mon.

CAY TRE £45 3 3 2

**42-43 DEAN ST, W1 020 7317 9118 5–2A
301 OLD ST, EC1 020 7729 8662 13–1B**

Some of the "tastiest Vietnamese food in town" is found at this pair in Hoxton and Soho from Hieu Trung Biu, a pioneer of pho and other southeast Asian specialties in the capital over two decades. Popularity means they can be "deafeningly loud". / www.caytrerestaurant.co.uk; caytrerestaurant.

CECCONI'S £87 2 2 4

**19-21 OLD COMPTON STREET, W1
020 7734 5656 5–2A
5A BURLINGTON GDNS, W1
020 7434 1500 4–4A
58-60 REDCHURCH STREET, E2
020 3841 7755 13–1C
THE NED, 27 POULTRY, EC2
020 3828 2000 10–2C**

"The original location is by far the best" – "almost Continental in feel, and opposite the back entrance of the Royal Academy in Burlington Arcade": "a regular haunt" for Mayfair types where "a seat at the bar is the best possible place in the world". "Always buzzy and with exceptional Bellinis, it's best for breakfast or brunch". On the downside, "the high prices of the food reflect the area and locale". Its simpler spin-offs (most notably pizza joints in Soho and Shoreditch) capture a fragment of this "fun and upmarket" style. / cecconis.co.uk; cecconislondon.

CEDRIC GROLET AT THE BERKELEY SW1 £90 3 4 4

**THE BERKELEY, WILTON PLACE
020 7107 8866 6–1D**

"OMG so good and so spectacular!" – Paris pâtissier par excellence Cédric Grolet opened his first permanent London showcase in this Knightsbridge 5-star in early 2022, and its 'kitchen table' is a place to ogle, then eat – "good-looking French chefs work in front of you" to create trompe-l'oeil fruit and flowers "made for Insta and for foodies". "Loved my experience here, expensive but so worth it". (The price shown is for the 'Gouter' 5-piece menu with tea, but the bookable counter described about is £135 per head; or take out from about £5 per item). / SW1S 8RL; www.the-berkeley.co.uk; @the_berkeley; Mon-Sun 7 pm.

CENT ANNI SW19 £58 3 2 2

33 HIGH STREET 020 3971 9781 11–2B

This "really consistent performer" serving "straightforward Italian classics" – "not haute cuisine" – is "a great place to go with the family", making it "a solid addition to the Wimbledon Village scene". Top Tip – "50% discount on wine on Wednesdays is a major attraction". / SW19 5BY; centanni.co.uk; Mon-Sat 11 pm, Sun 10.30 pm.

CEPAGES W2 £56 4 3 4

**69 WESTBOURNE PARK ROAD
020 3602 8890 7–1B**

"Sharing plates of classic French dishes" help make this Gallic bistro deep in Westbourne Park "perfect for a casual dinner with friends". "It can be crazy busy but has a lovely buzz". / W2 5QH; www.cepages.co.uk; Mon-Sat 11 pm, Sun 10 pm; closed Mon-Fri L.

CERU £41 3 2 2

**7-9 BUTE ST, SW7 020 3195 3001 6–2C
13 QUEENSWAY, W2 020 7221 2535 7–2C**

"Delicious food from the Levant, served with charm" has earned an enthusiastic following for Barry and Patricia Hilton's "interesting Middle Eastern" bistros: particularly the original, tucked away in South Kensington's 'Little France' in a quirky modernised unit with a Scandi-meets-North-Africa vibe. A thumbs-up too for its newer, year-old Queensway branch. / www.cerurestaurants.com; ceruLondon.

CEVICHE SOHO
W1 £72 3|2|3
17 FRITH ST 020 7292 2040 5–2A

This "buzzy and fun Peruvian with super-fresh ceviche and a range of interesting small plates" has become a "Soho staple" since it was launched in 2012. Reviews were more mixed this year, however. To fans, it's "hard to fault", with "a menu that's as vibrant and enjoyable as ever". To critics, "overhyped" – "perfectly nice, but not matching expectations" and "nothing special". / W1D 4RG; cevichelondon. com; @cevicheuk; Wed & Thu, Sat, Fri 8.30 pm, Sun 5 pm.

CHAKRA W8 £44 3|2|3
**33C HOLLAND STREET
020 7229 2115 6–1A**

The cute location is a highlight of this "hidden gem", obscurely tucked away in a plush Kensington backstreet, where the Indian food is "solid and great value for money". (It's actually part of a chain of four, but there's scant feedback on its siblings in Little Venice, Barnes and Kingston). / W8 4LX; www.chakralondon.com; @chakralondon; Tue-Thu 10 pm, Fri & Sat 10.30 pm, Sun 9 pm; closed Mon.

CHAMELEON NW1 £60 3|3|4
**ONE MARYLEBONE, 1 MARYLEBONE ROAD
020 7186 2444 9–4B**

Feedback is limited but full of praise for chef Elior Balbul's Tel Avivian sharing-style cuisine at this dramatic venue, which shares Grade I listed Holy Trinity Church (designed by Sir John Soane) with event space 'One Marylebone'. In summer there's a garden terrace ('God's Garden') and in winter the option to eat in a set of greenhouses. / NW1 4AQ; chameleon.london; @chameleonlondon; Tue-Sat 11.30 pm; closed Tue-Fri L, closed Sun & Mon; Jacket required.

CHAMPOR-CHAMPOR
SE1 £54 4|3|3
62 WESTON ST 020 7403 4600 10–4C

"Hidden away behind London Bridge", this "cute", eclectically decorated stalwart no longer attracts the outsized following it did many years ago, but continues to attract fans from across town for its interesting Thai-Malay cuisine. / SE1 3QJ; www.champor-champor.com; @champorchamporldn; Mon-Sat 10 pm, Sun 9.30 pm.

CHARLIE'S AT BROWN'S
W1 £93 4|5|5
**BROWN'S HOTEL, ALBEMARLE STREET
020 7493 6020 3–3C**

"Jesus has worked another miracle" at this Mayfair landmark: the Jesus in question being Jesus Adorno, former maître d' of Le Caprice, who joined in September 2021. It was an inspired appointment, and with his "quite exceptional" team he has helped further raise the game of this "beautiful" Mayfair dining room, where Adam Byatt (of Trinity) and his head chef Matthew Stirling have, since 2019, been brought on board to provide a "lovely" seasonal British menu of upscale brasserie fare. Despite its "well-spaced" tables and fine wood panelling, the venue has never in recent decades fully capitalised on its virtues as one of London's better traditional hotel dining spaces. That time is now! / W1W 4BP; @browns_hotel; Mon-Sun 10 pm.

CHATEAU W4 £35 3|4|2
**213 CHISWICK HIGH ROAD
020 8742 2344 8–2A**

Now celebrating its tenth anniversary, this Middle Eastern venture on Chiswick's main drag has gradually expanded its scope over the years from offering daytime "lovely loose-leaf tea and good coffee with a great selection of cakes". "At night, it transforms into a Lebanese / Eastern Med restaurant, serving a pretty traditional menu with fresh tasty dishes and Lebanese wines to hand". / W4 2DW; chateau-chiswick.com; @chateau_chiswick; Mon-Sat 10 pm, Sun 7 pm.

CHE COSA N19 £32 3|3|2
**653 HOLLOWAY ROAD
020 7018 7077 9–1C**

"Two minutes' walk from Archway tube", this "tiny Italian" comes "recommended for its homemade pasta and specials" and "delicious Italian sourdough pizza", all delivered by "polite and considerate staff". Top Menu Tip – "the olives Ascolana appetiser – fried breadcrumbed green olives stuffed with minced meat". / N19 5SE; www.checosa.co.uk; @checosa.restaurant; Sun-Thu 11.30 pm, Fri & Sat 12.30 am.

THE CHEESE BARGE
W2 £52 2|3|3
SHELDON SQUARE 07862 001418 7–1C

"Bonkers idea", but "great fun" – Matthew Carver's custom-designed, double-decker barge moored in Paddington Basin serves a "good cheese-based menu" that celebrates cheeses made in Britain and Ireland. "It makes for a jolly experience on a sunny day, but" – although true turophiles might disagree – can seem something of "a one trick pony". Stablemates include the world's first cheese conveyor belt, in Seven Dials. / W2 6HY; www.thecheesebar.com/paddington; @thecheesebarldn; Tue-Sun 2 pm; closed Tue-Sun D, closed Mon.

CHELSEA CELLAR
SW10 £51 3|4|4
9 PARK WALK 020 7351 4933 6–3B

This "treasured Chelsea local, tucked away in a cosy basement off the Fulham Road 'beach'", inspires a devoted following from its regulars, looking after them with "classy and delicious" Italian dishes and an impressive wine list. Tourists and casual passers-by are unlikely even to notice the all-but-hidden entrance, adding to the clubbish appeal. / SW10 0AJ; www.thechelseacellar.co.uk; @thechelseacellar; Tue-Sat midnight; closed Tue-Sat L, closed Sun & Mon.

CHER THAI SW4 £31 4|4|3
22 NORTH STREET 020 3583 3702 11–1D

"A new arrival in Clapham that's making a really good name for themselves" as a "neighbourhood gem". This small venture – the work of a husband-and-wife team – launched just before the February 2020 lockdown, and is finally winning recognition for its "really excellent Thai food: perhaps nothing ground-breaking, but the classics are prepared as well as I can remember having them in London in recent years". / SW4 0HB; www.cherthailondon.co.uk; @cherthailondon; Tue, Thu, Wed 10.30 pm, Fri & Sat 11 pm, Sun 10 pm; closed Mon.

CHEZ ANTOINETTE £43 3|4|3
**THE CAXTON, 22 PALMER STREET, SW1
020 3990 5377 2–4C**
**UNIT 30 THE MARKET BUILDING, WC2
020 7240 9072 5–3D**

"Invitingly tucked away off Victoria Street", "it feels like stepping into Paris" at this "good little bistro", where "helpful staff" deliver "a short but interesting" all-day menu of "simple but delicious fare" at "good value prices" ("excellent saucisson, and good bavette steak, duck leg… a very good tarte Tatin and reasonably priced house wine!"). Only fleeting mentions for the branch cutely located in the tourist hell of Covent Garden on the lower ground level of the market itself, but all good. /

CHEZ BRUCE
SW17 £100 5|4|3
2 BELLEVUE RD 020 8672 0114 11–2C

"The very definition of a neighbourhood star" – Bruce Poole's "unpretentious, yet ever-reliable" south London icon, on Wandsworth Common, is – for the 17th year running – Londoners' No.1 favourite in our annual diners' poll. For its legions of fans it's "the lodestar as to 'how to do it well' without making people feel ripped off" – "a proper grown-up restaurant, yet without being staid or stuffy". Matt Christmas's "unfussy" but "cleverly crafted" cuisine is "consistently superb" ("imaginative and expertly executed, with nothing just for show/colour, and with all constituents perfectly balanced"). "Engaging staff are knowledgeable without being intimidating" and if you're a wine connoisseur you'll be delighted by the "comprehensive and well-selected wine list" (although, "if you just want the house white then they won't be at all sniffy"). "The modest dining room is bright, with no background muzak, and always pleasantly buzzy and busy". A few reports do note the odd "Covid blip" or staffing issues, but (practically) all accounts say it's now "back to its best". "Year after year, this is one of the places I feel a sense of homecoming, gradually developing rituals around different reasons to justify a trip. Wonderfully comforting, satisfying and delightful all round!" ("If I were on Desert Island Discs, this would be my luxury item!")

Top Tip – "the £57.50 3-course lunch menu is some of the best value in town". / SW17 7EG; www.chezbruce.co.uk; @chez.bruce; Tue-Thu 9.15 pm, Fri & Sat 9.30 pm, Sun 9 pm; closed Mon.

CHEZ ELLES E1 £62 333

45 BRICK LN 020 7247 9699 13–2C

This "reliably good Gallic bistro" stands out from the crowd in Brick Lane, perhaps the last address you'd expect to find something "so French" in London. / E1 6PU; www.chezellesbistroquet.co.uk; @chezellesbistro; Tue-Sat 11.30 pm; closed Tue-Sat L, closed Sun & Mon.

CHICAMA SW10 £77 333

383 KING'S ROAD 020 3874 2000 6–3C

"Super-fresh fish", "inventive, well-cooked seafood dishes with a Peruvian slant" and a "great atmosphere" (boosted by "the best pisco sours") are the key ingredients of this King's Road "crowd-pleaser" – the younger stablemate of Pachamama in Marylebone – which can be "so warm you think you are somewhere tropical". Any gripes? – "just wish they'd turn the music down!" / SW10 0LP; www.chicamalondon.com; @chicamalondon; Mon-Fri 11 pm, Sat & Sun 4 pm; closed Sat & Sun D.

CHICK 'N' SOURS £41 433

1 EARLHAM STREET, WC2
020 3198 4814 5–2B
22 ASSEMBLY PASSAGE, E1 NO TEL
13–2D
390 KINGSLAND RD, E8
020 3620 8728 14–2A

"So good – I'm still daydreaming about it", say fans of "the most delicious fried chicken burgers" served up alongside sour cocktails and local beers at this former pop-up with branches in Haggerston and Covent Garden, and an evening-only take-away outlet in Whitechapel (Fri/Sat/Sun). Top Menu Tip – "best is the K-Pop burger with spicy Korean-style coleslaw. Yom!" / www.chicknsours.co.uk; chicknsours.

THE CHILTERN FIREHOUSE W1 £109 225

1 CHILTERN ST 020 7073 7676 2–1A

"Blindingly expensive, but unforgettable" – "you're paying for the experience not the food" at this sexy and enduringly fashionable Marylebone operation, which "everyone knows is about the 'scene' and rubbernecking the clientele". When it comes to its long, luxe-brasserie menu (burrata, oysters, steak, tuna tartare, pizza…), results are "OK, but not worth the cash, unless you are as super-rich as the rest of its customers". Top Tip – "go for breakfast, to get a sense of the ambience". / W1U 7PA; www.chilternfirehouse.com; Mon-Sun 10 pm; closed Mon-Sun L.

CHINA TANG, DORCHESTER HOTEL W1 £101 233

53 PARK LN 020 7319 7088 3–3A

The late Sir David Tang's take on 1930s Shanghai in the basement of this famous hotel divides opinion: some praise its "sublime food" including "wonderful Peking duck" (with the option of caviar) and other luxurious dishes to share (such as suckling pig or abalone) for £200-£300; others complain of "crazy prices" for "average meals" that are "no better than the standard Cantonese". On the plus side, the more affordable dim sum selection is available in the evening as well as at lunchtime, and plenty of guests have a good time (to the point one reporter found it "rowdy"). Top Tip – plan on a cocktail in the superbly atmospheric bar. / W1K 1QA; www.chinatanglondon.co.uk; @chinatanglondon; Mon-Sun 11 pm; closed Mon-Wed L.

LA CHINGADA SE8 £15 432

206 LOWER ROAD 020 7237 7448 12–2B

"Simple dishes are well-realised" at this basic Mexican, which has moved from its previous site (a take-away with a few seats at the counter) to this (marginally grander) former caff nearby in Surrey Quays. / SE8 5DJ; lachingada.co.uk; @lachingadalondon; closed Mon-Sat & Sun.

CHISHURU SW9 £49 332

UNIT 9 MARKET ROW
07960 002150 11–2D

"Wow! Wasn't sure what to expect of the African food, but it was mind-blowing" – Adejoke Bakara's "bold and beautiful" dishes win many converts to her "simple, warm and inviting" two-year-old in Brixton, where she channels her Nigerian heritage into contemporary West African cooking washed down with cocktails and funky wines. But does it risk over-exposure? A couple of diners this year judged it "overpriced for food that's good but not exceptional". / SW9 8LB; www.chishuru.com; @chishuru; Fri-Sun, Tue-Thu 10.30 pm; closed Tue-Thu L, closed Mon; payment – credit card only; booking online only.

CHISOU £70 322

22-23 WOODSTOCK STREET, W1
020 7629 3931 4–1A
31 BEAUCHAMP PL, SW3
020 3155 0005 6–1D

"High-quality sushi – the fish is super-fresh" and "very good tempura" are the highlights at this classic Japanese duo in Mayfair and Knightsbridge. A meal here is "certainly not cheap but it is fantastic": "there are one or two London restaurants that do better Japanese and sushi. But not at these prices". Top Tip – "ask for sea urchins in season". / www.chisourestaurant.com.

CHOOK CHOOK SW15 £55 433

137 LOWER RICHMOND ROAD
020 8789 3100 11–1B

"Generous portions of super-delicious food" – "the sort you would expect to find in India rather than Britain" – has won local acclaim for this three-year-old on the edge of Putney, with a luxury train theme linking cuisines from across the subcontinent. / SW15 1EZ; chookchook.uk; @chookchooklondon_; Mon-Thu 10.30 pm, Fri & Sat 11 pm, Sun 10 pm; closed Mon-Fri L.

CHOTTO MATTE £70 444

11-13 FRITH ST, W1 020 7042 7171 5–2A
26 PADDINGTON STREET, W1
020 7058 4444 2–1A

"Love the spin on the Peruvian x Japanese dishes" – Kurt Zdesar's Nikkei concept fueled by its 'Tokyo to Lima' cocktail menu is growing like topsy, expanding from its Soho home (undergoing 'an exciting restyle' as of summer 2022) to Marylebone Village in January 2022, with forthcoming debuts in Doha, Riyadh and San Francisco as part of a plan to expand to 20 sites globally in the next 5 years. The vibe is as energetic as its expansion plans: "too noisy for the seniors in our group, but all the youngsters loved it!" / chotto-matte.com; chottomatteldn.

CHOURANGI W1 £46 433

3 OLD QUEBEC STREET
020 3582 2710 2–2A

An "inventive menu" inspired by the melding of Indian, Chinese and British cuisines in historic Calcutta makes this Marble Arch yearling "a great addition to the area". Named after a central district of the city, it was founded by chef-patron Anjan Chatterjee and Indian airline entrepreneur Aditya Ghosh. / W1W 7DL; chourangi.co.uk; @chourangildn; Tue-Sat 10.30 pm, Sun 10 pm; closed Mon.

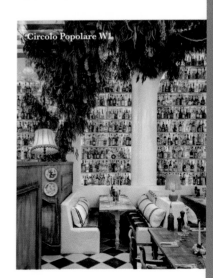

Circolo Popolare W1

CHRISKITCH N10   £44   3 3 3

7A TETHERDOWN   020 8411 0051   1–1C

"No menu and it's whatever is made on the day – I love it!". Australian chef Chris Honor's all-day neighbourhood café in Muswell Hill serves "Ottolenghi-style food" to a high standard. / N10 1ND; www.chriskitch.com; @chriskitchfood; Sat-Mon 5 pm, Tue-Fri 6 pm; closed Sat-Mon & Tue-Fri D; may need 3+ to book.

CHRISTOPHER'S WC2   £94   2 2 3

18 WELLINGTON ST   020 7240 4222   5–3D

This veteran American-style surf 'n' turf restaurant occupies a stunning Covent Garden mansion but for most of its long history (three decades) has been a missed culinary opportunity. So, "go to see the room, but don't expect much of the formulaic food", which often elicited criticism this year ("like an expensive McDonalds"). "One day someone will take this astonishing space with its magical stone spiral staircase and open a great destination". / WC2E 7DD; www.christophersgrill.com; @christopherswc2; Tue-Thu midnight, Fri & Sat 1.30 am, Sun 5 pm; closed Sun D, closed Mon; may need 6+ to book.

CHUCS   £94   2 2 3

25 ECCLESTON STREET, SW1
020 3827 3000   2–4B
65 LOWER SLOANE STREET, SW1
020 3827 2999   6–2D
31 DOVER ST, W1   020 3763 2013   3–3C
97 OLD BROMPTON ROAD, SW7
020 8037 4525   6–2B
226 WESTBOURNE GROVE, W11
020 7243 9136   7–1B
3 CIRCUS ROAD, NW8
020 4537 6277   9–3A

"A throwback to old-school dining" – this wittingly old-fashioned chain (created in the last 10 years) channels an imagined La Dolce Vita lifestyle into its "enjoyable if slightly stuffy" mix of chic Italian cafés and restaurants (if you are of a certain age, think 1980s Tatler). They look "pretty" and are "attractive in their own way": "not bad if a bit overpriced". That's the kind view anyway: harsher critics say they "could do better" and "don't deserve a revisit". But they must be doing something right, as in July 2021 they opened in St John's Wood. / www.chucsrestaurants.com; chucsrestaurants.

CHUKU'S N15   £40   4 4 3

274 HIGH ROAD   NO TEL   1–1D

Emeka and Ifeyinwa Frederick's vibey three-year-old in Seven Sisters (motto, 'Chop, chat, chill') has won a big name for its quirky Nigerian tapas (e.g. jollof quinoa, moi moi, honey suya prawns), fab soundtrack and upbeat service. Whether its recommendation by Diane Abbott is a plus or a minus is hard to call… / N15 5AJ; www.chukuslondon.co.uk; @chukusldn; Tue-Sat 10.30 pm, Sun 8.30 pm; closed Tue-Fri L, closed Mon; payment – credit card only; booking online only.

CHURCH ROAD SW13   £62   3 4 3

94 CHURCH ROAD   020 8748 0393   11–1A

"High quality reflects the Phil Howard influence" at the Elystan Street chef's relaxed operation on his home turf in Barnes, launched in 2019 with business partner Rebecca Mascarenhas, on the site of their previous, less ambitious offering, Sonny's (RIP). It's "a cosy yet elegant" use of the space, with food "better than at your average local, and with a very good wine list". / SW13 0DQ; www.churchroadsw13.co.uk; @churchroadsw13; Wed, Sat 10 pm, Thu & Fri 10.30 pm, Sun 3 pm; closed Wed L closed Sun D, closed Mon & Tue.

CHURCHILL ARMS W8   £44   3 2 3

119 KENSINGTON CHURCH ST
020 7792 1246   7–2B

This "neighbourhood landmark" on Kensington Church Street was built in 1750 and has won renown in recent decades, both for its lavish floral displays (which earned it recognition from the Chelsea Flower Show) and also for the "excellent, cheap 'n' cheerful Thai" that operates in its pretty and quirky dining annex, all "at a great price-point for the area". Long-term customers say "it's not as good as it once was, but still a reliable stalwart". / W8 7LN; www.churchillarmskensington.co.uk; @churchillarmsw8; Mon-Sat 11 pm, Sun 10.30 pm.

CHUTNEY MARY SW1   £90   4 3 4

73 ST JAMES'S STREET
020 7629 6688   3–4D

A trip to the "wonderful, fun cocktail bar" makes a brilliant introduction to this "spacious, elegant and bustling" operation, whose "marvellous décor truly gives it character". The original venture of Ranjit & Namita Mathrani, plus the latter's sister, Camellia Panjabi (who also now own Amaya, Veeraswamy and Masala Zone), it moved several years ago from SW10 to this swanky St James's address. The "sophisticated Indian cooking" has "superb spicing" with plenty of "depth and complexity" and "wonderful" flavours, and amongst London's posh Indians it remains one of the best known. / SW1S 1PH; www.chutneymary.com; @chutneymary.london; Sun-Wed 9.30 pm, Thu-Sat 10 pm; closed Mon L.

CHUTNEYS NW1   £25   3 3 2

124 DRUMMOND ST   020 7388 0604   9–4C

"Still offering great value" for "fresh and really tasty food", this canteen is one of the stalwarts of the 'Little India' enclave behind Euston station, where Indian students gathered to eat from the 1950s. The daily vegetarian buffet lunch is a steal at under £10, while the meat and fish options on the main menu are not much more expensive. / NW1 2PA; www.chutneyseuston.uk; @chutneysnw1; Mon-Sat 11 pm, Sun 10 pm; no Amex; may need 5+ to book.

CIAO BELLA WC1   £54   3 4 5

86-90 LAMB'S CONDUIT ST
020 7242 4119   2–1D

"Not completely cheap but extremely cheerful" – this "absolutely classic Italian restaurant" has wowed Bloomsbury for 40 years with "all your favourite dishes – pasta, antipasti, arancini, panna cotta". "Everything is just right" and there's "always a great atmosphere, good fun and friendly service". It's "perfect for groups and families, but not so much for intimate dinners" – although nobody told Boris Johnson, who wooed his paramour Jennifer Arcuri here over chips and red wine. / WC1N 3LZ; www.ciaobellarestaurant.co.uk; @ciaobella_london; Mon-Sat 10.45 pm, Sun 10.30 pm.

CIBO W14   £60   4 4 3

3 RUSSELL GDNS   020 7371 6271   8–1D

"Spankingly good Italian food" is found at this long-established modern venue in an "isolated location" behind Holland Park, whose "posh locals know a good thing when they see it". There are plenty of "unusual options on the menu", with an emphasis on "original and well-prepared fish dishes". / W14 8EZ; www.ciborestaurant.net; Mon-Sat 9.45 pm; closed Mon-Sat L, closed Sun.

CIGALON WC2   £51   3 3 3

115 CHANCERY LANE
020 7242 8373   2–2D

The sun-drenched flavours of Provence – both food and wine – are brought into focus at this Chancery Lane outpost of Pascal Aussignac's Club Gascon group, which occupies an engaging glass-ceilinged room, originally built as an auction house. The downstairs cocktail bar, Baranis, also boasts the UK's only indoor petanque pitch. The verdict comment? "OK but not inspiring". / WC2A 1PP; www.cigalon.co.uk; @cigalon_london; Tue-Fri 9 pm; closed Mon, Sat & Sun.

CIN CIN W1   £39   3 4 4

21A FOLEY ST   020 7436 0921   2–1B

This "lovely neighbourhood Italian" in Fitzrovia opened in April 2021 as a spin-off from a successful Brighton duo, and has made a "great transition to London" on an eye-catching corner site (formerly Bonnie Gull, RIP). The food is "delicious", although "portions are lady-sized rather than man-sized". The business was founded ten years ago when Italian-Australian lawyer David Toscano bought an old Fiat van to participate in a Brighton street-food festival. / W1; www.cincin.co.uk/london; @cincinuk; Wed-Sat 11.30 pm; closed Mon & Tue & Sun; no shorts.

CINCINNATI CHILIBOMB EC2   £23   3 4 2

26 CURTAIN ROAD   07910 010210   13–2B

"US-style dive bar" in Shoreditch "serving what may well be the finest bar-meal/hangover-cure in London – beef chili in a hollowed-out brioche bun, topped with cheese and your choice of chili sauce in varying levels of insanity". Tim Brice, aka 'Captain Chili', took over the former site of Rok (RIP) to open his little corner of Americana in February 2021. Apparently the Cincinatti chilibomb was developed by Greek immigrants who adapted Tex-Mex chili con carne in the 1920s. / EC2E 3NY; www.cincinnatichilibomb.co.uk; @cincinnatichilibomb; Tue-Sat 11 pm; closed Sun & Mon.

CINDER NW3   £68   2|2|2

66 BELSIZE LANE   020 7435 8048   9–2A

This "tiny" Belsize Park two-year-old from chef Jake Finn (ex-La Petite Maison and The Ritz) is a "buzzy neighbourhood spot", where most of the food has been 'kissed by flames' on the Josper grill. But while it's undoubtedly a boon "in an area of drought for decent restaurants", opinions divide on its performance: to fans it provides an "excellently judged, seasonally changing menu"; to sceptics, it's "somewhat underwhelming and a bit expensive". / NW3 5BJ; www.cinderrestaurant.co.uk; @cinder_london; Tue-Sat 10.30 pm, Sun 10 pm; closed Mon; payment – credit card only.

CINNAMON BAZAAR WC2   £56   4|4|4

28 MAIDEN LANE   020 7395 1400   5–4D

The "gorgeous food, with amazing flavours and presentation" at this Covent Garden café matches the high standards Vivek Singh sets at his grander Cinnamon restaurants, some of the best-known Indian kitchens in London. It's a useful destination pre-theatre. / WC2W 7NA; www.cinnamon-bazaar.com; @cinnamonbazaar_official; Mon-Sun 11 pm.

THE CINNAMON CLUB SW1   £75   4|3|4

OLD WESTMINSTER LIBRARY, GREAT SMITH ST   020 7222 2555   2–4C

"The atmospheric book-lined walls of Westminster's former public library are a highlight" and add "a lot of character" to Vivek Singh's famous venue a short stroll from the Palace of Westminster: one of the Top 40 most-mentioned restaurants in our annual diners' poll and the best-known top Indian destination. "It's worth a visit just for the bar!" – where an evening often commences – but the prime attraction is "clever", "high-end" nouvelle Indian food "that's truly different" and with "very delicate spicing". "The huge area can make service a challenge" but generally staff cope well. / SW1P 3BU; www.cinnamonclub.com; @thecinnamoncollection; Mon-Sat 11 pm; closed Sun; no trainers; booking max 14 may apply.

CINNAMON KITCHEN   £60   3|3|3

**4 ARCHES LANE, SW11
020 3955 5480   11–1C
9 DEVONSHIRE SQ, EC2
020 7626 5000   10–2D**

"Big flavoured, modern Indian dishes" from an "interesting and different menu" win praise for Vivek Singh's high quality duo: "a more affordable introduction to the Cinnamon Club's cuisine". The newer SW11 branch, "with service around an open kitchen in a lively railway arch" near Battersea Power Station is jollier than its longer-established City sibling, where "the décor is quite boring and service a tad patchy" (although the latter is also "pretty decent value in an area that has limited options for a weekend lunch". / www.cinnamon-kitchen.com; cinnamonrestaurants.

CINQUECENTO   £48   2|2|3

**1 CALE STREET, SW3   020 7351 9331   6–2C
233 PORTOBELLO ROAD, W11   NO TEL
7–2B**

Opinions diverge on this Neapolitan duo, whose year-old Portobello branch already eclipses the small, tucked-away Chelsea original in terms of feedback. Fans hail their "excellent pizzas and other dishes", while others find them "surprisingly average" and "inexplicably popular". /

CIRCOLO POPOLARE W1   £57   3|3|5

40-41 RATHBONE SQUARE   NO TEL   5–1A

"A fun place to go with mates" – the Big Mamma Group's "vibey" Fitzrovian has won renown as a ready-made party scene. The outsized portions of simple Italian fodder from a monthly changing menu are arguably "utterly bonkers" and deliver an affordable occasion, although one or two critics feel it's "losing some of its originality" and providing too many "unmemorable" dishes nowadays. / W1W 1HX; @bigmamma.uk; Mon-Sat 10.30 pm, Sun 10 pm.

CITRO N6   £52   4|3|2

15A SWAIN'S LANE   07840 917586   9–1B

This "fabulous local Italian" in Highgate ticks all the boxes, with "home-made pasta and great accompaniments" plus "fresh and original pizzas", delivered with the "personal family touch" that generates an "excellent vibe". / N6 6QX; www.eatcitro.com; @citro_restaurant; Tue-Sat 10 pm, Sun 3 pm; closed Tue, Wed L closed Sun D, closed Mon.

CITY BARGE W4   £68   2|2|3

**27 STRAND-ON-THE-GREEN
020 8994 2148   1–3A**

An "absolutely wonderful little pub" at Strand-on-the-Green, Chiswick, whose "riverside location and snug dining room" make any meal "a lovely experience from start to finish". A couple of reporters feel that the food "is not as good as it was pre-lockdown", but in general it's acknowledged as a "good standby". / W4 3PH; www.citybargechiswick.com; @CityBargeW4; Mon-Thu 11 pm, Fri & Sat midnight, Sun 10.30 pm.

CITY SOCIAL EC2   £107   3|3|4

**TOWER 42 25 OLD BROAD ST
020 7877 7703   10–2C**

"Jason Atherton's City branch is still guaranteed to wow guests – from the plush elevator to the stunning views, everything screams impressive" at this 24th-floor venue in Tower 42 (fka the NatWest Tower). The food is "tasty" – if "not the most adventurous" (i.e. plenty of steaks) – "but staking out a view in one of the deep booths, glass in hand, and watching the city spread out for miles is a pretty spectacular way to spend an evening". / EC2N 1HQ; www.citysociallondon.com; @citysocial_t42; Tue-Sat 9.30 pm; closed Sat L, closed Sun & Mon; booking max 4 may apply.

THE CLARENCE TAVERN N16   £61   3|4|3

**102 STOKE NEWINGTON CHURCH STREET
020 8712 1188   1–1C**

The food is "a comforting delight – never lacking in flavour" at this Stoke Newington boozer, for two years part of the Anchor & Hope group and with former Great Queen Street (RIP) chef Harry Kaufman at the helm. "There's the kind of consistency emerging that one would expect of the team – which is pleasing to see in a bit of town with no shortage of choice, but often very little of consistent note". Grade II-listed, the Clarence was known as the Daniel Defoe under its previous ownership before reverting to its original name. / N16 0LA; www.clarencetavern.com; @theclarencetavern; Tue-Sat 11 pm, Sun 5 pm; closed Tue L closed Sun D, closed Mon; payment – credit card only.

CLARETTE W1   £89   3|3|3

44 BLANDFORD ST   020 3019 7750   3–1A

Converted from a Tudorbethan pub in Marylebone (complete with black and white exterior and leaded-glass windows), this three-floor wine bar and restaurant is part-owned by a scion of the French dynasty behind Château Margaux, explaining the extensive list of vintages from the estate on the French-centric list, many available by the glass. The better-than-incidental French/Italian cooking is also well-rated. / W1W 7HS; www.clarettelondon.com; @clarettelondon; Tue-Fri 11 pm, Sat midnight; closed Tue-Thu L, closed Sun & Mon.

CLARIDGES FOYER & READING ROOM W1   £109   3|4|4

49 BROOK STREET   020 7107 8886   3–2B

"The epitome of Best of British" – "nobody does afternoon tea like Claridges": "it's a casually elegant delight from start to finish". "Everyone is made to feel like a VIP and the food is good without being intimidating" ("awesome cakes and a great range of sandwiches"). Top Tip – when you finish your tea, "don't forget the jewel that is the tiny Champagne bar". / W1W 4HW; www.claridges.co.uk; @claridgeshotel; Mon-Sun 10 pm.

CLARKE'S W8 £95 443

124 KENSINGTON CHURCH STREET
020 7221 9225 7–2B

"Sally Clarke remains very present" at her "sophisticated" and "welcoming" Kensington HQ, which she established in 1984 at the bleeding edge of a trend to a more seasonal, ingredient-led style of dining that's nowadays become an accepted norm. Consequently, for some fans, this has been "a 'go-to' for decades" owing to its "consistently superb cuisine", creating dishes "with fantastic attention to detail" that "are imaginative without seeming 'tricked up'". The décor has always divided opinions here: "quite formal" for some tastes, but to others "romantic" and "perfect for a relaxed evening with grown-up conversation". Ratings slipped a little this year across the board, though, as even those hailing it as "excellent" may note that "prices seem to have jumped here even more than most post-Covid". / W8 4BH; www.sallyclarke.com; @sallyclarkeltd; Tue-Sat 10 pm; closed Sun & Mon; booking max 8 may apply.

THE CLERK & WELL
EC1 £51

156 CLERKENWELL ROAD
0207 837 8548 10–1A

"Recently revamped" with eight 'boutique guestrooms', this handsome Clerkenwell establishment is one of the oldest public houses in central London. There are too few reports for a rating as yet, but it looks promising and "the Sunday roast sharing board is pretty impressive". / EC1E 5DU; www.clerkandwell.co.uk; @theclerkandwellpub; Mon-Sun 11 pm.

THE CLIFTON
NW8 £67 344

96 CLIFTON HILL 020 7625 5010 9–3A

"You never tire of the Clifton", a rather grand St John's Wood pub serving "delicious" food from a "perfect menu – not too much, not too little". There's "great service" too, led by the trio who relaunched the pub five years ago, having saved it from developers. The Clifton also has a bit of louche history: originally a hunting lodge, it was used by 'Bertie', the future King Edward VII, for assignations with his mistress Lillie Langtry. / NW8 0JT; www.thecliftonnw8.com; @thecliftonnw8; Mon-Sat 10 pm, Sun 9 pm.

CLIPSTONE W1 £85 432

5 CLIPSTONE STREET
020 7637 0871 2–1B

"Rocking something reminiscent of an upscale NYC-style neighbourhood vibe (a real triumph in the context of central London)" – Will Lander and Daniel Morgenthau's "unpretentious, relaxed and happy" corner site in Fitzrovia "keeps up very high standards": "the menu is always original", service is "charming", there's an "interesting wine list" and a "noisy buzzy atmosphere". It can be slightly "erratic" though, and arguably "in being rather cramped, it needs to get off the fence and either up the party mood, or space the tables and quieten down a little". / W1W 6BB; www.clipstonerestaurant.co.uk; @clipstonerestaurant; Tue-Sat 9.45 pm, Sun 8.45; closed Mon.

CLOS MAGGIORE
WC2 £95 335

33 KING ST 020 7379 9696 5–3C

"Get lucky and score a table in the conservatory and you've landed the most romantic rendezvous in town!" at this "lovely" oasis in bustling Covent Garden – for many years now, reporters' No.1 choice "for celebrating anniversaries, engagements, weddings, etc…". The "beautiful glazed dining room is hung with blossom and has both a roof that opens in warm weather and a cosy fire for cold days". And not everyone feels that all is lost if you don't nab one of these prime seats ("everyone raves about the garden room but there is a small dining room upstairs that we love too!"). Though it has never been a prime foodie destination, the kitchen typically wins acclaim for its "accomplished modern European cuisine", which is backed up by "the longest wine list ever seen" (although pricing of some vintages gave cause for complaint this year). There continues to be a school of thought that its food is "sadly not as good as it was pre-lockdown" or that "staff changes have made it seem less welcoming". But ratings recovered well here this year after a dive last year, and on most of the very many reports we receive: "you always feel special here!" / WC2E 8JD; www.closmaggiore.com; @clos_maggiore; Wed-Sun 10 pm; closed Mon & Tue; no shorts.

THE CLOVE CLUB
EC1 £206 443

SHOREDITCH TOWN HALL, 380 OLD ST
020 7729 6496 13–1B

"In the unlikely, understated but pleasant environs of Shoreditch Town Hall", this iconic modern venue – a UK flag-bearer on the World's 50 Best – is approaching its 10th year and, for the most part, "still knocking the ball out of the park". With its "calm, unpretentious room table setting" and "cool open-kitchen approach", it delivers "imaginative and precise cooking with a wide range of tastes and textures" that fans say is "the best of the best", and bolstered by novel wine and drink pairings. (Michelin, never exactly ahead of the curve, awarded it two stars in 2022). "Professional, attentive and caring service" plays its part and there's been "outstanding attention to detail since reopening post Covid". The whacking bill continues to be an issue here, though. Even many fans find it "disturbingly pricey" – although they note "you get what you pay for" – but others feel the value just doesn't stack up: "third visit probably now our last… at over £600 for two, it's now just tooooooo expensive". / EC1V 9LT; www.thecloveclub.com; @thecloveclub; Mon-Sat 11 pm; closed Mon L, closed Sun.

CLUB GASCON
EC1 £137 433

57 WEST SMITHFIELD
020 7600 6144 10–2B

"Reliably great after all these years" – Pascal Aussignac and Vincent Labeyrie's renowned institution near Smithfield Market occupies a stylishly converted former Lyons Tea House and continues to mine southwest France for its culinary inspiration: notably "very inventive presentations of foie gras" paired with "a different range of wines that one sees in most other restaurants, given its regional emphasis". / EC1A 9DS; www.clubgascon.com; @ClubGascon; Tue-Sat 9.30 pm; closed Tue-Sat L, closed Sun & Mon; no shorts.

THE COACH EC1 £65 233

26-28 RAY STREET 020 3954 1595 10–1A

The attractively converted garden room and beautiful upstairs dining room are highlights at this fine old pub (dating from 1790) in Clerkenwell. It hit foodie fame a couple of years ago under well-known chef, Henry Harris: since then the verdict on its gastroboozer fare has been: "variable, but still capable of hitting some top notes". / EC1E 3DJ; www.thecoachclerkenwell.co.uk; @thecoachlondon; Mon-Sat 9 pm, Sun 4 pm; closed Sun D.

The Coal Shed SE1

COAL OFFICE N1 £83 4|3|4

2 BAGLEY WALK 020 3848 6085 9–3C

"Amazing, and amazing fun… one of my best meals of the year and I wasn't expecting it at all!" – this "tightly packed" space from chef Assaf Granit and the Tom Dixon studio has a "wonderful location" next to the latter's HQ: which is adjacent to Granary Square and Coal Drops Yard. Deceptively simple in style, "it's great to take guests here and watch their faces as they realise this isn't just another noisy cocktail joint but a seriously good restaurant". The menu of "Middle Eastern food with a modern twist" delivers "dish after dish of mind-blowing flavours" – "original and fabulous… if in tiny portions". "It's tight on space, so get ready to snuggle up", or "sit outside on a sunny day, which is the perfect way to spend a couple of hours". "Only problem? Getting a booking!" / N1N 4PQ; coaloffice.com; @coaloffice; Mon-Wed, Sat & Sun, Thu & Fri 11 pm; closed Mon-Wed L.

COAL ROOMS SE15 £71 4|3|3

11A STATION WAY 020 7635 6699 1–4D

"Extra points on ambience for the Victorian toilets" at the 19th-century booking hall and goods rooms of Peckham Rye station, now transformed into an all-day café and evening restaurant. It serves a "limited" but "delicious" menu of modern European dishes and fans say results are "always spot-on". / SE15 4RX; www.coalroomspeckham.com; @coalrooms; Wed-Sat 11 pm, Sun 6 pm; closed Sun D, closed Mon & Tue; payment – credit card only.

THE COAL SHED SE1 £77 3|3|3

ONE TOWER BRIDGE 020 3384 7272 10–4D

"A restaurant of choice when you go to the nearby Bridge Theatre" – this five-year-old sibling to a Brighton original provides "a good welcome", plus "very good steaks" and a "short but acceptable" menu of other options. "If it were not a little pricey for what it offers, I would be even more enthusiastic!" / SE1 2SE; www.coalshed-restaurant.co.uk; @thecoalshed; Tue-Sat 11 pm, Sun 8 pm; closed Tue, Wed L, closed Mon.

COCORO W1 £39 4|3|2

31 MARYLEBONE LN 020 7935 2931 3–1A

"Don't let the décor fool you: the traditional sushi and other dishes here are really good and good value!", according to fans of this "cheap 'n' cheerful" small chain, whose most commented on outlets are the "really-Japanese-in-feel" Marylebone original and more deli-style Highgate spin-off (Bloomsbury and Bayswater inspire little feedback). / W1U 2NH; cocororestaurant.co.uk; @cocorolondon; Mon-Sun 10.30 pm.

COCOTTE £54 3|4|3

271 NEW KING'S ROAD, SW6
020 7610 9544 11–1B
11 HARRINGTON ROAD, SW7
020 7589 1051 6–2C
95 WESTBOURNE GROVE, W2
020 3220 0076 7–1B
8 HOXTON SQUARE, N1
020 7033 4277 13–1B
79 SALUSBURY ROAD, NW6
020 7625 6606 1–2B

"Delicious roast chicken, with sides such as potato purée and root veggies" – as well, of course, as fries and salads – have won a growing fanclub for Romain Bourrillon's upbeat French-rotisserie chain, whose most popular branches in our annual diners' poll are in Bayswater, Queen's Park and Parsons's Green. / www.mycocotte.uk; cocotte_rotisserie.

COLBERT SW1 £63 2|3|3

51 SLOANE SQ 020 7730 2804 6–2D

"A top location on a corner of Sloane Square" helps define this "Parisian-like café/brasserie", which is decorated "with minute attention to detail in the quintessential Corbin & King style". It's "always crowded and noisy", but doesn't inspire affection the way its siblings do; and it's nominated much more as a convenient rendezvous than as a destination in itself. "All the Gallic classics are there on the menu", and while the food is "reliable" enough, definitely don't expect fireworks. "Very efficient and friendly service" this year though. Top Tip – "good range of breakfast menus". / SW1W 8AX; www.colbertchelsea.com; @ColbertChelsea; Tue-Sat 10.30 pm, Sun & Mon 10 pm.

LA COLLINA NW1 £74 3|2|3

17 PRINCESS RD 020 7483 0192 9–3B

This "friendly and cosy" independent Italian with a "good garden space" has established a comfortable niche for itself in Primrose Hill over the past dozen years. It's run by Patrick Oberto and his partner Diana Rinaldo, who took over the site in 2011. / NW1 8JR; www.lacollinarestaurant.co.uk; @lacollinaprimrosehill; Tue, Sun 9.15 pm, Wed-Sat 9.45 pm; closed Tue-Fri L, closed Mon; booking max 8 may apply.

THE COLLINS ROOM SW1 £131 3|3|4

THE BERKELEY HOTEL, WILTON PLACE
020 7107 8866 6–1D

Pimp your Insta in fine style with a trip to this pretty chamber and its fashionista afternoon 'Prêt-à-Portea', whose exquisitely crafted cakes are regularly re-shaped to mirror the fashions of different designers. From April 2022 it is 'couture cakes inspired by designers from Saint Laurent to Schiaparelli': 'Schiaparelli's couture golden mini dress combines caramel sponge, dark Valrhona chocolate and hazelnut praline, all topped with a shimmering, chocolate oversized collar', apparently. Not one if you're counting the pennies of course, but something genuinely different and deftly realised for those with money to burn. / SW1X 7RL; www.the-berkeley.co.uk/restaurants-bars/collins-room; @the_berkeley; Mon-Sun 10.30 pm.

LE COLOMBIER SW3 £92 2|4|4

145 DOVEHOUSE STREET
020 7351 1155 6–2C

"You could be in Paris… except the staff are nicer" at Didier Garnier's stalwart "absolute old favourite" in a quiet Chelsea backstreet. For its silver-haired Francophile following, it ticks all the boxes for "a proper French restaurant", serving ultra-classic bistro fare ("the menu changes rarely"), "wonderful desserts" and a "fabulous Gallic wine list at very reasonable prices". More sceptical reporters feel it's "delightful", but that "it's a pity they don't put a bit more effort into the cuisine". They are drowned out, though, by the proportion who feel that "for a very relaxing meal, there's nowhere better". Top Tip – "try and get a table under the awning". / SW3 6LB; www.le-colombier-restaurant.co.uk; Tue-Sat 10.30 pm; closed Sun & Mon.

COLONEL SAAB WC1

HOLBORN HALL, 193-197 HIGH HOLBORN
020 3004 0004 5–1D

Will this late 2021 newcomer finally make a go of this marvellous site in Holborn's former Town Hall, that's so far seen off Shanghai Blues, Burger and Lobster, and most recently Gezellig (RIP)? Dubbed a 'Curry Catastrophe' by the Evening Standard's David Ellis, our feedback is a little more upbeat, but too limited for a safe rating. / WC1V; www.colonelsaab.co.uk; @colonelsaab; Mon-Sat 10.30 pm, Sun 8 pm.

COLONY GRILL ROOM, BEAUMONT HOTEL W1 £107 3|4|4

8 BALDERTON STREET, BROWN HART GARDENS 020 7499 9499 3–2A

Within a luxurious Art Deco hotel near Selfridges, this swish venue (majorly refurbished in 2021) has the "proper spacing", "low level of noise" and "expert management" that's ideal for a business meal ("particularly if you book a booth"). The menu aims to recreate that of 'a New York-style grill room with a timeless selection of transatlantic favourites, salads, crustacea and steaks', and by and large it succeeds. Top Tip – "afternoon tea like you're in a Wodehouse novel". / W1W 6TF; www.colonygrillroom.com; @thecolonygrillroom; Mon-Sat 9.30 pm, Sun 2.30 pm; closed Sun D.

LE COMPTOIR ROBUCHON W1 £132 3|4|3

6 CLARGES STREET 020 8076 0570 3–4C

With its marble bar and banquette seating, this gracious venue (which opened in late 2019) near Shepherd Market is the London flagship for the late Joel Robuchon's global luxury restaurant chain (Robuchon International). It inspires curiously little feedback for its luxurious, rather safe, modern French cuisine ('Le Burger', £36; 'La Sole Meunière', £59), but all reports are uniformly upbeat. Top Tip – "good-value fixed lunch menu with generous courses". / W1W 8AE; www.robuchonlondon.co.uk; @lecomptoirrobuchon; Tue-Sat 11 pm; closed Tue, Sat L, closed Sun & Mon.

THE CONNAUGHT GRILL
W1   £154

CARLOS PLACE   020 7107 8852   3–3B

Bearing no resemblance to the 'Connaught Grill' in operation from 1955-2000 (nowadays, the space occupied by Hélène Darroze), this relative newcomer opened in early 2020, closed for much of the pandemic, then re-emerged in April 2022 (too late for much feedback in our annual diners' poll). Occupying a newly converted area within the hotel, the sleek interior – with much bespoke woodwork – is a world away from the 'period piece' style of its former namesake. Likewise the menu, overseen by NYC chef Jean-Georges Vongerichten and much of it produced from the rotisserie and a wood-burning grill. Where, in its former incarnation, you might have enjoyed Consommé 'Prince of Wales', followed by Médaillons de Cailles 'Belle Epoque', now you can have Heirloom Tomato Salad followed by grilled Japanese Sirloin Black Beef. / W1K 2AL; www.the-connaught.co.uk/restaurants-bars/the-connaught-grill; @theconnaught; Wed-Sat 10.15 pm, Sun 4.30 pm; closed Wed-Sat L closed Sun D, closed Mon & Tue.

COPPA CLUB   £53   234

**29 BREWHOUSE LANE, SW15
020 3937 5354   11–2B
THREE QUAYS WALK, LOWER THAMES ST,
EC3   020 7993 3827   10–3D**

"An ideal location next to the Thames" is a plus for both London outposts of this national chain, which have "superb" situations near Tower Bridge and Putney Bridge and outside terraces with cute outside 'igloos'. In ethos, they resemble hotel brasseries… just without the attendant hotel: staff are "accommodating" and even if the food is not exciting it's dependable and relatively affordable.

COPPER & INK
SE3   £86   433

5 LEE ROAD   020 3941 9337   1–4D

"Why go into central London to eat?" – this "neighbourhood restaurant punches well above its location" in Blackheath, with "former Masterchef finalist Tony Rodd continuing to produce fine value for money": "his tasting menu which changes each month is always where the most fun is to be had, churning out some very special plates of food reflecting the seasons". Partner Becky Cummings runs the front of house and "they have put together a really special local restaurant with a fine drinks list to match". / SE3 9RQ; www.copperandink.com; @copperandink; Wed-Sat 11.30 pm; closed Mon & Tue & Sun.

COPPER CHIMNEY
W12   £41   333

**SOUTHERN TERRACE, WESTFIELD
LONDON   020 8059 4439   1–3B**

With 15 restaurants in five Indian cities, this long-established Indian chain (est 1972 in Mumbai) chose Westfield (near the main entrance) for its first UK branch, which opened a couple of years ago. We still don't get a huge volume of reports, but all are upbeat, especially from those with kids in tow: "authentic, fairly priced, and with something for the whole family to enjoy". / W12 7GA; www.copperchimney.uk; @copperchimney_uk; Sun-Thu 10 pm, Fri & Sat 10.30 pm.

COQ D'ARGENT
EC2   £96   223

1 POULTRY   020 7395 5000   10–2C

"The great location" atop No 1 Poultry, "in the heart of the City", makes this D&D London venue "perfect for entertaining out-of-town business guests" (who might recognise it from the James Bond sequence in the opening ceremony of the London Olympics). It's "slick and efficient", too, which helps for scheduling "a time-critical business lunch". On the debit side, "staff sometimes get overwhelmed by the number of diners", and "the nosh is upmarket but predictable" – "glad I wasn't paying for it!". / EC2R 8EJ; www.coqdargent.co.uk; @coqdargent; Mon-Sat midnight; closed Sun; booking max 10 may apply.

COQFIGHTER W1   £30   432

75 BEAK STREET   020 7734 4001   4–2C

Fried chicken specialists who have elevated the fast-food classic to delectable and "moreish" culinary heights – this Soho outfit was founded by a trio of transplanted Melburnians who missed one of their home city's prime nibbles. They also have outlets in King's Cross, Finsbury Park and the Boxparks in Shoreditch and Croydon, as well as delivery kitchens in Brockley and Balham. / W1W 9SS; www.coqfighter.com; @coqfighteruk; Sun-Thu 10 pm, Fri & Sat 11 pm.

CORA PEARL
WC2   £69   334

**30 HENRIETTA STREET
020 7324 7722   5–3C**

"Romantic but with a buzz", this Covent Garden crowd-pleaser excels for its "consistent mixture of ambience, service and quality food". Not surprisingly "a pre-theatre favourite", it offers "no real gastronomic experiences" but superior comfort food, such as the "delicious and imaginative mini ham-and-cheese toastie starter portions: to die for!". Like its older sister Kitty FIsher's in Shepherd Market, it's named after a courtesan who, in times gone by, frequented the area. / WC2W 8NA; www.corapearl.co.uk; @corapearlcg; Tue-Sat 10 pm, Sun 3.30 pm; closed Sun D, closed Mon.

CORD EC4

85 FLEET STREET   020 3143 6365   10–2A

The Paris-based Cordon Bleu culinary institute (est 1895) has one of the grander names in gastronomy to trade under, and opened a restaurant in the Lutyens-designed former Reuters building in Fleet Street in summer 2022, with former Plaza Athénée and Folie chef Christophe Marleix running the kitchen. One early visitor, Giles Coren of The Times, found it a "time machine", with classical cooking and "four chefs in vertiginous toques" – "how much you enjoy it will depend on what you think of the direction restauration was taken since Le Cordon Bleu was the sine qua non (1973?)". There's also a daytime café for anybody who wants to nosey around inside. / EC4E 1AE; www.cordrestaurant.co.uk; @cordrestaurant; Mon-Fri 11 pm; closed Sat & Sun.

CORE BY CLARE SMYTH
W11   £226   554

**92 KENSINGTON PARK RD
020 3937 5086   7–2B**

"The best restaurant in London" – Clare Symth's "supreme" Notting Hill five-year-old once again topped our diners' poll as the capital's No. 1 gastronomic experience: "a real triumph". And yet, while "it's a special place, the experience is not over-wrought": "it deftly straddles that line between fine dining but not being stuffy". "Clare and head chef Jonny Bone run a great kitchen", but they achieve "the finest cooking without it being up-your-arse mucked around, just with the beautiful presentation of seasonal ingredients" all "served with flair and precision in a fine dining room". "The friendly and very efficient front of house team is led by Rob Rose. And when it comes to wine we always rely on sommelier Gareth's recommendations. He has never let us down yet and works within a sensible budget". "Clare and Jonny always greet you: in fact, everyone says hi and has time to chat. Save up your money and spend it here!" / W11 2PN; www.corebyclaresmyth.com; @corebyclaresmyth; Thu-Sat 2.15 pm; closed Thu-Sat D, closed Mon-Wed & Sun.

CORK & BOTTLE
WC2   £58   244

**44-46 CRANBOURN ST
020 7734 7807   5–3B**

"Hidden right next to the horrors of Leicester Square!", this 50-year-old wine cellar rates highly for its "really special wine ambience" and "knowledgeable and helpful" service. Will Clayton still runs the place on the lines laid down by founder Don Hewitson, although "the food offering has improved over time – not gourmet, but always a good pairing for the wine". This year will see the millionth serving of the famous cheese & ham pie that is always on the menu. / WC2H 7AN; www.thecorkandbottle.co.uk; @thecorkandbottle; Mon-Sat 11.30 pm; closed Sun; no booking D.

Decimo WC1

CORNERSTONE
E9 £92 554

3 PRINCE EDWARD ROAD
020 8986 3922 14–1C

"Unbelievably good food…", "so clever…", "each dish was perfection…", "the best fish dishes I've eaten…", "mind blowing!" – Tom Brown inspires superlatives with the "small yet superbly composed" creations as his "truly innovative seafood destination". "The décor is industrial as you would expect in trendy Hackney Wick" and you can "sit at the counter and watch the chefs at work". Service that's "highly professional without being stuffy or offhand" completes an "unfailingly amazing" formula that's currently one of the strongest all-round performances in town. Top Menu Tip – "signature crab crumpet is changed for winter by adding a rarebit on top". / E9 5LX; cornerstonehackney.com; @cornerstonehackney; Wed-Sat, Tue 9 pm; closed Tue L, closed Sun & Mon.

CORRIGAN'S MAYFAIR
W1 £118 343

28 UPPER GROSVENOR ST
020 7499 9943 3–3A

Richard Corrigan's Mayfair HQ, just off Park Lane, aims to 'champion all game that is coastal and wild, furred and feathered' and the result is a selection of fairly traditional British dishes, infused "with the occasional Irish flavour" ("top-quality venison" and "perfectly cooked fish" inspired particular mention this year). In style, it's quite a "formal" space, although "service is efficient and not too stuffy for the type of establishment" and "if the great man himself makes an appearance, prepare to be entertained!"). One much-repeated complaint this year, though: it's becoming "heart-stoppingly expensive". / W1K 7EH; www.corrigansmayfair.com; @corrigans_mayfair; Tue-Sat midnight; closed Sun & Mon; booking max 12 may apply.

CÔTE
£59 222

BRANCHES THROUGHOUT LONDON

"Nothing to set the heart racing, but decent, plain food, friendly staff and reasonable prices" all continue to carve out a surprisingly massive fanclub for this middle-of-the-road bistro chain as a "tolerable and relatively reliable fall back". It's particularly liked for breakfast ("something for everyone"), pre-theatre, or a family meal ("unfussy" and "you know what you are getting"). Few reports are wild with enthusiasm though – even some fans fear their feedback reads "almost as if I am damning it with faint praise". And sagging ratings support those who feel it's now really coming "off the boil" (indeed, struggling to simmer), in particular when it comes to ambience. / www.cote.co.uk; cote_brasserie.

THE COW W2
£77 323

89 WESTBOURNE PARK RD
020 7221 0021 7–1B

Almost 30 years on, Tom Conran's Irish-themed gastropub is "still ace" – "all chaos and noise; with happy, if haphazard service; plus excellent prawns by the half-pint, and outstanding fish soup (of sonorous depth, with generous chunks of fish and a whopping kick of chilli and love)" – and of course "a fine pint of Guinness". Top Tip – "downstairs is where the atmosphere is", not the cramped first-floor dining room. / W2 5QH; thecowlondon.com; @thecowlondon; Mon-Sat 11 pm, Sun 11 pm; booking online only.

COYA
£114 333

118 PICCADILLY, W1 020 7042 7118 3–4B
ANGEL COURT, 31-33 THROGMORTON ST, EC2 020 7042 7118 10–2C

Resident DJs are intrinsic to the vibey style of Arjun Waney's "very opulent" Peruvians, which since their launch ten years ago now feature Paris, Monaco and Mykonos on their list of locations alongside those in Mayfair and near the Bank of England. The "exciting" Latino cuisine is "beautifully presented" and contributes to an "amazing overall experience". The crowd is "a bit flash" for some tastes, but you can always "ignore the bankers and the Gulf trust fund babies and focus on the plate". / www.coyarestaurant.com; coyamayfair.

THE CRABTREE
W6 £52 334

RAINVILLE ROAD 020 7385 3929 11–1A

A "wonderful location" on Fulham's Thames-side pedestrian path, with Craven Cottage and the River Café a few minutes' walk in either direction, is the strong suit of this spacious gastropub, which has a "quality food and drink offering". In milder weather there's a "fabulous asado grill in the garden, with a great range of vegan and vegetarian options". The atmosphere swings from tranquil midweek to rammed on sunny weekends and match days. / W6 9HA; www.thecrabtreew6.co.uk; @thecrabtreew6; Mon-Sat 11 pm, Sun 10.30 pm.

CRATE BREWERY AND PIZZERIA E9
£36 323

7, THE WHITE BUILDING, QUEENS YARD
020 8533 3331 14–1C

Just across the canal from the Olympic Park – and with a large waterside terrace – this warehouse microbrewery (nice brews!) in 'The White Building' has just the right mix of grunge and hipster vibe to inspire a trip to Hackney Wick. Decent pizza too… but be prepared for a wait at busy times. / E9 5EN; www.cratebrewery.com; @cratebrewery; Sun-Thu 11 pm, Fri & Sat 1 am; payment – credit card only.

CROCKER'S FOLLY
NW8 £55 434

23-24 ABERDEEN PL 020 7289 9898 9–4A

"Classic up-market Lebanese food" and "a good choice of Lebanese wines" from the Maroush group can be enjoyed in the unlikely surroundings of this lavish late-Victorian gin palace – a 'folly' constructed in the mistaken expectation that a railway terminus would be built nearby (the site turned out to be Marylebone). "The front bar is a reconstruction of the original pub, and is great for a pre-dinner drink". Top Tip – "avoid Lord's cricket days, when it gets busy with rowdy fans". / NW8 8JR; www.maroush.com/restaurant/crockers-folly; @maroush; Mon-Sun midnight.

THE CROOKED WELL
SE5 £69 333

16 GROVE LN 020 7252 7798 1–3C

"One of the very finest gastropubs in South London", this handsome Camberwell tavern is a "really solid and enjoyable local", and is run by landlord Hector Skinner, who set it up with three pals a dozen years ago. "If it was in Clapham it would be very famous and utterly heaving". Top Menu Tip – "the sharing roast chicken and the rabbit pie are the best mains". / SE5 8SY; www.thecrookedwell.com; @thecrookedwell; closed Mon-Sat & Sun; payment – credit card only; booking max 6 may apply.

THE CROSSING
SW13 £73 323

73 WHITE HART LN 020 8392 1617 11–1A

An "ambitious newcomer" in Barnes, where veteran hospitality operator Christian Arden has transformed a former pub (fka The Tree House) to the tune of £400k, with chef Anthony Demetre (of Arbutus and Wild Honey) consulting on the menu. "The food is really good, fully deserving of its recent rave review in the Telegraph from William Sitwell!" / SW13; www.thecrossing-barnes.co.uk; @thecrossingbarnes; Mon-Sun 11 pm.

THE CRYSTAL MOON LOUNGE, CORINTHIA HOTEL LONDON SW1
£104 344

WHITEHALL PLACE 020 7321 3150 2–3C

The "fabulous afternoon tea" in the lounge of this luxury hotel off Trafalgar Square makes for a "really special way to celebrate a birthday". "Impeccable service" and "inventive" cakes and pastries are a match for the plush surroundings. / SW1A 2BD; www.corinthia.com/en/hotels/london/dining/afternoon-tea; @corinthialondon; Mon-Sun midnight.

CUBÉ W1
£130 442

4 BLENHEIM STREET 020 7165 9506 3–2B

A short walk from Oxford Circus, this five-year-old izakaya is well-worth discovering. "Like with many Japanese restaurants the food rather than the ambience is the reason to visit: the sushi is exquisite, the chef is extremely accommodating and the experience is consistently good". / W1W 1LB; www.cubemayfair.com; @cubemayfairuk; Mon-Sat 11 pm, Sun 10 pm.

THE CULPEPER
E1 £58 3|3|3
40 COMMERCIAL ST 020 7247 5371 13–2C

This "upscale gastropub" in Spitalfields is a "beautifully refurbished" old boozer, now incorporating bedrooms and a roof garden. The "industrial chic" first-floor dining room may have a "simple menu, but the dishes are far from simple, packed full of flavour and balanced superbly – fine-dining food at gastroboozer prices". / E1 6LP; www.theculpeper.com; @theculpeper; Mon-Thu midnight, Fri & Sat 1 am, Sun 6 pm; closed Sun D.

CUT W1 £132 3|3|3
45 PARK LN 020 7493 4545 3–4A

"Puck never disappoints" according to fans of Wolfgang P's first European outpost across the road from The Dorchester's main entrance, who say its "amazing cocktails" and wide selection of prime cuts from both UK farms and also farther afield (including USDA steaks, Australian wagyu, and Japanese Pure A5 Wagyu) are ideal business entertaining fodder; and also well-suited "for a cheval evening" generally. Even some fans note that "it's very pricey" or that "you may have to make your own atmosphere", but the harsh critiques of some former surveys were absent this year. / W1K 1PN; www.dorchestercollection.com/en/london/45-park-lane/restaurants-bars/cut-45-park-lane; @45parklane; Mon-Sun 10.30 pm.

CYCENE E2
9 CHANCE STREET AWAITING TEL 13–1C

The renowned Mãos (RIP) has gone at James and Christie Brown's hipster retail happening in Shoreditch – 'The Blue Mountain School' – to be replaced by this late 2022 newcomer. A bigger (and more conventional) two-floor operation is promised, overseen by Theo Clench, who till recently was the executive chef at Fitzrovia's funky West African, Akoko and here we're told to expect a menu reflecting east Asia and Australasia. One course will be dedicated to bread alone, apparently, and guests will eat part of their meal behind the pass. / E2 7JB; Mon-Sun midnight.

CYPRUS MANGAL
SW1 £57 3|2|2
45 WARWICK WAY 020 7828 5940 2–4B

"The smell of the ocakbasi barbecue transports you to the eastern Med" at this good-value Turkish-Cypriot grill near Victoria station in Pimlico. It has satisfied appetites for nearly two decades with "flavourful and plentiful lamb dishes, plus piquant salads and salty rice to set them off". / SW1V 1QS; www.cyprusmangal.co.uk; @cyprusmangal; Mon-Sun 11 pm.

DA MARIO SW7 £49 2|3|3
15 GLOUCESTER RD 020 7584 9078 6–1B

Family-owned Italian near the Albert Hall that's "a good option for getting away from the chains". Open for five decades, it was apparently a favourite lunch haunt of Princess Diana, who would bring Princes Wills and Harry for pizza. / SW7 4PP; www.damario.co.uk; @Da-Mario-Kensington; Mon-Sun 11.30 pm.

DA MARIO WC2 £71 2|3|2
63 ENDELL ST 020 7240 3632 5–1C

"Narrow, buzzy and full of black-and-white photos of Sophia Loren, Audrey Hepburn and Marcello Mastroianni in their heyday" – this longstanding Covent Garden stalwart "is like a trattoria from one's dreams of holidays in Tuscany or Rome". "Andrea, the entertaining owner, loves a good chat with guests while they enjoy delicious Italian dishes just like mamma used to make. All ages have a great time". / WC2H 9AJ; www.da-mario.co.uk; @da_mario_covent_garden; Tue-Sat 11 pm, Sun 9 pm; closed Mon; no shorts.

DA TERRA, TOWN HALL
HOTEL E2 £223 5|4|4
8 PATRIOT SQUARE 020 7062 2052 14–2B

"Just blow-your-mind amazing!" – Rafael Cagali's "thought-provoking tasting menu extravaganzas" continue to affirm the status of this "wonderful dining room in Bethnal Green's old town hall" (previously The Typing Room and Viajante) as one of London's foremost culinary destinations. "Brazilian influences that you're unlikely to experience anywhere else" are "what really lift Da Terra from a splendid fine dining tasting experience to a really memorable and unique one". "Tastes and textures are sublime" and "presentation is consistently gorgeous (like works of art), with a charming and compelling degree of theatre". "With its open kitchen, many dishes are served by the chefs" and service is "highly professional and interactive". / E2 9NF; www.daterra.co.uk; @datearrestaurant; Wed-Sat 8 pm; closed Wed & Thu L, closed Mon & Tue & Sun; booking online only.

DADDY BAO SW17 £36 4|3|3
113 MITCHAM ROAD 020 3601 3232 11–2C

Taiwanese steamed buns with tasty fillings are the stars at the Tooting branch of Frank Leung's highly rated Bao family trio ('Mr' in Peckham, 'Master' in Westfield Shepherd's Bush), named in honour of his father, Joe, who retired after a lifetime in restaurants five years ago. / SW17 9PE; www.daddybao.com; @daddybao; Tue-Thu, Sun 09.45 pm, Fri & Sat 10.45 pm; closed Tue-Fri L, closed Mon.

DADDY DONKEY
EC1 £14 4|3|2
100 LEATHER LN 07950 448448 10–2A

"Still The Daddy!... I was glad to return to the office and find it was still trading!" – "Leather Lane Market may not be the most relaxing

venue for al fresco dining" but this busy takeaway draws fans with its "great burritos, plus a wide variety of toppings". / EC1N 7TE; www.daddydonkey.co.uk; @daddydonkeyburritos; Mon-Sun 5.30 pm.

DAFFODIL MULLIGAN
EC1 £75 3|4|3
70-74 CITY ROAD 020 7404 3000 13–1A

"Simple food and amazing produce served with a smile" is the premise at this Irish restaurant just south of Silicon Roundabout, backed by a team including chef Richard Corrigan, éminence grise of Irish gastronomy in London, and run by his son Richie. The beef is from Peter Hannan in Northern Ireland, and downstairs in the basement there's an outpost of Gibney's, a famous pub in Malahide near Dublin. / EC1E 2BJ; www.daffodilmulligan.com; @daffodilmulligan; Wed-Fri, Tue, Sat 10 pm, Sun 5 pm; closed Tue L closed Sun D, closed Mon.

DAI CHI W1 £16
16A D'ARBLAY STREET AWAITING TEL 4–1C

Angelina founders, Joshua Owens-Baigler and Amar Takhar, have overhauled the Soho bar they launched as Golden Gai last year, and reopened it in November 2021 as this 'kushikatsu' (deep-fried skewers coated in Panko crumbs) specialist, here served omakase style. Despite full-on raves from many press critics, including The Guardian's Grace Dent ("delightfully odd", but with "some of the most fantastic cooking in London"), it inspired curiously little feedback in our annual diners' poll – more reports please! / W1W; www.daichi.london; @daichi.london; Mon-Thu 11.30 pm, Fri & Sat midnight; closed Mon-Fri L, closed Sun.

DALLOWAY TERRACE,
BLOOMSBURY HOTEL
WC1 £80 2|3|4
**16-22 GREAT RUSSELL ST
020 7347 1221 2–1C**

The "beautiful terrace" with its "attentive staff" at this very central hotel makes for an oasis of calm close to busy Oxford Street. Named in reference to Virginia Woolf, the queen bee of the Bloomsbury set, it has a "fun atmosphere", and the heating and retractable roof make it ideal for afternoon tea throughout the year. / WC1B 3NN; www.dallowayterrace.com; @dallowayterrace; Mon-Sun 11 pm.

LA DAME DE PIC
EC3 £143 4|4|3
10 TRINITY SQUARE 020 7297 3799 10–3D

"As good as the London three star Michelin-rated restaurants", say advocates for this august dining room in a plush five-star near the Tower of London (which already holds two of the tyre man's gongs). Run from afar by Anne-Sophie Pic (Michelin's most decorated female chef, and owner of Maison Pic south of Lyon), it flies a little under the radar in terms of its local profile, but is perennially hailed in reports for its "exquisite cuisine and exemplary, un-clichéd service". Even those boosting it, though, note its heart-stopping bills, and it was more often judged as "overpriced" this year. / EC3E 4AJ; ladamedepiclondon.co.uk; @ladamedepiclondon; Wed-Sat 9 pm; closed Wed & Thu L, closed Mon & Tue & Sun; no shorts.

DANCLAIR'S SW9 £42

67-68 GRANVILLE ARCADE, COLDHARBOUR LANE
020 7733 9800 11–2D

A colourful, small new space in Brixton's Granville Arcade (Brixton Village as it's called nowadays) created in mid 2021 by Brian Danclair who also runs nearby 'Fish Wings & Tings' (now over a decade old). It's still off-radar in our survey, but both The Sunday Times's Marina O'Loughlin ("a restaurant on the verge of a party" with a "bass-heavy soundtrack and hectic colour scheme probably detectable from space") and The Evening Standard's Jimi Famurewa ("None of what is on offer… seeks to reinvent the wheel… yet, there is something quietly radical about its forceful sincerity") have raved in recent times. / SW9 3PR; danclairskitchen.co.uk; @danclairskitchen; Wed-Sat 11 pm; closed Wed-Sat L, closed Mon & Tue & Sun.

DAPHNE'S SW3 £89 223

112 DRAYCOTT AVE 020 7589 4257 6–2C

"A real favourite" of the Chelsea set since the 1960s, when it was launched by Daphne Rye, Richard Burton's agent (but most famous for its 1990s association with Princess Di) this smart Italian still has its cheerleaders, who insist that "it never fails" – "the best just get better". Others beg to differ, saying it's "sad to see such an establishment going downhill", or damning it with faint praise as "pleasant enough if rather undistinguished". These days it's part of Richard Caring's Caprice group, and feeds shoppers from nearby Brompton Cross. / SW3 3AE; www.daphnes-restaurant.co.uk; @Daphneslondon; Mon-Sat 11 pm, Sun 10.30 pm.

DAQUISE SW7 £58 223

20 THURLOE ST 020 7589 6117 6–2C

"Time has stood still" at this "old-fashioned and sedate" Polish institution by South Ken tube, since it opened in 1947: a "lovely, happy place that is utterly confident in what it does and sees no need to mess about with its authentic, filling and homely Polish cooking". ("It's perhaps a curious choice for romance, but my Polish wife loves it!") / SW7 2LT; www.daquise.co.uk; @daquise_london; Tue-Sun 11 pm; closed Mon; no Amex.

DARBY'S SW11 £82 334

3 VIADUCT GARDENS ROAD, EMBASSY GARDENS 020 7537 3111 11–1D

"It's in an odd area (unless you are the US Ambassador to the UK!)", but Robin Gill's "big, grand and stylish" two-year-old is "well worth the hike". "Sitting in the shadow of the imposing US Embassy" at Nine Elms, its "very polished" interior is "part oyster bar, part secluded booths" and feels "reminiscent of the grand steakhouses of NYC". "If you like oysters and Guinness, or even if you don't", it's "a great spot to waste an afternoon", serving "boldly flavoured" food: "great meat and fresh, beautifully cooked fish". But "while it's good, even so the pricing feels a little punchy". / SW11 7AY; www.darbys-london.com; @darbyslondon; Thu-Sat, Wed 10 pm, Sun 4 pm; closed Wed L closed Sun D, closed Mon & Tue.

DARWIN BRASSERIE EC3 £82 334

1 SKY GARDEN WALK
033 3772 0020 10–3D

The 36th-floor brasserie at the top of the City's Walkie-Talkie Tower may be the exception to the rule that restaurants with a "spectacular view" serve exorbitantly expensive menus of very ordinary grub. Yes, it's "fairly pricey", but consistent strong marks for food confirm reports that a meal here is "surprisingly good". / EC3E 8AF; skygarden.london/darwin; @sg_darwin; Sun-Thu 9.30 pm, Fri & Sat 10.30 pm.

DASTAAN KT19 £47 543

447 KINGSTON RD 020 8786 8999 1–4A

"The best-value for money inside the M25" is not a ridiculous claim for Sanjay Gour and Nand Kishor's "crowded" (and some would say "boring") suburban curry house "set in an anonymous row of shops, just off an anonymous main road between Epsom and Kingston". The cooking (with some dishes "based on Mumbai street food") is nothing short of "terrific": "the flavours are so big that you may feel knocked out the next day!". ("I've eaten in most of the renowned Indian restaurants in London, and Dastaan's cooking matches or surpasses all of them…", "This was our second visit only because it is a 200 mile round trip! And as previously, we were absolutely delighted with the food and service. You would have to travel far and wide to match the quality of the cuisine here!"). Top Menu Tip – "quail and duck kebabs are exceptional" and the lamb chops are "a must". / KT19 0DB; dastaan.co.uk; @dastaan447; Tue-Sat 10.30 pm, Sun 9.30 pm; closed Tue-Fri L, closed Mon; booking weekdays only.

DAYLESFORD ORGANIC £72 222

44B PIMLICO RD, SW1
020 7881 8060 6–2D
6-8 BLANDFORD ST, W1
020 3696 6500 2–1A
76-82 SLOANE AVENUE, SW3
AWAITING TEL 6–2C
208-212 WESTBOURNE GROVE, W11
020 7313 8050 7–1B

The food at the quartet of London cafés supplied by Lady Bamford's organic farm in the Cotswolds suffered a mauling from some reporters this year. The Daylesford brand does have some "huge fans", who praise its venues as "very pleasant for a good-quality snack". But critics – citing "long waits", "clueless staff" and "poor-quality, ropey ingredients" – feel they "may be a place to be seen but are overpriced and uninteresting". / www.daylesfordorganic.com; SRA-3 stars.

DEAN STREET TOWNHOUSE W1 £74 234

69-71 DEAN ST 020 7434 1775 4–1D

"Great atmosphere in the heart of Soho" is the big draw at this all-day brasserie from the Soho House group, which provides "simple food cooked well and friendly, attentive staff" – a winning package that's particularly "perfect for breakfast" or "great for pre-theatre". / W1D 3SE; www.deanstreettownhouse.com; @deanstreettownhouse; Mon-Thu midnight, Fri & Sat 1 am, Sun 1 am; closed Sun D.

DEAR GRACE W12 £48

195 WOOD LANE 020 8187 1039 1–2B

"A great addition to White City", this vast new all-day operation caters for everything from big parties – it can accommodate 350 guests, feeding them "fabulous small plates and lovely wine" – to weekday working lunches (£15 for any large plate and a drink). On the site of the former Wellbourne brasserie, it's from the team behind Lost in Brixton and the Pergolas at Paddington and Olympia. Feedback is too limited for rating, but early reports are very positive. / W12 7FQ; www.deargracelondon.co.uk; @deargracelondon; Tue-Fri 11 pm, Mon 10 pm, Sat 6 pm; closed Sun.

DECIMO WC1 £94 324

THE STANDARD, 10 ARGYLE ST
020 3981 8888 9–3C

"Trying very hard to be trendy and mostly succeeding" ("the views from the WC were a big hit in my party!") – Peter Sanchez-Iglesias's dramatic three-year-old occupies the high-ceilinged 10th-floor space of the über-funky Standard Hotel, with incredible views of St Pancras from its huge, floor-to-ceiling windows. (To enter, shoot up the side of the hotel in the red-pill-shaped, glass-sided lift). It's all very 1970s James Bond. "There are some really exceptional dishes" from a vibrant Spanish/Mexican menu (e.g. lobster with lime chilli, quail with mole glaze, even caviar tortilla). But while all reports rate it decently well, gripes about "silly prices and one or two disappointments" limit the overall verdict to good rather than outstanding. / WC1W 9JE; www.decimo.london; @decimo.london; Tue-Sat 10.30 pm; closed Tue-Thu L, closed Sun & Mon.

DEHESA W1 £66 222

25 GANTON STREET 020 7494 4170 4–2B

"Delicious" Spanish and Italian tapas and "a great choice of wines by the glass" win plaudits for this "romantic candlelit restaurant", "tucked away conveniently behind Liberty just off Carnaby Street". However, since its fabulous debut 15 years ago, it is undeniably "less superb than it used to be", but "that's partly due to standing still while everyone else continues to press forwards". / W1F 9BP; www.saltyardgroup.co.uk/dehesa; @dehesarestaurant; Mon-Sat 11 pm, Sun 9 pm.

DELAMINA £49 433

56-58 MARYLEBONE LANE, W1
020 3026 6810 3–1A
151 COMMERCIAL STREET, E1
020 7078 0770 13–2B

"Exceptional Middle Eastern food" and "lovely staff" tick all the boxes at this modern duo in Shoreditch and Marylebone, from Tel Aviv-born cook Limor Chen and husband Amir. "It's hard to find interesting and well-priced venues in Marylebone, but Delamina manages both". It's a "small-plates, sharing concept and every dish is delicious", with a "beautiful combination of flavours" – "great with allergies too". / www.delaminaeast.co.uk; delaminakitchen.

THE DELAUNAY
WC2 £69 244

55 ALDWYCH 020 7499 8558 2–2D

"Calmer in tone than The Wolseley" (although still "tending to be noisy"): its "understatedly glamorous" sibling is even more in the "Austrian Grand Salon style" than the mothership. And being "well-located for the City and West End" (just off Aldwych), combined with "professional service" and "well-spaced tables", all foster its massive popularity for a "textbook business lunch", or the "archetypal City power breakfast". True to the group's culinary DNA, the food can seem "unimaginative". Viewed more positively, "the undemanding but reassuring menu" is "solid" and "reliable" and the specials of schnitzel, tarte flambée and sausages add to a "pleasing and cosseting" effect that "transports you to Mittel Europe". So, "even if it's never going to provide a top gastronomic experience, a meal at The Delaunay always feels special". Given the recent changes at The Wolseley Hospitality Group (as the business is now called), many reporters voice "trepidation" at the recent loss of the founders: "it's an example of Corbin & King at their best… whither now that they're no longer running the show?" That said, the ratings, here, actually improved on last year in our annual diners' poll. Top Menu Tip – "wonderful gateaux to go with good coffee either after a meal or during the day. / WC2B 4BB; www.thedelaunay.com; @thedelaunay; Mon-Sat 10.30 pm, Sun 5.15 pm; closed Sun D.

DELFINO W1 £61 332

121A MOUNT ST 020 7499 1256 3–3B

This "consistently excellent" "family Italian restaurant" has knocked out "authentic pizza, pasta and secondi dishes" in Mount Street for more than 50 years – and all at decidedly un-Mayfair prices. It closed briefly for a make-over in summer 2022. / W1K 3NW; www.delfinomayfair.com; @Delfinomayfair; Mon-Sat 10.30 pm; closed Sun.

DELHI GRILL N1 £33 323

21 CHAPEL MKT 020 7278 8100 9–3D

This Punjabi 'dhaba' (roadside food stall) is a popular fixture in Islington's Chapel Market, winning praise for its light-hearted take on tasty Indian street food from fans (who have included

The Culpeper E1

veteran restaurant critic Fay Maschler). / N1 9EZ; www.delhigrill.com; @delhi_grill; Mon-Sat 10.30 pm, Sun 10 pm; cash only.

LES 2 GARCONS
N8 £72 543

143B CROUCH HILL 020 8347 9834 9–1C

"A great wallop of France at its best – superbe!". This Crouch Hill newcomer from a pair of industry veterans is "everyone's new favourite for good reasons" – "chef Robert Reid and his friend Jean-Christophe Slowik, who have worked at Michelin-starred restaurants in the past, have created a rural French bistro that is low on snobbery and pretence but has a genuine Gallic 'je ne sais quoi' that feels effortless. The food is delicious, the atmosphere is very pleasant and the worry is that it will soon become impossible to book here". / N8 9QH; www.les2garconsbistro.com; @les2garconsbistro; Tue-Sat 9.30 pm; closed Tue-Fri L, closed Sun & Mon.

DHABA@49 W9 £35 332

49 CHIPPENHAM ROAD
020 3489 2424 7–1B

"Top butter chicken and a great selection of chaats" win a thumbs-up for this snazzily decorated Punjabi fixture in Maida Vale. / W9 2AH; @dhabaat49; Tue-Sat, Mon 10.30 pm, Sun 10 pm; closed Mon L.

DIM SUM DUCK
WC1 £24 522

124 KING'S CROSS ROAD
020 7278 6018 9–3D

"Exactly what the name suggests" – "stunningly crafted dim sum and roast duck" – make this "minuscule" café, a short walk from King's Cross St Pancras, one of London's greatest cheap eats. "It's nothing to look at, but that doesn't matter at all as the array of different dumplings and cheung fun is truly fab, plus the prices are very reasonable". "You can't book and the queues can be long, so get here early or mid-late afternoon". / WC1X 9DS; dimsum-duck.business.site; @dimsumandduck; Mon-Sun 10 pm.

DIN TAI FUNG £57 222

5-6 HENRIETTA STREET, WC2
020 3034 3888 5–3D
CENTRE POINT, TOTTENHAM COURT ROAD, WC2 AWAITING TEL 5–1A

The London offshoots of a famous Taiwanese dumpling brand (in Covent Garden, Selfridges and, scheduled for late 2022 opening, a big 13,500 sq ft debut in Centre Point) are by most accounts "great fun", although "it's quite a different proposition to the Asian formula" – "more upmarket". There's plenty of enthusiasm for the "soup dumpling heaven" provided by the signature pleated dumplings (xiao long bao) – although be warned: they are "more expensive" than in Asia and "the bill can add up pretty fast". / www.dintaifung-uk.com.

THE DINING ROOM,
THE GORING HOTEL
SW1 £113 334

15 BEESTON PL 020 7396 9000 2–4B

"Hooray for The Goring!" – this "enormously charming" and "quintessentially English" hotel, just behind Buck House, remains, for most reporters, one of London's most treasured bastions. Built by Otto Goring in 1910, Jeremy Goring is currently at the helm, and its unchanging style and popularity with royalty have done nothing to harm its following over the years. For a business occasion in particular, the "delightful" dining room complete with "old-style, classy, traditional fare" is ideal and "never fails to impress a first-timer"; and for "afternoon tea done to perfection" look no further than its "lovely and calming" lounges. "The pandemic seems to have hit them hard, though, including the loss of their Michelin star chef". To be honest, it always seemed a slightly strange idea that fancy haute cuisine was key to its success, so no immediate need for panic there. What is more concerning, though, is the decline in rating for what has always been a benchmark level of "discreet and professional" service: "it has sometimes been rather offhand lately – an unwelcome development they would do well to reverse…" / SW1W 0JW; www.thegoring.com; @thegoring; Mon-Sun 9.30 pm; closed Sat L; no shorts; booking max 6 may apply.

Dai Chi W1

DININGS £101 5 4 2

22 HARCOURT ST, W1
020 7723 0666 9–4A
WALTON HOUSE, WALTON ST, SW3
020 7723 0666 6–2C

"It feels like you're in Tokyo at this tiny place" in Marylebone ('Dinings Harcourt') – the two-floor original of this authentic duo, which increasingly now trade as separate entities: "just trust the chef to get you the best sushi at the counter". The odd reporter pronounces the Chelsea branch ('Dinings SW3') as "not as good, but still a strong contender", but actually, although W1 inspires more feedback, there's little to choose between them in terms of their ratings. One distinguishing feature – in summer you can eat outside in SW3, which has a small courtyard garden. / dinings.co.uk.

DINNER BY HESTON BLUMENTHAL

SW1 £152 2 2 1

MANDARIN ORIENTAL, 66 KNIGHTSBRIDGE
020 7201 3833 6–1D

"Mystified as to why this place is considered special in any way…" – too often the reaction at this Heston Blumenthal-group chamber off Knightsbridge. True, it does still have some loyal fans who "have never had a bad meal" from the menu of historically inspired dishes ("I can't agree that the meat fruit is getting boring!"); and who swoon at the "lovely view of Hyde Park". But even some who acknowledge its plus points feel that "what was once innovative and stylish is now populated almost exclusively by Instagram wielding tourists who have yet to realise London cuisine has moved on". And harsher critics encounter "one of the most disappointing meals ever": "no ambience and so much money!" ("the nitro ice-cream had no flavour and felt like a gimmick"). Inexplicably, this place continues to hold two Michelin stars. Actually, it's completely explicable when you realise that Michelin often act like slaves to celebrity… / SW1X 7LA; www.dinnerbyheston.com; @dinnerbyhb; Mon-Thu 9 pm, Fri-Sun 9.30 pm.

DIPNA ANAND RESTAURANT & BAR WC2 £49 3 2 2

SOUTH WING, SOMERSET HOUSE, STRAND
020 7845 4646 2–2D

A "great location" in Somerset House provides a grand setting for this new central London offshoot from the venerable Brilliant, a leading light among the Indian restaurants of Southall – Dipna Anand is the niece of the founder. Early reports are all positive on the food front. / WC2W 1LA; dipnasomersethouse.co.uk; @dipnaatsomersethouse; Wed-Sat 10 pm, Sun 4 pm; closed Sun D, closed Mon & Tue.

DISHOOM £51 4 4 4

22 KINGLY ST, W1 020 7420 9322 4–2B
12 UPPER ST MARTINS LN, WC2
020 7420 9320 5–3B
THE BARKERS BUILDING, DERRY STREET,
W8 AWAITING TEL 6–1A
STABLE ST, GRANARY SQ, N1
020 7420 9321 9–3C
WOOD WHARF, 15 WATER STREET, E14
AWAITING TEL 12–1C
7 BOUNDARY ST, E2 020 7420 9324 13–1B

"I have yet to find the person who does not absolutely love Dishoom!" – Shamil and Kavi Thakrar's "must-visit chain" remains our poll's most-commented-on group, on the strength of its "exceptional" homage to the Irani cafés of Bombay. "A sense of nostalgia for a vanished India and quirky colonial notices add to the fun" of its "cool", "evocative" branches, where "outstanding staff, even when very busy" (which is to say always) preside over "borderline hectic" conditions with great verve and efficiency. The "slightly different Indian food" ("with spice rather than heat") is "far better than it has any right to be" given the volumes it's served in… "superb"… "so consistent" and "extremely fairly priced" too. The "left field" breakfast menu is famous nowadays, and "awesome bacon and egg naan rolls" have "redefined what brekkie is all about" for many Londoners. Founded in 2010, they will hit six branches in London in 2022, with a big (355 covers) new Canary Wharf outlet, complete with a bar and terrace overlooking the docks. On the downside, bookings at all the outlets are restricted and "queues are half way down the street". "It's worth it though!!". Top Menu Tips – "Finally got to try the black dal… a big hug in a bowl"

that's "to die for" and "Ruby Murray is a family favourite". And, with their burgeoning delivery business, "the fact you can now order the Bacon Naan for home consumption is a wonderful, wonderful thing". / www.dishoom.com; dishoom.

DIWANA BHEL-POORI HOUSE

NW1 £31 3 2 1

121-123 DRUMMOND ST
020 7387 5556 9–4C

This canteen has served "delicious, great-value vegetarian thalis" and other South Indian specialities in the 'Little India' enclave behind Euston station for almost as long as the Queen has been on the throne. "Long may they reign their dosas over us!" / NW1 2HL; www.diwanabph.com; @diwanabhelpoorihouse; Mon-Sat 10 pm, Sun 9 pm; no Amex; may need 10+ to book.

DONOSTIA W1 £59 4 3 3

10 SEYMOUR PL 020 3620 1845 2–2A

"What a fabulous restaurant!" – this tribute to the pintxo bars of San Sebastian (Donostia in Basque) maintains the highest of standards and is a "firm favourite" near Marble Arch, alongside its "sister across the road" (Lurra). / W1H 7ND; www.donostia.co.uk; @DonostiaW1; Thu & Fri, Tue, Wed, Sat 11 pm, Sun 9 pm; closed Tue, Wed, Sat & Sun L, closed Mon; booking max 8 may apply.

DOUBLE STANDARD

WC1 £60 3 5 5

THE STANDARD, 10 ARGYLE ST
020 3981 8888 9–3C

Award-winning 1970s-tastic décor isn't the sole appeal of this groovy bar, "in a convenient location opposite St Pancras Station": "a great venue", and not just for those waiting for a train. Its "buzzy and trendy" style makes it a superb rendezvous (it's very 'in' as a meeting place for creative types), although you have to like the sometimes deafening retro playlist. On the menu, "surprisingly good, simple food", delivered by unusually "friendly" and professional staff. / WC1H 8EG; www.standardhotels.com/london/features/standard_london_isla; @isla.london; Mon-Sun 11 pm.

DRAGON CASTLE

SE17 £48 3 2 2

100 WALWORTH RD 020 7277 3388 1–3C

"It was such a relief when Dragon Castle reopened" after a long post-Covid break – "it has long been a favourite, doing standard Cantonese dishes to a very high standard but also plenty of originals". It's a "huge, cavernous place with over-the-top Chinese décor", and proximity to the Elephant makes it "accessible from all parts of London". / SE17 1JL; www.dragoncastlelondon.com; @dragoncastle100; Mon-Sun 11 pm.

THE DRAPERS ARMS
N1 £65 3|3|3

44 BARNSBURY STREET
020 7619 0348 9–3D

This incredibly popular, early Victorian Islington boozer has been transformed into "the perfect city gastropub" by licensee Nick Gibson. The "well-cooked hearty food, great service and excellent wine list" ensure that it's typically rammed. / N1 1ER; www.thedrapersarms.com; @thedrapersarms; Mon-Sat 10.30 pm, Sun 8.30 pm; no Amex.

THE DRAWING ROOM AT THE DUKES HOTEL SW1 £67

35 SAINT JAMES'S PLACE
020 7318 6574 3–4C

"Very peaceful… staff were lovely… we had an extra plate of sandwiches and I chose the mini set of Martini which were totally lush…" – this posh St James's hotel's top culinary attraction, according to our survey, is afternoon tea in its very comfortable drawing room or conservatory. / SW1S 1NY; www.dukeshotel.com; Mon-Sun 6 pm; closed Mon-Sun L.

DROPSHOT COFFEE
SW19 £22 3|4|4

281 WIMBLEDON PARK ROAD
07445 673405 11–2B

This "great independent local coffee shop" on the road to the All England Club showcases an ever-changing list of coffees from different regions and roasteries, and serves "ace brunch food" all day (with tennis-themed names). Top Menu Tip – "the Break Point – eggs on muffins with ham and hollandaise is superb, with super-fresh deep-orange yolks". / SW19 6NW; dropshotcoffee.co.uk; @dropshotcoffeeldn; Mon-Fri 3 pm, Sat & Sun 4 pm; closed Mon-Sun D.

THE DRUNKEN BUTLER
EC1 £158 3|4|4

20 ROSEBERY AVENUE
020 7101 4020 10–1A

There's a host of no-choice, multi-course meals at this unusual Clerkenwell venture, where charismatic chef, Yuma Hashemi, showcases his Persian cuisine in a "fabulous room, set up like an affluent Tehran dining room c.1970". "The quality of the food is superb", and "the personal attention makes one feel as if eating at a friend's home – nothing commercial". There are "two mild flaws, though – 1) it's expensive for what it is; and 2) it's quite reliant on bread and rice". / EC1E 4SX; www.thedrunkenbutler.com; @thedrunkenbutler; Wed-Sun 11 pm; closed Wed-Sat L, closed Mon & Tue; booking online only.

THE DUCK & RICE
W1 £75 3|3|3

90 BERWICK ST 020 3327 7888 4–2C

"A Chinese pub" – in Berwick Street, Soho – "that works!". This contemporary 'concept' successfully combines enjoyable food (including house Cantonese roast duck) with an "interesting drinks list" and characterful interior. Launched in 2015, by Alan Yau of Wagamama, Hakkasan, Yauatcha and Busaba Eathai fame, it's never caught fire in quite the same way as his other operations. / W1F 0QB; www.theduckandrice.com; @theduckandrice; Tue-Sat 11 pm, Sun 9 pm; closed Mon.

DUCK & WAFFLE
EC2 £97 2|2|3

110 BISHOPSGATE, HERON TOWER
020 3640 7310 10–2D

Stunning 40th-floor views over London and 24/7 opening have drawn busy crowds to this perch at the top of the City's Heron Tower for 10 years now, and the signature "tasty duck and egg waffle" and other faux-rustic dishes go down well enough alongside a cocktail or two. / EC2N 4AY; www.duckandwaffle.com; @duckandwaffle; Mon-Wed 1.30 am, Thu-Sun midnight.

THE DUCK TRUCK
E1 £17 5|4|2

BISHOPS SQUARE 07919 160271 13–2B

"Quackers about this place!" – a fixture of Spitalfields Market, this street food truck delivers "duck in a wrap and much, much more" from an "eclectic" and "mouthwatering" menu. And the duck comes with a very modest… bill (geddit?). / E1 6AN; www.theducktruck.com; @theducktruck; Mon-Fri 4 pm; closed Mon-Fri D, closed Sat & Sun.

DUCKSOUP W1 £83 3|4|3

41 DEAN ST 020 7287 4599 5–2A

"A huge wine list packed with unfamiliar names" – all of them biodynamic or natural – "interesting, fairly priced, good-quality Mediterranean food" and a "guaranteed warm welcome" ensure this "fun place to eat always impresses". Now in its second decade, the "cool vibe" and funky atmosphere make it a pleasant throwback to the Soho of years past. / W1D 4PY; www.ducksoupsoho.co.uk; Wed-Sat, Tue 10.30 pm, Sun 5 pm; closed Tue L closed Sun D, closed Mon.

THE DUKE OF RICHMOND
E8 £55 3|3|3

316 QUEENSBRIDGE ROAD
020 7923 3990 14–1A

"The burgers and crab 'n' chip sarnies are great" at chef Tom Oldroyd's "brilliant local" with "charming staff" where Dalston meets Haggerston – "but be warned, you'll get messy!". ("I hope its sibling Oldroyd [in Islington, which closed under 2020 pandemic restrictions] returns as that was a perennial favourite, but until it does I'm happy to support the pub version!") / E8 3NH; www.thedukeofrichmond.com; @thedukeofrichmond; Mon-Thu 11 pm, Fri & Sat 9.30 pm, Sun 8 pm; closed Mon-Thu L.

THE DUKE OF SUSSEX
W4 £62 3|3|3

75 SOUTH PDE 020 8742 8801 8–1A

A "great stalwart for years" – this spacious Victorian tavern by Acton Green Common is a "good local" with the unexpected feature of a "Spanish-inspired" selection of tapas and other dishes, alongside more standard British roasts on a Sunday. Look out for the charming rear dining room, with small garden. / W4 5LF; www.thedukeofsussex.co.uk; @metropubco; Mon-Wed 11 pm, Fri & Sat midnight, Thu 11 am, Sun 10 pm; closed Thu D.

DULWICH LYCEUM
SE21 £54 3|4|4

7 CROXTED ROAD 020 8670 5837 1–4D

"Like its sister restaurant Peckham Bazaar, this Dulwich three-year-old serves great food" cooked over a custom-built charcoal grill by chef-patron John Gionleka and his team, who take guests on a culinary exploration of the Balkans, Greece and eastern Med. / SE21 8SZ; www.dulwichlyceum.com; @dulwichlyceum; Tue-Sat 11 pm; closed Tue-Sat L, closed Sun & Mon.

DUMPLING SHACK X FEN NOODLES E14 £25 5|3|1

THE COLLECTIVE, 20 CROSSHARBOUR PLAZA NO TEL 12–2C

"The best chilli pork dumplings freshly cooked to order" are amongst the acclaimed spicy treats at this culinary Mecca on the Isle of Dogs: the in-house restaurant of an aparthotel, a short walk from Crossharbour DLR. Part of John & Yee Li's street food business in Spitalfields Market, a new outlet is also opening in the basement of their London Fields, Sichuan Fry, in August 2022 (see also). / E14 9YF; www.dumplingshack.co.uk; @dumplingshack; Wed-Sat 8.45 pm; closed Mon & Tue & Sun.

DUMPLINGS' LEGEND
W1 £30 3|2|2

16 GERRARD ST 020 7494 1200 5–3A

This classic and efficient Chinatown operation is a popular choice for dim sum – especially for anyone "missing life in Hong Kong". The food is "all very tasty", if "nothing that really sets the world alight". / W1D 6JE; www.dumplingslegend.com; Mon-Thu 11 pm, Fri & Sat 3 am, Sun 10 pm.

DURBAR W2 £43 3|3|2

24 HEREFORD RD 020 7727 1947 7–1B

"The epitome of the local curry house", this "cosy" 65-year-old family-run tandoori off Westbourne Grove – one of London's oldest – serves "classic fare" that's "always delicious". / W2 4AA; www.durbartandoori.co.uk; closed Mon-Sat & Sun; booking evening only.

THE DUSTY KNUCKLE £37 **4**|**2**|**3**

**429 GREEN LANES, N4 NO TEL 9–1D
CAR PARK, ABBOT STREET, E8
020 3903 7598 14–1A**

"What a brilliant bakery!" – "the bread (especially the potato sourdough) is to die for"; "the pastries are also incredible" ("amazing sticky buns"), and "they serve a very decent filter coffee". "The sandwiches are massive and always filled with interesting and delicious things". Given that it's a social enterprise, providing job training and mentorship to at-risk young people, "this small chain (branches in Dalston and Haringey) deserves all the praise it gets". / www.thedustyknuckle.com; thedustyknuckle.

THE DYSART PETERSHAM TW10 £88 **4**|**4**|**4**

**135 PETERSHAM ROAD
020 8940 8005 1–4A**

In its "somewhat obscure location" bordering Richmond Park, this spacious Arts & Crafts home has "a wonderfully relaxed ambience". It is an ideal showcase for Kenneth Culhane's "original and beautifully cooked meals" – some of the most culinarily ambitious around leafy Richmond, and presented with "immaculate service". It's "almost a surprising find"… except, with the help of the folks from Clermont-Ferrand, it's increasingly well-known. / TW10 7AA; www.thedysartpetersham.co.uk; @thedysartpetersham; Sat, Wed-Fri, Sun 8.30 pm; closed Wed-Fri, Sun L, closed Mon & Tue.

E MONO NW5 £23 **4**|**3**|**2**

**285-287 KENTISH TOWN ROAD
020 7485 9779 9–2B**

The "exquisite kebabs" at this family-run Turk in Kentish Town (which takes its name from the original Victorian sign above the door) have "set the standard in north London for years". Don't be put off by the "limited menu and basic amenities (more like a local chippy)" – the food is "fresh, good quality and delicious", while "service is cheerful". / NW5 2JS; emonoturkishrestaurant.co.uk; Mon-Sun 11 pm; no booking.

E&O W11 £71 **4**|**3**|**4**

**14 BLENHEIM CRESCENT
020 7229 5454 7–1A**

"Still fab 20 years on" – Will Ricker's Notting Hill stalwart has proved amazingly enduring since its days as one of Madonna's fave raves: "it can be a bit hit and miss with its long-lasting Asian-fusion offering, but overall remains some of the tastiest food in Notting Hill" ("although they might change the menu occasionally"). There's a terrace with "excellent outdoor seating and heaters". / W11 1NN; www.eandolondon.com; @eandonotthill; Mon-Sat midnight, Sun 10 pm; booking max 6 may apply.

THE EAGLE EC1 £48 **3**|**3**|**4**

**159 FARRINGDON RD
020 7837 1353 10–1A**

"The original and still the best gastropub" – this no-frills boozer "just keeps churning out sublime, flavoursome food packed with punchy rustic flavours". Set on an anonymous stretch of the busy Faringdon Road, it has never striven to go upmarket or cash in on its fame. "The Mediterranean menu changes on a daily basis and always features something interesting that you hadn't tried before". Many reporters have "never had a bad meal". Any complaints? "It's still too noisy and seating is pot luck, but the standard of cooking more than compensates". / EC1R 3AL; www.theeaglefarringdon.co.uk; @eaglefarringdon; Mon-Sat 10.30 pm, Sun 3.30 pm; closed Sun D; no Amex; no booking.

EAT TOKYO £38 **3**|**2**|**1**

**16 OLD COMPTON ST, W1
020 7439 9887 5–2A
50 RED LION ST, WC1
020 7242 3490 2–1D
27 CATHERINE ST, WC2
020 3489 1700 5–3D
17 NOTTING HILL GATE, W11
020 7792 9313 7–2B
169 KING ST, W6 020 8741 7916 8–2B
14 NORTH END RD, NW11
020 8209 0079 1–1B
628 FINCHLEY RD, NW11
020 3609 8886 1–1B**

"Spartan surroundings…", "efficient service but can be stilted and without a smile…" yet "all is ultimately forgiven" at these "always busy" and "always reliable" Japanese canteens. "Given the price, you'd expect real mediocrity" and yet meals are almost invariably "acceptable and good quality (if somewhat formulaic)". Top Tip – "lovely bento boxes". (The 'G2' Golders Green branch specialises in Shabu Shabu – a variety of broths). / www.eattokyo.co.uk; eattokyoldn.

EATALY EC2 £52 **2**|**2**|**3**

135 BISHOPSGATE 07966 544965 10–2D

Entrepreneur Oscar Farinetti's glam food mall concept was a late arrival in London when it opened near Liverpool Street station in May 2021, given that he now has 42 scattered around the world. It offers a "fabulous selection of food and wine", alongside three restaurants (headed by the flagship Terra, where the dramatic centrepiece grill is apparently fired by wood shipped in from Calabria). Immediately very busy, the offerings include "super pizza", but, for a sceptical minority, "the whole place looks great but is merely a trap for wealthy, bored customers". / EC2E 3YD; www.eataly.co.uk; @eatalylondon; Mon-Sat 11 pm, Sun 10 pm.

EKSTEDT AT THE YARD, GREAT SCOTLAND YARD HOTEL SW1 £115 **4**|**4**|**4**

**GREAT SCOTLAND YARD
020 7925 4700 2–3C**

"Really amazing use of the smoke and fire they cook with" ("there's practically no gas or electricity in the kitchen!") "produces lots of novel flavours" at star Swedish chef, Nicklas Ekstedt's Whitehall yearling, which well-travelled reporters say "lives up to the Stockholm original" with its "inspired Nordic cuisine" (matched with "a novel selection of wines"). And "the lovely staff are really engaged with what they serve you" at this dining room within the five-star Hyatt: arguably, the most interesting culinary arrival of the year. One gripe, though: "some rather mean portions". / SW1S 2HN; www.ekstedtattheyard.com; @ekstedtldn; Tue-Thu, Sat, Fri 10.30 pm; closed Tue-Thu, Sat, Fri L, closed Sun & Mon.

EKTE NORDIC KITCHEN EC4 £55 **3**|**3**|**2**

**2-8 BLOOMBERG ARCADE
020 3814 8330 10–3C**

This "Nordic restaurant with classic and well-executed dishes from the region" is a more casual offering in the Bloomberg Arcade from Danish veteran City restaurateur Soren Jessen, of smart No 1 Lombard Street. There's a good choice of Danish smørrebrød – slices of rye bread with tasty toppings – and a matching selection of aquavit and Scandi gins. Although the odd reporter feels it's "rather let down by the austere ambience", it is "excellent for a quick work lunch". / EC4E 8AR; www.ektelondon.co.uk; @ektelondon; Mon-Sat 10.30 pm; closed Sun.

EL PASTOR £51 **3**|**2**|**3**

**BREWER STREET, W1
020 3092 4553 4–3C
7A STONEY STREET, SE1 NO TEL 10–4C**

"The tacos are tasty and the margaritas are fab" at this "fun and feisty" Mexican duo – part of the Hart Bros' empire (with the Borough Market original still being much more commented on than its Soho sibling, which opened in 2021 on the former site of Hix). "Sometimes the service is a little overwhelmed by how busy the place gets", and the "cheerful" ambience can be a bit "chaotic" as a result. /

ELA & DHANI SW13 £28 **4**|**5**|**3**

127 CHURCH ROAD 020 8741 9583 11–1A

A trio of childhood friends who grew up together in the Punjab joined forces to launch their first venture (meaning cardamom and coriander in Sanskrit) in early 2022 in Barnes. The locals are rapturous: "loving this new Indian and the staff are so nice!" / SW13 9HR; www.eladhani.co.uk; @ela_and_dhani; Tue-Sun 11 pm; closed Tue-Sun L, closed Mon.

THE ELDER PRESS CAFÉ
W6 £19 3 2 3

3 SOUTH BLACK LION LANE
020 3887 4258 8–2B

If it wasn't for the A4 running 100m from the front door, this stylish café would have a "perfect location a short walk from the river at Hammersmith". Inside, the funky interior is almost "yoga studio-esque" in its level of zen, and does superb coffee, plus "super hot choc and buns" as well as some good-but-pricey light bites. / W6 9TJ; www.theelderpress.co.uk; Mon-Sun 5 pm; closed Mon-Sun D.

ELDR AT PANTECHNICON
SW1 £79 3 3 4

19 MOTCOMB STREET
020 7034 5422 6–1D

Limited but mostly positive feedback this year at this second-floor dining space, within the gobsmackingly lovely Belgravia Pantechnicon building. Despite the ambition of its Nordic menu (the name means 'fire' in old Norse), though, it is still not making many waves. Maybe it's because a peek up the staircase takes you out onto the gorgeous rooftop… / SW1S 8LB; www.pantechnicon.com; @_pantechnicon; Mon-Sat midnight, Sun 11 pm.

ELIS E2

TOWN HALL HOTEL, PATRIOT SQUARE
AWAITING TEL 14–2B

On the site of The Corner Room, star chef Rafael Cagali is following the strategy adopted by former inhabitants of the main restaurant space with this large Bethnal Green hotel (Da Terra, see also) by opening a spin-off in these more humble quarters. From a 'Brazilian-Italian' menu, 'more rustic dishes' will feature than those at Da Terra – 'everything from my favourite street food to family meal celebration dishes that my grandma used to make'. / E2 9NF; @restaurant.elis; Mon-Sun midnight.

ELLIOT'S
£77 3 2 3

12 STONEY ST, SE1 020 7403 7436 10–4C
121-123 MARE STREET, E8
020 3302 5252 14–2B

This "fun little restaurant in Borough Market" has pioneered "very interesting natural wines" and wood-fire cooking for more than a decade, building a legion of fans in the process. "Have lost count of the number of times I've stopped for a glass of wine and cheesy puffs", says one. "Sam [co-owner Samantha Lim] is the best host in London and the food matches the service in every way". A second branch opened on Mare Street in Hackney in summer 2021. / www.elliots.london; elliotslondon.

ELYSTAN STREET
SW3 £103 3 2 3

43 ELYSTAN STREET 020 7628 5005 6–2C

Phil Howard – "in a former life, the chef at The Square, where he held two Michelin stars" – continues to deliver "sophisticated, precise

and light" 'flexitarian' cuisine at his "quietly situated" Chelsea HQ, where he has been ensconced for the last six years now. It's rather "grown up" in style – "the atmosphere is very much of understated wellbeing" and the room "spacious". As at some other establishments, though, the pressures of the era dent its ratings this year: "post Covid, the previously first class service is not quite as slick as it was: still professional, but just missing a beat every now and then", and this can sometimes lead to a "lacklustre" overall impression. Many fans, though, still feel "you can't go wrong" here. Top Tip – "fair wine prices". / SW3 3NT; www.elystanstreet.com; @elystanstreet; Mon-Thu 2145 pm, Fri & Sat 10.30 pm, Sun 4 pm; closed Sun D.

EMILIA'S CRAFTED
PASTA £51 3 4 3

12 GEORGE STREET, WOOD WHARF, E14
020 8176 1100 12–1C
77 ALIE STREET, E1 020 3358 0317 10–2D
UNIT C3 IVORY HOUSE, ST KATHARINE
DOCKS, E1 020 7481 2004 10–3D

The original – "a very friendly and very cosy little place with approximately 16 covers in St Katharine Docks" – is the most commented on of this small chain: "brilliant in its simplicity and delivery" of a straightforward pasta menu. Also with spin-offs near Aldgate and, more latterly, Canary Wharf. / www.emiliaspasta.com; emiliaspasta.

THE EMPRESS E9 £56 3 3 4

130 LAURISTON RD 020 8533 5123 14–2B

This well-known old tavern by Hackney's Victoria Park serves up "really good food" – and highly rated Sunday lunches – in "atmospheric" surroundings. "The new chef (Shannon James, ex-Angela Harnett's Murano) is a great refresher", with vegetarian dishes given equal billing on the menu. / E9 7LH; www.empresse9.co.uk; @the_empress_e9; Tue-Sat 10 pm, Mon 10.30 pm, Sun 9 pm; closed Mon L; no Amex.

ENDO AT THE ROTUNDA
W12 £285 5 5 5

THE HELIOS, TV CENTRE, 101 WOOD LANE
020 3972 9000 1–2B

"Quite possibly the best meal of my life!" – Endo Kazutoshi delivers "magical experiences, time after time" in his "tiny but scenic restaurant in the old BBC Television Centre" and "there's no superior restaurant in London". "Endo blends theatre, passion and extraordinary ingredients" and diners "really appreciate his dedication" in creating an omakase ('leave it to the chef') meal that provides "an unparalleled quality of food served with personal flair". "More than a meal, it was an experience poured out of the heart and hands of Chef Endo… I will return… far more impressive than most 3 Michelin starred meals I have had". / W12 7FR; www.endoatrotunda.com; @kazutoshi.endo; Tue-Sat 11 pm; closed Tue, Wed L, closed Sun & Mon; booking online only.

ENOTECA TURI
SW1 £84 3 5 3

87 PIMLICO ROAD 020 7730 3663 6–2D

Giuseppe & Pamela Turi's "phenomenal" stalwart was "a long-time favourite even before they moved from Putney to Pimlico" in 2015 (at an age when some couples would be considering retirement). "A place of calm refinement", they "rode out the pandemic with cheer and great service"; and by providing "precise northern Italian cooking with intense flavours". The special attraction, though, is Giuseppe's long term passion project: "one of the best Italian wine lists in London" offering a "to-die-for selection" that "starts at very reasonable price levels" (but "don't forget your wallet" if you want to do it full justice). / SW1W 8PH; www.enotecaturi.com; @enotecaturi; Mon-Sat 10 pm; closed Sun; no trainers; booking max 8 may apply.

THE ENTERPRISE
SW3 £71 2 3 4

35 WALTON ST 020 7584 3148 6–2C

"Just an icon" in Chelsea's chichi Walton Street – this "pricey" but "lively and very nice upmarket gastropub" caters stylishly to a "mainly posh, middle-aged-plus clientele". / SW3 2HU; www.theenterprise.co.uk; @theenterprise35; Mon-Sat 10.30 pm, Sun 10 pm.

L'ESCARGOT W1 £93 3 3 3

48 GREEK STREET 020 7439 7474 5–2A

London's oldest French restaurant (est 1927) has been beautifully maintained over the decades and is a charming relic of old Soho. It inspired diverging views this year though: recommended for top gastronomy by some but "rather average" or "a bit of a tourist trap" to others. A fair middle-ground report is as follows: "I have to admit that I had completely forgotten it existed, and it was actually very good. Seems impossible to imagine how well-regarded it was in its time, but still a perfectly decent place to go". / W1D 4EF; www.lescargot.co.uk; @lescargotsoho; Tue-Sat 10 pm, Sun 10.30 pm; closed Sun L, closed Mon.

ESCOCESA N16 £49 4 3 3

67 STOKE NEWINGTON CHURCH STREET
020 7812 9189 1–1C

"One of the very best restaurants in Stoke Newington" – this "crowded fish restaurant and oyster bar with rough and ready furnishings" serves "simple, fresh dishes in the style of tapas". (The owner, Glaswegian-born former record producer Stephen Lironi, is a fan of Spanish cuisine who learned that Scotland's best seafood was trucked to Spain – so he decided to 'hijack' some of it en route and serve it in London, alongside the pick of Spanish sherries, wine and produce). / N16 0AR; www.escocesa.co.uk; @escocesa_n16; Mon-Thu 10 pm, Fri & Sat 11 pm, Sun 9.30 pm; closed Fri L.

ESTIATORIO MILOS
SW1 £135 **4** **3** **4**

1 REGENT ST 020 7839 2080 4–4D

"Incredible, beautiful fish is displayed on ice and hosed down every five minutes for freshness" at this splendid St James's outpost of Costas Spiladis's glamorous Greek-based international chain. "Given the eye-watering prices", it's "a place for a special occasion", but if you're wallet is deep enough, it does deliver: "the food is memorably good", "service is silky smooth" and the interior design (complete with imported marble) is impressive (if, perhaps, "slightly cold"). / SW1Y 4NR; www.estiatoriomilos.com; @estiatoriomilos; Mon-Sat 11 pm, Sun 10 pm.

EVELYN'S TABLE AT THE BLUE POSTS W1 £153 **5** **4** **2**

28 RUPERT STREET 07921 336010 4–3D

The Selby brothers' "very snug little basement venue for counter-top fine dining" shows "levels of skill and technique to compete with much better-known places that leave you with a far higher bill"; with cooking that's "consistently well-thought-out, imaginative and bold". "Ultimately there can be a clash between the expectation of enjoying fine cuisine and fine wines, while being perched on a stool with people brushing past", so "file this under 'one to watch' as they plan to build out the ambition even further". / W1W 6DJ; www.theblueposts.co.uk/evelyns-table; @evelynstable; Tue-Sat 11 pm; closed Tue-Sat L, closed Sun & Mon.

EVEREST CURRY KING
SE13 £18 **4** **3** **2**

24 LOAMPIT HILL 020 8691 2233 1–4D

"A reliable canteen for the local Sri Lankan community" – this popular Lewisham caff (with chiller cabinets showing off all the different options) offers "authentic South Indian and Sri Lankan cuisine for locals in the know" who appreciate its "very tasty dishes and excellent value". / SE13 7SW; Sun-Wed 11 pm, Thu-Sat 1 am.

EVEREST INN SE3 £48 **3** **2** **2**

**41 MONTPELIER VALE
020 8852 7872 1–4D**

"A cut above your standard curry house", this Nepalese in Blackheath Village, overlooking the common, is a "decent destination in a culinary desert", offering "good cooking and very fair prices". / SE3 0TJ; www.everestinn.co.uk; @everestinn; Tue-Sun 10 pm; closed Tue-Fri L, closed Mon.

FACING HEAVEN E8 £38

1A BAYFORD STREET NO TEL 14–2B

Owner Julian Denis previously ran the super-popular vegan Chinese Mao Chow just up the road. This new venture (named for the medium-hot pepper) is twice the size (although still only 28 seats) and promises 'an evolution' of the food there, incorporating flavours and techniques from Puerto Rican, Portuguese and American cuisines. No survey reports, but The Evening Standard's Jimi Famurewa found, in his May 2022 review, the vibe of a "dangerously raucous east London house party circa 2009" matched with food that needed "a little more finesse, and… enough confidence… that they don't reach for the chilli-and-umami hose at every juncture". As of August 2022, the restaurant's website shows no availability and says it's currently closed for a refurb that should have ended in July 2022? So change may be afoot. / E8 3SE; www.facing-heaven.com; @facing heaven; Tue-Thu 9.30 pm, Fri & Sat 10 pm; closed Tue-Sat L, closed Sun & Mon; booking online only.

FADIGA W1 £36 **4** **4** **3**

71 BERWICK STREET 020 3609 5536 4–1C

This "casual pasta restaurant" and 'pastificio' in Soho conjures up the tastes of Emilia-Romagna "in a family environment – like your favourite grandma cooking you the Sunday dishes of a Bolognese family!". / W1W 8TB; www.fadiga.uk; @fadiga_ristorantebolognese; Tue-Thu 9.30 pm, Sat, Fri 10 pm, Sun 3 pm; closed Tue-Fri L closed Sun D, closed Mon.

FAIR SHOT CAFÉ W1

**17 SOUTH MOLTON STREET
020 7499 9007 3–2B**

'Fighting for diversity in the workplace, one coffee at a time…' – Bianca Tavella's December 2021 newcomer is a café on one of Mayfair's more fashionable shopping streets that aims to address the UK's current 94% unemployment levels for young people with learning disabilities. Amen to that. And it delivers great vibes. But it's being forced to leave its current premises in January 2023, due to the South Molton Regeneration triangle: wishing them a successful crowdfund appeal for a new site! / W1W 5QT; fairshot.co.uk; @fairshotcafe; Mon-Sat 5 pm, Sun 4 pm; closed Mon-Sun D.

FALLOW ST JAMES'S
SW1 £100 **4** **4** **4**

**2 ST JAMES'S MARKET
07785 937900 4–3B**

"Love the vibey new location even though it's big" – in late 2021, Jack Croft and Will Murray moved from 10 Heddon Street (where their original 12 weeks residency lasted over a year) to this "stylish" new 150-cover site in St James's, incorporating a bar, terrace and chef's counter. One or two diners dismiss the new version as "nothing special", but most accounts are full-on raves for the sharing-styles plates, originating from the UK and its Esher smallholding: "this has to be future of restaurants – sensational food, sustainably sourced, creatively used… magic!" / SW1S 4RP; www.fallowrestaurant.com; @fallowrestaurant; Mon-Sun 10.30 pm; credit card deposit required to book.

LA FAMIGLIA
SW10 £79 **2** **2** **4**

7 LANGTON STREET 020 7351 0761 6–3B

This "old favourite" Tuscan may "live on its reputation" (stretching back to 1966) and the appeal of its superb garden, but on "weekend lunches half of Chelsea appears here" (the half that's not somewhere in the country…) taking the grandchildren for Sunday lunch. Fans say the food is "not the very best but good…", sceptics that "the only thing that isn't average is the price… still, it is one of the poshest SWs!" / SW10 0JL; www.lafamiglia.co.uk; @lafamiglia.sw10; Tue-Sat 10 pm, Sun 9.30 pm; closed Mon.

FARANG N5 £49 **4** **4** **3**

72 HIGHBURY PARK 020 7226 1609 9–1D

"Brilliant Thai food" ("some of the best I've had outside Thailand, and properly spicy too") has won a loyal following for Sebby Holmes's former pop-up in Highbury. The menu has switched from tasting-only to offer à la carte, but the cooking is as uncompromising as ever. Top Tip – "the cook-at-home range sold in their 'larder' is great too". / N5 2XE; www.faranglondon.co.uk; @farangldn; Wed-Sat 9 pm; closed Mon & Tue & Sun; no Amex.

FARE EC1 £58 **3** **2** **3**

11 OLD STREET 020 3034 0736 13–1A

"A reliable spot for light Italian-style lunch or dinner" near Silicon Roundabout, with a strong drinks list courtesy of its co-founders: sommelier Michael Sager of Sager + Wilde and mixologist Marcis Dzelzainis. "The pizza dough is some of the best and the toppings are very different from your usual Italian", the pasta is home-made, and the grills are "just as good". / EC1E 9HL; farelondon.com; @fare_london; Mon-Sat 11 pm; closed Sun.

FARMACY W2 £71 **4** **3** **4**

**74 WESTBOURNE GROVE
020 7221 0705 7–1B**

A "delightful ever-changing menu of truly delicious and inventive vegan/vegetarian dishes" tickles the taste buds at Camilla Fayed's Bayswater venue, which is supplied by her Demeter-certified biodynamic farm in Kent. / W2 5SH; www.farmacylondon.com; @farmacyuk; Mon-Sun 10 pm.

THE FARRIER
NW1 £54 **3** **2** **4**

**CAMDEN MARKET, CHALK FARM ROAD
020 8092 4100 9–2B**

Cleverly converted from Victorian Grade II listed former stables into a faux-rustic gastroboozer, this Camden Town yearling has "a lovely atmosphere, looking out into buzzy Camden Market", and serves a "high-quality" menu of British comfort-food classics which are "a cut above your usual pub fare". There's also a hidden courtyard with a fire pit, and a good selection of locally brewed beers. / NW1 8AH;

Gaucho

www.thefarriercamden.com; @thefarriercamden; Mon & Tue 7 pm, Wed & Thu 11 pm, Fri & Sat midnight, Sun 10 pm; payment – credit card only.

THE FAT BADGER
TW10 £67 3|2|2
15-17 HILL RISE 01423 505681 1–4A

Not far from the Thames and Richmond High Street, the Gladwin family's fifth field-to-fork venture (with food and wines from their farm in Sussex) inspires the promising but mixed reviews that seem to be part of the DNA of their chain. Some excellent meals were enjoyed, but the odd disappointment sounds a warning note. / TW10 6UQ; www.thefatbadger-restaurant.com; @thefatbadger_resto; Mon-Sat 11 pm, Sun 5 pm.

FATT PUNDIT
£57 4|3|2
77 BERWICK STREET, W1
020 7287 7900 4–1C
6 MAIDEN LANE, WC2
020 7836 8883 5–3D

"Absolutely delicious" Indo-Chinese dishes (inspired by the Hakka-influenced cuisine of Kolkata) makes it worth discovering these slightly offbeat eateries in Soho and Covent Garden: ("delectable chops, and it even converted me to liking okra!"). /

FATTO PIZZA & BEER KX N1
UNIT 1, 3 PANCRAS SQUARE
020 3148 4900 9–3C

Since 2015, Fatto e Mano have taken Brighton by storm. This June 2022 newcomer is their first foray into the capital (well, if you leave out Croydon in 2020), occupying one of the glossy units near Google HQ in King's Cross, and serving, er, … / N1N; www.fattoamanopizza.com; @fattoamanopizza.

FENCHURCH RESTAURANT, SKY GARDEN
EC3 £106 3|3|4
20 FENCHURCH ST 033 3772 0020 10–3D

"Unbeatable views" from the 37th floor of the City's Walkie-Talkie building accompany chef Michael Carr's menus at this "high-end" operation from caterers Rhubarb. "The food varies from average to exceptional", but there "enough courses that succeed" to make dining here a worthwhile – even "romantic" – experience. / EC3M 3BY; skygarden.london/fenchurch-restaurant; @sg_skygarden; Fri & Sat 8.30 pm, Thu 9.30 pm, Sun 9 pm; closed Thu L, closed Mon & Tue & Wed; payment – credit card only; booking max 7 may apply.

FENN SW6
£61 5|4|3
194 WANDSWORTH BRIDGE ROAD
020 7371 9888 11–1B

"A top addition to West London's restaurant scene"; this quite basic, 30-seat sibling (plus terrace) to Hackney's Nest is "dreadful to get to" (unless you happen to live in Fulham near Wandsworth Bridge), but it more than repays the effort with "innovative and well-crafted

food" that's "well-priced" plus "a great selection of wines", all served by a "passionate" front-of-house team. / SW6 2UF; fennrestaurant.co.uk; @fennfulham; Tue-Sat 9.30 pm, Sun 3.30 pm; closed Tue, Wed L closed Sun D, closed Mon.

FEZ MANGAL W11
£49 4|4|2
104 LADBROKE GROVE
020 7229 3010 7–1A

"Tasty Turkish food" including "classic kebabs" combine with a "BYO policy and a mixed crowd to make for a fun and affordable meal out" at this Ladbroke Grove standby. For several years now it has been "full both at lunchtime and dinner". / W11 1PY; www.fezmangal.com; @fezmangal; Mon-Sun 11 pm; no Amex.

FIEND W10
£59 5|4|4
301 PORTOBELLO ROAD
020 3971 8404 7–1A

"Crazy food combinations that read so jarringly yet taste sensational", alongside "demonic cocktails" deserve to make a hell of a hit of Chris Denney's (ex 108 Garage) "dark and moody" yearling, just north of the Westway on the northerly section of the Portobello Road. You eat on the ground floor with its big open kitchen (with the option of a tasting menu as well as the à la carte), while in the basement there's a bar. Already something of an in-crowd hit amongst the fooderati, it deserves to be more widely known. / W10 5TD; www.fiend-portobello.com; @FIENDPORTOBELLO; Tue, Wed midnight, Thu-Sat 1 am; closed Tue, Wed L, closed Sun & Mon.

50 KALÒ DI CIRO SALVO
WC2 £47 5|2|3
7 NORTHUMBERLAND AVENUE
020 7930 9955 2–3C

"Properly Italian pizza" – "the best in London, possibly in the UK" – is hiding in plain sight in the heart of the West End, just off Trafalgar Square. Ciro Salvo is a third-generation pizza maestro based in Naples, and his London offshoot showcases his secret-formula high-hydration and long fermentation '50 Kalo' dough. "The dough is the fluffiest ever and every ingredient used is the best of the best, from olive taggiasche to Cetara anchovies to Piennolo pomodori. Incredible!". / WC2W 5BY; www.xn--50kal-yta.it/ciro__salvo.php; @50kalo; Mon-Sun 11 pm.

FIREBIRD W1
29 POLAND STREET 020 3813 1430 3–1D

St Petersburg restaurateurs, Madina Kazhimova and Anna Dolgushina opened this 46-cover restaurant and biodynamic wine bar in summer 2022 newcomer too late for our annual diners' poll, on the Soho site that was previously Corazon (RIP). Greek chef, Nikos Kontongiannatos (formerly head chef at Caravan) delivers plates cooked over fire in a low-lit space that's all concrete and exposed brickwork. In her July 2022 review, The Guardian's Grace Dent was well-impressed:

"The standard of cooking, matched with genuinely intriguing and appetising dishes, puts it right up there on my list of 2022's important openings". / W1W; @firebird.london; Mon-Sat 10 pm, Sun 6 pm.

FISCHER'S W1
£66 2|3|3
50 MARYLEBONE HIGH STREET
020 7466 5501 2–1A

"Treat the winter blues with a schnitzel" at this Wolseley Group brasserie in Marylebone – a "smaller, more casual cousin of the Delaunay", whose "understated" but cosy interior "whisks you off into an ambience of Continental sophistication" and provides a "lively" backdrop to a meal. True to the culinary DNA of the group, the "Austrian-style food" is "somewhat mediocre", and given its inspiration "you need to be up-for some heavy dishes". Prices are "fair", though, and, all in all, "it's a useful and reliable spot for lunch or a family meal". Top Tip – "they understand breakfast here!" / W1U 5HN; www.fischers.co.uk; @fischerslondon; Sun & Mon 9.30 pm, Tue-Sat 10 pm.

FISH CENTRAL
EC1 £40 3|4|2
149-155 CENTRAL ST
020 7253 4970 13–1A

"An institution" after more than 50 years, this "superior" Greek-Cypriot veteran "tucked away" in Clerkenwell, uses "Billingate's finest" to serve "really fresh fish at good prices". It's "always worth a visit, even when it gets too noisy for comfort". / EC1V 8AP; www.fishcentral.co.uk; @fishcentralrestaurant; Mon-Thu, Sat 10 pm, Fri 10.30 pm; closed Mon L, closed Sun.

FISH! SE1
£75 3|2|3
CATHEDRAL ST 020 7407 3803 10–4C

This "evergreen, upmarket fish restaurant in bustling Borough Market" has been a fixture of the area surrounding this foodie hub for more than two decades, noted for its glass frontage and "top-quality fresh fish". It gets "busy", though, and can be "a bit chaotic and unpolished". / SE1 9AL; www.fishkitchen.co.uk; @fishboroughmarket; Sun-Wed 10 pm, Thu-Sat 11 pm.

FISHERS SW6
£43 3|3|3
19 FULHAM HIGH STREET 02073715555 11–1B

"Doing the basic stuff brilliantly" – this "excellent neighbourhood fish restaurant", on the north side of Putney Bridge, provides "fish 'n' chips as they should be served", and "in huge portions". Meanwhile, "the cosy interior adds to the fishy charm!" / SW6 3JH; www.fishersfishandchips.co.uk; Mon-Sun 11 pm.

FISHWORKS
£79 3|3|2
7-9 SWALLOW ST, W1
020 7734 5813 4–4C
89 MARYLEBONE HIGH ST, W1
020 7935 9796 2–1A

2-4 CATHERINE STREET, WC2
020 7240 4999   5–3D

"Lovely fresh fish", "cooked simply" and "at prices which should shame its neighbours", is the attractive offer from this trio of straightforward seafood brasseries in some of the pricier parts of town – Covent Garden, Marylebone and Swallow Street, just of Piccadilly. Top Tip – "there's a fishmonger's attached", so you can take some "high-quality fish" home with you. / www.fishworks.co.uk.

FIUME SW8   £76   2 2 3

CIRCUS WEST VILLAGE, SOPWITH WAY
020 3904 9010   11–1C

The "best terrace in London" – on the south bank of the Thames near the newly redeveloped Battersea Power Station – provides "an amazing setting" for what should be a magnificent Italian restaurant. But it's hard to escape the feeling that restaurant group D&D London with their high-profile chef Francesco Mazzei have missed a trick, and that "far better food should be had at this price". / SW8 5BN; fiume-restaurant.co.uk; @Fiume.London; Mon-Sat 10 pm, Sun 4 pm; closed Sun D.

THE FIVE FIELDS SW3   £193   5 5 3

8-9 BLACKLANDS TER
020 7838 1082   6–2D

"Set in a quiet little street off the King's Road", Taylor Bonnyman's "discreet and elegant" Chelsea townhouse HQ flies under the radar in terms of PR, but is one of the survey's Top 40 most-mentioned restaurants, thanks to its "exceptional" quality. "Top-class ingredients are beautifully treated by a first-class team" overseen by Taylor and head chef Marguerite Keogh to deliver "classically inspired British seasonal food" that's "refined and sophisticated, but never overwrought". Service is "slick" and "classy" but "always with a smile" and the "soothing crisp lines" of the "beautiful dining room" create an "intimate" and "welcoming" atmosphere. "A truly special place for a celebration", especially of a romantic nature. / SW3 2SP; www.fivefieldsrestaurant.com; @the5fields; Tue-Sat 10 pm; closed Tue, Wed L, closed Sun & Mon.

500 N19   £56   3 4 2

782 HOLLOWAY RD   020 7272 3406   9–1C

"This gem of a restaurant" near Archway "doesn't look like much – tables are too close and it can be noisy" – but don't be put off: you'll find "excellent, inventive Italian food" and "always great service – I travel across London for a meal here". Milanese-born chef-patron Mario Mugli named it after the small but perfectly formed Fiat Cinquecento. / N19 3JH; www.500restaurant.co.uk; @500restaurant; Wed-Sat 10 pm, Sun 9 pm; closed Wed-Sat L, closed Mon & Tue.

500 DEGREES SE24   £36   3 2 3

153A DULWICH ROAD
020 7274 8200   11–2D

This "dependable, family-friendly pizzeria" by Brockwell Park is "still good value and the same quality after many years", with "nice chewy crusts to the pizza and plenty of flavour". It has an offshoot in Herne Hill. / SE24; www.500degrees.co; @500degreeshernehill; Mon-Sat 11 pm, Sun 10 pm.

FKABAM (BLACK AXE MANGAL) N1   £52   4 3 3

156 CANONBURY ROAD   NO TEL   9–2D

"Love it!" – Lee Tiernan's "amazing" heavy-metal take on the Anatolian grill is back after a long lockdown break with a modified name (with a nod to Prince) and some new graffiti. It's tiny (30 covers), loud, and the funky flatbreads are "beautiful stuff". Top Tip – the current set menu is released via Instagram weekly to its 62k followers. / N1; www.blackaxemangal.com; @blackaxemangal; Wed-Fri 10.30 pm; closed Wed-Fri L, closed Mon & Tue, Sat & Sun; payment – credit card only; credit card deposit required to book.

THE FLASK N6   £52   2 3 4

77 HIGHGATE WEST HILL
020 8348 7346   9–1B

"A classic venue for reliable pub grub after a walk across the Heath", this "atmospheric" Grade II listed gastroboozer, tucked away in its own backstreet behind Hampstead tube, boasts a "splendid courtyard", and gets "busy at weekends". / N6 6BU; www.theflaskhighgate.com; @itstheflask; Mon-Sat 10 pm, Sun 9 pm.

FLAT IRON   £37   3 4 3

17 BEAK ST, W1   020 3019 2353   4–2B
42-44 JAMES STREET, W1   NO TEL   3–1A
17 HENRIETTA ST, WC2
020 3019 4212   5–3C
9 DENMARK ST, WC2   NO TEL   5–1A
47-51 CALEDONIAN RD, N1   NO TEL   9–3D
112-116 TOOLEY STREET, SE1   NO TEL
10–4D
41-45 THE CUT, SE1   NO TEL   10–4A
SOHO WHARF, CLINK STREET, SE1   NO TEL   10–3C
88-90 COMMERCIAL STREET, E1   NO TEL
13–2C
77 CURTAIN ROAD, EC2   NO TEL   13–1B

"What they do – a limited repertoire – they certainly do well" at this "no-nonsense" steakhouse chain (which serves no starters or puds, just five or six mains and sides, plus "a tiny key they give you at beginning of meal to exchange for a delicious ice cream cornet to take with you as you go!"). It amounts to "amazing value for a good (ish) steak" – "tasty, not mind-blowing, but dependable and fairly priced, and elevated by the sides and sauces". On the site of a former Byron, the 10th branch opens in Waterloo in 2022. / www.flatironsteak.co.uk; flatironsteak.

FLAT WHITE W1   £12   3 3 2

17 BERWICK ST   020 7734 0370   4–2D

The original (back in 2005) and, say fans, still "best flat white in London" – this Antipodean-style indie in Soho's Berwick Street Market has launched imitators on every high street in Britain. / W1F 0PT; www.flatwhitesoho.co.uk; @flatwhitesoho; Mon-Sun 6 pm; payment – credit card only; no booking.

FLESH AND BUNS   £66   3 4 3

32 BERNERS STREET, W1
020 3019 3492   3–1D
BONE DADDIES, 41 EARLHAM STREET,
WC2   020 7632 9500   5–2C
1 PHILLIMORE GARDENS, W8
020 3019 3492   8–1D

"Very busy and bustling" – these "vibey" izakayas are part of Bone Daddies group, and provide an "inventive" mix of dishes from a wide-ranging menu: sushi, filled hirata buns, ceviche (not all branches) and a wide selection of other dishes. In addition to Fitzrovia and Covent Garden, they briefly added a Kensington site in 2022, but it is set to be converted to a Bone Daddies after just a few months. / www.fleshandbuns.com; fleshandbuns.

FLORA INDICA SW5   £55   3 2 3

242 OLD BROMPTON RD
020 7370 4450   6–2A

This "interesting" and unusual modern Indian in Earl's Court celebrates the Scottish botanists of the Victorian era who collected the flora of the subcontinent. There's a relatively short menu, but everything is "delicious" – "small portions, but they pack a fabulous punch of flavour". / SW5 0DE; www.flora-indica.com; @flora_indica; Mon-Sun 11 pm.

FLOUR & GRAPE SE1   £47   3 3 3

214 BERMONDSEY ST   (020) 7407 4682
10–4D

This "noisy and bustling Bermondsey restaurant" is one of the new wave of pasta-only specialists, with "attentive staff" who serve "indulgent food" to happy guests. "The excellent pasta is well complemented by a great all-Italian wine list". There's also a gin bar in the basement. / SE1 3TQ; www.flourandgrape.com; @flourandgrape; Mon-Sun 10 pm; closed Mon L; booking max 6 may apply.

FM MANGAL SE5   £49   3 3 2

54 CAMBERWELL CHURCH ST
020 7701 6677   1–3C

"The chargrilled onions and flatbreads to start soon grab the attention" at this popular family-run Anatolian in Camberwell, founded across town in Islington more than 25 years ago. "The grilled lamb that follows is still as good as ever. Thankfully!". / SE5 8QZ; www.fmmangal.co.uk; @fm_mangal; Mon-Sun midnight; no Amex; no booking.

FOLEY'S W1 £54 3 4 3

23 FOLEY STREET 020 3137 1302 *2–1B*

Most (but not all) the diverse menu is of East Asian-inspiration at this 70-seater in Fitzrovia, complete with outdoor bar. The "excellent seafood" is worth a special mention – "some of the best calamari ever" – and it's "good value, too". / W1W 6DU; www.foleysrestaurant.co.uk; @foleysrestaurant; Mon-Sat 10 pm, Sun 9 pm.

FOLIE W1 £89 3 4 4

37 GOLDEN SQUARE 020 7600 6969 *4–2C*

With a menu inspired by the French Riviera, this spacious outfit in Golden Square "quickly became a firm favourite for business lunches", despite the unfortunate timing of its launch in late 2019. Parisian patron Guillaume Depoix's vision of the 'perfect Soho brasserie', it delivers "delicious French food done simply and well", with a "great clubby feeling, especially when the DJ is there at weekends". / W1W 9LB; folie. london; @folie_london; Mon-Thu 12.30 am, Fri & Sat 2 am; closed Sun.

FOOD HOUSE W1 £39

46 GERRARD STREET
020 7287 2818 *5–3B*

In the late 1990s, Jonathan Meades in the Times regularly hailed the Harbour City – a previous Cantonese occupant of this site on Chinatown's main drag – as London's top choice for dim sum. Now this latest incumbent is receiving similar treatment on the back of an Eater article hailing it as "the trendiest restaurant in central London". According to The Observer's Jay Rayner, the new "very different" offering is "the grand, jumpy, thrilling, chilli and numbing peppercorn hullabaloo that those of us addicted to the Sichuan repertoire just adore". / W1W 5QH; Mon-Sat 11 pm, Sun 10 pm.

FORTNUM & MASON, THE DIAMOND JUBILEE TEA SALON W1 £86 3 3 4

181 PICCADILLY 020 7734 8040 *3–3D*

"Perfect for foreigners with high expectations of afternoon tea" – this "sedate" chamber provides "everything you would expect" of the occasion. Staff are "so accommodating" and the spread is "outstanding every time": "the hot starters are delicious, the cakes plentiful and they keep arriving – take a little box home of the ones you can't eat". / W1A 1ER; www.fortnumandmason.com; @fortnums; Mon-Sat 7 pm, Sun 7.30 pm; no trainers.

45 JERMYN ST. SW1 £80 2 3 3

45 JERMYN STREET 020 7205 4545 *3–3D*

Fortnum & Mason's "luxurious" and "cosseting" restaurant (with its own street entrance) makes "a top central destination at any time! – for breakfast, coffee, lunch, tea, dinner or for drinks" (as the bar does "superb cocktails"). "With its many booths, alcoves and corners, it's the ideal place to meet someone" (particularly on business), and "discreet staff will ensure your liaison goes swimmingly". Less kind reports feel "there's nothing to distinguish the inoffensive upmarket international food", but harsher critiques are absent. Top Menu Tip – "Be sure to try the caviar – served from a trolley". And, for breakfast, this is "an excellent alternative to the nearby Wolseley as it's much less frenetic" and available "with rare-breed eggs, caviar, winter or white truffles in season". / SW1S 6DN; www.45jermynst.com; @45jermynst; Mon-Sat 11 pm, Sun 6 pm; closed Sun D.

40 MALTBY STREET SE1 £62 3 3 2

40 MALTBY ST 020 7237 9247 *10–4D*

With its "carefully sourced and imaginatively prepared seasonal ingredients complemented by natural wines", this spartan venue in a Victorian railway arch behind London Bridge station has become a pilgrimage site for foodies in the past decade. Chef Steve Williams's menu is chalked up on a board each day, and there's no coddling of guests in what is still primarily a warehouse operated by the Gergovie biodynamic wine import business, who provide the in-house wines. A small minority feel the whole experience is "a bit overhyped", but there are no complaints about the quality of the food. / SE1 3PA; www.40maltbystreet.com; @40maltbystreet; Wed-Sat 10 pm; closed Wed-Fri L, closed Mon & Tue & Sun; no Amex; no booking.

FORZA WIN SE5

31 CAMBERWELL CHURCH STREET AWAITING TEL *1–3C*

Having stormed Peckham, then closed during lockdown, Bash Redford and Michael Lavery have chosen Camberwell for the latest iteration of their Italian brand. The formula has become increasingly 'grown up' since it started in 2012 as a pop-up pizzeria in the Truman Brewery: its new guise will be that of a traditional Italian restaurant with primo, secundi, dolce, etc. / SE5 8TR; www.forzawin.com; @forzawin; Mon-Sun midnight.

FORZA WINE SE15 £60 3 4 5

FLOOR 5, RYE LANE 020 7732 7500 *1–4D*

"Tremendous views over London" and sipping natural wines as you chill add to the handy experience of this "amazing rooftop restaurant and bar in the heart of Peckham Rye". Perched on the fifth floor of a co-working space, it is run by the team behind Peckham's Italian-focused Forza Win (no 'e', currently shifting sites). "It's a treat to work through the menu ('snacks' belies the culinary skills at work) while drinking a cocktail and admiring the sights". / SE15 4ST; www.forzawine.com; @forzawine; Sun-Thu 11.30 pm, Fri & Sat 12.30 am.

400 RABBITS £31 3 3 2

143 EVELINA ROAD, SE15
020 7732 4115 *1–4D*
16A ASH AVENUE, SE17
020 7703 1559 *1–3C*

30-32 WESTOW ST, SE19
020 8771 6226 *1–4D*
BROCKWELL LIDO, DULWICH ROAD, SE24
020 7737 8183 *11–2D*
521 NORWOOD ROAD, SE27
020 8761 0872 *1–4D*

"Always fresh sourdough pizza" has helped build a strong local following for this hip southeast London group, with outlets in Crystal Palace, Nunhead, West Norwood, Herne Hill and Elephant & Castle. A new natural wine selection from specialist importer Les Caves de Pyrène is now available alongside the craft beers on tap. Top Tip – "make sure you leave room for the ice cream". / www.400rabbits.co.uk; 4hundredrabbits.

FOUR REGIONS TW9 £55 3 2 2

102-104 KEW RD 020 8940 9044 *1–4A*

This "very solid local Chinese near Richmond" has plied its trade for more than 30 years, delivering "consistently good food with some great veggie choices" and "delicious dim sum". Named after China's four culinary regions, its menu covers the field from Cantonese seafood to spicy Sichuan dishes, and there are good-value set meal options. No wonder it's "often busy". / TW9 2PQ; www.fourregions.co.uk; Mon-Sat 10 pm, Sun 9 pm.

FOUR SEASONS £67 4 1 1

11 GERRARD STREET, W1
020 7287 0900 *5–3A*
12 GERRARD ST, W1 020 7494 0870 *5–3A*
23 WARDOUR ST, W1 020 7287 9995 *5–3A*
84 QUEENSWAY, W2 020 7229 4320 *7–2C*

"The roast duck is extraordinarily delicious and just melts in the mouth" (and the rest of the menu is worthy of exploration too) at these "squashed in" Cantonese pit stops in Bayswater and Chinatown, which waste little energy on interior design or customer service. (A new branch 'Chop Chop', is set to open in the basement of the Hippodrome casino, near Leicester Square, over summer 2022.) / www.fs-restaurants.co.uk.

14 HILLS EC3 £90 2 2 4

120 FENCHURCH STREET
020 3981 5222 *10–3D*

A 'forest in the sky' – 2,500 evergreens planted on the 14th floor of 120 Fenchurch Street by D&D London at a reputed cost of £5million – "brings something different to the usual City venue". It's a "buzzing room with good food to match" from a modern Anglo-French menu. It goes without saying that "you're paying for the views and the experience" – but it certainly makes for "a fun evening". / EC3E 5BA; www.danddlondon.com; @14hillsldn; Mon-Sat 10.30 pm, Sun 9.30 pm.

FOX & GRAPES SW19 £62 3 2 2

9 CAMP RD 020 8619 1300 *11–2A*

This Georgian boozer on the edge of Wimbledon Common is "just what you want from a London 'village' gastropub"

– "a reliable friendly local, with food that's a cut above the ordinary". / SW19 4UN; www.foxandgrapeswimbledon.co.uk; @foxandgrapeswimbledon; Wed-Sun 10.30 pm; closed Mon & Tue.

THE FOX & HOUNDS
SW11   **£64**   3 4 3

66-68 LATCHMERE ROAD
020 7924 5483   11–*1C*

"The perfect local" according to Battersea residents, who rate this old corner pub for its "well-kept beer, well-cooked food, and brilliant service every time". There's a "lovely hidden garden at the back" too. / SW11 2JU; www.thefoxandhoundspub.co.uk; @thefoxbattersea; Sun-Thu 9 pm, Fri & Sat 10 pm; closed Mon-Fri L.

THE FOX AND PHEASANT
SW10   **£59**   3 2 4

1 BILLING ROAD   **020 7352 2943**   6–*3B*

A "superb atrium out the back", with a glass roof that opens completely, gives this self-styled 'country pub' in a cute corner of Chelsea (est. 1846) an edge over rivals. It's generally well-rated, but perhaps at its best for Sunday lunch. / SW10 9UJ; www.thefoxandpheasant.com; @thefoxandpheasantpub; Mon-Sat midnight, Sun 11 pm; closed Mon L.

FRANCO MANCA
  £39   2 3 2

BRANCHES THROUGHOUT LONDON

"A safe option each time, every time" – "they have got the pizza formula spot-on" at this stormingly good chain, which has grown remorselessly throughout recent times on the back of its "enjoyable" offering of "chewy" sourdough pizzas ("I go simple, but they have a good choice of interesting toppings"); plus "a small selection of beers and pluggable Italian wines". Perhaps some small competitors "do pizza better these days", but – "despite expansion" – these simply decorated, upbeat venues are "hard to improve on": "the food tastes fresh and unprocessed", "they turn around the orders quickly" and "are friendly to boot". And prices are "very competitive" too ("I am constantly amazed by how they can produce such a good product at such a low price"). "There are never leftovers here. You have to remind yourself just how far things have moved on occasionally... and these places do that". / www.francomanca.co.uk; francomancapizza.

FRANCO'S SW1
  £88   3 3 3

61 JERMYN ST   **020 7499 2211**   3–*3C*

"An old classic that always feels fresh" – this spry 75-year-old Italian in St James's is "very consistent" and provides "a lovely, busy atmosphere" that's "suited to eating with clients or friends". That it's "a bit pricey" is a theme running through most reports on it, though ("very pleasant, but I have a strong sense that many – most? – diners are on expenses... lucky them!"; "...lovely for the deep-pocketed, with traditional fare that's well done, but at astronomical prices"). Top Tip – "they do a decent line in business breakfast". / SW1Y 6LX;

www.francoslondon.com; @francoslondon; Mon-Sat 11 pm; closed Sun.

FRANK'S CANTEEN
N5   **£45**   3 4 3

86 HIGHBURY PARK   **020 7354 4830**   9–*1D*

This Highbury operation started out as a catering company but has developed into a popular all-day café/restaurant serving highly rated modern European cooking, with evening meals on Thursday, Friday and Saturday. / N5 2XE; www.frankscanteen.com; @frankscanteen; Sun-Wed 4 pm, Thu-Sat 9.30 pm; closed Sun-Wed D; payment – credit card only; booking online only.

FRANKLINS SE22
  £61   3 3 3

157 LORDSHIP LN   **020 8299 9598**   1–*4D*

"A romantic neighbourhood favourite of longstanding" in East Dulwich, which has been serving "good modern European cooking with some unusual twists" for over 20 years now. / SE22 8HX; www.franklinsrestaurant.com; @franklinsse22; Mon-Sat midnight, Sun 10.30 pm; no Amex.

FRANTOIO SW10
  £62   2 4 4

397 KING'S RD   **020 7352 4146**   6–*3B*

"Enormous fun!" "Everyone is treated like a long-lost relative" at this "West London hangout", where charismatic host Bucci presides over a "wonderful local". "The food is perfectly OK without being special", and comes in "massive portions: never mind the quality, feel the width!" – which adds to its appeal as a firm family favourite. / SW10 0LR; frantoio. co.uk; @Frantonio_london; Mon-Sun 11 pm.

FREDERICK'S N1
  £66   3 4 4

106 CAMDEN PASSAGE   **020 7359 2888**   9–*3D*

The "cooking is as reliable as ever" at this calm and sprawling Islington institution – a fixture among the antiques shops of Camden Passage for more than half a century. Its modern European cuisine is "nothing wildly exciting, but assured and confident" and backed up by an "excellent wine list". Staff are "especially good to regulars" ("it's so nice to be recognised, welcomed and made to feel special"). And "when sitting in the quiet and civilised garden in the sunshine, it's hard to believe you're only moments from the fray of Upper Street". / N1 8EG; www.fredericks.co.uk; Tue-Fri 10.30, Sat 10.30 pm; closed Sun & Mon.

THE FRENCH HOUSE
W1   **£67**   3 4 4

49 DEAN STREET   **020 7437 2477**   5–*3A*

"Another reincarnation for the slightly cramped room above 'The French'... and this is a good one!" – Neil Borthwick and his team produce "simple and gutsy food, with big steaks, fresh fish, and tasty Gallic classics on a daily changing menu which will leave you full and pleased that you visit the old place": "a London fixture of decades' standing". / W1W 5BG;

El Pastor

www.frenchhousesoho.com; @FrenchHouseSoho; Mon-Sat 11 pm, Sun 10.30 pm.

FRENCHIE WC2
  £92   3 3 3

18 HENRIETTA STREET
020 7836 4422   5–*3C*

"Paris in Covent Garden" is, say fans, found at this "romantic" small six-year-old – part of a group run by Gregory & Marie Merchand (the former nicknamed 'Frenchie' when he worked for Jamie Oliver at Fifteen). Some reporters, though, "had high hopes but were disappointed": "it was great but very overpriced and too fashionable..." / WC2E 8QH; www.frenchiecoventgarden.com; @frenchiecoventgarden; Wed & Thu, Sun 9.30 pm, Fri & Sat 10.30 pm; closed Wed L, closed Mon & Tue.

FROG BY ADAM HANDLING
WC2   **£208**   4 4 3

35 SOUTHAMPTON STREET
020 7199 8370   5–*3D*

"Outstanding showmanship" ("food theatre for the TikTok generation") "but matched with exceptional cooking running behind the gimmicks" ("dry ice, melting bubbles etc thrill but don't hide the perfect texture and a palate of savoury flavour combinations") has carved an impressive reputation for Adam Handling's acclaimed Covent Garden flagship. Despite its status as a foodie temple, staff are "so relaxed and fun" and the atmosphere generally is very "informal", which fans feel "makes the experience even better": "you can really focus on the food". And with "the kitchen being open, it allows you to see Adam leading his very disciplined brigade". On the downside, ratings dipped a little this year, with some diners questioning "startling prices", or accusing the culinary pyrotechnics of allowing "a triumph of style over substance". ("The technical excellence is unquestionable, but really too much showing off... serving waffles with caviar and honey ought to be a capital offence!"). Success came in other respects, though: it was finally – not before time – awarded a Michelin star. / WC2W 7HG; www.frogbyadamhandling.com; @Frogbyah; Wed-Sat, Tue 11 pm; closed Tue L, closed Sun & Mon.

LA FROMAGERIE £59 322

2-6 MOXON ST, W1 020 7935 0341 3–1A
52 LAMB'S CONDUIT ST, WC1
020 7242 1044 2–1D
30 HIGHBURY PARK, N5
020 7359 7440 9–2D

"Lots of lovely cheese" is on the menu at this specialist trio in Bloomsbury, Marylebone and Highbury, complemented by a "truly interesting and well-curated wine list". The "delicious fondue and raclette go down well on a winter's day". / www.lafromagerie.co.uk.

THE FRONTLINE CLUB
W2 £49

13 NORFOLK PL 020 7479 8960 7–1D

There's an intriguing background to this quite smart venue near Paddington station, founded as a meeting place for international journos and snappers, and whose walls display iconic news photographs from around the world. Feedback has shrunk over the pandemic period, with the odd unsettled report, but it has in the past offered a useful dining option in this thin area, so we've included it but without a current rating. / W2 1QJ; www.frontlineclub.com; @frontlineclub; Fri, Mon-Thu 11 pm; closed Mon-Thu L, closed Sat & Sun; booking max 6 may apply.

FUMO WC2 £55 333

37 ST MARTIN'S LANE
020 3778 0430 5–4C

"Don't go if you have a phobia of crowds" and it's a little "touristy", but this outpost of the San Carlo group by the Coliseum gets the thumbs-up: it's "buzzy and fun"; "the great small plates" are "more than competent for a large, high turnover place"; and it has "a super location for pre-theatre meals". / WC2N 4JS; sancarlofumo.co.uk/restaurants/fumo-london; @sancarlorestaurants; Mon-Thu 11.30 pm, Fri & Sat midnight, Sun 10.30 pm.

GALLIPOLI AGAIN
N1 £49 344

119 UPPER STREET 020 7226 8099 9–3D

"This old Upper Street favourite" (no longer with a nearby offshoot) wins high marks for its "well-grilled Turkish food" and "just brilliant, warm service". Jolly décor, with lots of "quiet corners", suits it to a variety of meals: from a budget celebration to lunch with the fam. / N1 1QP; gallipolicafe.co.uk.

GALVIN AT WINDOWS, PARK LANE LONDON HILTON HOTEL W1 £130 233

22 PARK LN 020 7208 4021 3–4A

"Stunningly located on the 28th floor of the Park Lane Hilton" – the Galvin Bros have run this well-known eyrie since 2006. Its "chief selling point is the panorama of London" of course, and a fair judgement currently is that: "the cooking is sound, well-executed and nicely presented, rather than stellar; but the view over Hyde Park and Buckingham Palace Gardens justify the steep prices and it's great place for a special occasion". Top Top – "the bar is worth a visit too, with an evening setting sun providing wonderful lighting", and you can take in the skyline there just for the price of a cocktail. / W1K 1BE; www.galvinatwindows.com; @galvinatwindows; Wed-Sat 9.30 pm, Sun 2.45 pm; closed Wed L closed Sun D, closed Mon & Tue; no trainers; booking max 5 may apply.

GALVIN BAR & GRILL
WC1 £88 344

KIMPTON FITZROY, 1-8 RUSSELL SQUARE
020 7520 1800 2–1C

"The magnificent and historic, late-Victorian dining room makes for a truly stunning backdrop to any meal" at this "beautifully renovated" chamber: the main dining room of the monumental hotel (originally Hotel Russell) that dominates the north of Russell Square. Critics say the space is "the star of the show", feeling that the cuisine from the newly installed Galvin Brothers regime "fails to live up to it"; but taken overall, ratings for its "menu of British grill favourites" are good. Top Tip – "a very good family Sunday lunch option". / WC1W 5BE; galvinrestaurants.com/restaurant/galvin-bar-and-grill; @galvinbarandgrill; Tue-Sat 9.30 pm, Mon 10, Sun 3 pm; closed Sun & Mon D.

GALVIN BISTROT & BAR
E1 £65 323

35 BISHOPS SQUARE
020 7299 0404 13–2B

This "very reliable and enjoyable old-style bistrot" in Spitalfields is from "the same team as La Chapelle" (the Galvin brothers' deluxe flagship next door). Fans say that "means the food is top-notch for a bar" with a "well-prepared set menu that's great value", but ratings are capped by a minority of critics who feel it has "lost its magic since the revamp". Top Tip – "worth visiting for the Pilsner alone" – fresh unpasteurised Urquell delivered weekly and stored in copper tanks above the bar. / E1 6DY; galvinrestaurants.com; @galvinrestaurants; Tue-Sat 9.30 pm; closed Sun & Mon.

GALVIN LA CHAPELLE
E1 £111 335

35 SPITAL SQ 020 7299 0400 13–2B

"One of the most pretty and impressive dining rooms in London" – an "amazing and beautifully lit" space often mistaken for a church, but in fact originally a late-Victorian girls' school – helps underpin the appeal of the Galvin Brothers' long-established destination, near Spitalfields Market. Although its ratings have come under pressure since Covid struck due to some uneven reports, this remains an "all-round treat", much nominated for both important business and romantic occasions thanks to its "well-spaced" interior; service that is "spot-on"; and "fantastic French cuisine", with numerous diners voting for it in our poll as their top gastronomic experience of the year. / E1 6DY; www.galvinlachapelle.com; @galvinrestaurants; Wed, Sun 9 pm, Thu-Sat 9.30 pm; closed Wed L, closed Mon & Tue; no trainers; booking max 8 may apply.

THE GAME BIRD
SW1 £123 344

16-18 ST JAMES'S PLACE
020 7518 1234 3–4C

"A hidden gem in the heart of London" – this "discreet" dining room is tucked away in an Edwardian St James's five star, but well worth discovering nowadays as its "top-of-the-range", classic British cuisine is going from strength to strength, and its plush, traditional style is suited to many types of occasion including business and romance. In August 2021, Lisa Goodwin-Allen of Northcote in Lancashire (same ownership) was named as the new overseer from afar of the menu here. Perhaps she's behind the boost in ratings, although there's been no discernible revolution in its general culinary approach. / SW1S 1NJ; thestaffordlondon.com/the-game-bird; @thegamebirdlon; Mon-Fri 9 pm, Sun 5 pm, Sat 9 pm.

GANAPATI SE15 £44 422

38 HOLLY GROVE 020 7277 2928 1–4D

"A South London gem" – Claire Fisher's "authentic, fresh and delicious South Indian food" has been a "stalwart" of Peckham dining since 2004 (well before the area's gastro scene took off). It's a "lovely little restaurant", "if a bit cramped", especially if you "quite enjoy the fairly communal dining", and "its regularly changing menu still entices and surprises". Top Tip – "you must buy some jars of divine home-made pickles and chutneys to take home!". / SE15 5DF; www.ganapatirestaurant.com; @ganapati.peckham; Tue-Sat 10.30 pm, Sun 10 pm; closed Mon; no Amex.

GANYMEDE SW1 £88 443

139 EBURY STREET 020 3971 0761 2–4A

"A surprisingly good replacement for the much loved Ebury St Wine Bar" (long RIP) – this new Belgravia venture "is a great find in an area devoid of good restaurants". Daniel Mertl is acclaimed as "a talented chef" producing a "superior" brasserie menu that's "all from the very top of the drawer". / SW1S 9QU; ganymedelondon.co.uk; @ganymedesw1; Mon-Sat 11 pm, Sun 6 pm.

THE GARDEN CAFE AT THE GARDEN MUSEUM SE1 £64 433

5 LAMBETH PALACE RD
020 7401 8865 2–4D

The "fantastic food" is in a very different league to that of most museum cafés, in this attractive space off the gorgeous courtyard of Lambeth's Garden Museum, where former Padella chef, George Ryle, is responsible for "fresh and interesting cooking" with an Italian accent. But not all the typical norms have been neglected: there's also "delicious coffee and cakes". / SE1 7LB; www.gardenmuseum.org.uk; @gardenmuseumcafe; Mon, Wed & Thu, Sat & Sun 5 pm, Tue, Fri 9 pm; closed Mon, Wed & Thu, Sat & Sun D; no Amex; booking max 12 may apply.

LE GARRICK WC2 £61 334

10-12 GARRICK STREET
020 7240 7649 5–3C

"The cramped basement is super-cute and atmospheric" ("its booths and candles making it one of the more romantic venues in town") at this "little piece of Paris in the heart of Covent Garden". With its "decent French provincial-style cooking" it is particularly tipped as a "very acceptable pre-theatre option". / WC2E 9BH; www.legarrick.co.uk; @le_garrick; Mon-Sat 11 pm; closed Sun.

THE GARRISON SE1 £77 333

99 BERMONDSEY STREET
020 7089 9355 10–4D

A "stalwart of Bermondsey Street", this classy, green-tiled gastropub helped kick-start the area as a foodie destination with its launch 20 years ago. The team showed they still care with an "improved menu after lockdown". / SE1 3XB; www.thegarrison.co.uk; @thegarrisonse1; Mon-Thu 11 pm, Fri & Sat midnight, Sun 10.30 pm.

THE GATE £58 333

22-24 SEYMOUR PLACE, W1
020 7724 6656 2–2A
51 QUEEN CAROLINE ST, W6
020 8748 6932 8–2C
370 ST JOHN ST, EC1 020 7278 5483 9–3D

"Predictably good meat-free food that's worth a detour" has helped win a big fanclub for this small veggie chain, which vies with Mildreds as London's best multiple plant-based group. (The Gates are less well known than their rivals nowadays but score higher for food). In particular, there's high praise for "the original and best" location, which occupies a "lovely light-filled" space above a church, behind Hammersmith's Eventim Apollo (and with a 'secret garden' in summer). The St John's Wood spin-off closed this year, leaving two others near Sadlers Wells and in Seymour Village. If there's a gripe, it's the "somewhat unchanging menu", which has seemed more static of late. / thegaterestaurants.com; gaterestaurant.

THE GATEHOUSE N6 £60 333

1 NORTH ROAD 020 8340 8054 9–1B

"Surprisingly Spanish" – this "busy" former Wetherspoons in Highgate is taking the neighbourhood by storm with its very "decent" tapas. "Lovely Sunday lunches too" and they even have a small theatre upstairs! / N6 4BD; www.thegatehousen6.com; @thegatehousen6; Mon-Sat 10 pm, Sun 9 pm.

GAUCHO £87 222

BRANCHES THROUGHOUT LONDON

"Expensive but fun" is the upbeat take on this Argentinian steakhouse chain, where imported steaks are matched with an "excellent wine list" (including the largest selection of Argentinian wines outside the country). And the riverside branch in Richmond is a particular "go-to place for a celebration". On the downside, a worrying proportion of diners find it "overpriced" or plain "disappointing": "it's a good steak, but doesn't match the price tag". / www.gauchorestaurants.co.uk; gauchogroup; SRA-1 star.

GAUTHIER SOHO W1 £120 333

21 ROMILLY ST 020 7494 3111 5–3A

"If all vegan food was as good as this I'd convert… it's ceaselessly wonderful and served by brilliant staff in a fabulous setting" – that's the most upbeat view on Alexis Gauthier's "beautifully furnished and discreet townhouse smack in the middle of Soho", where you ring a doorbell to gain entry. Having been resolutely carnivorous on its launch in 2010, Alexis went vegan personally in 2016, and since June 2021 he has taken the restaurant meat-free as well. On the plus side, this is now one of the most ambitious and successful meat-free restaurants in town. But on the downside, practically none of his old meat-loving regulars like it so much now ("it was an old favourite, and I was interested to try the all-vegan menu, but it wasn't for us…"; "we so very much wanted to love this move to vegan cuisine from Gauthier Soho, but we were sadly disappointed…"; "excellent food, but I mourn the loss of the non-vegan options…"). Still, even those "who are not totally convinced" say "there is no doubt that Gauthier manages to marry vegan cuisine with a high-end, gourmet experience more successfully than most". And "what is stunning is their wine flights, which are amazing!" / W1D 5AF; www.gauthiersoho.co.uk; @gauthierinsoho; Tue-Thu 10 pm, Fri & Sat 10.30 pm; closed Tue-Sat L, closed Sun & Mon; payment – credit card only; booking max 6 may apply.

LE GAVROCHE W1 £147 434

43 UPPER BROOK ST 020 7408 0881 3–2A

"The pinnacle of traditional French cuisine" – "Michel Roux Jr's grand dame of London restaurants" is a cornerstone of "old-school brilliance". "Others may be more avant-garde, but if you want the classics, there's nowhere better" than this subterranean Mayfair venue, founded by his late father Albert and run by Michel since 1992. Under the former, it was the first UK restaurant with three Michelin stars, and has held two since 1993. "Some consider it old-fashioned" or even "dated"-looking (the décor is somewhat "akin to an old-style cruise ship of the 1980s"). But most reporters feel "it has what you want for a special night out": "classic Gallic cuisine of a kind that is hard to find even in France nowadays" delivered in a supremely cosseting setting ("the deep carpets, low hum of conversation and huge portraits of generations of Roux talent tell you you're in for a treat"). "Staff are knowledgeable and attentive, without being stuffy", although a decline in the service rating from its former formidable peak, perhaps reflects the fact that some diners feel "service is not as sharp of late – we miss Emanuel Landré!" (who relinquished the reins as GM to twins Sylvia & Ursula Perberschlager a couple of years ago). And, of course, there's no hiding that a meal here "costs an arm and a leg", particularly now that – due to post-Brexit staffing shortages – there is no longer the option of the much-mourned, marvellous-value set lunch (cancelled when the restaurant became dinner-only). Its food rating this year was more borderline, perhaps as a result. Still, "look up 'fine dining' in the dictionary and chances are a picture of Le Gavroche will appear before long"; and despite the ups and downs of recent times, the overall verdict is that it is "still keeping on top of its game". The fact that "Michel Roux regularly takes the time to speak with customers is an added bonus". Top Menu Tips – "The twice-baked cheese soufflé remains rightly famous as the stuff of many a fantasy last meal; and the epic cheese trolley really is a sight to behold". And, of course, the cellar is special here too: "a wonderfully deep wine list because of the establishment's longevity". / W1K 7QR; www.le-gavroche.co.uk; @le_gavroche_restaurraunt; Tue-Sat 10 pm; closed Tue-Sat L, closed Sun & Mon; no shorts.

GAZETTE £64 223

79 SHERWOOD CT, CHATFIELD RD, SW11
020 7223 0999 11–1C
147 UPPER RICHMOND RD, SW15
020 8789 6996 11–2B
218 TRINITY ROAD, SW17
020 8767 5810 11–2C
17-18 TOOK'S COURT, EC4
020 7831 6664 10–2A

This "buzzy" and "well-priced" modern Gallic quartet (Clapham, Putney and Wandsworth plus the City) keeps regulars happy with "interesting twists on the starters" and "some great weekly offers, eg 'Lobster Night'". One or two critics feel their performance is "half-hearted and disappointing", but on most accounts they are an "extremely likeable attempt to recreate a French bistro". / www.gazettebrasserie.co.uk.

GBR (THE GREAT BRITISH RESTAURANT) AT THE DUKES HOTEL SW1 £83 333

ST JAMES'S PL 020 7491 4840 3–4C

"Tucked away in Dukes Hotel, off St James's Street", this swish brasserie provides food that's "remarkably good and relatively inexpensive". "I have found it more or less empty at lunch-time, so peace and quiet reigns", but arguably "it deserves better support". Top Tips – "well-cooked breakfast" and "very reasonably priced set menus". / SW1A 1NY; www.dukeshotel.com; @gbr_london; Tue-Thu 9 pm, Fri & Sat 10 pm; closed Sun & Mon.

GEM N1 £45 443

265 UPPER ST 020 7359 0405 9–2D

"The name sums it up!" say fans of this busy spot near Angel serving "great Turkish grills with handmade relishes and sides" alongside "excellent" Greek and Kurdish dishes. Its 'Hidden Gem' basement can be booked for private parties. / N1 2UQ; www.gemrestaurant.org.uk; @gemrestaurantuk; Mon-Sat 11 pm; closed Sun; no Amex.

GERMAN GYMNASIUM N1   £70   123

1 KING'S BOULEVARD
020 7287 8000   9–3C

"The impressive building is the best part of the experience" at this D&D London operation, whose location – a Victorian former gym, immediately behind King's Cross station, could not make it handier as a rendezvous. Having opened in quite a promising vein in 2015, its ratings in recent times have started to match the "style-over-substance" performance too often discerned in the group's approach. Custom isn't a problem – it can be "so busy (and excessively noisy)". But service can be "perfunctory" ("they seem to think they do not have to try or otherwise expend any effort to retain customer loyalty") and although some fans do feel its "easygoing" menu of sausages, schnitzels, burgers and other brasserie fare are "great for your German food fix", too many find it "limited, unexciting and overpriced". Top Tips – most often recommended for business and/or breakfast. / N1C 4BU; www.germangymnasium.com; @thegermangym; Mon-Sat 10 pm, Sun 9 pm.

GIACOMO'S NW2   £48   342

428 FINCHLEY RD   020 7794 3603   1–1B

This traditional family-run "local Italian gem" in Child's Hill has provided "good home-cooked food, beautifully served" for more than two decades. / NW2 2HY; www.giacomos.co.uk; Tue-Sun 10.30 pm; closed Mon.

GIANNINO MAYFAIR W1   £119   243

8-10 BLENHEIM STREET
020 8138 1196   3–2B

Few restaurants can boast the heritage of this Mayfair two-year-old: the first ever spin-off from a Milanese original of over 120 years' standing. It's still a case of promise unfulfilled, though, with reports that are very up and down, despite a general acknowledgement of "friendly service and a pleasant interior" (the latter very classical in style). "Eye-watering prices" are key to the ambivalence felt by diners, despite some dishes that are "clearly wonderful" – if you give it a go, perhaps try the set lunch, which is "exceptional value by comparison to other options here". / W1W 1LJ; gianninomayfair.com; @gianninomayfair; Mon-Sat 11.30 pm; closed Sun.

GINGER & WHITE HAMPSTEAD NW3   £14   333

4A-5A, PERRINS CT   020 7431 9098   9–2A

This "ever-popular" haunt serves "excellent coffee", while "the food menu is perfectly acceptable", and includes a "really precise and delicious shakshuka". Any negatives? – "finding a spot can be a trial". / NW3 1QS; www.gingerandwhite.com; @gingerandwhitelondon; Mon-Fri 5.30 pm, Sat & Sun 6 pm; closed Mon-Sun D; no Amex; no booking.

GINZA ONODERA SW1   £100   323

15 BURY ST   020 7839 1101   3–3D

Some "outstanding fine Japanese cooking" is reported at this upmarket St James's basement, which has been through a number of names and owners in recent times, and re-opened in its current guise in Autumn 2021. It comprises a ground-floor bar, plus 70-seat subterranean dining space, incorporating three six-seat counters for teppanyaki, a robata chef's table, and a sushi counter. There is still the odd "disappointing" report, but the overall direction of travel here seems promising. / SW1S 6AL; www.ginza-stjames.com; @ginzastjames; Tue-Fri & Sat-Mon 10.30 pm.

GIULIA W12   £56   332

77 ASKEW RD   020 8743 0572   8–1B

"Replacing the much-loved Adams Cafe" is no easy task, but this "new family-run Italian" in up-and-coming 'Askew Village' is "a local winner" on all accounts. "The small team provides a short, straightforward menu (pasta is homemade and delicious) and the brief wine list hits the right notes". / W12; Tue-Sat 10.30 pm, Sun 10 pm; closed Tue-Sun L, closed Mon.

GLORIA EC2   £61   235

54-56 GREAT EASTERN STREET   NO TEL
13–1B

"It's such a lot of fun" (whether you eat "upstairs – think explosion in a china/flower shop; or downstairs – sexy booths") at the Big Mamma Group's "kitsch-but-in-a-great-way" Italian, which imports the brio of an imagined Amalfi coast, circa 1972, to this Shoreditch corner site. "You need to love a party" though – the filling cod-Italian cuisine is "not bad" but "doesn't match the buzz or the queues". / EC2E 3QR; www.bigmammagroup.com; @bigmamma.uk; Mon-Wed 10.45 pm, Thu-Sat 11 pm, Sun 10.30 pm.

LA GOCCIA WC2   £62   324

FLORAL COURT, OFF FLORAL STREET
020 7305 7676   5–3C

The "gorgeous setting", in Covent Garden's newish Floral Court development and with an outside courtyard, is a highpoint at this venture from the family who own Richmond's well-known Petersham Nurseries: "perfect for a date". Although "expensive", it was complimented more often this year for its "lovely", simple Italian cuisine. / WC2W 9DJ; petershamnurseries.com/dine/la-goccia; @petershamnurseries; Tue, Wed 10 pm, Thu-Sat 11 pm, Sun 6 pm; closed Sun D, closed Mon.

GODDARD & GIBBS E1   £69

100 SHOREDITCH HIGH STREET
020 7613 9802   13–1B

Occupying the former site of Hoi Polloi (RIP), this large, mid-2022 newcomer is part of the recently relaunched One Hundred Shoreditch hotel. Complete with Raw Bar, the menu focus is on fish, although with choices for non-pescatarians. An active PR campaign succeeded in dragging in both The Sunday Times's Marina O'Loughlin and The Guardian's Grace Dent, both of whom delivered a mixed verdict ("pleasurable rather than jaw-dropping…", "doing the very minimum it could to push out hundreds of covers a day, with few flourishes, scant innovation and often little flavour"). / E1 6JN; www.goddardandgibbs.com; @goddardandgibbs; Mon-Sun 11 pm.

GODDARDS AT GREENWICH SE10   £25   343

22 KING WILLIAM WALK
020 8305 9612   1–3D

"Pie 'n' mash is now fashionable" (as reported in GQ magazine) "and the grandkids love it". This "very friendly" outlet near Greenwich Park from the Goddard family – one of London's traditional pie-shop dynasties – is a good place to try the capital's original fast food, with some updates on the menu to offer more choice. / SE10 9HU; www.goddardsatgreenwich.co.uk; @goddardspies; Sun-Thu 7.30 pm, Fri & Sat 8 pm.

Evelyn's Table at The Blue Posts W1

GOLD W11 £71 2 2 4

95-97 PORTOBELLO ROAD
020 3146 0747 7–2B

"Youthful, hip and bursting at the seams", this "great W11 hang out" is a famous old pub once visited by Bill Clinton, now converted into a nightclubby setting by Nick House of Mahiki and Whisky Mist fame. The "tapas-style" food from ex-River Café chef Theo Hill "is hit and miss, with some great and some disappointing dishes" – "but that doesn't seem to bother the crowd, who are there mostly to drink, see and be seen" and soak up the "exciting", "Tel Aviv-style rustic ambience". It has a "beautiful courtyard" too, complete with palm trees and a glass ceiling. / W11 2QB; goldnottinghill.com; @goldnottinghill; Mon-Thu 12.30 am, Fri & Sat 1 am, Sun 11.30 pm.

GOLD MINE W2 £45 3 2 2

102 QUEENSWAY **020 7792 8331** 7–2C

"You'll likely find yourselves among Asian customers" at this classic Cantonese restaurant in Queensway. While perhaps "not the best Chinese food London has to offer", the cooking provides "the real thing", with roast duck the most recommended dish here. / W2 3RR; @goldmine.bayswater; Mon-Sun 11 pm.

GOLDEN DRAGON W1 £49 3 2 3

28-29 GERRARD ST **020 7734 1073** 5–3A

This "boisterous" stalwart is a prime choice on Chinatown's main drag – the dim sum especially is a cut above all its rivals, but all the dishes are just done better here". / W1 6JW; www.gdlondon.co.uk; @goldendragon_uk; Mon, Wed-Sun 10 pm; closed Mon, Wed-Sun L, closed Tue.

GOLDEN HIND W1 £49 3 2 2

73 MARYLEBONE LN **020 7486 3644** 2–1A

"Great fish 'n' chips" is to be found at this Maylebone veteran – one of London's oldest chippies, given that it first opened in 1914. Your order can be steamed with olive oil and oregano and accompanied with mozzarella fritters and asparagus for those who want a change from the standard deep-fried option, and there's a mouth-watering selection of old-school English puds including spotted dick, rhubarb crumble and treacle syrup sponge, all served with custard or ice cream. / W1U 2PN; www.goldenhindrestaurant.com; Mon-Sat 10 pm; closed Sun.

GOOD EARTH £75 3 3 2

233 BROMPTON RD, SW3
020 7584 3658 6–2C
143-145 THE BROADWAY, NW7
020 8959 7011 1–1B
11 BELLEVUE RD, SW17
020 8682 9230 11–2C

"Several clicks above your average Chinese..." – this "very popular" family-owned chain with sites in Knightsbridge, Mill Hill, Wandsworth Common and Esher – remains a long-running

success story. Purists might find the food too "safe" (and the menu "has changed little over the years"). Yet even one critic who has "yet to be convinced by the concept of a posh Chinese" feels "they give it a good go" here, and despite the "pretty punchy prices" most diners feel the experience is "well worth the extra money". / www.goodearthgroup.co.uk.

GOODMAN £95 3 3 2

24-26 MADDOX ST, W1
020 7499 3776 3–2C
3 SOUTH QUAY, E14 **020 7531 0300** 12–1C
11 OLD JEWRY, EC2 **020 7600 8220** 10–2C

"Still the go-to New York-style steak house" – this Russian-owned chain has "a distinct style from Hawksmoor" which it somewhat resembles; and though its fanbase is much smaller, it's held in equal regard by those who recommend it. Well located for expense accounters, its branches in Mayfair, the City and Canary Wharf are "a safe bet for good steak" and deliver a straightforward formula inspiring few grumbles. "The prices aren't dirt cheap, but those AAA steaks never were". / www.goodmanrestaurants.com; goodman_london.

GORDON RAMSAY SW3 £210 3 3 2

68-69 ROYAL HOSPITAL RD
020 7352 4441 6–3D

Fans do rave over the "beautiful cuisine from wonderful Matt Abé", "exceptional" service and "memorable" all-round experience created by the f-word chef's original HQ. And there's little question that the classical-ish cuisine here is highly "technically accomplished", service "friendly and well-informed" ("too much of it, if anything") and the overall impression "classy". But it continues to struggle against diners' sky-high expectations, often inspired by Michelin's somewhat unfathomable continuation of its three-star rating promoting it as being at the very pinnacle of UK dining. A relatively small venue in deepest Chelsea, "the dining room has the air of an art deco cruise ship, with its neutral tones and carpet", all of which creates a setting that's "tranquil", but too "cold" or "bland" to some tastes. And when it comes to gastronomy, a typical critical report of the cuisine would be that it's "not bad, some of it very good, but… frankly I was expecting outstanding… and it was a far cry from that… to the extent it was my biggest disappointment of the year". It doesn't help that it's "hugely expensive, which always puts on the dampers". (Footnote – a number of reporters wish ex-maître d' Jean-Claude Breton well: "thank you JC, enjoy your very well-deserved retirement!") / SW3 4HP; www.gordonramsay.com; @Restaurantgordonramsay; Tue-Sat 11 pm; closed Sun & Mon; No jeans; booking max 9 may apply.

GORDON'S WINE BAR WC2 £43 2 2 5

47 VILLIERS ST **020 7930 1408** 5–4D

"Love it… I always feel like a spy when I drink there…" – London's oldest wine bar (est. 1890), near Embankment tube, is worth a visit for its

"great interior" alone, with ancient brick-lined vaults, but it also boasts one of the capital's biggest outside terraces. You no longer queue for the cold cuts, cheese and pies – they bring them to you with waiter service. The "excellent selection of wines" is by far the greater attraction. / WC2N 6NE; gordonswinebar.com; @gordonswinebar; Mon-Sat 11 pm, Sun 10 pm; no booking.

GOURMET BURGER KITCHEN £37 3 2 2

BRANCHES THROUGHOUT LONDON

"Quality burgers at a great price point" make the capital's original posh burger chain "a family favourite" for many fans – "the kids always want to go back". Founded 22 years ago in Battersea's 'Nappy Valley' by a bunch of Kiwis, the group expanded rapidly and changed hands three times before hitting the buffers. Its fortunes appear to have stabilised since Birmingham-based 'chicken king' Ranjit Boparan bought it out of administration in 2020, although the 60-odd branches have been whittled down to 37 – half of them in London. / www.gbkinfo.com.

GOYA SW1 £42 3 3 2

34 LUPUS ST **020 7976 5309** 2–4C

"This tapas bar/restaurant has been around forever" – 30 years, to be precise, of serving solid Hispanic cuisine to a happy Pimlico clientele – "but the standard is hard to beat". "The place is a delight. It doesn't rock, but it does everything else brilliantly!". / SW1V 3EB; www.goyarestaurant.co.uk; Mon-Sat midnight, Sun 11.30 pm.

GRANARY SQUARE BRASSERIE N1 £49 2 2 3

1 GRANARY SQUARE **020 3940 1000** 9–3C

This "beautiful venue" near King's Cross with "lovely outside tables" is part of Richard Caring's Ivy Collection and comes with similar pros and cons. It's "lively and buzzy", and a handy location makes it "a fun place to meet friends", but it takes flak for "slow and unprofessional" service and food that's "the usual brasserie fare, but doesn't feel like it's cooked with love" and "isn't worth the price". / N1N 4AB; www.granarysquarebrasserie.com; @granarysquarebrasserie; Mon-Sat midnight, Sun 11 pm; booking max 12 may apply.

GRAND TRUNK ROAD E18 £68 4 4 3

219 HIGH STREET **020 8505 1965** 1–1D

"We are so lucky to have such a great restaurant on our doorstep!" – Rajesh Suri (who managed Mayfair's Tamarind for 14 years) "exceptional local" is "a far cry from your usual Indian restaurant, so any extra expense is worth it" for the "delicious and unusual flavours, all well presented". "Glad I live in E18!" / E18 2PB; www.gtrrestaurant.co.uk; @grandtrunk_road; Tue-Sat 10.30 pm, Sun 8.30 pm; closed Tue-Thu L, closed Mon; no shorts.

GRANGER & CO £62 ②②②

237-239 PAVILION RD, SW1
020 3848 1060 6–2D
105 MARYLEBONE HIGH STREET, W1
020 8079 7120 2–1A
175 WESTBOURNE GROVE, W11
020 7229 9111 7–1B
STANLEY BUILDING, ST PANCRAS SQ, N1
020 3058 2567 9–3C
THE BUCKLEY BUILDING, 50 SEKFORDE
ST, EC1 020 7251 9032 10–1A

"Best brunch in London!" is an oft-repeated claim for Aussie celeb chef Bill Granger's chain of "pleasant light and airy" spaces, which its army of fans see as "perfect breakfast venues, with great food, strong coffee, and a buzzy atmosphere". The "varied" menu has the "Antipodean slant" you'd expect, but arguably "the food doesn't quite live up to its style" and "it pays to be adventurous with your ordering: be bold and try something new! – the safe options are very… safe". In August 2022, the group adds a fifth Marylebone site in what older readers will remember as 'Maison Sagne'. / grangerandco.com; grangerandco.

THE GRAZING GOAT
W1 £83 ③③③

6 NEW QUEBEC ST 020 7724 7243 2–2A

Promising 'layers of country pub' on its website, this popular pub/restaurant (also with rooms) is tucked away in a Marylebone townhouse. Part of the posh Cubitt House group, it offers "decent upmarket pub fare with reliable cooking and service" in a buzzing setting. / W1H 7RQ; www.thegrazinggoat.co.uk; @cubitthouse; Mon-Sat 9 pm, Sun 8 pm.

GREAT NEPALESE
NW1 £42 ③④③

48 EVERSHOLT ST 020 7388 6737 9–3C

Time to kill near Euston station? Grab a bite at this "long standing, quality local" – a sweet-looking, little curry house (est 1982), still proudly displaying its Fay Maschler review from shortly after it opened. "It always delivers good dishes" – Nepalese specials are best – but prices are not as 'bargain basement' as its appearance might suggest. / NW1 1DA; www.great-nepalese.co.uk; Mon-Sat 10.30 pm; closed Sun.

GREEN COTTAGE
NW3 £48 ③②②

9 NEW COLLEGE PDE
020 7722 5305 9–2A

"We keep coming and they keep feeding us" – this "longstanding, basic Chinese restaurant" in Swiss cottage "never lets you down", serving some of the "best roast duck outside Chinatown and Queensway". / NW3 5EP; Mon-Sun 11 pm; no Amex.

GREENBERRY CAFÉ
NW1 £50 ③③④

101 REGENTS PARK ROAD
020 7483 3765 9–2B

"A favourite brunch venue" – this "lovely casual local café/restaurant" in Primrose Hill "offers all-day dining with plenty of choice from an eclectic menu". Top Tip – "winter lunch in one of their outdoor heated 'castaway shacks'". / NW1 8UR; greenberrycafe.co.uk; @greenberrycafe; Sun & Mon 3 pm, Tue-Sat 10 pm; closed Sun & Mon D.

THE GRILL AT
THE DORCHESTER
W1 £108 ④④④

53 PARK LANE 020 7629 8888 3–3A

This "stunning and beautiful dining room", off the hotel's main 'Promenade', inherited its Moorish décor from the 1930s and is currently riding high on the "wonderful dining experience" created by 27-year-old wunderkind chef, Tom Booton's cuisine: "a serious talent going right to the very top; and a humble and approachable guy whose restaurant reflects this ethos". Top Tip – "the set lunch is one of the capital's biggest bargains" and is great on a Sunday here. / W1K 1QA; www.dorchestercollection.com/en/london/the-dorchester; @thedorchester; Tue-Sat 10 pm, Sun 4 pm; closed Tue-Fri L closed Sun D, closed Mon; no trainers.

GRUMBLES SW1 £47 ③④③

35 CHURTON ST 020 7834 0149 2–4B

This "cosy, traditional and relaxed bistro" celebrates its 60th anniversary next year, and is proudly resistant to change: the wooden furnishings remain intact from the original £300 fit-out in 1964. It makes for "an unstuffy environment where you feel at home from the moment you walk in", and the food – solid, old-school British bistro fare – is "excellent" by the standards of "cheap 'n' cheerful" scoff. / SW1V 2LT; www.grumblesrestaurant.co.uk; @grumblesrestaurant; Mon-Sun 10 pm.

THE GUILDFORD ARMS
SE10 £56 ③③③

55 GUILDFORD GROVE
020 8691 6293 1–3D

"'Cut-above' pub food" is served in this "beautiful Georgian tavern" in Greenwich, whose garden has been "transformed into a well-designed and extensive eating area" ("far nicer than the makeshift tents that often emerged in the pandemic"). / SE10 8JY; www.theguildfordarms.co.uk; @guildfordarms_; Tue-Thu 9 pm, Fri & Sat 9.30 pm, Sun 8.30 pm; closed Mon; payment – credit card only.

THE GUINEA GRILL
W1 £101 ②②④

30 BRUTON PL 020 7409 1728 3–3B

"Proper man food!" is to be found at this "very old-school" Mayfair favourite – a dining room behind a well-known Young's pub in a cute central mews, which feels "like a different century" (est 1952). "If you like steak in a traditional environment", look no further: "there's an extensive menu including a mighty mixed grill, a variety of prime grass-fed steaks or tempting traditional pies". "Best of all, you can then go on for drinks in the attached pub!" No hiding, though, that its performance has taken a knock in these troubled times. While it's always been "a bit expensive (but completely unique)", some meals this year badly missed the mark due to service that was "nothing special" or poor preparation ("The Guinea used to be one of my favourite destinations for a sumptuous piece of charcoal-grilled beef, but the rib steak on my last visit was so tough it has hardly fit to eat"). BREAKING NEWS: In July 2022, Oisin Rogers, who has managed the dining room here for the last 6 years, announced he is moving on to pastures new. / W1J 6NL; www.theguinea.co.uk; @guineagrill; Mon-Sun 10 pm.

THE GUN E14 £69 ③③④

27 COLDHARBOUR 020 7515 5222 12–1C

Directly across the Thames from the O2 – and a short drive from Canary Wharf – this Grade II listed tavern benefits from a superb waterside location, characterful old interior and large modern terrace. Nowadays run by Fuller's, it's not a foodie pub as it was a few years ago, but still wins praise for "great food, super cocktails and friendly staff". / E14 9NS; www.thegundocklands.com; @thegundocklands; Mon-Sat 9.30 pm, Sun 7 pm.

GUNPOWDER £52 ④③③

20 GREEK STREET, W1
020 3813 7796 5–2A
ONE TOWER BRIDGE, 4 CROWN SQUARE,
SE1 AWAITING TEL 10–4D
11 WHITES ROW, E1 020 7426 0542 13–2C

"Tops for combining punchy tastes and value": this Indian street-food trio – in Spitalfields, near Tower Bridge, and – since late 2021 – now in Soho too – offers a "distinct" and "modern spin" on Indian cuisine. Although the plates are small, "it's amazing how they deliver such big flavours". / www.gunpowderlondon.com; gunpowder_london.

GURA GURA WC2

19 SLINGSBY PLACE NO TEL 5–3B

Set to be an October 2022 debut in Covent Garden's 'The Yards' development – this new pan-Asian bar and kitchen concept will be a 110-seater spread over two floors and offering a mix of sushi, sashimi, dim sum and small plates. A walk-through wine tunnel will feature at the entrance. / WC2W 9DL; Mon-Wed 10 pm, Thu-Sat 10.30 pm.

GUSTOSO RISTORANTE &
ENOTECA SW1 £58 ③②②

35 WILLOW PL 020 7834 5778 2–4B

A "solid performer", this "reliable Italian occupies an area not over-blessed with good places" – between Westminster Cathedral

Gloria EC2

and Victoria station in Pimlico. "Lovely wild boar ragu with pappardelle". / SW1P 1JH; www.ristorantegustoso.co.uk; @gustoso_ristorante; Mon-Sat 9.30 pm; closed Sun.

GYMKHANA W1 £84 5 3 3

42 ALBEMARLE ST 020 3011 5900 3–3C

The "standard-bearer for subcontinental food in London" – the Sethi family's "exceptional" Mayfair destination nowadays ranks in the Top-20 most-mentioned restaurants in our annual diners' poll, and is the highest-ranking Indian. "An amazing selection of traditional dishes not found anywhere else" delivers "top-quality flavours relying on taste, not heat" ("so delicious, I couldn't stop eating!"), all in a "vibey" two-floor setting, with Indian-inspired décor referencing Indian clubs and mansions. "Unbeatable… if you can get in, that is…" / W1S 4JH; www.gymkhanalondon.com; @gymkhanalondon; Mon-Sun 10.30 pm; payment – credit card only.

HACHÉ £47 4 3 3

95-97 HIGH HOLBORN, WC1
020 7242 4580 2–1D
329-331 FULHAM RD, SW10
020 7823 3515 6–3B
24 INVERNESS ST, NW1
020 7485 9100 9–3B
37 BEDFORD HILL, SW12
020 8772 9772 11–2C
153 CLAPHAM HIGH ST, SW4
020 7738 8760 11–2D
147-149 CURTAIN RD, EC2
020 7739 8396 13–1B

"Doing what they do very well" – "top burgers" are presented with a veneer of Parisian sophistication at this seven-strong chain, popular not just for their value but their "lovely" styling too. / www.hacheburgers.com.

HACKNEY COTERIE E8 £46 3 4 3

230B DALSTON LANE
020 7254 4101 14–1B

"Great value and unusual tasting menus, nice wines & lovely service" win all-round applause for this yearling in a Hackney Downs warehouse from Anthony Lyon (of Lyon's in Crouch End). Head chef Giuseppe Pepe (ex-Pidgin and Marksman) is responsible for the seasonal, minimal-waste menu, and his "food is beautifully presented and served". / E8 1LA; www.hackneycoterie.net; @hackneycoterie; Wed & Thu 10 pm, Fri & Sat 10.30 pm; closed Wed & Thu L, closed Mon & Tue & Sun.

HAKKASAN £120 3 1 2

17 BRUTON ST, W1 020 7907 1888 3–2C
8 HANWAY PL, W1 020 7927 7000 5–1A

"Fantastic, modern Chinese food" has long driven this famous Asian phenomenon. Launched in 2001, it has gone from a big, "overly dark" and nightclubby basement ("horribly loud music") near Tottenham Court Road to spawn a very glam Mayfair offshoot; as well as 12 international spin-offs from NYC to Mumbai. "Eye-watering prices" and a mixed record when it comes to service, have always inspired jibes of "style over substance" here. But perhaps due to post-Covid challenges, such problems are in the foreground this year. Given that there have been blips before, they will probably get a grip. But it's hard at present to ignore the many former fans saying "these ageing stalwarts need a refresh" ("I used to love it, but I think the bill now is silly and unjustified and the service is half-hearted and surly"). / www.hakkasan.com; hakkasanlondon; no trainers, no sportswear.

HALO BURGER EC2 £19 3 3 2

105 GREAT EASTERN STREET
020 7490 0444 13–1B

For a meat-free burger, this tiny brand (the first vegan restaurant in Europe to use 'Beyond Meat' in its patties) is well worth a try if you need a bite near the Old Street roundabout, or are down Pop Brixton way. / EC2E 3JD; haloburger.co.uk; @haloburgeruk; Sun-Thu 10.30 pm, Fri & Sat 11 pm.

HAM NW6 £68 4 4 3

238 WEST END LANE 020 7813 0168 1–1B

"We are lucky to have this place on our doorstep!" – this "cosy and informal" West Hampstead five-year-old is an "affordable luxury" for its local fan club, where "always-excellent bistro food" is "beautifully presented in sensible portions". Top Tip – "the 6pm early-bird offer makes it amazing value for money, too". / NW6 1LG; www.hamwesthampstead.com; @Hamwhampstead; Tue-Sat 10 pm, Sun 3 pm; closed Sun D, closed Mon.

HAM YARD RESTAURANT, HAM YARD HOTEL W1 £66 2 2 4

1 HAM YD 020 3642 1007 4–3D

"A quiet haven tucked away near Piccadilly Circus" – in summer, the outside courtyard is so peaceful it's hard to believe just how central you are. "A lovely afternoon tea at sensible prices" is the top culinary attraction here. At other times, the "stylish" setting is "conducive to a relaxed meal" but its "bistro-style fare" is a case of "nothing to criticise, but with vastly better places in easy reach". / W1D 7DT; www.firmdalehotels.com/hotels/london/ham-yard-hotel/ham-yard-bar-restaurant; @firmdale_hotels; Mon-Sat 11 pm, Sun 10.30 pm.

THE HAMPSHIRE W6 £57 3 4 3

227 KING STREET 020 8748 3391 8–2B

Formerly 'The Hampshire Hog' – this stylish pub near Hammersmith Town Hall has been taken over and 'gone Indian' in recent times. Nipping in for a pint, little has changed, but food-wise it's more like a modern curry house. They are trying hard and it shows in the quality food and responsive service. And the big investment in their large, attractive garden to the rear really pays dividends in summer months. / W6 9JT; www.the-hampshire.com; @thehampshire; Mon-Fri midnight, Sat & Sun 11 pm.

HANKIES £41 3 2 2

61 UPPER BERKELEY STREET, W1
020 7958 3222 2–2A
67 SHAFTESBURY AVENUE, W1
020 7871 6021 5–3A

Tapas based on Delhi street food is served in a roti at this Indian duo, with branches in Soho and in a smart hotel dining room near Marble Arch, for whom feedback remains limited but upbeat. (The Paddington branch has now closed). / www.hankies.london.

HANNAH SE1 £122 3 3 2

SOUTHBANK RIVERSIDE, BELVEDERE ROAD 020 3802 0402 2–3D

This little-known "hidden Japanese gem" near the London Eye showcases the skills of chef-parton Daisuke Shimoyama, who spent six years as head chef at Umu in Mayfair before launching his own venture at this hotel in the former County Hall. His omakase "tasting menu is particularly impressive" and is matched by an interesting sake list selected by the chef, while budget options at lunchtime include a bento box. / SE1 7PB; www.hannahrestaurant.london; @hannah_japanese_restaurant; Wed 9 pm; closed Wed L, closed Mon & Tue, Thu-Sat & Sun; no trainers; credit card deposit required to book.

HANS' BAR & GRILL SW1 £84 3 3 3

164 PAVILION ROAD 020 7730 7000 6–2D

On a most chichi little thoroughfare, this café/bar and all-day restaurant is part of nearby luxury boutique hotel 100 Cadogan Gardens. It charges Chelsea prices from breakfast on, but fans say it's a "perfect spot to have lunch when on a shopping expedition". / SW1S 0AW; www.hansbarandgrill; @hansbarandgrill; Mon-Sat 10 pm, Sun 7 pm.

HARE & TORTOISE £43 3 3 2

11-13 THE BRUNSWICK, WC1
020 7278 9799 2–1D
373 KENSINGTON HIGH ST, W14
020 7603 8887 8–1D
156 CHISWICK HIGH RD, W4
020 8747 5966 8–2A
38 HAVEN GRN, W5 020 8810 7066 1–2A
296-298 UPPER RICHMOND RD, SW15
020 8394 7666 11–2B
90 NEW BRIDGE ST, EC4
020 7651 0266 10–2A

The "mix of Asian food slightly adapted for all tastes" and offered at "really reasonable prices" makes this long-running chain "a family favourite". Founded at the Brunswick Centre in Bloomsbury 26 years ago, it now has branches in Ealing, Putney, Kensington and Chiswick, along with two delivery-only kitchens. Top Tip – "you can't beat the curry laksa". / https://www.hareandtortoise.co.uk.

HARRODS DINING HALL
SW1 £84 **3 3 4**

HARRODS, 87-135 BROMPTON ROAD NO TEL 6–1D

Worth it just for the gorgeous Edwardian tiling of this famous space: built to house the Harrods Food Hall's meat and fishmongers counters, and nowadays hosting London's swishest food court, with six outlets – Kama by Vineet; Kerridge's Fish & Chips; Pasta Evangelists; Caviar House & Prunier; as well as a grill and sushi bar. / SW1S 7XL; www.harrods.com/en-gb/restaurants; @harrodsfood; Tue-Sat 11 pm, Mon 9 pm, Sun 6 pm.

HARRODS SOCIAL
SW1 £78 **3 3 3**

**87-135 BROMPTON ROAD
020 7225 6800 6–1D**

"In the lower ground floor of Harrods opposite the wine department", this luxe brasserie from Jason Atherton's Social Group opened immediately after the pandemic. Unsurprisingly, prices are not bargain basement, but even those complaining about them rate the food as good, and the store at last has the comfortable, modern restaurant space it formerly lacked. Top Tip – very affordable set menu, but you must have booked ahead. / SW1S 7XL; www.harrods.com/en-gb/restaurants/harrods-social-by-jason-atherton; @harrodsfood; Tue-Sat 11 pm, Mon 9 pm, Sun 6 pm; closed Sun D.

HARRY'S BAR W1 £69 **2 2 3**

**30-34 JAMES STREET
020 3971 9444 3–1A**

Carrying the name of Richard Caring's famous Harry's Bar in Mayfair (which is still members only), this sub-brand spin-off near Selfridges aims to encapsulate classic La Dolce Vita-style glamour. All of the limited feedback acknowledges decent Italian cooking, but is riddled with quibbles feeding back to the level of expense ("good food but the tables are packed too tightly and we'll give it miss in future, as it did not have the right ambience for the price…"; "food was mediocre at the ridiculous price…"). / W1W 1EU; www.harrys-bar.co.uk; @harrysldn; Mon-Sun 11 pm.

HARWOOD ARMS
SW6 £81 **3 2 3**

WALHAM GROVE 020 7386 1847 6–3A

"The best scotch eggs in London!" are a renowned attraction at this "lovely" boozer in the backstreets of deepest Fulham, whose food aristocracy backers include the Ledbury's Brett Graham, as well as game expert Mike Robinson. On the back of its "excellent and robust" cooking – particularly "perfect game" – it is again voted London's No. 1 pub in our annual diners' poll but, unsurprisingly "trying to get a table takes some planning: it's not a pub you can pop into if the mood takes you, especially when Chelsea are playing at home". It's also the case that service has been "a bit

mixed" in recent times and that the cuisine – "though still pretty good, feels like it isn't quite at the standard it was when Sally Abé was in charge of the kitchen". / SW6 1QP; www.harwoodarms.com; @theharwoodarms; Mon-Thu, Sat 9.15 pm, Fri 9.15 pm, Sun 8.15 pm; closed Mon-Thu L; credit card required to book.

HASHI SW20 £53 **3 3 2**

54 DURHAM RD 020 8944 1888 11–2A

This "very good neighbourhood Japanese", one of the best in the Raynes Park enclave, earns plaudits year after year for its "excellent food and service". / SW20 0TW; @hashi_japanese_restaurant; Tue-Sat 10 pm, Sun 2.30 pm; closed Tue-Fri L closed Sun D, closed Mon; no Amex.

HATCHED SW11 £79 **4 3 2**

**189 SAINT JOHN'S HILL
020 7738 0735 11–2C**

This "buzzing local" brings "casual fine dining" to Battersea, with highly focused young chef Shane Marshall and his team striving to create an 'uncluttered' dining experience. That may sound like hard work, but "everything tastes good and portions are hearty". "Eat at the counter if you can for a great insight into how to inject maximum flavours into a dish". / SW11 1TH; www.hatchedsw11.com; @hatchedsw11; Tue-Sat 11 pm, Sun 1.30 pm; closed Tue-Thu L closed Sun D, closed Mon.

HAUGEN E20 £70 **2 2 2**

**9 ENDEAVOUR SQUARE
020 4568 1444 14–1D**

Spectacular design and proximity to Westfield Stratford are not enough to win this Alpine-themed D&D London property much in the way of feedback. Such as we received is downbeat ("disappointing… Schnitzel done badly") and it's hard to demur from Grace Dent's damning assessment in her October 2021 review: a "huge, tourist-magnet restaurant"… "utterly hampered by someone's desperate need to make profit". / E20 1JN; www.haugen-restaurant.com; @haugenldn; Sun-Thu 9.45 pm, Fri & Sat 10.30 pm.

THE HAVELOCK TAVERN
W14 £59 **3 2 4**

57 MASBRO RD 020 7603 5374 8–1C

"Popular in the neighbourhood and very easy to recommend" – this blue-tiled Victorian tavern behind Olympia excels for "good, slightly pimped gastropub fare". Launched as a more foodie operation in 1996, it still draws fans from across west London and beyond. / W14 0LS; www.havelocktavern.com; @havelocktavern; Mon-Sat 9.30 pm, Sun 9 pm.

HAWKER'S KITCHEN
N1 £22 **5 3 2**

**64 CALEDONIAN ROAD
020 8458 2064 9–3D**

Mano Muthu worked at Euston's legendary Roti King for many years, and opened this

simple shop-conversion caff, north of King's Cross, in mid 2021. The cooking here has more of a south Indian spin than its rival, with the inclusion of a selection of dosas, and fans (who include the Evening Standard's Jimi Famurewa) feel its "exceptional dishes potentially beat Roti King for the title of best rotis in London!" / N1 9DP; www.hawkerskitchen.com; @hawkers.kitchen; Mon-Sun 9.50 pm.

HAWKSMOOR £94 **2 2 2**

5A AIR ST, W1 020 7406 3980 4–4C
11 LANGLEY ST, WC2 020 7420 9390 5–2C
**3 YEOMAN'S ROW, SW3
020 7590 9290 6–2C**
**16 WINCHESTER WALK, SE1
020 7234 9940 10–4C**
**WOOD WHARF, 1 WATER STREET, E14
020 3988 0510 12–1C**
**157 COMMERCIAL ST, E1
020 7426 4850 13–2B**
**10-12 BASINGHALL ST, EC2
020 7397 8120 10–2C**

"Bloody good, succulent steaks", with "epic cocktails and wines", all served in "rather clubby", "classy" surroundings is a formula that's won fame and fortune for Huw Gott and Will Beckett's steakhouse phenomenon. "Many happy afternoons have been lost in these places!", which continue to be voted as London's "best steak chain by far", and "a go-to for business". "Everything is top-notch: the quality and cookery of the beef; the exemplary seafood (be it Salcombe crab on toast or their lobster); even down to their excellent sides of mac 'n' cheese, bone marrow or Caesar salad". However, a visit "is not exactly easy on the wallet". "It's verrrrry expensive" (and "if you go with mates who like to chug back the wine, the bill will be massive!"). And ratings are coming under ever-more pressure due to "staff who seem unable to cope", or meals with "too many misses at too heavy a price to be a reliable bet". Last year, the team expanded to Manhattan and also opened a "stunning floating boat/barge" in the docks at Canary Wharf. Later in 2022, the group will also add a Liverpool branch to rival Manchester's; and a few months later make a Dublin debut on College Green too. "Are they losing some of their je-ne-sais-quoi as they get bigger and badder? There's a sneaking suspicion the lustre is being slightly lost." / www.thehawksmoor.com; SRA-3 stars.

HAYA W11 £56 **3 4 3**

**184A KENSINGTON PARK ROAD
0203 995 4777 7–1B**

This attractive modern Notting Hill café is inspired by visits to Tel Aviv, and the "energetic kitchen produces a small range of well thought-out dishes". Staff are "really friendly" too. / W11 2ES; haya.london; @haya.ldn; Mon-Sun 11.30 pm; payment – credit card only.

HAZ £62 **3 3 2**

10 UPPER ST MARTIN'S LANE, WC2 NO TEL 5–3B
9 CUTLER ST, E1 020 7929 7923 10–2D
**14 FINSBURY SQUARE, EC2
020 7920 9944 13–2A**
34 FOSTER LN, EC2 020 7600 4172 10–2B

64 BISHOPSGATE, EC2
020 7628 4522 10–2D
6 MINCING LN, EC3 020 7929 3173 10–3D

"Super-fresh" food, including "especially good starters and mezze", "friendly service" and "very good value for money" are the hallmarks of this "very good Turkish chain in the City". There's also a "large range of vegetarian dishes". The six branches are all heaving at lunchtime, but "St Paul's is the most spacious, in a great setting near the cathedral and much quieter too, especially at the weekends". / www.hazrestaurant.co.uk.

HEDDON YOKOCHO
W1   £29 323

8 HEDDON STREET NO TEL 4–3B

This "wonderful Japanese noodle shop just off of Regent Street" is modelled on the 'yokocho' alleyways of old Tokyo, its retro 1970s theme lending itself well to pedestrianised Heddon Street. There's "great-tasting ramen with regular specials" and it "can be busy". Launched two years ago by the Japan Centre team, it also has branches in Panton Street, Soho, and Westfield Shepherd's Bush. / W1W 4BU; www.heddonyokocho.com; @ramenyokocho; Sun-Thu 10.30 pm, Fri & Sat 11 pm.

HÉLÈNE DARROZE, THE CONNAUGHT HOTEL
W1   £174 232

CARLOS PL 020 3147 7200 3–3B

"The food is sublime"; "exceptional service" is "very friendly and interactive"; "… but WOW! the bill!!" – that's the headline story this year on this famous French chef's London outpost in this most blue-blooded of hotels. Despite numerous "exquisite" dishes featuring in reports, very many reporters feel "the costs verge on criminal" (and that "once you have seen the prices, it's difficult to get past them as the food just doesn't compensate for the full-blown attack on your wallet!!"). It doesn't help that the restaurant was recently elevated by Michelin to three stars, and that an "interesting but not amazing" experience can now seem well below par ("how this dining room has the tyre maker's top rating is beyond us"). And those seeking an old-school Mayfair environment should also look elsewhere: "the days of the Connaught of old are well and truly over", with "a conscious decision to move away from the previous old-style look" – a move dismissed by critics as "suburban lounge décor in what used used to be one of the handsomest dining rooms in London". / W1K 2AL; www.the-connaught.co.uk; @theconnaught; Tue-Sat 9.30 pm; closed Sun & Mon; no trainers.

HELIOT STEAK HOUSE
WC2   £71 333

CRANBOURN STREET
020 7769 8844 5–3B

"To-die-for steaks" can be a surprise find in the restaurant overlooking the floor of London's biggest casino, on Leicester Square. It's a quirky space, in the circle of the former Hippodrome Theatre, and its USDA-imported meat and superior wines are something of a passion project for casino owner, Simon Thomas. / WC2H 7AJ; www.hippodromecasino.com; @hippodromecasino; Mon-Sat 1 am, Sun 11 pm; closed Mon-Fri L.

HELIX (SEARCYS AT THE GHERKIN) EC3
**   £86 335**

30 ST MARY AXE 0330 1070816 10–2D

"The food is as good as the view and worth a repeat-visit!", say fans of this iconic 40th-floor dining room, near the top floor of the Gherkin (run nowadays by the posh catering company, Searcys). "Great for a celebration and with reasonable prices (especially for London)", attractions include an "interesting and well-executed afternoon tea". / EC3E 8EP; searcysatthegherkin.co.uk/helix-restaurant; @searcysgherkin; Mon-Wed 10 pm, Fri & Sat 11 pm, Sun 6 pm; closed Sat L closed Sun D, closed Thu.

HEREFORD ROAD
W2   £56 443

3 HEREFORD RD 020 7727 1144 7–1B

St John alumnus chef Tom Pemberton "never disappoints" with his modern British cooking at the "small but not too noisy" Bayswater neighbourhood restaurant he opened in 2007, in a cleverly converted former butcher's shop. "Service is efficient, food is excellent and good value" and the "Sunday roasts are brilliant". / W2 4AB; www.herefordroad.org; Fri & Sat, Tue-Thu 10 pm, Sun 3.30 pm; closed Tue-Thu L closed Sun D, closed Mon.

HERITAGE SE21
**   £55 333**

101 ROSENDALE ROAD
020 8761 4665 1–4D

This "impressive newcomer to the usually disappointing Dulwich food scene" arrived with a top pedigree for "high-class, high-taste" Indian cuisine under chef Dayashankar Sharma, a veteran of Tamarind, Zaika and Grand Trunk Road. The Guardian's Grace Dent was an early champion – "by rights it should become a south London classic" – but ratings are capped by one or two locals who feel it's "OK but not worth the hype". / SE21 8EZ; www.heritagedulwich.co.uk; @heritageindiandulwich; Tue-Sat 10.30 pm, Sun 9 pm; closed Tue-Fri L, closed Mon.

THE HERO OF MAIDA
W9   £68 332

55 SHIRLAND RD 020 7266 9198 7–1C

This "great local Maida Vale gastropub" opened to considerable fanfare after an overhaul five years ago, and has now settled down with "a city-wide reputation for its Sunday lunches – you'll need to book well ahead". There's "a good selection of wine, beers and spirits", and it's "dog-friendly", too. / W9 2JD; theheromaidavale.co.uk; @theheroofmaida; Mon-Sat 11 pm, Sun 10 pm.

HICCE N1
**   £72 323**

COAL DROPS YARD 020 3869 8200 9–3C

"A stylish and trendy venue in stylish and trendy Coal Drops Yard" – Pip Lacey produces "an interesting menu of small plates" at this "lovely" venue, prominently situated within the development. There were some gripes this year about the "confusing wine list", and although everyone acknowledged some "superb" dishes, reservations remain about the value equation here ("great food, but the bill! For the size of the portions and overall amount of food and wine consumed it really felt steep!"). (Top Gear fans: Lacey now also has a side gig running the kitchen at Jeremy Clarkson's Diddly Squat Farm restaurant in the Cotswolds). / N1N 4AB; www.hicce.co.uk; @hiccelondon; Wed-Sat 11 pm, Sun 4 pm, Tue 10.30 pm; closed Tue L closed Sun D, closed Mon; payment – credit card only.

ABOVE AT HIDE
W1   £175 323

85 PICCADILLY 020 3146 8666 3–4C

"There can be fewer better outlooks in London than the view over Green Park from the first-floor windows" of this beautifully appointed, modern Mayfair dining room. Overseen by Ollie Dabbous, the kitchen achieves "phenomenal flavour combinations and presentation" and "exceptional" overall results ("one of my best meals in London, maybe in life…"). And the "extraordinary wine list" is perhaps even more impressive: you can order any vintage from the acclaimed list sold by Hedonism Wines (who are under the same ownership), "or you can opt for the unusual and interesting wine pairings". But "any temptation to choose a nice bottle can be financially crippling!" – "when the final bill comes, it's a good job that you're already sitting down…". / W1W 8JB; www.hide.co.uk; @hide_restaurant; Mon-Sun 10 pm.

HIDE GROUND
W1   £128 344

85 PICCADILLY 020 3146 8666 3–4C

Fans say it's "nicer eating on the ground floor than being restricted to the much more expensive tasting menu upstairs" at this glossy landmark, opposite Green Park. Open from early morning, it's "an unusual but sophisticated haunt for breakfast in the heart of Mayfair". And, as with upstairs, "the availability of Hedonism Wines via a tablet, means the wine list has more toys than Hamleys!" / W1W; www.hide.co.uk; @hide_restaurant; Tue-Sun 9 pm; closed Tue L, closed Mon.

HIGH ROAD BRASSERIE
W4   £67 223

162-166 CHISWICK HIGH RD
020 8742 7474 8–2A

The longstanding (est. 2006) Chiswick branch of Soho House seems to have been left behind as founder Nick Jones's empire spreads around the world. It occupies a prominent site on the busy High Road with a cute outside terrace, but generates precious little feedback these days –

Isla WC1

even by reporters who like its modern brasserie cooking. / W4 1PR; highroadbrasserie.co.uk; @highroadbrasserie; Sun-Wed 11 pm, Fri & Sat 1 am, Thu midnight; booking max 8 may apply.

HIGH TIMBER EC4 £66 343

8 HIGH TIMBER STREET
020 7248 1777 10–3B

This "high-grade hidden gem, just below the Millennium Bridge" – aka the Wobbly pedestrian bridge, directly opposite Tate Modern – is owned by a South African wine producer and "focuses on high-quality steaks and a Saffer-heavy wine list". If you're really interested, it's worth seeking out the "great off-menu wines". Top Tip – "the house biltong is delicious". / EC4V 3PA; www.hightimber.com; @hightimberrestaurant; Mon-Fri 10 pm; closed Sat & Sun.

HISPANIA EC3 £79 344

72-74 LOMBARD STREET
020 7621 0338 10–2C

This smart and expansive Hispanic spread over two floors in the heart of the City, opposite the Bank of England, scores well for its "classic tapas" and meat dishes, accompanied by a heavyweight wine list. / EC3V 9AY; www.hispanialondon.com; @hispanialondon; Mon-Fri 10 pm; closed Sat & Sun.

HITHE & SEEK EC4 £41

60 UPPER THAMES STREET
020 3988 0141 10–3B

"This low-key wine bar is an absolute gem", "hiding" in the new waterside Westin Hotel, "with a huge window looking across the Thames" to Tate Modern and Shakespeare's Globe theatre ("spending the evening watching the river drift by with a glass in hand is a really great way to end a tough week"). The interior has a contemporary Scandi look and the menu is put together by Jorge Colazo, ex-head chef at Aquavit. Feedback is too limited for a rating, but initial reports are upbeat, talking of "interesting wine and imaginative small plates". / EC4E 3AD; www.hitheandseek.com; @Hithe + Seek; Wed-Sat 11 pm; closed Wed-Sat L, closed Mon & Tue & Sun.

HOLBORN DINING ROOM WC1 £83

252 HIGH HOLBORN 020 3747 8633 2–1D

It's not been a vintage year for this grand British brasserie, known for its Pie Room,

grills and charcuterie. Feedback has been very unsettled, with poor ratings across the board and reports of "stodgy and tasteless dishes", "breathtaking mark-ups", and "famous pies that were poorly cooked and really not worth the hype or the money". In June 2022, after the conclusion of our survey, the executive chef for the last eight years, Calum Franklin, moved on. Given that change seems to be afoot, we have left it unrated. / WC1V 7EN; www.holborndiningroom.com; @holborndiningroom; Mon-Fri 10 pm, Sat 10.30 pm, Sun 9.45 pm.

HOLLY BUSH NW3 £76 224

22 HOLLY MOUNT   020 7435 2892   9–1A

"A cosy gem" – this postcard-pretty Grade II listed Georgian tavern in a "lovely location" down a narrow street has been a must-visit in Hampstead village since Dr Johnson dropped in. It's an "expensive" place to eat by pub standards, but it's by no means a standard pub. "Go just for the real fire!". / NW3 6SG; www.hollybushhampstead.co.uk; @thehollybushpubhampstead; Mon-Thu 11 pm, Fri & Sat 10 pm, Sun 8 pm.

HOLY CARROT SW1 £56 344

URBAN RETREAT, 2-4 HANS CRESCENT
020 3897 0404   6–1D

"Every course can be eaten by a gluten-free vegan and yet your everyday carnivore will still enjoy the meal" at this new all-day vegan in a chichi 'Wellness & Beauty Salon' near Harrods. It receives nothing but praise: "this is what I call an outstanding vegan: imaginative food presented beautifully and they use NO sugar!" / SW1S 0LH; www.holycarrot.co.uk; @holycarrotrestaurant; Mon-Sat 10 pm, Sun 5 pm; closed Sun D.

HOMESLICE £54 433

50 JAMES STREET, W1
020 3034 0621   3–1A
13 NEAL'S YD, WC2   020 7836 4604   5–2C
2 TV CENTRE, 101 WOOD LN WHITE CITY,
W12   020 3034 0381   1–2B
374-378 OLD STREET, EC1
020 3151 1121   13–1B
69-71 QUEEN STREET, EC4
020 3034 0381   10–3C

"Still delivering on what it set out to do" – Alan and Mark Wogan's (yes, the late Terry's sons) hip pizza chain is the best-rated of the mid-sized groups, thanks to its "huge and amazing pizzas with delicious and unusual toppings" ("now the choice is even easier with the 50/50 option!"). Top Menu Tip – "awesome vegan nduja pizza" is amongst a growing number of plant-based options (and, from June 2022, they now have a fully meat-free site, in their 135-cover Shoreditch branch). / www.homeslicepizza.co.uk; homesliceldn.

HONEST BURGERS £37 322

BRANCHES THROUGHOUT LONDON

"You get what it says on the tin" at this hugely popular, "no frills" ("no starters and no puds") brand – the most commented-on burger multiple in our annual diners' poll – which is "still consistently good, despite having turned into a massive chain". The "top-quality meat and a good variety of specials" ("check out the latter for something a little different") are "cooked to your liking from a basic menu" and "the wonderfully flavoured rosemary fries are a fab accompaniment". Having flirted with an all-vegan sub-brand in Leicester Square ('V Honest'), it was converted back to the core concept in June 2022. / www.honestburgers.co.uk.

HONEY & CO WC1 £70

54 LAMB'S CONDUIT STREET
020 7388 6175   2–1D

After 10 years in which they helped establish modern Israeli cuisine as a new London staple, Sarit Packer and Itamar Srulovich (husband and wife) have relocated their much-loved venue from Warren Street to a much better Bloomsbury site that's double the size of the bijou original (the corner site that was formally Cigala, RIP). In its old home, fans were happy to be shoehorned in tighter than sardines for their "stellar" mezze-style inventions. Not everyone felt its performance always matched the hype, though, so we've left it unrated after it's settled in here. But The Guardian's Grace Dent was impressed in a late July 2022 review, saying: "it's a little different now, perhaps more grown-up and formal, but the old loveliness is there in spades". / WC1N 3LW; www.honeyandco.co.uk; @honeyandcobloomsbury; Mon-Sat 10 pm; closed Sun.

HONEY & SMOKE W1 £69 422

216 GREAT PORTLAND STREET
020 7388 6175   2–1B

"Excellent Middle Eastern cooking, with some inventive dishes and excellent vegetarian options" continues to win applause for this grillhouse near Great Portland Street (sibling to Honey & Co). "First-class natural ingredients are perfectly seasoned and prepared": "in the wrong hands, these simple dishes could be bog-standard, but are lifted by excellent preparation (for instance, a simple tomato salad with a super, herby dressing)". "Shame the restaurant is so Spartan, noisy and uncomfortable", though – "it's not the place for a night out, but good for lunch or a quick bite". Top Menu Tip – the cheesecake, which Giles Coren from The Times says is "the business… life-changing. Epochal. Aeonic". / W1W 5QW; honeyandco.co.uk/

places/honey-smoke; @honeyandsmokerestaurant; Tue-Sat 10.30 pm; closed Sun & Mon.

HOOD SW2 £58 4 4 2

67 STREATHAM HILL
020 3601 3320   11–2D

"We're very fortunate to have Hood nearby", say fans of this notably "friendly" Streaham local which tries harder than most neighbourhood places, with "imaginative touches, such as foraged food". Produce is sourced as locally as possible, with a map on one wall pinpointing farms in the southern counties. / SW2 4TX; www.hoodrestaurants.com; @hoodstreatham; Wed-Sat 11 pm, Sun 3 pm; closed Sun D, closed Mon & Tue; booking online only.

HOPPERS £52 4 3 3

49 FRITH ST, W1   NO TEL   5–2A
77 WIGMORE STREET, W1
020 3319 8110   3–1A
UNIT 3, BUILDING 4, PANCRAS SQUARE, N1
020 3319 8125   9–3C

"Authentic flavours of Sri Lanka with superb, well-balanced spicing" won strong acclaim this year for JKS Restaurants' well-known, three-strong chain in Soho, Marylebone and King's Cross, where the eponymous 'hoppers' are coconut and rice flour pancakes with various fillings; highly rated for a "superior tasting and reasonably priced" bite. A fourth branch is on the cards for late 2022. Top Tip – "it has a good range of options for vegans and vegetarians". / www.hopperslondon.com; hopperslondon.

HOT STONE N1 £90 4 4 3

9 CHAPEL MARKET   020 3302 8226   9–3D

"What a great place to enjoy wagyu steak… which, as its name indicates, is cooked on a hot stone at the table" – Padam Raj Rai's Islington ishiyaki is one of only a handful of UK restaurants selling certified Kobe beef, and also serves high-quality sushi and sashimi. Most reports are hymns of praise – occasional niggles relate to service that is occasionally "hit or miss". Its former Fitzrovia sibling is now rebranded as Rai (see also). / N1 9EZ; www.hotstonelondon.com; @hotstonelondon; Mon-Thu 9 pm, Fri & Sat 9.30 pm, Sun 8 pm; closed Mon-Thu L.

HUMBLE CHICKEN W1 £38 3 3 4

54 FRITH STREET   020 7434 2782   5–2A

"Super busy with good reason" – "every part of a chicken is cooked to utter perfection married with moreish Japanese flavours" at Angelo Sato's "cool" yearling in Soho: "he's in front of you slaving away at the charcoal preparing yakitori skewers day after day" and "sitting at the bar you get a good view of the 'cogs' the delicious dishes have to go through to get to the counter in front of you". "The prices are high for the portion sizes though" and while fans "warm to tendon and giblets", and feel "there is something quite nice about the concept of using every part of a chicken", that doesn't float everyone's boat. / W1W 4SJ;

www.humblechickenuk.com; @humblechicken_uk; Tue-Thu 10 pm, Fri & Sat 11 pm; closed Tue-Thu L, closed Sun & Mon.

HUMBLE GRAPE £66 3 4 3

11-13 THEBERTON STREET, N1
020 3887 9287   9–3D
2 BATTERSEA RISE, SW11
020 3620 2202   11–2C
18-20 MACKENZIE WALK, E14
020 3985 1330   12–1C
8 DEVONSHIRE ROW, EC2
020 3887 9287   10–2D
1 SAINT BRIDE'S PASSAGE, EC4
020 7583 0688   10–2A

"The whole package – great food, staff and incredible wines" – wins hymns of praise for James Dawson's wine shop/club/bar/kitchen combination that now has five branches across central London. The focus is on sustainable, small-scale independent producers, with many wines available by the glass. / www.humblegrape.co.uk; humblegrape.

HUNAN SW1 £111 4 2 1

51 PIMLICO RD   020 7730 5712   6–2D

"Just say what you want and it keeps coming until you say 'stop!'" at this acclaimed, family-run veteran in Pimlico (founded in 1982), where, according to your preferences, Mr Peng orchestrates the ensuing "Chinese tapas-style" banquet. Many reporters "have been going for years, yet still find new dishes". And despite the odd concern this year about "staff turnover" and a slight "loss of touch", most are wowed "time after time" by the "amazing" results ("crazily good fun, if you go with an open mind"). "Talk to the owner about the wines too: he knows a lot and is very enthusiastic". / SW1W 8NE; www.hunanlondon.com; @hunanlondon; Mon-Sat 11 pm; closed Sun.

THE HUNTER'S MOON SW3 £75 3 4 3

86 FULHAM ROAD   07497 425819   6–2C

This "lively and friendly local" in South Ken rates well for its "high-quality menu complemented by daily specials". Opened three years ago by the Lunar Pub Company, it's "not somewhere for a quiet and romantic dinner, but the young local crowd make it a vibrant venue". / SW3 6HR; huntersmoonlondon.co.uk; @huntersmoonsw3; Mon & Tue, Thu 11 pm, Fri & Sat midnight, Sun 8.30 pm; closed Wed.

HUO SW10 £71 3 3 3

9 PARK WALK   020 3696 9090   6–3B

"A new find" just off 'Chelsea Beach' – this yearling on the former site of Farm Girl offers "stylish pan-Asian catering to a stylish crowd". There's substance, too, with a "varied menu which means there's always something tasty to choose". Founder Michael Lim has worked a similar formula with success for many years at Uli in Notting Hill. / SW10 0AJ; huo.london; @huo.london; Mon-Sat midnight, Sun 11 pm.

HUSH W1 £99 2 2 3

8 LANCASHIRE CT   020 7659 1500   3–2B

"An oasis away from the hustle and bustle of the West End" (and relatively "tourist-free"), with a "lovely quiet covered courtyard", this glitzy operation is pitched at those in the know – founding investors included Yegeny Lebedev, son of a Soviet spy, and our own 007, the late Roger Moore. "Easy to get to from Bond Street/Oxford Street/Regent Street", it's "perfect for business breakfast or lunch". But "this all comes at a price and it's one the food, whilst definitely pleasant, can struggle to fully justify". / W1S 1EY; www.hush.co.uk; @hushmayfair; Mon-Sat 10 pm; closed Sun; booking max 12 may apply.

HUTONG, THE SHARD SE1 £119 2 2 3

31 ST THOMAS ST   020 3011 1257   10–4C

"What an amazing place" – this Asian joint on the 33rd floor is never short of guests having a good time. However, "the prices are extremely steep"… just like the Shard's glass wall… which contributes to the mixed feelings it inspires. Business entertainers say it's "classy" ("I'm always willing to go… on someone else's budget!"), but even some fans feel that "even the stunning vista don't justify the bill". And others are more definite: "I'd rather eat at my local Chinese". / SE1 9RY; www.hutong.co.uk; @hutongshard; Mon-Sun midnight; no shorts.

IBÉRICA £64 2 2 2

ZIG ZAG BUILDING, 70 VICTORIA ST, SW1
020 7636 8650   2–4B
195 GREAT PORTLAND ST, W1
020 7636 8650   2–1B
12 CABOT SQ, E14   020 7636 8650   12–1C
89 TURNMILL ST, EC1
020 7636 8650   10–1A

For a "really enjoyable, reasonably authentic Tapas experience", all served in a "buzzing" environment, many would recommend this national chain's four London branches (in Victoria, Canary Wharf, Farringdon and Marylebone). "Uneven" service can make them "a bit hit 'n' miss" (especially in SW1) but one constant is "a particularly strong list of Spanish wines, many by the glass or carafe". / www.ibericarestaurants.com; ibericarestaurants.

ICCO PIZZA £19 3 3 2

46 GOODGE ST, W1   020 7580 9688   2–1C
21A CAMDEN HIGH STREET, NW1
020 7380 0020   9–3B

"It's cheap 'n' very cheerful, but with great-quality authentic pizzas" at this basic Goodge Street spot ("worth foregoing a fancier meal for, as its thin-crust pizzas are so good!"). You'll find "very fast and friendly service", and that's it: "this place is all about the pizza and nothing else (unless you love Snapple drinks)". Opened in 1999, it now has a branch in Camden and delivery outlets in Wood Green, Colindale and Croydon. / www.icco.co.uk.

IKEDA W1 £92 442

30 BROOK ST 020 7629 2730 3–2B

The "superb Japanese food" at this little-known Mayfair veteran, now in its fifth decade, stands out in "an increasingly crowded market for Japanese gastronomy". Like many traditional restaurants in Tokyo or Kyoto, it is understated and unflashy to a fault. The sashimi and sushi are "moderately expensive, but then fish this good should be". Top Tip – "the Tekkadon Chirashi is simply delicious – sashimi of tuna, fatty tuna and seared tuna on a bed of rice". / W1K 5DJ; www.ikedarestaurant.com; Tue-Thu 9 pm, Mon, Fri 9.45 pm; closed Mon, Fri L, closed Sat & Sun.

IKOYI SW1 £231 322

1 ST JAMES'S MARKET
020 3583 4660 4–4D

"Flavours not experienced before" – "inventive haute cuisine takes on West African dishes using ingredients like plantain and sorghum" – continue to propel Iré Hassan-Odukale and Jeremy Chan's St James's trail-blazer to ever-greater heights of fame, as confirmed by the restaurant's further promotion by Michelin in January 2022. "With the second star comes the elevated price tag" however, and formerly stellar ratings here have sagged under the heightened expectations. Many "masterpieces" are still reported amongst meals, but a worrying new vein of bitter disappointments has also crept into diner commentary ("I was excited to try Ikoyi and discover its new approach, but hand on heart it was not worth the money…"; "we were angry and so disappointed, the food was really average, massively over-spiced and too hot"). Perhaps it's no coincidence that shortly after our diners' poll results that Chan and Hassan-Odukale announced they were putting the original St James's Market site on the market with a view to moving to an upgraded site (with options mooted including a move to the 180 Strand building). / SW1S 4AH; www.ikoyilondon.com; @ikoyi_london; Thu-Sat, Mon-Wed 8.45 pm; closed Mon-Wed L, closed Sun.

IMAD'S SYRIAN KITCHEN W1 £26 333

KINGLY COURT, KINGLY STREET
07473 333631 4–2B

"A delight and an education": this "tiny restaurant with a tiny menu of Syrian food" – "hidden away on the second floor of Soho's Kingly Court" – is a "real favourite for its back story, for the quality of the dishes, and for the fact that you keep coming back". Chef Imad Alarnab fled Damascus in 2015, leaving behind his successful restaurant group, and cooked for fellow-refugees before making his comeback as a restaurateur in London two years ago. / W1W 5PW; imadssyriankitchen.co.uk; @imadssyriankitchen; Tue-Thu, Mon 8.30 pm, Fri & Sat 9.30 pm; closed Mon L, closed Sun.

IMPERIAL CHINA WC2 £55 322

25A LISLE ST 020 7734 3388 5–3A

"Higher quality than the run-of-the-mill Chinatown stalwarts" – this big, "reliable" three-storey Cantonese (est. 1993) benefits from a cute, tucked-away location in a small courtyard, complete with fish pond, just north of Leicester Square. / WC2H 7BA; www.imperialchina-london.co.uk; @imperialchinalondon; Mon-Thu 11 pm, Fri & Sat 11.30 pm, Sun 10.30 pm.

IMPERIAL TREASURE SW1 £124 442

9-10 WATERLOO PLACE
020 3011 1328 4–4D

"Some of the best Chinese cooking in London" is delivered at this West End three-year-old: the first London branch of a Singapore-based group with offshoots across mainland China. But even if the dishes are "divine", "you pay a serious premium" to dine here. And the atmosphere of this "beautiful" former banking hall, with "very smart" décor by the late Christian Laigre, "can end up either too manic or funereal, with little in between". Top Menu Tip – the Peking duck is as "exceptional" as its price tag. / SW1S 4BE; www.imperialtreasure.com; @imperialtreasureuk; Mon-Sun 11 pm.

INAMO £45 333

134-136 WARDOUR ST, W1
020 7851 7051 4–1D
11-14 HANOVER PL, WC2
020 7484 0500 5–2D

"So much fun for the kids!" – these "interactive, self-ordering 'Asian' feasts!" in Soho and Covent Garden feature funky projectors, so that the tabletop effectively operates as a touch-screen. "Placing an order here is really entertaining" and, though the food is not the main event, it's well-rated: "there's so much variety and their bottomless offers are amazing value". "The family always wants to go back…" / www.inamo-restaurant.com; W1: Mon - Thu 11.30pm, Fri & Sat midnight, Sun 10.30 pm – SW1: Mon - Thu 11pm, Fri & Sat 12.30pm, Sun 10.30pm.

INDIA CLUB, STRAND CONTINENTAL HOTEL WC2 £29 323

143 STRAND 020 7836 4880 2–2D

"Good scruffy fun with a side order of nostalgia" is to be had at this "hidden gem" in the Strand (a favourite with staff at the Indian High Commission opposite). "An almost anonymous doorway leads you up some stairs" where you "step back in time, not to a cheesy incarnation of the British Raj, but to the early days of independence". Founded in 1951 (Prime Minister Nehru was among the founding members), the 'club' is open to the public and serves food that can be (but is not invariably) "excellent" at a "great price", in an authentically "slightly chaotic atmosphere".

It's been under siege for the past five years from a landlord itching to redevelop, but it's "an institution that deserves to survive, and an oasis of good value in central London". Top Tip – it's unlicensed – "pause for a drink in the bar downstairs before or after eating" or carry your pint to the table. / WC2R 1JA; www.theindiaclub.co.uk; @indiaclublondon; Mon-Sun 10.50pm; booking max 6 may apply.

INDIAN MOMENT SW11 £36 322

44 BATTERSEA RISE 020 7223 6575 /
020 7223 1818 11–2C

This "smart, modern-style Indian" has established itself as a "really good-quality neighbourhood curry house" in its 20 years in Battersea. "Yes, it's a little cramped and can be noisy at its busiest times, but the food is always good and the fact it's BYOB helps keep the cost down" (£1.95 corkage fee). / SW11 1EE; www.indianmoment.co.uk; @indianmoment; Sun-Thu 11.30pm, Fri & Sat midnight; closed Mon-Fri L.

INDIAN OCEAN SW17 £31 333

214 TRINITY RD 020 8672 7740 11–2C

This "old-school curry house" near Wandsworth Common has for many years been a "reliable neighbourhood favourite", and fans say it "never fails" to produce the goods. / SW17 7HP; www.indianoceanrestaurant.com; Sun-Thu 11 pm, Fri & Sat 11.45 pm; closed Sun-Thu-Sat L.

INDIAN RASOI N2 £35 332

7 DENMARK TERRACE
020 8883 9093 1–1B

This cute family-run Muswell Hill curry house with a small terrace for outdoor dining prides itself on its Mughal-inspired north Indian cuisine, which goes down well with a local clientele. / N2 9HG; www.indian-rasoi.co.uk; @indianrasoigeneva; Tue-Sun 10 pm; closed Mon; no Amex.

INDIAN ROOM SW12 £37 443

59 BEDFORD HILL 020 8675 8611 11–2D

"Very helpful staff" add to the appeal of this Balham High Street Indian, of over 15 years' standing. Whether it should be a perennial inclusion in TripAdvisor's top 10 London restaurants is debatable, but the (limited) feedback we receive says it's worth a visit. / SW12 9EZ; www.indianroom.co.uk; @indianroombalham; Sun-Thu 11 pm, Fri & Sat 11.30 pm; closed Mon-Fri L.

INDIAN ZING W6 £58 433

236 KING ST 020 8748 5959 8–2B

"Always fine flavours" with deft and "delicate spicing" delight disciples of this deceptively ordinary-looking "local Indian" near Ravenscourt Park, which, they claim, could "easily go head-to-head with any of London's most famous Indian restaurants". Perhaps that's over-egging it a little, but it's very consistently supported. (The late Michael Winner was an early fan when chef-owner Manoj Vasaikar opened here in 2005). / W6 0RS; www.indian-zing.co.uk; Mon-Sun 10 pm.

INDIGO, ONE ALDWYCH WC2 £65 3|3|3

1 ALDWYCH   020 7300 0400   2–2D

This "well-situated" venue occupies an attractive mezzanine in a luxury hotel near Covent Garden that borrows buzz from the foyer below; and which makes a handy rendezvous for business or pleasure. Top Tip – "a most imaginative afternoon tea, and they cater automatically for those of us who are wheat and dairy free!" / WC2B 4BZ; www.onealdwych.com; @onealdwychhotel; Mon & Tue 10.30 am, Wed-Sat 9.30 pm, Sun 3 pm; closed Mon & Tue, Sun D.

INO W1

4 NEWBURGH STREET
020 3701 6618   4–2B

There are still too few reports to give a rating to this Greek 'gastrobar' in Soho, but it looks promising, with a combination of interesting Greek wines (the name derives from the Ancient Greek word for wine); cocktails from the barrel; and charcoal-grilled plates – they even finish their spanakopita pies on the grill. It is from the team behind well-rated Opso and avant-garde Athens restaurant Funky Gourmet. / W1W; www.inogastrobar.com; @inogastrobar; Mon-Sat 11 pm, Sun 5 pm; closed Sun D.

ISHTAR W1 £70 3|3|3

10-12 CRAWFORD ST   020 7224 2446   2–1A

"Particularly tasty grilled meats and mezzes" are the highlights of the menu at this well-established Marylebone outfit, which has served "excellent Anatolian fare" for almost 20 years. "Service is friendly", and "there's evening entertainment too". / W1U 6AZ; www.ishtarrestaurant.com; @ishtarlondon; Sun-Thu 11 pm, Fri & Sat midnight.

ISIBANI SW1

9 KNIGHTSBRIDGE GREEN
07553 051171   6–1D

This July 2022 newcomer on Knightsbridge Green arrived well after our annual diners' poll had concluded so too late for rating. It's a debut from 26-year-old Nigerian-born London chef Victor Okunowo, a semi-finalist on BBC MasterChef The Professionals in 2020. The vibrantly decorated West African restaurant has a 22-seat fine-dining room, with more relaxed eating available on the first floor and 16-cover roof terrace. / SW1S 7QL; www.isibani.com; Mon-Thu midnight, Fri & Sat 2 am, Sun 11 pm.

ISLA WC1 £62 3|5|4

THE STANDARD HOTEL, 10 ARGYLE STREET   020 3981 8888   9–3C

Next to the Double Standard (see also), the hotel's book-lined lounge and restaurant (the books were inherited from St Pancras Library, previously on this site) shares the "buzzy atmosphere, convenient location, good value short menu" and impeccably cheerful and efficient service of its neighbour. In summer, it also has a superb, quiet covered terrace that feels a millions miles from WC1. / WC1W 8EG; www.islalondon.com; Mon-Sun 10.30 pm; closed Mon-Sun L.

ISSHO-NI E2 £43 3|4|3

185 BETHNAL GREEN ROAD
020 7366 0314   13–1D

Upbeat Bethnal Green izakaya, created four years ago by Claire Su (who converted the premises her parents ran as Noodle King). Praised for its "fresh sushi and interesting small plates", it's also known as a venue for cocktails and bottomless brunch. / E2 6AB; issho-ni.com; @isshoniuk; Tue-Thu 10.30 pm, Fri & Sat 11 pm; closed Sun & Mon.

ITALIAN GREYHOUND W1 £57 2|2|3

62 SEYMOUR STREET
020 3826 7940   7–1D

Just off Edgware Road near Marble Arch, this attractive 80-seater yearling (with 20-seat outside terrace) serves a casual Italian menu, featuring pizza and pasta as well as some more substantial dishes. However, even those who feel the food is "good" say it can be "rather hit 'n' miss" and when full the interior becomes "noisy". / W1; theitaliangreyhound.co.uk; @greyhoundmarylebone; Wed-Sat 11 pm, Sun 7 pm; closed Mon & Tue.

ITALIKU W1 £68 3|3|3

110 GREAT PORTLAND STREET
020 7323 1885   2–1B

"Modern Italian with a Japanese twist" – this late summer 2022 launch in Great Portland Street from Jean-Bernard Fernandez-Versini, founder of legendary Cannes pop-up Cosy Box, marries the two food cultures to good effect. Italian-born chef Ivan Simeoli says he's "not limited by tradition, but uses it as an inspiration" for a menu dominated by fish and seafood with plenty of raw options, while Italian Fassona and Japanese wagyu beef have cameo roles. / W1W 6PQ; italiku.co.uk; @italikulondon; Mon-Sat 10.30 pm; closed Sun.

THE IVY WC2 £97 2|2|3

1-5 WEST ST   020 7836 4751   5–3B

"It's just so, so comforting… out-of-towners, especially those north of 50, always find it magical!" This "always buzzy" and still-famous Theatreland icon ('rolled out' by Richard Caring over the last ten years as a national chain) is, says fans, "still a wonderful experience". Such advocates often feel that

"it never fails to impress" (even if the A-listers moved on a few years ago) and – for business occasions – appreciate the fact that "clients love it!" Even such boosterism often acknowledges, however, that "these days better food can be found elsewhere" ("it's not remotely going to challenge or educate your palate"). And, while it's long been accepted that "you don't come here for its comfort food", its ratings nowadays support harsher critics who feel that "it's just become an overworked cliché" – "the food is moving to the disappointing level of the chain… and service too". / WC2H 9NQ; www.the-ivy.co.uk; @theivyweststt; Mon-Sat 11 pm, Sun 10.30 pm; no shorts; booking max 6 may apply.

THE IVY ASIA £72 2|3|4

8-10 NORTH AUDLEY STREET, W1
020 3751 4990   3–2A
201-203A KING'S ROAD, SW3
020 7486 6154   6–3C
20 NEW CHANGE PASSAGE, EC4
020 3971 2600   10–2B

"Great fun … despite lots of Instagram poseurs hanging around" – that's the most common view on Richard Caring's latest Ivy sub-brand: a mashup of "stunning" OTT interiors and a Pan-Asian menu which by-and-large totally avoids dishes from China to throw together Thai curries, wagyu beef and lots of fish and seafood (much of it presented as sushi or sashimi). Even fans would concede that "the food is secondary here – for entertainment value, this place has 'got it', but the menu is somehow lost in the mix". And there are those who discern "crazy levels of cultural appropriation (a floor-to-ceiling, fake banyan tree? Seriously?), stirred in with a menu that's less Asian-fusion than Asian-confusion, all creating a bit of a Caring-inspired mess". This year saw the addition of a Mayfair branch to the original one (in the shadow of St Paul's) and last year's opening in SW3 (where "very loud music can add to the already-high noise level"). / www.theivyasia.com.

THE IVY CAFÉ £65 1|2|2

96 MARYLEBONE LN, W1
020 3301 0400   2–1A
120 ST JOHN'S WOOD HIGH ST, NW8
020 3096 9444   9–3A
75 HIGH ST, SW19   020 3096 9333   11–2B
9 HILL STREET, TW9   020 3146 7733   1–4A

"You know what you are getting" according to fans of this sub-brand, spin-off chain, whose 'café' branches are a cut below those trading as a 'brasserie'. They laud its "acceptable" cooking and say, "it's great to see how well the Ivy's formula has been rolled out with very atmospheric décor". Even fans of the "really nice buzz" inspired by these "costly surroundings" can find the food "pretty average" though. And harsher critics (of which there are many) say "what is the point of this expensive and dreadful group? They just demean memories of the original Ivy". Top Tip – "really reasonable for breakfast with decent portions in a pleasant atmosphere" (and you can book in advance for it, too). / ivycollection.com/our-restaurants.

Imad's Syrian Kitchen W1

THE IVY GRILLS & BRASSERIES £72 223

66 VICTORIA STREET, SW1
020 3971 2404   2–4B
26-28 BROADWICK ST, W1
020 3301 1166   4–1C
1 HENRIETTA ST, WC2
020 3301 0200   5–3D
197 KING'S RD, SW3   020 3301 0300   6–3C
96 KENSINGTON HIGH ST, W8
020 3301 0500   6–1A
ONE TOWER BRIDGE, 1 TOWER BRIDGE,
SE1   020 3146 7722   10–4D
50 CANADA SQUARE, E14
020 3971 7111   12–1C
DASHWOOD HOUSE, 69 OLD BROAD ST,
EC2   020 3146 7744   10–2D

"You wouldn't go for 'haute cuisine', but as a jolly place to eat comfort food in a spectacular setting, it is hard to beat" – that's the upbeat view, anyway, on this now-"ubiquitous" brasserie chain. Eight years and 40 openings later, the spin-offs increasingly eclipse the Theatreland original (see also), whose Edwardian features provide the style-guide for its nationwide 'roll out'. "Even if the unchallenging food reaches no heights, there's a consistent buzz", which makes them a "posh", "fun" choice for a get-together, if not a particularly foodie one. This is particularly the case at the landmark London off-shoots: at 'Chelsea Garden' ("gorgeous greenery"); Kensington ("slick", with a "pretty glitzy crowd"); and on the Thames ("great views over Tower Bridge"). But while it's always been acknowledged that the mass offering is "a shadow of the mothership's" – with "average grub at not-so-average prices" – the feeling that the brand has become just "a chain that does not excite" is gaining ever-stronger currency. Service seems more "stretched" nowadays, and a sliding ambience rating is making the whole offering seem ever-more "overrated, for all its modern art and perky décor". / theivymarketgrill.com/menus.

JAMAVAR W1 £81 444

8 MOUNT STREET   020 7499 1800   3–3B

"Real Indian cuisine" – "exquisite flavours from top-quality ingredients and stunning preparation" – have won a major reputation for this "top-class Indian", founded by Samyukta Nair, whose family own India's luxurious Leela Palace group. It occupies a "fantastic", tastefully decorated Mayfair site, near Berkeley Square: "quiet enough for conversation whilst busy enough to create a reassuring hum". / W1K 3NF; www.jamavarrestaurants.com; @JamavarLondon; Mon-Sat 10.30 pm, Sun 9.30 pm; no shorts.

JASHAN N8 £42 322

19 TURNPIKE LN   020 8340 9880   1–1C

This 32-year veteran curry house in Turnpike Lane is of the type that inspires "love" and devotion in its regulars. Post-pandemic, it emerged with a new format and menu and some fans regret the change: "the quality of food is generally back to its previously high, but the menu seems to have shortened, and

service is now sometimes MIA". / N8 0EP; www.jashan.co.uk; Mon-Sat 10.30 pm, Sun 10 pm; closed Mon-Sun L; no Amex; may need 6+ to book.

JEAN-GEORGES AT THE CONNAUGHT W1 £130 333

THE CONNAUGHT, CARLOS PLACE
020 7107 8861   3–3B

It's primarily as an afternoon tea haunt that this Mayfair base for the NYC star-chef attracts attention in our diners' poll, for its "excellent sandwiches and beautiful pastries that almost look too good to eat" ("staff always ask us if we would like more… we always do"). At other times, this plush conservatory serves a pretty conventional brasserie menu (with little hint of the south east Asian specialities that established JGV's Manhattan reputation), and on which one of the most popular items is, curiously, pizza. / W1W 2AL; www.the-connaught.co.uk/mayfair-restaurants/jean-georges; @theconnaught; Mon-Sun midnight.

JERU W1 £105 424

11 BERKELEY STREET
020 3988 0054   3–3C

"You have to like loud and vibey" if you visit celeb Aussie chef, Roy Ner's nightclubby newcomer in Mayfair, "beautifully decorated with large open kitchen and bars". Its launch wasn't smooth – with incidents of "comically bad service in the first week" – leading one or two critics to query: "is it the worst launch of the year?". But practically all reporters feel that "the Middle Eastern-style food certainly hits the spot" and there's a general sense that "once it beds in they may be able to work out their problems". / W1W 8DS; jeru.co.uk; @jerulondon; Tue, Wed 11.30 pm, Thu-Sat 12.30 am; closed Sun & Mon.

JIJI N1 £66 434

6G ESTHER ANNE PLACE
020 7486 3929   9–3D

"In the gorgeous new location of Islington Square", this "fantastic" and unusual Israeli-Japanese newcomer is proving a promising addition to N1: "very buzzy, with cool vibes" and serving "small fusion plates" that are very "interesting". Even fans agree, however, that it's "very expensive… but definitely worth it… I'll be back!" / N1 1WL; jijirestaurants.com; @jijirestaurant; Tue-Sun 11 pm; closed Mon.

JIKONI W1 £76 333

21 BLANDFORD STREET
020 7034 1988   2–1A

Chef and food writer Ravinder Bhogal presents her "very original, beautifully prepared" take on East African Indian cuisine in a "homely" setting in Marylebone. The odd reporter accused it of being "hyped" but most reports do nothing but enthuse about the cooking's "inventive and surprising flavours". / W1U 3DJ; www.jikonilondon.com; @JikoniLondon; Wed-Sat 10 pm, Sun 3 pm; closed Wed-Fri L closed Sun D, closed Mon & Tue.

JIN KICHI NW3 £59 553

73 HEATH ST   020 7794 6158   9–1A

"Sit at the counter and you might almost think you were in Tokyo… until you step outside and walk back to town over Hampstead Heath" from this "favourite Japanese" – one of NW3's best claims to culinary fame. "A small place, it feels so down-to-earth and unassuming, and then blows you away with delicious sushi and yakitori grilled dishes, with even humbler items like seaweed salad made to perfection". We've rated it in accordance with its long-term trend, but – having closed for much of the last year – it reopens in summer 2022 almost doubled in size. Here's hoping they've kept the best facets of its former quaint and "most authentic" style. / NW3 6UG; www.jinkichi.com; Tue-Sat 10.30 pm, Sun 10 pm; closed Mon; payment – credit card only.

JINJUU W1 £71 423

16 KINGLY ST   020 8181 8887   4–2B

"You can't go wrong" at this modern take on Korean cuisine off Carnaby Street. "The décor is quirky and the interior a little dark, but the food is the star" (especially since the departure of high-profile founder – Korean-American TV chef Judy Joo): and it's "tremendous value for money in Soho". / W1B 5PS; www.jinjuu.com; @jinjuusoho; Mon-Thu 10 pm, Fri & Sat 11 pm, Sun 7 pm.

JOANNA'S SE19 £59 334

56 WESTOW HILL   020 8670 4052   1–4D

"Popular in these parts for over 40 years", this bastion of Crystal Palace (est. 1978) has endured thanks to its "reliable" bistro fare and charming welcome, including to those with kids in tow. Great views of the London skyline too if you get the right table. / SE19 1RX; www.joannas.uk.com; @joannas_1978; Wed-Sat 10 pm, Sun 4 pm; closed Wed L closed Sun D, closed Mon & Tue.

JOE ALLEN WC2 £61 245

2 BURLEIGH ST   020 7836 0651   5–3D

"Like a pair of comfy shoes that never let you down", this nostalgic Covent Garden sibling to an NYC Theatreland brasserie of the same name is a "go-to when we're in town" for its many fans ("I have been to many Michelin star establishments around the world but Joe Allen is my favourite restaurant"). It was moved – lock, stock and barrel – three years ago due to reconstruction on its original site: "the address has changed, but everything else is the same: thank god!". Even its fans concede that its unambitious staple menu "might not win prizes for the food" – it's a place for a bite post-show, not a foodie occasion (with its off-menu burger being its most celebrated culinary offering for those in-the-know). / WC2W 7PX; www.joeallen.co.uk; @joeallenlondon; Mon-Sat midnight, Sun 8 pm; closed Mon L.

JOE PUBLIC SW4   £16   3️⃣3️⃣2️⃣

4 THE PAVEMENT   020 7622 4676   11–2A

"Fab" California-style pizzas (bigger and fresher toppings, apparently) are all you can eat at this handy converted public convenience next to Clapham Common tube, apart from the breakfast butties served until 2pm. There's also red & white wine on tap, and own-label beers by the can. / SW4 7AA; www.joepublicpizza.com; @JOEPUBLICSW4; Sun-Wed 10 pm, Thu-Sat 11 pm; closed Mon-Fri L; no booking.

JOIA SW8

15TH FLOOR, BATTERSEA POWER STN, CIRCUS RD WEST   **AWAITING TEL**   11–1C

If you're of a certain age, your reading may have been punctuated since the 1980s with visuals in national newspapers of how a skyline bar/restaurant at the forever-about-to-be-redeveloped Battersea Power Station might look. Well, it's finally a reality! Portuguese chef Henrique Sá Pessoa will open these three distinct spaces – a 15th floor restaurant; a bar on the 14th floor; and a rooftop bar with infinity pool – as part of the new art'otel in the development. Sá Pessoa's existing interests include his two Michelin star Alma back home in his native Lisbon and acting as exec chef to art'otel Amsterdam. Authentic Portuguese and Catalonian cuisine is promised alongside other dishes of Iberian inspiration, with numerous items finished tableside for a bit of added glam. / SW8 5BN; artotellondonbattersea.com/joia; @joiabattersea; Mon-Sat midnight, Sun 11 pm.

JONES & SONS N16   £67   3️⃣3️⃣4️⃣

STAMFORD WORKS, 3 GILLETT STREET   020 7241 1211   14–1A

This industrial-style space in Dalston, with an 11-metre Carrara marble bar, serves a "great range of well-prepared and presented" modern British dishes – notably char-grilled steaks. The business celebrates its tenth anniversary this year, and moved to its current site in 2016 – a "cavernous place" that made it an ideal location for the Bafta-nominated film Boiling Point, shot in one take on the day before the first national lockdown in March 2020. / N16 8JH; www.jonesandsonsdalston.com; @jones.and.sons; Wed-Sat 10 pm, Sun 6 pm; closed Wed-Fri L, closed Mon & Tue; booking max 20 may apply.

THE JONES FAMILY AFFAIR WC2   £67   4️⃣3️⃣4️⃣

40-42 WILLIAM IV STREET   020 3750 2121   2–2C

"An excellent addition to the family!" – this new steakhouse from the eponymous clan is making a success of this big, well-located site off Trafalgar Square where a number of London's top restaurateurs have stumbled in the last decade, when it was Les Deux Salons, RIP. Its large interior is "beautiful"; and – "with superb meat, supplied by The Ginger Pig – it does one of the best steaks in London". And, leaving all that aside, it's just "great to have somewhere decent to eat so centrally".

/ WC2W 4DD; www.jonesfamilyaffair.co.uk; @jonesfamilyrestaurants; Tue-Sat midnight, Sun 7 pm; closed Mon.

THE JONES FAMILY KITCHEN SW1   £53   4️⃣4️⃣4️⃣

7-8 ECCLESTON YARD   020 3929 6000   2–4B

"Superb with meat, especially the steaks: simply the most perfectly grilled ever…" – the Jones Family (formerly in Shoreditch) are making a good go of this steakhouse "oasis in busy Victoria" – a "fabulous, bright space with great art" (part of the stylish new Eccleston Yards project), where service "is delivered with a smile". "The ambience of its outdoor courtyard is very pleasant in summer" too. / SW1S 9AZ; www.jonesfamilykitchen.co.uk; @jonesfamilyrestaurants; Tue-Sat 11 pm, Sun 8 pm; closed Mon.

JOSÉ SE1   £61   4️⃣3️⃣4️⃣

104 BERMONDSEY ST   020 7403 4902   10–4D

"No wonder it remains popular after all these years" – José Pizarro's "tiny" Bermondsey bar "is always packed with a good vibe" thanks to its "short, perfectly executed tapas menu". It didn't score quite as highly this year, not because of harsh critiques, but just a sense that "while great and truly buzzing, it's not the old standard it once was". / SE1 3UB; www.josepizarro.com; @josepizarrorestaurants; Mon-Sat 10.30 pm, Sun 10 pm; no booking.

JOSÉ PIZARRO EC2   £62   3️⃣2️⃣2️⃣

BROADGATE CIRCLE   020 7256 5333   13–2B

You find a "real taste of Spain" at this "small and friendly restaurant in Broadgate" from José Pizarro. Perhaps inevitably, the glossier surroundings here are a turn-off to those who know him via his revered Bermondsey original, for whom this "feels awfully like a franchise", but even so, all reports rate the food as good or better. / EC2M 2QS; www.josepizarro.com/jose-pizarro-broadgate; @josepizarrorestaurants; Mon-Fri 10.30 pm, Sat 9.45 pm; closed Sun.

JOSÉ PIZARRO AT THE RA W1   £55   4️⃣3️⃣3️⃣

ROYAL ACADEMY, BURLINGTON GARDENS, PICCADILLY   020 7300 5912   3–3D

"I was expecting this to be a luke-warm franchise type of place, but the food was really exceptional!" – José P has confounded any sceptics with his takeover of this "relaxing oasis" within the famous Piccadilly art institution: "a fantastic addition to the dining scene in London" with "fabulous tapas", "served impeccably" in a "stunning" dining room where you feel "surrounded by art". / W1W 0BD; josepizarro.com/venues/jose-pizarro-royal-academy-arts; @josepizarrorestaurants; Tue-Sun 6 pm; closed Mon.

THE JUGGED HARE EC1   £75   3️⃣2️⃣3️⃣

49 CHISWELL STREET   020 7614 0134   13–2A

"If you like game, this is the place for you" – a "lively" City gastropub with a focus on "fabulous British food" led by game in season, spit-roasted suckling pig and rare-breed meat. Handy for pre-show dining for visitors to the neighbouring Barbican arts centre, and "great-value Sunday lunches too". / EC1Y 4SA; www.thejuggedhare.com; @thejuggedhare; Mon-Sun 11 pm.

JULIE'S W11   £92   2️⃣3️⃣4️⃣

135 PORTLAND RD   020 7229 8331   7–2A

After a four-year closure, "Julie's enjoyed a brief revival under head chef Shay Cooper, but sadly since his departure post-pandemic together with some key FoH staff" (to the Lanesborough) feedback has dropped off, with the odd "at best mediocre" report. Still, this remarkable, louche warren of subterranean rooms has been a romantic, if not a foodie destination since 1969: it's too early to write it off yet. / W11 4LW; www.juliesrestaurant.com; @juliesw11; Tue-Sat midnight; closed Sun & Mon.

JUNSEI W1   £68   4️⃣4️⃣3️⃣

132 SEYMOUR PLACE   020 7723 4058   7–1D

"Great chicken skewers" are the USP at this Japanese yearling in Marylebone which specialises in yakitori cooking – different cuts of meat "butchered and prepared in-house" so that not a scrap is wasted, and cooked on a robata grill. / W1W 1NS; junsei.co.uk; @junsei_uk; closed Mon-Sat & Sun.

KAFFEINE   £17   2️⃣5️⃣3️⃣

15 EASTCASTLE ST, W1   020 7580 6755   3–1D
66 GREAT TITCHFIELD ST, W1   020 7580 6755   3–1C

"They go the extra mile" at this Antipodean-style outfit whose "excellent" brews, including "the perfect espresso", ensure that is "always packed". Its two "convenient" sites in Fitzrovia make "a great escape not far from the Oxford Street chain experience", and they serve "decent food (especially by coffee shop standards)". / kaffeine.co.uk; kaffeinelondon.

KAHANI SW1   £77   4️⃣4️⃣3️⃣

1 WILBRAHAM PLACE   020 7730 7634   6–2D

Ex-Tamarind exec chef, Peter Joseph's "real classic of an Indian" is tucked away in a tastefully decorated basement near Sloane Square (behind Cadogan Hall). Peter was raised in Tamil Nadu, and achieves "an exceptionally high standard" using British ingredients to create light, modern dishes with a focus on grills from the robata grill and tandoor. "Although it's a pricey curry, you certainly get some bang for your buck!" / SW1S 9AE;

www.kahanilondon.com; @kahanilondon; Mon-Sat 10.30 pm, Sun 8 pm; closed Mon-Fri L.

KAI MAYFAIR W1 £125 333

65 SOUTH AUDLEY ST
020 7493 8988 3–3A

"A cut above any Chinese restaurant I have been to" – Bernard Yeoh's "attentive but not overbearing" Mayfair stalwart celebrates its 20th birthday in 2023 and continues to offer a luxurious mix of "absolutely fantastic contemporary Chinese cooking" (what Yeoh describes as 'liberated Nanyang cuisine') twinned with an impressive wine list (swelling with Premiers Crus from Bordeaux, Burgundy and beyond). Even those who say the food is "lovely" though, feel it comes at "eye-watering prices". / W1K 2QU; www.kaimayfair.co.uk; @kaimayfair; Mon-Sun 11 pm.

KAIFENG NW4 £74 332

51 CHURCH ROAD 020 8203 7888 1–1B

This "consistently high-quality kosher Chinese" in Hendon has established a strong reputation across north London over more than 20 years. It is named after a Chinese city with a Jewish population dating back 1,000 years or more. / NW4 4DU; www.kaifeng.co.uk; Sun-Thu 10.30 pm; closed Sat L, closed Fri.

KAKI N1 £50 432

125 CALEDONIAN ROAD
020 7278 6848 9–3D

"Prepare to numb your senses" at "one of the best Sichuan restaurants around" – this smartly modernised pub between King's Cross and Islington serves "red-hot and authentic cuisine by the canal on Caledonian Road". "Service is quick and friendly, the food delicious", and "the outside deck gives a lovely view over the canal in warm weather". Top Menu Tip – "the specials board is always worth a look – cumin lamb skewers, three treasures, pig intestine and twice-cooked pork belly are among the many stand-outs". / N1 9RG; www.thekaki.co.uk; @kaki_london; Sun-Thu 10 pm, Fri & Sat 11 pm.

KALIMERA N8 £53 443

43 TOPSFIELD ROAD 07446 981139 1–1C

"Tasty and reasonably priced plates of Mediterranean food" make this yearling from Télémaque Argyriou "a nice new addition to Crouch End". "How rarely do you get authentic Greek cuisine in London? Mostly you find Cypriot (OK, but not at all the same thing) or tourist stuff. This is the real Greek in a London bistro style – wonderful!". (The ingredients are real, too – led by olives and oil from the patron's family farm in Greece). / N8 8PT; www.kalimera-streetfood.co.uk; @kalimeralondon; Tue-Sat 11 pm; closed Tue-Sat L, closed Sun & Mon.

KANADA-YA £39 422

3 PANTON ST, SW1 020 7930 3511 5–4A
28 FOUBERT'S PLACE, W1
020 3435 8155 4–1B
64 ST GILES HIGH ST, WC2
020 7240 0232 5–1B
35 UPPER STREET, N1
020 7288 2787 9–3D

The "very rich and extremely meaty pork broth" wins plenty of admirers for what some consider "London's top ramen". Founded by former cycle racer Kazuhiro Kanada in Kyushu 14 years ago, the small group now has four branches in the capital – Angel, Piccadilly, Covent Garden and Carnaby – and provide "food to savour on a chilly winter day". / www.kanada-ya.com; kanada_ya_ldn.

KANISHKA W1 £101 332

17-19 MADDOX STREET
020 3978 0978 4–2A

Atul Kochhar's "inventive" Northeastern Indian cuisine ("light and not too rich") continues to win a strong fanclub for this well regarded four-year-old in Mayfair. It would rate even higher, were it not for a few reporters for whom "it's sound all around but just not that next-level I'd expect at the price point". / W1W 2QH; kanishkarestaurant.co.uk; @kanishkamayfair; Mon-Sun 11 pm.

KAOSARN £42 333

110 ST JOHNS HILL, SW11
020 7223 7888 11–2C
181 TOOTING HIGH STREET, SW17
020 8672 8811 11–2C
BRIXTON VILLAGE, COLDHARBOUR LN,
SW9 020 7095 8922 11–2D

"Delicious Thai food" wins plaudits for this family-owned and run trio in Brixton, Battersea and Tooting, while the BYO policy keeps a lid on the bill. / www.kaosarnlondon.co.uk.

KAPPACASEIN SE1 £11 532

1 STONEY STREET NO TEL 10–4C

"Still simply the best cheese toastie after all these years" – perhaps "the best you'll ever find" – is to be treasured at the Borough Market stall of a Bermondsey dairy, which makes its cheese with organic cow's milk from Chiddingstone in Kent. / SE1 9AA; www.kappacasein.com; @kappacasein; Thu & Fri 3 pm, Sat 4 pm; closed Thu-Sat D, closed Mon-Wed & Sun; no booking.

KASA & KIN W1 £46 343

52-53 POLAND STREET
020 7287 5400 4–1C

"A brightly coloured space" – this November 2021 newcomer (which translates to 'Home and Family' in Filipino) is run by the same crew as Romulo Café and gets a thumbs-up for "broadening the offer of Philippine cuisine in the UK" – "it's great to have an upscale option for contemporary Filipino food in the heart of Soho". One Filipino reporter feels that some dishes are too modified for local tastes, but agrees it's "fun, lively and with very acceptable food". Top Tip – "an array of sinful merienda/ tea snacks in the adjoining bakery and patisserie counter". / W1W 7NQ; kasaandkin.co.uk; @kasaandkin; Mon-Wed 9 pm, Thu-Sat 10 pm, Sun 8 pm.

JOIA SW8

KASHMIR SW15 £49 332

18-20 LACY ROAD 07477 533888 11–2B

"Proper and authentic regional food" gives this Kashmiri restaurant – apparently the first of its kind in Britain – a real point of difference in Putney. Regulars agree that it's "so good to try new dishes here, which are always delicious" – "served with ongoing geniality by the lovely owners", Rohit and Shweta Razdan, who ran restaurants in New Delhi and Singapore before moving to SW15. / SW15 1NL; www.kashmirrestaurants.co.uk; @kashmirrestuk; Mon, Wed & Thu 10.30 pm, Fri-Sun 11 pm; closed Mon, Wed-Fri L, closed Tue.

THE KATI ROLL COMPANY W1 £26 322

24 POLAND STREET 020 7287 4787 4–1C

A taste of Kolkata, via New York – these "Indian fast-food" joints in Soho and Bethnal Green serve buttery paratha flatbreads rolled around fillings originally grilled on skewers (kati means skewer), the street food from home that founder Payal Saha missed when she moved to Manhattan 21 years ago. / W1W 8QL; www.thekatirollcompany.com; @thekatirollcompany; Mon-Sun 11 pm.

KAZAN SW1 £62 332

93-94 WILTON RD 020 7233 7100 2–4B

"A Pimlico gem for so many years now, and even better than ever" – this "good-value" joint serving "good, honest Turkish food" celebrates its 21st anniversary this year. It's "heartening to see it so popular (deservedly so) since the latest lockdown ended", although it now operates on just one side of Wilton Road, having had two venues for years. / SW1V 1DW; www.kazan-restaurant.com; no Amex.

KEBAB QUEEN WC2 £123 443

4 MERCER WALK 020 7439 9222 5–2C

"Real wow factor" inspires fans of this not-very-secret counter, in the basement of Kingly Court's Le Bab, which aims ' to push kebabs as far as they can go'. "The service experience – with food served by the chef onto the actual surface of the special heated counter directly in front of you" (no plates, you scoop it up in your fingers) – "brings a brilliant sense of fun to the whole meal". "But it's not at the expense of serious culinary intent": ex-Gavroche chef, Manu Canales creates "original food, with exceptional quality of ingredients and cooking". / WC2H 9FA; www.eatlebab.com; @eatlebab; Wed-Sat 11 pm; closed Mon & Tue & Sun.

KEN LO'S MEMORIES SW1 £67 332

65-69 EBURY ST 020 7730 7734 2–4B

"Still going strong after all these years" – although "long-since forgotten by the foodie fashionistas" – the late Ken Lo's veteran Belgravian "still produces decent-quality, if perhaps westernised Chinese dishes, served with charm in comfortable surroundings". / SW1W 0NZ; www.memoriesofchina.co.uk; @kenlosmemoriesofchina; Wed-Sat, Tue, Sun 10.30 pm; closed Tue L, closed Mon.

KENNINGTON TANDOORI SE11 £56 343

313 KENNINGTON RD 020 7735 9247 1–3C

The closest thing to 'Parliament's official curry house' – frequented by prominent Westminster forkmen from Ken Clarke and John Prescott to David Cameron and BoJo – this Kennington institution is run by vascular surgeon Kowsar Hoque, whose father opened in 1985. Fans say it's "difficult to go elsewhere when wanting an Indian dinner!" / SE11 4QE; www.kenningtontandoori.com; @Kennington tandoori; Mon-Sun 10.30 pm; closed Mon-Sun L; no Amex.

KERRIDGE'S BAR & GRILL WC2 £109 223

10 NORTHUMBERLAND AVENUE 020 7321 3244 2–3C

"A little bit of Marlow on Embankment", say fans of TV-Tom's London HQ: a "smooth operation", which occupies a vast, atmospheric chamber within one of London's most glamorous five stars (well, if it's good enough for Ivanka…). The posh brasserie food, overseen by chef Nick Beardshaw, is "quite heavy and meaty" and fans say "while it's a bit pricey, you will have an enjoyable meal". On the downside, there's a disappointed minority for whom the atmosphere "is very hotel dining room" and who see this as "another disappointing experience from a TV-star branded establishment". / WC2W 5AE; www.kerridgesbarandgrill.co.uk; @kerridgesbandg; Mon-Sat 10.30 pm, Sun 9 pm.

KERRIDGE'S FISH & CHIPS SW1 £115 335

HARRODS, 87-135 BROMPTON ROAD 020 7225 6800 6–1D

"Expensive but amazing fish 'n' chips" and other "very tasty" seafood classics win nothing but praise for this year-old outlet, within Harrods Dining Halls (see also). "Most definitely go for the cockle popcorn

and malted beer batter". / SW1S 7XL; www.harrods.com/en-gb/restaurants/kerridges-fish-chips; Tue-Sat 11 pm, Mon 9 pm, Sun 6 pm.

KHUN PAKIN THAI AT THE SALUTATION W6 £20 333

154 KING STREET 020 8748 3668 8–2C

A plug from Tom Parker Bowles in the Daily Mail did no harm at all to this Thai concession in an attractive old pub opposite the building site once known as 'Hammersmith Town Hall', where the cooking is a cut above that in a typical boozer. Top Tip – "if you get the chance, eat in the sun in the cute beer garden at the back: with some delish salt 'n' pepper squid, life is good!" / W6 0QU; www.salutationhammersmith.co.uk; Mon-Sat 11 pm, Sun 10.30 pm.

KIBOU LONDON SW11 £61 223

175-177 NORTHCOTE ROAD 020 7223 8551 11–2C

This "convenient neighbourhood Japanese" was a "welcome addition to Northcote Road" when it landed in Battersea's Nappy Valley in summer 2020 – vividly decorated and the first London branch of a popular Cheltenham-based group. Not all reporters are convinced, though, with gripes about "flustered service" or indifferent dishes weighing in the balance against those who continue to feel it's "good value". / SW11 6QF; kibou.co.uk; @kiboulondon; Tue-Sat 11 pm, Sun 10 pm; closed Mon.

KIKU W1 £70 442

17 HALF MOON ST 020 7499 4208 3–4B

This "classic Japanese stalwart" has offered an authentic taste of Tokyo in a Mayfair backstreet for 45 years – and is always "full of Japanese consular employees" from the nearby embassy. Top Tip – "go for the good-value lunchtime set menu". / W1J 7BE; www.kikurestaurant.co.uk; @kikumayfair; Mon-Sat 10.15 pm; closed Sun.

KILIG SE8

DEPTFORD ARCHES, 2 RESOLUTION WAY AWAITING TEL 1–3D

This July 2022 newcomer at Deptford Arches promises an interesting culinary mashup reflecting the founders' roots in the Philippines and Colombia. It opened too late for survey feedback, but The Evening Standard's Jimi Famurewa found it: "occasionally inspired and enormously likeable but also prone, here and there, to a kind of erratic overreach". / SE8 4NT; www.kiliglondon.co.uk; @kilig_ldn; Mon-Sat midnight, Sun 11 pm.

KILIS KITCHEN N1 £51 333

4 THEBERTON STREET 020 7226 5489 9–3D

This "excellent local" Turkish restaurant just off Islington's main drag offers a classic and extensive menu of "good food at a very

reasonable price", served up in a "buzzy and friendly setting". / N1 0QX; www.kilis.co.uk; @kilis_kitchen; Sun-Thu 11 pm, Fri & Sat midnight.

KILN W1 £50 544

58 BREWER STREET NO TEL 4–3C

"Exciting", "astonishingly good" and "incredible value" Thai-inspired BBQ fuels nothing but adulatory reviews for Ben Chapman's "incomparable" Soho destination ("we licked the plates clean and bemoaned the fact Manchester has nothing like this!"). This is "casual, bar-counter eating at its best", but the "buzzy, loud atmosphere is not conducive to a leisurely meal". Sitting upstairs "at the grill, watching the chefs cooking over the open flames is the highlight"; "downstairs is a bit grim and windowless" by comparison. "It's too good to be an occasional place, but the queues make it impossible for frequent visits" (and "with no booking, you have to chance it; and it can be a long queue, glaring at people to hurry up!)". Top Menu Tips – "the glass noodles, sausage, chicken glazing, larb squid and Cornish greens are exceptional". / W1F 9TL; www.kilnsoho.com; @kilnsoho; Mon-Sat 11 pm, Sun 9 pm.

KIN AND DEUM SE1 £47 423

2 CRUCIFIX LANE 020 7357 7995 10–4D

"Extremely good" Thai food helps win a fair-sized fan club for this white-walled pub-conversion, near London Bridge. But "when it's packed, it can be a bit noisy for a good conversation". / SE1 3JW; www.kindeum.com; @kindeum; Mon-Sun 10.30 pm.

KINDRED W6 £44 333

BRADMORE HOUSE, QUEEN CAROLINE STREET 020 3146 1370 8–2C

Slap bang in the middle of Hammersmith Broadway, it's easy to ignore Grade II listed 'Bradmore House', nowadays a hip coworking club. The food (from a menu created by chef Andrew Clarke) doesn't aim for foodie fireworks, but is way better than you would expect just seconds from the tube platforms, as is the stylish and cosy basement location. / W6 9YE; www.wearekindred.com; @londonkindred; Tue, Wed 11 pm, Thu-Sat midnight, Mon 6 pm; closed Sun.

KIPFERL N1 £54 333

20 CAMDEN PASSAGE 020 77041 555 9–3D

"Classic Austrian comfort food" is the order of the day at this Austrian-run all-day café, which opened in the City 20 years ago and moved to Islington's Camden Passage in 2011. The menu runs from "great coffee and cakes", via "delicious and decadent brunch" to "a choice of traditional main dishes, with very good veal in cream sauce or schnitzel and nice desserts". Commendably, there is little pandering to local tastes: everything is as close as possible to what you might eat in Vienna. / N1 8ED;

www.kipferl.co.uk; @kipferl_london; Mon-Thu 10 pm, Fri & Sat 11 pm, Sun 7 pm.

KISS THE HIPPO £27 3|3|2

51 MARGARET STREET, W1 NO TEL 3–1C
50 GEORGE STREET, TW9
020 3887 2028 1–4A

"The coffee is the best!", according to fans of this "zen" Scandi-style café in Fitzrovia, from an ambitious ethical importer and roastery that has won a clutch of barista awards in the five years since it was founded (including Top Coffee House at the Harden's London Restaurant Awards 2021). The shop offers "light snacks such as cinnamon rolls and cakes" – and "everything is good, not just the coffee". Their original venture, in Richmond, moved into a new address in summer 2022, and they also have kiosks in Shoreditch, King's Cross and Sloane Square. / kissthehippo.com; kissthehippo.

KITCHEN TABLE
W1 £330 4|4|4

70 CHARLOTTE STREET
020 7637 7770 2–1C

"Sublime on every level… if only it wasn't so expensive". James Knappett and Sandia Chang's 18-seater in Fitzrovia re-opened after a significant reformatting in July 2021 and "it's both an exceptional meal and quite a show" – "the arrangement of the counter makes for a theatrical experience, with lots of opportunity to chat with the people cooking and running front of house", while the multi-course menu (each course focused on a single ingredient) is, all reports agree, utterly "memorable". Practically all reports also mention the pricing though – "OUCH!"… "it was amazing but the bill's crazy…" / W1T 4QG; www.kitchentablelondon.co.uk; @kitchentable1; Tue-Sat 11 pm; closed Sun & Mon; booking online only.

KITCHEN W8 W8 £90 4|3|3

11-13 ABINGDON ROAD
020 7937 0120 6–1A

"Polished cuisine" with a "creative mix of ingredients" – overseen from afar by star chef Phil Howard – elevates this "classic neighbourhood restaurant" off High Street Kensington into something "top class" and one of London's better-known foodie destinations. If criticism is made, it's typically that a diner "had heard great things, but was underwhelmed despite finding nothing obviously wrong". In a similar variable vein, service veers from "very pleasant" to "sometimes chaotic"; and the "well-spaced" dining room is "lovely" to some, too low-key for others. / W8 6AH; www.kitchenw8.com; @KitchenW8; Tue-Thu, Sun 9.30 pm, Fri & Sat 10 pm; closed Mon.

KITTY FISHER'S
W1 £76 3|3|4

10 SHEPHERD'S MARKET
020 3302 1661 3–4B

This "very small, charming and romantic" venture in Shepherd Market was briefly the hottest ticket in town in the mid noughties (providing a much-PR'd date night for David & Samantha Cameron). Nowadays, those who remember the historic hype can find it "overrated" or "dependable rather than… wow!", but overall its food is well-rated. Top Menu Tip – Belted Galloway Wing Rib and "cosmic crispy potatoes!" / W1J 7QF; www.kittyfishers.com; @kittyfishers; Tue-Sat 9.30 pm; closed Sun & Mon.

KNIFE SW4 £73 4|4|3

160 CLAPHAM PARK ROAD
020 7627 6505 11–2D

"The best Sunday roasts… well cooked and hangover-busting!" are just one of the options for eating at this excellent, small brick-walled steakhouse on the Clapham/Brixton borders (a former winner of the Top Steaks category in the Harden's London Restaurant Awards). The menu has a good variety of choices, including beef sourced from farmers in the Lake District. / SW4 7DE; kniferestaurant.co.uk; @kniferestaurant; Wed-Sat 9.30 pm, Sun 4.30 pm; closed Wed-Sat L closed Sun D, closed Mon & Tue.

KOJI SW6 £84 3|3|4

58 NEW KING'S RD 020 7731 2520 11–1B

"A perfect place this side of town", say fans of this long-established pan-Asian – tucked away in Parson's Green – whose swish décor and diverse menu (sushi, sashimi tacos, udon noodles, wagyu steaks, kushiyaki skewers, wood-roasted fish…) can make it a good choice for a special celebration. But it doesn't attract the volume of feedback that it used to. / SW6 4LS; www.koji.restaurant; @kojirestaurant; Tue, Wed 10.30 pm, Thu-Sat 11 pm; closed Tue-Sat L, closed Sun & Mon; payment – credit card only.

KOL W1 £124 4|4|4

9 SEYMOUR STREET 020 3829 6888 2–2A

"Ex-Noma pop-up chef, Santiago Lastra's sort-of fine dining Mexican successfully redefines street food at this warm and high-end dining room", just off Portman Square – "a welcome addition to Marylebone" that "deserves the hype" and which is emerging as one of London's more "exciting" destinations right now. "The open kitchen allows the man himself to be seen" and a meal "feels like an occasion", but one that's "earthy" and "fun". "The innovative use of British ingredients to recreate Mexican flavours is what makes this a really interesting culinary experience" – providing "twists on the genre which tantalise the palate" and deliver "immensely thoughtful and innovative" dishes with "deep savoury notes". "And the wine list is both unusual and worth taking a risk on too: some hidden gems from small producers and uncommon countries which complement the food well". "You are helped in your journey by a knowledgeable and unpretentious sommelier" and service generally is "excellent". "Always buzzy, tables are hard to come by". Top Tips – "the lobster taco is a real highlight and the mole something very special indeed", while there's "one of the finest vegan tasting menus in London". / W1W 7BA; kolrestaurant.com; @kol.restaurant; Tue-Sat

midnight, Sun 2.30 pm; closed Tue L closed Sun D, closed Mon; payment – credit card only.

KOLAMBA W1 £36 3|3|2

21 KINGLY STREET 020 3815 4201 4–2B

"Knock-out Sri Lankan small plates" at this Soho three-year-old deliver "bright and fiery dishes". There are "amazing veggie options", and it's "well-priced and authentic". / W1W 5QA; kolamba.co.uk; @kolamba.ldn; Mon-Sat 10 pm, Sun 9 pm.

KOYA £45 3|4|3

50 FRITH ST, W1 020 7434 4463 5–2A
10-12 BROADWAY MARKET MEWS, E8 NO
TEL 14–2B
BLOOMBERG ARCADE, QUEEN VICTORIA
STREET, EC2 NO TEL 10–3C

"Portions are perfect for the price and they don't 'cheap out' on the protein" at these "solid udon places" in Soho (est. 2010), a newer offshoot in the City's Bloomberg Arcade and now also with the opening of 'Koya Ko' in Hackney's Broadway Market (this last with a slightly different menu). "Very Japanese-chic, super-cosy and cute", their "staff are kind and helpful with answering questions about ingredients". Udon are more traditional and subtler than ubiquitous ramen, and arrive in Japan's famous light dashi stock. / www.koya.co.uk.

KOYN W1

38 GROSVENOR STREET
020 3376 0000 3–2B

On gracious Grosvenor Square – a Japanese-inspired izakaya-style from Mei Mei's Samyukta Nair; and her family's LSL Capital's fifth Mayfair venture; opening September 2022. The two-storey space is apparently inspired by 'enigmatic' Mount Fuji: 'On the round floor is MIDORI, the green room, representative of vegetative life on the snow-capped peak, and below is MAGMA, the charred room, representing an active, bubbling volcano'. Who'd have guessed! A broad spectrum of Japanese cuisine is trailed, featuring specialist dishes in their sushi bar and robata grill selections. / W1W 4QA; www.koynrestaurants.com; Tue-Sun midnight.

KRICKET W1 £52 5|4|4

12 DENMAN ST 020 7734 5612 4–3C

As 10CC might have put it: "We don't like Kricket… we love it!". "Brilliant Indian sharing plates with an emphasis on taste, not heat" have bowled a hat-trick of successes for Rik Campbell and Will Bowlby since their street food pop-up went permanent in Soho, Brixton and White City. Their "interesting and flexible" small-plate menus are served in a "cool, vibey atmosphere", either eating at the counter or at tables – with more vibes next door in their speakeasy bar Soma for diners in Soho. / W1D 7HH; www.kricket.co.uk; @kricketlondon; Mon-Sat 10.30 pm; closed Sun.

KUDU SE15 £60 4|4|4

119 QUEEN'S RD 020 3950 0226 1–4D

"A fun spot, with super food and surroundings" – Patrick Williams and Amy Corbin's (yes, that Corbin) Peckham venture has earned its place on London's foodie map with "quality" South African-influenced cooking and "personable" service. On warmer days, you can eat in the back garden. / SE15 2EZ; www.kuducollective.com; @kudu_restaurant; Thu-Sun 10 pm; closed Thu L, closed Mon & Tue & Wed.

KUDU GRILL SE15 £49 4|4|4

57 NUNHEAD LANE 020 3172 2450 1–4D

"A simply stunning South African braai restaurant" – Amy Corbin and Patrick Williams's "cosy and classy" yearling (opened in September 2021) delivers "some of the best food in a long time" to excited local reporters, "with confident, bold flavours" ("a special shout out to the delectable peri peri butter and monkey gland sauce"). "Superb service too (catered for the veggie and the vegan in our group without batting an eyelid, and without sacrificing flavour!)". / SE15; www.kuducollective.com; @kudugrill; Wed-Sat 10 pm, Sun 2.30 pm; closed Wed-Fri L closed Sun D, closed Mon & Tue.

KUTIR SW3 £64 5|4|4

10 LINCOLN STREET 020 7581 1144 6–2D

"It's always a great pleasure to dine at this beautiful Chelsea townhouse with a lovely summer terrace upstairs" Rohit Ghai's "inventive" cuisine is some of the best Indian food in London: "heavily spiced" and delivered by "impeccable staff" in a "bright, airy and compact dining room". / SW3 2TS; kutir.co.uk; @kutirchelsea; Tue-Sun 10 pm; closed Mon; no shorts; booking online only.

THE LADBROKE ARMS W11 £65 3|2|4

54 LADBROKE ROAD 020 7727 6648 7–2B

With its flower-bedecked exterior and "relaxed neighbourhood vibe", this Ladbroke Grove local is "certainly one of the better pubs" in the capital, serving "delicious food that's definitely more restaurant than pub grub" alongside "good beer". It's close to Holland Park, and attracts a good Sunday lunch crowd. / W11 3NW; www.ladbrokearms.com; @Ladbrokearms; Mon-Sat 9.30 pm, Sun 9 pm.

LAHORE KEBAB HOUSE E1 £35 5|2|2

2-10 UMBERSTON ST
020 7481 9737 12–1A

"Still the best authentic Pakistani grilled meat and curry" is to be had at this grunge-tastic Whitechapel legend of 50 years' standing, where "tastes are genuine" and prices "cheap as chips". Top Menu Tip – "love the lamb chops". / E1 1PY; www.lahore-kebabhouse.com.

LAHPET £59 3|4|3

21 SLINGSBY PLACE, WC2
020 3883 5629 5–3C
58 BETHNAL GREEN ROAD, E1
020 3883 5629 13–1C

"Distinctive and exciting" flavours of Burma ("an under-represented cuisine in London") have now made their way from a stall near London Bridge, via a Hackney railway arch and a Shoreditch restaurant (still running) to the West End, in Covent Garden's newish 'The Yards' development, thanks to founders Dan Anton and Burmese chef Zaw Mahesh. Named after a salad of pickled tea leaves, Lahpet is "lively and noisy", and its food is "thrilling". Top Tip – "the luminescent ginger salad… so zingy and flavourful!" / lahpet.co.uk; lahpet.

LAKSAMANIA W1 £49 3|3|2

92 NEWMAN STREET 020 7637 9888 3–1D

"A topspot for Malaysian food", this three-year-old street-food specialist off Oxford Street serves "top-notch laksas", following both traditional recipes and chef Danny Tan's original variations. Service is overseen by the "friendly Aunties who run the front-of-house show". / W1W 3EZ; www.laksamania.co.uk; @laksamania; Mon, Wed & Thu 9 pm, Fri & Sat 9.30 pm, Sun 8 pm; closed Tue.

THE LANDMARK, WINTER GARDEN NW1 £88 2|3|5

222 MARYLEBONE RD
020 7631 8000 9–4A

"The most stunning venue, full of palm trees under a high glass roof", makes this eight-storey hotel atrium the perfect setting for brunch or an "excellent afternoon tea". "The pastries are wonderful" and there's a "fantastic choice of breakfast dishes" – but the real treat is the "superb ambience" created by one of London's most Insta-friendly spaces. / NW1 6JQ; www.landmarklondon.co.uk; @the_landmark_london; Mon-Sun 10 pm; no trainers; booking max 12 may apply.

THE LANESBOROUGH GRILL SW1 £132

HYDE PARK CORNER 020 7259 5599 6–1D

The "stunning" atrium setting has always been a highlight of the light-filled dining room of this ultra-luxe hotel on Hyde Park Corner, which has been transformed this year. In April 2022, out went its haute-cuisine menu (and Michelin star) – in came this new posh brasserie offering (overseen by former Julie's chef, Shay Cooper), putting an emphasis on seasonal British produce (and with a number of dishes served tableside on gueridon trolleys). The change was sufficiently close to our annual diners' poll that it's more appropriate to leave a rating till next year. / SW1X 7TA; www.oetkercollection.com/hotels/the-lanesborough/restaurants-bars/restaurants/celeste/; @the_lanesborough; no shorts.

LANGAN'S BRASSERIE W1 £73 1|2|3

STRATTON STREET 020 7491 8822 3–3C

"Not the old Langans by any means" – the relaunch in late 2021 of this treasured old-faithful brasserie (est. 1976) near The Ritz has proved "a little mixed" to say the least, and a return to its A-list past now seems a very distant prospect. One or two fans do "love the entire experience" of this business favourite and its plutocratic comfort food. But more common are those whose "excitement turned to huge disappointment in the face of abysmal service and astronomical prices" for staple dishes, to the extent that some diners loath the place: "arguably the most overrated restaurant in central London, made clear by all the Z-list celebrities I assume they get to dine for free…" – "should be rated zero zero zero!" / W1J 8LB; www.langansrestaurants.co.uk; @langansbrasserie; Mon-Sat 11 pm, Sun 9.30 pm.

PALM COURT, THE LANGHAM W1 £98 2|3|4

1C PORTLAND PLACE
020 7636 1000 2–1B

"Elegant silver and grey décor" helps set a refined tone in the plush lounge of this luxurious five star. Most reports of "very imaginative gateaux and sandwiches" suggest it lives up to its heritage (the ceremony of afternoon tea having, apparently, started here), but even fans can find the price tag "a little steep". / W1B 1JA; www.palm-court.co.uk; @langham_london; Mon-Sun 11 pm; no trainers.

LAO CAFE WC2 £39 3|3|2

60 CHANDOS PLACE 020 3740 4748 5–4C

This "modest but terrific" former pop-up near Trafalgar Square, from entrepreneurial Lao-Thai chef Saiphin Moore (of Rosa's Thai), is "well worth the visit" for "good-sized portions" of "authentic" Laotian food – a lesser-known Asian cuisine with meals revolving around the staple of sticky rice. / WC2N 4HG; laocafe.co.uk; @laocafelondon Follow; Mon-Sun 10 pm; may need 8+ to book.

LAUNCESTON PLACE W8 £102 4|3|3

1A LAUNCESTON PL 020 7937 6912 6–1B

"A special place to dine in stylish and intimate rooms" – this "quirkily laid-out" townhouse (est. 1986) in a quiet Kensington backstreet "exudes gracious hospitality" and "never fails to delight", particularly as a "romantic" destination. Chef Ben Murphy joined in January 2017 and why Michelin have failed to award him a star is anyone's guess: his cuisine "is delicious with subtle flavour combinations and artistically presented plates" that all make up for a "memorable" occasion. (You would never know it was owned by D&D London – it stands head and shoulders over the rest of their portfolio nowadays.) / W8 5RL; www.launcestonplace-restaurant.co.uk; @launcestonplace; Wed-Sat 10 pm, Sun 9 pm; closed Mon & Tue.

THE LAUNDRY
SW9 £62 343

374 COLDHARBOUR LANE
020 8103 9384 11–2D

This "impressive" three-year-old in Brixton is set in a handsome converted Victorian laundry. The first venture of Melanie Brown (a former chef and founder of the New Zealand and Australian Cellar wine businesses), it wins consistent ratings across the board for its "good food, great service and buzzy atmosphere". / SW9 8PL; thelaundrybrixton. com; @brixtonlaundry; Mon-Wed 11 pm, Thu-Sat midnight, Sun 9 pm; payment – credit card only.

LE BAB £53 322

TOP FLOOR, KINGLY COURT, W1
020 7439 9222 4–2B
4 MERCER WALK, WC2
020 7240 9781 5–2C
CIRCUS WEST VILLAGE, BATTERSEA
POWER STN, SW11 NO TEL 11–1C
408 COLDHARBOUR LANE, SW9
07756 943372 11–2D
KINGSLAND LOCKE, 130 KINGSLAND HIGH
ST, E8 020 3877 0865 14–1A
231 OLD STREET, EC1
020 3456 7890 13–1A

"Intriguing twists on the kebab theme" (plus "good beer brewed on site" at the Kraft Dalston branch) continue to win consistently good ratings across this expanding chain, which in September 2022 adds a 20-seater in Brixton to its roster of locations. See also Kebab Queen. / https://www.eatlebab.com.

THE LEDBURY
W11 £236 454

127 LEDBURY RD 020 7792 9090 7–1B

"Brett is indeed finally back!" at this Notting Hill luminary, which has often topped our annual diners' poll as London's top gastronomic destination, but which closed for the duration of the Covid pandemic. Virtually all feedback is ecstatic: "it's just so good to see it re-open!". "The dining room has had a thorough refresh" and the "slight reduction in the number of tables has significantly improved the ambience" ("you still feel you're in the same place, just with a more spacious feel"); and "service was top-notch even after just a couple of weeks of re-opening". When it comes to gastronomy, many fans feel that "while it didn't seem possible, if anything, Brett has raised his game even higher" since ditching the pre-pandemic à la carte menu format to focus on "a modern-style tasting menu", featuring 8 courses (and also at lunch with a cut-down option of 6 courses). A minority of reporters, though, are more cautious in their praise. The new "eye-watering level of prices" is the most widespread concern. But one or two deeper sceptics – while acknowledging "technically exquisite" or "knockout" cooking – think "it's not bad or disappointing, just not quite as good as it once was". So, as a result, The Ledbury food rating has not yet quite regained its customary level of 5/5. What's not in doubt, though, is that owner Nigel Platts-Martin's celebrated operation has survived its state of suspended animation to

compete successfully once again at the highest level. / W11 2AQ; www.theledbury.com; Mon-Sat 9.45 pm; closed Mon-Thu L, closed Sun.

LEGARE SE1 £48 443

CARDAMOM BUILDING, 31G SHAD THAMES
020 8063 7667 10–4D

"Top-top quality food" – from Matt Beardmore, formerly of Trullo – has established a glowing reputation for this small Italian on the South Bank near Tower Bridge. He opened it two years ago with ex-Barrafina manager Jay Patel, to immediate good reports – and "you can see why it has attracted all the hype". / SE1 2YB; legarelondon.com; @legarelondon; Wed-Sat, Tue 10 pm; closed Tue L, closed Sun & Mon.

LEMONIA NW1 £60 233

89 REGENT'S PARK RD
020 7586 7454 9–3B

"Been going for 30+ years and still love it" – this "shamelessly old-school Greek" is a longstanding north London destination, and fans say it's "such a nice change from the ubiquitous, pretentious, small-plates places" in serving "traditional taverna fayre that's perfectly decent, if not exciting". What people really go a bundle on though, is its "lovely family-friendly atmosphere", as fostered by "very approachable staff who have been there forever" (but who "can be slow at busy times"). / NW1 8UY; www.lemonia.co.uk; Mon-Sat 10.30 pm, Sun 4 pm; closed Sun D; no Amex.

LEROY EC2 £69 333

18 PHIPP STREET 020 7739 4443 13–1B

It's hard to review this funky Shoreditch five-year-old without mentioning its star from the French tyre firm – the latter setting up expectations that are not always met. Many reports do give the highest praise to its creative small plates and well-curated selection of wines. But there's a disgruntled minority, who stumble on their feelings that it's over-egged. ("I'm not a star chaser but I do want to have a good time, and somehow the whole experience felt a bit Spartan…"; "the food is indeed tasty, but is VERY overpriced. Is part of the problem that their Michelin star has pushed them into cramming as many tables in as possible?") / EC2E 4NP; www.leroyshoreditch.com; @leroyshoreditch; Mon-Sat 9.30 pm; closed Mon L, closed Sun; credit card deposit required to book.

LEVAN SE15 £60 332

3-4 BLENHEIM GROVE
020 7732 2256 1–4D

"Innovative cooking, good cocktails and a relaxed, cool setting" draw the "young hip crowd" to this "small Peckham restaurant" from the team behind Salon in Brixton (RIP). All reports remain fundamentally upbeat, but a variety of gripes and some dishes "not quite hitting the mark" took its rating lower this year. / SE15 4QL; levanlondon.co.uk; @levanlondon; Tue-Sat 10 pm, Sun 3 pm; closed Sun D, closed Mon.

THE LIBERTINE EC3
THE ROYAL EXCHANGE AWAITING TEL
10–2C

The vaults of The Royal Exchange are to become a posh Citified food court at the hands of the Incipio group, whose other operations include Pergola on the Wharf in Docklands and White City's Dear Grace. Open in October 2022, this is the business's seventh venue. / EC3E 3LR; Mon-Sat midnight, Sun 11 pm.

THE LIGHT HOUSE
SW19 £65 333

75-77 RIDGWAY 020 8944 6338 11–2B

Celebrating its 25th year, "this excellent, independent neighbourhood restaurant knocks out top-class Mediterranean dishes at no more than you'd pay in a nearby pub" – in an "imaginative" culinary style that's "not changed much over the years". It can seem pricey, or "hit and miss", but there's also an argument that it's "so underrated". / SW19 4ST; www.lighthousewimbledon.com; @lighthousewimbledon; Mon-Sat 10 pm, Sun 3.30 pm; closed Sun D.

THE LIGHTERMAN
N1 £58 222

3 GRANARY SQUARE 020 3846 3400 9–3C

"A great location on the canal with lots of outdoor seating" – and with "interesting views of the new developments around King's Cross" – are the trump cards of this strikingly designed canalside gastropub on Granary Square. On the downside, the food is "fairly standard pub fodder" and it can just be "too much, too busy, too noisy". / N1C 4BH; www.thelighterman.co.uk; @thelightermankx; Mon-Thu 11.30 pm, Fri & Sat midnight, Sun 10.30 pm.

LINA STORES £47 433

13 MARYLEBONE LANE, W1
020 3148 7503 3–1A
51 GREEK STREET, W1
020 3929 0068 5–2A
20 STABLE STREET, N1 AWAITING TEL
9–3C
19 BLOOMBERG ARCADE, EC4
020 3002 6034 10–3C

"Beautiful fresh pasta, served from the heart by knowledgeable Italians" is the attractive offer at this small group, spun out of a famous veteran Soho deli (est. 1944) in the past five years under private equity outfit White Rabbit. The "food is good and good value, though limited and very focused on the pasta". There are now branches in King's Cross, the City's Bloomberg Arcade and most recently Marylebone; the farthest-flung is in Tokyo, while Clapham Old Town has been long promised. / www.linastores.co.uk; linastores.

LINO'S NW6

6 LONSDALE ROAD NO TEL 1–2B

Though well-received, the original Lino's near St Barts never properly got off the ground before Covid struck and closed during the

Lisboeta WC1

pandic. This September 2022 newcomer adds to the expanding Queen's Park scene, a two-floor site plus outside dining too. / NW6 6RD.

LISBOETA WC1 £77 443

30 CHARLOTTE STREET
020 3830 9888   2–1C

"Nuno Mendes, London's most creative and friendly chef is back!" – partnering with MJMK Restaurants (who run Casa do Frango and Kol) – at this three-floor Fitzrovian in the thick of Charlotte Street, which "is set up for quick counter dining on the ground floor or longer meals upstairs". As usual, "his take on Portuguese food is outstanding", delivering "distinctive and gutsy flavours" with "flair". "The bill soon adds up", though, to the extent that one or two reporters find it "expensive and hyped". But the main complaint? – "the upstairs room can be painfully noisy". Top Menu Tip – 'abade de priscos' – the 'signature' custard pie pudding incorporating bacon. / WC1W 4AF; lisboeta.co.uk; @lisboeta.london; Tue-Sat 11.30 pm, Mon 11 pm, Sun 5 pm; closed Mon L closed Sun D.

LITTLE SOCIAL
W1 £77 433

5 POLLEN STREET   020 7870 3730   3–2C

"Opposite Jason Atherton's flagship in Pollen Street", its "high-class and intimate" younger sibling is in a more straightforward bistro style, and offers "simple food done exceptionally well". "Surroundings and service are warm" too, and "in summer you can eat outside on this pedestrianised street". / W1W 1NE; www.littlesocial.co.uk; @_littlesocial; Tue-Sat 9pm; closed Sun & Mon.

LITTLE TAPERIA
SW17 £53 333

143 TOOTING HIGH ST
020 8682 3303   11–2C

"A local delight" in southwest London – "tasty, unusual tapas", "super-knowledgeable staff" and "buzzy, upbeat atmosphere add to the feeling that you're anywhere but Tooting High Street". "The prices are more like central London than SW17, but the quality's right up there to justify the premium". / SW17; www.thelittletaperia.co.uk; @thelittletaperia; Mon-Thu 11 pm, Fri & Sat midnight, Sun 10.30 pm; may need 6+ to book.

LLEWELYN'S
SE24 £71 332

293-295 RAILTON RD
020 7733 6676   11–2D

A "local favourite" opposite Herne Hill station for its "hearty and tasty European bistro food", "this restaurant goes from strength to strength. The cooking is inventive without being gimmicky and skilled without being over the top". It's "a lovely place", but "the room is strangely laid out", with a "cramped interior and hard surfaces, so it gets noisy" ("or you could say buzzy"). / SE24 0JP;

www.llewelyns-restaurant.co.uk; @llewelynslondon; Tue-Thu 9 pm, Fri & Sat 9.30 pm, Sun 3.15 pm; closed Tue-Thu L closed Sun D, closed Mon; booking max 8 may apply.

LA LLUNA N10 £58 332

462 MUSWELL HILL BROADWAY
020 8442 2662   1–1B

This "wonderful local tapas bar with a buzzy vibe" in Muswell Hill wins strong ratings for its "surprisingly good food", served in a modern dining room with naked brick walls. A second branch (not listed) opened in Whetstone in summer 2021. / N10 1BS; www.lalluna.co.uk; @la_lluna_london; Mon-Thu 11 pm, Fri & Sat midnight, Sun 10 pm.

LOCANDA LOCATELLI
W1 £103 232

HYATT REGENCY, 8 SEYMOUR ST
020 7935 9088   2–2A

"Lovely to see Giorgio parading the floor and in the kitchen making sure everything is correct", say fans of his well-known, sophisticated and moodily "romantic" Italian, off Portman Square (run, with wife Plaxy, since 2002), for whom a visit is still "always a delight" with triumphant modern Italian cooking that's among London's best. Its ratings took a knock this year, though, from a number of former fans who said "it's not what it was" ("sorry, but we've had two or three disappointing meals here now"). / W1H 7JZ; www.locandalocatelli.com; @locandalocatelli; Tue-Sat 11 pm, Sun 10 pm; closed Tue, Wed L, closed Mon; booking max 8 may apply.

LONDON SHELL CO.
W2 £79 444

THE PRINCE REGENT, SHELDON SQUARE
07818 666005   7–1C

"A cruise through Regent's Park to Camden Lock on the Grand Union canal is the perfect complement to five flavoursome fishy dishes, sluiced down with sommelier-advised wines" aboard the Prince Regent. Sister barge the Grand Duchess offers a similar seafood menu, permanently docked by Paddington station. Top Tip – "go as a group of four – smaller groups will end up sharing a table due to the limited space onboard". / W2 6EP; www.londonshellco.com; @londonshellco; Wed-Sat 9.30 pm, Sun 3 pm; closed Wed-Fri L closed Sun D, closed Mon & Tue.

LONDON STOCK
SW18 £52 343

2 BUBBLING WELL SQUARE, RAM
QUARTER   020 8075 3877   11–2B

"They're trying hard with the food here… perhaps too hard" – but that's about the worst anyone has to say about this 'relaxed, fine-dining concept', whose bare-brick walls are part of Wandsworth's 'Ram Quarter'. It's the first venture of Cordon-Bleu-trained Assem Abdel Hady and Andres Bernal, plus chef Sebastian Rast and presents an 8-course tasting menu 'drawing inspiration from the multicultural melting pot of the community in

which it is based'. Even if "not every dish finds its mark, they are always beautifully presented" and some excellent overall meals are reported. Now entering its third year, it's yet really to make waves, but worth a try. / SW18 1UQ; londonstockrestaurant.co.uk; @lndstockrestaurant; Wed-Sat 8 pm, Sun 3 pm; closed Sun D, closed Mon & Tue; payment – credit card only.

LONG CHIM W1

HORSE & DOLPHIN YARD OFF
MACCLESFIELD STREET   AWAITING TEL
5–3A

Chef David Thompson has built international renown for his Thai cuisine, although his previous London venture of over a decade ago – Nahm (long RIP), in Belgravia's swanky Halkin Hotel – never quite hit the mark (despite achieving a Michelin star). This Chinatown newcomer joins branches in Sydney, Perth and Dubai and incorporates a big basement, with a small ground-floor mezzanine and sizable exterior courtyard for outside dining. As you'd expect, this is a more down-to-earth formula than Belgravia's was, with a more casual, street-food-style menu. / W1W 5AZ; @longchim; Wed-Sat midnight, Sun 9 pm.

THE LORDSHIP
SE22 £42 322

211 LORDSHIP LANE   020 8299 2068   1–4D

"This great local pub" in Dulwich excels for its "simple food – especially the pies". "It's always a big surprise to me that the Lordship isn't in Harden's. It's a huge room with lots of outdoor space, and very friendly, welcoming staff". / SE22 8HA; thelordshippub.co.uk; @lordshippub; Tue-Sat 10 pm, Mon 11 pm, Sun 9 pm; closed Mon L.

THE LORE OF THE LAND
W1 £68 334

4 CONWAY STREET   020 3927 4480   2–1B

This faux-rustic pub in deepest Fitzrovia from Guy Ritchie and David Beckham is "a class act", and serves some of the "best pub grub ever", including venison from Ritchie's Wiltshire estate. The pub has been around for almost 200 years and has previously been known as the Adams Arms and the Lukin. Two fires in the space of six months last year invited newspaper headlines about 'two smoking barrels'. / W1W 6BB; gritchiepubs.com; @loreofthelandpub; Tue, Wed 11 pm, Thu-Sat 11.30 pm, Sun 9 pm; closed Mon.

LORNE SW1 £71 553

76 WILTON ROAD   020 3327 0210   2–4B

"Fabulous Katie Exton and her team never disappoint" at her "lovely, small and intimate Pimlico restaurant", which "is coming into its own despite all the terrible setbacks when it opened" (including a flood closing it for months) and "hits a sweet spot of value and reliability". A major attraction is the "clean and well-executed modern European cuisine" – "with interesting ingredients and dishes on the right side of edgy" – but the rarer attraction is her "endearing" personal style and "enthusiastic gentle guidance to the right wine pairing" from the "supremely clever and wide-ranging wine list" she has assembled as "one of London's top sommeliers". Top Tip – "there is a great glassware selection too for a restaurant of its size, which is often overlooked in guides!" / SW1S 1DE; www.lorne restaurant.co.uk; @lorne_restaurant; Mon-Sat 9.30 pm; closed Mon L, closed Sun.

LOUIE WC2 £97 323
13-15 WEST STREET 020 8057 6500 5–2B

Rihanna celebrated her birthday in February 2022 at this lavish Creole haunt next to The Ivy, in Covent Garden, where the former site of L'Atelier de Joël Robuchon nowadays combines a restaurant (ground floor), bar (first floor) and roof garden. Whether the tastes of New Orleans are faithfully replicated is a matter of some dispute – there is the odd take-down of "overpriced and under-seasoned dross", but most reports actually say its gumbo, Louisiana crab cakes and other eclectic dishes are "very good". / WC2W 9NE; www.louie-london.com; @louielondon_restaurant; Tue-Sat 10.30 pm; closed Tue, Fri L, closed Sun & Mon.

LPM W1 £116 544
54 BROOK'S MEWS 020 7495 4774 3–2B

The Côte d'Azur comes to Mayfair at this glamorous, "super-slick" and "always busy" operation, tucked away near Claridges, which – since 2007 – has led the way with its "fantastic, light small plates": "not your typical French, heavy, creamy food" but heavenly dishes that "leave you feeling like you ate healthily". Even those rating it "outstanding all round" can find it "overpriced" – a better verdict would be "expensive but worth it". / W1K 4EG; www.lpmlondon.co.uk; @lpmlondon; Tue-Sat 10.30 pm, Sun 10 pm; closed Mon.

LUCA EC1 £90 434
88 ST JOHN ST 020 3859 3000 10–1A

"Subtle and original" cooking (from "the highest quality of ingredients", all of them British) wins high ratings at this "discreet, classic high-end Italian", which inhabits rambling and lovely premises north of Smithfield Market, complete with a beautiful rear conservatory. Other than being "a really special place", it bears no comparison to its sibling, The Clove Club. Top Tips – the Parmesan fries are a trademark; and it's "great for a business lunch". / EC1E 4EH; luca.restaurant; @luca.restaurant; Wed-Sat 11 pm; closed Mon & Tue & Sun.

LUCE E LIMONI WC1 £63 343
91-93 GRAY'S INN RD 020 7242 3382 10–1A

"Great food in a cosy, homely setting" – this Sicilian specialist on a stretch of the unlovely Gray's Inn Road "is a useful and reliable local restaurant in an area with limited options". Owner Fabrizio Zafarana "makes a real effort to get to know all his customers and

will happily amend a dish to suit personal taste". / WC1X 8TX; www.lucelimoni.com; @restaurant_luce_e_limoni; Mon-Thu 10 pm, Fri & Sat 11 pm; closed Sat L, closed Sun.

LUCIANO'S SE12 £58 343
131 BURNT ASH ROAD 020 8852 3186 1–4D

"Fabulous pizza and pasta (all made on site), friendly staff and an interesting wine list" add up to a "brilliant-value local Italian" in Lee – "a cut above neighbourhood standard". Named after Luciano Masiello, the one-time Charlton Athletic footballer and father of owner Enzo. / SE12; lucianoslondon.co.uk; @lucianoslondon; Mon-Sat 9.30 pm, Sun 8.30 pm; closed Mon-Fri L.

LUCIO SW3 £98 332
257 FULHAM RD 020 7823 3007 6–3B

Celebrating its 20th anniversary this year, this family-run Italian on the Fulham Road is "everything you'd expect in an upmarket Chelsea restaurant" – although the service, led by host Lucio Altana and his sons Dario and Mirko, "is rather better than you might anticipate". / SW3 6HY; www.luciorestaurant.com; @luciorestaurant; Tue-Sat 10.30 pm, Sun 3 pm; closed Sun D, closed Mon.

LUCKY & JOY E5 £46 434
95 LOWER CLAPTON ROAD 07488 965966 14–1B

This "ridiculously low-key venue in Clapton" serves perhaps the best Chinese food in town that's prepared by Westerners – chef-owners Ellen Parr (ex-Rochelle Canteen and Moro) and Peter Kelly (ex-Morito). "It's a small menu so order everything!" / E5 0NP; luckyandjoy.co.uk; @luckyandjoyldn; closed Mon-Sat & Sun.

LUCKY CAT W1 £84 222
10-13 GROSVENOR SQUARE 020 7107 0000 3–2A

This "loud" Gordon Ramsay-backed venue in Mayfair (on the former site of Maze, long RIP) aims to channel the glam 1930s drinking dens of the Far East and serves a hodgepodge of dishes: from sushi to steak; from salads to seafood. Dreary ratings overall support those who say there are "so many better places to get much better pan-Asian fare"… so it's just the time to start a roll-out then! with its first, much simpler spin-off – The Lucky Cat Noodle & Bar – taking over a Shoreditch site previously dedicated to chicken and waffles. / W1W 6JP; www.gordonramsayrestaurants.com/lucky-cat; @luckycatbygordonramsay; Mon-Wed midnight, Thu-Sat 3 am, Sun 11 pm.

LUME NW3 £87 332
38 PRIMROSE HILL ROAD 020 7449 9556 9–2A

The "most charming front of house", led by "delightful owner Guiseppe" adds brio to this "passionate and cute little local", which occupies a quiet corner of Primrose Hill. "Good wines… it's also a wine shop" add

to the gastronomic appeal of its "authentic" Sardinian/Sicilian gastronomia. / NW3 3AD; www.lume.london; @lumelondon; Tue-Sun 10 pm; closed Tue-Thu L, closed Mon.

LUPINS SE1 £51 443
66 UNION ST 020 3908 5888 10–4B

This "awesome little spot" near London Bridge ("handy for Tate Modern") serves "fresh and really interesting" 'British tapas', including some "innovative vegetarian options". Five years after the launch, founders Lucy Pedder and Natasha Cooke have a second venue, Pomelo, at the Goods Way food market in King's Cross. / SE1 1TD; www.lupinslondon.com; @lupinslondon; Wed-Sat 10 pm; closed Wed L, closed Mon & Tue & Sun; payment – credit card only.

LURE NW5 £52 323
56 CHETWYND RD 020 7267 0163 9–1B

"In some ways, an unremarkable eat-in experience but the fish is excellent" – this modern Dartmouth Park chippy is still recommended by locals for its "top-quality fish 'n' chips", but at times "its level of service can leave something to be desired". / NW5 1DJ; www.lurefishkitchen.co.uk; Wed-Sat 10 pm, Sun 9.30 pm; closed Wed-Fri L, closed Mon & Tue; booking weekends only.

LURRA W1 £67 433
9 SEYMOUR PLACE 020 7724 4545 2–2A

"A simple, understated oasis of calm and deliciousness, just a stone's throw from the hullabaloo of Marble Arch" – this accomplished Basque venue in Seymour Village serves a "concise but impressive menu" of "sublime Spanish food mixing tapas and some of the best meat and fish in London". In particular, "the steaks are pretty amazing", with cuts from "elderly dairy cows" a particular feature. Top Menu Tips – as well as steak, the grilled turbot is "perfectly cooked"; and "the cheesecake is, as everyone says, awe-inspiring… still thinking about it". / W1H 5BA; www.lurra.co.uk; Mon-Sat 10.30 pm, Sun 3.30 pm; closed Mon L closed Sun D.

LUTYENS GRILL, THE NED EC2 £106 324
27 POULTRY 020 3828 2000 10–2C

"Is there a better business venue?" query fans of this plush steakhouse, which sits within a panelled corner of the vast former HQ of Midland Bank, next to the Bank of England. It's the prime dining option within the hotel accessible to those not blessed with membership of Soho House, featuring top-quality British and imported steak. / EC2E 8AJ; www.thened.com/restaurants/lutyens-grill; @thenedlondon; Mon-Sat midnight, Sun 4 pm; closed Sat L closed Sun D.

LYLE'S E1 £97 5 4 3

THE TEA BUILDING, 56 SHOREDITCH HIGH STREET 020 3011 5911 13–1B

"Never failing to deliver extraordinary food" – James Lowe's famous (among foodies) canteen, at the foot of Shoreditch's well-known 'Tea Building', "is so consistent in delivering seemingly simple, but actually quite intricate flavour combinations". These are offered as small plates at lunch and in the evening as a tasting menu. Originally he was inspired by a stint working at St John, but his own cuisine is nowadays something of a benchmark in its own right for modern seasonal British cooking, with "a menu that changes all the time". / E1 6JJ; www.lyleslondon.com; @lyleslondon; Mon-Sat 11 pm; closed Sun.

LYON'S N8 £57 4 4 3

1 PARK ROAD 020 8350 8983 1–1C

"Big flavours and lots of spice" characterise the "inventive sharing plates of seafood" from the British Isles, prepared with influences from around the world, at this "lovely" (if "cramped" and "noisy") Crouch End three-year-old, where "there's always a great vibe and staff are super-friendly". Top Tip – "fabulous squid-ink bread and whipped butters". / N8 8TE; lyons-restaurant.com; @lyonsseafood; Tue-Sat 10 pm; closed Tue-Thu L, closed Sun & Mon.

M RESTAURANTS £99 2 2 3

ZIG ZAG BUILDING, VICTORIA ST, SW1 020 3327 7776 2–4B
NEWFOUNDLAND, E14 AWAITING TEL 12–1C
2-3 THREADNEEDLE WALK, EC2 020 3327 7770 10–2C

Martin Williams's "customer-centric ethos" is on display at these slickly run and business-friendly 'Gastro Playgrounds', in the City, Victoria and – launching in August 2022 – in Canary Wharf, which deliver a mix of "amazing steaks", plus extensive wine (and the availability of memberships with access to the 'M Den Portal'). Its ratings were dented slightly this year though by one or two disappointing reports relating to "pedestrian dishes" and "awful mark-ups". / www.mrestaurants.co.uk; mrestaurants.

MA GOA SW15 £43 3 3 3

242-244 UPPER RICHMOND RD 020 8780 1767 11–2B

The Kapoor family's "authentic Goan cuisine has been a stalwart in Putney for 30 years", at their well-known venue on the South Circular Road. Five years ago they implemented a complete make-over, modernising their offer in street-market style, with a new selection of "craft beers that are great accompaniments for the hot dishes". / SW15 6TG; www.magoaputney.co.uk; @magoalondon; Tue-Thu, Sun 9.30 pm, Fri & Sat 10.30 pm; closed Tue-Thu, Sun, Fri & Sat L, closed Mon.

MACELLAIO RC £68 2 2 3

39-45 SHAFTESBURY AVENUE, W1 020 3727 6161 5–3A
6 STORE STREET, WC1 020 3848 7230 2–1C
84 OLD BROMPTON RD, SW7 020 7589 5834 6–2B
ARCH 24, 229 UNION ST, SE1 07467 307682 10–4B
124 NORTHCOTE RD, SW11 020 3848 4800 11–2C
38-40 EXMOUTH MARKET, EC1 020 3696 8220 10–1A

"Just the place to stuff yourself silly with beef!", say loyal fans of Roberto Costa's successful chain, where you choose your cut from "amazing meat displays to get the juices flowing": a formula that's brought expansion over the years to six locations across the capital, including on Shaftesbury Avenue (where it's branded 'Teatro del Carne'). Ratings sank this year, though, on a number of "disappointing" reports, with recurring themes including "quality meat undermined by poor cooking" and "high prices for wines considering their middling status". / www.macellaiorc.com.

MADDOX TAVERN W1 £74

47 MADDOX STREET 020 3376 9922 3–2C

A very characterful Mayfair site – once a posh gentlemen's outfitters and more recently a branch of Browns – now hosts this July 2022 newcomer (which opened too late to be included in our annual diners' poll). Steaks feature prominently on a menu of 'elevated' British classics and there's also a seperate all-day 'tavern' selection. / W1W 2PG; www.maddoxtavern.com; @maddoxtavern; Mon-Thu midnight, Fri & Sat 12.30 am; closed Sun.

MADE IN ITALY £56 3 2 2

249 KING'S RD, SW3 020 7352 1880 6–3C
141 THE BROADWAY, SW19 020 8540 4330 11–2B

"Rustic décor, friendly service and great pizza" win recommendations for this long-running duo, whose Chelsea branch boasts a heated roof terrace. They make their own fresh cheeses at a factory in Battersea, and their "burrata heart on a pizza is a creamy delight". / www.madeinitalygroup.co.uk; madeinitalylondon.

MAGENTA NW1 £76 3 3 3

THE MEGARO HOTEL, 23 EUSTON ROAD 0203 146 0222 9–3C

"Trying to be different", this new bar/restaurant in King's Cross is bang opposite the station, yet aims to defy its touristy location with natty décor and a northern Italian menu of some ambition. We've rated it on limited feedback which mentions some aspects that were "underwhelming" offset by others that were "very good"; and which imply it's worth a whirl if you are in the area. / NW1 2SD; www.magentarestaurant.co.uk; @magenta_kx; Tue-Sat 10 pm; closed Sun & Mon.

MAGGIE JONES'S W8 £67 3 4 5

6 OLD COURT PL 020 7937 6462 6–1A

Named after the pseudonym used by the late Princess Margaret for incognito dining, this cosseting 1970s-style brasserie provides a "cosy and romantic setting" for aristos or commoners in search of comforting Anglo-French classics, washed down with wine in magnum bottles whose consumption is measured by a dipstick. It's on top form these days, with improved ratings across the board. / W8 4PL; www.maggie-jones.co.uk; @maggiejonesrestaurant; Mon-Fri 9.30 pm, Sat & Sun 9.15 pm.

MAGURO W9 £53 3 2 2

5 LANARK PL 020 7289 4353 9–4A

This tiny Japanese near Little Venice is "well worth seeking out". "The food is served in a friendly manner and the sushi and sashimi is always very fresh". / W9 1BT; www.maguro-restaurant.com; @maguro.london; Mon-Sat 11 pm, Sun 10.30 pm; closed Mon-Sun L; no Amex.

THE MAINE MAYFAIR W1 £116 3 2 4

6 MEDICI COURT, 20 HANOVER SQUARE 020 3432 2192 3–2C

"The burlesque show can come as a bit of a shock, but adds to the fun if somewhat tacky vibe" of this big, brash, American brasserie – all 350 covers of it, set over three floors of a grand Georgian townhouse in Mayfair. Fans feel "it's set to be a staple" aided by its enjoyable New England-style cuisine and glam, highly Instagrammable interior, but some reports do suggest that "while good, the food's nothing special and not cheap". Top Tip – recently they added a 100-cover foliage-filled terrace for lunch, dinner and drinks. / W1W 1JY; www.themainemayfair.com; @themainemayfair; closed Mon-Sat & Sun.

MAISON BERTAUX W1 £15 4 3 5

28 GREEK ST 020 7437 6007 5–2A

"Fight to get a seat and enjoy the best pâtisserie in town" at this "Soho institution" – founded by a Parisian exile in 1871 and frequented by generations of artists, revolutionaries and bohos. It's "eccentric to say the least", and not incidentally "one of the few pâtisseries still cooking on the premises – there are so few of these places left!". And while "still miles ahead of other French pâtisseries, they also offer a (very English) cream tea". "They do their utmost to squeeze you in (as it is always busy). I guess the ambience is a matter of taste but luxurious it isn't!" / W1D 5DQ; www.maisonbertaux.com; @maison_bertaux; Mon-Sun 6 pm; closed Mon-Sun D.

MAISON FRANÇOIS
SW1   £87   345

34 DUKE STREET ST JAMES'S
020 3988 5777   3–3D

"Paris comes to St James's" at this "beautiful and buzzy" two-year-old, which has been one of the more impressive arrivals of recent years (it opened in autumn 2020). "Proper, well-executed French-brasserie food" (snails, crab salad, roast chicken, veal, steak and chips…) – "such a relief after all of the faddy nonsense dominating the London restaurant scene" – is delivered by "first-rate" staff throughout the day, from breakfast onwards. And together with the "amazing" high-ceilinged interior, the overall combination makes for a superb "all-round experience", if one "with prices to match the location". Top Tips – "the best dessert trolley in London!" and a "fun" basement wine bar called Frank's. / SW1S 6DF; maisonfrancois. london; @maisonfrancoislondon; Thu-Sat 1 am, Mon-Wed midnight, Sun 6 pm; closed Sun D.

MALLOW SE1   £56   423

1 CATHEDRAL STREET
020 7846 8785   10–4C

"A fantastic new addition from the Mildreds group" – this autumn 2021 newcomer makes "a good place to take people who are sceptical about meat-free food". It's "a pretty location with an excellent view of Borough Market" that's "full of atmosphere" and "it doesn't overly virtue-sell the plant-based experience: they just get on with making it excellent" with a "slightly more innovative approach to the seasonally changing menu" than in the main chain. "The wine list is limited, but they do have cocktails". / SE1 1TL; www.mallowlondon.com; @mallowlondon; Mon-Sat 11 pm, Sun 10 pm.

MAMMA DOUGH
(GROUP)   £51   432

40 LADYWELL ROAD, SE13
020 8690 7550   1–4D
179 QUEEN'S RD, SE15
020 7635 3470   1–4D
76-78 HONOR OAK PK, SE23
020 8699 5196   1–4D
1 STATION ROAD, SE25
020 8653 2537   1–4D
299 KIRKDALE, SE26   020 8778 1234   1–4D
303-307 BALHAM HIGH ROAD, SW17
020 3409 4671   11–2D
354 COLDHARBOUR LN, SW9
020 7095 1491   11–2D

"Tasty thin-crust dough – cooked well in the middle, so no soggy bottoms" – is the secret to the appeal of this seven-strong South London sourdough pizzeria group, where the emphasis is on local ingredients (including Shipton Mill flour and British-made buffalo mozzarella) washed down with locally brewed craft beers and juices from Kent. / www.mammadough.co.uk.

MANDARIN KITCHEN
W2   £68   432

14-16 QUEENSWAY   020 7727 9012   7–2C

"Who would order anything but the lobster noodles?" ("the best way to get the most out of a crustacean, and surprisingly good value!") at this "unbeatable Cantonese classic" in Queensway: a "chaotic, crowded and noisy", if "efficiently run" stalwart (est 1978) which sells more lobster than just about any other restaurant in the UK. If you do, there are other delicious seafood dishes to try (scallops, crab, razor clams…) and the Peking Duck's not bad either. / W2 3RX; www.mandarin.kitchen; @mandarinkitchenlondon; Mon-Sat 11.15 pm, Sun 23.

MANGAL 1 E8   £34   532

10 ARCOLA ST   020 7275 8981   14–1A

"Succulent BBQ meat and great-value meze" have earned this Turkish grill in Dalston a major and well-earned reputation. For some, a meal here represents "the best value in London" – helped by a "liberal BYO policy that means you drink as well as your cellar allows". Top Tips: "the sweetbreads are sensational". And for an ambitious modern take on cooking over fire, head round the corner to Mangal 2, now run by owner Ali Dirik's sons Sertaç and Ferhat (see also). / E8 2DJ; www.mangal1.com; @mangal_ocakbasi; Sun-Wed midnight, Fri & Sat 1 am; closed Thu; cash only; no booking.

MANGAL 2 N16   £80   442

4 STOKE NEWINGTON RD
020 7254 7888   1–1C

"Mangal 2 has reinvented itself during the pandemic" with Ferhat and Sertaç Dirik (the sons of the founder), "transforming it from its previous incarnation as just another of one of the (good!) pile-'em-high Turkish restaurants on the Dalston/Stoke Newington strip into a totally new venue: still Turkish, but more small plates now than giant platters". All reports agree it's a successful switch, "standing on a solid par with the other good small-plates-and-wine joints around Hackney, while still doing something quite different". "The noisy room is a little Spartan, but the exciting and interesting food transports you" – "the Turkish influence is not that obvious" but the menu delivers "good ingredients very well cooked" (although "the wine list is a bit too natural, with no other conventional options)". / N16 8BH; www.mangal2.com; @mangal2restaurant; Mon-Sat 11 pm; closed Mon & Tue, Sat L, closed Sun.

MANICOMIO   £86   223

85 DUKE OF YORK SQUARE, SW3
020 7730 3366   6–2D
6 GUTTER LANE, EC2
020 7726 5010   10–2B

This modern Italian "favourite" makes good use of its large and attractive terrace in Chelsea's peaceful Duke of York's Square, and has a big and loyal following as a result. Fans say the food is "interesting" too, but more sceptical diners feel that's debatable. It also has a twin in the City, which attracts much less comment. / www.manicomio.co.uk; manicomiorestaurant.

MANTECA EC2   £50   524

49-51 CURTAIN ROAD
020 7033 6642   13–1B

"A fabulous range of super-tasty Italian small plates with some very memorable flavours (that pig skin ragu!!!!)" and incorporating "terrific homemade pasta" are making a smash hit of Chris Leach and David Carter's "absolutely rammed" venture, which relocated from Heddon Street to Shoreditch in October 2021. It wins nothing but praise and many nominations as "the top food experience of the last 12 months". "Enthusiastic" service can suffer under the weight of custom and – with its "deafening noise" – the setting does "slightly reek of (the former) PizzaExpress the site used to be" – but "given that it's exceptional, you'll get by… they can polish any rough edges later". / EC2E 3PT; mantecarestaurant.co.uk; @manteca_london; Mon-Sat 11 pm, Sun 5 pm; closed Sun D.

MANTHAN W1   £61   343

49 MADDOX STREET   020 7491 9191   3–2C

Rohit Ghai's "comfy and stylish" Mayfair yearling offers a homely menu inspired by the chef's Punjabi childhood. "Awesome" flavours from "the good variety of dishes" make it "a must-try" for fans. Sceptics, though – while acknowledging that "effort is put into both good food and service" – feel some results "lack punch" or "aren't quite at the top levels of food from the subcontinent in London". / W1W; manthanmayfair.co.uk; @manthanmayfair; Mon-Sun 10 pm.

MANUEL'S SE19   £60   453

129 GIPSY HILL   020 8670 1843   1–4D

Some of south east London's best Italian food is to be found at this attractive Gipsy Hill Sicilian, acclaimed for its "wonderful Mediterranean food, superb Sunday lunch… Live music events are always good fun (particularly the tribute acts!)". In summer the terrace comes into its own. / SE19 1QS; www.manuelsrestaurantandbar.com; @manuelsrestaurantgipsyhill; Tue-Sat 10.30 pm, Sun 9 pm; closed Mon.

MANUKA KITCHEN
SW6   £59   333

510 FULHAM RD   020 7731 0864   6–4A

This flexible and well-run New Zealand-inspired spot just off Parson's Green is an equally "dependable" option "for Chelsea pre-match brunches" and "candlelit dinners". / SW6 5NJ; manukakitchen.co.uk; @manukakitchen; Tue-Sat 11 pm, Mon 10 pm, Sun 4 pm; closed Mon L closed Sun D; booking max 8 may apply.

MANZI'S W1

1 BATEMAN'S BUILDINGS   NO TEL   5–2A

This long-planned and long pandemic-delayed Soho seafood restaurant may be delayed still further by the management changes at Corbin & King, now renamed as The Wolseley Hospitality Group. It is envisaged as a 'fun and affordable' venue along the lines of stablemate Brasserie Zédel. But – in the absence of Jeremy King and Chris Corbin – who will now provide the vision for recreating the original Manzi's, which was, for decades, a treasured standby for theatregoers on the south corner of Chinatown? / W1W 3EN; Tue-Sat, Mon 11 pm.

MAR I TERRA SE1 £54 443

14 GAMBIA ST 020 7928 7628 10–4A

"Very good-quality" tapas and a "nice, buzzy" atmosphere greet guests at this converted small backstreet pub near the South Bank, one of the longer-established Hispanic specialists in town. It's a "favourite for a casual night out" and "conveniently located for the NT, Young Vic, Tate Mod and so on". / SE1 0XH; www.mariterra.net; Tue, Thu, Wed, Fri & Sat midnight; closed Wed, Fri & Sat L, closed Sun & Mon.

MARCELLA SE8 £46 343

**165A DEPTFORD HIGH STREET
020 3903 6561 1–3D**

This hip five-year-old on Deptford High Street wins consistently high ratings for its simple and "authentic" Italian cooking, inspired by the great food writer Marcella Hazan. It is the younger sibling to Peckham star Artusi. / SE8 3NU; www.marcella.london; @marcelladeptford; Wed & Thu 10 pm, Fri & Sat 10.30 pm, Sun 4 pm; closed Sun D, closed Mon & Tue; may need 6+ to book.

MARCUS, THE BERKELEY SW1 £172 333

WILTON PL 020 7235 1200 6–1D

Marcus Wareing's Belgravia flagship keeps ploughing a steady course "at the level you would expect from a top Knightsbridge hotel", at this "well-spaced" venue which continues to be "run with expertise" despite a changeover of personnel this year (in January 2022, Mark and Shauna Froydenlund stepped down as chef-patrons, leaving head chef Craig Johnston and senior sous chef, Jack Hazell to take the reins). The modern French cuisine is "beautifully well-judged and thought out"; "service is wonderfully attentive and warm"; and "the wide range of wines provides interesting choices for any dish". There's the odd cavil that the food can be on the "rich" side, but the main objection here is the obvious: "the bill can get just a bit silly…" / SW1X 7RL; www.marcusrestaurant.com; @marcusbelgravia; Tue-Sat 10 pm; closed Sun & Mon; no trainers.

MARE STREET MARKET E8 £53 324

117 MARE STREET 020 3745 2470 14–2B

Funky chandeliers, plants and random artworks lend an eclectic and energetic vibe to the dining possibilities of this hiply transformed Hackney office block (nowadays a 10,000 square foot market), where you eat (the same menu) in either the 'Open Kitchen' or the 'Dining Room' (cosier, with a higher concentration of design pieces). An array of pizzas is a menu mainstay as is a selection of small plates and a few grills. It's not a foodie destination, but can be "good value". / E8 4RU; www.marestreetmarket.com; @marestreetmarket; Sun-Thu midnight, Fri & Sat 1 am.

MAREMMA SW2 £64 434

**36 BRIXTON WATER LANE
020 3186 4011 11–2D**

This "brilliant local in Brixton" scores well for its "delicious, light food", taking inspiration from the Maremma, a region of coastal marshes in the south of Tuscany. "A lovely candlelit ambience" makes it "perfect for a fun date night". / SW2 1PE; www.maremmarestaurant.com; @maremma_restaurant; Wed-Sat 10 pm, Sun 4 pm; closed Wed & Thu L closed Sun D, closed Mon & Tue.

MARGAUX SW5 £74 443

**152 OLD BROMPTON RD
020 7373 5753 6–2B**

"Boeuf bourguignon was done to perfection" – typical of the "very solid French cooking of meat and fish courses" at this "reliable neighbourhood restaurant", on the well-heeled borders of Earl's Court and South Kensington. Top Tip – "it's best to eat upstairs". / SW5 0BE; www.barmargaux.co.uk; @barmargaux; Tue-Sat 10.45 pm; closed Tue L, closed Sun & Mon.

MARGOT WC2 £84 344

**45 GREAT QUEEN STREET
020 3409 4777 5–2D**

"Suave" "classic, top-end Italian" in Covent Garden that's run by co-founder Nicolas Jaouën, who presides over "an elegant room, smooth service and capable cooking". It's "not cheap, but you leave feeling you have been looked after well". The "excellent list" numbers 350 wines. / WC2B 5AA; www.margotrestaurant.com; @margotldn_; Tue-Sat 9.30 pm; closed Sun & Mon.

MARIA G'S W14

**COE HOUSE, 1-4 WARWICK LANE
020 3479 3772 8–2D**

Retirement looks OK, judging by the glossy apartment buildings of the sprawling 'Riverstone Living' retirement complex in the former no-man's-land between the Tesco superstore on the A4 and Olympia. At the foot of one such building is this project overseen by Robin Gill – a neighbourhood Italian with a curt menu and a cute outside space. It opened too late for our annual diners' poll – hard to judge on initial reports whether it's more than a high-quality amenity for nearby residents. / W14 8FN; mariags.co.uk; @robin.gill.cook; Mon-Sat 10 pm, Sun 9 pm.

THE MARKSMAN E2 £75 333

**254 HACKNEY ROAD
020 7739 7393 14–2A**

The "short and desirable menu" of modern British dishes continues to win praise for this ambitious gastropub near Columbia Road Market, from former St John chefs Tom Harris and Jon Rotheram. A huge hit when it opened, it's adopted a lower profile over the years, but remains "just the place to take hard-to-impress young adult children". / E2 7SJ; www.marksmanpublichouse.com; @marksman_pub; Wed-Sat 10 pm, Sun 9 pm; closed Wed & Thu L, closed Mon & Tue.

MAROUSH £67 322

**5 MCNICOL DRIVE, NW10
020 3941 3221 1–2A**
**II) 38 BEAUCHAMP PL, SW3
020 7581 5434 6–1C**
**VI) 68 EDGWARE RD, W2
020 7224 9339 7–1D**

"Fun, reliable Lebanese cuisine served Beirut-style" – "shawarma and meze-type dishes at their best" – has built an empire over 40 years for Marouf and Houda Abouzaki's well-known chain (and its sister brand, 'Ranoush'). The pandemic brought branch closures, including of the original Edgware Road site, although Knightsbridge's Maroush II with its café-style ground floor (and including a sandwich wraps menu) is still going strong. And – showing the resilience for which the Lebanese are renowned – a large new "open plan" site opened in 2021 in distant Park Royal. / www.maroush.com.

MARU W1 £242 543

**18 SHEPHERD MARKET
020 3637 7677 3–4B**

This "minute restaurant" in Mayfair's Shepherd Market leapt "straight into the top tier of London's Japanese restaurants" when it opened in 2021, with its "top-class dishes centred around dry-aged fish". Taiji Maruyama, a third-generation sushi chef from Fukushima who has worked around the world, controls every aspect of the 20-course omakase (chef's choice) meal, from the crockery he made himself to the "food prepared in front of you", "expertly paired with sake, tea or wine". It's a "unique and intimate experience" – "very Tokyo" – and part of the new wave of tiny, ultra-focused Japanese operations in London, for those with deep enough pockets. / W1W 7QH; www.marulondon.com; @maru__london; Tue-Sat 11 pm; closed Tue-Sat L, closed Sun & Mon.

MARUGAME UDON £17 432

**ST CHRISTOPHER'S PLACE, W1 NO TEL
3–1B**
**UNIT 2.03 ENTERTAINMENT AVENUE, THE
O2, SE10 NO TEL 12–1D**
**THE ATRIUM KITCHEN, CABOT PLACE, E14
NO TEL 12–1C**

Luca EC1

114 MIDDLESEX STREET, E1
020 3148 2780   13–2B

"Decent noodles at rock-bottom prices" means these "new, authentic, incredibly reasonably priced Japanese canteens" are "always busy". An 800-strong global chain, it launched in London in July 2021 with a 100+ cover site just off Liverpool Street and is adding branches willy nilly, with the second half of 2022 seeing debuts in Oxford Circus, The Strand and Waterloo. "The food cannot be fresher than here: noodles are made on-site and tempura is fried just in front of you" and "they cater for both non-vegans and vegans". Finish your meal with "unlimited ice cream, which is unexpectedly delicious too". / marugame.co.uk; marugameuk.

MASALA ZONE   £60   ③③④

SELFRIDGES, 400 OXFORD STREET, W1
020 7287 9966   3–1A
9 MARSHALL ST, W1   020 7287 9966   4–2B
48 FLORAL ST, WC2   020 7379 0101   5–2D
147 EARL'S COURT RD, SW5
020 7373 0220   6–2A
75 BISHOP'S BRIDGE RD, W2
020 7221 0055   7–1C
25 PARKWAY, NW1   020 7267 4422   9–3B

"I keep coming back for the reliably distinctive range of Indian dishes… when I'm pushed to try new things I rarely regret it" – the "always interesting menu" at these longstanding pioneers of street food and thalis delivers "very tasty grub in generous portions that's good value for money". It's run by MW Eats (the family company behind some of the capital's most prestigious subcontinental restaurants). / www.masalazone.com; masalazone.

MASALCHI BY ATUL KOCHHAR HA9   £42

2 WEMBLEY PARK BOULEVARD
01494 728126   1–1A

A world away from the Mayfair luxury that made his reputation, Atul Kochhar gets more 'down and dirty' with this new, glass-walled 120-seater in the shadow of Wembley Stadium with a budget street-food formula. So far, we've only had limited feedback, but it says the food is "very good" and in a December 2021 review, Jay Rayner of The Observer told readers to "expect uncompromising fire and depth". / HA9 0HP; masalchi.co.uk; @masalchi_wembley; Mon-Thu 10 pm, Fri & Sat 10.30 pm, Sun 9.30 pm.

MASTER WEI WC1   £32   ④②②

13 COSMO PLACE   020 7209 6888   2–1D

"Excellent Xi'an hand-pulled noodles" ("pasta-like noodles with chillies to make your eyes water") "at reasonable prices" ensure that chef-proprietor Wei Guirong's central London canteen, "tucked away in a narrow pedestrian street near Russell Square", is always "buzzing". It is a sibling to Xi'an Impression near Arsenal's Emirates Stadium. / WC1N 3AP; master-wei. com; @master.wei.3150; Sun-Thu 10 pm, Fri & Sat 10.30 pm.

MATHURA SW1   £59   ③②②

4 GREYCOAT PLACE   020 4549 1906   2–4C

"In an old Fire station near Victoria", Atul Kochhar's October 2021 newcomer is "a massive undertaking (with over 170 covers)". It inspires a wide range of reactions, none of them terrible, some of them rapturous, but many of them mixed. The "unusual" food has "amazing spicing, with a focus on fish", but some dishes can appear "too ordinary" or "needing a rethink" and even fans note they are "expensive". In a similar vein, the "friendly" service can be "iffy" in its efficiency; and "ambience can be lacking" despite the "stylish conversion". Still, it's an ambitious venture still finding its feet, and perhaps the fairest overall verdict at this stage is: "enjoyable rather than brilliant". / SW1S 1SB; mathura.co.uk; closed Mon-Sat & Sun.

MAYA EC2   £67

81 GREAT EASTERN STREET
020 7550 1000   13–1B

With its "lovely setting on top of the Hoxton Hotel", this glam, loungey rooftop yearling (run by Soho House) is renowned mostly for its "fine selection of Tequilas and Mezcal". Reports are too scarce for a rating, but such as we have praise some "excellent modern Mexican dishes" too. / EC2E 3HU; thehoxton.com/london/ shoreditch/maya-restaurant; @thehoxtonhotel; Mon-Sun 11 pm.

MAZI W8   £77   ④④③

12-14 HILLGATE ST   020 7229 3794   7–2B

"The most delicious deconstructed Greek food" has earned this "buzzy" modern take on the taverna, tucked away near Notting Hill Gate station, an enviable reputation over the past 10 years. "I could just feast on their dip jars and the cheese pie". Top Tip – for the full Aegean summer atmosphere, "the outdoor courtyard is great". / W8 7SR; www.mazi.co.uk; @mazilondon; Mon-Sat midnight, Sun 11 pm.

THE MEAT & WINE CO MAYFAIR W1

17C CURZON STREET
0203 988 6888   3–4B

This August 2022 newcomer in Mayfair is the steakhouse chain's twelfth internationally. South African Bradley Michael started the business 'down under' in Oz 35 years ago. Here, the focus is on Australian and British beef 'energised by Afro-centric flavours and cooking techniques'. / W1W 5HU; www.themeatandwineco.co.uk/london/mayfair/ anic&utm_campaign=yext&utm_ content=homepage; @themeatandwinecouk; Mon-Sun midnight.

MEATLIQUOR   £46   ④②②

37-38 MARGARET STREET, W1
020 7224 4239   3–1C
15-17 BRUNSWICK CENTRE, WC1   NO TEL
2–1D
17 QUEENSWAY, W2   020 7229 0172   7–2C

133B UPPER ST, N1   020 3711 0104   9–3D
14-15 HOXTON MARKET, N1
020 7739 8212   13–1B
37 LORDSHIP LANE, SE22
020 3066 0008   1–4D
7 DARTMOUTH RD, SE23
020 3026 1331   1–4D
74 NORTHCOTE ROAD, SW11
020 7228 4777   11–2C
13-19 OLD TOWN, SW4
020 3026 8126   11–1D

"Dead hippie sauce is a must" at these "very loud" operations, which "remain at the head of the gourmet burger pack" for many fans with "lots of options available". After 14 years of growth from a food van to a national chain with 10 venues in the capital, they "don't seem to have lost their way yet". "The dark and grungy ersatz New Orleans interior vibe" is of the love-it-or-hate-it variety. / meatliquor.com; meatgram.

MEDITERRANEO W11   £68   ③②③

37 KENSINGTON PARK RD
020 7792 3131   7–1A

"The real Italian deal, just off Portobello Road", this "plain and simple" trattoria has "been going for ages and seems to be just as popular and noisy as ever" – and "always delivers solid good value". Founded 25 years ago, it has two sister restaurants in the same street, Essenza and Osteria Basilico. / W11 2EU; www.mediterraneo-restaurant.co.uk; Mon-Sun 10.30 pm; booking max 10 may apply.

MEDLAR SW10   £115   ④④③

438 KING'S RD   020 7349 1900   6–3B

"A class act that consistently punches above its weight": this low-key but high-quality Chelsea indie (opened in 2011) flies somewhat under the radar in terms of PR profile, but regularly ranks in the top 40 most-mentioned restaurants in our annual diners' poll. Joe Mercer Nairne's "superior" modern British cuisine is "always a delight", often "special" and comes at a "reasonable price". Service (overseen by co-owner David O'Connor) is "likewise expert" and it's "well worth asking the sommelier to recommend something offbeat", as there are "some unusual gems on the wine list". And while the interior is "low key", the atmosphere is "conducive to a wonderful evening". "It's not clear why it lost its Michelin star": "it should have regained it long ago". Top Tips – "the tarte Tatin for two is to die for. Corkage of £10 at lunchtimes and £25 in the evenings is one of London's great bargains". / SW10 0LJ; www.medlarrestaurant.co.uk; @medlarchelsea; Mon-Sat 10.30 pm, Sun 9.30 pm.

MEGAN'S   £50   ②②③

BRANCHES THROUGHOUT LONDON

With its inviting décor, this fast-expanding group has been a big "winner" since the pandemic, mushrooming to 18 sites, all of which have generally proved useful additions to their respective areas. But while "it certainly looks the part, and the staff look after you well enough", the brunch-friendly fare can be hit 'n' miss, with reports ranging from "surprisingly good" to "formulaic and really abysmal". Top Tip – "always a top option for feeding the family". / megans.co.uk; megansrestaurants.

MEI MEI SE1 £70 3|3|2

UNIT 52 BOROUGH MARKET KITCHEN, JUBILEE PLACE NO TEL 10–4C

"The tastes of Singapore" are still applauded at ex-Pidgin chef, Elizabeth Haigh's hawker-style stand (winner of Harden's Top Street Food in our September 2021 London Restaurant Awards), which sits amidst the clatter of the Market Kitchen area of Borough Market. But feedback was much more muted and a little more uneven this year, and it's hard not to conclude that the furore surrounding the cancelled launch of her recipe book hasn't taken some of the gloss off impressions here. / SE1 9AG; www.meimei.uk; @meimeilondon; Mon-Wed 4 pm, Thu & Fri 10.30 pm, Sat 11.30 pm; closed Mon-Wed D, closed Sun; payment – credit card only; no booking at lunch.

MELE E PERE W1 £54 2|3|2

46 BREWER STREET 020 7096 2096 4–3C

"Simple Italian dishes", with everything freshly made in the kitchen, are on the menu at this ten-year-old independent in Soho, whose standout culinary feature is the range of house-made vermouths in the bar. Praise is pretty muted, though – and "the room really lacks something despite good service". / W1F 9TF; www.meleepere.co.uk; @meleeperesoho; Mon & Tue, Sun 10 pm, Wed-Sat 11 pm; payment – credit card only; booking online only.

THE MELUSINE E1 £78 4|3|3

UNIT K, IVORY HOUSE, ST. KATHERINE DOCK 02077022976 10–3D

"Small and perfectly formed" two-year-old with a "wonderful waterside setting" in St Katharine Dock that serves "seafood that should appear on the end of Paul Whitehouse's rod – it's that fresh!". "On a sunny day with an outdoor table, it's the best" – the "fantastic shellfish" includes "the best langoustines ever and stellar scallops". Theodore Kyriakou, who set up both Livebait and The Real Greek back in the 1990s, is part of the founding team. / E1E 1AT; www.themelusine.co.uk; @themelusine_skd; Tue-Sat 10.30 pm, Sun 9.30 pm; closed Mon; cash only.

MERAKI W1 £78 4|3|4

80-82 GT TITCHFIELD ST 020 7305 7686 3–1C

This "slick operation" in Fitzrovia was created by restaurateurs Peter and Arjun Waney – of Zuma and Roka fame. It's not dissimilar to its pan-Asian stablemates: "buzzing, fun and loud, but with food that's very imaginative and well executed" – this time in a modern Greek idiom. They must be doing something right, as there are now branches in Mykonos, Riyadh and Porto Cervo on Sardinia's Costa Smeralda. / W1W 7QT; www.meraki-restaurant.com; @merakilondon; Tue-Thu 10.15 pm, Fri & Sat 10.45 pm; closed Sun & Mon.

MERCATO METROPOLITANO SE1 £43 3|2|5

42 NEWINGTON CAUSEWAY 020 7403 0930 1–3C

"Very reasonably priced, good food and great fun" is all yours for the taking at this former paper factory near Elephant & Castle, converted to host more than 40 different food and drink pop-ups. "You just wander from one to another, then find a place to sit and eat in the common area", which includes London's biggest beer garden – "a great outdoor space". There are now three other MMs in London, following a concept launched in Italy (hence the name). / SE1 6DR; www.mercatometropolitano.com; @mercatometropolitano; Mon-Thu 11 pm, Fri & Sat midnight, Sun 10 pm.

THE MERCER EC2 £79 3|3|3

34 THREADNEEDLE ST 020 7628 0001 10–2C

In a converted banking hall near the Bank of England, this well-established brasserie exists to serve a City clientele, from breakfast on. Opinions divide on whether it's a little "disappointing", like many in the Square Mile, or "perfect of its type and better than it needs to be". / EC2R 8AY; www.themercer.co.uk; @themercerrestaurant; Mon-Fri 9.30 pm; closed Sat & Sun.

LE MERCURY N1 £38 2|2|2

140A UPPER ST 020 7354 4088 9–2D

This "fun, old-style bistro with dishes to match" has been one of the dining bargains of Islington's main drag for the best part of 40 years. It serves brunch from 10am as well as the standard Gallic brasserie menu for lunch and dinner. / N1 1QY; www.lemercury.co.uk; @lemercury; Mon-Thu midnight, Fri & Sat 1 am, Sun 11 pm.

MERE W1 £115 3|4|2

74 CHARLOTTE STREET 020 7268 6565 2–1B

"Service from David, Monica and the team is always excellent", say fans of their Fitzrovia basement where "everyone seems keen to make your visit a very memorable experience". TV star Monica's "top-quality cuisine strikes a great balance between classic and innovative" ("refined and packed with flavour but paradoxically, robust at the same time without being unsubtle") and "the wine list is extremely well-curated and has a wide ambit, as you might expect from David as a former Gavroche Sommelier". As with many top London restaurants this year, though, ratings dipped a fraction – the pressures of the times? – with more reports along the lines of "a very pleasant experience but slightly underwhelming". But while the proportion of reporters saying they had their best meal of the year here has declined, more and more have taken it to their hearts as their "favourite" nomination. / W1W 4QH; www.mere-restaurant.com; @mererestaurant;

Tue-Thu 9 pm, Fri & Sat 9.30 pm; closed Sun & Mon.

MESON DON FELIPE SE1 £48 3|3|4

53 THE CUT 020 7928 3237 10–4A

"Top tapas in The Cut" – 'London's original tapas bar' still cuts it after 35 years, providing sterling pre- and post-show service to theatregoers visiting the nearby Young and Old Vic. The "very friendly, helpful owner" ensures there's a good atmosphere even when the joint is rammed. / SE1 8LF; www.mesondonfelipe.com; @mesondonfelipe; Mon-Sat 11 pm; closed Sun.

MEZA TRINITY ROAD SW17 £41 3|3|3

34 TRINITY RD 07722 111299 11–2C

This "lovely little café" was "the original Lebanese place in Tooting", and is known for its "great meze" and other Levantine plates, along with a warm welcome. The second branch in Mitcham Road has closed down. / SW17 7RE; www.mezarestaurant.com; @meza_res; Sun-Thu 11 pm, Fri & Sat 11.30 pm.

MICHAEL NADRA £71 3|3|2

42 GLOUCESTER AVE, NW1 020 7722 2800 9–3B

Just by the Regent's Canal, Michael Nadra's high-quality French restaurant serves some of the "best food in the area" at the top of Regent's Park. On sunny days, it particularly benefits from its cute courtyard (regarding the interior, some diners feel it's "a shame that the odd layout can detract from its other qualities"). It used to have an (older) Chiswick sibling, but this has now closed: seemingly a victim of the pandemic. / www.restaurant-michaelnadra.co.uk.

MIEN TAY £41 3|3|2

45 FULHAM HIGH ST, SW6
020 7731 0670 11–1B
433 LORDSHIP LANE, N22
020 3302 9530 1–1C
180 LAVENDER HILL, SW11
020 7350 0721 11–1C
122 KINGSLAND RD, E2
020 7729 3074 14–2A

This quartet of family-run restaurants have won a big reputation for their southwest Vietnamese dishes, including pho and their famed goat with galangal. They started out 15 years ago in Shoreditch before heading across the river to Battersea. / mientay.co.uk.

MIKE'S PECKHAM SE15 £45 4|4|3

UNIT 4.1, 133 COPELAND RD 020 7732 9012 1–4D

"Deliciously different pizza" comes by the slice in the "relaxed setting" of this yearling in a former grain warehouse (a former site of Forza Win). For all its "very basic" appearance, serious thought goes into the toppings, along with ingredients such as Sicilian datterini tomatoes, Calabrian tropea onions and Turkish figs. "The only problem is knowing when to stop ordering!" / SE15; mikespeckham.co.uk; @mikespeckham; Wed-Fri 10 pm, Sat 10.30 pm, Sun 5 pm; closed Sun D, closed Mon & Tue; payment – credit card only.

MILDREDS £52 333

45 LEXINGTON ST, W1
020 7494 1634   4–2C
79 ST MARTIN'S LANE, WC2
020 8066 8393   5–3B
200 PENTONVILLE RD, N1
020 7278 9422   9–3D
9 JAMESTOWN RD, NW1
020 7482 4200   9–3B
1 DALSTON SQUARE, E8
020 8017 1815   14–1A

Investment a few years ago turbo-charged this '100% plant-based' chain, whose stalwart original Soho branch (est 1988) suddenly spawned a handful of "airy" and "jolly" (somewhat "crammed") modern spin-offs across town. To this number, a new, two-floor Covent Garden branch opened its doors in February 2022 with 120 covers. The expansion has gone well and its "earnest" and "flavourful" cooking is not just favoured by veggies: "I was taken not entirely voluntarily as a dedicated meat-eater but have changed my tune after dining here!" / mildredsrestaurants.

MILK SW12 £23 323

20 BEDFORD HILL   020 8772 9085   11–2C

"Be prepared to queue for the delicious and original brunches" at this Antipodean champion that has had devotees beating a path to Balham for 11 years (It's "achingly hip, which I'm emphatically not, but the food is so good I love it anyway"). / SW12 9RG; milklondon.uk/info; @milk.london; Mon-Fri 3.30 pm, Sat & Sun 4 pm; closed Mon-Sun D; no booking.

MIMI MEI FAIR W1 £93 334

55 CURZON STREET   020 3989 7777   3–3B

"Tucked away in a lovely Mayfair conversion", Samyukta Nair's (who studied in China) year-old Shanghai-inspired venture has suffered some tough press reviews (notably from Giles Coren in The Times) but generally pleases diners. OK, even many fans concede that it is "super-expensive", but "apart from the bill, everything else is amazing", including the superior dim sum (from an ex-Hakkasan, Chinese-Singaporean chef, Peter Ho) and "fabled Peking duck" (which you must pre-order). / W1W 8PG; mimimeifair.com; @mimimeifair; Mon-Sat 10.30 pm, Sun 10 pm.

MIN JIANG, THE ROYAL GARDEN HOTEL W8 £100 435

2-24 KENSINGTON HIGH ST
020 7361 1988   6–1A

"The most difficult restaurant in W8 to bag a table at" for good reason: the rooftop dining room of the 5-star Royal Garden Hotel combines "top Hong Kong-standard Chinese food" with "wonderful views over Kensington Gardens" – "the dim sum is excellent" and

"I could cry with joy simply thinking about their Beijing duck", which is "one of the best in London". / W8 4PT; www.minjiang.co.uk; @minjianglondon; Mon-Sun 10.30 pm.

MIRCH MASALA SW17 £25 422

213 UPPER TOOTING RD
020 8767 8638   11–2D

This Pakistani canteen is one of the stars of Tooting's 'curry corridor', and had a moment in the limelight when it was recommended a few years back by the area's most famous son, London mayor Sadiq Khan. / SW17 7TG; mirchmasala-takeaway.co.uk; @Dish No. 87 at Mirch Masala; Sun-Thu 11.30 pm, Fri & Sat 11.45 pm; cash only; no booking.

MIRO MAYFAIR W1

15 OLD BURLINGTON STREET
020 7183 9661   4–3A

From Cream Group (owners of Cirque le Soir, Restaurant Ours, Wild and The Windmill Soho), this July opening in Mayfair occupies the erstwhile 120-cover site of XO (RIP). Former Elystan Street head chef Toby Burrowes heads up an extravagant offering, which includes a £3,000 'sunken treasure' caviar platter; and a cocktail listed at £5,000 (a rare 1950s gin and a bottle of 1970 Dom Perignon BTW). All good PR. Opening in mid-July 2022, this new spot calls itself a 'clubstaurant' – not a term we feel needs encouragement. / W1W 2JR; www.miromayfair.com; @miromayfair; Wed-Sun 11 pm.

MISCUSI £39 222

23 SLINGSBY PLACE, WC2
020 8089 8540   5–3B
80 UPPER STREET, N1
020 8089 5847   9–3D

One of Italy's recent hits, this sustainable fast-food pasta business with 12 branches arrived in Covent Garden in November 2021(and quickly opened a second in Islington in June 2022). The limited feedback in our annual diners' poll was somewhat in tune with The Telegraph's William Sitwell (who was so disappointed he suggested the chain "be summoned to the foreign office and expelled"): "I was so excited based on all the social media around the place: food was average (as in something you'd make at home when you're in a rush)". /

MIZNON LONDON W1

8-12 BROADWICK STREET   AWAITING TEL
4–1C

Tel Aviv, Paris, NYC… and now London – Soho (in July 2022) is the latest location for this eight-strong international chain, whose owner, Eyal Shani, is aiming for 150 locations once all is said and done. It's all about the filled pitas, with each branch's menu tailored to the locality. Soho's features an 'English Breakfast' option, alongside lots of fish and vegetarian possibilities. / W1W 8HN; @miznonlondon; Mon-Sat 11 pm, Sun 10 pm.

LOS MOCHIS W8 £44 334

2 FARMER ST   020 7727 7528   7–2B

This Mexican/Japanese hybrid in Notting Hill offers 'gangster tacos' served with Japanese elegance – and provides "the best fun dining out I have had in a long while", full of "exciting, flavour-packed mouthfuls". Finnish-born founder Markus Theslelf coined the label 'Baja Nihon' to cover a cuisine that does not exist elsewhere, and has taken over the site occupied by legendary fish 'n' chip restaurant Geales (RIP) for more than 50 years. Top Tip – "it's great for allergies – the entire menu is GF and you'd have no idea!" / W8; www.losmochis.co.uk; @osmochislondon; Mon-Sun midnight; closed Mon-Fri L; payment – credit card only.

MON PLAISIR RESTAURANT WC2 £69 224

19-21 MONMOUTH STREET
020 7836 7243   5–2B

"Mon Plaisir felt like an old-fashioned time warp when I first started coming here in the 1980s, and it hasn't changed since!" – this sprawling bistro in Covent Garden is set in "a French honeycomb of rooms" and many of its devotees say it's "still holding its own" thanks to its "delightful authenticity" ("serving French food – including proper snails and other bistro classics – in the French way") and its "beguiling" approach generally ("a great place to look starry-eyed into your partner's eyes"). Its ratings are sliding, though, due to numerous other long-term fans losing interest ("I hadn't been in years and found average food, variable service and a tired impression generally": "…a pity as it used to be so good!") / WC2H 9DD; www.monplaisir.co.uk; @monplaisiragram; Tue-Sun 9.30 pm; closed Sun & Mon.

MONMOUTH COFFEE COMPANY £7 343

27 MONMOUTH ST, WC2
020 7232 3010   5–2B
2 PARK ST, SE1   020 7232 3010   12–2A

"Amazing coffee" – "a wide selection from single estates that's carefully selected and optimally roasted" – together with "well-paired pastries and cakes as complements" continue to make these "lively and fun", artisanal brew stops "a good morning 'perk me up'", and some of the most popular destinations in town. Staff are "impressively calm and friendly" too; "worth queuing for". / www.monmouthcoffee.co.uk.

MORITO £58 433

195 HACKNEY ROAD, E2
020 7613 0754   14–2A
32 EXMOUTH MKT, EC1
020 7278 7007   10–1A

"The food is always a delight" at "the little brother of (and much cheaper than) Moro", nearby in Exmouth Market, which serves "excellent authentic tapas dishes washed down with delicious Spanish wine" or a "half-bottle of sherry". It's a notably "well run joint", with "staff who know their grub" and are "very welcoming without being fussy". Top Tip – "arrive early to nab one of their two outdoor tables on the paved street and imagine yourself in Spain as you watch life going by". / www.morito.co.uk; moritotapas.

MORO EC1 £77 3 3 2

34-36 EXMOUTH MKT
020 7833 8336   10–1A

"Still going strong (after all these 25 years)… the only downside is that it can feel noisy when full" – that's long been the classic view on Sam and Sam Clark's "old favourite" on Exmouth Market, where an "interesting range of tasty", "Spanish/Moorish-influenced dishes" are provided alongside an "oenological tour of Spain" from the extensive Iberian wine list (which has an "exciting selection of wines by the glass"). Its ratings have been drifting south, however, over a period of years, due to the minority who "really want to like it, but find the food lacking punch" nowadays. Top Tip – "on a weekday, at lunchtimes, Moro sets up a stall in the street outside the restaurant, and sells tagine with couscous to take away: some of the best street food in the UK!" / EC1R 4QE; www.moro.co.uk; @restaurantmoro; Mon-Sun 10.30 pm; closed Mon L.

MORSO NW8 £72 3 3 2

130 BOUNDARY ROAD
020 7624 7412   9–3A

A "modern" take on an Italian local in Abbey Road, with a menu built around "delicious small plates and brilliant pasta" with "lots of great vegetarian options". It's "community-centred" and "very reliable", with "fantastic, helpful staff". A second branch in Kensal Rise closed down after two years in May 2022. / NW8 0RH; www.morsolondon.co.uk; @morsolondon; Tue-Sat 10.30 pm, Sun 9.30 pm; closed Mon.

MOTCOMBS SW1 £65 2 3 4

26 MOTCOMB ST   020 7235 6382   6–1D

All agree on the attractive style of this long-established (since 1982) and rather old-fashioned Belgravia stalwart, with nice pavement tables. Not everyone agrees on the value provided by its eclectic international menu (shepherds pie, seared tiger prawns, Dover sole, Belgravia icing…) but it is sometimes tipped for business. / SW1X 8JU; www.motcombs.co.uk; @motcombsrestaurant; Mon-Sun 11 pm.

MR BAO SE15 £34 3 2 2

293 RYE LN   020 7635 0325   1–4D

"A really good bet" in Peckham, serving "superb Taiwanese bao buns". It's "friendly, affordable and fun – so perfect for these challenging times". On the weekend it's "brunch heaven – kimchi pancakes and hash browns with ma po beans are really different and yummy". Daddy Bao in Tooting and Master Bao in Westfield Shepherd's Bush complete the family. / SE15 4UA; www.mrbao.co.uk; @mrbaouk; Mon-Sat 10.30 pm, Sun 9.30 pm; closed Mon-Wed L.

MR FALAFEL W12 £9 5 4 2

15 UXBRIDGE RD   07307 635548   8–1C

"Run by two chef brothers", this "tiny restaurant" is crammed into the north end of Shepherd's Bush Market and does a "brisk trade". Motto: 'We Speak Falafel Fluently' – you can order your wrap in the style of Syria, Iran, Lebanon or the owners' native Palestine. You get "absolutely fresh food, a warm welcome and the best prices in town!" / W12 8AH; Mon-Sun midnight.

MR JI W1 £15 3 3 2

72 OLD COMPTON STREET
020 7052 5770   4–2D

"Taiwanese chicken that's fun, fast and cheap" (plus other "great, dirty Asian bites"), has created a buzz around this tapas-inspired haunt in Soho. Founder Samuel Haim started out selling street food in Camden, and has now teamed up with Ta Ta Eatery's Ana Gonçalves and Zijun Meng, with a second site slated to open in Camden's Parkway in the latter half of 2022. / W1W 4UN; mrji.co.uk; @mrjirestaurant; Tue-Sat 10.30 pm, Sun 5.30 pm; closed Sun D, closed Mon; payment – credit card only; credit card deposit required to book.

MR TODIWALA'S PETISCOS IG9 £43 4 4 3

75 QUEEN'S ROAD   020 8257 0816   1–1D

"Great atmosphere and something quite different!" – this "warm and welcoming" Buckhurst Hill operation mixes Goan and Portuguese influences. It's a partnership between Cyris & Pervin Todiwala and the Redman-Schaffer family from Woodford, delivering "great little dishes" ('petiscos') and "fantastic Portuguese wines from independent estates". / IG9 5BW; www.mrtodiwalaspetiscos.com; @mrtodiwalaspetiscos; closed Mon-Sat & Sun.

MUNAL TANDOORI SW15 £34 3 4 2

393 UPPER RICHMOND ROAD, PUTNEY
020 8876 3083   11–2A

This "great-value local Indian" is a landmark on the South Circular near Putney which has built a sterling reputation over 32 years for its classic north Indian dishes supplemented by interesting Nepalese specialities such as momo steamed dumplings – all served in "huge portion sizes!". / SW15 5QL; www.munaltandoori.co.uk; @Munal Nepalese Restaurant (Official); Sun-Thu 10 pm, Fri & Sat 11 pm; closed Sun-Thu-Sat L.

MURANO W1 £129 3 4 3

20-22 QUEEN ST   020 7495 1127   3–3B

"Technically accomplished", Italian-inspired cuisine (which, at heart, is quite "classical") from Angela Hartnett, served "in a sophisticated-yet-relaxed setting, by outstanding-yet-unobtrusive staff" continues to inspire the many fans of her unflashy-yet-luxurious venue in Mayfair. But, while most diners applaud its overall performance, it has inspired a variety of gripes of late: the décor can be too "muted" for some tastes, and some repeat visitors have admitted to feeling "underwhelmed" of late by the odd "uninspiring" dish. On most accounts, though "the main difficulty here is answering the question: 'how many courses?'" (the options being a 3-course, 4-course, 5-course or 6-course meal). / W1J 5PP; www.muranolondon.com; @muranolondon; Mon-Sat 10 pm; closed Sun.

MUSE SW1 £171 5 4 4

38 GROOM PLACE   020 3301 2903   6–1D

"Tom Aikens gave us a night of culinary genius on a plate. Unforgettable" – his "original, informal and fun" two-year-old Belgravia HQ continues to deliver a "superlative" experience. The "incredible plates of food are full of little flavour bombs" and "whilst the menu inspiration of dishes tied to his life story risks getting a little passé if you're a regular, Tom does cook it well" ("it's great that he is often actually there in person"). There's

Native at Browns W1

"lovely trendy décor on both floors, and it's a fantastic experience on the ground floor stools slap bang in front of Tom and the chefs who are so friendly and engaging". Top Tip – perhaps reflecting Tom's health-conscious, ultramarathon leanings, "dietary intolerances are well catered for" and "vegetables prepared in interesting and exciting ways". / SW18 7BA; www.musebytomaikens.co.uk; @musebytomaikens; Tue-Sat 11 pm; closed Tue, Wed L, closed Sun & Mon; booking online only.

MYRTLE SW10   £84   543

1A LANGTON STREET
020 7352 2411   6–3B

This "real gem of a restaurant" in a Chelsea townhouse is the work of Dublin-born chef Anna Haugh (who has worked for Phil Howard and Gordon Ramsay, among others). "Stunning Irish food" provides "course after course" tracing a route round the counties, and "all of them hit the mark". "The talent in the kitchen is matched by the warmth of the welcome and the efficiency of the service", all of which adds up to "one of the best and least expected openings in Chelsea of the past five years". Michelin don't even list it on their website, when they should be considering it for a star! / SW10 0JL; www.myrtlerestaurant.com; @myrtlerestaurant; Tue-Sat 10 pm; closed Sun & Mon.

NANDINE SE5   £34   343

45 CAMBERWELL CHURCH STREET
020 7703 3221   1–3C

"Kurdish delights in SE5!" – founder Pary Baban was forced to flee her home by Saddam Hussein's troops in 1989 and collected recipes on her travels. Now she shares them at her cafés in Camberwell and Peckham (Nandine means 'kitchen' in Kurdish), where you can "enjoy the great spicing and flavours" in a "lovely atmosphere". "Brunch is a particular highlight" – try Pary's "great shakshuka". / SE5 8TR; @nandineuk; Sun-Thu 10.30 pm, Fri & Sat 11 pm; closed Mon-Fri L.

THE NARROW E14   £76   223

44 NARROW ST   020 7592 7950   12–1B

"Great views" are by all accounts the main highlight of a meal at Gordo's Limehouse pub overlooking a bend in the river. But perhaps we expect too much of a chef happy to dish out a roasting to his peers: "I know a lot of people don't like it, but it did what it said on the tin – it's good pub food, and it's only if you anticipated more that you'll be disappointed". / E14 8DP; www.gordonramsayrestaurants.com/the-narrow; @thenarrowgordonramsay; Mon-Wed 11.30 pm, Thu-Sat midnight, Sun 10 pm.

NATIVE AT BROWNS
W1   £78   544

BROWNS, 39 BROOK STREET
020 7549 5999   3–2B

"Everything on the menu is a triumph!" at Imogen Davis and Ivan Tisdall-Downes's

"charming" yearling, in Mayfair's fashionable Browns store. "It has a cool vibe, having entered through the store" and the food can "far exceed expectations" – "wonderful, innovative dishes that will stick in the memory (for instance, the fudgy bone marrow crème brûlée, which got meatier as we got closer to the bone)". "It's not too expensive either, given the location". Top Tip – in summer, it has a 40-seat courtyard. / W1W 4JE; www.brownsfashion.com/uk/services/native-at-browns; @eatnative; Tue-Sat 9 pm; closed Sun & Mon.

NAUGHTY PIGLETS
SW2   £52   544

28 BRIXTON WATER LN
020 7274 7796   11–2D

Joe Sharratt and Margaux Aubry's informal French-inspired Brixton venue is a true leader of South London gastronomy, serving small sharing plates of "the best grub" and "most exciting wines" south of the river. "Margaux is a treasure – a Lyon-hearted wonder" who provides guests with expert guidance through the menu and excellent wine list. Foodie composer/impresario Andrew Lloyd Webber was such a fan that he invited the team to launch a spin-off at his 'The Other Place Theatre' in Victoria. / SW2 1PE; www.naughtypiglets.co.uk; @naughtypiglets; Fri & Sat, Tue-Thu 11 pm; closed Tue-Thu L, closed Sun & Mon; payment – credit card only.

NAUTILUS NW6   £38   322

27-29 FORTUNE GREEN RD
020 7435 2532   1–1B

"Old-fashioned in the best way", this veteran West Hampstead chippy is known for "fantastic fresh fish 'n' delicious chips" – hailed as "the best in the NWs". "Matzo meal batter is light as a feather and not too greasy, and they can also do great grilled fish when you're on a health kick". The dining room remains "no-frills" despite a lockdown revamp and still "has a strip lighting aesthetic… but you don't come for the ambience". / NW6 1DU; @nautilusfishandchip; Mon-Sat 10 pm, Sun 9 pm; no Amex.

NESSA W1

1 WARWICK STREET   AWAITING TEL   4–3B

This 100-cover, autumn 2022 Soho newcomer is the work of Guy Ivesha (founder of Mortimer House) and has well-known chef Tom Cenci (whose CV includes Duck & Waffle) as executive chef. A casual bistro format is the aim, delivering a classic seasonal menu. It will sit on the ground floor of 1 Warwick, a sibling members' club to the original. / W1W 5LR; @nessasoho; Mon-Sun midnight.

NEST E9   £48   443

177 MORNING LANE   020 8986 0065   14–1B

This "outstanding" four-year-old is an "engaging but cramped little venue" whose "absolute bargain of a menu" from co-owner Johnnie Crow (ex-Harwood Arms and Anglo), makes it "well worth the trip up to Hackney (booking essential!)". The meal is structured

around one type of meat each month – chicken, game, wagyu – to minimise waste, and "service is personal, enthusiastic and charming". "You're unlikely to find much better value in town, with some truly stellar dishes given the mid-range price-point". / E9 6LH; www.nest_food; @nest_food; Tue-Sat 10 pm, Sun 3 pm; closed Tue-Fri L closed Sun D, closed Mon.

NEWENS: THE ORIGINAL
MAIDS OF HONOUR
TW9   £40   333

288 KEW ROAD   020 8940 2752   1–3A

"Very touristy of course, but also very atmospheric… and the afternoon teas are so good!" – This "very traditional tea rooms opposite Kew Gardens" is seemingly unchanged in many decades and offers a comforting slice of post-war life, having been built in mock-Tudor style in the late 1940s. "Famed for their 'maids of honour' pastries", "their tea is a simple classic affair of scones, jam, clotted cream, savoury pastries, pies, and aforementioned tarts". "It never fails to please and I just keep coming back after 40 years!" / TW9 3DU; theoriginalmaidsofhonour.co.uk; @theoriginalmaidsofhonour; Mon-Sun 6 pm.

NGON W4   £28   322

195 CHISWICK HIGH ROAD
020 8994 9630   8–2A

"So much better than the chains" – this very no-frills canteen in the heart of Chiswick is worth remembering for its "simple but fresh" and vibrant Vietnamese dishes (bahn mi, salads, pho…) / W4 2DR; www.ngondeli.com; @ngondeli; Mon-Sat 8 pm, Sun 5 pm; closed Sun D.

THE NINTH LONDON
W1   £105   543

22 CHARLOTTE STREET
020 3019 0880   2–1C

"They don't need to try too hard" at Jun Tanaka's "relaxed" but extremely accomplished Fitzrovia fixture. "Everything that's on the plate is there for a reason… a good reason!" – his "very high-quality" cuisine is "very well-balanced" and service is "charming". Top Menu Tips – "seared mackerel with pickles works well, beef cheeks is a signature, and turbot head is wonderful". BREAKING NEWS: In summer 2022, a fire closed the restaurant, with no reopening date set as of mid August 2022. / W1T 2NB; www.theninthlondon.com; @theninthlondon; Mon-Sat 9.30 pm; closed Sun.

NO. FIFTY CHEYNE
SW3   £107   235

50 CHEYNE WALK   020 7376 8787   6–3C

This gorgeous-looking brasserie in the heart of Old Chelsea is "always busy", with chef Iain Smith (a former associate of Jason Atherton) presiding over high-quality but rather pricey surf'n'turf grills and "Sunday roast to die for". Proprietor Jenny Greene, the theatre impresario who restored the Old Vic and owns Ronnie Scott's jazz club, upgraded the premises several years ago; it is now a licensed wedding venue with an upstairs bar and salon boasting impressive views over Albert Bridge. / SW3 5LR; www.fiftycheyne.com; @50cheyne; Wed-Sat midnight, Sun 6 pm; closed Wed & Thu L closed Sun D, closed Mon & Tue; payment – credit card only.

NOBLE ROT WC1   £74   3 5 5

51 LAMB'S CONDUIT ST
020 7242 8963   2–1D

"Even the most jaded wine bore will find something new and special" at Mark Andrew and Daniel Keeling's "moody" watering hole in Bloomsbury – nowadays one of London's best-known destinations. Naturally the "expertly chosen and truly fascinating wine list" ("a top mix of classics and new wave/low intervention wines") is at the heart of its appeal, but its magic also owes much to its "fabulously knowledgeable staff" ("who really know their stuff and can make great recommendations to suit all price points"). A further major factor was the inspired choice six years ago of such splendidly apt premises: the "dark-lit" and charmingly mellow site that was for decades the forgotten-about, 1970s stalwart wine bar, 'Vats': "cosy and appealing with a lovely feel to it". And, while the "wine is always centre stage", the food is "surprisingly good" too – "on point with excellent ingredients". "Availability by the glass is fabulous" ("and by the bottle!"), but the "measures are small at 75 or 125ml" and – "be careful!" – prices of more exotic vintages can be "injurious to the bank account". But even those who feel "a visit quickly gets pricey given those tiny glasses" think it's "good for a treat". And for many aficionados "the fantastically diverse list encourages – nay insists! – that you blow your budget and reach for the stars!". Top Tip – "splendid set lunch". / WC1N 3NB; www.noblerot.co.uk; @noblerotsoho; Mon-Sat 9.30 pm; closed Sun.

NOBLE ROT SOHO W1   £59   3 4 4

2 GREEK STREET   020 7183 8190   5–2A

"After decades of being a Gay Hussar regular I now find myself at this fine replacement run by committed wine experts…" – this famous Soho address was resurrected in 2021 by Dan Keeling and Mark Andrew and fans are "happy to report standards just as high as at their original site in Holborn". Star of the show is the "gargantuan wine list" – "a treasure trove of interesting bins" (albeit "with some jaw-dropping prices") – "interpreted by knowledgeable and friendly staff", who help maintain the "charming and quirky" atmosphere of this "solid and comfortable" site (which, as its predecessor, opened in 1953). The "food is not as exceptional as the wine" but the "gutsy and value-led menu" of "good ingredients, served simply" is generally well-reviewed for its "delicious and unpretentious" qualities. Top Tip – "excellent-value set lunch". / W1W 4NB; noblerot.co.uk; @noblerotsoho; Mon-Sat 9.30 pm; closed Sun.

NOBU W1   £127   4 3 2

19 OLD PARK LN   020 7447 4747   3–4A

"Definitely not as fashionable as it once was… the décor is now a bit old hat… but the food at this Nobu still has the edge" – the original London branch of Nobu Matsuhisa's famous international chain is "still the place to go if you like Japanese fusion-style cuisine", and "if you ignore the prices then the rest is simply wonderful!" Perhaps realising that they need to work harder now that the A-list crowd has moved on, service is often "spot on" too, nowadays. / W1K 1LB; www.noburestaurants.com; @nobuoldparklane; Sun-Wed 10 pm, Thu-Sat 10.30 pm.

NOBU PORTMAN SQUARE W1   £104   3 3 4

22 PORTMAN SQUARE
020 3988 5888   2–1A

"More modern in style than its older Park Lane sister and far more trendy now" – this "large, dark and warmly" decorated venue, with outside terrace, beamed down into this latest outpost of the international chain in December 2020. But while "popular and packed", with Japanese-fusion cuisine that's often rated as "wonderful", it's "an expensive option compared with other Japanese venues" and "the food isn't quite as good as the original at The Met". / W1W 7BG; london-portman. nobuhotels.com; @nobulondonportman; Sun-Thu 10 pm, Fri & Sat 10.30 pm.

NOBU SHOREDITCH EC2   £127

10-50 WILLOW ST   020 3818 3790   13–1B

With its big, high-ceilinged basement restaurant looking out onto a cool sunken garden – this style-conscious Shoreditch hotel (launched in 2017) never felt like it fully established itself fully prior to the pandemic. It closed from 2020 till June 2022, just after the conclusion of our survey, so our rating will have to wait till next year. / EC2E 4BH; www.london-shoreditch.nobuhotels.com; @nobulondonshoreditch; Sun-Wed 10.30 pm, Thu-Sat 11.30 pm; closed Sat & Sun L.

NOCI N1   £41   2 2 3

4-6 ISLINGTON GREEN
020 3937 5343   9–3D

"A welcome recent addition to Islington" – this March 2022 newcomer from Louis Korovilas serves a short, seasonal menu of pastas and a modern take on Italian street-food snacks. But while "it's a handy neighbourhood option for fresh pasta", the overall verdict is that "it doesn't quite compare to the likes of Padella or Bancone" (Korovilas used to work at the latter). / N1 2XA; www.nocirestaurant.co.uk; @nocipasta; Mon-Sat 11 pm, Sun 10 pm.

NOIZÉ W1   £98   4 5 4

39 WHITFIELD ST   020 7323 1310   2–1C

"A corner of France in London" – this "unassuming" but increasingly well-known Fitzrovia dining room "is brought to life by charming and attentive owner, Mathieu Germond and his team". The "relaxed atmosphere is helped by widely spaced tables and the menu brought to the table on a blackboard" which delivers "classic French dishes from top-class ingredients". The prime attraction, though, is the wine. "Matthieu has an encyclopaedic knowledge" and the "cracking list has something new to discover every time and at all price ranges". / W1W 2SF; www.noize-restaurant.co.uk; @noize_restaurant; Wed-Fri, Tue, Sat 10 pm; closed Tue, Sat L, closed Sun & Mon.

NOMAD LONDON WC2   £117   3 4 5

4 BOW STREET   020 3906 1600   5–2D

A "simply brilliant addition to Covent Garden" – Grade II listed Bow Street Magistrates' Court, as was, is now the first London offshoot of Manhattan's hip NoMad hotel, with a dining room, 'The Atrium', that occupies a stunning indoors-outdoors glass-ceilinged space three storeys high. It's "great for breakfast (and lunch and dinner)", with exec chef Ashley Abodeely putting her NY/LA spin on the best seafood, meat and vegetables Britain can produce. "This is a really special dinner out… if you can stomach the prices", and while you're there you must slip into the Side Hustle, a bar occupying the old Bow Street police station, where Abodeely indulges a taste for tacos she developed while working in LA. "Special mention to the cocktails and very professional and friendly waiters". / WC2W 7AH; www.thenomadhotel.com/london; @thenomadhotel; Mon-Sat 10.30 pm, Sun 5 pm; closed Mon-Fri L closed Sun D.

NOOR JAHAN   £52   4 4 2

2A BINA GARDENS, SW5
020 7373 6522   6–2B
26 SUSSEX PLACE, W2
020 7402 2332   7–1D

This "ever-popular warhorse" has served "classic Indian food" in traditional curry house style to an appreciative audience on the Earl's Court-South Ken border for 60 years now. The "staff have been there forever and we love this happy and delicious place", say fans – it's "old-fashioned, but that's part of the appeal". /

NOPI W1   £92   3 3 2

21-22 WARWICK ST   020 7494 9584   4–3B

"Unique food to die for" from a "very inventive Middle Eastern-inspired menu" inspires followers of Yotam Ottolenghi and the acclaimed Israeli chef's "bustling" Soho flagship: "each plate is heaven" and "you may discover some new wines" along the way. As is so often the case with his ventures, though, the pricing gives nothing away – "the food's great, but I didn't award full marks as it's not outstanding value for money". / W1B 5NE; ottolenghi.co.uk/restaurants; @ottolenghi; Mon-Sat 10.30 pm; closed Sun.

THE NORFOLK ARMS WC1 £49 3|3|2

28 LEIGH ST   020 7388 3937   9–4C

"Superb tapas" are "served with a smile" in this deceptive Victorian pub in a sidestreet near King's Cross, that "still looks like a typical boozer". It's "very popular, justifiably, so booking ahead is required at busy times". / WC1H 9EP; www.norfolkarms.co.uk; Mon-Sat 11 pm; closed Sun; no Amex.

NORMA W1 £84 4|4|4

8 CHARLOTTE STREET
0203 995 6224   2–1C

"The décor feels wonderfully indulgent without descending into kitsch" at the Stafford Hotel Group's "stylish" three-year-old. Something similar could be said about the "interesting spin on Sicilian cuisine" that's "excellently prepared and full of authentic flavour", and delivered in generous portions. "Staff are brilliant" too. Top Menu Tip – "a top choice for inventive and not-too-excessive pasta" or small plates (e.g. prawns, monkfish, burrata); "top it all off with first-rate tiramisu and rose-flavoured panna cotta". / W1W 2LS; www.normalondon.com; @norma_ldn; Mon-Sat 10.30 pm; closed Sun.

NORMAH'S W2 £28 4|3|2

23-25 QUEENSWAY MARKET
07771 630828   7–2C

"The ambience might not be much (it is set inside a no-frills indoor market) but – oh boy! – the beef rending and mee goreng are deeeelicious" at this tiny, high-quality and exceptionally good-value Malaysian café in Bayswater, where Normah Abd Hamid has fulfilled a lifetime's ambition by sharing her brilliant home cooking with friends and strangers. / W2 4QP; www.normahs.co.uk; @normahs_place; Tue-Sat 9 pm; closed Tue-Sat L, closed Sun & Mon.

NORMANS CAFE N19 £25 4|4|4

167 JUNCTION ROAD   NO TEL   9–1C

"Bringing the greasy spoon into the 21st century – Norman's hits the spot of traditional British food with top-notch ingredients at bargain prices". Chefs Elliot Kaye and Richard Hayes ditched jobs at Leroy and Lyle's in 2020 to open this Tufnell Park café, complete with gingham curtains and a classic photo of Bobby Moore holding aloft the Jules Rimet trophy – it is one of the few places on earth where you can have ham, two eggs and chips washed down by a negroni or a skin-contact wine. "The queues around the corner says it all. Get there early to secure a table!" / N19 5PZ; www.normanscafe.co.uk; @Normanscafelondon; Wed-Sun 3 pm; closed Wed-Sun D, closed Mon & Tue.

EL NORTE W1 £108 3|3|3

19-20 DOVER STREET
020 3154 8182   3–3C

"Top-class Hispanic cuisine is served in an atmosphere of easy luxury" at this Mayfair yearling from Spanish twins Alberto and Arian Zandi – their third London restaurant following Zuaya and Como Garden in Kensington. "Both taste and texture of the food are spot on", but even fans who say "it really is a super restaurant" can fret that "prices are a bit out of control" (but for the most part feel "you get what you pay for"). / W1W 4LP; el-norte.co.uk; @elnortelondon; Sun-Thu 12.30 am, Fri & Sat 1.30 am.

NORTH CHINA W3 £43 4|3|3

305 UXBRIDGE RD   020 8992 9183   8–1A

The Lou family's West London fixture of almost 50 years' standing, was created by founder Hung Sun Lou (aka Chef Lou, now in his 80s) and more latterly has operated under his son Lawrence, the current owner, who virtually grew up in the restaurant. Lost on the outskirts of Acton, it provides northern Chinese cuisine of consistently "high quality". / W3 9QU; www.northchina.co.uk; @northchinafood; Tue-Sun 10.30 pm; closed Mon.

NORTH SEA FISH WC1 £51 3|3|2

7-8 LEIGH ST   020 7387 5892   9–4C

"Follow the black cabs and grab the battered goodies at this venerable chipper", say fans of this Bloomsbury fixture, run by the Beauchamp family since 1977. "The place has been spruced up since my first visit decades ago, but it still could do with more sprucing up! But these are small criticisms and one doesn't go for the décor, but for what's on the plate". "Friendly and well-informed service is a bonus, too". / WC1H 9EW; www.northseafishrestaurant.co.uk; @thenorthseafish; Mon-Sat 9.30 pm; closed Mon L, closed Sun.

THE NORTHALL, CORINTHIA HOTEL WC2 £96 3|3|3

10A NORTHUMBERLAND AVE
020 7321 3100   2–3C

Despite its gracious, high-ceilinged interior, this luxury five-star's comfortable dining room – with its own dedicated entrance, near the Embankment – is sometimes overlooked by reporters. Those who make the trip, however, say the cuisine (overseen by executive chef, André Garrett) is "good value" (especially the set option) and that, in particular, it's "a great lunch location". / WC2N 5AE; www.corinthia.com/london/restaurants-bars; @corinthialondon; Tue-Sat 11 pm, Mon 10.30 am, Sun 4 pm; closed Mon D.

NOVIKOV (ASIAN RESTAURANT) W1 £130 2|2|4

50A BERKELEY STREET
020 7399 4330   3–3C

"It feels like you're in a nightclub, and it's very expensive" at this oligarch playground in Mayfair, run by Arkady Novikov (who in past times boasted of his personal friendship with Vladimir Putin, but who more recently hoisted a 'Peace for Ukraine' flag on the restaurant website). For some folks the whole vibe is a complete turn off ("this is what's wrong with London!"), but for Eurotrash in party mood it's still just the job for nibbling on sushi, robata and other luxe bites. (There is also a grand Italian dining room to the rear, but it inspires practically no feedback this year). / W1J 8HA; www.novikovrestaurant.co.uk; @novikovrestaurant; Mon-Wed midnight, Thu-Sat 12.30 am, Sun 11 pm.

NUMERO UNO SW11 £63 2|3|2

139 NORTHCOTE RD
020 7978 5837   11–2C

"White table clothes, Italian staff serving good, honest food. What's not to love" about this "old-style (this is a compliment) local that's been on Northcote Road for years". That's the upbeat view, anyway, but – while a majority of its Nappy Valley regulars still sing its praises – marks dipped this year amid the odd report that it is "losing its charm", with "tables far too close together" for comfort. Perhaps popularity has come at a cost. / SW11 6PX; www.numerounorestaurant.co.uk; @numerounoclapham?hl=en; Mon-Sun 11 pm; no Amex.

NUOVI SAPORI SW6 £54 3|4|3

295 NEW KING'S RD   020 7736 3363   11–1B

This "very friendly family-owned restaurant" near Parsons Green offers a small menu of "reliable Italian food", at "very good value for money". / SW6 4RE; www.nuovisaporilondon.co.uk; @nuovi_sapori_14; Mon-Sat 11 pm; closed Sun; booking max 6 may apply.

NUSR-ET STEAKHOUSE SW1 £184 1|1|1

101 KNIGHTSBRIDGE   01821 687738   6–1D

"Suitable only for chavs and vulgarians" – social media hyperstar, Nusret Gökçe's "ludicrous" Knightsbridge outpost of his global steakhouse chain takes nothing but stiff flak in our annual diners' poll for its "grotesque" or even "filthy" pricing. Fair-minded reporters feel that "the steaks and dishes are good, however not at those prices! (which are much cheaper in Istanbul!"). Less forgiving ones say that "either Salt Bae is a pompous twat or just taking the piss out of morons with more money than sense!" (Whatever you feel, it's not a bad business model, posting £2m of profit in its first four months of operation.) / SW1S 7RN;

www.nusr-et.com.tr/en/home.aspx; @nusr_et;
Mon-Sat 1.30 am, Sun 12.30 am.

NUTSHELL WC2 £68 322

**30 SAINT MARTIN'S LANE
020 3409 7926 5–4C**

Mohammad and Marwa Paknejad's "sophisticated Iranian" in Theatreland serves a "short menu of very pretty, subtly flavoured dishes", from a modern open kitchen that uses fresh British ingredients along with Iranian spices. "The lightness of the cooking makes it perfect for a meal pre- or post-theatre". / WC2W 4ER; nutshelllondon.co.uk; @nutshelllondon; Tue-Sat 9.30 pm; closed Tue-Thu L, closed Sun & Mon.

O'VER £68 322

**1 NORRIS STREET, ST JAMES'S MARKET,
SW1 020 7930 9664 4–4D
44-46 SOUTHWARK STREET, SE1
020 7578 9933 10–4B**

"Pizza with imported sea water from Naples! What's not to like...?" ask fans of this studiedly authentic Neapolitan duo on Borough's main drag and in St James's Market. Portions are "generous", too. / www.overuk.com; over_uk.

OAK £67 324

**243 GOLDHAWK RD, W12
020 8741 7700 8–1B
137 WESTBOURNE PARK RD, W2
020 7221 3355 7–1B**

"Superb pizzas" and a "great local vibe" are the attractions at this smart pub conversion in "a trendy corner of Notting Hill" and its two offshoots (the Oak W12 off Ravenscourt Park and the Bird in Hand at Brook Green). "It's Roman-style pizza, with a thin, crispy base – not the chewy gooey style that is too popular". Top Tip – in W11, the upstairs lounge bar "is a gem for a pre- or post-dinner drink". /

OBICÀ MOZZARELLA BAR, PIZZA E CUCINA £60 333

**19-20 POLAND ST, W1
020 3327 7070 4–1C
1 WEST WINTERGARDEN, 35 BANK ST, E14
020 7719 1532 12–1C
UNIT 4 5 - 7 LIMEBURNERS LANE,, EC4
020 3327 0984 10–2A**

This international chain has three London representatives – in Soho, the City and Canary Wharf – and focuses on light Italian dishes (pizza, pasta and salads) showcasing the eponymous cheese from Campania alongside other Italian produce; plus a range of cocktails and wines. A good spot "for post-work drinks and nibbles". / obica.com; obicamozzarellabar; 10 pm - 11 pm; E14 Sat 8 pm; E14 & EC4 Closed Sun.

OBLIX SE1 £107 224

**LEVEL 32, THE SHARD, 31 ST. THOMAS
STREET 020 7268 6700 10–4C**

This all-day operation on the 32nd floor of the Shard celebrates its tenth anniversary this year, and still wows with its "amazing views" over London. The 'urban casual' menu from Rainer Becker (of Zuma and Roka) fits the (very expensive) bill without generating much excitement. It is divided in two, with Oblix East offering "excellent afternoon tea" and cocktails. / SE1 9RY; @oblixrestaurant; @oblixrestaurant; Mon-Wed, Sat, Fri, Sun 11 pm; Thu midnight; booking max 6 may apply.

ODETTE'S NW1 £82 322

**130 REGENTS PARK ROAD
020 7586 8569 9–3B**

This classy north London institution in the heart of pretty Primrose Hill "never disappoints and is really good value" under renowned chef-patron Bryn Williams, who has been in charge for the last 15 of its 45 years, and whose family farm in Wales supplies the kitchen (including with "excellent, tender beef"). It's the venue of choice for locals with something to celebrate – while many from further afield just "love Sunday lunch at Odette's, sitting outside on a sunny day". / NW1 8XL; www.odettesprimrosehill.com; @odettesrestaurant; Wed-Sun 9.30 pm; closed Mon & Tue.

OFF THE HOOK E1 £21

**27 GAUGING SQUARE, VAUGHAN WAY
020 7709 0834 10–3D**

"Sustainable, fresh, well-cooked with interesting Korean and Caribbean influences" – this avant-garde seafood operation in Wapping, from Dorset-based fish supplier Shaun Henderson and chef Neil Wager, opened in stages through 2022. The chippy came first – "but what fish 'n' chips!", with ten chip varieties, including 'extra-large smoked with togarashi and okono sauce' – followed by a full-service seafood restaurant and a 'butchery' specialising in dry-aged fish. Reports are too limited for a rating but initial feedback is very positive. / E1E 2AH; oth.fish; @offthehook.fish; Wed-Sat 10 pm; closed Mon & Tue & Sun.

OGNISKO RESTAURANT SW7 £60 345

**55 PRINCE'S GATE, EXHIBITION ROAD
020 7589 0101 6–1C**

"The magnificent interior of the entrance hall and dining room" of this characterful Polish émigré club in South Kensington (near the museums and Royal Albert Hall) creates a "lovely and airy" ambience boosted by its "warm and friendly" staff. And in recent years it has also added "a fabulous all-weather terrace" with "a marquee in the attractive garden" at the rear, where the atmosphere can be "incredible". The solid Polish fare is "good if not fantastic" but keenly priced and accompanied by a wide drinks list, including "full homemade flavoured vodkas". Top Tip – support Ukraine by buying a 'Zelenskyy' – "a special (delicious) cocktail in the national colours". / SW7 2PG; www.ogniskorestaurant.co.uk; Mon-Sat 11.15 pm, Sun 10.30 pm; no trainers.

OKA £57 332

**KINGLY COURT, 1 KINGLY COURT, W1
020 7734 3556 4–2B
19 NEW CAVENDISH STREET, W1
020 7486 4388 3–1A
251 KING'S ROAD, SW3
020 7349 8725 6–3C
71 REGENTS PARK RD, NW1
020 7483 2072 9–3B
88 CHURCH ROAD, SW13
020 8741 8577 11–1A**

These "busy and bustling fusion restaurants" offer a "wide choice" of East Asian dishes, headed by "Japanese-style favourites" – including various sushi or sashimi options and miso black cod – that are "competently and surprisingly well prepared". Israeli-born founder Ohad Kastro celebrates the 10th anniversary of the original launch in Primrose Hill this year; branches in Soho, Marylebone, Chelsea and Barnes have followed. / www.okarestaurant.co.uk.

OKLAVA EC2 £77 443

74 LUKE ST 020 7729 3032 13–1B

"Fabulous" Turkish-Cypriot cooking has won a major foodie reputation for Selin Kiazim's Shoreditch seven-year-old, aided by "genuine" service from business partner Laura Christie. It's a "lively" spot too (if "really noisy with chatter bouncing off the hard surfaces"). / EC2A 4PY; www.oklava.co.uk; @oklava_ldn; Wed-Sat, Tue 10 pm; closed Tue L, closed Sun & Mon; payment – credit card only; booking max 6 may apply.

OLIVETO SW1 £71 322

**49 ELIZABETH STREET
020 7730 0074 2–4A**

"Great thin-crust pizzas" and other "simple but delicious" staples get a good reception at this Belgravia Italian from Sardinian Mauro Sanna's classy stable. It "does what it does very well": namely "good honest, earthy food" made with "fresh ingredients". The wine list majors on interesting bottles and magnums from Sardinia. / SW1W 9PP; www.olivorestaurants.com/oliveto; @olivorestaurants; Mon-Sun 10.30 pm.

OLIVO SW1 £80 342

**21 ECCLESTON STREET
020 7730 2505 2–4B**

"An old favourite", the 33-year-old original in Mauro Sanna's Belgravia mini-empire was "ground-breaking, as one of the first London Italian restaurants to serve simple 'peasant' dishes – in this case Sardinian. Now everyone does it! However, Olivo has never marketed itself at foodies, just well-heeled locals" – who are "never disappointed". It's "not cheap, but definitely not expensive compared with glitzier competitors" in the area. / SW1S 9LX; www.olivorestaurants.com; @olivorestaurants; Tue-Sun 10.30 pm; closed Sat & Sun L, closed Mon.

OLIVOCARNE
SW1 £87 3|3|2

61 ELIZABETH ST 020 7730 7997 2–4A

This "reliable Sardinian restaurant" is the meat specialist in Maura Sanna's Belgravia group, serving several cuts of beef along with 'porceddu' (slow-roasted suckling pig) and "some really good Italian and Sardinian wines". The décor is a modern take on Sardinian folk imagery, and there's a heated terrace where you can enjoy a Havana cigar from the in-house collection. / SW1W 9PP; www.olivorestaurants.com; @olivorestaurants; Tue-Fri, Sun 10.30 pm, Sat 11 pm; closed Mon.

OLIVOMARE SW1 £82 3|3|2

**10 LOWER BELGRAVE ST
020 7730 9022 2–4B**

"This impressive neighbourhood restaurant" in Belgravia serves "wonderful seafood, Italian style". Opened in 2007, it is part of Sardinian-born Mauro Sanno's upmarket group in one of London's poshest enclaves. The interior design can seem a little "bleak" for some tastes: not an issue in summer at the outside tables. / SW1W 0LJ; www.olivorestaurants.com; @olivorestaurants; Tue-Sun 10.30 pm; closed Mon; booking max 10 may apply.

OLLEY'S SE24 £39 3|3|3

**65-69 NORWOOD RD
020 8671 8259 11–2D**

"Consistently excellent fish 'n' chips" have made their mark for more than 35 years at Harry Niazi's rustic spot by Brockwell Park, named after Oliver Twist (1837), in which Charles Dickens mentions a 'fried fish warehouse' – one of the earliest references to what became the national dish. / SE24 9AA; www.olleys.info; @olleysfishexperience; Tue-Sun 9.30 pm; closed Mon; no Amex.

OLYMPIC STUDIOS
SW13 £57 2|2|3

**117-123 CHURCH ROAD
020 8912 5170 11–1A**

"Barnes at brunch" is to be found at this "family-friendly" brasserie, on the ground floor of a complex created from legendary recording studios (The Beatles, The Rolling Stones, Ella Fitzgerald, Madonna, Prince… the list goes on) and which also incorporates an indie cinema and "very cool" members' bar. Fans say you get "decent food at reasonable prices" here at any time. Sceptics that "it has nice surroundings, but a limited and dull menu, which is pretty well executed, but just serves a purpose, nothing more". / SW13 9HL; www.olympiccinema.co.uk; @olympicstudios; Mon-Thu 10 pm, Fri & Sat 10.30 pm, Sun 9 pm; payment – credit card only.

OLYMPUS FISH
N3 £41 4|4|2

**140-144 BALLARDS LN
020 8371 8666 1–1B**

"Always welcoming, always fresh fish and always wonderful chips" are the priorities at this modern family-run fish 'n' chips restaurant in Finchley (est. 2000). The fish can be fried or charcoal-grilled, and is backed up by a choice of Turkish mezze and side dishes. / N3 2PA; www.olympusrestaurant.co.uk; Mon-Sun 10 pm.

OMBRA E2 £58 3|4|3

1 VYNER ST 020 8981 5150 14–2B

This "fabulously located" Italian on the Hackney stretch of Regent's Canal has shades ('ombra' in Italian) of Venice, although head chef Mitshel Ibrahim hails from Milan, where his parents had an Ethiopian restaurant. "Terrific tastes are delivered by an obviously enthusiastic kitchen and serving team" – "if we didn't live 200 miles away this would be a regular haunt". Its lockdown project has turned into a permanent pasta factory next door. / E2 9DG; www.ombrabar.com; @ombrabar.restaurant; Mon, Thu-Sat 10 pm, Sun 5 pm; closed Mon L closed Sun D, closed Tue & Wed.

108 BRASSERIE
W1 £73 3|2|3

**108 MARYLEBONE LN
020 7969 3900 2–1A**

This pavement brasserie, complete with outside seating in warmer months, is part of a well-situated hotel at the top of Marylebone Lane, near the High Street. The food is sometimes "variable", but can be "very good". / W1U 2QE; www.108brasserie.com; @108marylebonelane; Mon-Sat 11 pm, Sun 6 pm.

104 RESTAURANT
W2 £102 4|4|4

**104 CHEPSTOW ROAD
020 3417 4744 7–1B**

"Originally came here at the recommendation of a Michelin star chef – now it's our default treat". Richard Wilkins continues to win high ratings all round in reports on his Notting Hill 14-seater, praised for "generous portions of superb food" (with luxurious ingredients such as wagyu beef often a feature of the menu). / W2 5QS; www.104restaurant.com; @104restaurant; Wed-Sun 9.30 pm; closed Wed-Fri L, closed Mon & Tue.

101 THAI KITCHEN
W6 £45 3|2|2

352 KING ST 020 8746 6888 8–2B

"Whilst an unexciting-looking place, the food is consistently enjoyable" – both punchy Isaan dishes from the northwest and seafood from the south – at this "starkly decorated" canteen near Stamford Brook tube (often somewhat over-egged in fooderati 'best of' lists as a seminal cheap eat). / W6 0RX; www.101thaikitchen.uk; Mon-Sun 10.30 pm; no Amex.

116 AT THE ATHENAEUM
W1 £68 2|4|3

**ATHENAEUM HOTEL, 116 PICCADILLY
020 7499 3464 3–4B**

The "wonderful afternoon tea" at this "luxury" hotel on Piccadilly hogs the limelight since the former Galvin at the Athenaeum dining room was rebranded during the pandemic. The lunch and dinner menus offer contemporary British cuisine from chef Ian Howard. Top Tip – the cream tea is a steal at £10 for homemade scones, Cornish clotted cream and strawberry jam plus a pot of tea. / W1; www.athenaeumhotel.com; @theathenaeum; Mon-Sat 10 pm, Sun 2.30 pm; closed Sun D.

1 LOMBARD STREET
EC3 £72 3|2|3

1 LOMBARD ST 020 7929 6611 10–3C

"King of the City lunching scene" – Soren Jessen's "buzzing" stalwart in the very heart of the Square Mile, near Bank, continues to maintain its "consistent standards" and is "a decent if very 'City' restaurant". "Classic dishes" ("including some added when Mark Hix was still consultant chef") are served alongside "a well-chosen wine list" (and they do an "awesome breakfast" too). / EC3V 9AA; www.1lombardstreet.com; @1lombardstreet; Mon-Sat 11 pm; closed Sun; booking max 10 may apply.

123V W1 £57 3|2|3

**TERRACE & LOWER GROUND FLOOR
AT FENWICK, 63 NEW BOND STREET
020 8132 9088 3–2B**

"The basement of a department store doesn't lend itself to high ambience", but "half the fun of this place is the window shopping on the way in!" From Alexis Gauthier's "interesting all-vegan selection", the "amazingly crafted" sushi "looks amazing" and "is an engaging experience that comes close to 'the real thing' by look and taste". Fans say items like the vegan burgers "are also terrific", although there are also sceptics who find these other options "less convincing". But in summer, "any shortcomings are more than made up for by the brilliant outside location, with a large paved terrace abutting Bond street, where you could be in Cannes under the large umbrellas as you watch the fancy shopping bags and their owners wandering by". / W1W 1RQ; 123vegan.co.uk; @123vegan_w1; Mon-Sat 8 pm, Sun 5 pm; closed Sun D; payment – credit card only.

ONLY FOOD AND COURSES
SW9 £66

**POP BRIXTON, 49 BRIXTON STATION ROAD
07949 259067 11–1D**

In one of Pop Brixton's hip containers, Robbie Lorraine's 6-course tasting menu aims to take guests on a nostalgia trip to the 80s and 90s and is almost as much about pop culture as it is about the food. On limited feedback, though, the latter is much more than an afterthought. STOP PRESS: in July 2022, Lorraine announced that he would be leading the kitchen at the new Boys Hall in Kent and there's no availability shown here till for the remainder of 2022, so its future direction seems up in the air. / SW9 8PQ; www.onlyfoodandcourses.co.uk; @onlyfoodandcourses; Thu-Sat 10.30 pm, Sun 4 pm; closed Sun D, closed Mon & Tue & Wed; booking online only.

LES 110 DE TAILLEVENT W1 £90 3 3 3

16 CAVENDISH SQUARE
020 3141 6016   3–1B

Named for its "phenomenal wine list" – featuring 110 wines available by the glass using the Coravin wine storage system – this London outpost of a famous Parisian group offers a professional all-round formula, which also incorporates high-quality, modern French cuisine and "excellent service" (with particularly "superb sommelier knowledge"); all served in the "well-lit and welcoming" setting of a stylish dining room, looking onto Cavendish Square. On the downside, it can seem expensive; and "on a quiet night, atmosphere is lacking". / W1G 9DD; www.les-110-taillevent-london.com; @110london; Wed-Fri 2.30 pm, Tue, Sat midnight; closed Tue, Sat L closed Wed-Fri D, closed Sun & Mon; credit card deposit required to book.

OPERA TAVERN WC2 £58 2 2 3

23 CATHERINE STREET
020 7836 3680   5–3D

This former pub in Covent Garden (part of Urban Pubs & Bars) serves "dependable tapas-style" Spanish and Italian small plates in an atmosphere that "feels both private and buzzing". Marks have dropped off in recent years, though, and those who remember it back in the day, when it really fizzed along, feel it's "lost its game". / WC2B 5JS; www.saltyardgroup.co.uk/opera-tavern; @operatavern; Mon-Sat 11 pm; closed Sun.

OPSO W1 £93 3 2 3

10 PADDINGTON ST   020 7487 5088   2–1A

"Excellent modern Greek cuisine" (incorporating luxury non-traditional ingredients such as wagyu beef, English

asparagus and truffle mayonnaise) is to be found on the menu at this Marylebone venue from the Athens-based Modern Greek Food Group. It has a funkier 'gastrobar' stablemate, Ino, off Carnaby Street. / W1U 5QL; www.opso.co.uk; @opso_london; Mon-Sat 10.15 pm, Sun 9.45 pm; closed Sun L.

THE ORANGE SW1 £84 2 3 3

37 PIMLICO RD   020 7881 9844   6–2D

This "fun" rustic-chic pub/hotel/events space is a magnet for an "attractive crowd" on the Pimlico-Chelsea border, and serves a "varied range" of food, from wood-fired pizza in the bar to more formal meals in the dining room upstairs. / SW1W 8NE; www.theorange.co.uk; @theorangepublichouse; Mon-Sat 10 pm, Sun 9.30 pm.

ORANGE PEKOE SW13 £40 3 3 4

3 WHITE HART LN   020 8876 6070   11–1A

"A neighbourhood treasure", this well-run tea shop near the river in Barnes serves "every kind of tea possible", plus "super cakes and sandwiches". It's "highly sought-after" for its afternoon teas – "you'll need to book for a cuppa and a slice of cake at busy times". More substantial meals for brunch/lunch can be "disappointing". / SW13 0PX; www.orangepekoeteas.com; @orangepekoeteas; Mon-Sun 5 pm; closed Mon-Sun D.

THE ORANGE TREE N20 £66 3 3 3

7 TOTTERIDGE VILLAGE
020 8343 7031   1–1B

This 'country pub' in Totteridge village, on London's northern fringe, boasts a global menu that covers everything from oriental-inspired dishes to steaks from the grill, and wins a general thumbs-up from reporters. / N20 8NX; www.theorangetreetotteridge.co.uk; Tue-Sat 9 pm; closed Sun & Mon.

ORASAY W11 £59 5 4 4

31 KENSINGTON PARK ROAD
020 7043 1400   7–1A

"Every dish screams eat me!" – "Jackson Boxer is delivering some seriously bold cooking" – in particular "incredibly delicious seafood" (but also "wonderful wood-fired meats") – at his Notting Hill three-year-old, named for the Hebridean island where he spent many childhood summers. Top Menu Tip – "the Mull scallop in vin jaune is a highlight amongst many, many brilliantly executed dishes". / W11 2EU; orasay.london; @orasay.london; Tue-Thu 10 pm, Fri & Sat 11 pm, Sun 3.30 pm; closed Tue-Thu L closed Sun D, closed Mon.

OREN E8 £64 4 3 2

89 SHACKLEWELL LANE
020 7916 6114   14–1A

"I just love Oren's food", say the many fans of chef Oden Oren's simple 30-seater in Dalston, which catapulted into the front rank of new-wave Middle Eastern venues when it opened three years ago. The modern Israeli and eastern Med small plates, along with wines recommended by Zeren Wilson, "never disappoint". Top Tip – "pollock pastrami is really memorable". / E8 2EB; www.orenlondon.com; @orenlondon; Tue-Sat 11 pm; closed Tue-Fri L, closed Sun & Mon.

ORIENT LONDON W1 £51 4 3 2

15 WARDOUR STREET
020 7989 8880   5–3A

Near the gateway leading into Chinatown, this undistinguished looking Chinese venue is one of the better bets in the area: the food is "always tip top" and "less clichéd" than often is the case nearby. Seafood is tipped as is the "excellent dim sum". / W1W 6PH; www.orientlondon.com; @orientlondon; Sun-Thu 11.30 pm, Fri & Sat midnight.

ORMER MAYFAIR BY SOFIAN, FLEMINGS MAYFAIR HOTEL W1 £115 4 5 3

7-12 HALF MOON STREET
020 7016 5601   3–4B

"A choice of 6-course or 8-course tasting menus and a fantastic selection of wines" greets visitors to this 1930s-style, oak-panelled chamber in Mayfair, which scored uniformly high marks this year for Sofian Msetfi's accomplished, seasonal British cuisine. There are also vegetarian and vegan alternative menus (the latter of which requires 48 hours notice). / W1J 7BH; www.flemings-mayfair.co.uk/fine-dining-london/ormer-mayfair-restaurant; @ormer.mayfair; Mon-Fri 7 pm, Sat 5 pm; closed Sat D, closed Sun; no shorts.

Oklava EC2

ORO DI NAPOLI
W5 £40 342

6 THE QUADRANT, LITTLE EALING LANE
020 3632 5580 1–3A

This Neapolitan pizzeria vies with nearby Santa Maria as "the pizza place of choice" in the local Ealing battle for supremacy. They also offer fried pizza for a different slant on the fast-food classic. / W5 4EE; www.lorodinapoli-ealing.com; @lorodinapoliealing; Mon-Sun 10 pm.

ORRERY W1 £94 222

55 MARYLEBONE HIGH ST
020 7616 8000 2–1A

Above Marylebone's Conran Shop, this "well-spaced", first-floor dining room has historically been a D&D London flagship thanks to its stylish interior, charming views over a churchyard, professional standards and – a relatively recent addition – a "lovely outdoor rooftop terrace". For the second year since the pandemic struck, though, its ratings remain well below their historical levels. Some do still report their best meal of the year here, praising "outstanding modern French cuisine"; but sceptics are "disappointed because it used to be so much better". It doesn't help that "the ambience of this long and thin chamber has always been slightly precarious" and, at worst, reports are of "mediocre food (relative to the price) served in a very underwhelming manner in a dead environment". One regular, though, thinks it's just a passing phase: "after being through something of a culinary slump, I had an excellent meal!" / W1U 5RB; www.orrery-restaurant.co.uk; @the_Orrery; Mon-Sat 10 pm, Sun 9 pm; booking max 8 may apply.

OSCAR WILDE LOUNGE AT CAFE ROYAL W1 £97 335

68 REGENT ST 020 7406 3333 4–4C

If you're ticking off London's luxe afternoon teas, that offered in the Café Royal's former Grill Room needs to be on your list. Its succession of cakes and savouries is well-reviewed, but of course the star of the show is the rococo room, designed in 1865: a story-book riot of mirrors and painted ceilings (which, for many decades back in the day, was one of the capital's great restaurant destinations). / W1B; www.hotelcaferoyal.com/oscarwilde; @hotelcaferoyal; Tue-Sat midnight; closed Tue-Thu L, closed Sun & Mon.

OSLO COURT
NW8 £73 355

CHARLBERT STREET 020 7722 8795 9–3A

"Let's do the time warp again (…and again, and again, and again, and…)" – this happy relic at the foot of a Regent's Park apartment block "hasn't changed in 30 years, and why should it?" Stuck in perpetuity in the mid-1970s (complete with salmon-pink décor; long-serving waiters from that era; and a menu that's not wittingly nostalgic, it just never changed) "it would take the hardest of hearts not to be moved to inexplicable joy by an occasional visit here". The "amazing staff really look

after you", "you won't leave hungry", and the arrival of the dessert trolley provides a rapturous climax to the occasion. They are also terrific with kids, who often dine here as part of large family groups incorporating relatives at least 70 years their senior. / NW8 7EN; www.oslocourtrestaurant.co.uk; Mon-Sat 11 pm; closed Sun; No jeans.

OSTERIA, BARBICAN CENTRE
EC2 £53 322

LEVEL 2 SILK STREET
020 7588 3008 10–1B

It's pleasing that this monolithic arts centre boasts a respectable restaurant, in the form of this Searcy's-run operation, which is ideally situated for a meal around a performance, and uniformly well-rated. There are niggles though – even those who applaud "very decent Italian cuisine" can note "the odd lapse" in execution, or say the overall meal "lacked finesse". / EC2Y 8DS; osterialondon.co.uk; @SearcysLondon; Mon-Sat 7 pm; closed Sun.

OSTERIA ANTICA BOLOGNA
SW11 £67 332

23 NORTHCOTE RD 020 7978 4771 11–2C

"Genuine Italian home cooking" has made this rustic, wood-panelled trattoria a "favourite place for family celebrations" for more than three decades in one of South London's top family zones, Clapham's 'Nappy Valley'. It's a useful reminder that there's more to la cucina Italiana than pizza and pasta, and "the wild boar is to die for!". / SW11 1NG; www.osteria.co.uk; @osteriaanticabologna; Tue-Fri 21.45 pm, Sat 10 pm, Sun 8.45 pm; closed Mon.

OSTERIA BASILICO
W11 £73 333

29 KENSINGTON PARK RD
020 7727 9957 7–1A

"Friendly, neighbourhood Italian", now in its 31st year, that serves "good" if fairly standard food, and – following the lockdown puppy explosion – can appear to "welcome almost as many dogs as human customers". The only real problem is its popularity, which means it "can be a bit crowded as tables are very close to each other". If you can't squeeze in, its two younger siblings in the same street, Essenza and Mediterraneo, are worth a try. / W11 2EU; www.osteriabasilico.co.uk; Mon-Sun 10.30 pm; no booking, Sat L.

OSTERIA TUFO
N4 £63 343

67 FONTHILL RD 020 7272 2911 9–1D

"Simple but delicious Italian food" and a "pretty, light and airy interior" are key ingredients at this good neighbourhood trattoria in Finsbury Park. The formula is topped off by "friendly proprietress Paola" (and, on occasion a "genuine opera-singing waiter") guaranteeing a "lively and fun atmosphere". Top Menu Tip – "leave room for the perfectly sized Cafe Tufo coffee with mascarpone". / N4 3HZ; www.osteriatufo.co.uk; @osteriatufo; Mon-Fri 10.30

pm, Sat 22.30 pm, Sun 8.30 pm; closed Mon-Fri L closed Sat D; no Amex.

OTTO'S WC1 £98 445

182 GRAY'S INN ROAD
020 7713 0107 2–1D

"Unique and outstanding!" – "don't be fooled by the unprepossessing exterior" of Otto Tepasse's very "individual" venture, near Gray's Inn: "one of London's better restaurants". "Inside you find an eclectic, comfortable, old-fashioned interior" ("akin to the ambience of a country antique shop"), where le patron (much in evidence) and his "charming" team deliver "comforting and traditional, beautifully prepared French dishes", as part of an old-school and "romantic" experience that's "semi-theatrical in a very good way". "Their signature dish – ordered in advance – is Duck à la Presse": "quite a performance and possibly the richest three courses you'll ever eat" (safest "to be sampled only once in a lifetime!"). Other Top Menu Tips – "exceptional tournedos Rossini and steak tartare". / WC1X 8EW; www.ottos-restaurant.com; @ottos_restaurant; Wed-Fri, Tue, Sat 10 pm; closed Tue, Sat L, closed Sun & Mon.

OTTOLENGHI £71 432

28 PAVILION ROAD, SW1
020 3824 2818 6–2D
63 MARYLEBONE LANE, W1
020 3148 1040 2–1A
63 LEDBURY RD, W11 020 7727 1121 7–1B
287 UPPER ST, N1 020 7288 1454 9–2D
50 ARTILLERY PAS, E1
020 7247 1999 10–2D

Still "a gold standard", with their "lovely, beautifully displayed food" – this small group of deli-cafés has expanded slowly since the first one opened in Notting Hill 21 years ago; the latest arrived in Pavilion Road, Chelsea, in January 2022. Hugely influential Israeli-born chef and writer Yotam Ottolenghi has transformed the way much of the world sees Middle Eastern cuisine – and vegetables. "I'm not a vegetarian, but I love eating the veg dishes here and I find I don't need to order any meat". (See also the chef's two grander restaurants, Nopi and Rovi). / www.ottolenghi.co.uk.

THE OWO SW1

THE OLD WAR OFFICE, 57 WHITEHALL PLACE NO TEL 2–3C

Italian-Argentine megachef Mauro Colagreco, of Mirazur on the French Riviera, is the star gastronomic attraction of the late-2022 launch of the Raffles hotel and apartment complex, emerging from the Edwardian baroque shell of the Old War Office building opposite Whitehall Palace, owned since 2014 by the Hinduja Group. In all, there will be 11 restaurants and two bars on the sprawling site, with Colagreco responsible for 'a brasserie with a twist, a fine-dining restaurant and an avant-garde private chef's table'. / SW1S 2HB; www.theowo.london; @theowo.london; Sun-Thu 11 pm, Fri & Sat 11.30 pm.

OXEYE SW11 £169 544

14 NEW UNION SQUARE
020 8067 7532   11–1D

MasterChef: The Professionals winner, Sven-Hanson Britt has created something "super special" at this late 2021 newcomer, near the new American embassy in Nine Elms. "A Tardis-like journey takes you into such an intimate dining space" decked out with "dark industry-chic" décor. "Staff do a fantastic job of creating a welcoming atmosphere in a restaurant with only a few tables" and "having Sven the chef come out to tell you what each course is and the backstory of each dish is just brilliant!" The food is "sensational" too – "cooked with a lightness of touch which enables the flavours of excellent ingredients to sing" ("the only, minor, issue was that I couldn't eat all the food… just too much of it!"). "Well worth a trip south of the river (only a few minutes on the bus from Vauxhall station)!" / SW11 7AX; oxeyerestaurant.co.uk; @oxeyerestaurant; Wed-Sat 11 pm; closed Mon & Tue & Sun.

OXO TOWER, RESTAURANT SE1 £107 111

BARGE HOUSE ST   020 7803 3888   10–3A

"Great view… shame about the restaurant". This South Bank landmark provides "stunning views over the Thames to the lights of the City of London, bound to impress your date". But it remains "a pity that such an iconic location serves canteen-standard grub" that's "waaayyyyyyy overpriced" ("the night would have been too expensive if it was free! But as it was we paid a hefty sum for a crushing disappointment"). / SE1 9PH; www.harveynichols.com/restaurant/the-oxo-tower; @oxo_tower; Mon-Sun 10 pm; booking max 10 may apply.

OXO TOWER, BRASSERIE SE1 £92 112

BARGE HOUSE ST   020 7803 3888   10–3A

Some do tip it as "a great place for a special occasion", but the slightly cheaper section of this Art Deco landmark is rated almost as poorly as the (more expensive) main dining room. Here, "very average food" is served in a space that's "incredibly noisy and crammed", leading to an experience that can seem "stale and poor"; and with a hefty price tag too. / SE1 9PH; www.oxotowerrestaurant.co.uk; @Oxo_tower; Mon-Sun 10 pm.

THE OYSTERMEN SEAFOOD KITCHEN & BAR WC2 £77 322

32 HENRIETTA ST   020 7240 4417   5–3D

"Lovely oysters and fab fresh fish generally" from a "daily changing blackboard of specials" fuel a meal at this successful joint which is "just like eating in a seaside restaurant". It's "a bit cramped and uncomfortable" for some tastes, but conversely "feels surprisingly intimate for Covent Garden". / WC2W 8NA; oystermen. co.uk; @theoystermen; Tue-Sat 10 pm, Sun 9 pm; closed Mon.

OZONE COFFEE ROASTERS £45 344

EMMA STREET, E2   020 7490 1039   14–2B
11 LEONARD STREET, EC2
020 7490 1039   13–1A

"A top choice for breakfast and coffee" – the Shoreditch and London Fields outlets of this 20-year veteran of the Antipodean speciality coffee scene have imported the chilled, high-quality approach of its branches back home in Auckland and New Plymouth. In E2, the galvanising aroma of roasting coffee wafts up from the beans being ground in the basement, adding to its superb hipster vibe. / ozonecoffee. co.uk.

P FRANCO E5 £57 433

107 LOWER CLAPTON ROAD
020 8533 4660   14–1B

This "too-cool-for-school" Clapton bar and bottle shop has long been a 'must-mention' by journalists creating roundups of East End foodie hot spots. It serves "interesting" low-intervention wines and "inventive small plates" whose "deft cooking and wonderful flavours is hidden by the simplicity of the menu". "The ambience is great too… if you're looking for a slightly tatty and bustling wine bar spilling out onto the pavement in a seedy shopping parade in Hackney". / E5 0NP; www.pfranco.co.uk; @pfranco_e5; Tue, Wed 9 pm, Thu-Sun 10 pm; closed Tue-Sun L, closed Mon; no Amex; no booking.

PACHAMAMA £75 223

18 THAYER STREET, W1
020 7935 9393   3–1A
73 GREAT EASTERN STREET, EC2
020 7846 9595   13–1B

These "groovy Peruvian late-night bar/restaurants" make "a stylish and fun way to end a night out, with a multiplicity of delicious small dishes on the tasting menu". Best to go in a party mood: they can be "too noisy for conversation". /

PADELLA £42 433

6 SOUTHWARK ST, SE1   NO TEL   10–4C
1 PHIPP STREET, EC2   NO TEL   13–2B

"Still some of the very best pasta in London at half the price of most places" continues to inspire rave reviews for these genius pit stops, where "pound for pound the great value for money is always good" ("and extends to the drinks"). "For an unplanned midweek supper there's nothing better", although at the mega-popular Borough Market original it can feel "like a conveyor belt" at busier times. At "the funky newish premises in Shoreditch" there's "rather more space than in SE1, with proper booking… what's not to like". Top Menu Tip – "just go for the cacio e pepe… but everything else is good as well". /

PAHLI HILL BANDRA BHAI W1 £83 322

79-81 MORTIMER STREET
020 8130 0101   3–1C

This contemporary two-year-old near Selfridges (on the former site of Gaylord, RIP) is the first London venture from New Delhi-based Azure Hospitality, and serves an "intriguing" menu inspired by the posh Mumbai suburb it is named after. The kitchen uses high-quality British produce, including some "interesting veggies", to produce cooking that's "full of enjoyable flavours". Meanwhile, down in 'Bandra Bhai', the basement 'smugglers den', you can find some "dangerously delicious cocktails!". / W1W 7SJ; palihill.co.uk; @palihilluk; Tue-Sat 10 pm, Sun 4 pm; closed Sun D, closed Mon.

PALACE LOUNGE, THE RUBENS AT THE PALACE SW1

39 BUCKINGHAM PALACE RD
020 7834 6600   2–4B

"With window views of the back of Buckingham Palace and its comings and goings amidst refills of tea", this plush lounge can make a good stop-off for an afternoon treat. Feedback is limited, but praises "a lovely stack of sandwiches, pretty cakes and scones with fresh flavours". More substantial meals are available in the hotel's very comfortable and traditional dining room (The English Grill), complete with oil paintings and leather banquettes. / SW1W 0PS; www.rubenshotel.com; Sun-Wed 11 pm, Thu-Sat midnight; Jacket required.

PALADAR SE1 £62 445

4-5 LONDON ROAD   020 7186 5555   10–4A

"You go here to have an all-embracing 'good time'" if you pop down to this "quirky and fun" destination, near Elephant & Castle. "It specialises in Latin American recipes from across the continent" using "genuine ingredients" to produce "unusual and delicious dishes". "What also makes this restaurant stand out is the outstanding wine list and friendly and knowledgeable service": "they always make it feel that there is a big party on!" / SE1 6JZ; www.paladarlondon.com; @paladarlondon; Tue-Fri 9.30 pm, Mon 9 pm, Sat 10 pm, Sun 8 pm; closed Mon L; payment – credit card only.

THE PALOMAR W1 £63 444

34 RUPERT STREET   020 7439 8777   4–3D

"In the teeth of ever-growing competition in the Middle Eastern/eastern Med bracket", this funky Tel Aviv-inspired grill on the edge of Chinatown continues to justify its reputation, serving "fantastic sharing plates" with "good robust flavours" in a "fun" and "buzzy" – if "rather crowded and very noisy" – setting. / W1D 6DN; www.thepalomar.co.uk; @PalomarSoho; Mon-Wed, Fri & Sat 11 pm, Thu 10 pm, Sun 9 pm.

PARADISE W1 £60 `4` `3` `3`

61 RUPERT STREET   NO TEL   4–2D

"Top-quality Sri Lankan food" – full of "interesting flavours" – draws an appreciative crowd to this modern venue "in the heart of Soho", where the kitchen combines carefully sourced British produce with South Asian spicing. It's run by former Wasps rugby player Sam Jones, with consultant Zeren Wilson advising on the low-intervention wine list. / W1W 7PW; www.paradisesoho.com; @paradisesoho; Tue-Sat, Mon 11 pm; closed Mon L, closed Sun.

PARADISE HAMPSTEAD NW3 £35 `3` `5` `3`

49 SOUTH END RD   020 7794 6314   9–2A

This "wonderful and consistent Indian" has served generations of Hampstead locals for more than 50 years. Now run by the founder's son, its USP is the "very attentive service" – "we get a marvellous warm welcome each and every time". The food is "reliably tasty", too. Top Tips – "the lamb Ceylon and tarka dhal are to die for". / NW3 2QB; www.paradisehampstead.co.uk; Mon-Sun 11.30 pm.

PARK CHINOIS W1 £143 `3` `2` `4`

17 BERKELEY ST   020 3327 8888   3–3C

Flamboyant décor and regular live entertainment aim to recreate the decadence of 1930s Shanghai at this showy Mayfair mandarin. As in previous years, it takes some flak for its pricing, but ratings for its luxurious cuisine (which includes Scottish Rib-Eye and imported Wagyu steaks, alongside Peking Duck, dim sum and more evidently Chinese dishes) were consistently good this year. / W1S 4NF; www.parkchinois.com; @parkchinois; Mon & Tue, Sun midnight, Wed & Thu 1 am, Fri & Sat 2 am; closed Mon-Fri L; No jeans.

PARK ROW W1 £105 `2` `2` `4`

77 BREWER STREET   02037 453 431   4–3C

"A wonderful themed entrance, through a bookcase in a library and down dark, futuristic stairs" sets an appropriate scene at this Marvel-themed basement (in association with Warner Bros), just off Piccadilly Circus. "The décor of the restaurant itself, though, contains rather less fantasy… without the entrance you might not even guess the Marvel-connection… it feels more jazz-age New York or an ocean liner". ("Contrary to my impression from the website, it is essentially one big room containing most of the different restaurants and bars, although the differences between them are subtle.") "The food is a mixed bag": some items are "excellent", but "despite the talented chef, other dishes are overpriced or subpar". Overall, though, leaving aside the cartoonish prices, everyone accepts that there is some serious culinary endeavour going on here. And such feedback that we have on the most expensive option (the exotic tasting menu in the separate 'Monarch Theatre'

experience) says it's "exceptional". / W1W 9ZN; www.parkrowlondon.co.uk; @parkrowlondon; Tue, Wed 1 am, Thu-Sat 1, Sun 9 pm; closed Mon.

PARLOUR KENSAL NW10 £66 `4` `3` `4`

5 REGENT ST   020 8969 2184   1–2B

Limited but upbeat feedback this year on this Kensal Rise fixture (akin to a gastropub) run by Jesse Dunford Wood, which opens from breakfast on (with a break in the afternoons). The place really comes into its own during brunch or Sunday lunch. Top Menu Tip – 'Cow Pie'. / NW10 5LG; www.parlourkensal.com; @parlouruk; Mon-Sun 10 pm.

PARRILLAN £121 `3` `3` `3`

COAL DROPS YARD, N1 020 7018 3339   9–3C
BOROUGH YARDS, 4 DIRTY LANE, SE1   NO TEL   10–4C

"In an outdoor, but well-sheltered setting", the Hart Bros' outside-only terrace in Coal Drops Yard has won a good following: "dining outside on a sunny day is a highlight", and the tabletop 'parrilla' grills allow guests the fun of cooking their own meat, seafood and vegetables over coals. On the downside, though, "results can be very average at high prices" and "while it works as a novelty, having a proper chef to cook for you is generally a better option in a restaurant!" In May 2022 (too late for survey feedback), they opened a second Borough Yards location. Like its sibling, it too has an outside terrace (with 40 covers), also with grills. But, for the first time, you will not have to DIY here, there also being an indoor restaurant (with 60 covers) with a menu designed for sharing cooked for you in the open kitchen. /

PARSONS WC2 £65 `4` `4` `3`

39 ENDELL STREET   020 3422 0221   5–2C

"If you can squeeze inside this tiny restaurant off Covent Garden (which has expanded out onto the pavement in recent years thankfully) you will be in for a real treat" and one "at a very fair price". Over its five years in operation, it's become one of London's top destinations for "spankingly fresh fish and seafood", "accurately cooked with brio in a small, bright space". "The unique gimmick here is that what's on the menu depends entirely on what they can get from the day boats in the morning and so could be anything. Dishes and prices are scrawled on the wall tiles with a reassuring lack of upselling; and wine comes from the ever-evolving selection at their sibling '10 Cases' over the road so you never have the same meal twice". "Lively and helpful" service completes the excellent offering. Top Menu Tips – "super oysters at £1 each" are a feature, "potted shrimp croquettes feature amongst the excellent-but-small selection of staples; and if you go in the winter you might be lucky enough to sample their legendary lobster mash". / WC2W 9BA; www.parsonslondon.co.uk; @parsons_london; Tue-Sat 10 pm; closed Sun & Mon.

PASCOR W8 £61

221 KENSINGTON HIGH STREET 020 7937 3003   8–1D

Perhaps because it's easy to ignore amongst the dross of Kensington High Street, this two-year-old venue focused on the eastern Med doesn't inspire much feedback this year, but such as we received is all positive. In June 2022, Tomar Amedi (former head chef of The Palomar) joined, and it is now billed as a 'Levantine Fire Kitchen'. Could be one to watch. / W8 6SG; www.pascor.co.uk; @pascor_restaurant; Mon-Sun 10 pm; closed Mon-Thu L.

PASTAIO W1 £55 `3` `3` `3`

19 GANTON STREET   020 3019 8680   4–2B

"A great place for a bowl of really well-executed pasta after a hard day's shopping or pre-theatre". "It's only a shame that this Soho pasta-café is almost the only place you can now experience Stevie Parle's lovely cooking". / W1F 7BU; www.pastaio.london; @pastaiolondon; Sun-Thu 10.30 pm, Fri & Sat 11 pm.

PASTAN EC1 £48 `3` `4` `3`

12-14 ST JOHN STREET 020 7253 3333   10–1A

After successful pop-ups in Bristol and Notting Hill, this plant-based artisan pasta venture moved into its first permanent site in late 2021 (provocatively, perhaps, just off Smithfield meat market). Early reports are all positive – "I didn't even realise it was vegan!" / EC1E 4AY; pastan. co.uk; @pastanuk; Tue-Thu 9 pm, Fri & Sat 9.30 pm; closed Sun & Mon.

PATARA £74 `3` `3` `2`

15 GREEK ST, W1   020 7437 1071   5–2A
7 MADDOX ST, W1   020 7499 6008   4–2A
181 FULHAM RD, SW3
020 7351 5692   6–2C
9 BEAUCHAMP PL, SW3
020 7581 8820   6–1C
82 HAMPSTEAD HIGH ST, NW3
020 7431 5902   9–2A
18 HIGH ST, SW19   020 3931 6157   11–2B

With its "authentic Thai food" (the mother restaurant is in Bangkok), this international group is still a "go-to Thai brand in the capital" for many reporters, especially if you want an experience "more up-market than at many of its competitors". Restaurateur Khun Patara Sila-On opened her first London branch in South Ken 33 years ago, and has added five more in central London, Hampstead and Wimbledon. / www.pataralondon.com; pataralondon.

PATERNOSTER CHOP HOUSE EC4 £71 `2` `4` `2`

1 WARWICK COURT   020 7029 9400   10–2B

A dependable steak remains the menu highlight at this D&D London grill, but some regulars are "disappointed that it has moved location (from Paternoster Square to Ludgate Hill) and is no longer overlooking St Paul's". Oddly for a restaurant catering to City business diners, the previous venue became famous for hosting reality TV show 'First Dates'. / EC4M 7DX; www.paternosterchophouse.co.uk; @paternosterchophouse; Mon-Fri 10 pm, Sat 10.30 pm, Sun 4.30 pm; closed Sun D; booking max 12 may apply.

PATRI £47 3 3 2

139 NORTHFIELD AVENUE, W13
020 3981 3388 1–3A
103 HAMMERSMITH GROVE, W6
020 8741 1088 8–1C

"Delhi-style street food" from an "extensive menu with different descriptions" has won a fan club for these "fun", "small" and basic cantinas in Ealing (x2) and on gracious Hammersmith Grove. Reviews this year however weren't quite as enthusiastic as in times past. /

PATTY AND BUN £44 3 2 2

18 OLD COMPTON ST, W1
020 7287 1818 5–2A
26 KINGLY STREET, W1
020 7287 9632 4–2A
54 JAMES ST, W1 020 7487 3188 3–1A
156 PORTOBELLO ROAD, W11
020 3951 9675 7–1B
101 WOOD LANE, W12
020 7223 0900 1–2B
19 BOROUGH HIGH STREET, SE1
020 7407 7994 10–4C
12 NORTHCOTE ROAD, SW11
020 7223 0900 11–2C
20 WATER STREET, E14 NO TEL 12–1C
2 ARTHAUS BUILDING, 205 RICHMOND ROAD, E8 020 8525 8250 14–1B
22-23 LIVERPOOL ST, EC2
020 7621 1331 10–2D

"If you want your meal dripping down your chest, this is the place!" – "very consistent and superb-tasting burgers" again win a big thumbs-up for this expanding chain, which in 2022 adds branches in first Northcote Road, then Canary Wharf. Top Menu Tips – their classic 'Ari Gold' and 'Smokey Robinson' options are consistently great (cooked rare on request); vegetarian burgers get upvoted; and any "monthly specials are always worth a look" ("love the limited editions"); "decent sides too". / www.pattyandbun.co.uk; pattyandbun.

PEARL LIANG W2 £54 3 3 3

8 SHELDON SQUARE 020 7289 7000 7–1C

With its "superior dim sum", this unusually spacious modern basement venue in Paddington Basin is often tipped as "better than the Chinatown options". From the main menu, the "great Cantonese cooking" comes in "generous portions", with pretty much "everything of an exemplary standard" – while service is "particularly accommodating and cheerful". / W2 6EZ; www.pearlliang.co.uk; @pearl_liang_restaurant; Mon-Sun 11 pm.

PECKHAM BAZAAR
SE15 £61 4 3 3

119 CONSORT RD 020 7732 2525 1–4D

"Boom! – of the school of cooking that says 'let's set fire to it and then drown it in olive oil'… wonderful!" – Albanian-born John Gionleka's Peckham pub conversion is based around a charcoal grill, as inspired by the cuisine of the former Ottoman Empire, stretching all the way from Croatia via the Balkans and Greece to Anatolia. The wine list covers much the same territory, with excursions into France and the Lebanon. / SE15 3RU; www.peckhambazaar.com; @peckhambazaar; Mon-Sat 11 pm, Sun 4 pm; closed Mon-Wed L closed Sun D.

PECKHAM CELLARS
SE15 £59 4 4 3

125 QUEENS ROAD 020 7207 0124 1–4D

This "fantastic local wine bar is worth a trip" to Peckham, where it is a star of the foodie scene that has blossomed in recent years. An "informal" operation that "always has an interesting selection of food and unusual wines" – "the menu's not huge", but the modern European dishes are well thought-out, and "both food and wine represent very good value for what you're getting". (In 2023, they will launch a spin-off in Camberwell, called 'Little Cellars'.) / SE15 2ND; peckhamcellars.co.uk; @peckhamcellars; Tue-Sat 11 pm, Sun 3 pm; closed Tue-Thu L closed Sun D, closed Mon; credit card deposit required to book.

THE PELICAN
W11 £67 3 3 3

45 ALL SAINTS RD 020 4537 2880 7–1B

This "newly opened pub with excellent food and vibe" is the latest iteration of a Notting Hill tavern built in 1872 and now tastefully buffed up. Jimi Famurewa of the Evening Standard gave chef Owen Kenworth a big thumbs-up for his "gutsy, sneakily creative food". It is also one of very few pubs to offer Pilates classes. / W11 1HE; thepelicanw11.com; @thepelican_w11; Mon-Sat midnight, Sun 10.30 pm; closed Mon-Thu L.

E PELLICCI E2 £22 3 5 4

332 BETHNAL GREEN RD
020 7739 4873 13–1D

"This top-notch Bethnal Green café" is "the place to go for London's best breakfast" – not just on account of the full English and bacon sarnies, but for the Art Deco wood panelling (Grade-II listed!) and the atmosphere created by four generations of the Pellicci family, who have run it since 1900. "What makes it different is the warm and funny staff", who draw "a happy mix of locals, tourists and everyone in between". Top Tip – "don't ask for anything gluten-free or they might laugh!" / E2 0AG; epellicci.has.restaurant; Mon-Sat 4 pm; closed Mon-Sat D, closed Sun; cash only; no booking.

THE PEM SW1 £98 4 4 2

CONRAD LONDON ST. JAMES, 22-28 BROADWAY 020 3301 8080 2–3C

Sally Abé has equalled the "superb" standard of British cooking that she achieved at the Harwood Arms at this Westminster yearling, named for a pioneering suffragette. But while the traditional hotel dining room she was imported to revivify is an "amazingly spacious and comfy space" – and benefits from "quietly super-efficient and knowledgeable staff" – it doesn't yet generate the volume of reports it perhaps deserves: "why was it empty? This deserves to be one of London's most popular restaurants!" / SW1S 0BH; thepemrestaurant.com; @thepemrestaurant; Tue, Sat, Wed-Fri 9.30 pm; closed Tue, Sat L, closed Sun & Mon.

PENTOLINA W14 £61 4 4 4

71 BLYTHE RD 020 3010 0091 8–1C

This "lovely local restaurant" run by an Italian couple in a quiet backwater near Brook Green is a popular choice for its "really delightful staff" and "excellent range of dishes". It's a small but light and airy space, with "tables outside in summer". / W14 0HP; www.pentolinarestaurant.co.uk; @pentolina_london; Tue-Sat 9.30 pm; closed Sun & Mon; no Amex.

PERILLA N16 £77 4 4 3

1-3 GREEN LANES 020 7359 0779 1–1C

"Absolutely exceptional" modern European cuisine is created by chef Ben Marks (ex-Noma and The Square) at his former pop-up overlooking Newington Green. There's a "good-value tasting menu" (which incorporates a service charge), and an "excellent variety of dishes", making best use of relatively modest rather than 'luxury' ingredients. / N16 9BS; www.perilladining.co.uk; @perilladining; Fri & Sat, Tue-Thu 11 pm, Sun 6 pm; closed Tue-Thu L closed Sun D, closed Mon.

THE PERRY HILL
SE6 £53 3 4 4

78-80 PERRY HILL 020 8699 3334 1–4D

A welcome 2021 relaunch after being closed for years – this roadhouse on the South Circular between Sydenham and Catford serves "generous" dishes that "elevate it beyond pub grub, but without pretending to be a gastropub". The food comes courtesy of Jamie Younger, who runs Peckham's Begging Bowl and was formerly at the Palmerston in East Dulwich; his "smoked and slow-cooked options are a triumph (red chicken, short ribs)". The "huge outdoor areas" make "weekend lunch en famille with toddlers a jolly affair" – a market sector enticed by a discount club for parents with young kids. / SE6 4EY; www.perryhillpub.co.uk; @perryhillpub; Mon-Sat 11 pm, Sun 10.30 pm.

PERSIAN PALACE
W13 £32 3 4 2

143-145 UXBRIDGE ROAD
020 8840 4233 1–3A

"Consistently good food, huge portions and excellent value" win solid ratings for this Persian local in Ealing. There's a "great menu of traditional dishes including kebabs, kashk and ghormeh sabzi" – the classic Persian stew – while "the décor and ambience are authentic and make you feel like you're in another country". / W13 9AU; www.persianpalace.co.uk/ealing; @persianppalace; Mon-Thu 10.30 pm, Fri-Sun 11 pm.

THE PETERSHAM
WC2 £102 223
FLORAL COURT, OFF FLORAL ST
020 7305 7676 5–3C

The undoubtedly "beautiful central London location" of this Covent Garden spin-off from the famous Richmond plant nursery makes it – for some reporters – "worth paying for the pricey food" in its two restaurants, especially if you have romance in mind. Plenty of others disagree, complaining of "disappointing" food in an operation that is "not even a decent shadow of the home port". / WC2W 9DJ; petershamnurseries.com; @petershamnurseries; Thu-Sat, Mon-Wed 9.30 pm; closed Sun; no trainers.

PETERSHAM NURSERIES CAFE TW10 £123 235
CHURCH LANE (SIGNPOSTED 'ST PETER'S CHURCH'), OFF PETERSHAM ROAD
020 8940 5230 1–4A

"A stunning location – perfect for a summer's lunch" guarantees the appeal of this shabby-chic café, inside a garden centre amidst some of the plusher housing on the fringe of Richmond Park. When it comes to the ambitious cuisine, it's "always tempting and food is never disappointing… but when the bill arrives there's often a sense that it wasn't worth the final cost". / TW10 7AB; www.petershamnurseries.com; @petershamnurseriescafe; Tue, Wed, Sun 5 pm, Thu-Sat 11 pm; closed Tue, Wed, Sun D, closed Mon.

THE PETERSHAM RESTAURANT
TW10 £80 223
NIGHTINGALE LANE 020 8003 3602 1–4A

"Excellent views over the meadows and Thames" make this dining room of a grand Richmond hotel (built in 1865) "a lovely place for a romantic dinner". Sunday lunch and afternoon tea are also popular choices. It's "a bit of a time-capsule", though, and even if prices have moved with the times, standards generally can be reminiscent of a former, less demanding, era. / TW10 6UZ; petershamhotel. co.uk/restaurant; @thepetershamhotel; Mon-Sun 9 pm.

LE PETIT BEEFBAR
SW3 £179
27 CALE STREET 020 4580 1219 6–2C

Riccardo Giradui's Chelsea newcomer is the first UK offshoot in a collection with branches in Mykonos, Dubai, Mirabel, and Monte-Carlo (the original). Giradui describes the concept as a 'temple of beef' with meat sourced globally. Too limited feedback for a review, but one seasoned reporter who lives locally notes: "There's no doubt you get a great steak here. Just expect to pay top dollar for it. The Monaco/Dubai connection drives

the clientele, which is more Knightsbridge than Chelsea". / SW3 3QP; lepetit.beefbar.com; @lepetitbeefbar; Thu-Sat, Tue, Wed 10.30 pm, Sun 3 pm; closed Tue, Wed L closed Sun D, closed Mon.

LE PETIT CITRON
W6 £56 333
98-100 SHEPHERDS BUSH ROAD
020 3019 1175 8–1C

"A nice and buzzy local bistro" that's attractively styled and "a good choice in the area" (a barren stretch of trafficky road, north of Brook Green). The formula is classically French, including a handy prix-fixe option. / W6 7PD; lepetitcitron.co.uk; @lepetitcitronw6; Mon-Sat 10 pm, Sun 4 pm; closed Sun D; payment – credit card only.

PETIT MA CUISINE
TW9 £62 333
8 STATION APPROACH
020 8332 1923 1–3A

This "very satisfying French throwback bistro" certainly looks the part, with its gingham tablecloths, Impressionist posters and tiled floor – and the menu of Gallic classics lives up to expectations: "we took French friends who thought it was fantastic!" Top Tip – "the prix-fixe lunch is super", and combines well with a visit to nearby Kew Gardens. / TW9 3QB; www.macuisinebistrot.co.uk; Tue-Sun 11.30 pm; closed Mon; no Amex.

PÉTRUS SW1 £144 221
1 KINNERTON ST 020 7592 1609 6–1D

"Interesting and eclectic wine" continues to live up to the name of Gordon Ramsay's luxurious Belgravian (which is built around a large central wine cage), but its performance this year slipped well below its historic trend: no top meals of the year were reported and instead a big proportion of disappointments. It doesn't help that prices are "ridiculous" and that there's sometimes "no atmosphere". / SW1X 8EA; www.gordonramsayrestaurants.com; @petrusrestaurant; Wed-Sat 11 pm, Sun 6 pm; closed Sun D, closed Mon & Tue; no trainers.

PHAM SUSHI EC1 £49 333
159 WHITECROSS ST
020 7251 6336 13–2A

"Handily close to the Barbican", this Japanese venue provides "quick and friendly service" and fans say the food is "always very, very good," too, from a "varied menu". Not all reports were as stellar this year, though. / EC1Y 8JL; www.phamsushi.com; @phamsushi; Mon-Fri 9 pm; closed Sat & Sun.

PHAT PHUC SW3 £38 423
CHELSEA COURTYARD, 151 SYDNEY STREET 020 7351 3843 6–3C

"Unique, authentic and to a high standard" – the tasty Vietnamese and Singaporean bowls at this street noodle bar present some of the best eating value in expensive Chelsea. A South East Asian counterpart

to the 'dirty burger', the name apparently means 'happy Buddha' – and you can buy the T-shirt or cap to prove you've eaten here. / SW3 6NT; www.phatphucnoodlebar.co.uk; @phat_phuc_noodle_bar; Mon-Sun 7 pm.

PHOENIX PALACE
NW1 £64 322
5-9 GLENTWORTH ST 020 7486 3515 2–1A

"Always quick, always reliable" and "pretty authentic" – this vast and traditional Cantonese banqueting hall near Baker Street tube offers more than 300 different dishes on its eight menus – "so if you avoid the obvious, there are plenty of excellent choices". / NW1 5PG; www.phoenixpalace.co.uk; @thephoenixpalace; Mon-Sat 11.30 pm, Sun 10.30 pm.

PIAZZA ITALIANA
EC2 £71 333
38 THREADNEEDLE STREET
020 7256 7223 10–2C

Occupying an impressive Edwardian banking hall in the heart of the City, this high-ceilinged space provides a large, classic Italian menu and – if you still have space – makes a feature of a sizeable cheeseboard, showcasing Italian cheeses. Reports are uniformly upbeat, including as a business choice (and, if Accounts are on your case, there's a good-value lunchtime set menu). / EC2E 8AY; www.piazzaitaliana.co.uk; @piazzaitalianauk; Mon-Wed 10 pm, Thu-Sat 11 pm; closed Sat L, closed Sun.

PIDGIN E8 £85 432
52 WILTON WAY 020 7254 8311 14–1B

One of Hackney's better-known culinary destinations, this unassuming little spot wins high marks from everyone who reports on it for our annual diners' survey, on the basis of its "lovely tasting menu". On the downside, "the space is small so feels crammed" and – given all the excitement that's been whipped up over the years – the odd reporters find it "very good, but a mite underwhelming compared to the rave reviews". / E8 1BG; www.pidginlondon.com; @pidginlondon; Wed-Sun 11 pm; closed Wed-Fri L, closed Mon & Tue.

PIED À TERRE
W1 £138 444
34 CHARLOTTE ST 020 7636 1178 2–1C

"Still impressive, reinventing itself and going strong!" – David Moore is the "warmest of hosts" and his exceptional Fitzrovian townhouse has been at the vanguard of London's dining scene for three decades now. "Many chefs pass through his patronage" – the current incumbent being Asimakis Chaniotis, whose "surprising" and "fabulously flavoursome" dishes include the option of one of London's foremost vegan tasting menus: "particularly impressive, imaginative and fun – even carnivores don't miss the meat!" It's not a huge site, but clever conversions over the years have created a "comfortable" and "lively" space (with a chef's table and bijoux private dining room on the upper floors). There were a couple of 'off' reports this year, of the "maybe-I-caught-it-on-a-bad-night" variety. But all-round raves remain the norm here: "I have been coming to this restaurant for over two decades and have never failed to be delighted!". Top Tip – "the vegan feast was a highlight of lockdown" and has continued as a home delivery option – "a wide range of delicious dishes, all with tantalisingly deep flavours". / W1T 2NH; www.pied-a-terre.co.uk; @PiedaTerreRestaurant; Thu-Sat, Tue, Wed 10 pm; closed Tue, Wed L, closed Sun & Mon; may need 8+ to book.

PIERRE VICTOIRE W1   £55   3 2 3

5 DEAN ST   020 7287 4582   3–1D

Celebrating its quarter century this year, this Soho survivor of what was once a national chain is "bustling and busy, but you can't argue with really decent French bistro food at this price in central London" ("I was pleasantly surprised by the quality…" – "I don't know how they keep the prices so reasonable"). / W1D 3RQ; www.pierrevictoire.com/london/restaurant; Sun-Wed 11 pm, Thu-Sat 11.30 pm.

PIG & BUTCHER N1   £66   3 2 3

80 LIVERPOOL ROAD   020 7226 8304   9–3D

This "pretty decent gastropub" – "the best in Islington" by some reckoning – butchers its own meat for the table. Everyone agrees that the food is "high quality" – "even the snacks are great!" – but "it's a busy place and the service is a little chaotic". / N1 0QD; www.thepigandbutcher.co.uk; Mon-Sat 10 pm, Sun 9 pm.

THE PIG'S HEAD SW4   £77   3 3 3

87 RECTORY GROVE
020 4568 5830   11–1D

"A great conversion of a big old pub in Clapham" – this November 2021 newcomer is the fourth site of the team behind Smokehouse, The Pig & Butcher and The Princess of Shoreditch. It's a "stylish and high-spec" renovation to create a buzzy attractive space over two levels. The main area is "a bit of a noisy barn" – "the mezzanine (with views to the kitchen) is the more interesting/quieter area foodwise". The menu has a sustainability focus ("the more 'unfashionable' meats: bone marrow, pig's head, mutton"), but at the overview it "serves up really well-cooked British pub dining". / SW4 0DR; www.thepigshead.com; @thepigshead; Mon-Sat 10.30 pm, Sun 9 pm; closed Mon & Tue L; payment – credit card only; credit card deposit required to book.

PIQUE NIQUE SE1   £75   3 3 3

32 TANNER STREET   020 7403 9549   10–4D

"One of the most oddly-located restaurants you can imagine", this "authentically French" outfit (sibling to Casse-Croûte on nearby Bermondsey Street) "looks like an ex-tennis clubhouse opposite a kids' playground". It's a "charming

and delightful place", though, and the food is of "high quality" – sometimes "simply superb". / SE1 3LD; pique-nique.co.uk; @piquenique32; Mon-Sat 11 pm, Sun 5 pm; closed Sun D.

EL PIRATA W1   £54   2 3 3

5-6 DOWN ST   020 7491 3810   3–4B

This old-school tapas bar tucked away in Mayfair boasts an "interesting wine list, attentive staff and fun atmosphere". There's a "good selection of dishes – nothing spectacular, but a pretty decent effort across hot and cold tapas". It's "not particularly cheap" by most standards, but in this part of London prices are often astronomical. The most famous pirate of modern times, Johnny Depp, has apparently swung by for a tapa or two. / W1J 7AQ; www.elpirata.co.uk; @elpiratamayfair; closed Mon-Sat & Sun.

PIVOT BY MARK GREENAWAY WC2   £96   4 4 3

3 HENRIETTA STREET
020 3325 5275   5–3D

"Tucked away on the first floor of a Covent Garden townhouse", this late-2021 newcomer from top Scottish chef, Mark Greenaway, is "a great little venue" with a "beautiful setting overlooking Covent Garden piazza". "Pick the chef's counter and you'll be served by Mark himself – an engaging chef, but even if you can't sit at the counter, the restaurant seating has good views". The menu (including breakfast and a pre-theatre option) is versatile and "both delivers on taste and offers good value for the location". Top Menu Tip – beef and bone marrow pie. / WC2W 8LU; 3henrietta.com; @pivotbymarkgreenaway; Wed-Sat 11 pm, Sun 5 pm; closed Sun D, closed Mon & Tue.

PIZARRO SE1   £66   4 4 3

194 BERMONDSEY ST
020 7256 5333   10–4D

"A brilliant venue with its own distinct offer in a street not short of a restaurant or two" – José Pizarro's "buzzy", larger sibling to his nearby tapas bar is "not the place if you want a quiet night" but "consistently good" for its "excellent, authentic Spanish food" ("with lots of sharing options"). / SE1 3TQ; josepizarro.com/pizarro-restaurant-bermondsey; @josepizarrorestaurants; Mon-Sat 10.45 pm, Sun 5 pm; closed Sun D.

PIZZA DA VALTER SW17   £49   4 3 3

7 BELLEVUE ROAD   020 8355 7032   11–2C

"Really good and very Italian pizza" emerges from the oven at this "somewhat basic" pizzeria in the "lovely surroundings" of Wandsworth Common's foodie Bellevue Parade, where neighbours include Chez Bruce. / SW17 7EG; www.pizzadavalter.co.uk; @pizzadavalter; Mon-Sun 11 pm.

PIZZA EAST   £59   3 3 3

310 PORTOBELLO RD, W10
020 8969 4500   7–1A
56 SHOREDITCH HIGH ST, E1
020 7729 1888   13–1B

This "fun" Portobello pizzeria is "made by the excellent location" and has a less-commented-on twin in the equally funky post-industrial setting of Shoreditch's 'Tea Building'. Fans reckon it's "still the one to beat" for "great pizzas", nibbles and a small menu of dishes baked in the wood-fired oven, along with "one of the best Bloody Marys in town"; critics say the "food has lost a little sparkle from a couple of years ago". / www.pizzaeast.com.

PIZZA METRO SW11   £56   3 2 2

64 BATTERSEA RISE
020 7228 3812   11–2C

"Amazing pizza by the metre" has always been the offer at this Battersea Neapolitan that celebrates its 30th anniversary this year. The full 100 cm will set you back £65, and is the equivalent to four conventional circular pizzas. / SW11 1EQ; www.pizzametropizza.com; @pizzametropizza; Tue-Thu 10 pm, Fri, Sun 11.30 pm, Sat midnight; closed Tue-Fri L, closed Mon; no Amex.

PIZZA PILGRIMS   £41   3 3 2

BRANCHES THROUGHOUT LONDON

"Much better than the long-established, tired pizza chains!" – the Elliot brothers' growing group is the most-mentioned of London's more artisanal pizza multiples in our annual diners' poll, inspiring joy with their "authentic Neapolitan preparation, with quality ingredients" and featuring "yummy crusts and interesting flavour combinations". And you get "consistent quality irrespective of the branch visited" too, even if conditions can be "a little cramped and chaotic". / pizzapilgrims.co.uk; @pizzapilgrims.

PIZZAEXPRESS   £53   1 2 1

BRANCHES THROUGHOUT LONDON

"They have lost the plot since their glory days" and it's increasingly unclear why we continue to review this "vibeless" high-street brand (est. 1965): nowadays solely recommendable as a kid-friendly emergency stand-by. For decades it was the gold standard of chain dining in the UK, but poor scores support those who feel "its decline has sadly continued" since, in 2021, its ownership passed to its bond holders. Recent developments include a new logo, bold new colours, pizza wraps 'to go' and a major curtailing of the cut-price deals for which the group had become notorious. And yet still ratings slide and even more positive reviews are often muted ("some of the new offerings are quite good…"; "nothing to complain about which shows improvement…"). However you cut it, what's undeniable is that, "there are so many hugely better pizzerias around". / www.pizzaexpress.co.uk.

Pascor W8

PIZZERIA MOZZA
W1 £48 4|2|3

**TREEHOUSE HOTEL, 14-15 LANGHAM
PLACE 020 3988 4273 3–1C**

"Brilliant pizza" from Netflix star, Nancy
Silverton, justifies a trip to this bustling pit stop,
at the foot of a hotel opposite Broadcasting
House. As the FT's Tim Hayward so
memorably put it in his October 2021 review:
'Goethe thought architecture was music, frozen;
Silverton proves that meatballs are beatitude,
minced'! / W1W 2QS; @staytreehouse; Wed-Sat
10 pm, Sun 6 pm; closed Mon & Tue.

PIZZERIA PAPPAGONE
N4 £35 3|3|3

**131 STROUD GREEN RD
020 7263 2114 9–1D**

This well-known Finsbury Park fixture
celebrates its 25th anniversary this year, and
is well established as a hub for north London's
Italian community as well as locals drawn by its
reliable "cheap and cheerful" Italian comfort
food, led by pizza from the wood-fired stove.
There's a bar in case you have to wait for a
table, and bambini are made to feel welcome.
/ N4 3PX; www.pizzeriapappagone.co.uk;
@pizzeriapappagone; Mon-Sun midnight.

PLANQUE E8 £76 3|2|4

322 ACTON MEWS 020 7254 3414 14–2A

It helps to be a lover of funky offbeat wines,
if you visit this 'Wine Drinkers' Clubhouse'
(incorporating members' lounge, wine cellar,
and retail store) in two so-now Haggerston
railway arches, where much of the seating is
at communal benches (achingly hip in every
sense…). Its menu of creative small plates
inspire reports that vary between highs and
lows. / E8 4EA; www.planque.co.uk; @_planque_;
Wed-Sat 11 pm, Sun 8.30 pm; closed Wed-Fri L,
closed Mon & Tue; payment – credit card only;
booking online only.

PLATEAU E14 £87 2|2|3

**4TH FLOOR, CANADA SQ
020 7715 7100 12–1C**

This "calm dining room" – with a "great vibe
and nice vistas" – seems to have lost its former
pre-eminence in the Canary Wharf dining
scene, and no longer generates much feedback.
Part of the D&D London empire, it is pitched
at the expense-account trade. The "food is
generally good, but has the odd misstep".

/ E14 5ER; www.plateau-restaurant.co.uk;
@Plateaucanarywharf; Mon-Sat 11.30 pm; closed
Sun.

PLAZA KHAO GAENG
WC1 £36

**ARCADE FOOD HALL, 103-105 OXFORD
STREET NO TEL 5–1A**

This mid-2022 newcomer is the flagship
offering at JKS Restaurants' new Arcade Food
Hall (see also) at Tottenham Court Road. It
opened too late to general feedback in our
annual diners' poll, but an early-doors report
said its "very authentic impressive Thai food
makes it a must-try", while The Evening
Standard's Jimi Famurewa raved: it serves "food
to quicken the pulse, dampen the brow and
leave you gasping for more!" / WC1W 1DB;
plazakhaogaeng.com; @plazakhaogaeng; Tue-Sat
10 pm, Sun 3 pm; closed Sun D, closed Mon.

THE PLIMSOLL N4 £55 5|3|2

52 ST THOMAS'S ROAD NO TEL 9–1D

"The Dexter burgers are a cult classic by
now" ("well-seasoned, crisp and juicy, with
meat overflowing from the bun") and the
"top choices of the young and trendy crowd"
packed into Jamie Allan and Ed McIlroy's (aka
'Four Legs') new "loud and down-to-earth
spot in Finsbury Park". But "don't overlook
the other outstandingly great value dishes on
the menu which are just as delicious", such as
"a tasty cockle bouillabaisse or fresh lemon
sole". They haven't wasted too much cash on
their makeover of the knackered old boozer
(fka 'The Auld Triangle') providing their new
home – "a great spot for grabbing a pint", but
"it seems not to have been redecorated since
your great grandad called in on the way to the
pre-premiership Arsenal game". / N4 2QW;
@the.plimsoll; Mon-Fri 11 pm, Sat & Sun midnight;
closed Mon-Fri L.

THE PLOUGH SW14 £61

**42 CHRIST CHURCH RD
020 8755 7444 11–2A**

This large 18th-century inn – a survivor from
the era when East Sheen was a rural village
– closed down in 2021 following a dispute
between Fuller's and the landlord, to the
dismay of locals. It reopened after a refurb
last summer, and is likely to make a comeback
given its great location near Richmond Park
and gorgeous outside terrace. / SW14 7AF;
www.plougheastsheen.co.uk; @PloughSheen; Mon-
Thu 9.30 pm, Fri & Sat 10 pm, Sun 9 pm.

PLU NW8 £175 5|4|4

**12 BLENHEIM TERRACE
020 7624 7663 9–3A**

"It is a complete mystery how the Michelin
guide has failed to recognise Elliot Moss's
wonderful food creations", say followers of his
tiny but "opulent" three-year-old in St John's
Wood, where the only option is an extended
tasting menu. "The chef is a true artist who
does everything himself: each phenomenal
and fun dish looks too good to eat but the
visuals are actually secondary to the insanely
addictive deliciousness of the flavours" ("his
foie gras dish leaves you desperate for 'just
one more mouthful'… and I don't even like
foie gras!") Fooderati insiders, Koffmann &
Vines, also waxed lyrical over their meal here
this year, proclaiming it 'a true gastronomic
experience'. "May he go from strength to
strength." / NW8 0EB; www.plurestaurant.co.uk;
@PluRestaurant; Thu-Sat 10 pm; closed Thu-Sat
L, closed Mon-Wed & Sun; credit card deposit
required to book.

PLUM VALLEY W1 £50 3|2|2

20 GERRARD ST 020 7494 4366 5–3A

"Top dim sum" – "always well cooked
and presented" – is the prime draw to this
Gerrard Street Cantonese stalwart, which
also benefits from an outdoor terrace.
/ W1D 6JQ; www.plumvalleylondon.com;
@plumvalleyrestaurant; Mon-Sun 10 pm.

POLLEN STREET SOCIAL
W1 £136 3|3|3

8-10 POLLEN ST 020 7290 7600 3–2C

"A restaurant I love to return to more than
any other!" – Jason Atherton's "glamorous"
and "lively" Mayfair HQ inspires dedication
and adoration from its enthusiastic, large fan
base: "exemplary cooking with imaginative
touches" is the expected highlight and "it's
great seeing Jason so calm and professional at
the pass, which comes through in the staff".
That said, ratings this year slipped due to a
few more middling experiences: "I so wanted
to like Pollen Street Social but it never quite
reached the expected heights given the hype
and prices!!" Top Tip – "a top spot for a
business lunch or dinner". / W1S 1NQ;
www.pollenstreetsocial.com; @pollen_street_social;
Tue-Sat 9.30 pm, Sun 11 pm; closed Mon; booking
max 6 may apply.

LE PONT DE LA TOUR
SE1 £96 2|2|2

36D SHAD THAMES 020 7403 8403 10–4D

"It's great to sit outside on a sunny day and see
the beautiful London sights" – not least Tower
Bridge of course – from the superb, Thames-
side, heated terrace of this long-established
D&D London destination on the South Bank.
It can be "perfect for a quiet, professional
meal", aided by an "amazingly wide wine list".
In other respects, though, its atmosphere and
classical Gallic cuisine are very "subdued"
compared to yesteryear (when it was the famous
flagship of Sir Terence Conran's restaurant

empire). A fair summary? – "nice to eat by the river… not really worth the journey… food OK". / SE1 2YE; www.lepontdelatour.co.uk; @lepontdelatourldn; Mon-Sat 10 pm, Sun 9 pm; no trainers.

POPEYES E15　£14　433

WESTFIELD STRATFORD CITY, MONTFICHET ROAD　NO TEL　14–1D

"You get the best fried chicken, but practically nothing else" at this new Westfield Stratford outlet serving Louisiana-style fried chicken sandwiches: the first location of a big US fast-food chain that breezed into town in November 2021 and is aiming for 350 branches in no time flat. "There were huge queues even months after it was opened" and "the ambience is that of a food court", but fans (unexpectedly including The Times's Giles Coren) say "the chicken is worth it". / E15 1AZ; www.popeyesuk.com; @popeyesuk; Mon-Sat 10 pm, Sun 6 pm.

POPOLO EC2　£56　532

**26 RIVINGTON STREET
020 7729 4299　13–1B**

"One of the best meals I had all year" – this "noisy, little spot in Shoreditch" showcases "simply great cooking" from kickboxer-turned-chef Jon Lawson, who prepares "awesome sharing-style Italian plates" with Spanish and North African touches. "Perfect for a date night if you want to impress, while still keeping it hip and intimate". The occasional duff note concerns the low-intervention wines: "interesting" to some, to others "expensive" or "an acquired taste". Top Tip – "grab a seat at the counter for the best ambience/experience". / EC2A 3DU; popoloshoreditch.com; @popoloshoreditch; Mon-Wed 10.30 pm, Thu-Sat 11 pm; closed Mon-Sat L, closed Sun; no booking.

POPPIES　£50　322

**59 OLD COMPTON ST, W1
020 7482 2977　4–2D
30 HAWLEY CR, NW1　020 7267 0440　9–2B
6-8 HANBURY ST, E1
020 7247 0892　13–2C**

You can "travel back in time" at this trio of deliberately retro chippies, with their "Formica tables and period posters creating a great atmosphere" – "the fish 'n' chips are excellent, too". Founder Pat 'Pops' Newland, an East Ender who started working at the age 11, was still a hands-on owner in his 80s when he died in April 2022. /

POPPY'S　£36　324

**129-131 BRACKENBURY ROAD, W6
020 8741 4928　8–1C
30 GREYHOUND ROAD, W6
020 7385 9264　8–2C
78 GLENTHORNE ROAD, W6
020 8748 2351　8–2C**

"Good-value local Thai restaurants in Hammersmith (that do reliable take-away too)". BYO adds to the value of a trip, with the best branch – rammed with stuffed animals, foliage

and bric-a-brac – on the site that was for yonks, The Brackenbury (long RIP), complete with cute outside terrace in summer. /

PORTE NOIRE N1　£52

UNIT A GASHOLDER 10, 1 LEWIS CUBITT SQUARE　020 7930 6211　9–3C

"Set inside one of the old gasholders behind Coal Drops Yard", Idris Elba's "beautiful" new Gastronomic Wine Bar & Shop opened in late 2021 on the periphery of this up-and-coming area, with a peaceful position and attractive outlook. Fans say it's "no gimmick restaurant, despite its Hollywood royalty backing, but a wine bar for grown-up people serious about their food and wine". More reports please! / N1N 4BY; www.portenoire.co.uk; @portenoirekx; Mon & Tue 9.30 pm, Wed-Sat 11.30 pm, Sun 4.30 pm; closed Sun D.

IL PORTICO W8　£73　333

**277 KENSINGTON HIGH ST
020 7602 6262　8–1D**

This "old favourite" opposite the Design Museum, now in its sixth decade, is "always buzzing, with great Italian food and a sense that every patron is 'family'". It's family-run, too, with James Chiavarini having taken over from his father, Pino. "James has introduced some modernising touches but I love the feeling that you're in Italy when you walk in the door – there's nothing minimal or characterless about it". / W8 6NA; www.ilportico.co.uk; @ilportico.kensington; Mon-Sat 11 pm; closed Sun.

PORTLAND W1　£97　453

**113 GREAT PORTLAND STREET
020 7436 3261　2–1B**

"Incredible cooking at very fair prices" matched with excellent wines has built a major following for Will Lander and Daniel Morgenthau's "homely and calm" Fitzrovia destination, with open kitchen on view. "Knowledgeable and classy service" adds considerably to the experience: "it feels like a treat, and yet also has a real neighbourhood feel to it too, which for food of this standard and this central can be rare". / W1W 6QQ; www.portlandrestaurant.co.uk; @portlandrestaurant; Tue-Sat 9.45 pm; closed Sun & Mon.

PORTOBELLO RISTORANTE PIZZERIA W11　£70　333

7 LADBROKE ROAD　020 7221 1373　7–2B

"Always full for a good reason" – this "very friendly" and lively Notting Hill Italian has a large outside terrace and attractive covered area, and is one of the better, more affordable options in the 'hood (and they're "great with kids", too). Some regulars suggest that "the pizza is better than the rest of the menu". / W11 3PA; www.portobellolondon.co.uk; @portobello_ristorante_pizzeria; closed Mon-Sat & Sun.

POSTBOX SW13

201 CASTELNAU　07424 339379　11–1A

This July 2022 newcomer in north Barnes (just south of Hammersmith Bridge) is the work of Leo Noronha, who recently worked at Hoppers. Here, he and his family will present a short, seasonal menu focused on Portuguese-influenced Goan cuisine, with dishes marinated for 48 hours then cooked on a robata grill. / SW13 9ER; www.postboxrestaurantlondon.com; @postbox_ldn; Mon-Sun midnight.

POTLI W6　£53　433

319-321 KING ST　020 8741 4328　8–2B

"Every dish tastes different with wonderful, rich depths of flavour" at this "interesting street-food-style" café on Hammersmith's 'restaurant row' near Ravenscourt Park: "both north and south India are covered" on a "great, regional menu", incorporating "delicious vegetarian options": "the wide range favours going with a big group, or ordering lots to have at home afterwards!" / W6 9NH; www.potli.co.uk; @potlirestaurant; Mon-Thu 10 pm, Fri & Sat 10.15 pm, Sun 8.45 pm.

LA POULE AU POT SW1　£70　345

231 EBURY ST　020 7730 7763　6–2D

"A candlelit supper for two here first is a surefire route to romance later!" according to fans of this "timeless" Gallic corner of Pimlico, which has "been a favourite for decades" (and which perennially nears the top of our list of London's most romantic destinations). With its "cosy and intimate" hidden nooks, the "warren-like" interior "oozes rural France", as do the "charming" and characterful waiters. Its "solid and traditional French bistro-style fare" is entirely in keeping: cassoulet, coq au vin, escargot, onion tart, steak frites, tarte Tatin, all washed down with "vin rouge from the large bottle" (with consumption measured by a dipstick). "Why would you change anything about it?" Top Tip – in summer, the "good outside tables" come into their own. / SW1W 8UT; www.pouleaupot.co.uk; @lapouleaupotrestaurant; Mon-Sun 11 pm; no trainers.

PRAWN ON THE LAWN N1　£68　532

**292-294 ST PAUL'S RD
020 3302 8668　9–2D**

"It's almost as good as eating on the beach" at this "very intimate" (as in "tables too close together") "small" restaurant on Highbury Corner, which serves "wonderful fresh fish and seafood". "The menu is on a blackboard because it changes every day" – depending on what is delivered fresh from Devon or Cornwall (where it has a sister establishment in Padstow). Perches are in high demand, so it pays to book ahead. / N1 2LH; prawnonthelawn.com; @prawnonthelawn; Wed-Sat 10 pm, Sun 5 pm; closed Sun D, closed Mon & Tue; no Amex.

PRIMEUR N5 £61 343

116 PETHERTON RD 020 7226 5271 1–1C

A "good local bistro with a short but punchy menu", set in a 1940s car showroom between Highbury and Stoke Newington. "The sort of place where you happily over-order because you want to try as many things as possible – and nothing disappoints." The same team are behind the nearby Westerns Laundry and Jolene bakery. / N5 2RT; www.primeurN5.co.uk; @menuprimeur; Tue-Sat 11 pm, Sun 20.30 pm; closed Tue-Fri L, closed Mon; booking max 7 may apply.

PRINCESS OF SHOREDITCH EC2 £75 533

76 PAUL ST 020 7729 9270 13–1B

"Superb food with a real eye for detail and quality" – Ruth Hansom's "outstanding modern cuisine" is really "going places" at this well-established gastroboozer, just off Great Eastern Street. The pleasant-enough dining area is quirkly located on the mezzanine, up a spiral staircase from the main bar: choose from either a five-course or eight-course tasting menu. / EC2A 4NE; www.theprincessofshoreditch.com; @princessofshoreditch; Mon-Sat 10 pm, Sun 8 pm; no Amex; booking D only.

THE PRINCESS ROYAL W2 £82 333

7 HEREFORD ROAD 020 3096 6996 7–1B

It briefly traded as The Commander and then Pomona's (both RIP), but this attractive Notting Hill tavern (nowadays part of the upscale Cubitt House group) returned in February 2022 to being essentially the same pub it had been since the late 1800s. Despite punchy prices, reports are upbeat on its posh-for-a-pub menu, which includes a selection of oysters and dishes from the 'Raw Bar'. / W2 5AH; www.cubitthouse.co.uk/the-princess-royal; @cubitthouse; Mon-Sat 11.30 pm, Sun 11 pm.

THE PRINCESS VICTORIA W12 £52 333

217 UXBRIDGE ROAD 020 8749 4466 8–1B

This "beautifully restored, nearly 200-years-old gin palace" on the Uxbridge Road was named at its 1829 launch after the 10-year-old princess who went on to reign as Queen Victoria. These days it serves "really good pub food" – "I've never had a bad meal here" – and stocks 100 different gins at its dramatic horseshoe bar. Top Tip – "the pizza and gin-and-tonic lunch offer is a bargain (if a slippery slope)". / W12 9DH; www.princessvictoria.co.uk; @threecheerspubs; Mon-Thu 11 pm, Fri & Sat midnight, Sun 10.30 pm.

PRIX FIXE W1 £47 322

39 DEAN ST 020 7734 5976 5–2A

"Affordable French bistro cooking", a "wide range of dishes" and "decent portion sizes" make this Gallic outfit (like its nearby stablemate Pierre Victoire) "just the thing for a Soho bite". It provides truly "exceptional value" for lunch and pre-theatre, but beware the price jump from 6pm, when it switches to an à la carte format. / W1D 4PU; www.prixfixe.net; @prixfixesoho; Mon & Tue, Sun 11 pm, Wed-Sat 11.30 pm.

THE PROMENADE AT THE DORCHESTER W1 £157 344

THE DORCHESTER HOTEL, 53 PARK LANE 020 7629 8888 3–3A

Afternoon tea in this "stunning" luxury hotel shows "England at its best", whether served in the Promenade (scheduled for a refurb) or the Orchid Room. It's a timeless experience, but one that moves with the times – they now serve what may be the poshest vegan afternoon tea in London. / W1K 1QA; www.dorchestercollection.com/en/london/the-dorchester/restaurant-bars/afternoon-tea; @thedorchester; Mon-Sun 10.30 pm; no shorts.

PROVENDER E11 £45 342

17 HIGH ST 020 8530 3050 1–1D

This "real local gem" on Wanstead High Street serves "well-executed French bistro food which never disappoints" – and "at a fair price". Max Renzland, the veteran restaurateur who ran it for a decade stepped down in late 2021, with equally experienced Christophet Huber and Robin Tarver taking over the reins. / E11 2AA; www.provenderlondon.co.uk; @provenderwanstead; Tue-Thu 10 pm, Fri & Sat 11 pm, Sun 9 pm; closed Mon; booking max 10 may apply.

PRUFROCK COFFEE EC1 £15 322

23-25 LEATHER LN 020 7242 0467 10–2A

"Great coffee" (and also stone-rolled and limited-edition tea) wins praise for this well-known brew stop near Hatton Garden, which also offers pastries, sarnies and other light bites. / EC1N 7TE; www.prufrockcoffee.com; @prufrockcoffee; Mon-Fri 4.30 pm, Sat & Sun 5 pm; closed Mon-Sun D; no Amex.

PUNJAB WC2 £46 423

80 NEAL ST 020 7836 9787 5–2C

This veteran curry house to the north of Covent Garden has survived for 76 years by providing "fine-value and well-above-average cooking". Founded in 1946 and claiming to be the first north Indian restaurant in London, it is now owned and operated by the fourth generation of the same family and still sticks close to its gastronomic roots ("ate with a friend whose family come from the Punjab and he said the food was thoroughly authentic"). In recent years, "real effort has gone into the wine list, but the best wine to drink with curry remains… beer". / WC2H 9PA; www.punjab.co.uk; @punjabcoventgarden; Mon-Sat 11 pm, Sun 10 pm; booking max 8 may apply.

PURE INDIAN COOKING SW6 £52 343

67 FULHAM HIGH STREET 020 7736 2521 11–1B

"A real gem", serving "top-quality modern Indian cooking at sensible prices" on Fulham High Street near Putney Bridge. The "delicious, unusual food" comes courtesy of chef-owner Shilpa Dandekar, who trained with both India's Taj Group and Raymond Blanc. She and her husband Faheem Vanoo, who runs the front of house, have made a good impression on locals ("it's run by really nice people"). / SW6 3JJ; www.pureindiancooking.com; @pureindiancooking; Mon-Wed, Sat, Thu & Fri 11 pm, Sun 10.30 pm; closed Mon-Wed, Sat L.

QUAGLINO'S SW1 £93 234

16 BURY ST 020 7930 6767 3–3D

As one of the late Sir Terence Conran's landmark openings, this big D&D London basement bar/brasserie in St James's was the talk of the town back in the 1990s, complete with racily dressed cigarette girl, and signature 'Q' ashtrays (a collectible selling for £70 online nowadays). Increasingly left to tourists and business-accounters, it still has fans for whom it's "exceptional all-round", but the proportion of disappointments over the years often hinders a more whole-hearted endorsement. / SW1Y 6AJ; www.quaglinos-restaurant.co.uk; @quaglinos; Mon-Thu midnight, Fri & Sat 1 am, Sun 7 pm; closed Mon-Fri L; no trainers.

THE QUALITY CHOP HOUSE EC1 £92 444

88-94 FARRINGDON RD 020 7278 1452 10–1A

"A London institution" since 1869, when it opened to feed the working classes of Clerkenwell – this 'Progressive Working Class Caterer' now attracts a more bourgeois crowd with "food cooked to melt-in-mouth perfection and informative, informal service. You feel that everyone loves their job". The menu still leans heavily on chops and steaks, leavened by good fish and vegetable options, and it's a "favourite place to show off to people" with its listed Victorian wooden booths and "very uncomfortable bench seats", softened by cushions. These days it is part of Will Lander and Daniel Morgenthau's Woodhead Group, alongside Portland and Clipstone, and has its own larder, daytime café and wine bar next door. / EC1R 3EA; thequalitychophouse.com; @qualitychop; Tue-Sat 10 pm, Sun 3.30 pm; closed Sun D, closed Mon.

QUARTIERI NW6 £51 333

300 KILBURN HIGH ROAD 020 7625 8822 1–2B

"Top Neapolitan pizza" (with a very wide range of choices and featuring ingredients shipped from Italy weekly) helps inspire fans of this casual, brick-walled Kilburn independent. / NW6 2DB; www.quartieri.co.uk; @quartierilondon; Mon-Sun 11 pm.

QUEENS OF MAYFAIR W1 £37 **3 4 4**

17 QUEEN STREET 020 7459 4617 3–3B

"A great change to the ghastly chains" – Victoria & Grace Sheppard's elegant, "friendly" café is tipped for its "terrific coffee", as well as a quiet bite or their 'bottomless brunch'. / W1W 5PH; www.queensofmayfair.com; @queensofmayfair; Mon-Fri 5.30 pm, Sat & Sun 6 pm; closed Mon-Sun D.

LE QUERCE SE23 £54 **4 3 2**

66-68 BROCKLEY RISE 020 8690 3761 1–4D

The "great Italian/Sardinian food" at this family-run Brockley Rise trat is a regular treat for fans in this corner of SE London. Top Tip – leave room for the "delicious and unusual ice creams/sorbets" – including chilli, garlic and aubergine, if you're brave enough! / SE23 1LN; www.lequerce.co.uk; @le_querce; Wed-Sat 8 pm, Sun 4 pm; closed Wed-Sat L closed Sun D, closed Mon & Tue.

QUILON SW1 £86 **5 4 2**

41 BUCKINGHAM GATE 020 7821 1899 2–4B

"Superb, delicate and fragrant cuisine" from Kerala in southwest India, has been a top attraction for more than 20 years at this luxurious but muted hotel dining room in St James's, run by the luxury Taj Group (and still under founding chef Sriram Aylur). Seafood dishes are particularly good, and there's a tasting menu matched with beers. Top Tip – "weekend brunch is super value". / SW1E 6AF; www.quilon.co.uk; @thequilon; Wed & Thu, Sat & Sun 9 pm, Fri 9.30 pm; closed Mon & Tue.

QUO VADIS W1 £90 **4 4 5**

26-29 DEAN ST 020 7437 9585 4–1D

"Jeremy Lee continues to deliver seasonal excellence in elegant surroundings with an atmosphere to match" at the Hart Bros' "delightful" and "unfailing" bastion of old Soho (which also incorporates an eponymous members' club for the foodie in-crowd on the upper floors of this rambling property, whose blue plaque celebrates former tenant, Karl Marx). Lee's deft British cooking is "always thoughtful and cheering" and "the wonderful room is compact enough to ensure great service". / W1D 3LL; www.quovadissoho.co.uk; @quovadissoho; Tue-Sat 10 pm; closed Sun & Mon.

RABBIT SW3 £69 **3 2 2**

172 KING'S RD 020 3750 0172 6–3C

This quirky, faux-rustic venture in Chelsea was the second in the Gladwin family's nowadays fast-growing farm-to-fork group. Its sustainable small-plates can be "very good", but there are also a few gripes in reports, including service that can be so-so and a feeling that "tables are too close together". / SW3 4UP; www.rabbit-restaurant.com; @rabbit_resto; Mon-Sat 10.30 pm, Sun 8 pm; closed Mon L.

RABOT 1745 SE1 £72 **2 2 3**

2-4 BEDALE ST 020 7378 8226 10–4C

"This Caribbean plantation-themed coffee shop" makes "amazing hot chocolate that scores highly in terms of VFC (Value For Calories!)". "The upstairs restaurant has a nice terrace overlooking Borough Market, which is a great space to enjoy drinks or dinner" (with chocolate cropping up at every possible juncture on the menu). / SE1 9AL; www.rabot1745.com; @rabot1745; Sun & Mon 4.30 pm, Wed-Sat 10 pm, Tue 5 pm; closed Mon & Tue, Sun D.

RADICI N1 £70 **2 2 2**

30 ALMEIDA ST 020 7354 4777 9–3D

"Reliable pasta and pizza" and a setting that's "buzzy, not noisy, and not overcrowded" do win praise for this D&D London operation in the heart of Islington (on the site of Almeida, long RIP). But, especially given that renowned chef Francesco Mazzei is nominally in charge of the food here, enthusiasm seems rather muted. / N1 1AD; www.radici.uk; @radici_n1; Tue-Sat 10 pm, Sun 3.45 pm; closed Tue, Wed L closed Sun D, closed Mon.

RAGAM W1 £35 **4 2 2**

57 CLEVELAND ST 020 7636 9098 2–1B

This Keralan veteran near the Telecom Tower is "still producing good food after all this time" (almost 40 years), offering "super value" and "friendly service". The new interior "hasn't made it a looker, but there are so many great dishes on the menu, so who cares?" / W1T 4JN; www.ragamindian.co.uk; Mon-Thu 11 pm, Fri & Sat 11.30 pm; closed Sun.

RAI W1 £112 **4 4 3**

3 WINDMILL STREET 020 7419 0305 2–1C

"Melt-in-the-mouth Wagyu and exemplary sashimi" inspire rave reviews for Shrabaneswor Rai and chef Padam Raj Rai's Fitzrovia newcomer (previously a second branch of Hot Stone, which they also own). There's no à la carte – the format is one of a multi-course, omakase-style tasting menu and fans are "blown away by the quality of the food". / W1W; rairestaurant.com; @rai.restaurant; Wed-Sun 1 am.

RAMBUTAN SE1

10 STONEY STREET NO TEL 10–4C

On the Borough Market site of a Konditor bakery, this 60-cover, two-floor spot will soon host the debut restaurant of Coventry-born Sri Lankan chef Cynthia Shanmugalingam. Opening in October 2022, it promises regularly changing menus featuring street food snacks and more substantial options. / SE1 9AD; www.rambutanlondon.com; @rambutan_ldn; Mon-Sun 7 pm.

RANDALL & AUBIN W1 £83 **4 4 5**

14-16 BREWER ST 020 7287 4447 4–2D

"A true Soho classic", with "the most fun front-of-house staff in London" and "fantastic fresh seafood" – served for the past quarter-century in a "lovely old butcher's shop" from 1911. "It isn't that romantic, but you can have the best times in this delightful spot", which is "great for pre-theatre or a post-matinee restorative". "When in need of a pick-me-up, one can't go wrong with huitres and champers at R&A". / W1F 0SG; www.randallandaubin.com; @randallandaubin; Mon-Sat midnight, Sun 11 pm; booking L only.

RANGREZ W6 £41 **3 3 3**

32 FULHAM PALACE ROAD 020 8563 7176 8–2C

Limited but good all-round feedback on this family-run Punjabi stalwart, which has long been a feature of the restaurant strip just to the south of Hammersmith's Eventim Apollo (and which sometimes only serves a restricted menu in the early evening during events there). It also has a branch in Ealing (not listed). / W6 9PH; www.rangrez.co.uk; Mon, Wed & Thu 10.30 pm, Fri-Sun 11 pm.

RASA N16 £42 **5 4 3**

55 STOKE NEWINGTON CHURCH ST 020 7249 0344 1–1C

"It never fails to impress", chorus the many fans of Keralan-born Das Sreedharan's bright-pink Stokie fixture, which celebrates its 30th anniversary next year. Even if one can debate whether it's perhaps "not quite as good as it was at its peak", for some folks it's still "the best South Indian vegetarian" in town, and no-one suggests other than that "the food here is delicious (and I'm not even a vegetarian!)" Over the years, it has spawned several spin-offs, but now operates only out of this single, original, venue (and for delivery). / N16 0AR; www.rasarestaurants.com; Sat & Sun 2.30 pm; closed Sat & Sun D, closed Mon-Thu & Fri.

RAVI SHANKAR NW1 £32 **3 2 2**

133-135 DRUMMOND ST 020 7388 6458 9–4C

"Really good and cheap veggie food" has established this fixture as a popular dining choice in the Little India street behind Euston station. The buffet lunch is even better value. / NW1 2HL; www.ravishankarbhelpoori.com; Mon-Sun 11 pm.

THE RED DUCK SW12 £44 **4 2 2**

1 RAMSDEN ROAD 020 8154 6838 11–2C

"Top-class Chinese food, served in canteen-style surroundings" has arrived in Balham with the pandemic-delayed opening of this first solo project from Chi San, former right-hand man to Alan Yau of Yauatcha and Hakkasan fame. The relatively short menu is filled with standard

Pastaio W1

dishes from the Cantonese culinary canon, modernised through the use of high-quality produce, and there's an interesting selection of beers, wines and teas. / SW12 8QX; theredduck. co.uk/ @_theredduck_; Tue-Sun 11 pm; closed Tue-Sun L, closed Mon.

RED FARM WC2 £88 323

9 RUSSELL STREET 020 3883 9093 5–3D

This modern pan-Asian in Covent Garden – an import from NYC – offers "playful dim sum", alongside other "cut-above" dishes. There are "relaxed long tables for groups or cosy red-checked spots for two diners", and the atmosphere is set by the "fun 90s playlist and friendly team". / WC2W 5HZ; redfarmldn.com; @redfarmldn; Mon-Thu 10 pm, Fri & Sat 10.30 pm, Sun 8.30 pm.

THE RED LION & SUN N6 £63 333

25 NORTH ROAD 020 8340 1780 9–1B

"Top-notch" Highgate Village local that's arguably "the best gastropub in north London" currently – and perfect "for a late lunch after a walk on the heath". The menu stretches from a "generous Sunday roast" and "gastropub favourites" to "a great selection of seafood" and "Asian-accented dishes" – "all cooked with style and attention to flavour". "Great beer" too, but perhaps more notably an "excellent range of wines". / N6; www.theredlionandsun.com; @theredlionandsun; Mon-Sun 11 pm.

REGENCY CAFE SW1 £14 335

17-19 REGENCY STREET
020 7821 6596 2–4C

"A Westminster institution loved by its regulars" – this "greasy spoon experience" occupies a site that's little changed since its opening in 1946, and continues to "plough its furrow regardless of modern fashion". "Fishy Fridays are a must" but, most vitally, it's "a great choice for a cheap breakfast, any time of the day". / SW1S 4BY; regencycafe.co.uk; Mon-Fri 7.15 pm, Sat 12 pm; closed Sat D, closed Sun.

LE RELAIS DE VENISE L'ENTRECÔTE £58 323

120 MARYLEBONE LN, W1
020 7486 0878 2–1A
5 THROGMORTON ST, EC2
020 7638 6325 10–2C

"Formulaic… but it works a treat". These "jolly" French steakhouses thrive on their "excellent and simple" format. "There's just one choice on the menu, but it's brilliant": salad to start; then steak ("tender and delicious") with "their magic secret sauce" ("the start of addiction"), plus "piles of hot fries". (To follow there's "a wide selection of desserts.") "No wonder there's always a queue, but it's worth it, even though the inside is really crammed and can be chaos." With the closure of the Soho branch, the remaining outposts are in Marylebone and the City. Top Tip – "ideal for a business lunch". / www.relaisdevenise.com.

REPUBLIC W4 £49 443

301-303 CHISWICK HIGH ROAD
020 8154 2712 8–2A

"Really innovative Indian food" is making its mark at this newbie from Kuldeep Mattegunta and Mustaq Tappewale, who met while working at Kricket in Soho and have taken over the former premises in deepest Chiswick of much-lamented Hedone (RIP) – including the open kitchen ("sitting at the counter watching the food being cooked is fun"). "Unusual and superbly made dishes" put it "in a different league from most Indian restaurants." / W4 4HH; republicw4.com; @republic_chiswick; Mon-Sat 10 pm; closed Sun; booking online only.

THE RESIDENCY W2

50 WESTBOURNE GROVE NO TEL 7–1B

Regular DJs feature on the entertainment programme at this May 2022 newcomer in Bayswater (which opened too late for feedback in our annual diners' poll). Extensive wood panelling is the most eye-catching feature of the cosy interior, while the short dinner menu (earlier in the day there's one dedicated to brunch) looks more aimed at good-value sustenance than foodie fireworks. / W2 5SH; www.theresidencynottinghill.com; Sun-Thu 9.30 pm, Fri & Sat 10.30 pm.

RESTAURANT 1890 BY GORDON RAMSAY WC2 £144 344

STRAND 020 7499 0124 5–3D

"A beautiful small and intimate newcomer" with gorgeous gold-hued décor, created by Gordon Ramsay in the bijou first-floor space above the Savoy Grill and overlooking the hotel entrance that some will remember as 'Upstairs' (long RIP). Chef James Sharp provides an accomplished nine-course tasting menu "well-prepared in classic Ramsay style" (and necessarily quite straightforward given the lack of kitchen facilities nearby) matched with "great attentive service from Sarah Rhone" and her team. The position, with many windows overlooking the entrance, provides many a talking point with the comings and goings down below. / WC2W 0EZ; www.gordonramsayrestaurants.com/ restaurant-1890; @restaurant1890gordonramsay; Tue-Sat 11 pm; closed Tue-Sat L, closed Sun & Mon.

THE RESTAURANT AT THE CAPITAL SW3 £91 343

22-24 BASIL STREET 020 7591 1202 6–1D

A short walk from the back of Harrods, the bijou dining room of this luxury hotel changed its stripes a couple of years ago. Under chef Chris Prow, it now offers a much less formal dining style – with an all-day menu (majoring in dishes from the Josper grill) showcasing British cuisine – and an outside terrace in summer. Some regret the passing of the former incarnation, but overall ratings are good all round. / SW3 1AT;

www.therestaurantatthecapitallondon.com; @thecapitalhotel; Mon-Sun 10 pm.

RESTAURANT ST. BARTS EC1

63 BARTHOLOMEW CLOSE NO TEL
10–2B

A new, even more ambitious venture from the team behind two of London's favourite neighbourhood restaurants, Nest in Hackney and Fulham's Fenn (Johnnie Crowe, Luke Wasserman and Toby Neill); the 15-course tasting menu (£120) from chef Kate Austen will focus on hyper-seasonal food. Opening September 2022, it's named after the church next door (St Bartholomew The Great), not the luxury island. / EC1E 7BG; www.restaurant-stbarts.co.uk; Wed-Sat 9.30 pm.

REUBENS W1 £47 222

79 BAKER ST 020 7486 0035 2–1A

"One of very few places in town certified kosher" – this 50-year-old classic Jewish deli (with basement restaurant) in Baker Street is often tipped for its "excellent salt beef" and also lays claim to the title of longest-running kosher restaurant in Britain (although it has only operated on this site for about half of that time). Three years ago it was rescued from closure by restaurateur Lee Landau. / W1U 6RG; www.reubensrestaurant.co.uk; @reubens_restaurant; Sun-Thu 10 pm, Fri 2 pm; closed Fri D, closed Sat; no Amex.

REVOLVE EC2 £86

UNIT G02 BROADGATE ,100 LIVERPOOL STREET 020 3146 9603 13–2B

With a terrace overlooking Broadgate Circle, this May 2022 newcomer is an all-day, 115-cover operation that's part of the City's glossy, new 100 Liverpool Street building and serves a menu of French brasserie classics such as escargots, beef tartare, coq au vin…. The name hints at its guest chef series concept; some of the country's top culinary talents are promised as part of a programme to transform the offering each month via special dishes and ticketed events. / EC2E 2RH; www.revolve.london; @revolve.london; Mon-Wed 10 pm, Thu-Sat 10.30 pm; closed Sun.

RHYTHM & BREWS W4 £23 334

22 WALPOLE GARDENS
020 7998 3873 8–2A

"An absolute treasure to have on the doorstep" for Gunnersbury residents – this funky café south of Turnham Green dispenses excellent coffee and has an ace vinyl collection to rifle through and choose a tune. "The food is always delicious too, and imaginatively served. We love it!" / W4 4HA; rhythmandbrews.co.uk; Mon-Sat 6 pm, Sun 5 pm; closed Sun D.

THE RIB MAN E1 £14 4️⃣4️⃣

BRICK LANE, BRICK LANE MARKET NO TEL 13–2C

"East London is where you get the best pork rolls in town" – courtesy of Mark Gevaux, a former butcher who has perfected the art of BBQ baby-back ribs, from pigs reared outdoors in Norfolk and Suffolk, and his own famous 'Holy Fuck' sauces. Available only in Brick Lane Market on Sundays (they sell out early) and at West Ham home games. / E1 6HR; www.theribman.co.uk; @theribman; Sun 2 pm; closed Sun D, closed Mon-Fri & Sat; no booking.

RICCARDO'S SW3 £53 3️⃣4️⃣3️⃣

126 FULHAM RD 020 7370 6656 6–3B

This "welcoming neighbourhood spot" on a Chelsea corner "won't win awards – but it won't let you down" with its "reliably tasty" Tuscan cooking. "The only downside is if you go late, the noise level is high." / SW3 6HU; www.riccardos.it; @riccardoslondon; Mon-Sun 11.30 pm.

RICHOUX W1 £56 3️⃣4️⃣3️⃣

172 PICCADILLY 020 3375 1000 3–3D

"Good to see Richoux return" on its old Mayfair site, and the new incarnation is "an improvement on the old chain" (which fell into administration in 2021). Its patisserie and all-day menu are still "excellent for a light meal or afternoon tea", but the cuisine generally (overseen by ex-Moor Hall chefs, Jamie Butler and Lewis Spencer) rises much above the workaday standards of its former format: "a simple French selection of dishes that's excellently executed", delivered by "friendly and charming service" and which provides very solid value too. / W1Y 9DD; www.richoux.co.uk; @RichouxUK; Tue-Sat 11 pm, Sun 5 pm; closed Sun D, closed Mon.

RICK STEIN SW14 £85 1️⃣2️⃣2️⃣

TIDEWAY YARD, 125 MORTLAKE HIGH ST 020 8878 9462 11–1A

"The superb setting on the Thames by Barnes Bridge" provides appropriately "lovely views over the river" for this famous Cornish fish and seafood brand's London outpost. But while fans do applaud "fresh fish at its best", a huge proportion of sceptics discern a "tired" performance with "perfunctory" service and "uninteresting" food that can be plain "poor". / SW14 8SN; www.rickstein.com/eat-with-us/barnes; @ricksteinrestaurants; Mon-Sun 10 pm.

RIDING HOUSE £61 2️⃣3️⃣4️⃣

43-51 GREAT TITCHFIELD ST, W1 020 7927 0840 3–1C
BERNARD STREET, WC1 020 3829 8333 2–1D

"Brilliant brekkie" has always been a star turn at this Fitzrovia haunt, whose attractions are heightened by its stylish setting and "friendly" staff. For more substantial meals, it can seem "competent, but not worth a detour". It celebrated 10 years in business by opening a sibling in a former branch of Carluccio's in Spring 2022 (no reports as yet). It's set within Bloomsbury's love-it-or-hate-it Brunswick Centre: a fine example of late-1960s modernist (brutalist?) architecture. /

THE RISING SUN NW7 £68 3️⃣4️⃣2️⃣

137 MARSH LN 020 8959 1357 1–1B

This "busy, picturesque pub" – a Grade-II listed 16th-century building in Mill Hill – serves "delicious and beautifully presented Anglo-Italian grub". It's run by "energetic brothers" Luca and Matteo Delnevo, who have "developed a loyal and upmarket following". / NW7 4EY; www.therisingsunmillhill.com; @therisingsunmillhill; Tue-Sat 9.30 pm, Sun 8 pm; closed Tue, Wed L, closed Mon.

RISTORANTE FRESCOBALDI W1 £88 3️⃣2️⃣2️⃣

15 NEW BURLINGTON PLACE 020 3693 3435 4–2A

The "superb Italian food and great wine list" are everything you would expect from its ownership, the Florentine Frescobaldi dynasty, bankers to English monarchs as far back as Edward I, who have been producing wine on their Tuscan estates since 1308. Needless to say, the opulent venue is "very expensive", but comes into its own in warm weather, with a "large outdoor terrace right in the heart of Mayfair that's perfect for spring and summer". / W1S 5HX; www.frescobaldi.london; @frescobaldi_london; Mon-Sat 11 pm; closed Sun.

RITA'S SOHO W1 £60 3️⃣4️⃣4️⃣

49 LEXINGTON STREET NO TEL 4–2C

This well-travelled ten-year-old cult pop-up has been "a great addition to Soho" since it alighted in 2021 on the cute, quirky site formerly occupied by Aurora (RIP), opposite the venerable Andrew Edmunds on Lexington Street. Gabriel Price's highly rated cooking takes an American-inspired approach to the best of English ingredients, pleasing critics as disparate as Jimi Famurewa and Tom Parker Bowles, while Missy Flynn looks after the front of house and guarantees "so much fun". / W1W 0AP; www.ritasdining.com; @ritasdining; Tue, Wed, Fri, Thu, Sat midnight; closed Tue, Wed, Fri L, closed Sun & Mon.

THE RITZ W1 £116 4️⃣5️⃣5️⃣

150 PICCADILLY 020 7493 8181 3–4C

"A wow all-round that will live long in the memory" – this "dreamy" Louis XVI-style dining room is renowned for its "magical" décor (a rival for any Disney castle) and has long been a top choice for an 'expense-be-damned' celebration, particularly a romantic one. But, these days, many feel that "the mindblowing food can match it too!" While the classical cuisine has long been respected for its consistent quality, its current performance is notably "at the top of its game". "John Williams' masterful orchestration of his very fine kitchen, produces some of the best and most interesting food in London": "perfectly executed luxury dishes" with spoiling ingredients and "with sauces to die for". "The outstanding flavours will have you running out of superlatives and there is the added bonus of theatre via cooking at the table" ("the crêpes are pure visual and gustatory pleasure!!"). "Immaculate service" is "silky smooth" too and arguably "it is a mystery why Michelin award it only one star as there are many worse two and three star restaurants in the UK". It is mightily expensive, of course, but "sometimes it is worth forking out for a truly fantastic time". It is also – with its regular dinner dances and strictly enforced dress code – a bastion of how to celebrate in traditional fine style: "How marvellous to dine to the sounds of a live pianist or band, and in a dining room where everyone has been forced to dress properly. Tie-less slobs are still turned away!" and "not a pair of jeans or trainers in sight!" / W1J 9BR; www.theritzlondon.com; @theritzlondon; Mon-Sun 9.30 pm; Jacket & tie required.

THE RITZ, PALM COURT W1 £105 3️⃣4️⃣5️⃣

150 PICCADILLY 020 7493 8181 3–4C

"You just can't beat the amazing old-world atmosphere, décor, service… and delicious afternoon tea" at this "world-beating" destination. "Yes it's a cliché, but it never fails to impress", "you feel like royalty for the afternoon" and "you won't need to eat in the evening afterwards". "You're either putting on The Ritz or just don't bother!" / W1J 9BR; www.theritzlondon.com; @theritzlondon; Mon-Sun 11 pm; Jacket & tie required.

RIVA SW13 £79 3️⃣4️⃣2️⃣

169 CHURCH RD 020 8748 0434 11–1A

With the closure of Hammersmith Bridge, this Barnes stalwart of over 30 years' standing is no longer an easy Uber ride away for much of the fooderati (it's oft-cited by celeb chefs and the foodie in-crowd as a go-to Italian). Perhaps that's why feedback is post-pandemic is very much more limited and more local than it was in times gone by. Devotees, though, still say it's an "old favourite", with "the same dependable Northern Italian cooking… What more can one ask?" / SW13 9HR; Tue-Sat 10 pm, Sun 9 pm; closed Mon.

THE RIVER CAFÉ W6 £132 3️⃣2️⃣3️⃣

THAMES WHARF, RAINVILLE RD 020 7386 4200 8–2C

"Soldiering on with flair and confidence" – Ruth Rogers' world-famous café is "still the 'go-to' location for "exceptional quality", "ingredient-led", "expertly served" Italian cooking ("even Italian winemakers are impressed by its authenticity and quality!") Stuck, "out-of-the-way", between a quiet Hammersmith backstreet and the Thames, a chic crowd (many of them regulars who live in the centre of town) cram themselves into this bright, unadorned room which started life as the staff canteen for Ruthie's late husband, Richard Rogers' architectural practice ("is it my

Prawn on the Lawn N1

imagination or are the tables getting even closer together nowadays?"). But, while practically "no one can doubt the quality of the food, even so the gobsmacking prices are hard to justify" and it is yet again voted the most overpriced restaurant in London in our annual diners' poll. As is now customary, comments mix awe at its virtues with frustration at the level of value: "I do love it, but I always get buyer's remorse afterwards" as "the pricing leaves a bitter taste after a fine meal"… "and yet we still go back…" Top Tips – 1) On a warm day, its location becomes a reliable attraction in itself: "it's enchanting sitting outside on the terrace beside the Thames". 2) When it comes to the menu, "it changes so much that it's pointless to pick out too many individual dishes but the fish and shellfish are cooked with great skill and attention to detail; and timeless favourites include the Ribollita and the Chocolate Nemesis". / W6 9HA; www.rivercafe.co.uk; @therivercafelondon; Mon-Sat 9.30 pm, Sun 3 pm; closed Sun D.

THE RIVER RESTAURANT, THE SAVOY WC2   £101   2 3 2

THE SAVOY, 91 THE STRAND
020 7499 0122   5–3D

In its heyday, this elegant room overlooking the Thames was one of London's key options for any kind of major occasion. But its relaunch and rebranding (from Kaspar's Seafood Bar & Grill, RIP) to this – its original identity, but now under Gordon Ramsay Holdings – in late 2021 inspired surprisingly limited survey feedback this year (and indeed few press reviews). It is sometimes recommended for the top fish and seafood that is its focus, but all-in-all reactions are muted and uneventful for what should be a top destination. / WC2R 0EU; www.gordonramsayrestaurants.com/ river-restaurant; @riverrestaurantbygordonramsay; Mon-Sat midnight, Sun 10.30 pm; no trainers.

RIVIERA SW1

23 ST JAMES'S ST   020 7925 8988   3–4D

On the prime but quirky St James's site that was Sake No Hana (RIP), Arian and Alberto Zandi are to relaunch this 170-cover space in November 2022 (which also has a 35-cover terrace). This time, as the name hints, the culinary inspiration will be the luxurious lifestyle of the south of France. / SW1 1HA; Mon-Sun midnight.

ROAST SE1   £76   2 2 4

STONEY ST   0845 034 7300   10–4C

Occupying in part a glazed portico that was originally part of the Royal Opera House, the "bright, airy location overlooking Borough Market" and "adorable room" make this restaurant "a great place to take colleagues or clients". There's generally more muted enthusiasm for the "overpriced" retro-British menu – prawn cocktail, beef Wellington, knickerbocker glory. / SE1 1TL; www.roast-restaurant.com; @roast_restaurant; Tue-Fri, Mon, Sat 10 pm; Sun 6.30 pm; closed Sun L.

ROCCA   £48   3 3 3

73 OLD BROMPTON RD, SW7
020 7225 3413   6–2B
75-79 DULWICH VILLAGE, SE21
020 8299 6333   1–4D

This duo of traditional local Italians are "perfectly good for a cheap 'n' cheerful meal", with pasta and pizza cooked to order and a "great atmosphere". Both branches have terraces for al fresco dining – both front and back in Dulwich Village; heated and covered in South Ken. / www.roccarestaurants.com.

ROCHELLE CANTEEN E2   £70   3 4 4

16 PLAYGROUND GARDENS
020 7729 5677   13–1C

"Delightful in every way" – this "hidden-away" venue occupies the bike sheds of a former school near Spitalfields, converted in 2006 by Melanie Arnold and Margot Henderson (wife of St John's Fergus). "Super relaxed" in style and with a "great outdoor space", it's in particular a "gorgeous setting" in summer, but, at any time of year, you can enjoy "robust British cooking with beautiful ingredients". (Its ICA branch was one of the more prominent victims of Covid, closing in September 2020.) / E2 7ES; www.arnoldandhenderson.com; @rochellecanteen; Sun-Wed 5 pm, Thu-Sat 10 pm; closed Thu-Sat L closed Sun-Wed D.

ROCK & ROSE   £61

270-272 CHISWICK HIGH ROAD, W4
020 4537 4566   8–2A
106-108 KEW RD, TW9
020 8948 8008   1–4A

'Food, Passion, Glamour' is the mantra of this funky neighbourhood bar/restaurant, owned by restaurateur Lorraine Angliss (of Annie's and Little Bird), who – having operated in Richmond for many years – opened a second site on Chiswick's main strip in Spring 2022. /

ROJI W1

56B SOUTH MOLTON STREET
AWAITING TEL   3–2B

Tucked away in a Mayfair alleyway, this promising Japanese 10-seater opened in July 2022. Husband-and-wife team Tomoko Hasegawa and Tamas Naszai met at Tokimeite and are backed here by the owners of Chisou and Sushi Atelier. Japanese preparation is applied to top British ingredients to produce an omakase-style menu (which must be paid for on booking), which includes a sushi course and can be paired with a hand-picked selection of sake and wine. / W1W 5SH; ro-ji.co.uk; @ro_ji_ldn; Mon-Sat 11 pm, Sun 9 pm.

ROKA   £91   4 3 3

30 NORTH AUDLEY ST, W1
020 7305 5644   3–2A
37 CHARLOTTE ST, W1
020 7580 6464   2–1C
ALDWYCH HOUSE, 71-91 ALDWYCH, WC2
020 7294 7636   2–2D
UNIT 4, PARK PAVILION, 40 CANADA SQ,
E14   020 7636 5228   12–1C

"Nailing it every time" – Arjun Waney and Rainer Becker's upscale Japanese-inspired operations endure on a deceptively simple formula of "great buzz… awesome food". Centre stage are the "expertly prepared" small plates – "a lovely combination of hot and cold Japanese-fusion dishes" featuring "gorgeous sushi, sashimi and robata" (from the centrally placed grill) – that are "pricey yet exceptional". As an offering, you could quibble that "it hasn't really evolved" in recent years, or you could say 'if it ain't broke, why fix it?' / www.rokarestaurant.com.

ROKETSU W1   £285   5 4 3

12 NEW QUEBEC STREET
020 3149 1227   2–2A

"A little bit of Kyoto in London" – Daisuke Hayashi's highly ambitious new 10-seater in Marylebone opened in early 2022, and is hailed in most reports as one of London's foremost Japanese restaurants. Sitting at the counter, is "like a trip to Japan" – you sample "a stunning 10-course tasting menu: a sublime experience with top-quality ingredients", where "every dish has a story… and it's wonderful". One or two reporters would only say it's only "good enough" at the "eye-watering prices", but even so Hayashi looks set to earn the renown here that he failed to garner during his short stint at Tokimeite. Wash down your meal with one of the 70 sakes assembled by former UMU sommelier, Ryosuke Mashio. / W1W 7RP; www.roketsu.co.uk; @roketsulondon; Tue-Sat 10 pm; closed Tue-Sat L, closed Sun & Mon.

ROMULO CAFÉ W8   £63   343

343 KENSINGTON HIGH STREET
020 3141 6390   8–1D

"Flying the flag for Philippine cuisine in the UK" – this "pioneering" Kensington fixture (owned by the grandchildren of a famous general) "was one of a handful of Filippino places when it opened" and its "consistently good" cooking and striking interior design has made it a good culinary ambassador, showcasing heirloom dishes from within the founding family. They also have three cafés under the same brand in the Philippines. / W8 6NW; www.romulocafe.co.uk; @romulocafelondon; Tue-Thu 9.30 pm, Fri-Sun 10.30 pm; closed Tue-Thu L, closed Mon.

ROOF GARDEN AT PANTECHNICON SW1   £82   335

19 MOTCOMB ST   020 7034 5426   6–1D

"Come rain or shine the rooftop is always buzzing" at this "simply super space" – a gorgeously decorated, 130-seat terrace on top of Belgravia's landmark Pantechnicon building, complete with retractable glass roof for rainy weather. Although some reporters say you only go for the great location, most accounts give it a thumbs-up all round, and "presenting something 'Nordic' and different" as its cuisine (from the kitchen at downstairs Eldr) goes down well (as do the "fab cocktails"…). / SW1S 8LB; www.pantechnicon.com/roof-garden; @_pantechnicon; Tue-Sat midnight, Sun 11 pm; closed Mon.

THE ROSENDALE SE21   £56   333

65 ROSENDALE RD   020 8761 9008   1–4D

This former coaching inn in West Dulwich is "a good pub for family gatherings", with its consistently well-rated food, "relaxed good service" and generous sense of space, both inside and in the garden and play area. / SE21 8EZ; www.therosendale.co.uk; @therosendalepub; Mon-Thu 11 pm, Fri & Sat midnight, Sun 10.30 pm; no Amex.

ROSMARINO SW17   £43   344

23 TRINITY ROAD   020 8244 0336   11–2C

"A stylish, family-run Italian" just a stone's throw from Tooting Bec: "an area in desperate need of a decent restaurant or three!" "Everyone always enjoys themselves and the food is really good"… "so popular that now they're expanding next door!" / SW17 7SD; Mon & Tue, Sun 9.30 pm, Wed-Sat 10 pm.

ROSSLYN COFFEE EC4   £8   543

78 QUEEN VICTORIA STREET   NO TEL   10–3B

"The best coffee in the City of London" – not to mention "exceptional espresso-based drinks", "outstanding hot chocolate" and even yummy soft-serve ice cream – win rave reviews for James Hennebry and Mat Russell's artfully neutral brew-stops, founded in 2018 to 'combine the standards of an Australian Cafe with the warmth and community of an Irish Pub'. / EC4E 4SJ; Mon-Thu 10.30 pm, Fri-Sun 11 pm.

ROTI CHAI W1   £44   332

3 PORTMAN MEWS SOUTH   020 7408 0101   3–1A

"An interesting menu of Indian street-food" that is both "good value and delicious" has long been an attraction at this dependable spot near Selfridges. It's probably "best suited for lunch" to punctuate a day's shopping nearby (the evenings-only dining room is a little more formal, serving tandoor grills and regional specialities). / W1W 6AY; www.rotichai.com; @rotichai; Mon-Sat 9.45 pm, Sun 8.45 pm; booking D only.

ROTI KING   £20   523

IAN HAMILTON HOUSE, 40 DORIC WAY, NW1 020 7387 2518   9–3C
CIRCUS WEST VILLAGE, BATTERSEA POWER STATION, SW8   AWAITING TEL 11–1C

"Arrive early and expect to queue" at this "cramped basement" near Euston Station: an "absolute favourite" that's "100% worth the wait" thanks to its "really authentic Malaysian food" – "divine rotis", plus curries and noodle dishes that are "packed with flavour" and "so cheap". The sleek environs of the new Battersea Power Station development seem like the antithesis of the original's ethos, but a spin-off opened here in early 2022 in one of the railway arches adjacent to the old power station. / rotikinguk.

ROTUNDA BAR & RESTAURANT, KINGS PLACE N1   £57   233

90 YORK WAY   020 7014 2840   9–3C

Development after development is emerging around King's Cross, so it's easy to forget this early arrival, by Regent's Canal, at the foot of the Kings Place art centre. Run by top figures in 'the Murphia' (Green & Fortune's John Nugent alongside the building's owner Peter Millican) its top culinary attraction is beef sourced from its own dedicated Northumberland farm. In summer, enjoy the huge outside terrace by the water. / N1 9AG; www.rotundabarandrestaurant.co.uk; @rotundalondon; Mon-Wed 11 pm, Thu-Sat midnight, Sun 9 pm; closed Mon & Tue L.

ROVI W1   £89   323

59-65 WELLS STREET
020 3963 8270   3–1D

"I could become a vegetarian if I could cook like this!" – star chef Yotam Ottolenghi's Fitzrovia fixture is posher than his delis, and "while not a vegetarian restaurant, vegetables take centre stage". Set around a central bar, the clean-lined design of this 90-seater creates a "fresh and airy" atmosphere. Foodwise there's an emphasis on cooking over fire, but while most reports hail his "interesting and delectable dishes", ratings are dented by those who "wanted to love it, but while it was fine, didn't really feel the vibe, especially at the prices charged". Top Menu Tip – "the vegetarian shawarma with celeriac is next level". / W1W 3AE; www.ottolenghi.co.uk/rovi; @rovi_restaurant; Sun-Fri & Sat 10.30 pm.

ROWLEY'S SW1   £85   323

113 JERMYN ST   020 7930 2707   4–4D

"Steak. Chips. Wine. As much as you can eat. Luvverly." That's the formula at this straightforward St James's steakhouse, now in its fifth decade, which, fans say, manages to stay "traditional without being stuffy". It occupies the former site of Wall's butchers, of sausage fame since the 19th century. It was rated higher this year as it seemed to avoid the typical complaints about pricing often present in feedback. / SW1Y 6HJ; www.rowleys.co.uk; @rowleys_restaurant; Tue-Sat 11 pm; closed Sun & Mon.

ROYAL CHINA   £65   312

24-26 BAKER ST, W1   020 7487 4688   2–1A
805 FULHAM RD, SW6
020 7731 0081   11–1B
30 WESTFERRY CIRCUS, E14
020 7719 0888   12–1B

"It can be very crowded so get there early" if you visit this well-known Cantonese chain: still a top choice for "very tasty dim sum". With the famous Queensway branch closing a couple of years ago, you now have to go to Baker Street, Canary Wharf or Fulham for your fix (although the latter is little commented on). "Whatever else keeps people coming back here, though, it's certainly not the service!" / www.royalchinagroup.co.uk.

ROYAL CHINA CLUB W1   £76   322

38-42 BAKER STREET
020 7486 3898   2–1A

"The cooking as always is wonderful" – "especially the great dim sum at lunchtime" – at the relatively smart Marylebone flagship of the well-known Royal China group. The ratings have slipped a little, but there are still plenty of fans who appreciate its "top authentic Cantonese food". / W1U 7AJ; www.royalchinagroup.co.uk/rccb.html; @royal_china_uk; Mon-Sun 9 pm; booking weekdays only.

RUDY'S W1 £34 3|3|3

80-82 WARDOUR ST 020 7734 0195 4–2D

"Excellent value and decent pizzas" using ingredients imported from Naples win a solid thumbs up – if not quite full-on raves – from fans of this Mancunian import, on the Soho site recently vacated by Wahaca (which nowadays is expanding countrywide). A Birmingham branch is in the pipeline, and more locations around the capital are on the wishlist. / W1; www.rudyspizza.co.uk/soho; @wearerudyspizza; Sun-Thu 9 pm, Fri & Sat 10 pm.

RUDY'S VEGAN DINER £42 3|3|2

206A UPPER STREET, N1
07547 832545 9–2D
729-731 CAMDEN STABLES MARKET, NW1
07384 342144 9–2B

"Delicious" plant-based versions of classic American comfort food – from burgers, seitan hot dogs and pastrami to milk-free shakes – cut the mustard at this pair of 'dirty vegan diners' in Camden Market and Islington. The Islington branch has a vegan butcher next door, touted as the world's first, with a concession in Selfridges. / rudysvegan.com; rudysDVD.

RULES WC2 £83 3|4|5

35 MAIDEN LN 020 7836 5314 5–3D

"It could so easily be a tacky tourist trap and is a bit pricey", but there remains a whole lot of love for this Dickensian landmark in Covent Garden (London's oldest restaurant to operate continuously on the same site – since 1798). The "beautiful" period dining room is "steeped in West End history and character" and the menu is "proper old-school" too – "no surprises, nothing extraordinary, but well-cooked and professionally served" grills, game, pies and puds. "And they do wonderful cocktails upstairs" too in the "splendid bar". Top Menu Tip – "well worth it for old favourites like steak 'n' kidney pudding followed by sponge pudding". / WC2E 7LB; www.rules.co.uk; @rules_restaurant; Mon-Sat 11.30 pm, Sun 5 pm; closed Sun D; no shorts.

THE RUSHMERE SW19 £47

89 RIDGWAY 020 8946 1652 11–2B

Formerly known as The Swan, this Wimbledon pub was extensively refurbed by the Metropolitan Pub Co, and reopened with a new name in March 2022. Too little feedback for a rating as yet, but one early-days visitor reported of "superior pub fare". / SW19 4SU; www.therushmeresw19.com; @RushmereSW19; Mon-Thu 11 pm, Fri & Sat midnight, Sun 10.30 pm.

RYE BY THE WATER TW8 £50 3|2|2

CATHERINE WHEEL ROAD
020 8560 9512 1–3A

This "charming waterside café/restaurant" headed by Ben Rand, former head chef at The Dairy in Clapham (RIP), is set in a new development in Brentford, where the Grand Union Canal connects with the Thames. "The food on the small menu is lovely", but it's a largely daytime-only operation, with occasional supper club evenings. / TW8 8BD; www.ryebythewater.com; @ryebythewater; Wed-Sun 3 pm; closed Wed-Sun D, closed Mon & Tue; no booking.

SABOR W1 £64 5|5|5

35 HEDDON ST 020 3319 8130 4–3A

"A little bit of San Sebastián in the heart of the West End" – "grab a seat at the counter and watch the magic unfold in front of you" at Nieves Barragan and José Etura's tapas bar (ground floor) and 'Asador' (first floor), an "all-time-favourite" which – despite the travails of the era – "just goes from strength to strength as one of the strongest Spanish restaurants in London". "Top-notch Iberian food is served with élan" – "heart and soul-filling, happy and warm, tear-inducing dishes" – and service is "so lovely and welcoming". "Limited bookings mean that there is always a queue to get in from when the doors open at lunch" and "the queue can be long". But "it's pleasing to hear that there are now bookable small tables upstairs", as many feel that "the Asador has got better now they have replaced the sharing benches with a proper arrangement". Top Tip – Asador means BBQ of a complete animal, and "if you crave suckling pig, this is the place!" / W1W 4BP; www.saborrestaurants.co.uk; @sabor_ldn; Wed-Sat 10.30 pm; closed Mon & Tue & Sun.

SACHI AT PANTECHNICON SW1 £80

19 MOTCOMB STREET
020 7034 5425 6–1D

The luxurious mix of sushi plus meat and seafood grills has inspired too little feedback as yet to rate the large, barrel-vaulted lower-ground floor of this Belgravia food and retail emporium. But such as we have is all positive. / SW1X 8LB; www.pantechnicon.com/sachi; @_pantechnicon; Mon-Sat midnight, Sun 11 pm; closed Mon-Fri L.

LE SACRÉ-COEUR N1 £48 3|3|2

18 THEBERTON ST 020 7354 2618 9–3D

This long-serving "no-nonsense bistro" just off Islington's main drag is a "hardy local stand-by at a very moderate price for those who like French bistro-style food and ambience". Top Tip – "escargots followed by steak frites for lunch at under £15 is an absolute steal". / N1 0QX; lesacrecoeurbistro.co.uk; @lesacrecoeurfrenchbistro; Sun & Mon 10 pm, Tue-Thu 10.30 pm, Fri & Sat 11 pm.

SACRO CUORE N8 £43 4|2|2

10 CROUCH END HILL, N8
020 8348 8487 1–1C
45 CHAMBERLAYNE RD, NW10
020 8960 8558 1–2B

"Genuine Neapolitan pizza" is what they strive for at this 10-year-old Kensal Rise spot and its "compact" Crouch End spin-off – and it earns them higher marks for food than most competitors, year after year. / www.sacrocuore.co.uk; sacrocuorepizza.

SAGAR £41 3|2|2

37 PANTON STREET, SW1
020 3093 8463 5–4A
17A PERCY ST, W1 020 7631 3319 3–1D
31 CATHERINE ST, WC2
020 7836 6377 5–3D
157 KING ST, W6 020 8741 8563 8–2C

"Very tasty dosas" headline the "wide range of delicious, South Indian vegetarian dishes", "with many unusual choices" at this "unassuming-looking" small chain, whose most central branch is just off Leicester Square. "The food is good enough even to silence grumbling carnivores like me!" / www.sagarveg.co.uk.

SAIGON SAIGON W6 £48 2|3|2

313-317 KING ST 020 8748 6887 8–2B

Stalwart Vietnamese, complete with characterful, battered themey interior, that continues to thrive but somewhat divides opinion. To critics it's "what I would call watered-down Asian food" with flavours lacking bite, but its large local fan club remain delighted and "pleasantly surprised" by its "good value". / W6 9NH; www.saigon-saigon.co.uk; Sun & Mon 10 pm, Tue-Sat 11 pm.

SAINT JACQUES SW1 £80 3|3|3

5 ST JAMES'S ST 020 7930 2030 3–4D

"This beautiful and impressive dining room and outside terrace has a rich restaurant history" (most recently as Boulestin and L'Oranger), and its latest "pricey-but-good" incarnation is proving "a useful addition to St James's". "Solid and traditional" in style, it provides "accomplished French cooking and helpful service" in a luxurious interior that's "very stylish and relaxed". And come summer, "the courtyard is a destination" in itself. / SW1 1EF; www.saintjacquesrestaurant.com; @saintjacquesrestaurant; Mon-Fri 22, Sat 10 pm; closed Sat L, closed Sun.

ST JOHN BREAD & WINE E1 £69 3|2|3

94-96 COMMERCIAL ST
020 7251 0848 13–2C

"Move away from the ordinary and enjoy something special" at this "cracking venue" – an über-functional, white-walled Spitalfields canteen whose "great, innovative menu" of offbeat British dishes (such as chitterlings) is a stripped-down version of

Trevor Gulliver and Fergus Henderson's world-famous Smithfield original. To some, it is even better: "I now prefer B&W to the mothership – it's more lively and wears the 'nose-to-tail' cloak a little more lightly". / E1 6LZ; www.stjohngroup.uk.com/spitalfields; @st.john.restaurant; Mon-Sun 9.30 pm.

ST JOHN SMITHFIELD
EC1 £82 4|4|3
26 ST JOHN ST 020 7251 0848 10–1B

"Not for the faint hearted… you need to have some courage to eat at St John with its challenging menu and stark industrial aesthetic" (complete with "harsh acoustics"). But the "uncompromising ethos" of "nose-to-tail eating at its very best" is what's carved the international renown of Trevor Oliver and Fergus Henderson's ex-smokehouse near Smithfield Market. "No wonder many of the best chefs in the UK are alumni of this amazing kitchen": fans feel "this is the only place that treats every part of the animal with respect" and it remains an "all-time favourite" for very many diners ("been going for over 25 years, faultless food and personally I love the minimalism of the décor too"). Ratings did slip quite a bit this year, though, with one or two reports that "menus have been more routine of late, with execution below old standards". Perhaps the general strain of these post-Covid and post-Brexit times? / EC1M 4AY; stjohnrestaurant.com; @st.john.restaurant; Mon-Sat 10.30 pm, Sun 4 pm; closed Sun D.

ST JOHNS N19 £60 3|4|5
91 JUNCTION RD 020 7272 1587 9–1C

"Still one of the best gastropubs in North London", this Archway tavern "bounced back" from the pandemic and "the food remains as interestingly reliable as ever". It's a "lovely place for a treat", especially under the "beautiful vaulted ceiling in the dining room" (originally built as a ballroom). / N19 5QU; www.stjohnstavern.com; @stjohnstavern; Mon-Sat 10 pm, Sun 6 pm; closed Tue-Thu L closed Sun D, closed Mon; no Amex; booking max 12 may apply.

ST MORITZ W1 £62 3|3|3
161 WARDOUR STREET
020 7734 3324 4–1C

This retro-Swiss veteran in Soho which celebrates its half-century next year is "about the only place in London you can get real fondue", along with other classics of "authentic Swiss cuisine" (including rösti, spätzli and bratwurst) in appropriately chalet-style surroundings. The cooking is generally "excellent & generous" – so "pröschtli" (cheers!) / W1F 8WJ; www.stmoritz-restaurant.co.uk; Mon-Sat 11.30 pm, Sun 10.30 pm.

SAKONIS £34 3|2|2
127-129 EALING RD, HA0
020 8903 9601 1–1A
330 UXBRIDGE ROAD, HA5
020 8903 9601 1–1A

A "surprise find" for the uninitiated, this veggie Indian trio has actually grown out of a family-run Wembley stall set up in 1984. The food is "freshly prepared" and "full of flavours", with the Wembley and Kingsbury branches offering an unlimited buffet; Hatch End is à la carte only. / sakonis.co.uk; sakonis_uk.

SALAAM NAMASTE
WC1 £50 3|3|2
68 MILLMAN STREET 020 7405 3697 2–1D

Sabbir Karim's "reliably consistent" modern curry house near Great Ormond Street Hospital boasts an "extensive menu that goes well beyond the traditional Indian dishes"; offering "very good quality across the board". / WC1N 3EF; www.salaam-namaste.co.uk; Sun-Fri & Sat 11 pm; closed Sat L.

SALE E PEPE
SW1 £83 3|5|3
9-15 PAVILION ROAD 020 7235 0098 6–1D

"Never lets you down… always fun… always noisy… always great food" – this "buzzy longstanding trattoria" (est. 1974), a short walk from the rear of Harrods, is "always a favourite" for a very loyal fan club, serving a long and traditional menu. "Ideal for date night" too. / SW1X 0HD; www.saleepepe.co.uk; @saleepepelondon; Mon-Sat 10.30 pm, Sun 10 pm.

SALLOOS SW1 £68 3|3|2
62-64 KINNERTON ST 020 7235 4444 6–1D

Tucked away in a mews townhouse, this "dependable" Belgravia haunt has served upscale Pakistani cuisine to a wealthy crowd for 45 years. It particularly hits the spot for "meat-lovers" – "the lamb chops are seriously loveable" – while "the friendliness of the staff makes up for the rather boring Gulf and Russian clientele". / SW1X 8ER; www.salloos.co.uk; @salloos_restaurant; Mon-Sat 11 pm; closed Mon-Sat L, closed Sun; may need 5+ to book.

LE SALON PRIVÉ
TW1 £58 3|3|3
43 CROWN RD 020 8892 0602 1–4A

A "classy" option deep in the 'burbs – chef-patron Gianluca di Monaco's (who worked under retired über-chef, Pierre Koffmann, for a time) "lovely little French spot" occupies a cute, if "understated" St Margaret's site long associated with gastronomy. For the odd sceptic, "sticking so strictly to the script of Gallic classics can seem a bit stifling in 2022", but for most customers that's exactly what makes it "a memorable place to visit". / TW1 3EJ; lesalonprive.net; @lesalon_prive; Tue-Sat 21.30 pm, Sun 4 pm; closed Sun D, closed Mon.

SALT YARD £56 3|2|2
54 GOODGE ST, W1 020 7637 0657 2–1B
THE SOUTHERN TERRACE, WESTFIELD LONDON, ARIEL WAY, W12 NO TEL 1–3B
NEW HIBERNIA HOUSE, WINCHESTER WALK, SE1 07585 338748 10–4C

"A variety of excellent tapas" (mixing Spanish and Italian inspirations) and an appealing, "buzzy" (if sometimes "loud") atmosphere created huge interest in the original Fitzrovia branch, when it opened back in 2005. But while still retaining a loyal fan club, it can seem overhyped nowadays ("it's always listed as a go-to place, but there are much better tapas available elsewhere now"). Having spawned various spin-offs (Dehesa, Opera Tavern, Ember Yard), since 2018 it's been part of Urban Pubs & Bars who have decided to roll it out: first to Westfield in Shepherd's Bush (which opened in July 2022) and coming soon to Borough Market if local planning objections can be overcome. / www.saltyardgroup.co.uk; saltyardgroup.

SALTIE GIRL W1
15 NORTH AUDLEY STREET NO TEL 3–2A

A renowned Boston seafood chain is opening in Mayfair in late 2022; expect lobster rolls, oysters, 'seafood towers', chowder and very likely dishes from their established tinned seafood collection. / W1W 6WZ; @saltiegirl.london; Mon-Sat 9.30 pm, Sun 9 pm.

SALUT N1 £72 3|4|4
412 ESSEX ROAD 020 3441 8808 9–3D

"A bit out of the way, on Islington's generally unlovely Essex Road", this "small neighbourhood spot" is worth discovering. "The open kitchen gives it a lovely and buzzy vibe", as well as providing "interesting" and "good value" modern European cooking. "It's open for Sunday lunch, but doesn't serve the ubiquitous roast." / N1 3PJ; www.salut-london.co.uk; @salut.restaurant; Mon-Sat 10 pm; closed Mon-Thu L, closed Sun.

SAM'S CAFÉ NW1 £27 3|3|3
40 CHALCOT ROAD 020 7916 3736 9–3B

This artfully down-to-earth, all-day (and most evenings) café, run by Primrose Hill locals actor Sam Frears and writer Andrew O'Hagan, is "the best place to start the day", with "delightful staff delivering decent coffee and lovely food". The fortnightly supper club provides "simple but tasty food" and the opportunity to "meet unknown neighbours in a friendly environment". Artists are invited to display their work on the walls; broadcaster and writer Andrew Marr exhibited a selection of his abstract drawings. / NW1 8LS; www.samscafeprimrosehill.com; @samscafeprimrosehill; Mon & Tue, Thu-Sun 10 pm, Wed 5 pm; closed Wed D.

SAMS RIVERSIDE
W6 £78 4|4|5
1 CRISP WALK 020 8237 1020 8–2C

"A superb position by the river" helps set the scene at this "outstanding, modern and really well designed" independent venue by Hammersmith Bridge – part of the revamped Riverside Studios complex – which has "a very buzzy atmosphere inside and lovely terrace outside". "Sam is a great host" (some regulars recall his Sam's Brasserie in Chiswick) and inspires "prompt and caring" service from his staff who give a "lovely welcome". "Very well-sourced seafood" is the highlight of a luxurious brasserie menu that "if not quite exceptional, is very good". "It's a place of real quality and a genuine alternative to the River Café down the towpath if they're full or your budget doesn't quite stretch that far". / W6 9DN; samsriverside.co.uk; @samsriversidew6; Mon-Sat 10 pm, Sun 4 pm; closed Sun D.

SAMBAL SHIOK N7 £45 322

171 HOLLOWAY ROAD 020 7619 9888 9–2D

"The food is simply wonderful, from fiery laksas to cool and piquant gado-gado" at this "buzzy, crowded, hawker-style stall" on the Holloway Road, presided over by Kuala Lumpur-born Mandy Lin and her team. "One of London's increasing number of properly good Malaysian restaurants." / N7 8LX; www.sambalshiok.co.uk; @sambalshiok; Tue-Thu 9 pm, Fri & Sat 10 pm; closed Tue L, closed Sun & Mon; payment – credit card only; booking online only.

SAN CARLO SW1 £78 334

2 REGENT STREET SAINT JAMES'S 020 3778 0768 4–4D

This "sophisticated Italian restaurant" north of Pall Mall, from Sicilian-born Carlo Distefano's national group, inspires relatively limited feedback despite (because of?) its heart-of-the-West-End location. It's consistently well-rated, though – fans say it "can always be relied on for business and social meals". / SW1S 4AU; sancarlo.co.uk/restaurants/san-carlo-london; @sancarlorestaurants; Tue-Sun 11 pm, Mon 10 pm.

SAN CARLO CICCHETTI £66 333

215 PICCADILLY, W1 020 7494 9435 4–4C 30 WELLINGTON ST, WC2 020 7240 6339 5–3D 6 HANS ROAD, SW3 020 7846 7145 6–1D

These "slick and professional" Italians (offshoots of the national San Carlo chain) are "buzzy and convenient sorts of places, where you can enjoy an upbeat bite without hanging around too long". They serve "an extensive menu of small Venetian sharing plates": "at best they're excellent" and almost invariably a meal is "good fun". The best known outlet is steps from Piccadilly Circus – "it might look like a tourist trap in its prime location but it's a reliable and smartly decorated venue". / www.sancarlocicchetti.co.uk.

SAN PIETRO W8 £52 323

7 STRATFORD ROAD 020 7938 1805 6–1A

"Really excellent Italian local" that occupies a smart, if tightly packed, two-floor site in an off-the-beaten-track Kensington backwater. It's a "cheerful place" with lovely fresh fish, "beautifully displayed packed in ice". / W8 6RF; www.san-pietro.co.uk; @Sanpietro7; Mon-Sun 10 pm.

SANTA MARIA £45 333

160 NEW CAVENDISH ST, W1 020 7436 9963 2–1B 92-94 WATERFORD ROAD, SW6 020 7384 2844 6–4A 11 BOND STREET, W5 020 8579 1462 1–3A 189 UPPER STREET, N1 020 7288 7400 9–2D

"Pizza of similar quality to those you'd find in a Naples basement" (with "authentic slow fermentation of the dough") inspire followers of this growing, twelve-year-old group, which they say is "second-to-none for texture and flavour". But the relocated original site in Ealing is "cramped" and seems "really dull" compared to the old one: "the pizza remains good, but it's lost the sense that you were part of something special and secret". (In recent times, they've also added an Islington branch and one in Brentford – not listed – that's part of a car showroom!) / www.santamariapizzeria.com.

SANTA MARIA DEL SUR SW8 £58 332

129 QUEENSTOWN RD 020 7622 2088 11–1C

"Tremendous steaks" are to be found at this "friendly" Argentinian steakhouse that has made itself at home in Battersea for almost 15 years – "worth the trip south of the river!" / SW8 3RH; www.santamariadelsur.co.uk; @stamariadelsur; Mon-Sun 10 pm.

Sarap Filipino Bistro W1

SANTINI SW1 £111 233

29 EBURY ST 020 7730 4094 2–4B

This "time-capsule" version of the classic Belgravia Italian restaurant attracted the likes of Frank Sinatra in its 1980s heyday. These days it is run by Laura Santini, daughter of the founder, Gino – and the food is by all accounts "undeniably delicious". Even fans, though, can find it "outrageously expensive". / SW1W 0NZ; www.santinirestaurant.com; @santinirestaurant; Mon-Sat 10.30 pm; closed Sat L, closed Sun.

SANTO MARE W1 £90 333

87-89 GEORGE STREET 020 7486 0377 2–1A

"You feel like you're in Italy as soon as you step in the door" of this chichi seafood specialist in Marylebone – "a tank of live lobsters and beautifully presented fresh fish on a bed of crushed ice give you the flavour of the specialities". The restaurant is supplied by fresh fish flown in from the Tyrrhenian sea, where the dynamic young owner Andrea Reitano has a twin restaurant in Porto Cervo, Sardinia. Top Menu Tips – "great fritto misto – and pasta with lobster, or langoustines, also delight". / W1U 8AQ; www.santomare.com/london-restaurant; @santomare; Mon-Sun 11 pm.

SANTO REMEDIO £66 322

152 TOOLEY STREET, SE1 020 7403 3021 10–4D 55 GREAT EASTERN STREET, EC2 020 7403 3021 13–1B

Edson and Natalie Diaz-Fuentes's authentic cuisine – washed down with delicious margaritas – wins consistently high ratings, if from a small fan club, for their Bermondsey restaurant. No feedback on their newer cafe in Shoreditch – a return to the area where they began their career in the capital seven years ago. /

SANTORE EC1 £56 322

59-61 EXMOUTH MKT 020 7812 1488 10–1A

This "very authentic Italian local" has been filling happy bellies in Exmouth Market for more than 20 years, with Neapolitan pizzas, pastas and other dishes – "nothing too refined, but plenty of choice and not expensive". The only complaint: "some options are just too big and hearty". / EC1R 4QL; www.santorerestaurant.london; @santorerestaurant_ldn; Sun-Thu 10 pm, Fri & Sat 11 pm.

SARAP FILIPINO BISTRO W1 £41 333

10 HEDDON STREET 020 3488 9769 4–3B

"Amongst the surging number of Filipino places, this is one to recommend!" – Ferdinand 'Budgie' Montoya brings his "upscale and creative Filipino food" to Mayfair's Heddon Street in this new venture, which follows his Sarap try-outs in Dalston, Soho and Brixton.

The dishes are "original and delicious" although it's perhaps no surprise that they come at "eye-watering prices, if you've ever been to the Philippines" (and Filipino diners don't always rate the cuisine as highly as non-natives). Top Tip – "memorable crispy stuffed pig's trotter!" / W1W 4BX; saraplondon.com; @sarap_london; Tue, Fri & Sat 11 pm, Wed & Thu 10.30 pm, Sun 4 pm; closed Tue L closed Sun D, closed Mon.

SARAVANAA BHAVAN HA0 £50 3 3 2

531-533 HIGH RD   020 8900 8526   1–1A

A "massive range of dosas" and other "very authentic, traditional South Asian options" ensure that this Chennai-based vegetarian chain's London branches are "very popular with the local Asian community". It's "not fancy", but there are "lots of dishes that don't make it on to many English Indian menus". Founded in 1981, the chain now operates in 23 countries. Founder P Rajagopal was imprisoned for the murder of an employee whose wife he wanted to marry, and died behind bars four years ago. / HA0 2DJ; saravanabhavanlondon.com; Sun-Thu 10.30 pm, Fri & Sat 11 pm.

SARTORIA W1 £92 3 4 3

20 SAVILE ROW   020 7534 7000   4–3A

This swish "old-fashioned Italian" with "very smooth and welcoming staff" has "real style" befitting its environs alongside the bespoke tailors of Savile Row (for which it is named). Owned by D&D London, the kitchen nowadays is run by distinguished Calabrian-born chef Francesco Mazzei. Prices have never been bargain basement here, but most reporters reckon the expense is "worth it for the excellent cooking using top-class ingredients" and the "divine selection of Italian wines". / W1S 3PR; www.sartoria-restaurant.co.uk; @sartoriarestaurant; Mon-Sat 10 pm; closed Sun.

THE SAVOY HOTEL, SAVOY GRILL WC2 £147 2 2 3

STRAND   020 7592 1600   5–3D

In Thatcher's day, this was London's power dining scene par excellence, and this "luxurious, opulent and dark" panelled chamber, just off the hotel foyer, remains "a fabulous room", especially in which to do business. Run by Gordon Ramsay since 2003, it has ploughed a safe-if-unexciting culinary course in recent times, focused on classics such as Beef Wellington and Lobster Thermidor, with results being consistently decent, if unexceptional. But reports this year took a dive due to concerns about the very poor level of value. Even a positive account hailing "outstanding Arnold Bennett soufflé starters and a superb all-round experience" noted that "the eye-watering bill makes it one just for a special occasion". For more sceptical souls, "the food is fine, but certainly not worth the price tag put on it". In particular, critical wine buffs feel the "list is borderline robbery, with incomprehensible mark-ups that seem extreme even for the capital… and unfortunately there aren't as many oligarchs around now daft

enough to pay such prices!" / WC2R 0EU; www.gordonramsayrestaurants.com/savoy-grill; @savoygrillgordonramsay; Mon-Sat midnight, Sun 11.30 pm.

THE SAVOY HOTEL, THAMES FOYER WC2 £112 2 3 4

THE SAVOY, THE STRAND   020 7420 2111   5–3D

The "typically English afternoon tea", "beautifully presented by polished staff" in the elegant foyer of this landmark hotel, is "everything you want it to be" – "and the little extras, such as the pianist, make it a real treat". "I've had a lot of afternoon teas and this one is second to none!" / WC2W 0ER; www.thesavoylondon.com/restaurant/thames-foyer-restaurant; @TheSavoyLondon; Mon-Sat midnight, Sun 11.30 pm.

SCALINI SW3 £93 3 4 3

1-3 WALTON ST   020 7225 2301   6–2C

"Classic" old-school trattoria (down to the photo gallery of visiting celebs), five minutes from Harrods, that's "bonkers expensive", but keeps its well-heeled crowd powerfully happy. "Portions are huge (they assume you're starving)" and it's "good fun, reliably noisy and… well… Italian" – a formula that has served it well for 35 years, and brought spin-offs in Cannes and across the Middle East in recent years. / SW3 2JD; www.scalinilondon.co.uk; @scaliniuk; Mon-Sun 11.30 pm; no shorts.

THE SCARSDALE W8 £59 3 3 5

23A EDWARDES SQ   020 7937 1811   8–1D

In one of London's prettiest squares, this "lively" pub classic has the dubious honour of being Piers Morgan's local – he claims to have met the then-actress Meghan Markle here on the day she later met Prince Harry. (TV crime buffs will also remember it from the late-70s series The Professionals.) The scoff's mostly unreformed pub grub, but good value. / W8 6HE; www.scarsdaletavern.co.uk; @scarsdalew8; Mon-Sat 11 pm, Sun 10.30 pm.

SCHNITZEL FOREVER N16 £47 3 2 2

119 STOKE NEWINGTON CHURCH STREET   020 7419 0022   1–1C

The humble schnitzel – a flattened cut of meat or fish, even cheese or mushrooms, covered in breadcrumbs and fried – is rescued from semi-oblivion and celebrated at this black-and-white-tiled Stoke Newington newbie that started life in 2020 as a delivery-only business that managed to achieve "remarkably crisp and fresh" results. There was not enough feedback for a rating this year, but longstanding schnitzel aficionado Jay Rayner was an instant convert, declaring it "the cornerstone of a blossoming high street chain with many outposts across the country. It just doesn't quite know it yet." / N16 0UD; www.schnitzelforever.co.uk; @schnitzel_forever; Mon, Wed & Thu, Sat 10 pm, Fri 10.30 pm, Sun 9.30 pm; closed Tue.

SCOTT'S W1 £99 4 4 4

20 MOUNT ST   020 7495 7309   3–3A

"Eternally elegant" – this "discreet and yet see-and-be-seen" Mayfair A-lister (007's preferred lunch spot) "always feels like a special occasion" ("people spotting here becomes a game"), and its mix of "glamour" with "very fine seafood and effective service" helps to put it in London's Top-5 most-mentioned restaurants in our annual diners' poll (and it's only narrowly beaten by its stablemate J Sheekey in nominations for the capital's best fish). "The menu is both familiar and innovative, with frequent new dishes and specials in addition to the classic fish and fruits de mer it is famous for" (of the former, for example, "top Dover sole"). "It is even more expensive than it ever was, but somehow one never minds the bill because the food and service seem to justify every penny." And while it has "an upmarket and lovely interior", if you can nab one of the pavement tables "sitting outside on Mount Street and watching the world go by adds to the ambience". / W1K 2HE; www.scotts-restaurant.com; @scottsmayfair; Mon-Sat 1 am, Sun 12.30 am; booking max 6 may apply.

SCOTT'S ON THE RIVER TW9

WHITTAKER AVENUE   NO TEL   1–4A

Not content with pimping 'The Ivy', Richard Caring is now setting about knocking off copies of the famous Mayfair seafood veteran, starting with this two-floor opening on the Richmond riverside. Finally, after months of wrangling, the planning objections of the original architect for the site have been overcome and it debuts in Autumn 2022. Open seven days a week, we are promised 'the finest fish and shellfish alongside a variety of meat and seasonal game, in an atmosphere exuding urbane sophistication'. The lower floor will have a crustacea and Champagne bar and the upstairs bar will host DJs every Thursday to Saturday. Hmmm… the latter doesn't sound at all like Scott's Mayfair – couldn't he have called it 'The Ivy Seafood', rather than knackering a second great name? Top Tip – a 32-cover terrace promises splendid al fresco dining. / TW9 1EH; caprice-holdings.co.uk; Sun-Thu 12.30 am, Fri & Sat 1.30 am.

SCULLY SW1 £91 3 3 2

4 ST JAMES'S MARKET   020 3911 6840   4–4D

"Wildly different and by-and-large exceptional" – Ramuel Scully's "brilliantly creative food" delivers "subtly spiced, multiply layered, classy and novel tastes" at his St James's Market five-year-old. "For those close to the open kitchen, it's almost like a chef's table" and the "kitchen brigade and front-of-house team deliver an experience that is at the same time other-worldly and disarmingly intimate". Even its strongest fans can feel the trip is "let down by the interior", however, and ratings more generally were undercut this year by those who found it pricey or felt there were "too many odd combinations". / SW1S 4QU; www.scullyrestaurant.com; @scully_chef; Tue, Wed, Sat, Thu & Fri 9.30 pm; closed Tue, Wed, Sat L, closed Sun & Mon; booking online only.

SEA CONTAINERS, MONDRIAN LONDON SE1 £78 ②②③

20 UPPER GROUND   020 3747 1000   10–3A

"It feels like a place to see and be seen, which can account for the expense, but fun and with good river views…" – not a bad overview of this "buzzy" dining room, designed by Tom Dixon, near Blackfriars Bridge. (A harsher view is that it's "a typically over-priced hotel joint, trying to be smarter than it really is".) Top Tip – "super weekend brunch, lots of choice, and the bar is good too". / SE1 9PD; www.seacontainerslondon.com; @seacontainersldn; Sun-Wed 11 pm, Thu & Fri 6.30 pm; closed Sun L, closed Sat.

THE SEA, THE SEA £70 ⑤④④

174 PAVILION ROAD, SW3
020 7824 8090   6–2D
337 ACTON MEWS, E8
020 7824 8090   14–2A

"Extraordinary food served with commitment" in a "cutting-edge omakase" format makes the new Haggerston branch of this seafood duo one of the most exciting culinary arrivals of the year. "In a very stylishly decorated railway arch venue", it is focused on a 12-seat chef's table overseen by chef Leandro Carreira: "a beautiful sea-like resin counter", where the "very skilled and friendly chefs are centre stage in front of diners, preparing the food as you watch". "This is perfect fish cooking with innovation in each course, where you can fully differentiate the taste of each fish"; and with "dishes that are Noma-like in their execution and quality". (Our meal ran: "sea urchin with almond milk, savoury custard with jus, fabulous churrasco of tuna belly, monkfish with leek, roasted fennel seed ice cream and Portuguese sponge cake and caviar".) And while the focus is on £8 this year, the original SW3 branch in a quiet mews near Sloane Street still wins favourable mention for "wonderfully fresh fish excellently prepared". / www.theseathesea.net; theseathesea_.

SEABIRD AT THE HOXTON, SOUTHWARK SE1 £82 ③②⑤

THE HOXTON, 40 BLACKFRIARS ROAD
020 7903 3000   10–4A

"Fabulous views", "delicious seafood"… "it ticks every box" according to fans of this 14th-floor rooftop: part of a Southwark hotel, which sets a glam tone. Ratings have softened a little since it opened a couple of years ago, however, with mounting concern that the height of the prices is starting to match that of the venue! / SE1 8NY; thehoxton.com/london/southwark/hotels; @thehoxtonhotel; Sun-Thu midnight, Fri & Sat 1 am.

THE SEAFOOD BAR W1 £101 ④④④

77 DEAN STREET   020 4525 0733   4–1D

"No frills or pretension – just generous platters of great seafood" in a "variety of options (raw and roasted)" help make the De Visscher family's new import from Amsterdam into "a great addition to Soho". "Unless you have a serious appetite, the plates may serve two or even three with a bowl of fries, making the evening a steal." And "it's not a place to worry about table manners – just grab one of their complimentary bibs and your claw crackers and have at it!" / W1W 3SH; www.theseafoodbar.com; @theseafoodbar; Sun-Thu 10 pm, Fri & Sat 10.30 pm.

SEAFRESH SW1 £59 ③③②

80-81 WILTON RD   020 7828 0747   2–4B

"Great fish" and "friendly staff" attract a steady crowd of regulars to this veteran Pimlico fish specialist, run by the same family since 1961. It's been modernised in relatively recent times, and serves classic fish 'n' chips alongside more elevated seafood options, including octopus, lobster and Dover sole meunière. / SW1V 1DL; www.seafresh-dining.com; Mon-Sun 10.30 pm.

SEARCYS ST PANCRAS GRAND NW1 £77 ②③④

UPPER CONCOURSE   020 7870 9900   9–3C

"Better than anything the Gare du Nord can offer (although perhaps that's not saying much!)" – this "beautiful" operation overlooking the Eurostar tracks comprises a "comfortable and well-spaced", large interior with a stylish concourse bar (Europe's longest, apparently) whose seating runs along the platforms from on high (the latter closing in summer 2022 for a major upgrade and a new focus on its extensive Champagne range of bottles and magnums). The brasserie fare (served seven days a week from breakfast) is sometimes criticised for being "unimaginative", but one or two reports felt it had "stepped up a gear" this year, with recommendations as a business or romantic rendezvous; or for its luxurious afternoon tea. It's certainly "convenient" (and, in the bar, "you can't beat it for a view of the trains"). / NW1 2QP; stpancrasbysearcys.co.uk; @searcystpancras; Mon-Sat 10.30 pm, Sun 10 pm.

THE SEA SHELL NW1 £57 ③③②

49-51 LISSON GROVE
020 7224 9000   9–4A

"Really good fish 'n' chips, big portions, always tasty"; the not-so-secret recipe for this legendary family-owned chippy's century – and more – of success. There are multiple cooking choices for the "lovely fish", which can be grilled or fried with panko, matzo-meal and gluten-free options and is served with 'bottomless' chips. Despite its heritage, though, it's been through various owners and refurbs over the decades – the interior is fine, but don't go expecting quirky period charm. / NW1 6UH; www.seashellrestaurant.co.uk; @seashellrestaurant; Tue-Sat 10.30 pm, Sun 7 pm; closed Tue, Wed L, closed Mon.

SEASONS W1 £123 ②②②

6-10 BRUTON STREET
020 3725 7700   3–2C

In the former Mayfair home of The Square (RIP), it's hard to know quite what to make of this high-end fish and seafood venture, which opened in late 2021 (and which, according to its website, is soon to open in Miami and New York). This basement site has always seemed a bit "corporate", and it still does, although visiting jazz singers can sometimes inject a sense of brio. Meanwhile, the luxurious, sustainable seafood menu (which curiously also incorporates black truffle or lobster pizza to share, and a few random meat options) inspires a range of opinions: from "very good" to "such a disappointment". / W1W 6PU; seasonsdream.com; @seasons_bistrot; Tue-Sat 1 am; closed Sun & Mon.

SESSIONS ARTS CLUB EC1 £60 ③③⑤

24 CLERKENWELL GREEN
020 3793 4025   10–1A

"Believe the gushy reviews!" This "stunning" dining room – part of "a glorious Georgian building" in Clerkenwell which features in Dickens's 'Oliver Twist' – is London's highest profile opening of the year and "worth the hype!": "it's a restaurant that has everything!". "From the moment you start looking for the inconspicuous entrance, to the concierge and the lift, then the big reveal into the dining room upstairs: it's the perfect place to surprise someone". And "what an interior!" – like "a faded palazzo" – "there's something about the high ceilings and the ambient lighting and the rugs on the floor that makes it the ultimate in shabby chic glamour" "can somehow combine ingredients that appear unpromising and end up with the most delicious, adventurous and unusual dishes": "delectable small plates for sharing, with some meat but mainly fishy/veggie options". "It's just a shame it's almost impossible to get a table now… it's so hot!" Top Menu Tip – "the smoked eel and potato sandwich is unmissable, crisp outside and meltingly smoky and fishy within". / EC1E 0NA; sessionsartsclub.com; @sessionsartsclub; Wed-Sat, Tue 10 pm; closed Tue L, closed Sun & Mon; payment – credit card only.

SEVEN PARK PLACE SW1 £170 ③③③

7-8 PARK PL   020 7316 1621   3–4C

"In a part of Mayfair heaving with Michelin stars, William Drabble and his team (operating out of a townhouse hotel) continue to knock it out of the park", providing a "wonderful and very extravagant time". "William is always in the kitchen where he belongs, not in the TV studios" and some fans feel he "doesn't get all the plaudits he deserves" for his "exceptional cuisine, with big bold flavours. Nothing is done only for effect, as every ingredient on a plate serves a purpose. The tasting menu delivers upon this, course after course. Combine all that with knowledgeable and approachable staff and this really is a place to rave about".

Sabor W1

/ SW1A 1LS; www.stjameshotelandclub.com; @stjameshotelandclub; Tue-Sat 10 pm; closed Sun & Mon; no trainers.

7 SAINTS W11 £64 344

7 ALL SAINTS ROAD 020 7460 8566 7–1B

"What a find!" – this "intimate" spot on a "beautiful cosy corner" off Portobello Road boasts a "small but perfectly formed menu" of "exciting food". Owner James Gummer (ex-maître d' at The Wolseley) leads the front of house, looking after guests so well that "it feels as if you're in New York". / W11 1HA; 7saints. co.uk; @7saintsrestaurant; Tue-Sat 10 pm; closed Tue-Fri L, closed Sun & Mon.

SEXY FISH W1 £103 113

1-4 BERKELEY SQ 020 3764 2000 3–3B

"So loud" in every aspect – Richard Caring's prominently sited seafood scene is an orgy of ostentatious styling, luxe seafood and sushi, and a crowd that's Mayfair's answer to 'Love Island'. The kind view is that it's "fun and full of life" ("they made our daughter feel very special for her 15th birthday"). The majority view is that "service is sloppy and prices absolutely outrageous". / W1J 6BR; www.sexyfish.com; @sexyfishlondon; Sun-Wed 1 am, Thu-Sat 2 am; booking max 6 may apply.

SHACKFUYU W1 £49 322

14A OLD COMPTON ST 020 3019 3492 5–2A

This "tasty" and fun Soho side project from the Bone Daddies group sounds like a post-modern culinary joke – a western take on a Japanese take on western cuisine! It started out as a pop-up, but proved popular enough to stick around on a permanent basis, serving hits from Korean fried wings and tuna tacos to kinako French toast with soft-serve ice cream. / W1W 4TJ; bonedaddies.com/shack-fuyu; @shackfuyu; Mon-Sat 10 pm, Sun 9 pm; no booking.

SHAHI PAKWAAN N2 £36 332

25 AYLMER PARADE, AYLMER ROAD 020 8341 1111 1–1B

"A local gem", this "high-quality" five-year-old takes its cue from the royal cuisine of Hyderabad in south-central India, and attracts regulars from beyond its East Finchley neighbourhood. / N2 0PE; www.shahipakwaan.co.uk; @Shahi Pakwaan; Mon-Sat 11 pm; closed Sun.

THE SHED W8 £66 344

122 PALACE GARDENS TER 020 7229 4024 7–2B

"A bit of an oddball" – this "quirky little place with a fun atmosphere" off Notting Hill serves a selection of creative dishes using sustainably sourced produce that's foraged or from the Gladwin family's farm in Sussex and is one of their better-rated venues. The Gladwins have now opened six restaurants under their 'Local & Wild' brand across west and central London,

with more expected to follow. / W8 4RT; www.theshed-restaurant.com; @theshed_resto; Tue-Sat, Mon 11.30 pm; closed Mon L, closed Sun.

J SHEEKEY WC2 £88 334

28-34 ST MARTIN'S CT 020 7240 2565 5–3B

"Tucked away in a side alley in the centre of Theatreland", this "old school" veteran (est. 1896) regained its No. 1 slot in this year' poll, both as London's most-mentioned destination; and also for providing the capital's best fish and seafood. "All the classics are perfectly prepared" ("the freshest shellfish, unforgettable dressed crab, oysters and huge portions of Dover sole, washed down with a chilled bottle of Chablis… perfection"). And, they are served in a "quirky and atmospheric" series of picture-lined rooms, whose nooks and "intimate booths" further buoy its traditional appeal. Post-Covid, meals here did not always seem as sure-footed as in the past, with staffing often diagnosed as a problem. But recovering ratings this year suggest more of a return to the "classy" form that's typically the norm here. "It's pricey, but Sheekey's still keeps its spot as one of the capital's greats!" / WC2N 4AL; www.j-sheekey.co.uk; @jsheekeyldn; Mon-Sat 11.30 pm, Sun 10.30 pm; booking max 6 may apply.

J SHEEKEY ATLANTIC BAR WC2 £88 434

28-32 ST MARTIN'S CT 020 7240 2565 5–3B

A semi-independent addition to the original venue next door, its "reliably fresh fish" and glam, casual styling make this American-style seafood bar "a great post-theatre favourite". There are no specific gripes about food or service, but "the pricing seems to be approaching the level of the main restaurant, taking away some of its raison d'être". / WC2N 4AL; www.j-sheekey.co.uk; @sheekeys; Mon-Sat 11.30 pm, Sun 10.30 pm; booking max 3 may apply.

SHIKUMEN, DORSETT HOTEL W12 £70 423

58 SHEPHERD'S BUSH GRN 020 8749 9978 8–1C

"One of the best Chinese restaurants in London" is where you might least expect it – in a modern hotel overlooking one side of Shepherd's Bush Green. Better still, it occupies a "smart, spacious room, so has a calm atmosphere with reasonable noise levels". The menu comprises "great-quality Cantonese plus other regions", including "consistently superior dim sum – all well and freshly cooked, with some unusual items alongside old favourites". / W12 5AA; www.shikumen.co.uk; @shikumen.w12; Mon-Sun 11 pm.

SHILPA W6 £36 322

206 KING ST 020 8741 3127 8–2B

Ignore the "very downmarket ambience" – "authentic dishes" and "good value" are the cornerstones of this "first-class", "cheap 'n'

cheerful" South Indian café on Hammersmith's main drag. / W6 0RA; shilpahammersmith.co.uk; @shilpa-indian-restaurant; Sun-Wed 11 pm, Thu-Sat midnight.

SHORYU RAMEN £59 332

9 REGENT ST, SW1 NO TEL 4–4D
3 DENMAN ST, W1 NO TEL 4–3C
5 KINGLY CT, W1 NO TEL 4–2B
35 GREAT QUEEN STREET, WC2 NO TEL 5–1D
190 KENSINGTON HIGH STREET, W8 NO TEL 8–1D
45 GREAT EASTERN STREET, EC2 NO TEL 13–1B
BROADGATE CIRCLE, EC2 NO TEL 13–2B

"Genuine Japanese-style ramen and dumplings" from Japan Centre owner Tak Tokumine hit the spot with "generous portions, excellent flavours" and "very good service" at his expanding group based in the West End. There are now seven venues in London, plus Ichiba food hall in Westfield Shepherd's Bush and offshoots in Oxford and Manchester. The summer 2022 launch of a branch in Kensington High Street was expected to be the first of several under a new franchising arrangement. /

THE SICHUAN EC1 £45 432

14 CITY ROAD 020 7588 5489 13–2A

This "cracking Sichuanese restaurant on the unglamorous and busy City Road" (near the Honourable Artillery Company) is "not for the chilli-hater!" "Go for the authentic and freshly cooked regional specialities" from chef Zhang Xiao Zhong, whose grandfather was personal chef to Sichuan-born Deng Xiaoping, Chairman Mao's successor as China's leader. / EC1Y 2AA; www.thesichuan.co.uk; Mon-Sun 11 pm.

SICHUAN FOLK E1 £52 432

32 HANBURY ST 020 7247 4735 13–2C

This "tiny place near Truman's old brewery" serves an "excellent and authentic take on Sichuan cuisine, in a calm atmosphere, away from the agitation of Brick Lane". Top Tip – "'numb and spicy' dumplings live up to their name". / E1 6QR; www.sichuan-folk.co.uk; @sichuanfolklondon; Sun-Thu 10.30 pm, Fri & Sat 10.45 pm; no Amex; booking online only.

SICHUAN FRY E8

2 WESTGATE STREET NO TEL 14–2B

Above a new branch of Dumpling Shack in the basement, John and Yee Li's ground-floor operation in London Fields will host this new outlet based on spicy burgers ('The Sichuan', 'The Vegan' and 'The Hot and Mala Mapo') in potato rolls plus 'shake shake' fries, as road-tested over a couple of years at Spitalfields Market. / E8 3RN; Mon-Sun midnight.

SIGNOR SASSI
SW1 £70 3 3 3

14 KNIGHTSBRIDGE GREEN
020 7584 2277 6–1D

Near Harrods, this Italian of 35 years' standing is recently part of the San Carlo brand, but fits well into the glamorous, traditional mould of that Manchester-based group. "The food can be excellent, but is also erratic at times." / SW1X 7QL; www.signorsassi.co.uk; @sancarlorestaurants; Mon-Sun 11 pm.

SILK ROAD SE5 £26 5 2 2

49 CAMBERWELL CHURCH ST
020 7703 4832 1–3C

"Basic room, basic service… but man, the food is good!!" – and "incredible value" – at this Camberwell canteen, which is renowned as one of the capital's better cheap eats. It knocks out "fiery but tasty" dishes from Xinjiang in China's northwest, home of the Muslim Uighurs. / SE5 8TR; silkroadlondon.has.restaurant; Mon-Sun 11 pm; closed Mon-Sun L; cash only; no booking.

SILO E9 £61 4 4 3

THE WHITE BUILDING, UNIT 7
QUEENS YARD, WHITE POST LANE
020 8533 3331 14–1C

Very limited feedback (but all of it upbeat) for Douglas McMaster's more-eco-than-eco, zero-waste project, above Crate in Hackney Wick's canalside White Building, which – in its drive for 'quality through purity' and 'a more primitive diet… born from clean farming' serves a menu of wacky, meat-free small plates and very off-piste wines. / E9 5EN; silolondon. com; @silolondon; Wed-Sat 11 pm; closed Wed-Fri L, closed Mon & Tue & Sun.

THE SILVER BIRCH
W4 £77 3 4 3

142 CHISWICK HIGH ROAD
020 8159 7176 8–2A

This "fantastic independent neighbourhood restaurant" in Chiswick serves an "adventurous" modern European menu of "delicious and unusual dishes". Approaching its second birthday, it's the first solo project from well-travelled American-born Kimberley Hernandez, previously head chef at XU and Kym's, and is more ambitious than most such locals – "still finding its feet, but with so much potential". / W4 1PU; silverbirchchiswick.co.uk; @silverbirchchiswick; Wed-Sun 9.30 pm; closed Mon & Tue.

SIMPSON'S IN THE STRAND
WC2 £93 2 3 4

100 STRAND 020 7420 2111 5–3D

"The roast beef commands attention!" – carved at the trolley in this famous grill room near The Savoy, serving "quintessentially British cooking in very generous portions". Its performance has been very inconsistent in recent times and it was closed for an extended period over Covid, making it hard to recommend unequivocally, other than as a 'slam dunk' for entertaining foreigners on business. / WC2R 0EW; www.simpsonsinthestrand.co.uk; @simpsons1828; closed Mon-Sat & Sun; no trainers.

SIMPSON'S TAVERN
EC3 £50 2 3 5

38 1/2 BALL CT, CORNHILL
020 7626 9985 10–2C

This "unique" institution – a traditional City chophouse founded in 1757 – is "the sort of place cooking the kind of food that doesn't exist any more… except it does here!". Guests seated in 19th-century oak-panelled stalls feast on full English breakfasts and grills or pies for lunch followed by the signature stewed cheese pudding (there is no evening or weekend service). "My father took me there 65 years ago – it's hardly changed, but there's no longer an open fire!" / EC3V 9DR; www.simpsonstavern.co.uk; @simpsonstavern; Mon-Fri 3.30 pm; closed Mon-Fri D, closed Sat & Sun.

SINGAPORE GARDEN
NW6 £56 4 2 2

83A FAIRFAX RD 020 7624 8233 9–2A

"Always good, always reliable, always full… which is unfortunate if you want a table last minute" – this Singaporean/Malaysian "old favourite" in a shopping parade near Swiss Cottage is sought out by hungry regulars, "as it has been for decades" (fans include Giles Coren, restaurant critic of The Times). Service is "fast", but it can also be a little "rushed and unsmiling". / NW6 4DY; www.singaporegarden.co.uk; @singapore_garden; Mon-Thu 10.30 pm, Fri & Sat 11 pm, Sun 10 pm; closed Mon-Thu L.

SINGBURI ROYAL THAI CAFÉ
E11 £26 4 4 3

593 LEYTONSTONE HIGH RD
020 8281 4801 1–1D

This "vibrant" shopfront Thai in Leytonstone is "full of fun" and fans say they could "eat here every night of the week" thanks to its excellent dishes and the BYO policy which helps keep prices down. / E11 4PA; @Singburi_e11; Tue-Sat 11 pm, Sun 10 pm; closed Mon; cash only.

SIX BY NICO £64 3 3 3

33-41 CHARLOTTE STREET, W1
020 7580 8143 2–1C
6 CHANCELLOR PASSAGE, E14
020 3912 3334 12–1C

"Such amazing value for a six-course, themed, tasting menu" that changes every six weeks – that's the USP of Nico Simeone's national chain, which, over five years, has grown from its Glasgow base to number nine in total (with London having two: in Fitzrovia and Canary Wharf). Of course it's "slightly gimmicky", but on the whole it's "a good effort at a budget experience": "you get what you pay for, and while not all dishes hit the mark, and service can be a bit hit 'n' miss (particularly at busy times), it is innovative, has a great buzz and is a lot of fun". / www.sixbynico.co.uk; sixbynico.

SIX PORTLAND ROAD
W11 £80 3 4 2

6 PORTLAND ROAD 020 7229 3130 7–2A

"Low-key but capable of great cooking" – Jesse Dunford Wood's "friendly neighbourhood spot" does sterling service for Holland Park, serving a "short but well-curated menu" for lunch and dinner, seven days a week, alongside an "awesome wine list", in an "understated setting that makes clear that the food is the main attraction". With just 36 seats, it can get a little loud with larger groups. / W11 4LA; www.sixportlandroad.com; @SixPortlandRoad; Mon-Sun 10 pm.

THE SIX RESTAURANT &
BAR HAMPTON COURT
KT8 £60 3 3 3

2 LION GATE 020 8016 6630 1–4A

A couple of excellent reports suggest it's worth considering this old pub reinvented as a hotel and restaurant (a couple of years ago), between the maze of Hampton Court Palace and Bushy Park. The refit is very attractive and the menu of superior gastropub fare is well-rated. / KT8 9DD; www.thesixrestaurant.com; @kingsarmshamptoncourt; Mon-Sun 9 pm.

SKAL NORDIC DINING
N1 £37 4 4 3

149 UPPER STREET 07308 031151 9–2D

This "small" Swedish restaurant in Islington serves "amazing", "absolutely delicious" meals based around Nordic 'husmanskost', meaning home cooking. It took over the Grade-II listed premises vacated by fellow-Scandi Rök (RIP) three years ago, making for an easy transition for locals with a taste for the north. / N1 1RA; www.skalnordicdining.co.uk; @skalnordic; Tue-Fri 11 pm; closed Mon, Sat & Sun.

SKETCH, LECTURE ROOM AT
LIBRARY W1 £223 3 4 5

9 CONDUIT ST 020 7659 4500 4–2A

"In an utterly fairytale setting full of glamour, you can't help but feel a sense of occasion" on the "unbelievably OTT" top floor of this grand Mayfair palazzo: "from the entrance to the fine-dining experience, it makes for a fabulous date night!" But its "pocket-bursting prices" are a source of widespread complaint, and one or two reporters feel that its elevation by Michelin to its highest echelons was misjudged ("three stars! REALLY? Nowhere near"). While converts are "over the moon due to the stunning reality" of the "joyful intricacy of the cuisine" from a "wacky but delightful" menu designed (from afar) by Gallic superstar Pierre Gagnaire, others discern "a confusing medley of French fiddliness that feels rather outdated". Service is "faultless" on most accounts, if "in the breathless French-formal style". Top Tip – "best to go for lunch if you want value for money". / W1S 2XG; sketch.london; @sketchlondon; Fri & Sat, Wed & Thu 9 pm; closed Wed & Thu L, closed Mon & Tue & Sun; no trainers; booking max 6 may apply.

SKETCH, GALLERY
W1　　　　**£98**　**3**|**3**|**4**

9 CONDUIT ST　020 7659 4500　4–2A

You pay top dollar to eat quite literally inside an art installation in this room within Mourad Mazouz's idiosyncratic Mayfair venue, where artist Yinka Shonibare's pan-African vision replaced the former lurid pink-walled David Shrigley showcase in spring 2022. It makes for "great artefacts to look at", while the food – either a lavish all-day 'afternoon tea' or dinner – is "very, very good". "But my word it's expensive" – even "unbelie overpriced" – is a repeated lament even from very enthusiastic reporters. / W1S 2XG; sketch.london; @sketchlondon; Sun-Thu 10 pm, Fri & Sat 11 pm.

SKEWD KITCHEN
EN4　　　　**£64**　**3**|**3**|**3**

12 COCKFOSTERS PARADE
020 8449 7771　1–1C

This "really buzzy upmarket Turkish restaurant" puts a modern slant on the traditional Anatolian grill. It makes a "great local addition" to Cockfosters, and celebrates its tenth year in 2023. / EN4 0BX; www.skewd.com; @skewdkitchen; Mon-Thu, Sat, Fri 11 pm, Sun 10 pm; closed Mon-Thu L.

SKYLON, SOUTH BANK CENTRE SE1
　　　　　　£78　**2**|**2**|**3**

BELVEDERE RD　020 7654 7800　2–3D

"Great views over the Thames" and a vast interior (it was built as 'The People's Palace' – the destination restaurant originally at the heart of the Brutalist South Bank centre), make this D&D London operation "good for both business and social" dining. The cuisine has often seemed like an afterthought here, but was mostly well-rated this year. / SE1 8XX; www.skylon-restaurant.co.uk; @skylonrestaurant; Mon-Sat 9 pm, Sun 5 pm; closed Sun D; no trainers.

SMITH & WOLLENSKY
WC2　　　　**£109**　**2**|**2**|**3**

THE ADELPHI BUILDING, 1-11 JOHN ADAM ST　020 7321 6007　5–4D

Fans proclaim "excellent steaks" (including imported prime, dry-aged USDA fillets) and "not a fault to find" at this plush steakhouse off the Strand: the first international branch of the famous NYC chain. Its pricing, though, has often struck Londoners as "totally out of order", leading to poor ratings across the board. / WC2N 6HT; www.smithandwollensky.co.uk; @sandwollensky; Mon-Thu 11.30 pm, Fri & Sat midnight, Sun 10 pm; closed Mon L.

SMITH'S WAPPING
E1　　　　**£76**　**4**|**3**|**3**

22 WAPPING HIGH ST
020 7488 3456　12–1A

"Stunning views of Tower Bridge and brilliant seafood" are twin highlights at this popular destination (sibling to a similar veteran,

in Ongar), which is "right on the river" in Wapping. "It's a bit out of the way, but well worth going off the beaten track for". "As for the décor, who doesn't love a restaurant with white tablecloths and smartly presented staff?" / E1W 1NJ; www.smithsrestaurants.com; @Smithsofwapping; Mon-Sat 10 pm, Sun 9 pm; no trainers.

SMITHS OF SMITHFIELD, TOP FLOOR EC1
　　　　　　£81　**2**|**3**|**3**

67-77 CHARTERHOUSE ST
020 7251 7950　10–1A

The City views are splendid at this rooftop venue, in the fine Grade II-listed former Smithfield market warehouse – converted into a multi-floor destination in the 1990s, of which this is the flagship dining option. Though it can seem a little 'City' in its approach, fans feel it's "still a solid choice for lunch". But not everyone's wild about the new menu ("just say no to small plate hell – this should have remained a steak restaurant!") / EC1M 6HJ; www.smithsofsmithfield.co.uk; @Thisissmiths; Mon-Fri 9.30 pm, Sat 9 pm, Sun 3 pm; closed Sun D; booking max 10 may apply.

SMOKE & SALT
SW17　　　　**£52**　**5**|**4**|**3**

115 TOOTING HIGH ST　NO TEL　11–2C

"Fine food in a casual setting" wins exceptional ratings for this former pop-up that is contributing to Tooting's rising reputation as a gastronomic destination. Remi Williams and Aaron Webster celebrate the ancient preserving techniques of salting, smoking and curing with "a menu of universally delicious sharing plates", served in a "bustling, vibrant atmosphere". / SW17; www.smokeandsalt.com; @smokeandsaltldn; Tue-Sat 10 pm; closed Sun & Mon; payment – credit card only.

SMOKEHOUSE ISLINGTON
N1　　　　**£63**　**3**|**3**|**3**

63-69 CANONBURY RD
020 7354 1144　9–2D

"Quality meat and good value" have carved a fine reputation for this Canonbury gastropub (part of Noble Inns), which is entering its 10th year in 2023. Whole carcasses are butchered

on-site, fish is delivered daily, and it's a beer-lovers dream, with 20 on tap and 60 bottled. / N1 2RG; www.smokehouseislington.co.uk; @smokehousen1; Mon-Sat 10.30 pm, Sun 10 pm; closed Mon-Thu L.

SMOKESTAK E1
　　　　　　£51　**5**|**3**|**4**

35 SCLATER STREET
020 3873 1733　13–1C

"The hint is in the name" at David Carter's "funky" Brick Lane venue, whose moody interior is inspired by southern US grill houses. Alongside the fingerlickin' smoked meats and pickled chillies, there are "some surprise hits – who knew that chargrilled cabbage is totally delicious?". "The dining room can be a bit smoky" – but that's why you should never BBQ indoors at home! / E1 6LB; www.smokestak.co.uk; @smokestakuk; Mon-Sat 11 pm, Sun 10 pm.

SMOKING GOAT
E1　　　　**£57**　**4**|**3**|**3**

64 SHOREDITCH HIGH STREET　NO TEL
13–1B

"Just superb flavours… and those chicken wings are to die for!" – Ben Chapman's "sensational" Thai has it all: "the Shoreditch location, the vibe, and the plates of fresh and inventive dishes". It "can be cramped" but folks "travel across town just to eat here". / E1 6JJ; www.smokinggoatbar.com; @smokinggoatbar; Mon-Sat 11 pm, Sun 10 pm.

SOCCA W1
　　　　　　

41 SOUTH AUDLEY STREET
020 3376 0000　3–3A

Set to open in the second half of 2022, on a Mayfair site that was formerly a branch of Richoux – this collaboration between Claude Bosi and Samyukta Nair will 'pay homage to the coastal towns of Cannes, Marseille and Nice, with an emphasis on French-Italian style dishes and wines'. It will all be more homespun than Bosi's Bibendum, apparently, with rustic options like rabbit with garlic cited as typical of the fairly traditional fare. / W1W 2PS; soccabistro.com; Mon-Sun 7 pm.

The Tent (at the End of the Universe) W1

SOCIAL EATING HOUSE
W1 £104 3|3|3

58-59 POLAND ST 020 7993 3251 4–1C

With its "sexy and atmospheric interior" and accomplished cuisine, the 10-year-old Soho branch of Jason Atherton's 'Social' brand is a venue recommended both for business meals and for "secret assignations" – kick off the occasion in his speakeasy 'The Blind Pig', which is hidden upstairs. / W1F 7NR; www.socialeatinghouse.com; @socialeathouse; Tue-Sat 10 pm; closed Sun & Mon.

SOFFICE LONDON
SW15 £44 3|4|3

236 UPPER RICHMOND ROAD 020 3859 4335 11–2B

"Wonderful and authentic Sicilian food" – in particular, "incredible fresh pasta" – can be found at this "deli/restaurant, newly opened in Putney". It calls itself a 'gastro-bakery', so all sorts of Sicilian nibbles are available alongside the "unusual pasta". "Staff are friendly and welcoming", and "the ambience is lively". / SW15 6TG; www.sofficelondon.com; @soffice_london; Mon-Sun 11 pm.

SOIF SW11 £64 3|2|2

27 BATTERSEA RISE 020 7223 1112 11–2C

This rustic French spot on Battersea Rise is operated by the pioneer importer of organic and biodynamic wines, Les Caves de Pyrène, and, although its mix of small plates and offbeat vintages no longer seems as original as once it did, it's consistently well-rated. / SW11 1HG; www.soif.co; @soif_sw11; Wed-Sat, Tue 11 pm, Sun 5 pm; closed Tue L closed Sun D, closed Mon.

SOLA W1 £104 5|3|2

64 DEAN STREET 020 7734 8428 5–2A

"One of London's finest gastronomic experiences" – Victor Garvey's "slightly unorthodox" Californian in Soho ('SO'ho via 'LA') had its late-2019 debut slightly stymied by Covid, but is nowadays "consistently serving some of the most interesting food in London, using exceptional produce"; and with "brilliant ideas and concepts in each dish". Staff are "chatty" – "overly so" for one or two diners, but "passionate and knowledgeable" to others – while the setting is "lacking atmosphere" or cleanly designed according to your taste. Dishes inspiring comment have included "amazing extra-large langoustines", "superb tuna and caviar" and a "delicious grapefruit dessert". / W1W 4QQ; solasoho.com; @solasoho; Wed-Sat 11 pm; closed Mon & Tue & Sun.

SOLLIP SE1 £98 5|4|3

8 MELIOR STREET 020 7378 1742 10–4C

"Truly an epic fusion of Asian and French cooking techniques, flavours and produce" justify the trip to husband-and-wife Woongchul Park and Comee Ki's French/Korean passion project, in the grungy streets surrounding London Bridge and Guy's Hospital (winner of the Top Gastronomic category at Harden's

London Restaurant Awards 2021). The "austere" interior can seem "clinical", but fans feel that "every part is beautiful and considered like the food itself". "You have to try the Insta-famous daikon tarte Tatin, but something even as humble as a cassoulet is raised to life-enriching memorableness here". / SE1 3QQ; www.sollip.co.uk; @sollip_restaurant; Tue-Thu 11 pm, Fri & Sat 11.30 pm; closed Tue-Sat L, closed Sun & Mon; payment – credit card only.

SOM SAA E1 £55 5|3|3

43A COMMERCIAL ST 020 7324 7790 13–2C

"Better than any Thai food I had in Thailand… and with a cool Shoreditch vibe" – this former factory near Spitalfields Market offers dishes with an "intensity and complexity of flavours that's second to none" – the "real Thai tastes (spicy, hot, sour, sweet and sharp) are tongue tingling!" "The front of the restaurant is more light and airy. The back gives a kitchen view but is dark"; "the team are relaxed, friendly and informative about the dishes (an essential point, as many options do require explanation for those not 'au fait' with Thai cuisine)". / E1 6BD; www.somsaa.com; @somsaa_london; Mon-Wed 10 pm, Thu-Sat 10.30 pm, Sun 9 pm; closed Mon & Tue L.

SÔNG QUÊ E2 £42 3|3|2

134 KINGSLAND RD 020 7613 3222 14–2A

"Great pho" and other Vietnamese crowd-pleasers is the attraction at this well-known "cheap and cheerful" canteen on the 'Pho Mile' stretch of Shoreditch's Kingsland Road. / E2 8DY; www.songque.co.uk; @songquecafe; Mon-Sat 11 pm, Sun 10.30 pm; no Amex.

SORELLA SW4 £66 4|3|2

148 CLAPHAM MANOR STREET 020 7720 4662 11–1D

"The neighbourhood Italian restaurant that you always wanted to have" is now chef Robin Gill's Clapham flagship following the closure of near-neighbour Dairy (RIP). It's "noisy and buzzy" in the proper Italian manner, and the cooking is "interesting and delicious", with highlights including "arancini to die for". / SW4 6BX; www.sorellarestaurant.co.uk; @sorellaclapham; Wed-Sat 10 pm, Sun 3 pm; closed Wed L closed Sun D, closed Mon & Tue; no Amex.

SOUTINE NW8 £65 2|4|4

60 ST JOHN'S WOOD HIGH STREET 020 3926 8448 9–3A

"Oh là là – looking 100 years old and dripping with charm" this "slick and relaxing" brasserie in St John's Wood is proving "another instant Corbin & King classic": "the décor is delightful and service is warm and graceful under pressure". True to the form, the "food could be more ambitious", but "for a family meal this lovely place is hard to beat". (With the founders recently sacked, "will the new regime ruin everything?"). / NW8 7SH; soutine.co.uk; @soutinestjohn; Mon-Sat 10 pm, Sun 9 pm.

THE SPANIARD'S INN
NW3 £42 2|2|4

SPANIARDS RD, HAMPSTEAD HEATH 020 8731 8406 9–1A

This ancient (circa 1585) wood-panelled inn at the top of of Hampstead Heath is drenched in historical and literary associations: Dick Turpin's father was the landlord, Byron, Dickens and Bram Stoker all drank here, and Keats reputedly composed his Ode to a Nightingale in what is now a walled beer garden. But if you're just after Sunday lunch, its leafy location and affordable scoff mean it's "always popular and well attended". / NW3 7JJ; www.thespaniardshampstead.co.uk; @thespaniardsinn; Mon-Sat 11 pm, Sun 10.30 pm.

SPARROW SE13 £55 4|3|4

RENNELL STREET 020 8318 6941 1–4D

"Don't be misled by the nondescript exterior" at this little local restaurant in Lewisham – "this is a serious kitchen, producing delectable and innovative small sharing plates". Husband-and-wife chef team Terry Blake and Yohini Nandakumar bring together their combined European and Asian heritages to create an unusual and ever-changing menu – which is always well received. / SE13 7HD; sparrowlondon.co.uk; @sparrow.london; Wed-Sat 10 pm, Sun 3 pm; closed Wed & Thu L closed Sun D, closed Mon & Tue.

SPARROW ITALIA W1

1 - 3 AVERY ROW AWAITING TEL 3–2B

Hot on the heels of a debut in LA, this US Italian restaurant concept is set to launch on this 190-cover site in Mayfair in late 2022, which will incorporate a ground floor bar, first floor dining room and terrace, and cigar lounge. It will offer an Italian/Mediterranean menu including pizza and pasta. More branches are planned both in the capital and back home in the US of A. / W1W 4AJ; Mon-Sun midnight.

SPEEDBOAT BAR W1

30 RUPERT STREET AWAITING TEL 4–3D

Named to be reminiscent of the canals of Bangkok's Chinatown, JKS Restaurants and chef Luke Farrell launch their second Thai concept together (the first was at the Arcade Food Hall) in September 2022 in Soho, to offer curries plus 'fast and furious wok cookery with roasted meats and zingy seafood salads', using UK-grown Thai herbs from Farrell's Forest nursery. / W1W 6DL; @speedboatbar; Mon-Sun midnight.

SPRING RESTAURANT
WC2 £116 3|3|4

NEW WING, LANCASTER PLACE 020 3011 0115 2–2D

"One of the prettiest chambers in London" – Skye Gyngell's "wonderful, light and airy venue" has a "lovely and calming vibe" and makes "beautiful use of the Somerset House dining room". Her "assured and imaginative" modern cuisine makes it a major favourite, although it was much less often recommended this year for hitting the peaks of gastronomy. Top Menu Tip – "the ethics, creativity, utility and value for money of the 'Scratch Menu' are brilliant!" ("delicious reimagined 'leftovers' served from a no-choice menu between 17.30 and 18.30"). / WC2R 1LA; www.springrestaurant.co.uk; @spring_ldn; Wed-Sat 9.30 pm; closed Sat L, closed Mon & Tue & Sun; credit card required to book.

ST MARTIN'S HOUSE WC2 £70

4A UPPER ST MARTIN'S LANE
020 7836 7591   5–3B

Styling itself as 'Your new home in Covent Garden' – this new all-day British brasserie in London's Theatreland opened in spring 2022 (just before our survey) in the prominent and convenient site formerly occupied by Tredwell's (RIP). In limited initial feedback, reports are of highs and lows – it seems safest to leave a rating till next year. / WC2W 9NY; www.stmartinshouselondon.co.uk; @stmartinshouselondon; Sun-Thu 11 pm, Fri & Sat 1 am.

STANLEY'S SW3   £93   323

151 SYDNEY STREET   020 7352 7664   6–3C

Just off the King's Road, this two-year-old courtyard bar and restaurant (with outside booths) is a "lovely" venue in partnership with the nearby Chelsea Gardener. The straightforward British seasonal food is consistently well-rated, but no-one suggests it's going to set the earth on fire. / SW3 6NT; www.stanleyschelsea.co.uk; @stanleys_chelsea_; Mon-Sat 11.30 pm, Sun 7.30 pm.

STEM & GLORY   £44   332

60 BARTHOLOMEW CLOSE, EC1
020 3969 9392   10–2B
100 LIVERPOOL STREET, EC2
07970 646 779   10–2D

"A vegan delight", say fans of this meat-free three-year-old near Barts Hospital: a crowdfunded spin-off from an acclaimed Cambridge venture. Results can be uneven ("maybe I chose badly…"; "some of the food missed but more was a hit…"), but they must be doing something right as a new Broadgate branch launches in September 2022. / www.stemandglory.uk; stemandglory.

STEVEN EDWARDS BINGHAM RIVERHOUSE TW10 £80   424

61-63 PETERSHAM ROAD
020 8940 0902   1–4A

"Lovely views of the Thames" and "fabulous food" combine to make this Richmond boutique hotel dining room "difficult to beat". The "exceptional tasting menu you can adapt to as many courses as you want" – from highly rated chef Steven Edwards (who owns etch in Brighton) – can be enjoyed "at a window table overlooking the river", "on the terrace or in a garden dome". /

TW10 6UT; www.binghamriverhouse.com; @binghamriverhouse; Fri & Sat 08 pm, Thu 8 pm, Sun 1.30 pm; closed Thu L closed Sun D, closed Mon & Tue & Wed; no trainers.

STICKS'N'SUSHI   £66   322

3 SIR SIMON MILTON SQ, VICTORIA ST, SW1   020 3141 8810   2–4B
40 BEAK STREET, W1   020 3141 8191   4–2C
11 HENRIETTA ST, WC2
020 3141 8810   5–3D
113-115 KING'S ROAD, SW3
020 3141 8181   6–3C
1 NELSON ROAD, SE10
020 3141 8220   1–3D
58 WIMBLEDON HILL RD, SW19
020 3141 8800   11–2B
1 CROSSRAIL PLACE, E14
020 3141 8230   12–1C

The "surprisingly delicious and wide-ranging menu" combines sushi with yakitori skewers (the so-called 'sticks') at this extremely popular Japanese-inspired group, whose "bustling" branches betray the Scandi style of their Copenhagen-based owners. It's "a perfect choice if not everyone wants sushi" (even if it's "expensive and portions are a bit on the small side"). A tenth branch is promised in late 2022 in Westfield W12. / www.sticksnsushi.com; sticksnsushi.

STICKY MANGO SE1 £61   322

33 COIN STREET   020 7928 4554   10–4A

"Not out of the ordinary, but what it does it does well" – chef Peter Lloyd's transformation of the revered South Bank French restaurant RSJ (RIP) into a "Malaysian-style" venue over three storeys disappointed former regulars, but has become a "firm favourite" with a new crowd for its "imaginative food, friendly service and a buzzy celebratory atmosphere". / SE1 9NR; www.stickymango.co.uk; @stickymangoldn; Tue-Sun, Mon 10.30 pm; closed Mon L.

STORY SE1 £272   333

199 TOOLEY ST   020 7183 2117   10–4D

"Love the edible candle that drips into the best sourdough bread you have ever tasted…" – Tom Sellers "isn't frightened of including strong flavours and rich, unctuous sauces" at his acclaimed foodie hotspot in "a slightly cultural/culinary desert" near Tower Bridge. "Dishes are served by all the staff including the chefs as the 'story' is told" over ten courses – "a great range of tastes and textures keeps you guessing" and there are some "unusual wine pairings". "The quirky approach can be annoying" but most reporters feel "the whole experience is phenomenal". But, even those who rate it as "exceptional all round" can still feel it is becoming significantly "overpriced"; and ratings were also undercut this year by one or two "gruesomely unbalanced" or "unsubstantial" meals. In January 2023, the restaurant will close for several months as a new storey is added to the building. BREAKING NEWS – also in 2023, Sellers will open a new restaurant in Mayfair, near The Ritz: at '1

Hotel Mayfair' which promises 'eco-conscious luxury and contemporary design'. / SE1 2UE; www.restaurantstory.co.uk; @rest_story; Thu-Sun 8.30 pm; closed Mon & Tue & Wed; no shorts.

STRAKER'S W10

91 GOLBORNE ROAD   07502 300962   7–1A

Thomas Straker spent lockdown becoming an Instagram star uploading cooking videos. His debut restaurant was going to be 'Acre' in Queen's Park, but his plan had an upgrade and name change to this 40-seater in Notting Hill. His aim is for it to be an 'epic neighbourhood restaurant' with 'east London wine bar vibes'; and a local-sourcing ethos designed to 'really ensure each ingredient has its moment in the spotlight'. / W10 5NL; www.strakers.london; @strakers_london; Mon-Sat 10 pm, Sun 9 pm.

STREET BURGER   £47   222

13-14 MAIDEN LANE, WC2
020 7592 1214   5–3D
24 CHARING CROSS ROAD, WC2
020 7592 1361   5–4B
222 KENSINGTON HIGH STREET, W8
020 7592 1612   8–1D
341 UPPER STREET, N1
020 7592 1355   9–3D
ENTERTAINMENT DISTRICT, THE O2, SE10
020 7352 2512   12–1D
26 COWCROSS STREET, EC1
020 7592 1376   10–1A
17 UPPER CHEAPSIDE PASSAGE, ONE NEW CHANGE, EC4   020 7592 1217   10–2B

In looks they are often "almost indistinguishable from the Byron that was replaced", and Gordon Ramsay's expanding chain (which has snapped up many of its rival's former sites) does have fans who say it's "better than expected" for "a decent burger". On the flipside, though, there are almost an equal number of sceptics who feel "it trades on the Ramsay name with cooking that's below par": "we went not long after this branch had opened hoping for a reliable burger like we used to get there when it was Byron… never have we eaten one so awful". Still, the roll-out continues with a recent addition near Farringdon station. / www.gordonramsayrestaurants.com/street-burger; gordonramsaystreetburger.

SUCRE LONDON W1 £80   344

47B GREAT MARLBOROUGH STREET
020 3988 3329   4–1B

Everyone "loves the décor" of this import from Buenos Aires, overseen by star Latino chef, Fernando Trocca: the glamorous makeover of a 300-year-old Soho building that once housed the London College of Music, complete with chandeliers, open kitchen and fire pit! Staff are "convivial" too and "the downstairs bar (Abajo) really helps round off an evening". The vibrant South American food? Marina O'Loughlin in The Sunday Times was not impressed, but some diners had their "best meal of the year" here, and even a reporter who found it "ever so slightly underwhelming" said "but it feels like it could really gain traction!" / W1W 7HS;

www.sucrerestaurant.com; @sucre.london; Mon-Sat 1 am, Sun midnight.

SUDU NW6

30 SALUSBURY ROAD
020 7624 3829   1–2B

Fatizah and Irqam Shawal (whose parents opened the venerable Satay House in 1973) are set to open this Malaysian style 'kopitiam' (a kind of South East Asian coffee shop) in ever-more happening Queen's Park late in 2022. Many of the fave rave dishes from Satay House will feature on the menu here. / NW6 6NL; @sudu.ldn; Mon-Sun midnight.

SUKHO FINE THAI CUISINE
SW6   £52   **4 5 2**

855 FULHAM RD   020 7371 7600   11–1B

"Delicious Thai food, served with charm" has won a very loyal local following and something of a wider reputation for this long-established café-style venture in a Fulham shop conversion. Arguably "tables are too close together", but most feel "even if it's cramped, it's still worth it". / SW6 5HJ; www.sukhogroups.com; @sukho_thairestaurant_fulhamsw6; Mon-Sat 10.30 pm, Sun 9.30pm.

SUMAK N8   £44   **3 4 2**

141 TOTTENHAM LANE
020 8341 6261   1–1C

"A favourite Turkish spot" – this well-run Crouch End local offers a "reliably delicious range of vegetarian, meat and fish dishes", and "treats regulars as old friends, eating at a 'home from home'". It's "not as cheap as the majority of Turkish/Kurdish restaurants in nearby Green Lanes, but the standard is higher and well worth the extra pound or two". / N8 9BJ; sumakrestaurants.com; @sumakrestaurant; Mon-Thu 11.30 pm, Fri & Sat midnight, Sun 11 pm.

SUMI W11   £94   **4 5 4**

157 WESTBOURNE GROVE
020 4524 0880   7–1B

Endo Kazutoshi's "cute little local" on the edge of Notting Hill – the more casual spin-off from White City's exceptional Endo at Rotunda – "punches above its weight". Named after the sushi master's mother, it offers a taste of his artful creations at much more approachable prices, and "a wonderful and delicious take on traditional Japanese food". In September 2022, it reopens having expanded (from 45 to 60 covers) and with a new chef: Christian Onia. / W11 2RS; www.sushisumi.com; @sumilondon; Tue-Sat 10 pm, Sun 5 pm; closed Sun D, closed Mon; booking online only.

THE SUMMERHOUSE
W9   £73   **3 3 5**

60 BLOMFIELD RD   020 7286 6752   9–4A

"Ducks and houseboats drift slowly by" at this tranquil spot that's all decked out in a white-and-blue nautical theme in Little Venice, which has a "perfect location right on Regent's Canal". But while nobody questions the "views

and great vibe", there's a minority "who wanted to like the place, but wish the food was more consistent". For most folks though, "what is not to like about this buzzing restaurant right on the canal serving lovely fresh fish?" / W9 2PA; www.thesummerhouse.co; Mon-Sat 11 pm, Sun 10.30 pm; no Amex.

SUNDAY IN BROOKLYN
W2   £72   **3 3 4**

98 WESTBOURNE GROVE
020 7630 1060   7–1B

This Notting Hill yearling, an offshoot of a modish Williamsburg original, hits the spot for lovers of NY-style comfort nosh. Most of it is "delicious" – "OK, not the most sophisticated, but hey – it's American brunch", and "sometimes they're trying a bit too hard to be hip", but ratings are good across the board. / W2 5RU; sundayinbk.co.uk; @sundayinbrooklyn_ldn; Mon & Tue 4.30 pm, Wed & Thu 10 pm, Fri & Sat 11 pm, Sun 9 pm; closed Mon & Tue D; payment – credit card only.

SUPA YA RAMEN E8

499 KINGSLAND ROAD   NO TEL   14–1A

Luke Findlay launched his first 15-cover restaurant on Hackney Road in March 2020, only to close just a few days later due to the first lockdown. This Dalston 20-seater with open kitchen is the hard-fought-for sequel and opened in September 2021. Feedback in our annual diners' poll remains surprisingly limited given the rave-review delivered on opening by The Evening Standard's Jimi Famurewa: "a verve, simplicity and slurpable magic that feels, thrillingly, like the future". / E8 4AU; supayaramen.myshopify.com/products/bubble-booking; @supa_ya_ramen; Tue-Sat 10 pm, Sun 4 pm; closed Tue-Fri L closed Sun D, closed Mon.

SUPAWAN N1   £54   **5 4 3**

38 CALEDONIAN ROAD
020 7278 2888   9–3D

"By day a florist, by night an exceptional Thai restaurant" – Wichet Khonghoon's "refined and authentic" spot in King's Cross is "one of the best Thai eateries in town" and certainly the most unusual – "it always feels celebratory to eat among the colourful blooms". The "high-quality and interesting food is not your western-style menu", but reflects Wichet's upbringing on Phuket in southern Thailand. / N1 9DT; www.supawan.co.uk; @supawan_thaifood; Mon-Sat 11 pm, Sun 10.30 pm.

SUPER TUSCAN
E1   £65   **4 3 3**

8A ARTILLERY PASSAGE
020 7247 8717   13–2B

"So tiny you could miss it" – this "authentic Italian" is a "very cosy and friendly" spot of a type rare for somewhere near the City (it's in the warren of streets around Spitalfields). "Impeccable" dishes are served with "minimal fuss" – "joyous!" / E1 7LJ; www.supertuscan.co.uk; @enoteca_super_tuscan; Mon-Fri 9 pm; closed Sat & Sun.

SUSHI ATELIER
W1   £61   **4 4 3**

114 GREAT PORTLAND STREET
020 7636 4455   2–1B

This contemporary Japanese outfit near Oxford Circus from the Chisou group is – according to its biggest fans – "simply outstanding" ("the head chef gave us personal advice and even created tailor-made sushi for us"… "sublime"). Not everyone would go quite as far, but all reports rate the food here as good or better. / W1W 6PH; www.sushiatelier.co.uk; @sushiatelierlondon; Tue-Sat 11 pm; closed Sun & Mon.

SUSHI BAR MAKOTO
W4   £38   **4 3 1**

57 TURNHAM GREEN TERRACE
020 8987 3180   8–2A

"Very consistent and reliable sushi" wins a loyal local following for this no-frills, family-run pit stop, a short walk from Turnham Green tube. / W4 1RP; www.sushibarmakoto.co.uk; @sushi_makoto; Mon-Sat 10 pm, Sun 9 pm.

SUSHI MASA NW2   £47   **3 3 2**

33B WALM LANE   020 8459 2971   1–1A

"The best food in Willesden Green" is arguably a double-edged compliment, but should do nothing to detract from this accomplished Japanese, acclaimed by locals for its "super-fresh, true-tasting sushi" and other "exquisitely prepared dishes". As with its long-time predecessor on this site (Sushi Say, long RIP), what is potentially a "dull" space is enlivened by the "charming" service. / NW2 5SH; Mon-Sat 10 pm; closed Sun.

SUSHI MURASAKI
W9   £56   **4 4 2**

12 LAUDERDALE ROAD
020 3417 8130   7–1C

"Exceptional", "really high-quality, fresh sashimi and moreish sushi" make this "on-point Japanese neighbourhood spot" a "regular favourite of Maida Vale locals". It also serves "good-value lunchtime bento boxes". / W9 1LU; sushi-murasaki.co.uk; @sushimurasakiuk; Mon-Sat 11 pm, Sun 10.30 pm.

SUSHI ON JONES N1   £56

GOODS WAY, 11 GOODS WAY
020 3179 2800   9–3C

This NYC sushi sensation, with its 45-minute, 12-course omakase formula, created barely a ripple of interest in our annual diners' survey. It could be the poor timing of the pandemic relative to its March 2020 debut, or it could be the rather peripheral location, near Google HQ on the edge of King's Cross's Pancras Square development. / N1N 4PW; www.sushionjones.com; @sushionjones; Wed-Sun 10 pm; closed Wed-Sun L, closed Mon & Tue.

SUSHI REVOLUTION SW9 — £31 3|3|2

240 FERNDALE ROAD
020 4537 4331 11–1D

Local reporters are full of praise for this Brixton newbie from Aidan Bryan and Tom Blackshaw, which has a perch in the swanky conversion of the old Bon Marché department store (now the HQ of Squire & Partners architectural practice). It doesn't generate huge amounts of feedback, but fans say "the menu's varied and the sushi's as good as it gets". / SW9 8FR; www.sushirevolution.co.uk; @sushirevolution; Mon-Sun 10 pm; payment – credit card only.

SUSHI SHOW — £22 3|3|2

28 CAMDEN PASSAGE, N1
020 7354 1329 9–3D
136 BETHNAL GREEN ROAD, E2
020 7613 1926 13–1C

Kaz Tateishi's "conscientious and consistent" (and therefore very Japanese) sushi shop with eat-in seats is tucked away in Islington's cute Camden Passage. A meal here (or taken away in a box) "always feels like money well spent". There is now a second outlet in Shoreditch. / www.sushishowlondon.com; sushi_show_london.

SUSHISAMBA — £116 2|2|3

OPERA TERRACE, 35 THE MARKET, WC2
020 3053 0000 5–3D
HERON TOWER, 110 BISHOPSGATE, EC2
020 3640 7330 10–2D

"Views are to die for" on the "glitzy" 38th floor of the Heron Tower, which – with its swish bar, outside terrace and vibrant dining space is "still a great place to see and be seen!" With "imaginative" and luxurious Japanese/South American fusion cuisine, the City branch of this US-based group should have it all, but enjoyment is blunted by the "exorbitant bill" and "service that seems like it's 'dialled in'". The Covent Garden location, on the first floor of the market itself and with a large outside terrace overlooking the back of the Royal Opera House, also occupies a prime London site: feedback is more limited, but similar in tone. / sushisamba.com; SUSHISAMBA.

SUSSEX W1 — £52 3|4|3

63-64 FRITH STREET 020 3923 7770 5–2A

"Creative food, interested staff and a pleasant space" (formerly Arbutus, RIP) have made this 'farm-to-fork' venue from the prolific Gladwin family "a great addition to Soho". Launched in 2019, it's their only outpost in the West End but they now have six London restaurants stretching from 'The Shed' in Notting Hill to 'The Fat Badger' in Richmond – this is the best-rated of the bunch. / W1W 3JW; www.sussex-restaurant.com; @sussex_resto; Tue-Sat 10.30 pm; closed Sun & Mon.

SUZI TROS W8 — £66 3|3|3

18 HILLGATE STREET
020 7221 2223 7–2B

"Delicious food served in a relaxed and, at times, noisy ambience" earns consistent praise for this Notting Hill three-year-old which focuses on the cuisine of Thessalonica and northern Greece. It's a "more casual" spin-off from Adrien Carre and Christina Mouratoglou's Mazi nearby, and is named after a classic Greek film that has come to symbolise the good life and eating well. / W8 7SR; www.suzitros.com; @suzitros; Tue-Sat 11 pm; closed Sun & Mon.

THE SWAN W4 — £64 3|4|4

1 EVERSHED WALK,119 ACTON LN
020 8994 8262 8–1A

With "one of West London's top pub gardens", this "great local" – on the Acton-Chiswick border – with a green-tiled Art Deco facade excels for its "delicious food and welcoming service" under the direction of "a proper landlady". There's also a "charming nook-filled room" for "Sunday lunch gatherings in the winter". / W4 5HH; www.theswanchiswick.co.uk; @theswanchiswick; Mon-Thu 10 pm, Fri & Sat 10.30 pm, Sun 9.30 pm; closed Mon-Fri L.

THE SWAN AT THE GLOBE SE1 — £70 2|2|4

21 NEW GLOBE WALK
020 7928 9444 10–3B

The "amazing setting" – part of Shakespeare's Globe with "spectacular views" over the Thames – is the USP of this venue. There's an "excellent range of cakes, sandwiches and teas" (including the oddly named 'Mr Falstaff's' savoury afternoon tea… forgetting Sir John's knighthood). But more generally, while the food's fine, "it's not a serious challenger for the title of restaurant rather than gastropub". / SE1 9DT; www.swanlondon.co.uk; @swanglobe; Mon-Sat 9.30 pm, Sun 9.45 pm.

SWEET THURSDAY N1 — £48 3|3|2

95 SOUTHGATE RD 020 7226 1727 14–1A

This handy De Beauvoir Town pizzeria and bottle shop majors on "delicious" Neapolitan-style pizzas, backed up with a range of 'pizza sandwiches' and 'no-dough starters' by Portuguese superchef Nuno Mendes (of Chiltern Firehouse and Lisboeta fame). / N1 3JS; www.sweetthursday.co.uk; @sweetthursdaypizza; Mon-Thu 10 pm, Fri & Sat 10.30 pm, Sun 9 pm.

SWEETINGS EC4 — £89 3|2|4

39 QUEEN VICTORIA ST
020 7248 3062 10–3B

"Sitting cheek by jowl at a counter that dates from the 19th century… bliss!" – this "City legend amongst fish restaurants" is "such a haven of bygone days, which gives it its special ambience and devoted following". Founded in the 1830s, and on its current site since the 1920s, it's "still serving sensational oysters (washed down with a pewter tankard of Black Velvet) after all these years" alongside "very traditional fish cooked simply and well" (e.g. "divine whitebait"). "It's a bit pricey and you can't book but otherwise excellent." / EC4N 4SA; sweetingsrestaurant.co.uk; @#Sweetingslondon; Mon-Fri 3 pm; closed Mon-Fri D, closed Sat & Sun; booking lunch only.

SYCAMORE VINO CUCINA, MIDDLE EIGHT HOTEL WC2 — £66 3|2|2

MIDDLE EIGHT HOTEL, 66 GREAT QUEEN STREET 020 7309 9300 5–1D

This "stylish" two-year-old in Covent Garden, "puts a different, modern spin on the usual Italian type offerings". Service is only "good in parts", though, and that it can feel compromised by being "too near the hotel lobby" (or "too integral to the lively bar of the hip hotel it's part of") is a repeat complaint. / WC2W 5BX; www.middleeight.com; @middle_eight_hotel; Mon-Fri 11 pm, Sat 10 pm, Sun 5 pm; closed Sun D.

TA KE SUSHI W5 — £34 4|3|2

3-4 GROSVENOR PARADE
020 8075 8877 1–3A

"A top Japanese restaurant in an area full of Japanese restaurants" – this "very reasonably priced" Ealing two-year-old serves "a wide-ranging menu covering every avenue – ramen, maki, sashimi, donburi – delivering all with panache and a friendly smile". "Reminds me of Japan… by the looks of the large number of Japanese customers, they think so too!" / W5 3NN; takesushiealing.co.uk; Sun, Mon-Wed 10 pm, Thu-Sat 10.30 pm.

TAB X TAB W2 — £31 4|4|3

WESTBOURNE HOUSE, 14-16 WESTBOURNE GROVE 020 7792 3445 7–1B

"Incredible coffee" (roasted by Kiss the Hippo) is the star turn at Mathew and Charmain Tabtabai's four-year-old Bayswater venture. They do a "great breakfast", too, with "excellent scrambled eggs" – and a range of cocktails for later in the day. / W2 4UJ; tabxtab.com; @tabxtablondon; Wed & Thu, Sun 4 pm, Sat, Fri 5 pm; closed Wed & Thu, Sat & Sun, Fri D, closed Mon & Tue; payment – credit card only; booking online only.

TABLE DU MARCHE N2 — £59 3|3|2

111 HIGH ROAD 020 8883 5750 1–1B

Happy habitués of this "reasonably priced French bistro" in East Finchley applaud its "good-quality" cuisine and a properly Gallic atmosphere around the marble-topped bar. Top Tip – "the lunch menu at £15 to £19 is extremely good value". / N2 8AG; tabledumarchelondon.co.uk; @tabledumarche; Mon-Sat 11 pm, Sun 10 pm.

TACOS PADRE
SE1 £38 3 3 4

BOROUGH MARKET KITCHEN, WINCHESTER WALK 07582 636186 10–4C

This "small" Borough Market taqueria is the brainchild of Nick Fitzgerald, who worked at Pujol (one of Mexico's most famous restaurants before coming to London), starting as a pop-up in 2017 and going permanent here in 2019. "It's a great location with a lovely atmosphere" and all reports rate the food as good or better. / SE1 5AG; www.tacospadre.com; @tacospadre; Fri, Thu 10 pm, Sun, Mon-Wed 3 pm, Sat 11.30 pm; closed Sun, Mon-Wed D.

TAKA MARYLEBONE
W1 £99 2 2 3

109 MARYLEBONE HIGH STREET 020 3637 4466 2–1A

Views diverged this year on this modern Marylebone Japanese – an exponent of 'Shun' (meaning 'food should only be eaten when it is at its best and at the height of its season'). Fans say it's a "lovely" place offering "novel and delicious" flavours from its wide-ranging, funky menu ('rock and rolls', 'plant-based power', 'raw to the core', 'robata'…) – sceptics say that it's "overpriced, with miniscule portions". / W1W 4RX; takalondon.com; @takarestaurants; Fri & Sat 10.30 pm, Tue-Thu 10 pm; closed Tue-Thu L, closed Sun & Mon.

TAKAHASHI SW19 £57 5 5 3

228 MERTON ROAD 020 8540 3041 11–2B

"Like a work of art!" – the "beautifully presented, elegant, superior-quality food and delightful service" at this tiny and "minimalist" Japanese restaurant in the unlikely surroundings of a parade of shops near South Wimbledon tube are a match for anything in the West End. Taka, a former Nobu chef, and his wife Yuko have consistently earned our highest possible food ratings since opening seven years ago. / SW19 1EQ; www.takahashi-restaurant.co.uk; @takahashi_wimbledon; Wed-Sat 10.30 pm, Sun 7.30 pm; closed Wed-Sun L, closed Mon & Tue.

TAMARIND W1 £81 5 4 3

20 QUEEN ST 020 7629 3561 3–3B

"An absolutely fabulous place", this pioneer of upscale Indian food for almost 30 years (and the first in the world to bag a Michelin star) is flying high again after a major refurb doubled the size of its Mayfair premises a couple of years ago. "Despite newcomers" taking curry to new levels, fans say "this remains the best Indian food" – "the brilliant taster menu is exceptional and demonstrates the skill and versatility of the kitchen" (now run by Karunesh Khanna, formerly head chef of Amaya). / W1J 5PR; www.tamarindrestaurant.com; @tamarindofmayfair; Mon-Sat 10.15 pm, Sun 9.15 pm; no trainers.

TAMARIND KITCHEN
W1 £62 4 4 4

167-169 WARDOUR ST 020 7287 4243 4–1C

This "sparky version of its parent Tamarind" in a "busy part of Soho" knocks out "delicious twists on quintessential Delhi street food" in a "large, stylish and comfortable dining room". "Jovial staff" add to the "very special" package. / W1W 8WR; tamarindkitchen.co.uk; @tamarindkitchenlondon; Tue, Mon, Wed-Sat 10.30 pm, Sun 9.30 pm; closed Mon, Wed-Sat L.

THE TAMIL PRINCE N1

115 HEMINGFORD ROAD 07988 750721 9–2D

The people behind Tamila in Hackney, chef Prince Durairaj and Glen Leeson (both ex-Roti King), took over the former Cuckoo pub in the middle of Barnsbury to launch this June 2022 newcomer: a South Asian restaurant, mixing small and large plates, accompanied by cocktails. In his early doors review, the Evening Standard's Jimi Famurewa found dishes inspiring "plate-licking, wanton lust". / N1 1BZ; www.thetamilprince.com; @the_tamil_prince; Tue-Sat 11 pm, Sun 10.30 pm; closed Mon.

TAMP COFFEE W4 £27 3 4 3

1 DEVONSHIRE ROAD NO TEL 8–2A

"Wonderful coffee and great pastries" are served at this rustic Chiswick spot, inspired by the cultural coffee shops where artists and politicos gather in Rio. All the baked goods – empanadas, croissants and pasteis de nata – are made daily on the premises, and they have begun to roast their own Brazilian coffee beans. / W4; www.tampcoffee.co.uk; @tampcoffee; Mon-Fri 3.30 pm, Sat & Sun 4 pm; closed Mon-Sun D; no booking.

TANDOOR CHOP HOUSE
WC2 £61 3 3 3

8 ADELAIDE STREET 020 3096 0359 5–4C

"Buzzy" Anglo-Indian hybrid in a "perfect central location" just off Trafalgar Square that serves "tapas-sized selections of delicious Indian food to share"; there's "not a huge choice", but there are "plenty of vegetarian options". An offshoot in Notting Hill is no longer in operation. / WC2N 4HW; tandoorchophouse.com; @tandoorchop; Mon-Thu 11 pm, Fri & Sat 11.30 pm, Sun 10 pm; booking max 6 may apply.

TAPAS BRINDISA £64 3 2 2

46 BROADWICK ST, W1
020 7534 1690 4–2B
7-9 EXHIBITION RD, SW7
020 7590 0008 6–2C
18-20 SOUTHWARK ST, SE1
020 7357 8880 10–4C
UNIT 25 BATTERSEA POWER STATION, 25 CIRCUS ROAD WEST, SW11
020 8016 8888 11–1C

HOTHAM HOUSE, 1 HERON SQUARE, TW9
020 8103 8888 1–4A

"Delicious tapas with a view of the River Thames" from "a large open terrace" is going down a storm at the instantly popular, new Richmond branch of the well-known chain (occupying the prominent site that was formerly Jackson & Rye, RIP). Backed by the firm of wholesalers of the same name, the group has steadily grown from its Borough Market origins over the last 10 years, and fans feel "it's exactly what you would expect from a place run by Spanish produce importers". On the downside, though, there is a school of thought that "while the food's done decently, it's serviceable but unexciting". / www.brindisakitchens.com; brindisaspanishfoods.

TAQUERIA £42 4 4 3

141-145 WESTBOURNE GROVE, W11
020 7229 4734 7–1B
8-10 EXMOUTH MARKET, EC1
020 3897 9609 10–1A

With its "shortish menu of delicious small plates of tacos, fajitas and quesadillas" plus "lots of tequila and five flavours of margarita cocktails", this Notting Hill original and its Exmouth Market spin-off serve "some of the best Mexican food in London" – both "authentic" and "good value". A veteran of the capital's taco scene, it started out with a stall in Portobello Road before moving into permanent premises 18 years ago. / taqueria.co.uk; taqueriauk.

TARO £36 3 3 2

1 CHURTON STREET, SW1
020 7734 5826 2–4B
61 BREWER STREET, W1
020 7734 5826 4–3C
356 REGENTS PARK ROAD, N3
020 7734 5826 1–1B
414 KENNINGTON ROAD, SE11
020 7735 7772 1–3C
193 BALHAM HIGH ROAD, SW12
020 8675 5187 11–2C
76 HIGH STREET, E17
020 7734 5826 1–1D

"It's easy to walk past" these "unassuming" Japanese canteens, but "don't – go on in!" There's a "great choice on the menu of both cooked plates and sushi"; "the food is always delicious" and prices are keen for a cuisine that can be very expensive. After two decades in Soho, the group has now pushed into Balham, Kennington and Finchley, with Pimlico and Walthamstow scheduled for late 2022. / tarorestaurants.uk; tarorestaurants.

TAS PIDE SE1 £40 3 3 3

20-22 NEW GLOBE WALK
020 7928 3300 10–3B

"Good food at reasonable prices" is just what's called for at this "great spot" adjacent to Shakespeare's Globe theatre on the South Bank. An offshoot of the well-known Turkish mezze chain, it is decked out in cosy Anatolian style and specialises in stuffed 'pide' flatbreads. / SE1 9DR; www.tasrestaurants.co.uk;

@tasrestaurantuk; Sun & Mon 10.30 pm, Tue-Sat 11.30 pm.

TATALE SE1

THE AFRICA CENTRE, 66 GREAT SUFFOLK STREET   020 8004 6436   10–4B

African cuisine has come a long way in London since Calabash – the capital's first African restaurant in the basement of the former Africa Centre in Covent Garden – opened in 1964. On the site of the new Africa Centre, in a repurposed Southwark office block, this Summer 2022 50-seater is run by Ghanaian-British restaurateur Akwasi Brenya-Mensa. Named after a form of plantain pancake, it aims to reflect the spirit of busy African roadside 'chop bars'. On the menu: omo tuo nkatenkwan sesame (mashed rice with groundnut, peanut soup); and buttermilk chicken burger topped with shito chilli, citrus yogurt and basil oil. / SE1 0BL; www.tataleandco.com; @tataleandco; Tue-Thu 10 pm, Fri & Sat 11 pm, Sun 4 pm.

TATTU LONDON WC2   £111   233

THE NOW BUILDING ROOFTOP, DENMARK STREET   020 3778 1985   5–1A

This scene-y Chinese operation from a Manchester-based chain is the signature restaurant of Oxford Street's 'The Now Building' (newly opened near Centre Point, featuring giant digital video screens). It's an Instagrammer's dream, but reports are mixed on the culinary front: the "food looks sensational", but is "overpriced" by a number of accounts and – although it may well find its market – foodies are likely to see it as an "example of how money and pretentions can go a long way". / WC2W 8LH; tattu.co.uk; @tattulondon; Mon-Sun 10.30 pm; closed Mon-Wed L.

TAVERNAKI W11   £29   322

222 PORTOBELLO ROAD 07510 627752   7–1A

A "delightful neighbourhood Greek restaurant, where real Greeks eat!" opened two years ago in Portobello by chef Harris Mavropoulos, with a straightforward menu of classic taverna dishes. It's a cosy place, with a downstairs bar, 'Mykonos'. / W11 1LJ; www.tavernakiportobello.co.uk; @tavernaki.portobello; Mon-Sun 11 pm.

TAVOLINO SE1   £52   213

UNIT 1, 2 MORE LONDON PLACE 020 8194 1037   10–4D

"Because of the fabulous view of the Tower of London and the river", this modern Italian (with large outside terrace) in the More London development by City Hall will attract custom come what may. Even those who consider it "overpriced" however, say the food's "OK" and fans say it has it all: "really good pizzas", "excellent pasta" and "a wonderful location thrown in". / SE1 2JP; www.tavolino.co.uk; @tavolinokitchen; Mon-Wed 9 pm, Thu-Sat 10 pm, Sun 8 pm.

TAYYABS E1   £34   412

83 FIELDGATE ST   020 7247 6400   10–2D

"You come to eat, not dine" at this "loud and popular" 500-seater, which "lives up to its reputation as the go-to curry house in (well, near to) Brick Lane". Top Menu Tip – "the lamb chops are meatilicious and the dry meat curry is rich and very tasty"; BYO. / E1 1JU; www.tayyabs.co.uk; @1tayyabs; Mon-Sun 11.30 pm.

TEA HOUSE THEATRE SE11   £   334

139 VAUXHALL RD   AWAITING TEL   11–1D

'Where there's tea there's hope' is the philosophical underpinning of this "quirky café", which occupies a converted pub by Vauxhall Pleasure Gardens, and "does amazing breakfasts" and "unusual teas", plus yummy buns. "They are a tea house though, so there is no coffee available!!" / SE11 5HL; Mon-Sun midnight.

THE TELEGRAPH SW15   £51   344

TELEGRAPH ROAD, PUTNEY HEATH 020 8194 2808   11–2A

Billing itself as "a country pub in London", this beautifully located hostelry on leafy Putney Heath is "much nicer since the change in ownership and refurb," having been purchased by Chester-based Brunning & Price a couple of years ago. "Food and beer are consistently good, with a choice of spacious indoor or attractive outdoor settings", the latter in the big beer garden. (For history buffs, the "wonderful site" itself was originally an optical telegraph station linking London to Portsmouth during the Napoleonic wars). / SW153TU; www.brunningandprice.co.uk/telegraph; @telegraphputneyheath; Mon-Thu 11.30 pm, Fri & Sat midnight, Sun 10 pm.

TEMPER   £54   324

25 BROADWICK STREET, W1 020 3879 3834   4–1C
5 MERCERS WALK, WC2 020 3004 6669   5–2C
78 GREAT EASTERN STREET, EC2 020 3879 3834   13–1B
ANGEL COURT, EC2   020 3004 6984   10–2C

"Sitting at the counter with all of its theatre is amazing" at Neil Rankin's "noisy, buzzy and fun" outlets, whose "really cool (well, hot) feature are the 'fire pit' cooking stations", from which they offer "a great mix of meat dishes" (including rare-breed steaks), plus fish options. There were some "off days" reported this year, though: in particular, service has sometimes been "under pressure" or even "shambolic". / temperrestaurant.com; temperlondon.

THE 10 CASES WC2   £77   343

16 ENDELL ST   020 7836 6801   5–2C

"Cramped, buzzy, with a great wine list" to accompany "innovative and reliable food" – it's

no surprise that this "very different" 'bistrot à vin' a couple of minutes' walk from the Opera House is such a Covent Garden "favourite". They only order ten cases of any wine (hence the name), which means you'll always find something "interesting" to drink – and "the head sommelier is wonderful!" / WC2H 9BD; www.10cases.co.uk; @The 10 Cases; Mon-Thu 10 pm, Fri & Sat 11 pm; closed Sun.

10 GREEK STREET W1   £69   433

10 GREEK ST   020 7734 4677   5–2A

"As good as ever" – this modern and understated Soho wine bar favourite provides "good food, if in rather cramped and noisy surroundings". A key feature is its handwritten 'Black Book' which lists the fine wines available each day. / W1D 4DH; www.10greekstreet.com; @10greekstreet; Tue-Sat 10.30 pm; closed Sun & Mon; No jeans; booking L only.

TENDIDO CERO SW5   £61   444

174 OLD BROMPTON ROAD 020 7370 3685   6–2B

"Innovative and exquisite tapas" and "excellent (if pricey) Spanish wines" have long attracted Hispanophiles to this bar, directly opposite its older sibling, Cambio de Tercio. "Lighting and service are top-notch", too. The only complaint is that "the buzzy ambience can change quickly to unpleasantly loud when there are too many groups in". / SW5 0BA; www.cambiodetercio.co.uk; @cambiodeterciogroup; Tue-Sat 11.30 pm, Sun, Mon 11 pm.

TENDRIL EC1   £56   433

102 BUNHILL ROAD   07842 797541   4–2C

"Wow. Who would believe it? A vegan restaurant that's amazing" – Rishim Sachdeva (ex-Fat Duck and Chiltern Firehouse) was a 'hard-core carnivore' until he challenged himself to see if he could create plant-based dishes that would satisfy himself as both a meat-eater and a chef. The answer was 'yes', the experiment changed his life, and he has spent three years doing pop-ups and residencies – most recently at a handy site just off Regent Street – while crowdfunding to raise capital for a permanent site. He has also gained a body of fans who have "visited several times for the unusual combinations and elevated vegan plates", which represent "superb value for money". Note – technically, Tendril is "mostly vegan", with cheese making an occasional guest appearance. / EC1E 8ND; www.tendrilkitchen.co.uk; @tendril_kitchen; Wed & Thu 10 pm, Fri & Sat 10.30 pm; closed Wed & Thu L, closed Mon & Tue & Sun.

THE TENT (AT THE END OF THE UNIVERSE) W1

17 LITTLE PORTLAND STREET AWAITING TEL   3–1C

Initially launched as part of an invite-only private members' club, John Javier's small (34-cover) August 2022 newcomer in Fitzrovia

is his first venture featuring Middle Eastern cuisine, zhushed up with – for instance – Asian seasonings, plus funky cocktails and wines. Expect Bedouin-style décor, DJs and live music. / W1W 8BP; Mon-Sun midnight.

TERRA ROSSA N1 £61 333

139 UPPER STREET 020 7226 2244 9–3D

"An absolute hidden gem" – this "unassuming Italian in the heart of Angel", close to the Almeida Theatre, is a "perfect neighbourhood spot", serving "generous portions of fantastic rustic food" and "well-selected wines" that make a meal "like being on holiday". It takes its name from the red earth of the Salento peninsula, the 'heel' of Puglia. / N1 1QP; terrarossa-restaurant.co.uk; @terrarossa.london; Mon-Sat 10.30 pm, Sun 9.30 pm.

THALI SW5 £49 333

166 OLD BROMPTON RD 020 7373 2626 6–2B

"Well worth seeking out on South Ken's 'Curry Corner'" – this "family-run restaurant with Bollywood paraphernalia on the walls" certainly "punches above its weight", with "a good selection of north-Indian dishes" and especially "delicious starters". / SW5 0BA; @thali_london; Mon-Sat midnight; closed Mon-Sat L, closed Sun.

THEO RANDALL AT THE INTERCONTINENTAL LONDON PARK LANE W1 £81 542

PARK LANE, 1 HAMILTON PLACE 020 7318 8747 3–4A

"In spite of many renovations it is still difficult to get away from the 'hotel dining room' feel" at this windowless and "bland" chamber, off the foyer of a large 1970s hotel on Hyde Park Corner. "Theo Randall's cooking does make up for it", though, and – in contrast to many top London destinations this year – ratings are going from strength to strength for its "fabulous Italian dining experience using stunning produce". In particular, Theo's series of "interesting, themed, regional menus are tremendous and very good value"; while "friendly and attentive" staff bring some conviviality to the "calm" space. Top Tip – "the set-price lunch menu may be the best-value lunch in the whole of London". / W1J 7QY; www.theorandall.com; @theo.randall; Tue-Sat 10 pm, Mon 10.30 , Sun 11 am; closed Sun & Mon D.

THEO'S SE5 £39 332

2 GROVE LN 020 3026 4224 1–3C

"Excellent, well-charred sourdough bases with interesting toppings" are knocked out at these "buzzy neighbourhood pizza indies", with locations in Camberwell and Elephant & Castle. "In the Franco Manca vein", it's "just as good as it was when it opened". / SE5; www.theospizzeria.com; @theospizzeria; Tue-Thu 10.30 pm, Sun & Mon 10 pm, Fri & Sat 11 pm; no Amex; may need 6+ to book.

34 MAYFAIR W1 £117 233

34 GROSVENOR SQ 020 3350 3434 3–3A

"You need deep pockets" to have a good time at this luxurious, rather conventional-looking American-style grill near the old US Embassy in Mayfair, from Richard Caring's Caprice group – but those who do say it "never disappoints"… "couldn't have asked for more (apart from a smaller bill!!)" / W1K 2HD; www.34-restaurant.co.uk; @34mayfair; Mon-Sun 11 pm; closed Sat & Sun L.

THE THOMAS CUBITT PUB BELGRAVIA SW1 £75 223

44 ELIZABETH ST 020 7730 6060 2–4A

This "posh and busy pub with a lovely buzz throughout" was named after the master builder who developed surrounding Belgravia in the Georgian era. It's "fab for people-watching" in smart Elizabeth Street, while "the food is good without wowing". / SW1W 9PA; www.thethomascubitt.co.uk; @thethomascubitt; Mon-Sat 10 pm, Sun 9.30 pm.

THREE UNCLES £34 533

UNIT 199 HAWLEY WHARF, 2ND FLOOR FOODHALL, NW1 07597 602281 9–2B
UNIT 19&20, BRIXTON VILLAGE, SW9 020 3592 5374 11–2D
12 DEVONSHIRE ROW, EC2 020 7375 3573 10–2D

"Excellent Cantonese roast meats on rice" ("the Hainan chicken rice fills your heart with the warmth of a hug and a blanket from childhood!") at prices that represent "very good value for money" inspire the highest praise for these Cantonese operations, near Liverpool Street and "tucked away" in Camden Town's Hawley Wharf. The brainchild of Hong-Kong-raised pals, Pui Sing, Cheong Yew and Mo Kwok, they opened a new branch in March 2022 in Brixton Market (praised by The Evening Standard's Jimi Famurewa for its "cooking of immense focus, skill and real endorphin-spiking intensity"). /

TILA SE8 £48

14 DEPTFORD BROADWAY 020 8692 8803 1–3D

On limited (but positive) feedback, this casual two-year-old bar / restaurant is worth knowing about, particularly in the thinly-served environs of Deptford. Many dishes are cooked over fire, and come with some eastern-Med influences. / SE8 4PA; www.tiladeptford.com; @tila.deptford; Wed-Fri 11 pm, Sat 10 pm, Sun 5 pm; closed Wed-Fri L closed Sun D, closed Mon & Tue.

TING SE1 £95 234

LEVEL 35, 31 ST THOMAS ST 020 7234 8108 10–4C

"Fantastic views" are the universally acknowledged highpoint of a visit to this swish Asian / British restaurant on the Shard's 35th floor. It is most often recommended for its "great twist on a traditional afternoon tea" (including an "exceptional vegan tea") – for more substantial meals, it is too often "not worth the price you pay for uninspiring dishes". / SE1 9RY; www.ting-shangri-la.com; @tinglondon; Mon-Sun 10.15 pm; no trainers; credit card required to book.

TISH NW3 £90 334

196 HAVERSTOCK HILL 020 7431 3828 9–2A

"Excellent modern kosher food in a beautiful setting" wins solid praise for this Belsize Park brasserie with a large and attractive outdoor terrace. The menu's European dishes include family favourites handed down to the owner, David Levin, by his Hungarian-Jewish mother and grandmother. / NW3 2AG; www.tish.london; @tish_london; Sun-Thu midnight; closed Fri & Sat.

TOFF'S N10 £51 432

38 MUSWELL HILL BROADWAY 020 8883 8656 1–1B

"Top-quality fish" has kept this Muswell Hill chippy high on the list of North London favourites for more than five decades, with two generations of the Greek-Cypriot Georgiou family maintaining the legacy left by the original 'Toff', Andreas Ttofalli. / N10 3RT; www.toffsfish.co.uk; @toffsfish; Mon-Sat 10 pm; closed Sun.

TOFU VEGAN £22 432

105 UPPER STREET, N1 020 7916 3304 9–3D
28 NORTH END ROAD, NW11 NO TEL 1–1B

"Wonderfully yummy plant-based food with no compromise on flavour" – "and so much more interesting than the standard Chinese offering" too – has made a big hit of this Islington yearling, whose mix of Sichuan, Cantonese and other influences make it "one of the best places ever!" It's already on to branch number two, which opened in April 2022 – "a brilliant addition to Golders Green, all vegan and very tasty!" /

TOKII W1 £94

THE PRINCE AKATOKI HOTEL, 50 GREAT CUMBERLAND PLACE 020 7724 0486 2–1A

Within the first international branch of a Japan-based group of five-star luxury hotels, this dining room near Marble Arch serves a non-traditional menu, focused on sushi, sashimi, seafood and meat cooked on the robata grill. Reports are too thin for a rating, but the odd exceptional meal is reported here. Top Tip – to give it a go, look out for their extremely keenly priced set menus. / W1W 7FD; www.tokii.co.uk; @tokiilondon; Mon-Sun 10 pm.

TOKIMEITE W1 £96

23 CONDUIT ST 020 3826 4411 3–2C

Too limited feedback for a rating on this Mayfair Japanese centred around an open kitchen, which – in its six years of operation – has never seemed quite to fulfil its potential.

Trivet SE1

Nowadays owned by famous food importers Atariya and supplied by Zen-Noh (Japan's agricultural cooperative), it should be an undisputed champion of NIpponese cuisine, but is still sometimes accused of being "incredibly expensive for what it delivers". / W1S 2XS; www.tokimeite.com; Tue-Sat 10.30 pm; closed Sun & Mon.

TOKLAS WC2   £70   4|2|3

1 SURREY STREET   020 3930 8592   2-2D

"A sparse interior in a Brutalist building" off the Strand "disguises a fantastic place to enjoy excellent food" at this new arrival from the founders of the art fair, Frieze: "a big, classy concrete space", complete with "a massive terrace that looks like a brilliant draw once the weather turns summery". "British seasonal dishes" are done to a high standard, although service is "a bit hit 'n' miss". / WC2W 2ND; www.toklaslondon.com; @toklas_london; Tue-Sat 11 pm; closed Tue L, closed Sun & Mon.

TOKYO SUKIYAKI-TEI & BAR SW3

85 SLOANE AVENUE   020 3583 3797   6-2C

Just off Sloane Avenue, this 'Japanese Wagyu Specialist' features a number of interesting, offbeat dishes on its menu, including Wagyu & truffle sushi, Wagyu shabu-shabu and yakiniku with Wagyu, ox tongue and Kobe beef (although there's also lots for fish-lovers too). Feedback is too limited for a rating. / SW3 3DX; www.tokyosukiyakitei.com; @tokyosukiyakitei; closed Mon-Sat & Sun; no shorts.

TOMMI'S BURGER JOINT   £36   3|3|2

30 THAYER ST, W1   020 7224 3828   3-1A
37 BERWICK STREET, W1
020 7494 9086   4-2D

The "Scandi bro-burger" consistently "hits the spot" at this Marylebone and Soho duo from Icelander Tómas Tómasson, who has 41 years in the burger business and a mini empire that stretches from his native Reykjavik to Copenhagen, Berlin, London and Oxford. Fun fact: Tómasson became the oldest first-time member of the Althing (Iceland's parliament) in its 1,000-year history when he won election at the age of 72 last year. / www.burgerjoint.co.uk; burgerjointuk

TOMOE SW15   £42   4|4|2

292 UPPER RICHMOND ROAD
020 3730 7884   11-2B

This "very popular" Japanese nook in Putney wins strong local support for its authentic sushi and other classics – with cooking, produce and service of a standard that belies its (authentically) downbeat appearance. / SW15; www.tomoe-london.co.uk; @tomoe.london; Wed & Thu 9 pm, Fri & Sat 9.30 pm; closed Mon & Tue & Sun.

TONKOTSU   £47   2|2|2

BRANCHES THROUGHOUT LONDON

This "slurpy Japanese noodles" outfit has grown from a 2011 pop-up to a fledgling national chain (14 branches in London, plus Brighton and Brum). These days it "feels formulaic, but the ramen does the business – the tonkotsu (pork broth, from which the place gets its name) is satisfyingly porky and the chilli chicken has a spicy hum". Critics are not so sure, pointing to "very disappointing noodles" and "drab stock". / www.tonkotsu.co.uk; tonkotsulondon.

TOSA W6   £39   3|4|2

332 KING ST   020 8748 0002   8-2B

"Down-to-earth", small Japanese, a short walk from Stamford Brook tube, that's "a perfect local": "service is patient and thoughtful" and the "menu covers all the bases (sushi, sashimi, tempura, etc) in good style but with the real winners coming from the robata grill" ("succulent morsels that help the beer go down... grilled mackerel is stunning"). / W6 0RR; www.tosa.uk; @tosa_hammersmith; Wed-Sun 11.30 pm; closed Mon & Tue.

TOULOUSE LAUTREC SE11   £68   3|4|3

140 NEWINGTON BUTTS
020 7582 6800   1-3C

Complete with regular jazz in its upstairs club, this Gallic brasserie near Kennington's Imperial War Museum is one of the brighter sparks in this thin area, and open all day (most days the hours are noon till midnight). / SE11 4RN; www.toulouselautrec.co.uk; @tlvenue; Mon-Sat midnight, Sun 10.30 pm.

TOWNSEND @ WHITECHAPEL GALLERY E1   £46   3|3|3

77-82 WHITECHAPEL HIGH ST
020 7539 3303   10-2D

This "excellent gallery restaurant" has proved "a great addition to the Whitechapel area", with "well-cooked small plates of British food on an ever-changing menu". Chef Nick Gilkinson is making a speciality of this type of venue – he was previously at the Garden Museum in Lambeth. Here, he is joined by Joe Fox, ex-head chef at Petersham Nurseries. (The name refers to the gallery's architect, Charles Harrison Townsend.) / E1; www.whitechapelgallery.org/townsend; @whitechapelgallery; Tue, Sun 6 pm, Wed-Sat 11 pm; closed Tue & Sun D, closed Mon.

TOZI SW1   £61   3|2|3

8 GILLINGHAM ST   020 7769 9771   2-4B

"The place I return to over and over again" – this popular Pimlico spot in a hotel near Victoria station excels for its modern Venetian cicchetti ("Italian small/sharing plates") and "demon cocktails". Top Tip – "the airy room comes out best at lunchtime". / SW1V 1HN; www.tozirestaurant.co.uk; @tozirestaurant; Tue-Sat 9.30 pm; closed Sun & Mon.

TRATTORIA RAFFAELE SE26   £32   3|3|2

94 SYDENHAM ROAD   020 8778 6262   1-4D

"All ages have a great time in true Italian style" at this Sydenham fixture, a "family-owned trattoria with a devoted following of regulars" who come for the classic, fresh-cooked pasta and pizzas. / SE26 5JX; www.trattoriaraffaele.com; Tue-Sat 10 pm, Sun 4 pm; closed Tue-Sat L closed Sun D, closed Mon.

TRINITY SW4   £113   5|4|3

4 THE POLYGON   020 7622 1199   11-2D

"You would pay a fortune to eat here if it was in Mayfair" – "Adam Byatt's excellent flagship" near Clapham Common is "so much more than a neighbourhood local" and "perfect for a fancy meal, especially if you live in south London!" Often inviting comparisons with nearby Chez Bruce, with ratings tracking its rival's closely, it is never quite as high in our ranking of London's Top 40 most-mentioned destinations (and has taken a little more flak for "high prices" of late). "Tastefully decorated" – the fact that it's "not pretentious, with just the right amount of friendliness from the staff" is key to its "pleasant" appeal, as, of course, is the "top-class food and wines". Top Tip – a large outside terrace is a relatively recent addition. / SW4 0JG; www.trinityrestaurant.co.uk; @Trinityclapham; Mon-Sun 8 pm.

TRINITY UPSTAIRS SW4   £64   3|3|3

4 THE POLYGON   020 3745 7227   11-2D

Upstairs from Adam Byatt's classy Clapham flagship Trinity, is "a casual space with big windows letting in plenty of light". It's frequented by locals in the know, who reckon that "Adam shoots and scores on a formula of tapas-themed sharing plates and accessible wine list". A mild dip in ratings this year backs up those who feel it's "slightly slipped from previous peaks", but no-one questions that it delivers "delicious, albeit simple food" and it's still very much "the local place to go if you can get a booking for a Sunday lunch". / SW4 0JG; www.trinity-upstairs.co.uk; @trinityclapham; Tue-Sat 8.30 pm, Sun 4 pm; closed Tue-Sat L closed Sun D, closed Mon.

TRISHNA W1 £74 **5** **4** **3**

15-17 BLANDFORD ST
020 7935 5624 2–1A

"Absolutely flawless…", "exceptional and memorable…", "consistently superb" – the superlatives just keep coming for JKS Restaurants' original venture, which scores just as highly as its sibling, Gymkhana, even if the latter is much better known nowadays. It's a cosy and "upscale" experience, set in quirky U-shaped premises, off Marylebone High Street, and enlivened by "discreet and friendly" staff. Top Menu Tips – "don't leave without trying the lamb chops"; "mushroom biryani is a standout"; and "crazy as it may sound for a mere piece of bread, the duck keema naan is a real highlight." / W1U 3DG; www.trishnalondon.com; @trishnalondon; Mon-Sat 10.15 pm, Sun 9.45 pm; closed Mon & Tue L.

TRIVET SE1 £142 **3** **3** **3**

36 SNOWSFIELDS 020 3141 8670 10–4C

Since its opening in late 2019, this Bermondsey three-year-old from Fat Duck alumni Jonny Lake (chef) and Isa Bal (sommelier) has burnished a formidable reputation as one of the more interesting culinary arrivals of recent years. Jonny's cuisine is "superb and delicate" and "if the food is outstanding, then the wine list is outstanding-er!" – "an incredible and esoteric range" with "a focus on Georgia, Turkey and Armenia". And it's a "comfortable" space too where, for once, "you can hear yourself think". It would score higher were there not a less wowed minority of reporters who either found the overall approach "excessively serious", or who were "not convinced by the menu combinations despite having high hopes". / SE1 3SU; trivetrestaurant. co.uk; @trivetrestaurant; Wed-Sat, Tue 11 pm; closed Tue L, closed Sun & Mon.

LA TROMPETTE W4 £101 **4** **3** **2**

5-7 DEVONSHIRE RD 020 8747 1836 8–2A

"Still worth the schlep across town", says an E18-based fan of this "elegant corner of Chiswick" – "a brilliant, upscale neighbourhood restaurant in a quiet backwater off the high street, which fans say is "pretty much on a level with its sibling Chez Bruce"; and which regularly features in the Top 40 most-mentioned restaurants in our annual diners' poll. Like its famous Wandsworth Common stablemate, its culinary attractions include modern British cuisine that's "up to date, with

ingredients centre stage," "complemented by a very fine wine list," and with "a very good cheese selection". But whereas reports this year often match the flawless pattern established over two decades ("just effortlessly excellent…"; "we have been regulars for a decade…never disappoints…"; "post-lockdown it continues to shine…"), there is also a growing minority concern that "while the food is still very good, the service has slipped", with quite a few accounts of a "haphazard and brusque" experience. "Maybe it's just because of these difficult times…" / W4 2EU; www.latrompette.co.uk; @latrompettechiswick; Wed & Thu 9 pm, Fri & Sat 10 pm, Sun 3 pm; closed Sun D, closed Mon & Tue.

TRULLO N1 £78 **3** **3** **3**

300-302 ST PAUL'S RD
020 7226 2733 9–2D

"It's so good to have on my doorstep" – Tim Sidiatan and Jordan Frieda's "teeming local favourite" is "precisely the type of neighbourhood spot everyone wants to have": "a relaxed, chic atmosphere makes for a stress-free, no-frills meal out that just feels special" ("choose downstairs for romance"). "Italian-inspired open-fire cooking is a focus, with frequently changing fish and meat dishes," but "it's worth a visit for the pasta alone". And it all comes at "sensible prices". Top Tip – "mouthwatering ragu!" / N1 2LH; www.trullorestaurant.com; Mon-Sat 10.30 pm, Sun 9.30 pm; no Amex.

TSUNAMI SW4 £57 **4** **3** **2**

5-7 VOLTAIRE RD 020 7978 1610 11–1D

"Excellent modern Japanese food with a twist" has given this Clapham local a cutting-edge vibe that has barely faltered since its launch in 2001 by a trio of ex-Nobu chefs. Top Menu Tips – "perfect black cod (gin dara) and the best scallops ever: presented flaming in a sea shell with enoki mushrooms in a creamy chilli sauce with the crunch of tobiko. Sublime!" / SW4 6DQ; www.tsunamirestaurant.co.uk; @tsunami_restaurants; Sun-Thu 9.30 pm, Fri & Sat 10.30 pm; closed Mon-Fri L; no Amex.

TURNIPS WITH TOMAS LIDAKEVICIUS SE1 £120 **4** **3** **3**

43 BOROUGH MARKET, OFF BEDALE STREET 020 7357 8356 10–4C

Tomas Lidakevicius produces "very innovative dishes using seasonal produce" at this zeitgeisty venture, attached to a greengrocer's stall in Borough Market, where a pop-up quickly went permanent in 2021. You book either for the sharing plates or full (£90) tasting menu experience – in either case "the place feels like being in a market stall to create an evening to remember; and it's close to the Thames for a nice walk home". / SE1 9AH; www.turnipsboroughmarket.com/restaurant; @turnipsborough; Wed-Sat 11.30 pm; closed Mon & Tue & Sun.

12:51 BY CHEF JAMES COCHRAN N1 £54 **3** **2** **3**

107 UPPER STREET 07934 202269 9–3D

"When the food is good it can be amazing" at former Ledbury chef James Cochran's Islington venue, which fans say "deserves to be better known" for his "fantastic tasting menu at sensible prices" (including "interesting" ingredients such as mutton and goat that reference the chef's part-Caribbean heritage). Even some fans can acknowledge one or two "samey" results, though, and grades slipped a fraction this year due to a few disappointments. Perhaps any unevenness is due to distraction from other projects: in June 2022 he opened Valderrama's – a 90s-themed sports bar a short walk along Upper Street featuring the buttermilk fried chicken he developed for his Around The Cluck lockdown project. / N1 1QN; www.1251.co.uk; @1251_twelve_fifty_one; Tue-Sat 11 pm, Sun 8 pm; closed Tue-Thu L, closed Mon; payment – credit card only; booking online only.

28 CHURCH ROW NW3 £57 **4** **4** **3**

28 CHURCH ROW 020 7993 2062 9–2A

Serving "the best tapas in Hampstead" – this "wonderful little hideaway" serves "simply exceptional vegetable plates" as well as "great fish and meat", with Italian as well as Spanish dishes on the menu. In the gracious approach to St John-at-Hampstead – it's "a brilliant conversion: they really got the ghost out of this basement", ensuring a "fun visit every time". / NW3 6UP; www.28churchrow.com; @28churchrow; Mon-Sat 10.30 pm, Sun 9.30 pm; closed Mon-Thu L.

28-50 £90 **2** **2** **2**

15-17 MARYLEBONE LANE, W1
020 7486 7922 3–1A
4 GREAT PORTLAND STREET, W1
020 7420 0630 3–1C
300 KING'S ROAD, SW3
020 7349 9818 6–3C
96 DRAYCOTT AVE, SW3
020 7581 5208 6–2C

An "impressive wine list" is the undoubted highlight of this small group, with branches in the West End and Chelsea – the newest branch is a 120-cover site near Oxford Circus. No-one has terrible things to say about its food selection, though, which is judged "passable…", "OK…", "…tasty if a little pricey". /

24 THE OVAL SW9 £50 **3** **4** **3**

24 CLAPHAM ROAD 020 7735 6111 11–1D

'Old-fashioned, modern British cooking' is the promise at this "very enjoyable" bistro near Oval tube – sister restaurant to Clapham's Knife and with a menu that similarly makes a feature of both top steaks and Sunday lunch. / SW9 0JG; www.24theoval.co.uk; @24theoval; Wed-Sat 9.30 pm, Sun 4.30 pm; closed Wed-Sat L closed Sun D, closed Mon & Tue.

TWIST CONNUBIO W1

£69 332

42 CRAWFORD ST 020 7723 3377 2–1A

"Fantastic food and professional service" combine at this Marylebone tapas bar, where Amalfi-born chef Eduardo Tuccillo creates a 'connubio' or marriage of Mediterranean flavours, drawing broadly on Spain for the meat dishes and his native Italy for vegetables. If choosing is tricky, there is a range of tasting menus to ease ordering. / W1H 1JW; www.twistconnubio.com; @twistconnubio; Sun-Wed-Sat 11 pm; closed Sun-Wed L.

TWO BROTHERS N3

£38 322

297-303 REGENT'S PARK RD
020 8346 0469 1–1B

"Excellent fish" and "friendly and helpful" staff ensure that this smart and well-run chippy remains a Finchley favourite after more than a quarter of a century. "Been eating here for years – it's always good!" / N3 1DP; www.twobrothers.co.uk; Tue-Sun 10 pm; closed Mon.

222 VEGGIE VEGAN W14

£45 332

222 NORTH END RD 020 7381 2322 8–2D

"Excellent food and service" earns the thumbs-up for this small, 100% vegan café, just north of the gyratory joining Fulham's North End Road with the Lillie Road. Their version of a 'burger' is made with asparagus and petits pois, served on house gluten-free bread. / W14 9NU; www.222vegan.com; @222vegancuisine; Tue-Sun 9 pm; closed Mon.

2 VENETI W1

£54 322

10 WIGMORE STREET
020 7637 0789 3–1B

This "honest Italian" near Wigmore Hall is "one of the few places in London where you can eat cuisine of the Veneto region"; "the dishes are simply prepared with high-quality ingredients," and there's a good wine list to match. It's not wildly fashionable, but "always provides an enjoyable meal served by professional staff in a relaxed ambience". / W1U 2RD; www.2veneti.com; @2veneti; Mon-Fri 9.45 pm, Sat 10.30 pm; closed Sat L, closed Sun.

ULI W11

£73 344

5 LADBROKE ROAD 020 3141 5878 7–2B

A "wonderful local with delicious Thai/China/Singapore-inspired Asian food" that's now in its second incarnation – a stripped-wood and pastel-shades venue in Ladbroke Grove, having moved from All Saints Road, where it opened in 1997. "Great service under owner Michael Lim's watchful eyes." "There is a large outdoor covered terrace at the front, warm in winter and cool in summer". BREAKING NEWS: in late 2022 a new branch will open in Seymour Village. / W11 3PA; www.ulilondon.com; @ulilondon; Mon-Sat midnight, Sun 11 pm.

UMU W1

£153 443

14-16 BRUTON PL 020 7499 8881 3–2C

The "amazing" Kyoto-style kaiseki menu is a longstanding fixture of this low-key stalwart, in a quiet Mayfair mews (which was sold out of administration in 2020 after the collapse of the M.A.R.C. group). But, under executive chef, Ryo Kamatsu, it also offers a luxurious à la carte ranging from caviar to British game to sushi created from the finest Cornish fish. Predictably, there are complaints of "small portions at exquisite prices", but this remains one of London's most notable addresses for Japanese cuisine. / W1J 6LX; www.umurestaurant.com; @umurestaurant; Tue-Sat 10 pm; closed Sun & Mon; no shorts; booking max 10 may apply.

UNWINED SW17

£33 342

21-23 TOOTING HIGH STREET
020 3583 9136 11–2C

Laura Aitkin & Kiki Evans's "quirky" wine bar in Tooting Market is "worth a visit for a fun evening" spent with an "eclectic wine list and food menu" – the latter from a succession of guest chefs ("go for the unusual wines based on themes e.g. myths"). The pair have a second wine bar in a shipping container by Waterloo station. / SW17 0SN; unwinedbars.co.uk; @UnwinedSW17; Wed-Sat 11 pm; closed Wed L, closed Mon & Tue & Sun; booking online only.

UPSTAIRS AT THE GEORGE W1

£80

55 GREAT PORTLAND STREET NO TEL
2–1B

The upstairs dining room of this 18th-century pub close to Oxford Circus has reopened under a dream team of owners JKS (the group behind Gymkhana, Bao, Arcade Food Hall etc), chef James Knappett of Kitchen Table and publican Dominic Jacobs of the Running Horse. The same formula has been an uneven success at The Cadogan Arms, but early feedback here is more encouraging. / W1W 7LQ; thegeorge.london; @thegeorgepublichouse; Wed-Sat 10 pm, Sun 6 pm; closed Mon & Tue.

LE VACHERIN W4

£71 443

76-77 SOUTH PARADE
020 8742 2121 8–1A

"Authentic bourgeois French cuisine" is on the menu at this "old-fashioned" but "superbly run" Gallic fixture with a "lovely atmosphere" by Acton Green. "Classic and reliable but with real flair", locals consider themselves "lucky to have this in W4", while plenty of regulars from further afield appreciate the "very good value for a full-service French restaurant". / W4 5LF; www.levacherin.com; @le_vacherin; Mon-Sat 10.30 pm, Sun 9 pm.

VARDO SW3

£72 223

9 DUKE OF YORK SQUARE
020 7101 1199 6–2D

With its "great location" and "lovely outside tables" on Duke of York Square, together with the bold contemporary architecture of its circular premises (complete with roof garden), this three-year-old – named after the traditional Romany horse-drawn wagon – has much going for it. Fans would say this includes its diverse menu (similar to its Caravan group siblings) which "ranges from tasty Levantine dishes to delicious pizzas, so giving great variety for families to enjoy". But ratings are undercut by complaints of "disappointing food" and a feeling that "they need to do something about the service". / SW3 4LY; vardorestaurant.co.uk; @vardorestaurant; Mon & Tue, Sun 10 pm, Wed & Thu 11 pm, Fri & Sat midnight.

VASCO & PIERO'S PAVILION W1

£72 454

11 D'ARBLAY STREET
020 7437 8774 4–1C

"Welcome back!" Every cloud has a silver lining and "having been unceremoniously evicted from its longtime Poland Street location during Covid", this "delightful" Soho veteran has "found a new, better site just round the corner" (it's actually the second time the restaurant, founded in 1971, has had to move). "Traditional, Tuscan food as it is meant to taste, with a wine list to match" are served by the "superb" staff in a "most convivial" setting. "They are good at remembering their customers" and "it's a great place to have a conversation, as they play no music". / W1W 8DT; www.vascosfood.com; Tue-Sat 10 pm; closed Sat L, closed Sun & Mon.

VEERASWAMY W1

£94 444

VICTORY HS, 99-101 REGENT ST
020 7734 1401 4–4B

Approaching its centenary, London's oldest Indian, near Piccadilly Circus, continues to thrive as part of the high-quality group that also owns Chutney Mary. It may be an "old favourite" for many fans of decades' standing, but the "relaxing" interior is modern and without any 'heritage' appeal. "Service is friendly and professional – not pushy, but there when you want them" – and the cooking has "sublime flavours and fragrances". / W1B 4RS; www.veeraswamy.com; @veeraswamy.london; Mon-Sat 10.30 pm, Sun 10 pm; closed Mon L; booking max 12 may apply.

VERMUTERIA N1

£56

38-39 COAL DROPS YARD
020 3479 1777 9–3C

The vintage styling – that of a classic European café – is at odds with ever-more über-sleek Coal Drops Yard. Reports on Anthony Demetre's all-day operation (named for the vermouth which is a feature of its drink offering) are still few, but suggest its well-sourced tapas, charcuterie and more substantial fare (including steak) can make it a handy refuge, from breakfast onwards (for which there's a dedicated selection). / N1N 4AB; vermuteria.cc; @vermuteria_london; Sun-Wed 10 pm, Thu-Sat 11 pm.

VIA EMILIA N1 £48 332

37A HOXTON SQUARE
020 7613 0508 13–1B

"Exemplary small-plates and pasta" is the focus at this small Hoxton showcase for the marvellous cuisine of Emilia-Romagna (think Bologna, Modena, Parma, etc). The dishes are even named in the local dialect. / N1 6NN; www.via--emilia.com; @viaemilia.restaurant; Mon-Sat 11 pm, Sun 10.30 pm.

IL VICOLO SW1 £67 332

3-4 CROWN PASSAGE
020 7839 3960 3–4D

"A real 'find' amongst the big beasts", tucked away in a St James's alleyway, "this small family-run Italian is welcoming and good value" – "intimate when quiet, a nice buzz when fuller". They are "clearly passionate about their ingredients", and offer "absolutely delightful service". / SW1Y 6PP; www.ilvicolorestaurant.co.uk; @Ilvicolo.restaurant; Mon-Sat 10 pm; closed Sun.

THE VICTORIA SW14 £60 333

10 WEST TEMPLE SHEEN
020 8876 4238 11–2A

Close to Richmond Park's Sheen Gate, this sprawling and "very friendly local pub" serves "outstanding food" from TV chef and owner Paul Merrett. A refurbished Victorian tavern, it has six boutique bedrooms, a large garden and a conservatory where family Sunday lunches are a big feature. / SW14 7RT; victoriasheen. co.uk; @thevictoriasheen; Wed-Sun 10.30 pm; closed Mon & Tue; no Amex.

VIET FOOD W1 £41 323

34-36 WARDOUR ST 020 7494 4555 5–3A

"Delicious" Vietnamese street-food classics and original creations from the founder, ex-Hakkasan chef Jeff Tan, draw a bustling crowd to this two-storey warehouse-style venue in Chinatown, which is "perfect pre- or post-theatre". It now has a sibling in South Ken, Go Viet. Top Menu Tip – "the green garlic sauce is a must". / W1D 6QT; www.vietnamfood.co.uk; @vietfoodlondon; Sun-Thu 10.30 pm, Fri & Sat 11 pm.

VIET GARDEN N1 £34 332

207 LIVERPOOL RD 020 7700 6040 9–3D

This "reliable" family-run Vietnamese in Islington welcomes a steady crowd, and "almost everyone eating here is local". It has "a friendly atmosphere created by people who love their native cuisine". Top Menu Tip – "the pork kho is deeply savoury, warming and comforting on cold winter nights". / N1 1LX; www.vietgarden.co.uk; @vietgardenuk; Sun-Thu 11 pm, Fri & Sat 11.30 pm; closed Mon-Fri L; no Amex.

VIJAY NW6 £38 441

49 WILLESDEN LN 020 7328 1087 1–1B

"Proper Indian food, proper paper napkins" – this Kilburn institution, which claims to have been Britain's first South Indian restaurant when it opened in 1964, remains "exactly as it was when the great Michael Winner recommended it back in 1990-something. 'Historic', said the old boy, and it still is". "Unfortunately you have to eat in drab surroundings" – which is a tactful way of putting it – but fans (who apparently include luminaries ranging from Diana Ross and Harrison Ford to the Indian cricket team), reckon it's worth it for the "top-notch" food and "really polite and professional" service. It caters equally for "meat-eaters, vegetarians and vegans". Top Tip – you may be tempted to eat in the more salubrious quarters of your own home, but the nosh is "so much better fresh than take-away". / NW6 7RF; www.vijayrestaurant.co.uk; @vijayindiauk; Sun-Thu 10.45 pm, Fri & Sat 11.45 pm; no booking.

VILLA BIANCA NW3 £71 223

1 PERRINS CT 020 7435 3131 9–2A

"Classic old-school Italian" in a "lovely setting in Hampstead", with white linen and walls living up to its name. Even some who consider it "an old favourite" acknowledge that the experience is "hit 'n' miss", with sometimes "snooty service" but it still draws an enthusiastic crowd: "my business days are over, but judging by the other diners there must be plenty of business going on!" / NW3 1QS; villabiancagroup.com/villabianca; @villabiancanw3; Tue-Sat 11.30 pm, Sun 10.30 pm; closed Mon.

VILLA DI GEGGIANO W4 £87 344

66-68 CHISWICK HIGH ROAD
020 3384 9442 8–2B

"A little piece of super-smooth Chiantishire dropped into W4" – this "spacious and comfortable" venue on a trafficky highway between Chiswick and Hammersmith makes "an amazing neighbourhood restaurant – very lucky locals!". Named after the 500-year-old Tuscan estate that owns it and supplies organic wines for the list, it "isn't cheap but the food is generally excellent" and "presentation and service are impeccable". / W4 1SY; www.villadigeggiano.co.uk; @villa_di_geggiano_london; Tue-Fri 10.30 pm, Sun 9 pm; closed Mon & Sat.

THE VINCENT ROOMS, WESTMINSTER KINGSWAY COLLEGE SW1 £45 323

76 VINCENT SQ 020 7802 8391 2–4C

"Top-quality food from third-year students at ridiculously low prices" is the term-time offer at this Vincent Square venue operated by Westminster Kingsway College. "Service by first-years can be very random but is always entertaining!" Choose between the formal Escoffier Room and the more relaxed brasserie. Top Tip – "excellent sourdough bread also at knockdown prices for sale in the foyer". / SW1P 2PD; www.thevincentrooms.co.uk; @thevincentrooms; Mon, Fri 3 pm, Tue-Thu 9 pm; closed Mon & Fri D, closed Sat & Sun; no Amex.

VINOTECA £63 222

18 DEVONSHIRE RD, W4
020 3701 8822 8–2A
ONE PANCRAS SQ, N1
020 3793 7210 9–3C
BOROUGH YARDS, STONEY STREET, SE1
020 3376 3000 10–4C
7 ST JOHN ST, EC1 020 7253 8786 10–1B
BLOOMBERG ARCADE, QUEEN VICTORIA STREET, EC2 AWAITING TEL 10–3C

"It's wonderful being able to choose so many wines by the glass" from the "eclectic list" at these popular modern wine bars, liked for their approachable contemporary style. "Obviously the liquid refreshment is the main point here", but the "simple" cooking can be "more assured than you might expect", if from a "limited menu". A new branch opened in late 2021 at Borough Yards in SE1, while in late 2022 its oldest site, on Seymour Place in Marylebone, shut up shop. Other particularly notable branches include the one right by King's Cross station (with a convenient and excellent terrace) and Chiswick. / www.vinoteca.co.uk.

VIVAT BACCHUS £72 333

4 HAY'S LN, SE1 020 7234 0891 **10–4C**
47 FARRINGDON ST, EC4
020 7353 2648 **10–2A**

This duo of venues in Farringdon and London Bridge have some of the capital's best collections of South African wine, alongside a selection of 'Old World' vintages. To soak them up, there's a miscellaneous assortment of dishes majoring in steaks, with some Saffa-inspired garnishes, and SA-style dried meats providing the most exotic options. Save space for the cheese, chosen in a walk-in room. / www.vivatbacchus.co.uk

VOLTA DO MAR WC2 £66 443

13-15 TAVISTOCK STREET
020 3034 0028 **5–3D**

An "always good", culinarily interesting Covent Garden three-year-old, from Salt Yard founder Simon Mullins and his Portuguese wife Isabel Almeida Da Silva. Named after the 'return from the sea': it serves a menu not just from Portugal but from the territories it traded with or colonised, from Brazil in the west via parts of Africa to Goa, Macau and Nagasaki in the east. / WC2W 7PS; voltadomar.co.uk; @voltadomar_ldn; Thu-Sat, Tue, Wed 10.30 pm; closed Tue, Wed L, closed Sun & Mon.

VQ £55 223

ST GILES HOTEL, 111A GREAT RUSSELL STREET, WC1 020 7636 5888 **5–1A**
325 FULHAM RD, SW10
020 7376 7224 **6–3B**
9 ALDGATE HIGH ST, EC3
020 3301 7224 **10–2D**

"Don't think high end, but these local 24-hour cafés are reliable and pleasant for a plain meal at any hour of the night or day", but particularly come into their own in the wee hours. In fact, only the well-known Chelsea original and the Aldgate spin-off (in a hotel) are open 24/7: opening hours in Bloomsbury are more selective. (Aldgate also has a standalone bar with a 24-hour alcohol licence). / www.vingtquatre.co.uk; vqrestaurants.

WAGAMAMA £51 222

BRANCHES THROUGHOUT LONDON

"You know what you'll get" at this Japanese-inspired chain, which celebrated its 30th birthday last year: "quick, tasty noodles with something for everyone", all at a "relatively cheap" price. True, it can seem merely "fine" or "unexciting in every sense" and ("anyone wanting spice might need to look elsewhere)". But, in particular, it's "a solid family bet" – "very child-friendly" and "kids love it". (Now with over 150 branches in the UK, in May 2022 they launched a new London flagship at Marble Arch, complete with outside seating by Hyde Park and a new cocktail menu). / www.wagamama.com; SRA-3 stars.

WAHACA £46 233

BRANCHES THROUGHOUT LONDON

"A fun, cheerful Mexican atmosphere" and "enjoyable, fresh tasting" street food dishes can still make "an excellent standby" of this stalwart chain, which has 10 sites in London nowadays. "Even if nothing on the menu is going to wow, its consistent quality and value are reassuring", with ratings and popularity starting to regain their historic high standing since a majority stake was sold to Nando's owner, Dick Enthoven, a couple of years ago. / www.wahaca.com; wahaca; SRA-3 stars.

THE WALLACE, THE WALLACE COLLECTION W1 £45 225

HERTFORD HS, MANCHESTER SQ
020 7563 9505 **3–1A**

The "fabulous atrium" of the famous Wallace Collection, just north of Oxford Street, makes "a perfect setting for a lovely tea" – which is also "very good value compared with many places providing afternoon tea in London". The lunch offering is not nearly as enticing. / W1U 3BN; www.peytonandbyrne.co.uk; @peytonandbyrne; Mon-Sun 4 pm; closed Mon-Sun D; no Amex; booking max 10 may apply.

THE WALMER CASTLE W11 £45

58 LEDBURY RD 020 4580 1196 **7–1B**

A perpetual hit with the minted ne'er-do-wells of Notting Hill, this chichi old boozer changed hands in early 2022. Previously a plaything of Guy Ritchie and David Beckham, its new owner is posh nightclub owner, Piers Adam, owner of Prince Harry's old favourite, Mahiki. Nowadays billed as 'in collaboration with The Craigellachie Hotel' (also owned by Adam), the website promises that 'The Walmer brings the essence of Speyside to London' although – cue cynical laughter – this apparently includes such Caledonian specialities as Crispy Monkfish Tacos, Truffled Lobster Macaroni, and Salmon Ceviche. Whether the trustafarians who cram the place will notice anything other than the fun new refurb and more single malts at the bar is debatable. / W11 2AJ; www.walmercastlenottinghill.co.uk; @walmercastle_nottinghill; Mon-Thu 11.30 pm, Fri & Sat midnight, Sun 10.30 pm; closed Mon & Tue L.

WALTER'S SE21 £67 334

84 PARK HALL ROAD 020 8014 8548 **1–4D**

Off the beaten track, in a shopping parade near Dulwich College, this "very traditional brasserie" was opened a year ago by "the guys behind The Oystermen, seafood royalty of Covent Garden", in a surprise move that avoided the danger of being typecast. It has "a very strong vibe of a good neighbourhood restaurant serving solid local fare" – prawn cocktail, lamb, ox cheek – "it's not food to blow your socks off, but it's not intended to". /

SE21 8SW; waltersdulwich.co.uk; @waltersdulwich; Wed-Sat 11 pm, Sun 6 pm; closed Mon & Tue.

THE WATER HOUSE PROJECT E2 £152 434

1 CORBRIDGE CRESCENT
07841 804119 **14–2B**

"A really exceptional experience… a real find… a fantastic night out" – Gabriel Waterhouse inspires acclaim for his relocated Bethnal Green supper club, whose gracious permanent home occupies a high-ceilinged space in Cambridge Heath. Every night, there's "a one-sitting, 9-course tasting menu with low-intervention wine" (or non-alcoholic pairings) delivering "some really innovative dishes". Ratings would be even higher, were it not for one or two reports along the lines of "love the new menu, but too many foams…" / E2 9DS; www.thewaterhouseproject.com; @thewaterhouseproject; Wed-Sat 11 pm; closed Wed-Sat L, closed Mon & Tue & Sun.

THE WELLS TAVERN NW3 £69 343

30 WELL WALK 020 7794 3785 **9–1A**

"Possibly the best overall eating experience in NW3" – this characterful Georgian tavern in Hampstead (run for two decades by Beth Coventry, sister of the veteran restaurant critic Fay Maschler) is a great all-rounder. The "consistent food is excellent for a local pub", "the setting is delightful" (choose from three different dining rooms) and "it's a friendly place that combines well with a walk on the Heath". / NW3 1BX; thewellshampstead.london; @thewellshampstead; Mon-Sat 10 pm, Sun 9.30 pm; no Amex.

WEST 4TH SW6 £52 322

175 NEW KING'S ROAD
020 8161 1776 **11–1B**

This Parson's Green yearling is a tribute to the Canadian West Coast, and is named after the Vancouver street where founders Livia Boumeester and Louisa Stevenson-Hamilton hung out when they lived there. "Don't expect stars; do expect earthy comfort food." Poutine – the chips, cheese curds and gravy combo that is Canada's gift to a hungry world – is on the menu, along with "the best mac 'n' cheese around". / SW6 4SW; www.west4thlondon.co.uk; @west4thkitchen; Tue-Thu 10 pm, Fri & Sat 11 pm, Sun 4 pm; closed Sun D, closed Mon; payment – credit card only.

WESTERNS LAUNDRY N5 £68 334

34 DRAYTON PARK 020 7700 3700 **9–2D**

"Beautifully prepared fish-centric tapas and a super-cool setting" make this "fab Holloway Road local" small-plates venue "a perfect place to impress your out-of-towner mates… or even those that live in London!" There's a "small but interesting list" of "brilliant orange and other low-intervention wines". Top Tip – "leave space for the rum baba – you'll need to share". / N5 1PB; www.westernslaundry.com;

@westernslaundry; Tue-Sat 10.30 pm, Sun 9 pm; closed Tue-Fri L, closed Mon.

THE WET FISH CAFÉ
NW6
£53 **3 3 3**

242 WEST END LANE 020 7443 9222 1–1B

"A top local that's still going strong". This "cut above" West Hampstead fixture, set in the conversion of a 1930s fishmongers (and still selling retail) has a large fan club fostered by its "quirky and passionate" approach. The top draw is the "short selection of well-priced, very fresh fish", but it's "everything a true café should be," too (serving all day). "It might score even higher if the menu offered more choice." / NW6 1LG; www.thewetfishcafe.co.uk; @thewetfishcafe; Mon-Sun 11 pm; booking evening only.

THE WIGMORE, THE LANGHAM W1
£63 **4 4 4**

**15 LANGHAM PLACE, REGENT STREET
020 7965 0198 2–1B**

Michel Roux Junior has reimagined the British pub as only a French master chef could at this fine hostelry near Oxford Circus – a partnership with the neighbouring Langham Hotel, who carved the pub out of some under-used space. "Simple British dishes are presented as you have never tasted them before" ("shepherd's pie and Scotch eggs were particularly memorable, but everything was delightful") and its "great buzzy ambience" helps make it an excellent West End meeting place. / W1W 3DE; www.the-wigmore.co.uk; @wigmorelondon; Tue-Sat 11 pm; closed Sun & Mon.

WILD HEART W1
£39

**20 WARWICK STREET
020 7292 6100 4–3B**

"Great name… even better food" say fans of this casual, Japanese-inspired dining experience within a Soho hotel, whose all-day dining possibilities (breakfast, lunch, dinner, and afternoon tea…) were conceived by star chef Garry Hollihead. Too limited feedback as yet, though, for a full rating of its mix of poke bowls, salads, sliders and main plates, complemented by an oriental cocktail list and sake menu. / W1W 5NF; www.sanctumsoho.com/restaurant; @karmasanctumldn; Mon & Tue 11, Wed-Sat 10 pm, Sun 11.30; closed Mon & Tue, Sun D.

WILD HONEY ST JAMES
SW1
£96 **3 3 3**

**SOFITEL, 8 PALL MALL
020 7389 7820 2–3C**

"Perfect, joyous French cooking with pitch-perfect flavours" inspires fans of Anthony Demetre's well-regarded venture, which he moved here from Mayfair pre-Covid. The very "spacious" and "tasteful" dining room and its superb position – just off Trafalgar Square, but away from the madding crowds – makes it an excellent business choice (or pre/post-theatre). In terms of value, many diners tip any set

options here over the à la carte. / SW1S 5NG; www.wildhoneystjames.co.uk; @wildhoneystjames; Wed-Sat 9.30 pm, Tue 2.30 pm; closed Tue D, closed Sun & Mon.

WILD TAVERN
SW3
£111 **2 3 3**

2 ELYSTAN STREET 020 8191 9885 6–2C

"Hopping Chelsea local" (overlooking Chelsea Green), whose owners George Bukhov-Weinstein and Ilya Demichev also play a part in other casual luxury brands such as Beast and Burger & Lobster. Here, a vaguely Alpine interior hosts an offering whose menu incorporates a raw bar and pastas, plus prime steaks and fish grills sold by the 100g. Results are generally good, but whether they represent fair value is debated ("such an exceptional bill should not be presented to anyone with a weak heart…") / SW3 3NS; www.wildtavern.co.uk; @wildtavern; Mon-Sat 10 pm, Sun 9.30 pm.

WILTONS SW1
£108 **3 3 3**

55 JERMYN ST 020 7629 9955 3–3C

"Like a London club but with infinitely better food" – this "very civilised" St James's veteran (London's oldest restaurant, established in 1742, but not on this site) is "a real throwback to another era" ("it's probably not the place to attract 'influencers', whoever or whatever they are!"). The menu (which majors in fish and seafood) is "as traditional as one can expect (as is the clientele)" – you are served "classic food, classically executed and classically served" and at its best results are "simply exceptional". "Service is old-school professional" although, perhaps due to the strains of Covid, did not enjoy its customary 5/5 rating this year. Even so, Wiltons remains "a great place for meeting on business" and its pricing is such that it's best to let the corporate credit card take the strain whenever possible. Top Menu Tips – "the Dover sole is still the best in the capital" and "their lobster thermidor is rich and everything you want in an indulgent food item". Game is excellent in season and they do a "magnificent bone-in rib served from the trolley". / SW1Y 6LX; www.wiltons.co.uk; @wiltons1742; Mon-Sat 10.30 pm; closed Sat L, closed Sun.

THE WINDMILL
W1
£60 **3 2 3**

6-8 MILL ST 020 7491 8050 4–2A

"Great home-made pies (in five flavours) and mash to go with a pint of Young's bitter – what's not to like?" about this "traditional pub" just off Regent Street, from the same stable as the Guinea Grill. There's a newish (est. 2020) upstairs restaurant and terrace which is more what you might expect in Mayfair, white tablecloths and all. / W1S 2AZ; www.windmillmayfair.co.uk; @windmill_pub; Mon-Sat 11 pm, Sun 6 pm.

THE WINE LIBRARY
EC3
£48 **2 2 4**

43 TRINITY SQ 020 7481 0415 10–3D

This 19th-century vaulted wine cellar near Tower Hill offers "an amazing and enjoyable selection of wines to buy and then open and drink right there" (at off-licence prices plus £9.50 corkage). "Service is 'fetch your own'", and platters of buffet-style "finger food" – charcuterie, French cheeses, and more – contribute to an "always agreeable visit". / EC3N 4DJ; www.winelibrary.co.uk; Tue-Fri 8 pm, Mon 6 pm, Sat 5.30 pm; closed Sat D, closed Sun.

THE WOLSELEY
W1
£77 **1 2 4**

160 PICCADILLY 020 7499 6996 3–3C

"The sheer style of the room" helps create an "unbeatable buzz" at this "very classy and smartly located" Continental Grand Café by The Ritz, which has, for nearly 20 years, established itself as London's premier venue for a "reliably impressive" business occasion; and as "the absolute go-to for a totally unrivalled breakfast" ("a cliché, but really it is the best place to enjoy eggs Benedict in London"). And "afternoon tea is excellent too, with a good choice of sandwiches and cakes." Established by Christopher Corbin and Jeremy King in 2003 in an erstwhile Edwardian car showroom (which provided the restaurant's name), it has perennially been "the permanent buzz not the average food that's created the magic of the place". The "simple comfort fare at West End prices" has often rated poorly next to the "sparkling" atmosphere and "star-studded people watching" carefully cultivated by its well-connected founders. So "whether the place will survive the recent departure of those same founders remains to be seen". A shareholder battle post-Covid saw Corbin & King edged out by their financial backers, the Thai Minor group, and many reporters fear "a ravens-leaving-the-tower moment" ("fingers crossed they don't let the money-men spoil this…"; "it's wait-and-see time…"; "if they ruin it, we will revolt…"). The schism happened in April 2022, immediately prior to our survey, and ratings this year are significantly down across the board. It could be that Brexit-induced staffing shortages bear some of the blame, but already some reporters fear the reason is clear: "it's lost its soul now Jeremy and Chris have been ousted". / W1J 9EB; www.thewolseley.com; @thewolseley; Mon-Sat 11 pm, Sun 10 pm.

WONG KEI W1
£32 **3 1 1**

41-43 WARDOUR ST 020 7437 8408 5–3A

"Tasty mountains of food" served with "no frills" make this Cantonese landmark one of London's most enduring low-budget eats. "Yes, it's basic" and the "super-quick" service "no longer has the 'rudeness' of the 1990s" that had its own masochistic entertainment value. But many reporters note that "they are still visiting after decades, so something works": "it's great cheap food". "The ambience is tired with token Chinese decoration … wouldn't have it any other way!" / W1D 6PY; Mon-Sat 11.30 pm, Sun 10.30 pm; cash only.

WRIGHT BROTHERS £71 323

56 OLD BROMPTON RD, SW7
020 7581 0131   6–2B
11 STONEY ST, SE1   020 7403 9554   10–4C
26 CIRCUS ROAD WEST, SW8
020 7324 7734   11–1C

"The best oysters and crustacea in a bustling market-facing venue" is how many restaurant-goers think of this "buzzy and packed" small group, whose SE1 branch at Borough Market is better known than its Battersea Power Station sibling. "Order from the blackboard for the freshest catch." "You come for the seafood, not the sparkling repartee" and service "can get a bit frazzled". (We have continued to list the South Kensington outlet, but as we go to press it is 'temporarily closed' due to staff shortages. / thewrightbrothers.co.uk; WrightBrosLTD.

WULF & LAMB £53 322

243 PAVILION ROAD, SW1
020 3948 5999   6–2D
66 CHILTERN STREET, W1
020 8194 0000   2–1A

Plant-based versions of comfort-food classics such as black-bean burgers and "interesting mac'n'cashew cheese" are menu highlights at this pair of meat-free cafés, out to prove that vegan dining has graduated from shabby to chic. Its menu of plant-based borrowings from cuisines around the world impresses even the occasional carnivore – "I forget I'm not vegan!" / www.wulfandlamb.com.

WUN'S W1 £61 323

24 GREEK STREET   020 8017 9888   5–2A

A "very good" modern take on classic Cantonese cuisine from Z He and Alex Peffly (of Bun House) is presented in an atmospheric "neon-lit underground parlour in Soho, with the menus on newspapers, giving a gentlemen's club/opium den vibe". / W1W 4DZ; tearoom. bar; @wunstearoom; Tue-Fri midnight; closed Tue-Fri L, closed Mon, Sat & Sun; booking online only.

XI'AN IMPRESSION N7 £37 321

117 BENWELL RD   020 3441 0191   9–2D

"Cheap and authentic": the noodles are so unctuous and delicious" at this canteen opposite the Emirates stadium – "and it's BYO to boot". For Gooners, the "excellent food tastes even better if Arsenal win". / N7; www.xianimpression.co.uk; @Xianimpression; Mon-Sun 10 pm; no booking.

YAMA MOMO SE22 £64 322

72 LORDSHIP LN   020 8299 1007   1–4D

This "great local Japanese" in East Dulwich is the "small, younger brother of Tsunami in Clapham", and attracts a "buzzing crowd of local regulars" with its "good sushi and sashimi, crisp tempura, and sizzling hot plates of steak, chicken and fish". Service is "cheerful if occasionally haphazard". / SE22 8HF; www.yamamomo.co.uk; @yamamomo_eastdulwich; Mon-Thu 10 pm, Fri & Sat 10.30 pm, Sun 9.30 pm; closed Mon-Thu L.

YARD SALE PIZZA £43 442

54 BLACKSTOCK ROAD, N4
020 7226 2651   9–1D
46 WESTOW HILL, SE19
020 8670 6386   1–4D
39 LORDSHIP LANE, SE22
020 8693 5215   1–4D
393 BROCKLEY ROAD, SE4
020 8692 8800   1–4D
63 BEDFORD HILL, SW12
020 8772 1100   11–2C
622 HIGH ROAD LEYTONSTONE, E11
020 8539 5333   1–1D
15 HOE STREET, E17   020 8509 0888   1–1D
184 HACKNEY ROAD, E2
020 7739 1095   14–2A
105 LOWER CLAPTON RD, E5
020 3602 9090   14–1B

"Such good pizza in very decent sizes for the price" earns this (south) east London chain some of the highest ratings for pizza in the capital and they're "consistently quick" too. The latest addition to the group is a branch in Crofton Park. / yardsalepizza.com; yardsalepizza.

YASHIN £109 433

117-119 OLD BROMPTON RD, SW7
020 7373 3990   6–2B
1A ARGYLL RD, W8   020 7938 1536   6–1A

Flying under the radar, as they have for over a decade now, Yasuhiro Mineno's and Shinya Ikeda's offbeat duo – a two-floor site in a Kensington backstreet (est. 2010), and the newer 'Ocean House' spin-off (est. 2013, in the quirky former Brompton Library) – never inspire a huge volume of feedback, perhaps because they are by no means cheap. The owners have fine CVs though and all reports continue to say the sushi here can be exceptional. / yashinsushi.com.

YAUATCHA £104 322

BROADWICK HOUSE, 15-17 BROADWICK ST, W1   020 7494 8888   4–1C
BROADGATE CIRCLE, EC2
020 3817 9888   13–2B

"Exquisite" dim sum – in particular "addictive cheung fun and venison puffs" – have won fame for these Hakkasan spin-offs, which are quite different in nature. The original site occupies a "blingy, dark, rammed-full Soho basement" (and you can also eat in the ground-floor tea room); while the Broadgate spin-off is vast by comparison and much more swish and corporate, with large outside terraces for cocktails. Both outlets share the shortcomings of Hakkasan, though: they can be "soooooo pricey", and service can be "slow" or "entitled". Top Tip – their "cakes are incredible; small and perfectly formed!" / www.yauatcha.com.

THE YELLOW HOUSE SE16 £52 343

126 LOWER RD   020 7231 8777   12–2A

"A true local gem to be cherished in a downbeat area for restaurants" – this endearing local near Surrey Quays station wins applause for its "small and friendly team" and "always amazing" wood-fired pizza and other fare. "I could not be more relieved that these guys survived the pandemic!" / SE16 2UE; www.theyellowhouse.eu; @theyellowhouserestaurant; Wed & Thu 9.30 pm, Fri & Sat 10 pm, Sun 6.30 pm; closed Wed-Sun L, closed Mon & Tue.

YUCA W1

10 - 11 LANCASHIRE COURT
020 7518 9388   3–2B

The duo behind Brazilian-Japanese spot Mano, Alexis Colletta and Romain Fargette, are opening another Mayfair fusion haunt in the neighbourhood in summer 2022. This one will be Japanese-Mexican, sited where Mews of Mayfair (RIP) was, and will feature a 300-cover restaurant and a club in the basement. / W1W 1EY.

ZAFFERANO SW1 £96 433

15 LOWNDES ST   020 7235 5800   6–1D

A short stroll from Knightsbridge, this Belgravia stalwart seems increasingly forgotten about, certainly compared with its mid-'90s glory days when it was the talk of the town. Its fans, though, continue to regard it as a "fantastic premium Italian", with a capable wine list and deftly realised pasta and other classic dishes. / SW1X 9EY; zafferanorestaurant.com; @zafferanorestaurant; Mon-Sun 10 pm.

ZAFFRANI N1 £48 222

47 CROSS ST   020 7226 5522   9–3D

This "handy local Indian restaurant" near the Almeida Theatre in Islington is rather smarter than the average curry house, and has a wide choice of fish and seafood dishes in addition to the standard meat and veg range. / N1 2BB; www.zaffrani.co.uk; @zaffrani_restaurant; Mon-Sun 10.30 pm; closed Mon-Sun L.

ZAHTER W1 £89 323

30-32 FOUBERT'S PLACE
07775 156768   4–1B

"An impressive addition to the Carnaby Street scene" – this modern Eastern-Med newcomer from Turkish chef Esra Muslu is decorated in an informal café style that's deceptive given the high quality of the cuisine. The open kitchen and counter on the ground floor "give you so much to talk about (I just love watching the flames in the oven)" and "the food can be as light or heavy as you wish" according to which small plates you go for. "Love it"… but it can be "ridiculously noisy", "staff don't always seem to know what they're doing" and the small dishes come at chunky prices. / W1W 7PS; zahter.co.uk;

@zahterlondon; Tue-Thu 11.30 pm, Fri & Sat 12.30 am; closed Sun & Mon.

ZAIBATSU SE10 £41 3 3 2

96 TRAFALGAR RD   020 8858 9317   1–3D

"Rough and ready, cramped, but charming" – this unassuming Japanese BYO on the edge of Greenwich is "mostly known for perfectly decent sushi at reasonable prices", along with some less commented-on pan-Asian dishes. / SE10 9UW; www.zaibatsufusion.co.uk; Tue-Sat 11 pm, Sun 9 pm; closed Mon; cash only.

ZAIKA OF KENSINGTON W8 £67 3 4 4

1 KENSINGTON HIGH STREET 020 7795 6533   6–1A

The "beautiful dining room" ("an old bank building") hosts a menu inspired by the historic royal cuisine of Lucknow, at this smart restaurant near Kensington Gardens. It "never seems to make it into the 'top' lists", unlike its highly rated stablemate Tamarind in Mayfair, "but the modern cooking never disappoints and is of the highest quality". W8 5NP; www.zaikaofkensington.com; @zaikaofkensington; Mon-Sat 10.15 pm, Sun 9.15pm; closed Sun & Mon L; no trainers; credit card required to book.

ZEPHYR W11

100 PORTOBELLO ROAD 020 4599 1177   7–2B

In Notting HIll, this summer 2022 newcomer from Pachamama Group occupies a sizable 3,000 sq ft site. A restaurant and late-night cocktail bar, it aims to apply the bold flavours of Asian cuisine to a Greek-inspired formula… that's a new one on us. / W11 2QD; www.zephyr.london/book-a-table; Mon-Sun midnight.

ZHENG SW3 £69 3 3 2

4 SYDNEY ST   020 7352 9890   6–2C

"Really interesting Malay/Chinese combo" cuisine sets this smart, if low key, Chelsea venue apart, minimally decked out with painted black walls. Spun off from an original in Oxford, it is named after the Chinese admiral who explored South East Asia 600 years ago. "Staff are very friendly and helpful" in navigating the menu, with its collision of Chinese, Malay and Indian food cultures. / SW3 6PP; www.zhengchelsea.co.uk; Mon, Wed-Sun 11 pm; closed Mon, Wed-Fri L, closed Tue; no shorts.

ZIA LUCIA £52 4 2 2

61 BLYTHE ROAD, W14 020 7371 4096   8–1C BOXPARK WEMBLEY, 18 OLYMPIC WAY, HA9   020 3744 4427   1–1A 61 STOKE NEWINGTON HIGH STREET, N16 020 8616 8690   1–1C 157 HOLLOWAY ROAD, N7 020 7700 3708   9–2D 65 BALHAM HIGH ROAD, SW12 020 3093 0946   11–2C 356 OLD YORK ROAD, SW18 020 3971 0829   11–2B

12A PIAZZA WALK, E1 020 7702 2525   10–2D

"Love the different pizza-base options such as charcoal and gluten-free" (there's also wholemeal and 'traditional') at these popular pizza pit stops, where the dough is fermented for 48 hours then cooked in purpose-built gas and wood ovens. Two branches were added in 2022: in Stoke Newington in April and in Canary Wharf in summer. / zialucia.com; zialuciapizza.

ZIANI'S SW3 £66 3 3 3

45 RADNOR WALK   020 7351 5297   6–3C

This diminutive but "highly enjoyable" Venetian trattoria off Chelsea's King's Road (named in honour of the Doge who laid out Venice's Piazza San Marco) is "really popular with the locals" for its "great buzz", led by the "loud and funny waiters". Founder Roberto Colussi died five years ago, but it has carried on in the way he intended, and will celebrate its 40th anniversary next year. / SW3 4BP; www.ziani.co.uk; Mon-Sun 10 pm.

ZOILO W1 £84 3 3 3

9 DUKE ST   020 7486 9699   3–1A

Grilled beef, both Argentine and British, is the star of the show at Argentinian chef-patron Diego Jacquet's comfortable modern outfit near the Wallace Collection – and, after more than a decade, it "hasn't lost the quality", while the "service is always good and friendly". Oenophiles enjoy the range of Argentinian wines, while the prix fixe lunch is a steal. / W1U 3EG; www.zoilo.co.uk; @zoilolondon; Tue-Sat 10 pm; closed Tue, Wed L, closed Sun & Mon.

ZUMA SW7 £105 4 3 5

5 RAPHAEL ST   020 7584 1010   6–1C

The crowd (especially in the bar) can be "bling personified", but Rainer Becker and Arjun Waney's glitzily glam scene, a short walk from Harrods, delivers way more than "a fun cocktail", serving luxurious Japanese-fusion dishes that are "just heaven". For fine food with a pulse, this remains "one of the best dining experiences in London". Top Menu Tips – "outstanding Wagyu tartare, crispy langoustines and seared tuna salads, and melt-in-the-mouth otoro sushi". / SW7 1DL; www.zumarestaurant.com; @Zumalondonofficial; Mon-Sat 11 pm, Sun 10.30 pm; booking max 8 may apply.

CENTRAL

SOHO, COVENT GARDEN & BLOOMSBURY (PARTS OF W1, ALL WC2 AND WC1)

£200+	Frog by Adam Handling	British, Modern	4	4	3
£180+	Aulis London	British, Modern	4	4	4
£150+	Evelyn's Table	British, Modern	5	4	2
£140+	The Savoy Hotel, Savoy Grill	British, Traditional	2	2	3
	Restaurant 1890	French	3	4	4
£130+	Bustronome	British, Modern	2	3	4
£120+	Gauthier Soho	Vegan	3	3	3
	Kebab Queen	Turkish	4	4	3
£110+	NoMad London	American	3	4	5
	Spring Restaurant	British, Modern	3	3	4
	Sushisamba	Fusion	2	2	3
	Thames Foyer, Savoy	Afternoon tea	2	3	4
	Tattu London	Chinese	2	3	3
£100+	SOLA	American	5	3	2
	Kerridge's Bar & Grill	British, Modern	2	2	3
	Park Row	"	2	2	4
	Social Eating House	"	3	3	3
	River Rest', Savoy	Fish & seafood	2	3	2
	The Seafood Bar	"	4	4	4
	The Petersham	Italian	2	2	3
	Smith & Wollensky	Steaks & grills	2	2	3
	Yauatcha	Chinese	3	2	2
£90+	Christopher's	American	2	2	3
	Clos Maggiore	British, Modern	3	3	5
	The Ivy	"	2	2	3
	The Northall	"	3	3	3
	Pivot by Mark Greenaway	"	4	4	3
	Quo Vadis	"	4	4	5
	Simpson's in the Strand	British, Traditional	2	3	4
	L'Escargot	French	3	3	3
	Frenchie	"	3	3	3
	Louie	"	3	2	3
	Otto's	"	4	4	5
	Nopi	Mediterranean	3	3	2
	Decimo	Spanish	3	2	4
	Hawksmoor	Steaks & grills	2	2	2
	Oscar Wilde Lounge	Afternoon tea	3	3	5
	aqua kyoto	Japanese	3	3	4
	Roka, Aldwych House	"	4	3	3
£80+	Balthazar	British, Modern	1	2	3
	Bob Bob Ricard	"	2	4	5
	Ducksoup	"	3	4	3
	Galvin Bar & Grill	"	3	4	4
	Holborn Dining Room	British, Traditional	–	–	–
	Rules	"	3	4	5
	Randall & Aubin	Fish & seafood	4	4	5
	J Sheekey	"	3	3	4
	J Sheekey Atlantic Bar	"	4	3	4
	Folie	French	3	4	4
	Margot	Italian	3	4	4
	Dalloway Terrace	Afternoon tea	2	3	4
	Cecconi's Pizza Bar	Pizza	2	2	4
	Sucre London	Argentinian	3	4	4
	Zahter	Turkish	3	2	3
	Red Farm	Chinese	3	2	3
£70+	Big Easy	American	2	2	3
	Dean Street Townhouse	British, Modern	2	3	4
	Heliot Steak House	"	3	3	3
	The Ivy Market Grill	"	2	2	3
	Noble Rot	"	3	5	5
	St Martin's House	"	–	–	–
	The Ivy Soho Brasserie	British, Traditional	2	2	3
	Fishworks	Fish & seafood	3	3	2
	The Oystermen	"	3	2	2
	The 10 Cases	International	3	4	3
	Café Murano	Italian	2	2	2
	Da Mario	"	2	3	2
	Vasco & Piero's	"	4	5	4
	Toklas	Mediterranean	4	2	3
	Lisboeta	Portuguese	4	4	3
	Barrafina	Spanish	5	4	4
	Cakes and Bubbles	"	3	4	3
	Burger & Lobster	Burgers, etc	3	3	3
	Ceviche Soho	Peruvian	3	2	3
	The Barbary	North African	4	3	4
	The Duck & Rice	Chinese	3	3	3
	Chotto Matte	Japanese	4	4	4
	Jinjuu	Korean	4	2	3
	Patara Soho	Thai	3	3	2
£60+	Paradise	Sri Lankan	4	3	3
	Rita's Soho	Mexican	3	4	4
	Joe Allen	American	2	4	5
	Andrew Edmunds	British, Modern	3	4	5
	Cora Pearl	"	3	3	4
	Double Standard	"	3	5	5
	The French House	"	3	4	4
	Ham Yard	"	2	2	4
	Indigo, One Aldwych	"	3	3	3
	Isla	"	3	5	4
	The Jones Family Affair	"	4	3	4
	Riding House Bloomsbury	"	2	3	4
	10 Greek Street	"	4	3	3
	The Delaunay	East & C. European	2	4	4
	Parsons	Fish & seafood	4	4	3
	Blanchette	French	3	4	3
	Brasserie Blanc	"	2	2	2
	Le Garrick	"	3	3	4

Mon Plaisir Restaurant	"	2 2 4
Bocca di Lupo	Italian	4 3 3
Dehesa	"	2 2 2
La Goccia	"	3 2 4
Luce e Limoni	"	3 4 3
Obicà	"	3 3 3
San Carlo Cicchetti	"	3 3 3
Sycamore Vino Cucina	"	3 2 2
Volta do Mar	Portuguese	4 4 3
Tapas Brindisa Soho	Spanish	3 2 2
Il Teatro della Carne	Steaks & grills	2 2 3
St Moritz	Swiss	3 3 3
L'Antica Pizzeria da Michele	Pizza	5 3 2
The Palomar	Middle Eastern	4 4 4
Berenjak	Persian	4 4 4
Nutshell	"	3 2 2
Haz	Turkish	3 3 2
Little Four Seasons	Chinese	4 1 1
Wun's	"	3 2 3
Masala Zone	Indian	3 3 4
Tamarind Kitchen	"	4 4 4
Tandoor Chop House	"	3 3 3
Flesh and Buns	Japanese	3 4 3
Sticks'n'Sushi	"	3 2 2

£50+

Hoppers	Sri Lankan	4 3 3
El Pastor Soho	Mexican	3 2 3
The Black Book	British, Modern	3 4 4
Café Deco	"	3 2 2
Noble Rot Soho	"	3 4 4
Sussex	"	3 4 3
VQ, St Giles Hotel	"	2 2 3
Cork & Bottle	British, Traditional	2 4 4
Cigalon	French	3 3 3
Pierre Victoire	"	3 2 3
Boulevard	International	2 3 3
La Fromagerie Bloomsbury	"	3 2 2
Ave Mario	Italian	3 3 4
Bancone	"	4 4 3
Ciao Bella	"	3 4 5
Fumo	"	3 3 3
Mele e Pere	"	2 3 2
Pastaio	"	3 3 3
Opera Tavern	Spanish	2 2 3
Blacklock	Steaks & grills	3 4 3
Mildreds	Vegetarian	3 3 3
North Sea Fish	Fish & chips	3 3 2
Poppies	"	3 2 2
Homeslice	Pizza	4 3 3
temper Covent Garden	"	3 2 4
temper Soho	BBQ	3 2 4
Le Bab	Middle Eastern	3 2 2
Lahpet	Burmese	3 4 3
Barshu	Chinese	5 2 2
Fatt Pundit	"	4 3 2
Imperial China	"	3 2 2
Orient London	"	4 3 2
Plum Valley	"	3 2 2
Din Tai Fung	Chinese, Dim sum	2 2 2

Cinnamon Bazaar	Indian	4 4 4
Dishoom	"	4 4 4
Fatt Pundit	"	4 3 2
Gunpowder Soho	"	4 3 3
Kricket	"	5 4 4
Salaam Namaste	"	3 3 2
Oka, Kingly Court	Japanese	3 3 2
Shoryu Ramen	"	3 3 2
Kiln	Thai	5 4 4

£40+

The Norfolk Arms	British, Modern	3 3 2
Brasserie Zédel	French	1 4 5
Chez Antoinette	"	3 4 3
Prix Fixe	"	3 2 2
Gordon's Wine Bar	International	2 2 5
Casa Tua	Italian	4 2 3
Lina Stores	"	4 3 3
Haché	Burgers, etc	4 3 3
MEATliquor	"	4 2 2
Patty and Bun Soho	"	3 2 2
Street Burger	"	2 2 2
50 Kalò di Ciro Salvo	Pizza	5 2 3
Chick 'n' Sours	Chicken	4 3 3
The Barbary Next Door	North African	4 2 2
Bubala Soho	Middle Eastern	4 4 3
Golden Dragon	Chinese	3 2 3
Kasa & Kin	Filipino	3 4 3
Hankies	Indian	3 2 2
Punjab	"	4 2 3
Sagar	"	3 2 2
Dipna Anand	Indian, Southern	3 2 2
Bone Daddies	Japanese	3 3 3
Koya-Bar	"	3 4 3
Shackfuyu	"	3 2 2
Bibimbap Soho	Korean	3 3 2
Hare & Tortoise	Pan-Asian	3 3 2
Inamo	"	3 3 3
Cay Tre	Vietnamese	3 3 2
Viet Food	"	3 2 3

£35+

Kolamba	Sri Lankan	3 3 2
Bar Italia	Italian	2 4 5
Fadiga	"	4 4 3
Miscusi	"	2 2 2
Flat Iron	Steaks & grills	3 4 3
Tommi's Burger Joint	Burgers, etc	3 3 2
Food House	Chinese	- - -
Baozi Inn	Chinese, Dim sum	3 2 2
Eat Tokyo	Japanese	3 2 1
Humble Chicken	"	3 3 4
Kanada-Ya	"	4 2 2
Taro	"	3 3 2
Wild Heart	"	- - -
C&R Café	Malaysian	3 2 2
Lao Cafe	Thai	3 3 2
Plaza Khao Gaeng	"	- - -
Bao Soho	Taiwanese	3 4 4

£30+

Café in the Crypt	British, Traditional	2 2 4

Rudy's	Pizza		3 3 3
Coqfighter	Chicken		4 3 2
Master Wei	Chinese		4 2 2
Wong Kei	"		3 1 1
Dumplings' Legend	Chinese, Dim sum		3 2 2
£25+	Imad's Syrian Kitchen	Syrian	3 3 3
	India Club	Indian	3 2 3
	The Kati Roll Company	"	3 2 2
	Heddon Yokocho	Japanese	3 2 3
£20+	Bageriet	Sandwiches, cakes, etc	4 2 2
	Dim Sum Duck	Chinese, Dim sum	5 2 2
£15+	Mr Ji	Fusion	3 3 2
	Maison Bertaux	Afternoon tea	4 3 5
	Bun House	Chinese	4 3 3
	Dai Chi	Japanese	– – –
£10+	Flat White	Sandwiches, cakes, etc	3 3 2
£5+	Monmouth Coffee Company	Sandwiches, cakes, etc	3 4 3

MAYFAIR & ST JAMES'S
(PARTS OF W1 AND SW1)

£380+	The Araki	Japanese	5 4 3
£240+	Maru	Japanese	5 4 3
£230+	Ikoyi	International	3 2 2
£220+	Alain Ducasse	French	2 3 2
	Sketch, Lecture Rm	"	3 4 5
£190+	Amethyst	British, Modern	– – –
£170+	Above at Hide	British, Modern	3 2 3
	Hélène Darroze	French	2 3 2
	Seven Park Place	"	3 3 3
£150+	The Connaught Grill	British, Modern	– – –
	The Promenade	Afternoon tea	3 4 4
	Umu	Japanese	4 4 3
£140+	Le Gavroche	French	4 3 4
	Park Chinois	Chinese	3 2 4
£130+	Pollen Street Social	British, Modern	3 3 3
	Estiatorio Milos	Fish & seafood	4 3 4
	Le Comptoir Robuchon	French	3 4 3
	Galvin at Windows	"	2 3 3
	Cut	Steaks & grills	3 3 3
	Cubé	Japanese	4 4 2
	Jean-Georges	Pan-Asian	3 3 3
	Novikov (Asian restaurant)	"	2 2 4
£120+	Hide Ground	British, Modern	3 4 4

The Game Bird	British, Traditional		3 4 4
SeaSons	Fish & seafood		2 2 2
Il Borro	Italian		3 3 3
Murano	"		3 4 3
Hakkasan Mayfair	Chinese		3 1 2
Kai Mayfair	"		3 3 3
Nobu	Japanese		4 3 2
£110+	Corrigan's Mayfair	British, Modern	3 4 3
	The Maine Mayfair	"	3 2 4
	Ormer	"	4 5 3
	The Ritz	British, Traditional	4 5 5
	Bar des Prés	French	3 4 4
	LPM	"	5 4 4
	Giannino Mayfair	Italian	2 4 3
	34 Mayfair	Steaks & grills	2 3 3
	Coya	Peruvian	3 3 3
	RAI	Japanese	4 4 3
£100+	Colony Grill Room	American	3 4 4
	The Grill at The Dorchester	British, Modern	4 4 4
	Wiltons	British, Traditional	3 3 3
	Sexy Fish	Fish & seafood	1 1 3
	Bocconcino Restaurant	Italian	2 2 2
	El Norte	Spanish	3 3 3
	The Guinea Grill	Steaks & grills	2 2 4
	Claridges Foyer	Afternoon tea	3 4 4
	The Ritz, Palm Court	"	3 4 5
	Jeru	Middle Eastern	4 2 4
	China Tang	Chinese	2 3 3
	Kanishka	Indian	3 3 2
	Ginza Onodera	Japanese	3 2 3
£90+	Charlie's at Brown's	British, Modern	4 5 5
	Hush	"	2 2 3
	Quaglino's	"	2 3 4
	Wild Honey St James	"	3 3 3
	Bentley's	Fish & seafood	4 4 3
	Scott's	"	4 4 4
	Sketch, Gallery	French	3 3 4
	Amazonico	International	3 3 4
	Scully	"	3 3 2
	Chucs Dover Street	Italian	2 2 3
	Sartoria	"	3 4 3
	Aquavit	Scandinavian	2 3 2
	Goodman	Steaks & grills	3 3 2
	Hawksmoor	"	2 2 2
	MiMi Mei Fair	Chinese	3 3 4
	Benares	Indian	4 4 4
	BiBi	"	5 5 4
	Chutney Mary	"	4 3 4
	Veeraswamy	"	4 4 4
	Ikeda	Japanese	4 4 2
	Roka	"	4 3 3
	Tokimeite	"	– – –
£80+	Apricity	British, Modern	2 4 3
	45 Jermyn St.	"	2 3 3
	GBR, Dukes Hotel	British, Traditional	3 3 3

	Boudin Blanc	French		3 3 4
	Maison François	"		3 4 5
	Saint Jacques	"		3 3 3
	Cecconi's	Italian		2 2 4
	Franco's	"		3 3 3
	Ristorante Frescobaldi	"		3 2 2
	Theo Randall	"		5 4 2
	Rowley's	Steaks & grills		3 2 3
	Drawing Room (Browns)	Afternoon tea		3 4 4
	Diamond Jub (F&M)	"		3 3 4
	Gymkhana	Indian		5 3 3
	Jamavar	"		4 4 4
	Tamarind	"		5 4 3
	Lucky Cat	Pan-Asian		2 2 2
£70+	The American Bar	American		2 3 5
	The Avenue	"		3 3 3
	Kitty Fisher's	British, Modern		3 3 4
	Langan's Brasserie	"		1 2 3
	Little Social	"		4 3 3
	Maddox Tavern	"		– – –
	Native at Browns	"		5 4 4
	The Wolseley	"		1 2 4
	Fishworks	Fish & seafood		3 3 2
	Café Murano	Italian		2 2 2
	San Carlo	"		3 3 4
	Burger & Lobster	Burgers, etc		3 3 3
	Bombay Bustle	Indian		5 4 4
	Chisou	Japanese		3 2 2
	Kiku	"		4 4 2
	The Ivy Asia Mayfair	Pan-Asian		2 3 4
	Patara Mayfair	Thai		3 3 2
£60+	Bellamy's	British, Modern		3 5 4
	116 at the Athenaeum	"		2 4 3
	The Windmill	British, Traditional		3 2 3
	Al Duca	Italian		3 2 2
	Il Vicolo	"		3 3 2
	Sabor	Spanish		5 5 5
	Drawing Room, Dukes	Afternoon tea		– – –
	Delfino	Pizza		3 3 2
	O'ver	"		3 2 2
	Manthan	Indian		3 4 3
£50+	123V	Vegan		3 2 3
	José Pizarro at the RA	Spanish		4 3 3
	El Pirata	"		2 3 3
	Richoux	Sandwiches, cakes, etc		3 4 3
	Shoryu Ramen	Japanese		3 3 2
£40+	Sarap Filipino Bistro	Filipino		3 3 3
	Chourangi	Indian		4 3 3
£35+	Queens of Mayfair	British, Modern		3 4 4

FITZROVIA & MARYLEBONE (PART OF W1)

£330+	Kitchen Table	British, Modern		4 4 4
£280+	Roketsu	Japanese		5 4 3
£140+	Akoko	West African		4 4 4
£130+	Pied à Terre	French		4 4 4
£120+	Kol	Mexican		4 4 4
	Beast	Steaks & grills		2 2 2
	Hakkasan	Chinese		3 1 2
£110+	Mere	East & C. European		3 4 2
	Ampéli	Greek		3 4 3
£100+	The Chiltern Firehouse	American		2 2 5
	The Berners Tavern	British, Modern		2 2 5
	The Ninth London	"		5 4 3
	Locanda Locatelli	Italian		2 3 2
	Arros QD	Spanish		2 2 2
	Dinings	Japanese		5 4 2
	Nobu Portman Square	"		3 3 4
£90+	Cavita	Mexican		– – –
	Portland	British, Modern		4 5 3
	28-50 Marylebone	"		2 2 2
	Santo Mare	Fish & seafood		3 3 3
	Noizé	French		4 5 4
	Les 110 de Taillevent	"		3 3 3
	Orrery	"		2 2 2
	Opso	Greek		3 2 3
	Palm Court, The Langham	Afternoon tea		2 3 4
	Roka	Japanese		4 3 3
	Taka Marylebone	"		2 2 3
	TOKii	"		– – –
£80+	Clipstone	British, Modern		4 3 2
	The Grazing Goat	"		3 3 3
	Upstairs at The George	"		– – –
	Clarette	French		3 3 3
	La Brasseria Milanese	Italian		3 3 3
	Norma	"		4 4 4
	ROVI	Mediterranean		3 2 3
	Zoilo	Argentinian		3 3 3
	The Bright Courtyard	Chinese		3 2 2
	Pahli Hill Bandra Bhai	Indian		3 2 2
£70+	Brasserie of Light	British, Modern		2 2 5
	108 Brasserie	"		3 2 3
	Fishworks Marylebone	Fish & seafood		3 3 2
	Chotto Matte	Fusion		4 4 4
	Meraki	Greek		4 3 4
	Carousel	International		4 3 2
	Caffè Caldesi	Italian		3 2 2
	Blandford Comptoir	Mediterranean		3 3 3
	Ottolenghi	"		4 3 2
	Burger & Lobster	Burgers, etc		3 3 3
	Daylesford Organic	Sandwiches, cakes, etc		2 2 2
	Pachamama	Peruvian		2 2 3
	Honey & Co	Middle Eastern		– – –

Ishtar	*Turkish*	3 3 3
Royal China Club	*Chinese*	3 2 2
Jikoni	*Indian*	3 3 3
Trishna	*"*	5 4 3

£60+

Granger & Co	*Australian*	2 2 2
The Ivy Café	*British, Modern*	1 2 2
The Lore of the Land	*"*	3 3 4
The Wigmore, The Langham	*British, Traditional*	4 4 4
Fischer's	*East & C. European*	2 3 3
Italiku	*Fusion*	3 3 3
Twist Connubio	*"*	3 3 2
Six by Nico	*International*	3 3 3
Briciole	*Italian*	3 3 2
Harry's Bar	*"*	2 2 3
Riding House Café	*Mediterranean*	2 3 4
Ibérica	*Spanish*	2 2 2
Lurra	*"*	4 3 3
Honey & Smoke	*Middle Eastern*	4 2 2
Royal China	*Chinese*	3 1 2
Masala Zone at Selfridges	*Indian*	3 3 4
Flesh and Buns Fitzrovia	*Japanese*	3 4 3
Junsei	*"*	4 4 3
Sushi Atelier	*"*	4 4 3

£50+

Hoppers	*Sri Lankan*	4 3 3
Wulf & Lamb	*Vegan*	3 2 2
Caravan	*British, Modern*	2 2 2
La Fromagerie Café	*International*	3 2 2
Circolo Popolare	*Italian*	3 3 5
Italian Greyhound	*"*	2 2 3
2 Veneti	*"*	3 2 2
Donostia	*Spanish*	4 3 3
Salt Yard	*"*	3 2 2
Relais de Venise	*Steaks & grills*	3 2 3
The Gate	*Vegetarian*	3 3 3
Homeslice	*Pizza*	4 3 3
Oka	*Pan-Asian*	3 3 2
Foley's	*Thai*	3 4 3

£40+

The Wallace	*French*	2 2 5
Lina Stores	*Italian*	4 3 3
MEATLiquor	*Burgers, etc*	4 2 2
Patty and Bun	*"*	3 2 2
Golden Hind	*Fish & chips*	3 2 2
Pizzeria Mozza	*Pizza*	4 2 3
Santa Maria	*"*	3 3 3
Reubens	*Kosher*	2 2 2
Delamina	*Middle Eastern*	4 3 3
Hankies Marble Arch	*Indian*	3 2 2
Roti Chai	*"*	3 3 2
Sagar	*"*	3 2 2
Bone Daddies	*Japanese*	3 3 3
Laksamania	*Malaysian*	3 3 2

£35+

Cin Cin	*Italian*	3 4 4
Flat Iron Marylebone	*Steaks & grills*	3 4 3
Tommi's Burger Joint	*Burgers, etc*	3 3 2
Ragam	*Indian*	4 2 2
CoCoRo	*Japanese*	4 3 2

Bao Fitzrovia	*Taiwanese*	3 4 4

£25+

Kiss the Hippo	*Sandwiches, cakes, etc*	3 3 2

£15+

Icco Pizza	*Italian*	3 3 2
Kaffeine (Great Titchfield Street)	*Sandwiches, cakes, etc*	2 5 3
Marugame Udon	*Japanese*	4 3 2

£10+

Boxcar Baker & Deli	*Sandwiches, cakes, etc*	3 3 3

BELGRAVIA, PIMLICO, VICTORIA & WESTMINSTER (SW1, EXCEPT ST JAMES'S)

£240+

The Aubrey	*Japanese*	3 4 3

£180+

Nusr-Et Steakhouse	*Steaks & grills*	1 1 1

£170+

Marcus, The Berkeley	*British, Modern*	3 3 3
Muse	*"*	5 4 4

£150+

Dinner	*British, Traditional*	2 2 1

£140+

Pétrus	*French*	2 2 1

£130+

The Lanesborough Grill	*British, Modern*	- - -
The Collins Room	*Afternoon tea*	3 3 4

£120+

Imperial Treasure	*Chinese*	4 4 2

£110+

Goring Dining Rm	*British, Traditional*	3 3 4
Kerridge's Fish & Chips	*Fish & seafood*	3 3 5
Santini	*Italian*	2 3 3
Ekstedt at The Yard	*Scandinavian*	4 4 4
A Wong	*Chinese*	5 5 3
Hunan	*"*	4 2 1

£100+

Fallow St James's	*British, Modern*	4 4 4
Crystal Moon Lounge	*Afternoon tea*	3 4 4

£90+

The Pem	*British, Modern*	4 4 2
Chucs	*Italian*	2 2 3
Zafferano	*"*	4 3 3
Al Mare	*Mediterranean*	3 3 3
M Restaurant	*Steaks & grills*	2 2 3
Cedric Grolet	*Sandwiches, cakes, etc*	3 4 4

£80+

Ganymede	*British, Modern*	4 4 3
Hans' Bar & Grill	*"*	3 3 3
The Orange	*"*	2 3 3
Olivomare	*Fish & seafood*	3 3 2
Harrods Dining Hall	*International*	3 3 4
Enoteca Turi	*Italian*	3 5 3
Olivo	*"*	3 4 2
Olivocarne	*"*	3 3 2
Sale e Pepe	*"*	3 5 3
Roof Garden	*Scandinavian*	3 3 5
Boisdale of Belgravia	*Scottish*	2 2 3

	Amaya	*Indian*	5 3 4
	Quilon	*Indian, Southern*	5 4 2
	Sachi at Pantechnicon	*Japanese*	– – –
£70+	Alfred Tennyson	*British, Modern*	2 2 3
	Blue Boar Pub	"	3 2 2
	Daylesford Organic	"	2 2 2
	The Ivy Victoria	"	2 2 3
	Lorne	"	5 5 3
	Thomas Cubitt	"	2 2 3
	La Poule au Pot	*French*	3 4 5
	Harrods Social	*International*	3 3 3
	Caraffini	*Italian*	3 4 3
	Signor Sassi	"	3 3 3
	Eldr at Pantechnicon	*Scandinavian*	3 3 4
	Burger & Lobster	*Burgers, etc*	3 3 3
	Oliveto	*Pizza*	3 2 2
	Ottolenghi	*Middle Eastern*	4 3 2
	The Cinnamon Club	*Indian*	4 3 4
	Kahani	"	4 4 3
£60+	Granger & Co	*Australian*	2 2 2
	Colbert	*French*	2 3 3
	Motcombs	*International*	2 3 4
	Tozi	*Italian*	3 2 3
	Ibérica, Zig Zag Building	*Spanish*	2 2 2
	Kazan	*Turkish*	3 3 2
	Ken Lo's Memories	*Chinese*	3 3 2
	Sticks'n'Sushi	*Japanese*	3 2 2
	Salloos	*Pakistani*	3 3 2
£50+	Holy Carrot	*Vegan*	3 4 4
	The Jones Family Kitchen	*British, Modern*	4 4 4
	Gustoso	*Italian*	3 2 2
	Wulf & Lamb	*Vegetarian*	3 2 2
	Seafresh	*Fish & chips*	3 3 2
	Cyprus Mangal	*Turkish*	3 2 2
	Mathura	*Indian*	3 2 2
£40+	Vincent Rooms	*British, Modern*	3 2 3
	Chez Antoinette	*French*	3 4 3
	Grumbles	*International*	3 4 3
	Goya	*Spanish*	3 3 2
	Sagar	*Indian*	3 2 2
	Bone Daddies, Nova	*Japanese*	3 3 3
£35+	Kanada-Ya	*Japanese*	4 2 2
	Taro	"	3 3 2
£25+	Bleecker Burger	*Burgers, etc*	4 2 2
	Aloo Tama	*Indian*	4 4 3
£20+	Café Kitsuné at Pantechnicon	*Japanese*	3 3 4
£10+	Regency Cafe	*British, Traditional*	3 3 5

WEST

CHELSEA, SOUTH KENSINGTON, KENSINGTON, EARL'S COURT & FULHAM (SW3, SW5, SW6, SW7, SW10 & W8)

£210+	Gordon Ramsay	*French*	3 3 2
£190+	The Five Fields	*British, Modern*	5 5 3
	Bibendum	*French*	4 3 4
£170+	Le Petit Beefbar	*Steaks & grills*	– – –
£110+	Medlar	*British, Modern*	4 4 3
	Wild Tavern	*Italian*	2 3 3
£100+	Elystan Street	*British, Modern*	3 2 3
	Launceston Place	"	4 3 3
	No. Fifty Cheyne	"	2 3 5
	Min Jiang	*Chinese*	4 3 5
	Dinings	*Japanese*	5 4 2
	Yashin Ocean House	"	4 3 3
	Zuma	"	4 3 5
£90+	Bluebird	*British, Modern*	2 1 4
	Clarke's	"	4 4 3
	Kitchen W8	"	4 3 3
	Stanley's	"	3 2 3
	28-50 South Kensington	"	2 2 2
	Restaurant, Capital Hotel	*British, Traditional*	3 4 3
	Le Colombier	*French*	2 4 4
	Chucs	*Italian*	2 2 3
	Lucio	"	3 3 2
	Scalini	"	3 4 3
	Hawksmoor Knightsbridge	*Steaks & grills*	2 2 2
£80+	Harwood Arms	*British, Modern*	3 2 3
	Bibendum Oyster Bar	*Fish & seafood*	4 3 4
	Myrtle	*Irish*	5 4 3
	Daphne's	*Italian*	2 2 3
	Manicomio Chelsea	"	2 2 3
	Cambio de Tercio	*Spanish*	5 4 4
	Bombay Brasserie	*Indian*	3 3 3
	Akira at Japan House	*Japanese*	3 3 2
	Koji	"	3 3 4
£70+	Big Easy	*American*	2 2 3
	Daylesford Organic	*British, Modern*	2 2 2
	The Enterprise	"	2 3 4
	The Hunter's Moon	"	3 4 3
	The Ivy Chelsea Garden	"	2 2 3
	The Sea, The Sea	*Fish & seafood*	5 4 4
	Wright Brothers	"	3 2 3
	Margaux	*French*	4 4 3
	Mazi	*Greek*	4 4 3

Vardo	International	2 2 3
La Famiglia	Italian	2 2 4
Il Portico	"	3 3 3
Chicama	Peruvian	3 3 3
Alexandrie	Egyptian	3 3 3
Good Earth	Chinese	3 3 2
Chisou	Japanese	3 2 2
Huo	Pan-Asian	3 3 3
The Ivy Asia	"	2 3 4
Patara	Thai	3 3 2

£60+	The Abingdon	British, Modern	3 3 3
	Brinkley's	"	2 2 3
	Brook House	"	3 3 3
	The Cadogan Arms	"	2 2 3
	FENN	"	5 4 3
	Rabbit	"	3 2 2
	The Shed	"	3 4 4
	Maggie Jones's	British, Traditional	3 4 5
	Suzi Tros	Greek	3 3 3
	Cicchetti Knightsbridge	Italian	3 3 3
	Frantoio	"	2 4 4
	Ziani's	"	3 3 3
	Pascor	Mediterranean	- - -
	Ognisko Restaurant	Polish	3 4 5
	Tapas Brindisa	Spanish	3 2 2
	Tendido Cero	"	4 4 4
	Macellaio RC	Steaks & grills	2 2 3
	Maroush	Lebanese	3 2 2
	Royal China	Chinese	3 1 2
	Romulo Café	Filipino	3 4 3
	Kutir	Indian	5 4 4
	Masala Zone	"	3 3 4
	Zaika of Kensington	"	3 4 4
	Flesh and Buns	Japanese	3 4 3
	Sticks'n'Sushi	"	3 2 2
	Zheng	Malaysian	3 3 2

£50+	West 4th	Canadian	3 2 2
	The Fox and Pheasant	British, Modern	3 2 4
	Manuka Kitchen	"	3 3 3
	VQ	"	2 2 3
	The Scarsdale	International	3 3 5
	Chelsea Cellar	Italian	3 4 4
	Made in Italy	"	3 2 2
	Nuovi Sapori	"	3 4 3
	Riccardo's	"	3 4 3
	San Pietro	"	3 2 3
	The Atlas	Mediterranean	3 2 3
	Daquise	Polish	2 2 3
	Cocotte	Chicken	3 4 3
	Dishoom	Indian	4 4 4
	Flora Indica	"	3 2 3
	Noor Jahan	"	4 4 2
	Pure Indian Cooking	"	3 4 3
	Oka	Japanese	3 3 2
	Shoryu Ramen	"	3 3 2
	Sukho Fine Thai Cuisine	Thai	4 5 2

£40+	Churchill Arms	British, Traditional	3 2 3
	Los Mochis	Fusion	3 3 4
	Aglio e Olio	Italian	3 2 2
	Da Mario	"	2 3 3
	Haché	Steaks & grills	4 3 3
	Street Burger	Burgers, etc	2 2 2
	Fishers	Fish & chips	3 3 3
	Cinquecento	Pizza	2 2 3
	Rocca	"	3 3 3
	Santa Maria	"	3 3 3
	Ceru	Middle Eastern	3 2 2
	Best Mangal	Turkish	4 4 2
	Chakra	Indian	3 2 3
	Thali	"	3 3 3
	Addie's Thai Café	Thai	3 2 2
	Mien Tay	Vietnamese	3 3 2

£35+	Phat Phuc	Vietnamese	4 2 3

£25+	Big Fernand	Burgers, etc	4 4 2

NOTTING HILL, HOLLAND PARK, BAYSWATER, NORTH KENSINGTON & MAIDA VALE (W2, W9, W10, W11)

£230+	The Ledbury	British, Modern	4 5 4
£220+	Core by Clare Smyth	British, Modern	5 5 4
£110+	Caractère	Mediterranean	4 5 4
£100+	104 Restaurant	British, Modern	4 4 4
£90+	Julie's	British, Modern	2 3 4
	Chucs Westbourne Grove	Italian	2 2 3
	Sumi	Japanese	4 5 4
£80+	The Princess Royal	British, Modern	3 3 3
	Six Portland Road	"	3 4 2
	La Brasseria	Italian	3 3 3
£70+	Sunday in Brooklyn	American	3 3 4
	Daylesford Organic	British, Modern	2 2 2
	Gold	"	2 2 4
	London Shell Co.	Fish & seafood	4 4 4
	The Summerhouse	"	3 3 5
	The Cow	Irish	3 2 3
	Assaggi	Italian	3 4 3
	Osteria Basilico	"	3 3 3
	Portobello	"	3 3 3
	Ottolenghi	Mediterranean	4 3 2
	Farmacy	Vegetarian	4 3 4
	E&O	Pan-Asian	4 3 4
	Uli	"	3 4 4
£60+	Granger & Co	Australian	2 2 2
	The Hero of Maida	British, Modern	3 3 2
	The Ladbroke Arms	"	3 2 4
	The Pelican	"	3 3 3

7 Saints	"	3 4 4
Buvette	French	2 2 3
Mediterraneo	Italian	3 2 3
The Oak W2	"	3 2 4
Maroush	Lebanese	3 2 2
Four Seasons	Chinese	4 1 1
Mandarin Kitchen	"	4 3 2
Bombay Palace	Indian	5 4 3
Masala Zone	"	3 3 4

£50+

Fiend	British, Modern	5 4 4
Orasay	"	5 4 4
The Cheese Barge	British, Traditional	2 3 3
Hereford Road	"	4 4 3
Cepages	French	4 3 4
Haya	Mediterranean	3 4 3
Pizza East Portobello	Pizza	3 3 3
Cocotte	Chicken	3 4 3
Pearl Liang	Chinese	3 3 3
Noor Jahan	Indian	4 4 2
Maguro	Japanese	3 2 2
Sushi Murasaki	"	4 4 2

£40+

Taqueria	Mexican	4 4 3
The Frontline Club	British, Modern	- - -
The Walmer Castle	Scottish	- - -
MEATliquor	Burgers, etc	4 2 2
Patty and Bun Portobello	"	3 2 2
Cinquecento	Pizza	2 2 3
Ceru	Middle Eastern	3 2 2
Fez Mangal	Turkish	4 4 2
Gold Mine	Chinese	3 2 2
Durbar	Indian	3 3 2

£35+

Dhaba@49	Indian	3 3 2
Eat Tokyo	Japanese	3 2 1

£30+

Tab X Tab	International	4 4 3

£25+

Tavernaki	Greek	3 2 2
Normah's	Malaysian	4 3 2

£20+

Books for Cooks	International	3 4 4

HAMMERSMITH, SHEPHERD'S BUSH, OLYMPIA, CHISWICK, BRENTFORD & EALING (W4, W5, W6, W12, W13, W14, TW8)

£280+	Endo at The Rotunda	Japanese	5 5 5
£130+	The River Café	Italian	3 2 3
£100+	La Trompette	French	4 3 2
£80+	Villa Di Geggiano	Italian	3 4 4
£70+	Sams Riverside	British, Modern	4 4 5

The Silver Birch	"	3 4 3
Le Vacherin	French	4 4 3
Shikumen, Dorsett Hotel	Chinese	4 2 3

£60+

The Anglesea Arms	British, Modern	4 4 4
The Broadcaster	"	3 3 3
City Barge	"	2 2 3
The Duke of Sussex	"	3 3 3
High Road Brasserie	"	2 2 3
Rock & Rose	"	- - -
Vinoteca	"	2 2 2
Brasserie Blanc	French	2 2 2
Annie's	International	3 3 4
L'Amorosa	Italian	4 4 4
Cibo	"	4 4 3
The Oak W12	"	3 2 4
Pentolina	"	4 4 4
The Swan	Mediterranean	3 4 4

£50+

Brackenbury Wine Rooms	British, Modern	2 3 3
The Crabtree	"	3 3 4
The Havelock Tavern	"	3 2 4
The Princess Victoria	"	3 3 3
Le Petit Citron	French	3 3 3
Giulia	Italian	3 3 2
The Carpenter's Arms	Mediterranean	3 3 3
Salt Yard	Spanish	3 2 2
The Gate	Vegetarian	3 3 3
The Bird in Hand	Pizza	4 4 4
Homeslice	"	4 3 3
Zia Lucia	"	4 2 2
The Hampshire	Indian	3 4 3
Indian Zing	"	4 3 3
Potli	"	4 3 3

£40+

222 Veggie Vegan	Vegan	3 3 2
Dear Grace	British, Modern	- - -
Kindred	"	3 3 3
Patty and Bun	Burgers, etc	3 2 2
Oro Di Napoli	Pizza	3 4 2
Santa Maria	"	3 3 3
Angie's Little Food Shop	Sandwiches, cakes, etc	2 4 2
Best Mangal	Turkish	4 4 2
North China	Chinese	4 3 3
Copper Chimney	Indian	3 3 3
Patri	"	3 3 2
Rangrez	"	3 3 3
Republic	"	4 4 3
Sagar	"	3 2 2
Hare & Tortoise	Pan-Asian	3 3 2
101 Thai Kitchen	Thai	3 2 2
Saigon Saigon	Vietnamese	2 3 2

£35+

Base Face Pizza	Pizza	3 4 3
Chateau	Lebanese	3 4 2
Shilpa	Indian, Southern	3 2 2
Eat Tokyo	Japanese	3 2 1
Sushi Bar Makoto	"	4 3 1
Tosa	"	3 4 2

	Poppy's Thai Eatery 3	*Thai*	3 2 4

£30+	Avanti	*Mediterranean*	3 3 2
	Persian Palace	*Persian*	3 4 2
	Ta Ke Sushi	*Japanese*	4 3 2
£25+	Bleecker Burger	*Burgers, etc*	4 2 2
	Tamp Coffee	*Sandwiches, cakes, etc*	3 4 3

	Ngon	*Vietnamese*	3 2 2
£20+	Rhythm & Brews	*Sandwiches, cakes, etc*	3 3 4
	Khun Pakin Thai	*Thai*	3 3 3
£15+	The Elder Press Café	*British, Modern*	3 2 3
£5+	Mr Falafel	*Middle Eastern*	5 4 2

NORTH

HAMPSTEAD, WEST HAMPSTEAD, ST JOHN'S WOOD, REGENT'S PARK, KILBURN & CAMDEN TOWN (NW POSTCODES)

£170+	PLU	*French*	5 4 4
£90+	Chucs	*Italian*	2 2 3
	Tish	*Kosher*	3 3 4
£80+	Booking Office 1869	*British, Modern*	3 3 5
	Landmark (Winter Gdn)	"	2 3 5
	Odette's	"	3 2 2
	Lume	*Italian*	3 3 2
	Carmel	*Mediterranean*	5 4 4
£70+	Searcys St Pancras Grand	*British, Modern*	2 3 4
	Holly Bush	*British, Traditional*	2 2 4
	L'Aventure	*French*	4 4 4
	Michael Nadra	"	3 3 2
	Oslo Court	"	3 5 5
	Bull & Last	*International*	3 3 3
	La Collina	*Italian*	3 2 3
	Magenta	"	3 3 3
	Morso	"	3 3 2
	Villa Bianca	"	2 2 3
	Good Earth	*Chinese*	3 3 2
	Kaifeng	"	3 3 2
	Patara	*Thai*	3 3 2
£60+	Bradley's	*British, Modern*	2 2 2
	The Clifton	"	3 4 4
	Ham	"	4 4 3
	The Ivy Café	"	1 2 2
	Parlour Kensal	"	4 3 4
	The Wells Tavern	"	3 4 3
	Lemonia	*Greek*	2 3 3
	Soutine	*International*	2 4 4
	Anima e Cuore	*Italian*	4 2 2
	The Rising Sun	"	3 4 2
	L'Antica Pizzeria da Michele	*Pizza*	5 3 2
	Cinder	*BBQ*	2 2 2
	Chameleon	*Israeli*	3 3 4
	Maroush Park Royal	*Lebanese*	3 2 2
	Skewd Kitchen	*Turkish*	3 3 3
	Phoenix Palace	*Chinese*	3 2 2

	Masala Zone	*Indian*	3 3 4
£50+	The Wet Fish Café	*British, Modern*	3 3 3
	The Farrier	*British, Traditional*	3 2 4
	Lure	*Fish & seafood*	3 2 3
	Greenberry Café	*Fusion*	3 3 4
	L'Artista	*Italian*	2 4 3
	Calici	"	3 2 2
	Quartieri	"	3 3 3
	28 Church Row	*Spanish*	4 4 3
	Mildreds	*Vegetarian*	3 3 3
	Poppies Camden	*Fish & chips*	3 2 2
	The Sea Shell	"	3 3 2
	Zia Lucia	*Pizza*	4 2 2
	Cocotte	*Chicken*	3 4 3
	Crocker's Folly	*Lebanese*	4 3 4
	Bonoo	*Indian*	3 3 3
	Saravanaa Bhavan	"	3 3 2
	Jin Kichi	*Japanese*	5 5 3
	Oka	"	3 3 2
	Singapore Garden	*Malaysian*	4 2 2
£40+	Rudy's Vegan Diner	*Vegan*	3 3 2
	Authentique Epicerie & Bar	*French*	3 3 3
	The Spaniard's Inn	*International*	2 2 4
	Giacomo's	*Italian*	3 4 2
	Haché	*Steaks & grills*	4 3 3
	Sacro Cuore	*Pizza*	4 2 2
	Green Cottage	*Chinese*	3 2 2
	Great Nepalese	*Indian*	3 4 3
	Masalchi by Atul Kochhar	"	- - -
	Sushi Masa	*Japanese*	3 3 2
	Bang Bang Oriental	*Pan-Asian*	3 2 2
£35+	Nautilus	*Fish & chips*	3 2 2
	Paradise Hampstead	*Indian*	3 5 3
	Vijay	"	4 4 1
	Asakusa	*Japanese*	4 3 2
	Eat Tokyo	"	3 2 1
£30+	Ali Baba	*Egyptian*	3 2 2
	Balady	*Middle Eastern*	4 2 1
	Three Uncles	*Chinese*	5 3 3
	Diwana Bhel-Poori House	*Indian*	3 2 1
	Ravi Shankar	"	3 2 2
	Sakonis	"	3 2 2

Anjanaas	*Indian, Southern*	3 2 2

£25+	Sam's Café	*British, Traditional*	3 3 3
	Chutneys	*Indian*	3 3 2
£20+	E Mono	*Turkish*	4 3 2
	Tofu Vegan	*Chinese*	4 3 2
	Roti King	*Malaysian*	5 2 3
£15+	Icco Pizza	*Pizza*	3 3 2
£10+	Ginger & White Hampstead	*Sandwiches, cakes, etc*	3 3 3

HOXTON, ISLINGTON, HIGHGATE, CROUCH END, STOKE NEWINGTON, FINSBURY PARK, MUSWELL HILL & FINCHLEY

£120+	Parrillan	*Spanish*	3 3 3
£90+	Hot Stone	*Japanese*	4 4 3
£80+	Coal Office	*Mediterranean*	4 3 4
	Mangal 2	*Turkish*	4 4 2
£70+	Casa Pastór & Plaza Pastór	*Mexican*	3 2 2
	Hicce	*British, Modern*	3 2 3
	Perilla	"	4 4 3
	Les 2 Garcons	*French*	5 4 3
	German Gymnasium	*German*	1 2 3
	Salut	*International*	3 4 4
	Radici	*Italian*	2 2 2
	Trullo	"	3 3 3
	Ottolenghi	*Mediterranean*	4 3 2
	Barrafina	*Spanish*	5 4 4
£60+	Granger & Co	*Australian*	2 2 2
	The Bull	*British, Modern*	3 3 3
	The Clarence Tavern	"	3 4 3
	The Drapers Arms	"	3 3 3
	Frederick's	"	3 4 4
	Humble Grape	"	3 4 3
	Pig & Butcher	"	3 2 3
	The Red Lion & Sun	"	3 3 3
	Westerns Laundry	"	3 3 4
	St Johns	*British, Traditional*	3 4 5
	Prawn on the Lawn	*Fish & seafood*	5 3 2
	Jiji	*Fusion*	4 3 4
	The Orange Tree	*International*	3 3 3
	Primeur	"	3 4 3
	Osteria Tufo	*Italian*	3 4 3
	Terra Rossa	"	3 3 3
	Vinoteca	*Mediterranean*	2 2 2
	Bar Esteban	*Spanish*	3 3 3
	Camino King's Cross	"	2 3 2
	The Gatehouse	"	3 3 3
	Smokehouse Islington	*Steaks & grills*	3 3 3
£50+	Caravan King's Cross	*British, Modern*	2 2 2

The Lighterman	"	2 2 2
The Plimsoll	"	5 3 2
Porte Noire	"	- - -
Rotunda	"	2 3 3
12:51 by chef James Cochran	"	3 2 3
Kipferl	*East & C. European*	3 3 3
Lyon's	*Fish & seafood*	4 4 3
Bellanger	*French*	2 2 3
Table Du Marche	*French*	3 3 2
Kalimera	*Greek*	4 4 3
Banners	*International*	2 3 3
FKABAM (Black Axe Mangal)	"	4 3 3
The Flask	"	2 3 4
La Fromagerie	"	3 2 2
Citro	*Italian*	4 3 2
500	"	3 4 2
La Lluna	*Spanish*	3 3 2
Vermuteria	"	- - -
Mildreds	*Vegetarian*	3 3 3
Toff's	*Fish & chips*	4 3 2
Zia Lucia	*Pizza*	4 2 2
Cocotte	*Chicken*	3 4 3
Arabica KX	*Middle Eastern*	3 4 2
Kilis Kitchen	*Turkish*	3 3 3
Kaki	*Chinese*	3 3 2
Dishoom	*Indian*	4 4 4
Hoppers	"	4 3 3
Sushi on Jones	*Japanese*	- - -
Supawan	*Thai*	5 4 3

£40+	Rudy's Vegan Diner	*Vegan*	3 3 2
	Chriskitch	*British, Modern*	3 3 3
	Frank's Canteen	"	3 4 3
	Granary Square Brasserie	"	2 2 3
	Schnitzel Forever	*East & C. European*	3 2 2
	Caravel	*French*	3 3 4
	Le Sacré-Coeur	"	3 3 2
	Attimi	*Italian*	3 3 3
	Lina Stores	"	4 3 3
	Noci	"	2 2 3
	Via Emilia	"	3 3 2
	Escocesa	*Spanish*	4 3 3
	MEATliquor Shoreditch	*Burgers, etc*	4 2 2
	Street Burger	"	2 2 2
	Olympus Fish	*Fish & chips*	4 4 2
	Sacro Cuore	*Pizza*	4 2 2
	Santa Maria	"	3 3 3
	Sweet Thursday	"	3 3 2
	Yard Sale Pizza	"	4 4 2
	Chuku's	*West African*	4 4 3
	Gallipoli Again	*Turkish*	3 4 4
	Gem	"	4 4 3
	Sumak	"	3 4 2
	Jashan	*Indian*	3 2 2
	Zaffrani	"	2 2 2
	Rasa	*Indian, Southern*	5 4 3
	Sambal Shiok	*Malaysian*	3 2 2
	Farang	*Thai*	4 4 3
	Mien Tay	*Vietnamese*	3 3 2

£35+			
Two Brothers	Fish & seafood	3 2 2
Le Mercury	French	2 2 2
Miscusi	Italian	2 2 2
Pizzeria Pappagone	"	3 3 3
Skal Nordic Dining	Scandinavian	4 4 3
Flat Iron	Steaks & grills	3 4 3
The Dusty Knuckle	Sandwiches, cakes, etc	4 2 3
Xi'an Impression	Chinese	3 2 1
Indian Rasoi	Indian	3 3 2
Shahi Pakwaan	"	3 3 2
Kanada-Ya	Japanese	4 2 2
Taro	"	3 3 2
Bund	Pan-Asian	3 3 3
Cafe Bao	Taiwanese	3 4 4

£30+			
Che Cosa	Italian	3 3 2
Afghan Kitchen	Afghani	3 2 2
Delhi Grill	Indian	3 2 3
Viet Garden	Vietnamese	3 3 2

£25+			
Big Jo Bakery	British, Modern	3 3 3
Normans Cafe	"	4 4 4

£20+			
Tofu Vegan	Chinese	4 3 2
Sushi Show	Japanese	3 3 2
Hawker's Kitchen	Malaysian	5 3 2

SOUTH

SOUTH BANK (SE1)

£270+			
Story	British, Modern	3 3 3

£140+			
Trivet	British, Modern	3 3 3

£120+			
Turnips	International	4 3 3
Parrillan	Spanish	3 3 3
Hannah	Japanese	3 3 2

£110+			
Aqua Shard	British, Modern	2 2 3
Hutong, The Shard	Chinese	2 2 3

£100+			
Oblix	British, Modern	2 2 4
Oxo Tower, Restaurant	"	1 1 1

£90+			
Oxo Tower, Brasserie	British, Modern	1 1 2
TING	"	2 3 4
Le Pont de la Tour	French	2 2 2
Sollip	"	5 4 3
Hawksmoor	Steaks & grills	2 2 2

£80+			
Butlers Wharf Chop House	British, Traditional	2 2 3
Seabird	Fish & seafood	3 2 5
La Barca	Italian	3 3 3

£70+			
Elliot's	British, Modern	3 2 3
The Garrison	"	3 3 3
The Ivy Tower Bridge	"	2 2 3
Sea Containers	"	2 2 3
Skylon, South Bank Centre	"	2 2 3
The Swan at the Globe	"	2 2 4
Roast	British, Traditional	2 2 4
Applebee's Fish	Fish & seafood	3 3 3
fish!	"	3 2 3
Wright Brothers	"	3 2 3
Vivat Bacchus	International	3 3 3
Cafe Murano	Italian	2 2 2
Barrafina	Spanish	5 4 4
The Coal Shed	Steaks & grills	3 3 3

Pique Nique	Chicken	3 3 3
Rabot 1745	Caribbean	2 2 3
Mei Mei	Malaysian	3 3 2

£60+			
Santo Remedio	Mexican	3 2 2
The Anchor & Hope	British, Modern	3 3 3
40 Maltby Street	"	3 3 2
Garden Cafe	"	4 3 3
Vinoteca Borough	"	2 2 2
Brasserie Blanc	French	2 2 2
Casse-Croute	"	4 4 4
Macellaio RC	Italian	2 2 3
José	Spanish	4 3 4
Pizarro	"	4 4 3
Tapas Brindisa	"	3 2 2
O'ver	Pizza	3 2 2
Paladar	South American	4 4 5
Antillean	Caribbean	3 2 3
Bala Baya	Middle Eastern	3 3 3
Sticky Mango	Pan-Asian	3 2 2

£50+			
El Pastór	Mexican	3 2 3
Bermondsey Larder	British, Modern	4 4 3
Boiler & Co	"	5 4 3
Caravan Bankside	"	2 2 2
Lupins	"	4 4 3
BOB's Lobster	Fish & seafood	3 4 2
Tavolino	Italian	2 1 3
Bar Douro	Portuguese	4 4 4
Casa do Frango	"	4 2 3
Andanza	Spanish	4 3 3
Mar I Terra	"	4 4 3
Salt Yard	"	3 2 2
Mallow	Vegetarian	4 2 3
Arabica Bar and Kitchen	Lebanese	3 4 2
Gunpowder	Indian	4 3 3
Champor-Champor	Thai	4 3 3

£40+			
Flour & Grape	Italian	3 3 3
Legare	"	4 4 3
Mercato Metropolitano	"	3 2 5

Padella	"	433
Meson don Felipe	*Spanish*	334
Patty and Bun	*Burgers, etc*	322
Tas Pide	*Turkish*	333
Kin and Deum	*Thai*	423

£35+			
	Tacos Padre	*Mexican*	334
	Flat Iron Clink Street	*Steaks & grills*	343
	Baozi Inn	*Chinese*	322
	Bao Borough	*Taiwanese*	344

£10+			
	Kappacasein	*Sandwiches, cakes, etc*	532

£5+			
	Monmouth Coffee Company	*Sandwiches, cakes, etc*	343

GREENWICH, LEWISHAM, DULWICH & BLACKHEATH (ALL SE POSTCODES, EXCEPT SE1)

£80+			
	Copper & Ink	*British, Modern*	433

£70+			
	Coal Rooms	*British, Modern*	433
	Llewelyn's	"	332

£60+			
	The Alma	*British, Modern*	334
	Bobo Social	"	333
	The Camberwell Arms	"	444
	The Crooked Well	"	333
	Franklins	"	333
	Levan	"	332
	Walter's	"	334
	Toulouse Lautrec	*French*	343
	Peckham Bazaar	*Greek*	433
	Forza Wine	*Italian*	345
	Manuel's	"	453
	Kudu	*South African*	444
	Sticks'n'Sushi	*Japanese*	322
	Yama Momo	"	322

£50+			
	The Guildford Arms	*British, Modern*	333
	Peckham Cellars	"	443
	The Perry Hill	"	344
	The Rosendale	"	333
	Sparrow	"	434
	Joanna's	*International*	334
	The Yellow House	"	343
	Artusi	*Italian*	433
	Luciano's	"	343
	Le Querce	"	432
	Dulwich Lyceum	*Mediterranean*	344
	Mamma Dough	*Pizza*	432
	Babur	*Indian*	553
	Heritage	"	333
	Kennington Tandoori	"	343
	The Begging Bowl	*Thai*	443

£40+			
	The Lordship	*British, Modern*	322
	Tila	"	- - -
	Brookmill	*International*	333

Marcella	*Italian*	343
MEATliquor ED	*Burgers, etc*	422
Street Burger	"	222
Mike's Peckham	*Pizza*	443
Rocca	"	333
Yard Sale Pizza	"	442
Kudu Grill	*South African*	444
FM Mangal	*Turkish*	332
Dragon Castle	*Chinese*	322
Everest Inn	*Indian*	322
Ganapati	"	422
Bone Daddies	*Japanese*	333
Zaibatsu	"	332

£35+			
	Olley's	*Fish & chips*	333
	500 Degrees	*Pizza*	323
	Theo's	"	332
	Taro	*Japanese*	332

£30+			
	Trattoria Raffaele	*Italian*	332
	400 Rabbits	*Pizza*	332
	Nandine	*Middle Eastern*	343
	Mr Bao	*Taiwanese*	322

£25+			
	Goddards At Greenwich	*British, Traditional*	343
	Silk Road	*Chinese*	522

£15+			
	La Chingada	*Mexican*	432
	Everest Curry King	*Sri Lankan*	432
	Marugame Udon	*Japanese*	432

BATTERSEA, BRIXTON, CLAPHAM, WANDSWORTH BARNES, PUTNEY & WIMBLEDON (ALL SW POSTCODES SOUTH OF THE RIVER)

£160+			
	Oxeye	*British, Modern*	544

£110+			
	Trinity	*British, Modern*	543

£100+			
	Chez Bruce	*British, Modern*	543

£80+			
	Black Radish	*British, Modern*	453
	Rick Stein	*Fish & seafood*	122
	Darby's	*Irish*	334

£70+			
	The Crossing	*British, Modern*	323
	Hatched	"	432
	The Pig's Head	"	333
	Wright Brothers	*Fish & seafood*	323
	Fiume	*Italian*	223
	Riva	"	342
	Knife	*Steaks & grills*	443
	Good Earth	*Chinese*	332
	Patara	*Thai*	332

£60+			
	The Laundry	*Australian*	343
	Bistro Union	*British, Modern*	342

The Black Lamb	,,	–	–	–
Brunswick House Café	,,	3	2	5
Church Road	,,	3	4	3
Humble Grape	,,	3	4	3
The Ivy Café	,,	1	2	2
Only Food and Courses	,,	–	–	–
Trinity Upstairs	,,	3	3	3
The Victoria	,,	3	3	3
Fox & Grapes	British, Traditional	3	2	2
The Plough	,,	–	–	–
Gazette	French	2	2	3
Soif	,,	3	2	2
Brinkley's Kitchen	International	2	2	3
The Light House	,,	3	3	3
Artisans of Sardinia	Italian	3	4	3
Maremma	,,	4	3	4
Numero Uno	,,	2	3	2
Osteria Antica Bologna	,,	3	3	2
Sorella	,,	4	3	2
The Fox & Hounds	Mediterranean	3	4	3
Tapas Brindisa	Spanish	3	2	2
Macellaio RC	Steaks & grills	2	2	3
Cinnamon Kitchen Battersea	Indian	3	3	3
Kibou London	Japanese	2	2	3
Sticks'n'Sushi	,,	3	2	2

£50+

The Brown Dog	British, Modern	3	2	3
Coppa Club Putney	,,	2	3	4
Hood	,,	4	4	2
London Stock	,,	3	4	3
Olympic Studios	,,	2	2	3
The Telegraph	,,	3	4	4
24 The Oval	,,	3	4	3
Canton Arms	British, Traditional	3	3	4
Smoke & Salt	,,	5	4	3
Augustine Kitchen	French	4	4	3
Cent Anni	Italian	3	2	2
Made in Italy	,,	3	2	2
Pizza Metro	,,	3	2	2
Boqueria	Spanish	3	3	2
Little Taperia	,,	3	3	3
Naughty Piglets	Steaks & grills	5	4	4
Mamma Dough	Pizza	4	3	2
Zia Lucia	,,	4	2	2
Santa Maria del Sur	Argentinian	3	3	2
Le Bab	Middle Eastern	3	2	2
Chook Chook	Indian	4	3	3
Hashi	Japanese	3	3	2
Oka	,,	3	3	2
Takahashi	,,	5	5	3
Tsunami	,,	4	3	2

£40+

The Rushmere	British, Modern	–	–	–
Danclair's	International	–	–	–
Rosmarino	Italian	3	4	4
Soffice London	,,	3	4	3
Black Bear Burger	Burgers, etc	4	3	2
Haché	,,	4	3	3
MEATliquor	,,	4	2	2

Patty and Bun	,,	3	2	2
Bravi Ragazzi	Pizza	4	2	2
Pizza da Valter	,,	4	3	3
Yard Sale Pizza	,,	4	4	2
Orange Pekoe	Sandwiches, cakes, etc	3	3	4
Chishuru	West African	3	3	2
Meza Trinity Road	Lebanese	3	3	3
The Red Duck	Chinese	4	2	2
Black Salt	Indian	5	3	2
Kashmir	,,	3	3	2
Ma Goa	,,	3	3	3
Bone Daddies	Japanese	3	3	3
Tomoe	,,	4	4	2
Hare & Tortoise	Pan-Asian	3	3	2
Kaosarn	Thai	3	3	3
Mien Tay	Vietnamese	3	3	2

£35+

BabaBoom	Middle Eastern	3	3	2
Indian Moment	Indian	3	2	2
Indian Room	,,	4	4	3
Taro	Japanese	3	3	2
Awesome Thai	Thai	3	3	2
Daddy Bao	Taiwanese	4	3	3

£30+

Amrutha	Vegan	4	5	2
Unwined	Mediterranean	3	4	2
Three Uncles	Chinese	5	3	3
Indian Ocean	Indian	3	3	3
Munal Tandoori	,,	3	4	2
Sushi Revolution	Japanese	3	3	2
Cher Thai	Thai	4	4	3

£25+

Ela & Dhani	Indian	4	5	3
Mirch Masala	Pakistani	4	2	2

£20+

Dropshot Coffee	British, Modern	3	4	4
Milk	Sandwiches, cakes, etc	3	2	3
Roti King	Malaysian	5	2	3

£15+

Joe Public	Pizza	3	3	2

OUTER WESTERN SUBURBS KEW, RICHMOND, TWICKENHAM, TEDDINGTON

£120+

Petersham Nurseries Cafe	British, Modern	2	3	5

£80+

The Dysart Petersham	British, Modern	4	4	4
The Petersham Restaurant	,,	2	2	3
Steven Edwards	,,	4	2	4

£70+

Bacco	Italian	3	3	2

£60+

The Fat Badger	British, Modern	3	2	2
The Ivy Café	,,	1	2	2
Six Restaurant	British, Traditional	3	3	3
Petit Ma Cuisine	French	3	3	3
A Cena	Italian	3	3	3
Tapas Brindisa Richmond	Spanish	3	2	2

Rock & Rose	Pan-Asian	- - -

£50+	Black Dog Beer House	British, Modern	443
	Rye by the Water	"	322
	Le Salon Privé	French	333
	Four Regions	Chinese	322

£40+	Newens	Afternoon tea	333
	Dastaan	Indian	543

£25+	Kiss the Hippo	Sandwiches, cakes, etc	332

EAST

SMITHFIELD & FARRINGDON (EC1)

£200+	The Clove Club	British, Modern	443
£150+	The Drunken Butler	French	344
£130+	Club Gascon	French	433
£100+	Anglo	British, Modern	542
£90+	The Quality Chop House	British, Traditional	444
	Luca	Italian	434
£80+	St John Smithfield	British, Traditional	443
	Smiths (Top Floor)	Steaks & grills	233
£70+	The Jugged Hare	British, Modern	323
	Daffodil Mulligan	Irish	343
	Moro	Spanish	332
£60+	Granger & Co	Australian	222
	The Coach	British, Modern	233
	Sessions Arts Club	"	335
	Vinoteca	"	222
	Bleeding Heart Bistro	French	334
	Apulia	Italian	322
	Macellaio RC	"	223
	Ibérica	Spanish	222
	Berber & Q Shawarma Bar	Middle Eastern	544
£50+	Tendril	Vegan	433
	Caravan	British, Modern	222
	The Clerk & Well	"	- - -
	Café du Marché	French	345
	Santore	Italian	322
	Fare	Mediterranean	323
	Morito	Spanish	433
	The Gate	Vegetarian	333
	Homeslice by Symplicity	Pizza	433
	Le Bab	Middle Eastern	322
£40+	Stem & Glory	Vegan	332
	Taqueria	Mexican	443
	Fish Central	Fish & seafood	342
	Trattoria Brutto	Italian	345
	Pastan	"	343
	The Eagle	Mediterranean	334
	Black Bear Burger	Burgers, etc	432

	Street Burger	"	222
	The Sichuan	Chinese	432
	Bone Daddies, The Bower	Japanese	333
	Pham Sushi	"	333
	Cây Tre	Vietnamese	332
£30+	Balady	Middle Eastern	421
£15+	Prufrock Coffee	Sandwiches, cakes, etc	322
£10+	Daddy Donkey	Mexican	432

THE CITY (EC2, EC3, EC4)

£140+	La Dame de Pic	French	443
£120+	Nobu Shoreditch	Japanese	- - -
£110+	Angler, South Place Hotel	Fish & seafood	334
	Coya	Peruvian	333
	Sushisamba	Japanese	223
£100+	City Social	British, Modern	334
	Fenchurch, Sky Garden	"	334
	Aviary	Steaks & grills	234
	Lutyens Grill, The Ned	"	324
	Yauatcha City	Chinese	322
£90+	Duck & Waffle	British, Modern	223
	14 Hills	"	224
	Coq d'Argent	French	223
	Goodman City	Steaks & grills	332
	Hawksmoor Guildhall	"	222
	M Restaurant	"	223
£80+	Bread Street Kitchen	British, Modern	233
	Darwin Brasserie	"	334
	Helix	"	335
	Sweetings	Fish & seafood	324
	Bob Bob Ricard City	French	245
	Cecconi's, The Ned	International	224
	Revolve	"	- - -
	Manicomio City	Italian	223
£70+	The Ivy City Garden	British, Modern	223
	The Mercer	"	333
	1 Lombard Street	"	323
	Princess of Shoreditch	"	533

Paternoster Chop House	British, Traditional	2 4 2
Cabotte	French	3 5 4
Vivat Bacchus	International	3 3 3
Piazza Italiana	Italian	3 3 3
Bibo by Dani García	Spanish	2 2 3
Hispania	"	3 4 4
Burger & Lobster	Burgers, etc	3 3 3
Pachamama East	Peruvian	2 2 3
Oklava	Turkish	4 4 3
Brigadiers	Indian	5 4 4
The Ivy Asia	Pan-Asian	2 3 4

£60+

Maya	Mexican	– – –
Santo Remedio Café	"	3 2 2
High Timber	British, Modern	3 4 3
Humble Grape	"	3 4 3
Leroy	"	3 3 3
Vinoteca City	"	2 2 2
Brasserie Blanc	French	2 2 2
Gazette	"	2 2 3
Caravaggio	Italian	2 3 2
Gloria	"	2 3 5
Obicà	"	3 3 3
Camino Shoreditch	Spanish	2 3 2
José Pizarro	"	3 2 2
Haz	Turkish	3 3 2
Cinnamon Kitchen	Indian	3 3 3

£50+

The Anthologist	British, Modern	2 2 3
Caravan	"	2 2 2
Coppa Club Tower Bridge	"	2 3 4
VQ	"	2 2 3
Simpson's Tavern	British, Traditional	2 3 5
Eataly	Italian	2 2 3
Manteca	"	5 2 4
Osteria, Barbican Centre	"	3 2 2
Popolo	"	5 3 2
Casa do Frango	Portuguese	4 2 3
Ekte Nordic Kitchen	Scandinavian	3 3 2
Blacklock	Steaks & grills	3 4 3
Relais de Venise	"	3 2 3
temper Shoreditch	"	3 2 4
Homeslice	Pizza	4 3 3
temper City	BBQ	3 2 4
Shoryu Ramen	Japanese	3 3 2

£40+

Stem & Glory Broadgate	Vegan	3 3 2
Hithe & Seek	British, Modern	– – –
The Wine Library	International	2 2 4
Lina Stores	Italian	4 3 3
Padella Shoreditch	"	4 3 3
Haché	Burgers, etc	4 3 3
Patty and Bun	"	3 2 2
Street Burger	"	2 2 2
Ozone Coffee Roasters	Sandwiches, cakes, etc	3 4 4
Koya	Japanese	3 4 3
Hare & Tortoise	Pan-Asian	3 3 2

£35+

Flat Iron	Steaks & grills	3 4 3

£30+ Three Uncles	Chinese	5 3 3
£25+ Bleecker Burger	Burgers, etc	4 2 2
£20+ Cincinnati Chilibomb	American	3 4 2
£15+ Halo Burger	Burgers, etc	3 3 2
£5+ Rosslyn Coffee	Sandwiches, cakes, etc	5 4 3

EAST END & DOCKLANDS (ALL E POSTCODES)

£220+ Da Terra	Fusion	5 4 4
£150+ The Water House Project	British, Modern	4 3 4
£110+ Galvin La Chapelle	French	3 3 5

£90+

Brat at Climpson's Arch	British, Modern	4 3 3
Lyle's	"	5 4 3
Cornerstone	Fish & seafood	5 5 4
Goodman	Steaks & grills	3 3 2
Hawksmoor	"	2 2 2
M Restaurant	"	2 2 3
Roka	Japanese	4 3 3

£80+

Brat	British, Modern	4 3 3
Bright	"	4 4 3
Pidgin	"	4 3 2
Plateau	French	2 2 3
Cecconi's Shoreditch	Italian	2 2 4

£70+

Big Easy	American	2 2 3
Elliot's	British, Modern	3 2 3
The Ivy in the Park	"	2 2 3
The Narrow	"	2 2 3
Rochelle Canteen	"	3 4 4
Smith's Wapping	"	4 3 3
The Marksman	British, Traditional	3 3 3
Behind	Fish & seafood	5 5 4
The Melusine	"	4 3 3
The Sea, The Sea	"	5 4 4
Planque	French	3 2 4
Casa Fofó	International	5 4 3
Canto Corvino	Italian	2 2 3
Brawn	Mediterranean	– – –
Ottolenghi	"	4 3 2
Haugen	Swiss	2 2 2
Burger & Lobster	Burgers, etc	3 3 3

£60+

Allegra	British, Modern	3 3 3
The Gun	"	3 3 4
Humble Grape	"	3 4 3
Jones & Sons	"	3 3 4
Silo	"	4 4 3
St John Bread & Wine	British, Traditional	3 2 3
Goddard & Gibbs	Fish & seafood	– – –

The Boundary	*French*	– – –
Chez Elles	"	3 3 3
Galvin Bistrot & Bar	"	3 2 3
Angelina	*Fusion*	4 2 3
Six by Nico	*International*	3 3 3
Obicà	*Italian*	3 3 3
Super Tuscan	"	4 3 3
Oren	*Mediterranean*	4 3 2
Boisdale of Canary Wharf	*Scottish*	3 2 4
Ibérica	*Spanish*	2 2 2
Berber & Q	*Middle Eastern*	5 4 4
Haz	*Turkish*	3 3 2
Royal China	*Chinese*	3 1 2
Café Spice Namaste	*Indian*	5 4 4
Grand Trunk Road	"	4 4 3
Sticks'n'Sushi	*Japanese*	3 2 2
£50+ Cafe Cecilia	*British, Modern*	2 2 3
Caravan	"	2 2 2
The Culpeper	"	3 3 3
The Duke of Richmond	"	3 3 3
The Empress	"	3 3 4
Mare Street Market	"	3 2 4
P Franco	"	4 3 3
Il Bordello	*Italian*	3 2 3
Emilia's Crafted Pasta	"	3 4 3
Ombra	"	3 4 3
Morito	*Spanish*	4 3 3
Mildreds	*Vegetarian*	3 3 3
Burger & Beyond	*Burgers, etc*	4 3 2
Ark Fish	*Fish & chips*	3 3 2
Poppies	"	3 2 2
Pizza East	*Pizza*	3 3 3
Zia Lucia Aldgate	"	4 2 2
Smokestak	*BBQ*	5 3 4
Le Bab at Kraft Dalston	*Middle Eastern*	3 2 2
Lahpet	*Burmese*	3 4 3
Sichuan Folk	*Chinese*	4 3 2
Dishoom	*Indian*	4 4 4
Gunpowder	"	4 3 3
Smoking Goat	*Thai*	4 3 3
Som Saa	"	5 3 3
£40+ Hackney Coterie	*British, Modern*	3 4 3
NEST	"	4 4 3
Townsend	"	3 3 3
Provender	*French*	3 4 2
Mr Todiwala's Petiscos	*Portuguese*	4 4 3
Black Bear Burger	*Burgers, etc*	4 3 2
Patty and Bun	"	3 2 2
Yard Sale Pizza	*Pizza*	4 4 2
Ozone Coffee Roasters	*Sandwiches, cakes, etc*	3 4 4
Chick 'n' Sours	*Chicken*	4 3 3
Acme Fire Cult	*BBQ*	– – –
Andina Spitalfields	*Peruvian*	2 1 3
Bubala	*Middle Eastern*	4 4 3
Delamina East	"	4 3 3
Lucky & Joy	*Chinese*	4 3 4
Issho-Ni	*Japanese*	3 4 3
Koya Ko	"	3 4 3
Mien Tay	*Vietnamese*	3 3 2
Sông Quê	"	3 3 2
£35+ Flat Iron	*Steaks & grills*	3 4 3
Crate Brewery and Pizzeria	*Pizza*	3 2 3
The Dusty Knuckle	*Sandwiches, cakes, etc*	4 2 3
Facing Heaven	*Chinese*	– – –
Taro	*Japanese*	3 3 2
Lahore Kebab House	*Pakistani*	5 2 2
Bao Noodle Shop	*Taiwanese*	3 4 4
£30+ Alter	*Vegan*	4 3 2
Mangal 1	*Turkish*	5 3 2
Tayyabs	*Pakistani*	4 1 2
£25+ Bleecker Burger	*Burgers, etc*	4 2 2
Dumpling Shack	*Chinese*	5 3 1
Singburi Royal Thai Café	*Thai*	4 4 3
£20+ Off the Hook	*Fish & seafood*	– – –
E Pellicci	*Italian*	3 5 4
Attawa	*Indian*	3 3 2
Sushi Show	*Japanese*	3 3 2
£15+ The Duck Truck	*Burgers, etc*	5 4 2
Marugame Udon	*Japanese*	4 3 2
£10+ The Rib Man	*Burgers, etc*	4 4 –
Popeyes	*Chicken*	4 3 3
£5+ Brick Lane Beigel Bake	*Sandwiches, cakes, etc*	4 2 1

Koya

Cinnamon Kitchen

Circolo Popolare W1

Dishoom

MAP 1 – LONDON OVERVIEW

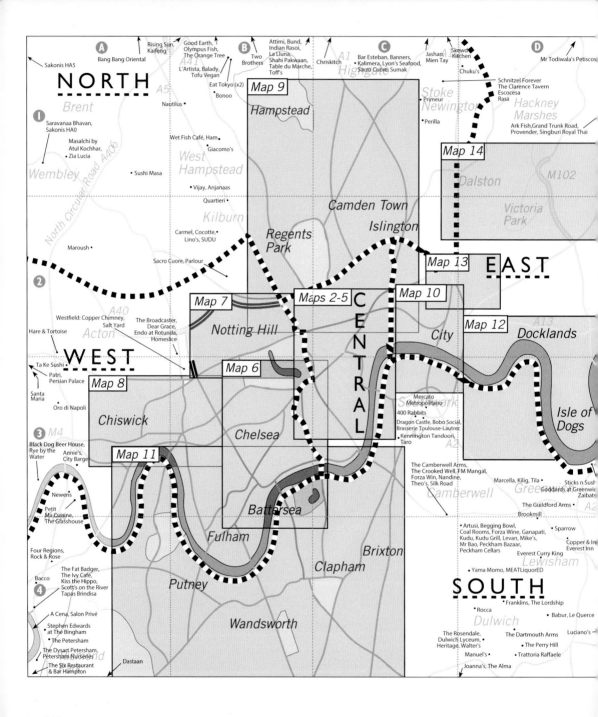

NORTH

WEST

CENTRAL

EAST

SOUTH

Brent

Wembley

Acton

Chiswick

Fulham

Putney

Wandsworth

West Hampstead

Hampstead

Kilburn

Regents Park

Notting Hill

Chelsea

Battersea

Clapham

Brixton

Camden Town

Islington

City

Southwark

Camberwell

Dulwich

Lewisham

Highgate

Stoke Newington

Dalston

Victoria Park

Hackney Marshes

Docklands

Isle of Dogs

Greenwich

Sakonis HA5

Bang Bang Oriental

Rising Sun, Kaifeng

Good Earth, Olympus Fish, The Orange Tree

L'Artista, Balady, Tofu Vegan

Eat Tokyo (x2)

Bonoo

Nautilus

Two Brothers

Attimi, Bund, Indian Rasoi, La Lluna, Shahi Pakwaan, Table du Marché, Toff's

Chriskitch

Bar Esteban, Banners, Kalimera, Lyon's Seafood, Sacro Cuore, Sumak

Jashan, Mien Tay

Skewd Kitchen

Chuku's

Mr Todiwala's Petiscos

Schnitzel Forever
The Clarence Tavern
Escocesa
Rasa

Primeur

Perilla

Ark Fish, Grand Trunk Road, Provender, Singburi Royal Thai

Saravanaa Bhavan, Sakonis HA0

Masalchi by Atul Kochhar, Zia Lucia

Wet Fish Café, Ham

Giacomo's

Vijay, Anjanaas

Quartieri

Sushi Masa

Maroush

Carmel, Cocotte, Lino's, SUDU

Sacro Cuore, Parlour

Westfield: Copper Chimney, Salt Yard

Hare & Tortoise

The Broadcaster, Dear Grace, Endo at Rotunda, Homeslice

Ta Ke Sushi

Patri, Persian Palace

Santa Maria

Oro di Napoli

Black Dog Beer House, Rye by the Water

Annie's, City Barge

Newens

Petit Ma Cuisine, The Glasshouse

Four Regions, Rock & Rose

Bacco

The Fat Badger, The Ivy Café, Kiss the Hippo, Scott's on the River
Tapas Brindisa

A Cena, Salon Privé

Stephen Edwards at The Bingham

The Petersham

The Dysart Petersham, Petersham Nurseries

The Six Restaurant & Bar Hampton

Dastaan

Mercato Metropolitano
400 Rabbits
Dragon Castle, Bobo Social, Brasserie Toulouse-Lautrec
Kennington Tandoori, Taro

The Camberwell Arms, The Crooked Well, FM Mangal, Forza Win, Nandine, Theo's, Silk Road

Marcella, Kilig, Tila

Goddards at Greenwich

Sticks n Sush

Zaibatsu

The Guildford Arms

Brookmill

Artusi, Begging Bowl, Coal Rooms, Forza Wine, Ganapati, Kudu, Kudu Grill, Levan, Mike's, Mr Bao, Peckham Bazaar, Peckham Cellars

Sparrow

Copper & Ir
Everest Inn

Everest Curry King

Yama Momo, MEATLiquorED

Rocca

Franklins, The Lordship

Babur, Le Querce

Luciano's

The Rosendale, Dulwich Lyceum, Heritage, Walter's

The Dartmouth Arms

The Perry Hill

Manuel's

Trattoria Raffaele

Joanna's, The Alma

Map 9

Map 14

Map 13

Maps 2-5

Map 10

Map 12

Map 7

Map 6

Map 8

Map 11

MAP 2 – WEST END OVERVIEW

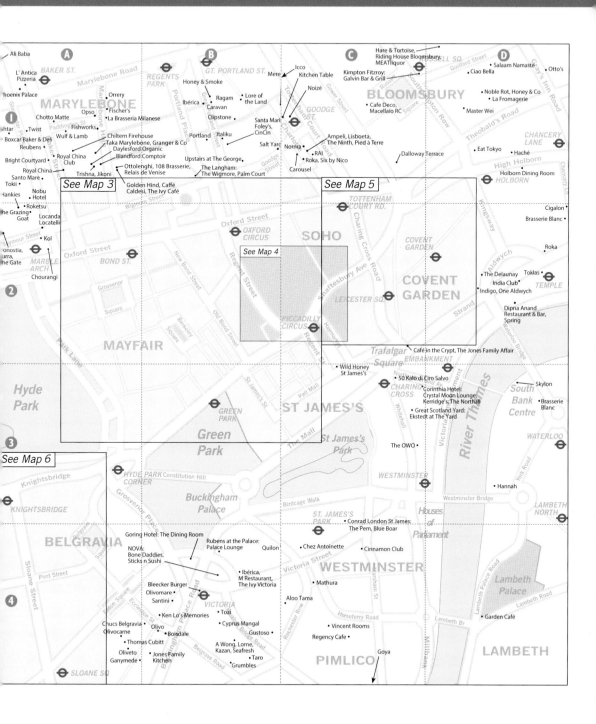

Ali Baba

L' Antica Pizzeria

Phoenix Palace

MARYLEBONE

Chotto Matte
Opso
Fischer's

Ishtar
Twist
Wulf & Lamb
Boxcar Baker & Deli
Reubens

Bright Courtyard

Santo Mare

Tokii
Hankies
Nobu Hotel
Roketsu
The Grazing Goat

Sonostia,
Hurra,
the Gate

Chourangi

A BAKER ST.

Maryebone Road

REGENTS PARK

Orrery

Ibérica

Ragam
Caravan

Clipstone

La Brasseria Milanese
Portland Place

Chiltern Firehouse
Taka Marylebone, Granger & Co
Daylesford Organic
Blandford Comptoir

Royal China Club
Royal China

Trishna, Jikoni
Ottolenghi, 108 Brasserie,
Relais de Venise

Golden Hind, Caffé
Caldesi, The Ivy Café

Locanda
Locatelli

Kol

MARBLE ARCH
Oxford Street
BOND ST.
Grosvenor Square

B GT. PORTLAND ST.

Honey & Smoke

Fischer's

Lore of the Land

Santa Maria
Foley's,
CinCin

Portland
Italiku

Salt Yard

Upstairs at The George,
The Langham:
The Wigmore, Palm Court

Icco
Mere
Kitchen Table

Noizé

GOODGE
ST.

Norma

Carousel

See Map 4

OXFORD
CIRCUS

SOHO

Regent Street

New Bond Street
Old Bond Street

PICCADILLY
CIRCUS

Shaftesbury Avenue

LEICESTER SQ.

MAYFAIR

Berkeley Square

Park Lane

**Hyde
Park**

GREEN
PARK

**Green
Park**

C Hare & Tortoise,
Riding House Bloomsbury,
MEATliquor

Kimpton Fitzroy:
Galvin Bar & Grill

Cafe Deco,
Macellaio RC

Ampeli, Lisboeta,
The Ninth, Pied à Terre

RAI
Roka, Six by Nico

BLOOMSBURY

See Map 5

TOTTENHAM
COURT RD.

Charing Cross Road

**COVENT
GARDEN**

**COVENT
GARDEN**

Dalloway Terrace

D Salaam Namaste
Ciao Bella
Otto's

Noble Rot, Honey & Co
La Fromagerie

Master Wei

**CHANCERY
LANE**

Eat Tokyo
Haché

Holborn Dining Room
HOLBORN

Cigalon

Brasserie Blanc

Roka

The Delaunay
India Club
Indigo, One Aldwych
Toklas
TEMPLE

Dipna Anand
Restaurant & Bar,
Spring

Strand

Café in the Crypt, The Jones Family Affair

Trafalgar
Square
EMBANKMENT

Wild Honey
St James's

ST JAMES'S

Pall Mall

St James's
Park

The Mall

**St James's
Park**

The OWO

50 Kalò di Ciro Salvo

**CHARING
CROSS**

Corinthia Hotel:
Crystal Moon Lounge,
Kerridge's, The Northall

Great Scotland Yard:
Eksted at The Yard

Whitehall

WESTMINSTER

**South
Bank
Centre**

Skylon

Brasserie
Blanc

WATERLOO

Hannah

River Thames

Victoria Embankment

See Map 6

Knightsbridge

KNIGHTSBRIDGE

BELGRAVIA

Sloane Street

Pont Street

Goring Hotel: The Dining Room

NOVA:
Bone Daddies,
Sticks n Sushi

Bleecker Burger
Olivomare
Santini

Chucs Belgravia
Olivocarne
Thomas Cubitt
Oliveto
Ganymede

SLOANE SQ

**HYDE PARK
CORNER**
Constitution Hill

Grosvenor Place

**Buckingham
Palace**

Rubens at the Palace:
Palace Lounge
Quilon

Ibérica,
M Restaurant,
The Ivy Victoria

Ken Lo's Memories

VICTORIA
Tozi

Cyprus Mangal
Gustoso

A Wong, Lorne,
Kazan, Seafresh
Taro
Grumbles

Olivo
Boisdale
Jones Family
Kitchen

Birdcage Walk

**ST. JAMES'S
PARK**

Chez Antoinette

Victoria Street

WESTMINSTER

Mathura

Aloo Tama

Vincent Rooms

Regency Cafe

PIMLICO

Houses
of
Parliament

Conrad London St James:
The Pem, Blue Boar

Cinnamon Club

Horseferry Road

Goya

Westminster Bridge

WESTMINSTER

**LAMBETH
NORTH**

**LAMBETH
PALACE**

Lambeth Palace Road

Garden Café

LAMBETH

Millbank

MAP 3 – MAYFAIR, ST. JAMES'S & WEST SOHO

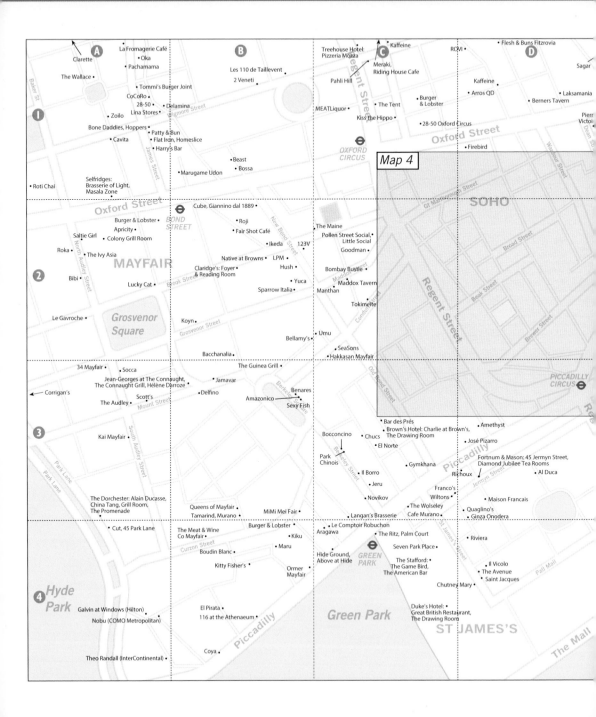

Map 4

Baker St

Clarette
La Fromagerie Café
Oka
Pachamama
The Wallace
Tommi's Burger Joint
CoCoRo
28-50
Delamina
Wigmore Street
Lina Stores
Zoilo
Bone Daddies, Hoppers
Patty & Bun
Cavita
Flat Iron, Homeslice
Harry's Bar
James Street
Beast
Marugame Udon
Bossa
Roti Chai
Selfridges:
Brasserie of Light,
Masala Zone

Les 110 de Taillevent
2 Veneti

Treehouse Hotel:
Pizzeria Mozza
Pahli Hill
MEATLiquor
Kiss the Hippo

Kaffeine
ROVI
Flesh & Buns Fitzrovia
Meraki,
Riding House Cafe
Sagar
Kaffeine
Arros QD
Burger
& Burger
& Lobster
Laksamania
Berners Tavern
The Tent
28-50 Oxford Circus
Pierr
Victoi
Firebird

OXFORD
CIRCUS

Oxford Street

Oxford Street
BOND
STREET
Cube, Giannino dal 1889
Roji
Burger & Lobster
Apricity
Fair Shot Café
Saltie Girl
Colony Grill Room
Ikeda
123V
Roka
The Ivy Asia
Native at Browns
LPM
MAYFAIR
Claridge's: Foyer
Hush
& Reading Room
Bibi
Yuca
Lucky Cat
Sparrow Italia
Manthan

The Maine
Pollen Street Social,
Little Social
Goodman
Bombay Bustle
Maddox Tavern
Tokimeite

SOHO

Regent Street

Le Gavroche
Grosvenor
Square
Koyn
Grosvenor Street
Bellamy's
Umu
Bacchanalia
SeaSons
Hakkasan Mayfair

Beak Street
Brewer Street
PICCADILLY
CIRCUS

34 Mayfair
Socca
The Guinea Grill
Jean-Georges at The Connaught,
Jamavar
The Connaught Grill, Hélène Darroze
Corrigan's
Scott's
Delfino
Benares
The Audley
Amazonico
Sexy Fish

Kai Mayfair
Bocconcino
Brown's Hotel: Charlie at Brown's,
Chucs
The Drawing Room
El Norte
Park
Chinois
Gymkhana
Il Borro
Richoux
Jeru
Franco's
Novikov
Wiltons
The Wolseley
The Dorchester: Alain Ducasse,
China Tang, Grill Room,
The Promenade
Queens of Mayfair
Tamarind, Murano
MiMi Mei Fair
Langan's Brasserie
Cafe Murano
Cut, 45 Park Lane
The Meat & Wine
Burger & Lobster
Le Comptoir Robuchon
Co Mayfair
Aragawa
The Ritz, Palm Court
Kiku
Boudin Blanc
Maru
Seven Park Place
Hide Ground,
Above at Hide
Kitty Fisher's
Ormer
Mayfair
Chutney Mary

Park Lane
South Audley Street
Berkeley Street
Curzon Street
GREEN
PARK
Jermyn Street
Bar des Prés
Amethyst
José Pizarro
Fortnum & Mason: 45 Jermyn Street,
Diamond Jubilee Tea Rooms
Al Duca
Maison Francais
Quaglino's
Ginza Onodera
Riviera
Il Vicolo
The Avenue
Saint Jacques

Hyde
Park
Galvin at Windows (Hilton)
Nobu (COMO Metropolitan)
El Pirata
116 at the Athenaeum
Piccadilly
Coya
Theo Randall (InterContinental)

Piccadilly
Green Park
Duke's Hotel:
Great British Restaurant,
The Drawing Room
ST JAMES'S
The Mall

The Stafford:
The Game Bird,
The American Bar

MAP 9 – HAMPSTEAD, CAMDEN TOWN & ISLINGTON

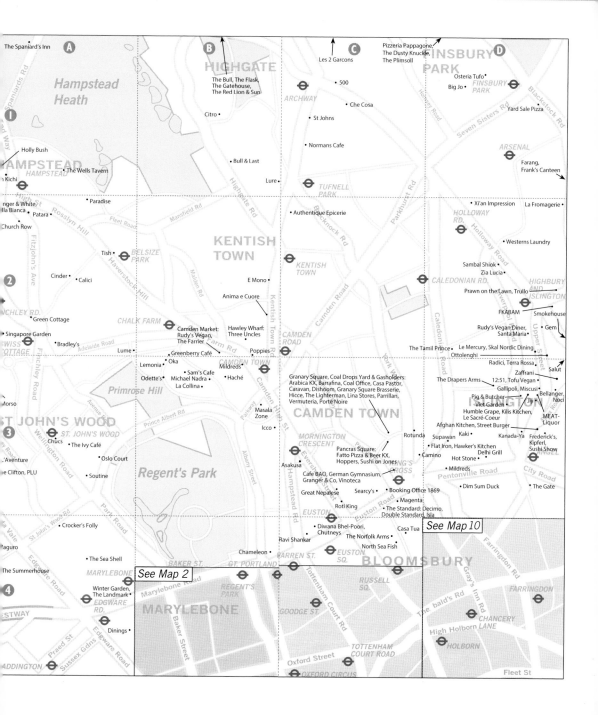

The Spaniard's Inn **A**

B

HIGHGATE

Les 2 Garcons **C**

Pizzeria Pappagone,
The Dusty Knuckle,
The Plimsoll

FINSBURY
PARK **D**

Hampstead
Heath

The Bull, The Flask,
The Gatehouse,
The Red Lion & Sun

• 500

Osteria Tufo •

Big Jo •   FINSBURY
PARK

I

ARCHWAY

• Che Cosa

Yard Sale Pizza •

Citro •

• St Johns

Seven Sisters Rd.

Blackstock Rd.

Holly Bush

• Bull & Last

• Normans Cafe

ARSENAL

HAMPSTEAD
HAMPSTEAD

• The Wells Tavern

Lure •

TUFNELL
PARK

Farang,
Frank's Canteen

n Kichi

nger & White,
lla Bianca •

• Paradise

Mansfield Rd.

• Authentique Epicerie

• Xi'an Impression   La Fromagerie •

HOLLOWAY
RD.

Patara •

Fleet Road

Church Row

Rosslyn Hill

KENTISH
TOWN

Parkhurst Rd.

• Westerns Laundry

Holloway Road

Fitzjohn's Ave.

2

Tish •   BELSIZE
PARK

Haverstock Hill

Cinder •   • Calici

E Mono •

KENTISH
TOWN

Sambal Shiok •
Zia Lucia •

CALEDONIAN RD.

HIGHBURY
AND
ISLINGTON

Prawn on the Lawn, Trullo •

NCHLEY RD.

Anima e Cuore •

Maiden Rd.

FKABAM •

Smokehouse •

• Green Cottage

CHALK FARM

Kentish Town Rd.

Camden Road

Caledonian Road

Rudy's Vegan Diner, •
Santa Maria •

• Gem

• Singapore Garden

Camden Market:
Rudy's Vegan,
The Farrier

Hawley Wharf:
Three Uncles

CAMDEN
ROAD

The Tamil Prince •   Le Mercury, Skal Nordic Dining •

Ottolenghi •

SWISS
OTTAGE

• Bradley's

Adelaide Road

Farm Rd.

Lume •

Greenberry Café •

Poppies •

Radici, Terra Rossa •

Salut •

Finchley Road

Lemonia •

Oka •

CAMDEN
TOWN

Zaffrani •

Odette's •

• Sam's Cafe
Michael Nadra •

Mildreds•

• Haché

The Drapers Arms •   12:51, Tofu Vegan •

Morso •

La Collina •

Gallipoli, Miscusi •

Pig & Butcher •

Bellanger,
Noci •

Primrose Hill

Avenue Road

Masala
Zone

Granary Square, Coal Drops Yard & Gasholders:
Arabica KX, Barrafina, Coal Office, Casa Pastor,
Caravan, Dishoom, Granary Square Brasserie,
Hicce, The Lighterman, Lina Stores, Parrillan,
Vermuteria, Porte Noire

Viet Garden •

Jiji •

Humble Grape, Kilis Kitchen,
Le Sacré-Coeur

MEAT-
Liquor

3

ST. JOHN'S WOOD

Prince Albert Rd.

Icco •

CAMDEN TOWN

Afghan Kitchen, Street Burger •

ST. JOHN'S WOOD

Chucs •

• The Ivy Café

MORNINGTON
CRESCENT

Rotunda •   Supawan •   Kaki •   Kanada-Ya •   Frederick's,
Kipferl,
Sushi Show

L'Aventure

• Oslo Court

Eversholt St.

• Flat Iron, Hawker's Kitchen

Delhi Grill •

e Clifton, PLU

• Soutine

Pancras Square:
Fatto Pizza & Beer KX,
Hoppers, Sushi on Jones

• Camino

Hot Stone •

City Road

Regent's Park

Albany Street

Asakusa

Hampstead Road

• Mildreds

Pentonville Road

• Dim Sum Duck   • The Gate

Cafe BAO, German Gymnasium,
Grangér & Co, Vinoteca

Great Nepalese •

Searcy's •

• Booking Office 1869

4

• Crocker's Folly

Park Road

Roti King •

• Magenta

aguro

EUSTON

• The Standard: Decimo,
Double Standard, Isla

See Map 10

• The Sea Shell

Chameleon •

• Diwana Bhel-Poori,
Chutneys

Casa Tua •

The Summerhouse •

Ravi Shankar •

WARREN ST.

The Norfolk Arms •

North Sea Fish •

Farringdon Rd.

MARYLEBONE

GT. PORTLAND

EUSTON
SQ.

BLOOMSBURY

FARRINGDON

Winter Garden,
The Landmark •

See Map 2

REGENT'S
PARK

RUSSELL
SQ.

Gray's Inn Rd.

EDGWARE
RD.

Maryle bone Road

Baker St.

The bald's Rd.

CHANCERY
LANE

STWAY

MARYLEBONE

GOODGE ST.

Tottenham Court Rd.

High Holborn

HOLBORN

Dinings •

Praed St.

Edgware Road

Oxford Street

OXFORD CIRCUS

TOTTENHAM
COURT ROAD

Fleet St

ADDINGTON

Sussex Gdns.

MAP 10 – THE CITY

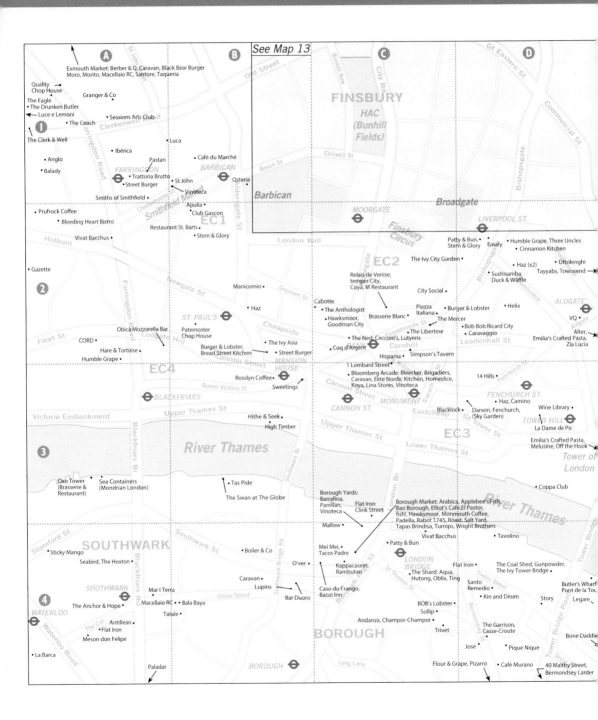

MAP 11 – SOUTH LONDON (& FULHAM)

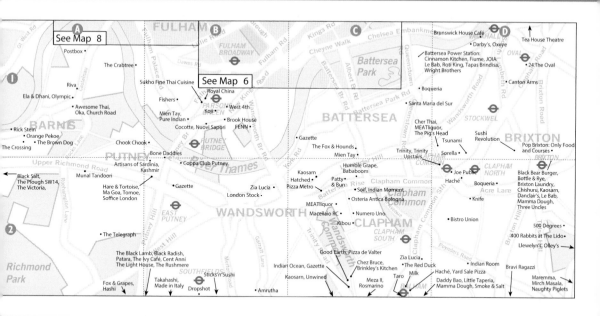

A See Map 8

FULHAM

B

FULHAM
BROADWAY

See Map 6

C

Chelsea Embankment

Cheyne Walk

Battersea
Park

D

VAUXHALL

Brunswick House Café •
• Darby's, Oxeye

Tea House Theatre

Postbox •

The Crabtree •

Sukho Fine Thai Cuisine •

OVAL

Battersea Power Station:
Cinnamon Kitchen, Fiume, JOIA,
Le Bab, Roti King, Tapas Brindisa,
Wright Brothers

•• 24 The Oval

Riva •

Ela & Dhani, Olympic •

Fishers •

Royal China
• West 4th
Koji •

• Boqueria

• Canton Arms

BARNS

• Rick Stein
• Orange Pekoe
• The Brown Dog

The Crossing

Mien Tay,
Pure Indian •

Chook Chook •

Cocotte, Nuovi Sapori

• Brook House
FENN •

• Santa Maria del Sur

BATTERSEA

STOCKWEL

Cher Thai,
MEATliquor,
The Pig's Head

Sushi
Revolution

BRIXTON

Bone Daddies •

• Gazette

The Fox & Hounds •

Mien Tay •

Tsunami

Sorella •

Pop Brixton: Only Food
and Courses

Upper Richmond Road

PUTNEY

Artisans of Sardinia,
Kashmir

• Coppa Club Putney

Thames

PUTNEY
BRIDGE

Humble Grape,
Bababoom

Trinity, Trinity
Upstairs

• Joe Public

CLAPHAM
NORTH

Black Salt,
The Plough SW14,
The Victoria,

Munal Tandoori •

Hare & Tortoise,
Ma Goa, Tomoe,
Soffice London

• Gazette

Kaosarn
Hatched •
Pizza Metro

Patty
& Bun •

• Soif, Indian Moment

Clapham Common
Rise

Haché •

Boqueria •

Acre Lane

Black Bear Burger,
Bottle & Rye,
Brixton Laundry,
Chishuru, Kaosarn,
Danclair's, Le Bab,
Mamma Dough,
Three Uncles

Zia Lucia
London Stock •

• Knife

EAST
PUTNEY

WANDSWORTH

MEATliquor •

Macellaio RC •

Kibou •

CLAPHAM

• Osteria Antica Bologna

• Numero Uno

Clapham
Common

• Bistro Union

500 Degrees •

400 Rabbits at The Lido •

Llewelyn's, Olley's •

• The Telegraph

CLAPHAM
SOUTH

The Black Lamb, Black Radish,
Patara, The Ivy Café, Cent Anni
The Light House, The Rushmere

Richmond
Park

SOUTHFIELDS

Fox & Grapes, •
Hashi

Takahashi,
Made in Italy •

Sticks'n'Sushi

Dropshot •

• Amrutha

Good Earth, Pizza de Valter

Indian Ocean, Gazette

Kaosarn, Unwined

Chez Bruce,
Brinkley's Kitchen

Meza II,
Rosmarino

Zia Lucia

• The Red Duck

Taro •

Milk •

• Indian Room

Haché, Yard Sale Pizza

Daddy Bao, Little Taperia,
Mamma Dough, Smoke & Salt

Bravi Ragazzi •

Maremma,
Mirch Masala,
Naughty Piglets

MAP 12 – EAST END & DOCKLANDS

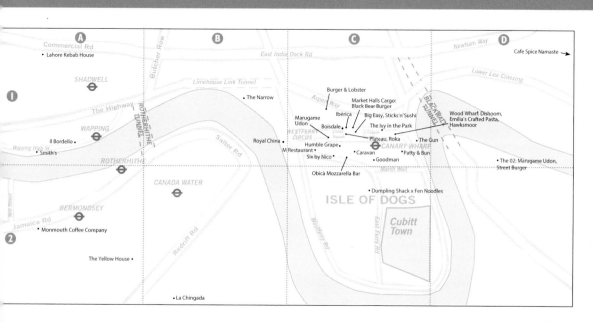

Commercial Rd

A

Butcher Row

B

East India Dock Rd

C

Newham Way

Lower Lea Crossing

D

Cafe Spice Namaste →

• Lahore Kebab House

SHADWELL

Limehouse Link Tunnel

The Highway

WAPPING

ROTHERHITHE TUNNEL

• The Narrow

Aspen Way

WESTFERRY
CIRCUS

Burger & Lobster

Market Halls Cargo:
Black Bear Burger

Iberica

Marugame
Udon

Boisdale

BLACKWALL TUNNEL

Big Easy, Sticks'n'Sushi

The Ivy in the Park

Wood Wharf: Dishoom,
Emilia's Crafted Pasta,
Hawksmoor

Il Bordello •

• Smith's

Wapping High St

Royal China •

Humble Grape

M-Restaurant •

Plateau, Roka •

CANARY WHARF

• The Gun

ROTHERHITHE

Salter Rd

Six by Nico •

• Caravan

• Goodman

• Patty & Bun•

• The 02: Marugame Udon,
Street Burger

Obicà Mozzarella Bar •

Marsh Wall

CANADA WATER

• Dumpling Shack x Fen Noodles

ISLE OF DOGS

BERMONDSEY

Cubitt
Town

Jamaica Rd

Redriff Rd

• Monmouth Coffee Company

Westferry Rd

East Ferry Rd

The Yellow House •

• La Chingada

MAP 13 – SHOREDITCH & BETHNAL GREEN

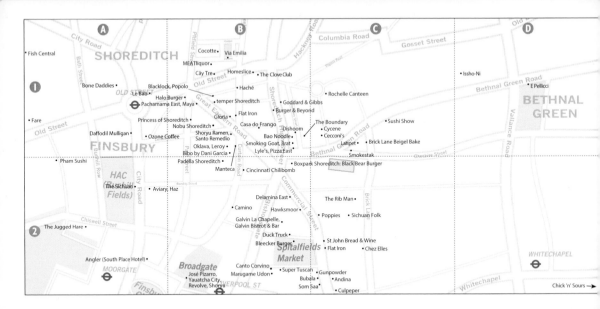

MAP 14 – EAST LONDON

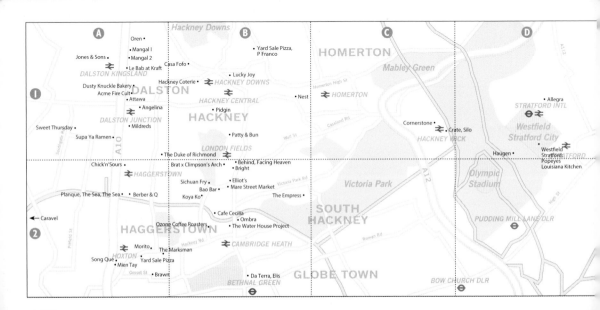

Dean Banks at The Pompadour, Edinburgh

Moor Hall, Aughton

Lympstone Manor, Exmouth

Andrew Fairlie, Gleneagles Hotel, Auchterarder

Opheem, Birmingham

TOP SCORERS

All restaurants whose food ratings is **5**; plus restaurants whose formula price is £60+ with a food rating of **4**.

Price	Restaurant	Ratings
£410	Ynyshir Restaurant and Rooms *(Eglwys Fach)*	4 3 3
£320	Midsummer House *(Cambridge)*	4 4 3
£290	L'Enclume *(Cartmel)*	5 5 5
£270	Aulis at L'Enclume *(Cartmel)*	5 5 4
	Moor Hall *(Aughton)*	5 5 4
	Raby Hunt *(Summerhouse)*	4 3 2
£260	Belmond Le Manoir aux Quat' Saisons *(Great Milton)*	5 5 5
£220	Waterside Inn *(Bray)*	5 5 5
£200	Lympstone Manor *(Exmouth)*	5 4 4
	Mana *(Manchester)*	4 4 4
£190	Restaurant Sat Bains *(Nottingham)*	4 4 3
	The Black Swan *(Oldstead)*	4 3 3
	Sosban & The Old Butcher's *(Menai Bridge)*	4 3 2
£170	The Ethicurean *(Wrington)*	4 3 4
£160	Sorrel *(Dorking)*	5 4 4
	ChefsTable at TRUEfoods *(Melmerby)*	5 5 3
	Gidleigh Park *(Chagford)*	4 4 5
	Carters of Moseley *(Birmingham)*	4 5 4
	Roots *(York)*	4 4 4
	The Latymer, Pennyhill Park Hotel *(Bagshot)*	4 3 4
£150	The Forest Side *(Grasmere)*	5 5 4
	Andrew Fairlie, Gleneagles Hotel *(Auchterarder)*	5 4 4
	Condita *(Edinburgh)*	5 4 4
	Hjem *(Wall)*	5 4 4
	Paul Ainsworth at No6 *(Padstow)*	5 4 4
	Pine *(East Wallhouses)*	5 4 4
	The Cellar *(Anstruther)*	5 4 4
	Cail Bruich *(Glasgow)*	5 4 3
	Loch Bay Restaurant *(Stein)*	5 4 3
	The Samling *(Windermere)*	4 4 5
	Number One, Balmoral Hotel *(Edinburgh)*	4 4 4
	Restaurant Hywel Jones by Lucknam Park *(Colerne)*	4 4 4
	The Clock House *(Ripley)*	4 4 4
	Winteringham Fields *(Winteringham)*	4 4 3
£140	The Kitchin *(Edinburgh)*	5 4 4
	The Whitebrook, Restaurant with Rooms *(Whitebrook)*	5 4 3
£130	Morston Hall *(Morston)*	5 4 5
	Adam Reid at The French *(Manchester)*	5 4 4
	Fraiche *(Oxton)*	5 4 3

Price	Restaurant	Ratings
	SY23 *(Aberystwyth)*	5 4 3
	The Olive Tree, Queensberry Hotel *(Bath)*	5 3 2
	Allium at Askham Hall *(Penrith)*	4 3 4
£120	Hambleton Hall *(Hambleton)*	5 5 5
	Alchemilla *(Nottingham)*	5 4 4
	Karrek, St Enodoc Hotel *(Rock)*	5 4 4
	House of Tides *(Newcastle upon Tyne)*	5 3 4
	Adam's *(Birmingham)*	5 5 3
	Restaurant Martin Wishart *(Edinburgh)*	5 5 3
	Salt *(Stratford upon Avon)*	5 4 3
	Unalome by Graeme Cheevers *(Glasgow)*	5 4 3
	The Idle Rocks *(St Mawes)*	4 4 4
	Where The Light Gets In *(Stockport)*	4 4 4
	Kintsu *(Colchester)*	4 4 3
	Lunar *(Barlaston)*	4 4 3
	Rafters *(Sheffield)*	4 4 3
	The Fernery, Grove of Narberth *(Dyfed)*	4 4 3
	The Hare Inn Restaurant *(Scawton)*	4 4 3
	Lake Road Kitchen *(Ambleside)*	4 3 3
£110	Paris House *(Woburn)*	5 4 5
	Fhior *(Edinburgh)*	5 4 3
	Old Stamp House *(Ambleside)*	5 4 3
	Outlaw's Fish Kitchen *(Port Isaac)*	5 4 3
	Roski *(Liverpool)*	5 4 3
	The Little Fish Market *(Brighton)*	5 4 3
	21212 *(Edinburgh)*	4 5 4
	Etch *(Brighton)*	4 4 4
	Fischers at Baslow Hall *(Baslow)*	4 4 4
	Longueville Manor *(Jersey)*	4 4 4
	The Box Tree *(Ilkley)*	4 4 4
	The Glenturret Lalique Restaurant *(Crieff)*	4 4 4
	L'Ortolan *(Shinfield)*	4 4 3
	64 Degrees *(Brighton)*	4 3 2
£100	Mash Inn *(Radnage)*	5 4 4
	The Small Holding *(Goudhurst)*	5 4 4
	Coombeshead Farm *(Lewannick)*	5 3 4
	Elderflower *(Lymington)*	5 4 3
	The Angel *(Hetton)*	5 4 3
	The Wilderness *(Birmingham)*	5 4 3
	Osip *(Bruton)*	5 3 3
	Harry's Place *(Great Gonerby)*	5 5 2
	Bohemia *(Jersey)*	4 5 4
	Dean Banks at The Pompadour *(Edinburgh)*	4 4 4
	Monachyle Mhor *(Balquhidder)*	4 4 4
	Purnells *(Birmingham)*	4 4 4
	Simpsons *(Edgbaston)*	4 4 4
	The Bow Room Restaurant *(York)*	4 4 4
	Lerpwl *(Liverpool)*	4 3 4
	Home *(Leeds)*	4 3 3
	The Peacock at Rowsley *(Rowsley)*	4 3 3
	Le Champignon Sauvage *(Cheltenham)*	4 5 2

£90	Northcote *(Langho)*	5	5	4
	Joro *(Sheffield)*	5	4	4
	The Muddlers Club *(Belfast)*	5	4	4
	The Sportsman *(Seasalter)*	5	4	4
	Upstairs by Tom Shepherd *(Lichfield)*	5	4	4
	The Shore *(Penzance)*	5	3	4
	Lumière *(Cheltenham)*	5	5	3
	Docket No.33 *(Whitchurch)*	5	4	3
	Etive *(Oban)*	5	4	3
	Heaney's *(Cardiff)*	5	4	3
	Hide & Fox *(Saltwood)*	5	4	3
	John's House *(Mountsorrel)*	5	4	3
	Meadowsweet *(Holt)*	5	4	3
	One Fish Street *(St Ives)*	5	4	3
	Orwells *(Shiplake)*	5	4	3
	Restaurant Roots *(Southbourne)*	5	4	3
	Restaurant Twenty Two *(Cambridge)*	5	4	3
	The Neptune *(Old Hunstanton)*	5	4	3
	The Newport *(Newport On Tay)*	5	4	3
	The Peat Inn *(Cupar)*	5	4	3
	Vanderlyle *(Cambridge)*	5	4	3
	White Swan at Fence *(Fence)*	5	4	3
	The Dining Room, Beaverbrook *(Leatherhead)*	4	4	5
	Pale Hall Hotel Restaurant *(Bala)*	4	4	4
	Read's *(Faversham)*	4	4	4
	Tyddyn Llan *(Llandrillo)*	4	4	4
	Freemasons at Wiswell *(Wiswell)*	4	3	4
	Seafood Restaurant *(Padstow)*	4	3	4
	The Ingham Swan *(Ingham)*	4	3	4
	Ox *(Belfast)*	4	5	3
	Artichoke *(Amersham)*	4	4	3
	Chef Jono at V&V *(Leeds)*	4	4	3
	Coast *(Saundersfoot)*	4	4	3
	HRiSHi, Gilpin Lodge *(Windermere)*	4	4	3
	Menu Gordon Jones *(Bath)*	4	4	3
	The Royal Oak *(Whatcote)*	4	4	3
	The Silver Cup *(Harpenden)*	4	4	3
	Bulrush *(Bristol)*	4	3	3
	Harborne Kitchen *(Birmingham)*	4	3	3
	So-lo *(Aughton)*	4	3	3
	The Old Inn *(Drewsteignton)*	4	3	3
	The Rattle Owl *(York)*	4	3	3
	The Three Chimneys *(Dunvegan)*	4	3	3
	The Walnut Tree *(Llandewi Skirrid)*	4	3	3
	Inver Restaurant *(Strachur)*	4	2	3
£80	Robin Wylde *(Lyme Regis)*	5	5	4
	Stark *(Broadstairs)*	5	4	4
	The Tudor Room, Great Fosters Hotel *(Egham)*	5	4	4
	The Bridge Arms *(Bridge)*	5	3	4
	Aizle *(Edinburgh)*	5	4	3
	Outlaw's New Road *(Port Isaac)*	5	4	3
	The Bailiwick *(Englefield Green)*	5	4	3
	The Beehive *(White Waltham)*	5	4	3
	The Little Chartroom *(Edinburgh)*	5	4	3
	Verveine Fishmarket Restaurant *(Milford-on-Sea)*	5	4	3
	The Clockspire *(Milborne Port)*	5	3	3
	Vaasu by Atul Kochhar *(Marlow)*	5	3	3
	Wilson's *(Bristol)*	5	4	2
	The Seafood Ristorante *(St Andrews)*	4	3	5

	The Greyhound *(Beaconsfield)*	4	5	4
	Melton's *(York)*	4	4	4
	Old Downton Lodge *(Ludlow)*	4	4	4
	Roux at Skindles *(Taplow)*	4	4	4
	The Barn at Moor Hall *(Aughton)*	4	4	4
	The Coach *(Marlow)*	4	4	4
	The Pig & Pastry *(York)*	4	4	4
	Vero Gusto *(Sheffield)*	4	4	4
	Beach House *(Oxwich)*	4	3	4
	The Woodspeen *(Newbury)*	4	3	4
	Arras *(York)*	4	4	3
	Dining Room *(Rock)*	4	4	3
	Heft *(Newton in Cartmel)*	4	4	3
	Hypha *(Chester)*	4	4	3
	La Chouette *(Dinton)*	4	4	3
	Rafters at Riverside House *(Ashford-in-the-Water)*	4	4	3
	Red Lion Freehouse *(East Chisenbury)*	4	4	3
	Catch at The Old Fish Market *(Weymouth)*	4	3	3
	Henry's Restaurant *(Bath)*	4	3	3
	Sindhu *(Marlow)*	4	3	3
	The Old Bank *(Westerham)*	4	3	3
	Elephant Restaurant & Brasserie *(Torquay)*	4	4	2
	The Hardwick *(Abergavenny)*	4	2	2
£70	Opheem *(Birmingham)*	5	4	4
	Peace & Loaf *(Newcastle upon Tyne)*	5	4	4
	Pensons at Netherwood Estate *(Stoke Bliss)*	5	4	4
	The Art School *(Liverpool)*	5	4	4
	Prithvi *(Cheltenham)*	5	4	3
	The Fordwich Arms *(Fordwich)*	5	4	3
	The French Table *(Surbiton)*	5	4	3
	The Pack Horse *(Hayfield)*	5	4	3
	Glebe House *(Southleigh)*	5	3	3
	Terre à Terre *(Brighton)*	5	3	3
	The Pig at Harlyn Bay *(Harlyn)*	4	4	5
	Pierhouse Hotel *(Port Appin)*	4	3	5
	The Cottage In The Wood *(Keswick)*	4	5	4
	Penrose Kitchen *(Truro)*	4	4	4
	The Horse Guards Inn *(Tillington)*	4	4	4
	The Hut *(Colwell Bay)*	4	4	4
	The Pipe & Glass *(Beverley)*	4	4	4
	The Pot Kiln *(Frilsham)*	4	4	4
	Wild Flor *(Brighton)*	4	4	4
	The Guildhall Tavern *(Poole)*	4	3	4
	The Sir Charles Napier *(Chinnor)*	4	3	4
	36 on the Quay *(Emsworth)*	4	4	3
	Jew's House Restaurant *(Lincoln)*	4	4	3
	La Popote *(Marton)*	4	4	3
	Nathan Marshall Prestor House *(Liss)*	4	4	3
	Scran & Scallie *(Edinburgh)*	4	4	3
	The Auldgirth Inn *(Dumfries)*	4	4	3
	The Cross at Kenilworth *(Kenilworth)*	4	4	3
	The Hammer & Pincers *(Loughborough)*	4	4	3
	Tolcarne Inn *(Penzance)*	4	4	3
	1921 Angel Hill *(Bury St Edmunds)*	4	3	3
	21 *(Newcastle upon Tyne)*	4	3	3
	Chapter One *(Locksbottom)*	4	3	3
	Hotel Endsleigh *(Milton Abbot)*	4	3	3
	Purslane *(Edinburgh)*	4	3	3
	The Bay Horse *(Hurworth)*	4	3	3

The Olive Branch (Clipsham)			4 3 3
The Potted Lobster (Bamburgh)			4 3 3
The Seaview Restaurant (Saltburn)			4 3 3
The Vanilla Pod (Marlow)			4 3 3
The Westwood Restaurant (Beverley)			4 3 3
Waterside Bistro (Shipley)			4 3 3
Wedgwood (Edinburgh)			4 3 3
Ugly Butterfly (St Ives)			4 2 3
Haywards Restaurant (Epping)			4 4 2
Gingerman (Brighton)			4 3 2
The Ollerod (Beaminster)			4 2 2

£60	Edinbane Lodge (Edinbane)			5 4 4
	Maison Bleue (Bury St Edmunds)			5 4 4
	Kota (Porthleven)			5 3 4
	Haar (St Andrews)			5 4 3
	Jon & Fernanda's (Auchterarder)			5 4 3
	Prévost at Haycock (Wansford)			5 4 3
	Skosh (York)			5 4 3
	Tallow (Southborough)			5 4 3
	The Moorcock Inn (Sowerby Bridge)			5 4 3
	The Parkers Arms (Newton-in-Bowland)			5 4 3
	The Poet (Matfield)			5 4 3
	The Wild Mushroom (Westfield)			5 4 3
	Upstairs at Landrace (Bath)			5 4 3
	Eusebi Deli (Glasgow)			5 3 3
	Shaun Rankin at Grantley Hall (Grantley)			4 4 5
	Riddle & Finns On The Beach (Brighton)			4 3 5
	The Rat Inn (Hexham)			4 3 5
	Noble (Holywood)			4 5 4
	Pea Porridge (Bury St Edmunds)			4 5 4
	Chapters (Hay-on-Wye)			4 4 4
	Gilpin Spice, Gilpin Lodge (Windermere)			4 4 4
	Hawksmoor (Manchester)			4 4 4
	Heritage (Slaugham)			4 4 4
	Ondine (Edinburgh)			4 4 4
	Rico's (Edinburgh)			4 4 4
	Sticky Walnut (Chester)			4 4 4
	Stones (Matlock)			4 4 4
	The Alice Hawthorn (Nun Monkton)			4 4 4
	The Man Behind The Curtain (Leeds)			4 4 4
	The Parsons Table (Arundel)			4 4 4
	El Gato Negro (Manchester)			4 3 4
	Riddle & Finns (Brighton)			4 3 4
	Shibden Mill Inn (Halifax)			4 3 4
	The Oyster Shack (Bigbury-on-Sea)			4 3 4
	Y Polyn (Nantgaredig)			4 3 4
	Fat Olives (Emsworth)			4 5 3
	Augustus (Taunton)			4 4 3
	Bilash (Wolverhampton)			4 4 3
	Coast (Oban)			4 4 3
	Fish and Forest (York)			4 4 3
	Hispi Bistro (Manchester)			4 4 3
	Hitchen's Barn (Oakham)			4 4 3
	Lasan (Birmingham)			4 4 3
	Pasta Loco (Bristol)			4 4 3
	Prawn on the Lawn (Padstow)			4 4 3
	Root (Bristol)			4 4 3
	Samphire (Whitstable)			4 4 3
	The Curlew (Bodiam)			4 4 3

	The Scallop Shell (Bath)			4 4 3
	The Walrus (Shrewsbury)			4 4 3
	The Woolpack Inn (Slad)			4 4 3
	Watson & Walpole (Framlingham)			4 4 3
	YU (Copster Green)			4 4 3
	Eileen's (Ampthill)			4 3 3
	Fishers Leith (Edinburgh)			4 3 3
	Gem 42 (Newport)			4 3 3
	Goodfellows (Wells)			4 3 3
	Indian Essence (Petts Wood)			4 3 3
	No.1 Ship Street (Oxford)			4 3 3
	Pompette (Oxford)			4 3 3
	Purslane (Cheltenham)			4 3 3
	Severn & Wye Smokery (Westbury-on-Severn)			4 3 3
	The Bay Horse (Ellel)			4 3 3
	The Black Bear Inn (Usk)			4 3 3
	The Black Bull Inn (Sedbergh)			4 3 3
	The Cartford Inn (Little Eccleston)			4 3 3
	The Dog & Gun (Skelton)			4 3 3
	The Gaff (Abergavenny)			4 3 3
	The Harbourside Refuge (Porthleven)			4 3 3
	The Inn at Welland (Welland)			4 3 3
	The Owl (Leeds)			4 3 3
	Thomas by Tom Simmons (Cardiff)			4 3 3
	Trakol (Gateshead)			4 3 3
	Tytherleigh Arms (Tytherleigh)			4 3 3
	Buoy & Oyster (Margate)			4 4 2
	Fishmarket (Edinburgh)			4 3 2
	Landgate Bistro (Rye)			4 3 2
	5 North Street (Winchcombe)			4 2 2
	Butley Orford Oysterage (Orford)			4 2 2

£50	Crab House Cafe (Weymouth)			5 4 4
	Angela's (Margate)			5 4 3
	Loch Leven Seafood Café (Onich)			5 4 3
	Noya's Kitchen (Bath)			5 4 3
	Riley's Fish Shop (Tynemouth)			5 4 3
	The Feathers Inn (Hedley On The Hill)			5 4 3

£40	Engine Social Dining (Sowerby Bridge)			5 4 4
	Sonny Stores (Bristol)			5 4 3
	Ebi Sushi (Derby)			5 4 2
	Seafood Shack (Ullapool)			5 4 2
	The Cumin (Nottingham)			5 4 2
	The Magpie Café (Whitby)			5 4 2
	Umi (Twickenham)			5 4 2
	The Cod's Scallops (Wollaton)			5 3 2

£30	Riley's Fish Shack (Tynemouth)			5 4 5
	Eleanore (Edinburgh)			5 4 3
	Paesano Pizza (Glasgow)			5 4 3
	Beefy Boys (Hereford)			5 3 3
	Kushi-ya (Nottingham)			5 3 3
	Anstruther Fish Bar (Anstruther)			5 3 2

£25	Erst (Manchester)			5 4 4

£15	Burger Brothers (Brighton)			5 3 2

Dean Banks at The Pompadour, Edinburgh

L'Enclume, Cartmel

Aizle, Edinburgh

Coworth Park, Ascot

ABERAERON, CEREDIGION   4–3C

HARBOURMASTER £57   3 3 3

2 QUAY PDE   SA46 0BT   01545 570755

Cardigan Bay fish and shellfish is the menu highlight at this boutique hotel in a "stunning setting at the end of the quay in Aberaeron" – backed up by Welsh lamb and Ceredigion cheeses. "A bustling gastropub with the restaurant off to one side, it feels lively and fun". Wells & Louise Jones of the Cardigan-based Flatrock hospitality group took the Harbourmaster over last year from longtime owners Glynn & Menna Heulyn. / www.harbour-master.com; hmaberaeron; Mon-Sun 9 pm; payment – credit card only.

ABERDEEN, ABERDEENSHIRE   9–2D

SILVER DARLING £62   3 3 4

NORTH PIER HOUSE, POCRA QUAY AB11 5DQ   01224 576229

"With great views over Aberdeen Harbour", this "unique fish restaurant" is perched on top of the old customs house, "with extensive glass windows" (through which you may see seals as well as "boats coming and going in the docks"). It wins praise for "assured, innovative cooking" where "quality rather than quantity" is the prime objective. / www.thesilverdarling.co.uk; thesilverdarlingrestaurant; Mon-Fri 8.30 pm, Sat 9 pm, Sun 8 pm; Cash & all usual cards; children: +16 after 8 pm.

ABERDOUR, FIFE   9–4C

ROOM WITH A VIEW, FORTH VIEW HOTEL £47   4 4 3

HAWKCRAIG POINT   KY3 0TZ 01383 860 402

"A seafood restaurant that never fails to please, with constantly changing menus that reflect what is available seasonally". That's the take on this small (24 covers) family-run fish restaurant and 'seasonal hotel' which sits on Hawkcraig point, with views of Edinburgh and the islands of the Forth. "The owners really do pull out all the stops to give a nice dining experience. Great for that special occasion!" / www.roomwithaviewrestaurant.co.uk; Wed-Sun midnight; closed Mon & Tue; Cash & all usual cards.

ABERGAVENNY, MONMOUTHSHIRE 2–1A

THE ANGEL HOTEL £82   3 4 3

15 CROSS ST   NP7 5EN   01873 857121

"This old coaching inn is always a pleasure to visit", with its "cosy warren of bars" and "carefully modernised and light dining room", serving "delicious and inventive seasonal food with an air of understated luxury". It's also "the best place" for an "unbeatable hand-crafted afternoon tea that delivers on detail, taste and presentation". / www.angelabergavenny.com/dining; the_angel_abergavenny; Sun-Thu 11 pm, Fri & Sat 11.30 pm; Cash & all usual cards.

THE CHAPEL £9   3 3 3

8 CROSS STREET   NP7 5EH 01873 736430

"Still the best coffee for a hundred miles", insist devotees of this independent arts centre café that serves "delightful soups, salads and unusual dishes using local ingredients" – all "thoughtfully prepared with great flavours". / www.artshopandgallery.co.uk; theartshopandchapel; Tue-Sat 4 pm; closed Tue-Sat D, closed Sun & Mon.

THE GAFF £63   4 3 3

4 THE COURTYARD, LION STREET NP7 9SZ   01873 739310

"A lovely little find that's something different from the norm" – these three sheds decorated with local art sit in a courtyard in the centre of the town. It offers "a well thought out small-plate menu from an open kitchen, showcasing the chefs working with love and care over plates of food which are beautifully presented and taste fantastic". "Definitely worth a visit for everyone when in the area". / www.thegaffrestaurant.co.uk; thegaffrestaurant; Wed-Sat 8.30 pm, Sun 2 pm; closed Wed L closed Sun D, closed Mon & Tue.

THE HARDWICK £80   4 2 2

OLD RAGLAN RD   NP7 9AA 01873 854220

This "fabulous" and famous venue near Abergavenny, "run by the great chef Stephen Terry", is "in many ways the gastropub archetype, with its heavy focus on local ingredients and suppliers, cooked expertly but without pretension". "Lunch on a quiet weekday didn't have many people there, but the chef pulls out all the stops. The menu is inspiring and imaginative, and the portions very generous". / www.thehardwick.co.uk; the_hardwick; Mon-Sat 9 pm; closed Sun; No Amex.

ABERYSTWYTH, CEREDIGION   4–3C

SY23 £132   5 4 3

2 PIER STREET   SY23 2LJ   01970 615935

"We live in West Wales and none of us ever thought we might, one day, say 'Let's go and eat in Aberystwyth'. But we did. And it was good!!". Nathan Davies's brave venture is "very much in the mould of Ynyshir" (from which he's an alumnus) "but not to be dismissed for that!". With its "chunky industrial decor and loud heavy metal, it has a totally different vibe" from typical rural restaurants. "The food is primarily cooked over coals" and its ten-course tasting menu delivers "unusual flavours, beautifully presented" and realised "to an exemplary standard". It quickly won recognition from the Tyre Men in February 2022 and was named their 'Opening of the Year'. But it stands out from the typical 'haute' norm: "perhaps there is a sameness in most one-stars now, or maybe we are world-weary and have eaten out too often, but this place is well worth the detour!". "The best meal we have had for a long time!" / sy23restaurant.com; sy23restaurant; Mon-Sun 11 pm.

TREEHOUSE

14 BAKER STREET   SY23 2BJ 01970 615791

Set to open early 2023 on Deansgate, the second offshoot of a US-based hotel chain aiming to make a splash in the city-centre with this 216-bedroom launch: we are promised "a breath of fresh air for a thriving global city in its ascent… designed to appeal to the youthful spirit in all of us and inspired by life's joys". Foodwise, this will include collaborations with chefs and restaurateurs Mary-Ellen McTague, Sam Grainger and Luke Cowdrey and there will be a ground-floor restaurant, 14th-floor bar and restaurant and 'crowning rooftop' bar and terrace, with views for miles. / www.treehousewales.co.uk; Tue-Sat 3.30 pm; closed Tue-Sat D, closed Sun & Mon.

ULTRACOMIDA £46   4 3 2

31 PIER ST   SY23 2LN   01970 630686

"A wonderful selection of tapas and lovely well-priced wines" has built a solid reputation over two decades for this stalwart Spanish deli/bar/wine merchant. "The only drawback is that the seating area has shrunk to a few high-stools, with all food eaten on a counter" nowadays. / www.ultracomida.com; ultracomida; Mon-Sat 3.30 pm; closed Mon-Sat D, closed Sun; payment – credit card only; no bookings.

SUMMER ISLES HOTEL 4|3|5

IV26 2YG 01854 622282

"The freshest fish/seafood you will get – from halibut and turbot to lobster and others – all prepared to perfection" – and with "top-class presentation" – win raves for this renowned but remote Highlands landmark, named for the islands it looks out onto. "All courses of the à la carte are top class, and the view just adds to the experience". Top Tip – "on days when you do not want a full dinner, the bistro also serves the freshest ingredients such as lobster simply presented but still excellent". / www.summerisleshotel.com; Sun-Thu 10 pm, Fri & Sat 11 pm; No Amex; No jeans; children: 8+.

THE GINGER FOX £63 3|3|3

MUDDLESWOOD ROAD BN6 9EA 01273 857 888

This "picture-book thatched country gastropub" from Brighton's Gingerman group in a "beautiful, isolated setting nestled under the South Downs", is "just perfect on a sunny day when you can eat in the attractive garden". It's "much more than a pub", serving "inventive dishes", "done with refinement", along with "a wine list including bottles from 10 Sussex vineyards". / thegingerfox.com; gingerfoxbrighton; Tue-Sun 8.30 pm; closed Mon; Cash & all usual cards.

ALDEBURGH FISH AND CHIPS £15 3|2|1

226 HIGH ST IP15 5DB 01728 454685

There's "always a queue" at this "very popular" fish 'n' chips fixture operated for 56 years by the Cooney family, just a step or two from Aldeburgh's pebble beach – where much of the "really fresh" fish is consumed and, by tradition, beak-loads of chips are stolen by fearless seagulls. "It's better now that the pub next door allows you to use their outside seating, so long as you buy some drinks!". / www.aldeburghfishandchips.co.uk; aldefishnchips; Mon-Wed, Fri 8.30 pm, Thu, Sat 8 pm, Sun 7.30 pm; Cash only.

ASH SMOKED FISHES 4|4|2

CRAG PATH IP15 5BP

This black-painted shack opposite Aldeburgh's Moot Hall sells "seriously brilliant smoked fish right on the beach". The seafood is either hot- or cold-smoked on site, using a light smoke to enhance flavour rather than the more commercial heavy smoke used as a preservative. Top Tip – "noon tarts to die for". / ashsmokedfishes; Mon-Sat 4 pm, Sun 5 pm; closed Mon-Sun D.

THE LIGHTHOUSE £55 3|5|4

77 HIGH STREET IP15 5AU 01728 453377

An "Aldeburgh stalwart" for almost three decades, this "wonderful local restaurant" is noted for its "absolutely charming service" led by owner Sam Hayes, "and an all-pleasing menu" with plenty of "delicious" options. It's "reliable, great value and good fun". Top Tip – "go for the fresh catch of the day, especially the Dover sole accompanied by a bottle of Chablis". / www.lighthouserestaurant.co.uk; aldelighthouse; Mon-Sun 9.30 pm; Cash & all usual cards.

THE SUFFOLK (FKA L'ESCARGOT SUR MER) £73 3|3|3

152 HIGH STREET IP15 5AQ 07557 333453

George Pell's August 2022 newcomer (converted from a former pub) started life as 'L'Escargot Sur-Mer' – a transplant of the Soho landmark he co-owns necessitated by Covid-19. It incorporates a 60-cover restaurant now named just 'Sur-Mer', a rooftop terrace complete with sea views, wine bar, private dining rooms and bedrooms. Chef James May only joined in March 2022, so the ratings we use (from its previous pop-up incarnation) must be guidelines only. Fans expect a continuation of the "great locally caught fish and shellfish, cooked in a great French style from a good bistro-type menu and wine list". / the-suffolk. co.uk; thesuffolkaldeburgh; Tue-Sun 9 pm; closed Mon.

THE GROSVENOR ARMS £51 3|3|4

CHESTER RD CH3 6HJ 01244 620228

"Looking for a fantastic, well-priced supper? Look no further than The Grosvenor Arms at Alford". This rather grand country pub ("library, conservatory, bar and snug") on the edge of the Duke of Westminster's Cheshire estate maintains "consistently high standards despite being a member of a large chain" – Brunning & Price – for whom this was the group's first property. / www.brunningandprice.co.uk/grosvenorarms; grosvenor.arms; Mon-Sun 11 pm; No Amex.

THE TASTING ROOM, RATHFINNY WINE ESTATE 3|4|4

RATHFINNY WINE ESTATE BN26 5TU 01323 870 022

Lush local wines are not the only attraction at this vineyard restaurant (also with accommodation), which enjoys gorgeous views of the vines and South Downs. There are weekly changing seasonal tasting menus, or "take the incredible picnic amongst the vineyards on a summer's afternoon... bliss!" / www.rathfinnyestate.com/tasting-room; rathfinnyestate; Wed & Thu, Sun 3 pm, Fri & Sat 8.30 pm; closed Wed & Thu, Sun D, closed Mon & Tue; Cash & all usual cards; credit card deposit required to book.

BISTRO 23 £47 3|3|3

23 NORTHUMBERLAND ST NE66 2RH 01665 830393

"By day it's a tea shop but 3 nights a week it transforms into a truly lovely restaurant", serving a "short menu of absolutely delicious dishes" including locally caught fish and Northumberland lamb. Family-run and celebrating its 20th anniversary this year, this is "the most reasonably priced 'quality' restaurant you'll find". / bistro23.co.uk; Mon-Thu, Sat 10 pm, Fri, Sun 4 pm; closed Fri & Sun D.

THE GEORGE £83 3|4|4

DE6 2FX 01335 310205

"The days when this was a pub have long gone: it is an unashamedly ambitious restaurant which charges a full price for some very good cooking" – so say fans of this Peak District gastropub near the Dove Valley, who say "the chef knows what he is doing, and as long as you can afford it this is one of the best places to eat in the Peak District". William Sitwell of The Telegraph paid it a visit in September 2022 and gave a similar but more nuanced view: the "cooking really is excellent and delicate with clever flavours" and "there is talent and charm by the bucket-load", but he felt the dishes on the menu were presented and served in tiny portions, and he was encouraged to think of them as tapas. He declared, they "are the most un-tapassy things I've ever seen". / www.thegeorgeatalstonefield.com; thegeorgestonefield; Thu-Sat 10.30 pm, Sun 5 pm; closed Sun D, closed Mon & Tue & Wed; Cash & all usual cards; credit card deposit required to book.

ALTRINCHAM MARKET £41 4|2|4

GREENWOOD STREET WA14 1SA

Nick Johnson's "wonderfully vibrant" transformation of a covered Victorian market into an artisan food hall has a "great atmosphere", and the "mix of food from different suppliers means that in a group, everyone has something they want to eat". "The novelty has gone but it's still holding up standards" – although "queues are too long" and it can be "a battle to get a table". / altymarket; Tue-Sat 10 pm, Sun 6 pm; closed Sun D, closed Mon.

CALIFORNIA COFFEE & WINE £53 3|3|3

3 OXFORD ROAD WA14 2DY
0161 928 8800

Founders Diana & Justin have backed up their passion for Californian-style coffee with a "relatively cheap" menu of sandwiches and nachos plus biodynamic wines, at the Altrincham café they opened five years ago in an "ideal location near the end of the M62". / www.californiacoffee.co.uk; CaliCoffeeWine; Sun-Thu 5 pm, Fri & Sat 11 pm; closed Sun-Thu D.

SUGO £52 4|3|3

22 SHAW'S RD, ALTRINCHAM WA14 1QU
0161 929 7706

A "perfect little Italian restaurant with a fantastic buzz" serving "outstanding authentic pasta dishes – no frills, just great food" – accompanied by "jugs of good inexpensive wine". It's "great fun", but you "need to book ahead" – or trek into Manchester, to the larger offshoot in Ancoats. / www.sugopastakitchen.co.uk; sugopastakitchen; Tue-Sat 10 pm, Sun 8.30 pm; closed Tue-Thu L, closed Mon; Cash & all usual cards.

AMBERLEY, WEST SUSSEX   3–4A

AMBERLEY CASTLE £120 2|3|5

BN18 9LT 01798 831992

The "stunning surroundings" of a semi-ruined medieval castle dating from 1103 complete with ramparts and working portcullis make this hotel (part of Andrew Brownsword's group) a "beautiful venue for a romantic date which you won't forget". With a rare and original barrel-vaulted dining room ceiling, the dining room is situated upstairs in the castle: "the food is average but the staff are helpful and obliging". / www.amberleycastle.co.uk; brownswordhotels; Wed-Sun 9 pm; closed Mon & Tue; Cash & all usual cards; No jeans; booking max 6 may apply; children: 8.

AMBLE, NORTHUMBERLAND   8–1B

THE OLD BOAT HOUSE AMBLE £51 4|3|3

LEAZES STREET NE65 0AA
01665 711 232

"If you like fresh fish, this is as good as it gets", say fans of this "harbourside restaurant" with "great views of the sea" – "you can see the boats coming in", and also survey "the Coquet estuary up to Warkworth Castle". A former fishing hut, it was extended and refurbished a few years ago by the owners, who also run the nearby Fish Shack – which some "enjoy even more". / www.boathousefoodgroup.co.uk/old-boat-house-amble; theoldboathouseamble; Mon-Sun 9 pm.

AMBLESIDE, CUMBRIA   7–3D

DRUNKEN DUCK £77 3|2|4

BARNGATES LA22 0NG 01539 436347

This "out-of-the-way gem" in a "wonderful rural location beyond Ambleside" is a "brilliant pub with terrific food and very tasty ale" from its own Barngates Brewery, out the back. It gets "very busy" at holiday times, but – even when "full of tourists and short of staff" – "the food is well prepared and presented". / www.drunkenduckinn.co.uk; Mon-Sat 8 pm, Sun 10.30 pm; No Amex; booking evening only.

KYSTY £50 4|4|3

3-4 CHEAPSIDE LA22 0AB
015394 33647

"Perfect food" and "friendly service" are to be found at this more relaxed spin-off from the nearby Old Stamp House, where head chef Dan Hopkins's interesting modern British cooking might be described as 'smart casual'. 'Kysty' is apparently a Cumbrian term for 'fussy'. / www.kysty.co.uk; kystyamble; Wed-Sat, Tue 9.30 pm; closed Tue L, closed Sun & Mon; credit card deposit required to book.

LAKE ROAD KITCHEN £129 4|3|3

3 SUSSEX HOUSE, LAKE ROAD
LA22 0AD 015394 22012

This "small but perfectly formed restaurant" from former Noma chef James Cross brings the full 'new Nordic' experimental dining experience to the Lake District – including wooden walls, sheepskin chairs and beef aged for as long as 430 days. "Dishes are varied and delicious and there's a great wine list to accompany them". Gripes, such as they are, tend to be relatively minor ("still excellent, but preferred it when there seemed to be a stronger emphasis on foraging"). / www.lakeroadkitchen.co.uk; lakeroadkitchen; Wed-Sun 9 pm; closed Wed-Sun L, closed Mon & Tue; booking is online only; children: 14.

OLD STAMP HOUSE £117 5|4|3

CHURCH ST LA22 0BU 01539432775

"A delicious plated journey around Cumbria's fields, lakes, woods, coast and fells – sublime from the off" and "smashing it out of the park as always". Chef Ryan Blackburn and his general manager brother Craig opened their 28-seater to wide acclaim in 2014, and it's now performing "better than ever". "We've loved this restaurant for years for its inventive local food and its unexpectedly tiny and cosy interior, down some hidden steps". The historic building was once William Wordsworth's office, in his sinecure as distributor of stamps for Westmoreland. / www.oldstamphouse.com; oldstamphouseambleside; Tue-Thu 1.30 pm, Fri & Sat 8.30 pm; closed Tue-Thu D, closed Sun & Mon; No Amex.

Andrew Fairlie, Gleneagles, Auchterarder

ROTHAY MANOR 3|3|4

ROTHAY BRIDGE LA22 0EH
01539 433605

This elegant-looking country house hotel has long been one of the better known choices in the Lakes, though arguably more as a place to stay more than as a standalone dining destination. But chef Daniel McGeorge holds a hard-to-win three AA rosettes, and our feedback this year – though limited – is upbeat: "visited twice of late, once for Sunday lunch and then for a special package: faultless both times". / www.rothaymanor.co.uk; rothaymanor; Mon-Sun 9 pm; closed Mon-Sat L; No Amex; children: 7+ at D.

ZEFFIRELLI'S £49 2|2|3

COMPSTON RD LA22 9AD 01539 433845

"I love the ethos – vegetarian which doesn't shout about it" – of the kitchen at this veteran indie "which is part of a complex that also includes a cinema and a jazz bar". It serves a "great range" of "enjoyable", "mainly Italian" meat-free dishes. But given that "Ambleside is rammed with visitors", "service can afford to be a bit take-it-or-leave-it" and some diners judged the food as "pretty ordinary" this year. / www.zeffirellis.com; zeffsfellinis; Mon & Tue, Thu-Sat 10 pm, Wed 11 pm, Sun 9 pm; No Amex.

AMERSHAM, BUCKINGHAMSHIRE   3–2A

ARTICHOKE £98 4|4|3

9 MARKET SQ HP7 0DF 01494 726611

Laurie Gear's "exceptional restaurant nestling in Old Amersham" has been "a favourite for two decades" and – having opened in 2002 – was "belatedly awarded a Michelin star" in 2019. "The best restaurant for miles" in this part of the outer burbs, it is one of the most commented-on restaurants in our annual diners' poll. One or two reports did include some 'rough edges' this year ("a return to form after a former disappointment…"; "a couple of dishes were odd, but never boring!") but the main theme was of "divine" food, "exceptional value tasting menus" and "delightful matching wines", all delivered by "attentive and knowledgeable staff". "I almost hate to give a good review as more people will find this true gem!" / www.artichokerestaurant.co.uk; artichokechef; Thu-Sat, Wed 11 pm; closed Wed L; No shorts.

GILBEY'S £69 233

1 MARKET SQ HP7 0DF 01494 727242

A fixture of Old Amersham for more than 30 years, this bistro from Michael Gilbey of the gin dynasty is a "fab example of old-school dining" – quite literally, given that the seventeenth-century premises were originally part of Dr Challoner's Grammar School. Even long-time fans, though, have begun to grumble that "having been a favourite for years, it has become more ordinary – not bad but no longer worth a journey". There's a sister branch in Eton. / www.gilbeygroup.com/home; gilbeysoldamersham; Mon-Sat 9.30 pm, Sun 3 pm; closed Sun D; Cash & all usual cards.

HAWKYNS BY ATUL KOCHHAR, THE CROWN INN £65 334

16 HIGH STREET HP7 0DH 01494 721541

If you remember 'Four weddings', this very characterful, beamed sixteenth-century pub in the town centre was the filming location for the bit where Hugh and Andie first start getting it together. Its food in recent years has been overseen by star Indian chef, Atul Kochhar, and is a highly rated curry favourite in (nearly) all reports. / www.hawkynsrestaurant.co.uk; hawkynsamersham; Thu-Sun, Mon-Wed 9.30 pm; closed Mon-Wed L.

PLUMA £86 333

18 HIGH STREET HP7 0DJ 01494 728383

This "stylish and buzzing local" serves good-quality tapas and other Hispanic dishes "that wouldn't look out of place in London", making it a "very welcome addition to the Amersham scene". "The food is great (the Iberico pork is amazing), cocktails are really innovative and service is top-notch". It was launched two years ago in a former high street Chinese take-away by experienced hospitality professionals Charlie Baxter and Arantxa Fuentes (ex-Heston B's Hind's Head). / www.plumarestaurants.com; pluma_amersham; Tue-Sat 9 pm; closed Sun & Mon.

TOM YUM £36 432

101 SYCAMORE ROAD HP6 5EJ 01494 728806

"Really good Thai cooking" inspires high ratings and positive feedback for this simple local fixture. "It's a bit cramped when it's full, but the take-home is good". / www.tomyum.net; Tue-Thu 9 pm, Fri & Sat 10 pm; closed Sun & Mon.

EILEEN'S £66 433

86A DUNSTABLE STREET MK45 2JP 01525 839889

This "small & intimate" spot from MasterChef: The Professionals finalist Steve Barringer offers "very popular tasting menus (5 & 8 courses) that change monthly" – and "you need to book well in advance" to taste this "adventurous cooking – especially for Ampthill!". It is named after his grandmother, who introduced Steve to cooking as a young boy. / www.eileensampthill.co.uk; eileensampthill; Wed-Sat 11 pm; closed Wed-Sat L, closed Mon & Tue & Sun.

THE LAMB AT ANGMERING £56 333

THE SQUARE BN16 4EQ 01903 774300

"A great pitstop whilst in the area" – the Norbury family's gastropub next to the South Downs is consistently well reviewed in our annual diners' poll. As well as a selection of pub 'classics' the menu includes a number of more ambitious brasserie-style items. / www.thelamb-angmering.com; thelambatangmering; Mon-Sat 8.30 pm, Sun 3 pm; closed Sun D; Cash & all usual cards.

THE TORRIDON RESTAURANT £69 333

THE TORRIDON IV22 2EY 01445 791242

This Victorian gothic shooting lodge-turned-boutique hotel benefits from a "stunning setting" by Loch Torridon. Its contemporary-style restaurant, 1887, offers a "very well presented menu", but while many reports praise some "wonderful dishes" and "very good cooking", some diners found it "disappointing" or encountered "limited availability" of dishes this year. As of October 2022, you have to stay to sample the food here as it's currently residents-only (unless you head for tea, coffee and cake in the Beinn Bar). / www.thetorridon.com; thetorridon; Mon & Tue 10 am, Wed-Sun 9 pm; closed Mon & Tue D.

ANSTRUTHER FISH BAR £36 532

42-44 SHORE ST KY10 3AQ 01333 310518

"Fresh and tasty fish" of an extremely high quality is always on the menu at this famous Scottish chippy, taken over 20 years ago by Robert & Alison Smith, whose families have been in the local fishing industry for generations. The couple also run the Argofish processing business, named after the Smith family's 'Argonaut' boats. / www.anstrutherfishbar.co.uk; anstrutherfishbar; Mon-Fri 8.30 pm, Sat & Sun 9 pm; No Amex; no bookings.

THE CELLAR £150 544

24 EAST GREEN KY10 3AA 01333 310378

Billy Boyter is two years away from his decade at this former smokehouse, which was a renowned culinary destination before his tenure started in 2014. "Outstanding tasting menus served with flair and knowledge" feature in all reports, as do numerous best meals of the year resulting from "perfectly-judged" preparation, with interesting tastes and combinations" and "great care and attention paid to ingredients and provenance". "Good wine pairings with some interesting choices" are the accompaniment, while "charming service and an "intimate atmosphere" complete the experience. / www.thecellaranstruther.co.uk; Wed-Sat 8.30 pm; closed Mon & Tue & Sun; No Amex.

APPLECROSS INN £46 434

SHORE ST IV54 8LR 01520 744262

"A little bit of Heaven", dropped beside the sea in the West Highlands: "the best seafood, some of the best views, a wonderful selection of drams, and simply a great pub" – this famous and remote destination made its debut (as the Temperance Hotel) in the 1911 Michelin Guide, and is still worth the detour. Top Tip – "always, always have the scallops". / www.applecrossinn.co.uk; Wed, Mon, Thu-Sun 10 pm; closed Wed L, closed Tue; No Amex; may need 6+ to book.

THE PARSONS TABLE £65 444

2 & 8 CASTLE MEWS, TARRANT STREET BN18 9DG 01903 883477

"Delightful, fresh and delicious food served by friendly staff" make this "great local restaurant" an "exceptional find". Chef Lee and foh Liz Parsons met working at Claridge's and had a successful career in Vancouver before returning to open under their own name in 2015. "The fish is especially good, with delicate seasoning", and there's a "great-value set lunch". / theparsonstable.co.uk; tpt_restaurant; Tue-Sat 9 pm; closed Sun & Mon; Cash & all usual cards.

THE PIG IN THE SOUTH DOWNS £52 344

MADEHURST BN18 0NL 01243 974500

"You really can't go wrong with Pig food... great bar, great restaurant full of people all enjoying themselves with tasty food and wine" at the eighth and latest in the shabby-chic litter of Pig hotels, in a "stunning location" on the South Downs. It also serves "great local wines", which will soon be joined by bottles from the 4,000 vines planted on the estate, due to be harvested for the first time this year. A small but vocal minority complain of "bistro food (just!), London prices and cafe service". / www.thepighotel.com; thepig_hotel; Mon-Sun 9.30 pm.

WOVEN, COWORTH PARK £146

BLACKNEST RD SL5 7SE 01344 876 600

Revamped and relaunched in September 2022 under this new stand-alone identity, the flagship dining room at the Dorchester Collection's 240 acre estate near Virginia Water still sits at the heart of the property and is still overseen by acclaimed chef, Adam Smith. It has been an open secret for years that the former design of the dining room didn't do justice to the setting, which the new space created by Martin Hulbert Design aims to put right. There's a new locally focused menu too. According to the press release: "inspiration from the idyllic landscape, will be woven [geddit? Ed] into the menus, and the dishes, whilst refined, will be presented in playful and contemporary ways". Over the years, Adam Smith's cuisine has been steadily acclaimed here in our diners' poll – perhaps even more so in future? Top Tip – in the lounges, Adam also oversees "lovely afternoon tea: traditional and reasonably priced too compared to some hotels in central London!" / www.dorchestercollection.com; coworthpark; closed Mon-Sat & Sun; Cash & all usual cards; No trainers; children: 9.

CRAB & LOBSTER £71 334

DISHFORTH RD YO7 3QL 01845 577286

Once very well known, this stalwart destination is known for its interesting location, filled with bric-a-brac, and notably good fish and seafood. It also has a lovely garden, and accommodation in eighteenth century Crab Manor, complete with individually themed bedrooms. All feedback we have suggests it remains very good all-round. / www.crabandlobster.co.uk; crabandlobster_; Sun-Fri & Sat 9 pm; Cash & all usual cards_;

THE HUNDRED OF ASHENDON £58 343

LOWER END HP18 0HE 01296 651296

"The team is small but work incredibly hard to create beautifully presented dishes that always hit the spot" at this "lovely pub" between the Chilterns and the Cotswolds, where Matt Gill's cuisine provides "excellent food" from an à la carte menu that, while "rustic", bears no relation to pub grub. / www.thehundred.co.uk; thehundredofashendon; Mon-Sat 11 pm, Sun 6 pm; closed Mon-Thu L closed Sun D.

RAFTERS AT RIVERSIDE HOUSE £81 443

RIVERSIDE HOUSE HOTEL, FENNEL STREET DE45 1QF 01629 814275

"Perhaps better than the parent restaurant in Sheffield?" – Tom Lawson and Alistair Myers opened this 14-bedroom rural hotel just before the first lockdown struck. All reports on it are very upbeat for its "romantic" style and "very good tasting menus with good wine pairings". / riversidehousehotel.co.uk; raftersrh; Wed-Sat 8.30 pm, Sun 6 pm; closed Wed L, closed Mon & Tue.

ANDREW FAIRLIE, GLENEAGLES HOTEL £152 544

PH3 1NF 01764 694267

"Andrew Fairlie may no longer be with us but his spirit lives on in this restaurant which bears his name" – the "elegant" flagship dining room of this world-renowned golf resort, which this year topped our annual diners' poll as No.1 in our Top 100 Best UK Restaurants. "And it still maintains its high standards and coveted 2 Michelin stars, which are well deserved". Chef Stephen McLaughlin and GM Dale Dewsbury have been on the team since 2001, and the former provides both an à la carte or 7-course tasting menu: seasonal, luxurious ingredients are prepared with impeccable skill and creativity to deliver a spoiling experience that's "well worth the money and a memory to be treasured". "Attentive" staff, who are "especially knowledgeable in all respects" are also often mentioned. / www.andrewfairlie.co.uk; restaurant_andrew_fairlie; Mon-Sat 10 pm; closed Mon-Sat L, closed Sun; Cash & all usual cards; No shorts; children: 12+.

JON & FERNANDA'S £63 543

34 HIGH STREET PH3 1DB 01764 662442

"Any trip to Scotland and in particular Gleneagles would not be complete without dinner at Jon & Fernanda's!" – so say fans of this "great find" near the famous resort, whose "friendly and welcoming" style helps make it "a firm favourite" for those who have discovered it over the last 22 years. The "locally sourced" à la carte menu is an accomplished but relatively down-to-earth antidote to the fancier fare found down the road: "it is so hard to choose from, with so many stunning dishes and wonderful presentation". / www.jonandfernandas.co.uk; Wed-Sat 9 pm; closed Wed-Sat L, closed Mon & Tue & Sun; Cash & all usual cards; No shorts; booking evening only; children: 10+.

STRATHEARN RESTAURANT, GLENEAGLES HOTEL 343

PH3 1NF 0800 731 9219

This famous resort's traditional fine-dining venue (as opposed to the more avant-garde Restaurant Andrew Fairlie, along the corridor) is "a wonderful throwback to a bygone age of elegance and sophistication" – "complete with live pianist", silver service and a trolley bearing the roast of the day, beef Wellington and Dover sole. "Despite all this, the ambience is not stuffy", and the culinary skills on display are thoroughly "modern". / gleneagles.com; Mon-Sun 9 pm; Cash & all usual cards.

THE BARN AT MOOR HALL £82 444

PRESCOT RD L39 6RT 01695 572511

The "modern and well-designed" alternative to the hall's main dining room is much more casual, and makes a top choice to enjoy the environs of the venue and its "professional" standards, but in a more relaxed vein. The "assured" cooking has won it a Michelin star, but that's something of a distraction really. Though interesting and impeccably sourced, the menu is quite straightforward, not particularly 'haute', and much more affordable than the main hall (especially with the early-in-the-week deals at lunch and dinner). Kids' menus and good outside tables in summer complete a likeable but conventional picture. / moorhall.com/the-barn/about; thebarnmh; Wed-Fri 9 pm, Sun 6 pm; closed Wed L closed Sun D, closed Mon & Tue & Sat.

MOOR HALL £273 554

PRESCOT RD L39 6RT 01695 572511

"What can I say that's not already been said? Just superb!" – Mark Birchall's converted manor house north of Liverpool is five years old now, but still has the golden glow of one of the UK's most fast-rising culinary stars, and some fans say they "thought it had a chance of its third Michelin star this year". That would be an achievement anywhere – never mind in a corner of West Lancashire long seen as a gastronomic wasteland. The long drive, the lake, the grounds, the cleverly refurbished medieval buildings… all create a "perfect and luxurious experience". "The dining room and lounges are sleek and welcoming and the attention to detail from the kitchen garden to the cheese room, even to the cutlery is flawless". "Best of all, every mouthful from its tasting menu is fresh, clean and sublime" and a clear reflection of the "dedication, high standards and clear technical expertise" in the kitchen. Fame is bringing one drawback though – even those who judge it a "fabulous" experience sometimes think it risks becoming an "outrageously expensive" one. And – amidst praise for "fun and unintimidating staff who don't miss a beat" – there is also the odd fear of "an over-focus on creating theatre rather than making the customer totally relaxed". Top Tip – "the food bonanza continues at breakfast so stay over if you can". / www.moorhall.com; restaurantmoorhall; Thu-Sun, Wed 8.30 pm; closed Wed L, closed Mon & Tue; Cash & all usual cards.

SO-LO £95 433

17 TOWN GREEN LANE L39 6SE 01695 302170

"Opened in late 2021, we visited on only their second night open, but the cooking was faultless and we're looking forward to going back at the earliest opportunity" – Tim Allen's year-old operation may not yet attract quite the same volume of feedback as Moor Hall, just down the road, but his 40-seater is highly rated by its small fanclub. In the evening, the format is a 6-course tasting menu for £75 – lunch is a more conventional (and cheaper) £35 for three courses. / www.restaurantsolo.co.uk; Mon, Thu-Sat 9 pm, Sun 4 pm; closed Mon L closed Sun D, closed Tue & Wed.

THE TRADDOCK HOTEL   £65   3 3 3

LA2 8BY   01524 251224

This Georgian manor house hotel in the Dales has been run by the Reynolds family for 21 years, with a kitchen that sends out everything from lavish afternoon teas to a "delicious" 10-course tasting menu – and "the quality and consistency are excellent whether you go down the fish route, meat or vegetarian". / www.thetraddock.co.uk; the_traddock; Mon-Sun 8.30 pm.

HARTWELL HOUSE £71   2 3 4

OXFORD ROAD   HP17 8NR   01296 747444

"Old-school service and food" are cornerstones of this Jacobean/Georgian stately home spa hotel with grounds by Capability Brown, owned by the National Trust. "Afternoon tea in one of the ante-rooms whilst sat on a sofa is a delight" and it's a "lovely place for a few days' stay, too!". / www.hartwell-house.com/wine-and-dine; hartwellhouse; Mon-Sun 9 pm; payment – credit card only; No jeans; children: 6+.

RIVERSIDE INN   £51   4 3 3

HR6 9ST   01568 708440

"Dreamily good" food from chef/co-owner Andy Link's eco-conscious menu inspires enthusiastic reports on this "historic" half-timbered pub, dating from 1600, perched beside the River Lugg, "with good walks nearby". "Every course is memorable, imaginative and perfectly executed" – while Sunday lunch "sets a new bar". The business became carbon-neutral last year, and adds a voluntary donation of £1.50 to each diner's bill to offset the footprint of their meal. Top Menu Tip – "rye and truffle bread with nettle butter" and "gorse fudge". / www.riversideaymestrey.co.uk; therivkitchen; Mon-Sat 9 pm; closed Mon L, closed Sun.

THE LATYMER, PENNYHILL PARK HOTEL   £168   4 3 4

LONDON ROAD   GU19 5EU   01276 486150

The "small, intimate dining room" at this luxury resort hotel has long been a top gastronomic destination, and currently has "the wow factor" under chef Steve Smith, who made his name at Bohemia in Jersey and is "at the top of his game". His "interesting and enjoyable 6-course tasting menu" is a "real pleasure", and comes with "stunning wine pairings", while "staff are able to swap out foods without any fuss". / www.exclusive.co.uk/pennyhill-park/food/latymer;

pennyhill_park; Wed-Sun 8.30 pm; closed Wed-Sun L, closed Mon & Tue; payment – credit card only; booking max 8 may apply; children: 12+.

PIEDANIELS   £58   4 3 3

BATH ST   DE45 1BX   01629 812687

"A good standard is maintained" at Eric & Christiana Piedaniel's Gallic venture of over 25 years' standing – a smartly decorated and comfortable venue, which inhabits a high-ceilinged, characterful oak-beamed room and which serves traditional French cuisine that's "good value". / www.piedaniels-restaurant.com; Tue-Sat 11 pm; closed Sun & Mon; Cash & all usual cards.

RESTAURANT LOVAGE BY LEE SMITH   £55   3 4 3

BATH STREET   DE45 1DS   01629 815 613

"Delightful food", "prepared with love and care", is on Derbyshire-born chef Lee Smith's menu at the crowdfunded restaurant he opened three years ago, having quit as head chef at Michelin-starred Samphire on Jersey. There's a "lovely ambience" in the cleverly modernised historic building, and everything tastes "fresh and delicious". / www.restaurantlovage.co.uk; lovagerestaurant; Thu-Sat, Wed 9 pm; closed Wed L, closed Mon & Tue & Sun.

PALE HALL HOTEL RESTAURANT   £93   4 4 4

PALE ESTATE, LLANDDERFEL   LL23 7PS   01678 530 285

"What joy to return to Palé Hall, and their standards of welcome, service, presentation and flavour". If this plush Relais & Châteaux property (the Duke of Westminster's former hunting lodge) near the River Dee was not stuck out in the sticks of North Wales, it would likely be much better known. Chef Gareth Stevenson offers a five-course or eight-course menu that receives limited but exceptional feedback in our annual diners' poll. Another attraction here is the afternoon tea: "a fine variety, beautifully set and well-served. A treat indeed. Unhurried and unstinting. Well done!" / www.palehall.co.uk; palehallhotel; Mon-Sun 9 pm; Cash & all usual cards; No trainers; children: 12.

MONACHYLE MHOR   £102   4 4 4

FK19 8PQ   01877 384622

"Well worth the lengthy detour" – "hidden away up a long narrow road", with views over Lochs Voil and Doine – Tom Lewis's "unique" boutique hotel puts a contemporary slant on traditional Highlands hospitality, while chef Marysia Paszkowska's menus rely heavily on home-grown produce. / www.mhor.net; themhorcollection; Mon, Thu-Sun 9 pm; closed Tue & Wed; Cash & all usual cards.

THE POTTED LOBSTER   £71   4 3 3

3 LUCKER ROAD   NE69 7BS   01668 214088

"Fabulous fresh seafood" – "the best for miles" – plays to packed houses at this "delightful" spot from well-known Alnick-born chef Richard Sim, which is generally agreed to be "one of the best restaurants in Northumberland" – "no wonder it's so hard to get a table". "For a seafood restaurant they serve amazing veggie food", while the menu also stretches to local beef and "delicious desserts". There's now a spin-off far away in Abersoch on the Llyn Peninsula in Wales. / www.thepottedlobster.co.uk; thepottedlobster; Mon-Sun 9 pm.

THE SWAN   £53   4 3 3

STATION RD   EX16 9NG   01398 332 248

This "great gastropub" from Paul & Donna Berry has earned a stellar reputation over a decade and more, and is "not to be missed when in Devon". "The excellent food is served by warm and friendly staff", and there's a "good range of beers". / www.theswan.co; theswanbampton; Mon-Sat 11 pm, Sun 8.30 pm; Cash & all usual cards.

LUNAR   £125   4 4 3

WEDGWOOD DRIVE   ST12 9ER   07494 073091

"Everything about this place is wonderful, most importantly the food but also the staff, the building and the decor. Incredible!". So say fans of this mouldbreaking late 2021 newcomer, whose high falutin' fine dining formula challenges expectations of both The Potteries generally, and the large unit it inhabits in particular (with 80 covers and a chef's table for 12). Overseen by local lad Niall Keating, head chef Craig Lunn produces a twelve-course tasting menu for just under £100 per person – "local Staffordshire produce plus hints of Japan and Asia". Feedback is still quite limited however, and the overall rating moderated by those who feel the performance is merely "good" rather than "outstanding". / www.lunarwedgwood.com; lunarwedgwood; Thu-Sat midnight, Sun 4 pm; closed Thu & Fri L closed Sun D, closed Mon & Tue & Wed.

ODOS   £40   4 5 3

238-240 HIGH STREET   EN5 5TD   020 8440 6222

This "posh Greek" which opened in 2019 is widely held to be "the best local restaurant" in the Barnet area, and popular owner Louis "has it bang-off" with "great fish and excellent meats". There are "lots of little sharing plates, with surprising dishes such as ceviche which are incredible", while "service is fantastic". "All the locals have discovered the secret, so this

is one to book in advance!". / odosrestaurant.
co.uk; odosrestaurant; Tue-Sat 10 pm, Sun 9 pm;
closed Mon.

BARNT GREEN, WEST MIDLANDS   5–4C

BLACK & GREEN   £85

49 HEWELL ROAD   B45 8NL
0121 655 5550

In June 2022 (after our annual diners' poll had
concluded), Andrew Sheridan of Birmingham's
Eight (see also) with partners Sam & Emma
Morgan opened this new 16-seat restaurant in a
small village outside Brum (near the intersection
of the M6 and M42). It serves a duo of seven-
course and eight-course 'micro-seasonal' menus
for £60 per person and £70 per person. /
aboutblackandgreen.co.uk; Wed-Sat 10.30 pm;
closed Wed-Sat L, closed Mon & Tue & Sun.

BARRASFORD, NORTHUMBERLAND   8–2A

BARRASFORD
ARMS   £50   333

NE48 4AA   01434 681237

Overlooking Houghton Castle, this two-
hundred-year-old pub boasts a "beer garden
with lovely views". Feedback is limited, but
continues to give a good all-round impression
regarding the "locally sourced food". /
www.barrasfordarms.co.uk; barrasfordarms; closed
Mon-Sat & Sun; No Amex; children: 18 + in bar
after 9.30pm.

BARTLOW, CAMBRIDGESHIRE   3–1B

THE THREE HILLS,
BARTLOW   £60   323

DEAN ROAD   CB21 4PW   01223 890500

"The kitchen has the knack of turning pot-
boilers into something special, and finding
unusual combinations that work, and work
very well", say fans of this big rural gastropub,
whose menu includes wood-fired pizza.
In summer you can eat in the large beer
garden, and there's also a heated, covered
outdoor terrace. / www.thethreehills.co.uk;
thethreehillsbartlow; Wed-Sat 9 pm, Sun 4 pm;
closed Sun D, closed Mon & Tue; payment – credit
card only.

BARTON-ON-SEA, HAMPSHIRE   2–4C

PEBBLE BEACH   £66   334

MARINE DRIVE   BH25 7DZ   01425 627777

This "high-quality" restaurant with rooms
excels for its "very good seafood" on an Italian-
influenced menu from Andy Waters, one of
vanishingly few British chefs to have worked
under the great Paul Bocuse in Lyons. "A
table on the terrace on a good day cannot be
beaten", with "great views" across the Solent
to the Isle of Wight. / www.pebblebeach-uk.com;
pebblebeachuk; Wed-Sun 10 pm; closed Mon &
Tue; Cash & all usual cards.

BASLOW, DERBYSHIRE   5–2C

FISCHERS AT BASLOW
HALL   £114   444

CALVER RD   DE45 1RR   01246 583259

"Fischers is almost a by-word for elegant
country-house dining in the Peak District" –
"the food is creative and tasty", and "a really
attentive team looks after you". "The setting is
hugely impressive", too: "a grand house that
still feels warm and friendly", a short drive
from the even more impressive Chatsworth.
Top Menu Tip – "they have a fantastic
pastry chef" – so leave room for pudding. /
www.fischers-baslowhall.co.uk; FischersBaslow;
Wed-Sun 8 pm; closed Mon & Tue; Cash & all
usual cards; No trainers.

BATCOMBE, SOMERSET   2–3B

THE THREE HORSESHOES

BA4 6HE   01749 850359

Owner Max Wigram has known Margot
Henderson of Rochelle Canteen in Shoreditch
since he was a teen and asked her to take
over the stoves at this restored 17th-century
Somerset inn with rooms, which is scheduled to
reopen after refurbishment in November 2022.
According to a September 2022 interview in
Wallpaper, he asked her because he "wanted
it to be really good, with no poncey rubbish"
and it will open all day from breakfast onwards.
There's a walled garden which will come into its
own in the summer months. / Fri & Sat 11 pm.

BATH, SOMERSET   2–2B

THE BATH PRIORY   £120   224

WESTON RD   BA1 2XT   01225 331922

Long a bastion of traditional fine dining in
Bath, this luxury hotel was the first acquired
by Andrew & Christine Brownsword almost 30
years ago, as they started to put together their
portfolio of leading properties. Ratings have
slipped in the past couple of years, though, with
a high proportion of reports even from fans
suggesting that "the prices are too much" for
"food and service not at the level expected".
Damning critiques are absent, however – it's
a question of value. / www.thebathpriory.co.uk;
brownswordhotels; Wed-Sun 8.30 pm; closed Wed-
Sun L, closed Mon & Tue; Cash & all usual cards;
No jeans; children: 5+ L, 12+ D.

THE BECKFORD BOTTLE
SHOP   £61   344

5-8 SAVILLE ROW   BA1 2QP
01225 809302

"Delicious small plates and a great wine list
make this a real treat" – as the name suggests,
it is primarily a vintner's with "excellent
wine served by knowledgeable and charming
staff", but "the tapas-style food is great", with
"interesting seasonal-inspired small plates" full
of "punchy flavours". Top Tip – "a steal on a
Monday when you can choose any wine from
the shop at retail and enjoy it with your meal".
/ www.beckfordbottleshop.com; beckfordbottles;
Tue-Sat 11 pm; closed Sun & Mon.

CHEZ DOMINIQUE   £66   332

15 ARGYLE STREET   BA2 4BQ
01225 463482

A "lovely" spot for a "nice, well-presented
family meal" in Bath, this six-year-old from
chef Chris Tabbitt (who trained at Simon
Hopkinson's Bibendum) and Sarah Olivier
has built a solid following for its "very
proficient" modern European menus. /
www.chezdominique.co.uk; chezdominique; Mon-
Sat 9.30 pm, Sun 9 pm.

THE CIRCUS   £56   342

34 BROCK ST   BA1 2LN   01225 466020

"Outstanding fish" is one of the better bets
at this popular independent close to the town
centre, and "service is outstanding too". The
"excellent pre-theatre menu is delightful and
a bargain". / www.thecircusrestaurant.co.uk;
thecircusrestaurant; Mon-Sat midnight; closed Sun;
Cash & all usual cards; children: 7.

CLAYTON'S
KITCHEN   £73   333

15A GEORGE ST   BA1 2EN
01225 585 100

"Dining is always special in this lovely Georgian
townhouse bistro", where chef Rob Clayton
has served "really great" modern French meals
in a "bustling, bright dining room" for more
than 10 years. A veteran of the legendary Chez
Nico in London, Rob first came to Bath to head
up the kitchen at the luxury Priory Hotel. /
www.claytonskitchen.com; claytons_kitchen; Wed &
Thu, Sun 9.30 pm, Fri & Sat 10 pm; closed Mon &
Tue; Cash & all usual cards.

COLONNA &
SMALLS   £13   444

6 CHAPEL ROW   BA1 1HN   07766 808067

This "absolutely spot-on coffee shop" is the
"perfect place to kill time time, and the coffee
is sensational" – "served by knowledgeable
staff" led by Maxwell Colonna-Dashwood,
a three-time UK barista champion and
pioneer who studied 'third wave' coffee in
Melbourne before founding his shop in 2009.
/ www.colonnaandsmalls.co.uk; Sun-Fri 4 pm, Sat
5 pm; closed Mon-Sun D; No Amex; booking max
6 may apply.

CORKAGE (CHAPEL
ROW)   £46   334

5 CHAPEL ROW   BA1 1HN   01225 423417

A range of "eclectic English seasonal tapas/
small plates" – with plenty of modern
European influences – is served alongside "a
very credible but affordable wine list" at this
wine shop and bar off Queen Square that
started life as a pop-up social project. "There's
now a huge barn extension that allows for a
pleasant summer evening" spent sampling
"interesting and unusual wines". / corkagebath.
com; corkagebath; Mon-Sat midnight; closed Mon-
Thu L, closed Sun.

The Terrace, Montagu Arms Hotel, Beaulieu

THE ELDER AT THE INDIGO HOTEL 3|3|4

2 SOUTH PARADE   BA2 4AB
01225 530616

Wild game is the highlight of dining at this venture from specialist Mike Robinson (co-owner of the Harwood Arms in Fulham), who manages deer herds on local estates to produce venison for chef Gavin Edney's "very good" menu. The stylish 166-bedroom boutique hotel opened in 2020 following the renovation of several adjoining Grade I and Grade II listed Bath stone townhouses. / theelder.co.uk; theelderrestaurant; Mon, Wed & Thu, Sun, Fri & Sat 11 pm; closed Mon, Wed & Thu, Sun L, closed Tue.

GREEN PARK BRASSERIE 3|3|3

GREEN PARK STATION   BA1 1JB
01225 338565

A converted old railway station provides a "pretty setting amongst the trees, next to the (currently) abandoned Ironbridge railway line" at this 'casual dining steakhouse and jazz bar'. On limited feedback, it remains well-rated all-round for its "basic-but-honest menu, with local ingredients from local suppliers and beer supplied by a local microbrewery". / www.greenparkbrasserie.com; GreenParkBraz; Tue-Thu 10 pm, Sat, Fri 10.30 pm, Mon 2.30 pm, Sun 3 pm; closed Sun & Mon D; Cash & all usual cards.

HENRY'S RESTAURANT £84 4|3|3

4 SAVILLE ROW   BA1 2QP   01225 780055

"Consistently excellent food, both set lunch and evening tasting menu" (and including a "lovely vcg tasting menu") confirm that chef Henry Scott is back on top form, after a drop in the ratings post-Covid. A single complaint this year: "chairs could be a bit more comfortable!". The former Hibiscus chef opened his Georgian townhouse venture in 2016. / www.henrysrestaurantbath.com; henrysrestaurantbath; Wed-Sat, Tue 8.30 pm; closed Tue L, closed Sun & Mon.

INDIAN TEMPTATION £39 3|3|2

09-10 HIGH STREET (CHEAP STREET)
BA1 5AQ   01225464631

"A fantastic array of vegan options, all served with a smile and conversation" win nothing but praise for this "friendly" restaurant next to the Roman baths and cathedral. "We had two small plates dishes highlighting different areas of India which were both excellent!" / www.indiantemptation.com; indiantemptationuk; Mon-Sun 10.30 pm; Cash & all usual cards.

THE IVY BATH BRASSERIE £77 2|3|4

39 MILSOM ST   BA1 1DS   01225 307 100

The "particularly pleasant outdoor terrace" and "lovely interior" are – as is typical for the brand – key attributes at this link in the ubiquitous national chain, which is one of the more commented-on destinations in the city. Gastronomically, it "does not excite", although some reporters are "pleasantly surprised at the food". / theivybath.brasserie.com; theivybath; Mon-Thu 10.30 pm, Fri & Sat 11 pm, Sun 10 pm.

MARLBOROUGH TAVERN £47 3|2|2

35 MARLBOROUGH BUILDINGS   BA1 2LY
01225 423731

This "top-notch gastropub" offers both "good vegetarian options" and "great Sunday roasts". Its popularity and "buzzy atmosphere" owe much to a "lovely pub garden" and handy town-centre address, around the corner from the Royal Crescent. / www.marlborough-tavern.com; marlboroughtavern; Mon-Sat 9 pm, Sun 8 pm; No Amex.

MENU GORDON JONES £97 4|4|3

2 WELLSWAY   BA2 3AQ   01225 480871

The "food and wine are always interesting" and are "still as good as ever" at engaging Anglo-Scottish chef Gordon Jones's former sandwich shop on the southern edge of town. There's "a single tasting menu available" (the only choice is whether to have 7 or 9 courses) and it comes as a complete surprise, with each dish introduced as it arrives at your table (and no vegetarian or other options). / www.menugordonjones.co.uk; menugordonjones; Wed-Sat 8 pm; closed Mon & Tue & Sun; No Amex; children: 12.

NOYA'S KITCHEN £56 5|4|3

7 SAINT JAMES'S PARADE   BA1 1UL
01225 684439

Noya Pawlyn's "delightful Vietnamese food" – "varied, interesting and full of fresh flavours, with a vibrant and zesty edge" – "delivers on every single visit" and has made the small restaurant she opened five years ago "justifiably popular". "How little Noya does it so well is a mystery" – but it may have something to do with the skills she learnt as a child, cooking for her siblings in a Hong Kong refugee camp while her parents went out to work. And it's not just a cheap and cheerful option: there's a "surprisingly good wine list", and "it's a great place for a date". / www.noyaskitchen.co.uk; noyaskitchen; Wed & Thu, Sat 9 pm, Tue 3.30 pm, Fri 10 pm; closed Tue D, closed Sun & Mon.

OAK £32 4|3|3

2 NORTH PARADE PASSAGE   BA1 1NX
01225 446059

"The food is astonishing" – "creative vegetarian fare (actually vegan when I went)" – and the "service is wonderful" at this "warm and friendly" outfit in one of Bath's oldest buildings. "They used to be called Acorn but changed their whole approach to small plates" a couple of years ago. "Food is imaginative and prepared flawlessly", and there's a "short but varied wine list". / www.oakrestaurant.co.uk; oakrestaurantbath; Mon-Sun 9.30 pm.

THE OLIVE TREE, QUEENSBERRY HOTEL £131 5|3|2

RUSSELL ST   BA1 2QF   01225447928

"Chris Cleghorn produces high-quality fare with a range of tasting menus" at this long-established and well-renowned venture (currently Bath's only Michelin-starred establishment), in the cellar of a comfortable independently run hotel. This year's average food scores were particularly high. There are still quibbles raised by some about the "slightly sterile basement dining room" and that a visit is "not cheap". Such concerns were mostly drowned out this year, though, by the majority who pronounce it "virtually perfect in every respect: a Treat with a capital 'T'!" / www.thequeensberry.co.uk; thequeensberry; Tue-Sun 9 pm; closed Tue-Thu L, closed Mon; Cash & all usual cards; No shorts.

THE SCALLOP SHELL £67 4|4|3

22 MONMOUTH PLACE   BA1 2AY
01225 420928

"Amazing fish 'n' chips and a good selection of utterly fresh seafood" have made this "upmarket" chippy (which over the pandemic acquired "a nice roof terrace with heaters") into "a bit of an institution in Bath". / www.thescallopshell.co.uk; thescallopshell; Mon-Sat 9.30 pm, Sun 3.30 pm; closed Sun D; payment – credit card only.

UPSTAIRS AT LANDRACE £61 5|4|3

61 WALCOT STREET   BA1 5BN
01225 424722

"Such a fabulous place! Relaxed but with great attention to detail" – within a year of opening above the popular Landrace bakery, ex-Quality Chophouse and Brawn chef Rob Sachdev's "austere" Med-inspired spot was being tipped by its fanclub as "the best restaurant in Bath" (in particular, of a more hip and casual variety). The weekly changing menu has an "amazing range of small plates to start, including the lightest, most delicious cheese puffs", while "mains are typically one meat, fish or veggie pasta option". Top Tip – "I'm still dreaming of those parmesan fritters". / landracebakery.com; landraceupstairs; Wed-Sat 9.45 pm; closed Mon & Tue & Sun.

THE WHITE HART INN £64 3|3|4

WIDCOMBE HILL   BA2 6AA
01225 338053

A "quirky and interesting" local with a "good atmosphere" serving a "creative menu, with cooking of a consistent high standard". It makes a "fantastic pub for Sunday lunch", with "outstanding roasts". / www.whitehartbath.co.uk; whitehartbath; Tue-Sat 11 pm, Sun 4 pm; closed Tue L closed Sun D, closed Mon; No Amex.

BAUGHURST, HAMPSHIRE   2–3D

THE WELLINGTON ARMS £70 3|3|3

BAUGHURST RD   RG26 5LP
0118 982 0110

"Superb food" – "a well-crafted blend of pub classics and more ambitious dishes" – is on the menu at this attractive gastropub run by chef Jason King and FOH Simon Page. It benefits from a "beautiful setting – especially if you can sit in the garden", where they grow much of their produce. Top Tip – "they also sell their own preserves". / www.thewellingtonarms.com; thewellingtonarms; Tue-Sat 8.30 pm; closed Sun & Mon; No Amex.

BEACONSFIELD, BUCKINGHAMSHIRE   3–3A

THE CAPE GRAND CAFE & RESTAURANT £58 3|3|3

6A, BURKES PARADE   HP9 1NN
01494 681137

This "friendly and popular local cafe" has won an enviable reputation over two decades for its "spectacular breakfast or brunch, with South African specialities". On Friday and Saturday nights they gear up for proper evening meals with various bobotie and braai variations, too. / www.thecapeonline.com; thecapebeaconsfield; Mon-Sat 4 pm, Sun 3 pm; closed Mon-Sun D; No Amex.

THE GREYHOUND £87 4|5|4

33 WINDSOR END   HP9 2JN
01494 671315

"Beautiful building… beautiful food… beautiful people" – Daniel Crump and Margriet Vandezande-Crump have transformed this old pub (since they took it over in 2019) to create a "wonderful" destination in this chichi town, once devoid of much in the way of culinary interest. They are not only "amazing hosts" ("and have put together a fantastic team") but also "constantly innovating as well as working actively in the local community". "The menu changes rapidly to reflect the best seasonal ingredients at any time of year" and the "strong standard of cooking" adds to a "wonderful" offering all-round. / greyhoundbeaconsfield.co.uk; greyhoundbeaconsfield; Tue-Sat 8.30 pm; closed Sun & Mon.

RIWAZ BY ATUL KOCHHAR £78 3|4|3

41 AYLESBURY END   HP9 1LU
01494 728126

Big-hitting London chef Atul Kochhar (of Mafair's Kanishka) opened this "excellent" new venue in Beaconsfield's old town last year, to general agreement that "staff are attentive and the food is wonderful", full of "clean and light flavours". On the debit side, "the music is way too loud" for some tastes, while "prices that are acceptable when restaurateurs are paying West End rents might just seem too much in this setting". / riwazrestaurants.co.uk; riwazbucks; Wed-Sat 10 pm, Sun 9.30 pm; closed Mon & Tue.

THE ROYAL STANDARD OF ENGLAND £61 2|3|4

FORTY GREEN   HP9 1XT   01494 673 382

This "atmospheric 900-year-old pub" – quite possibly the oldest free house in England – is "full of nooks and crannies" and has "bags of charm and character" (it's a popular film and TV set, and sometimes is closed for filming). There's a menu of "very good pub classics", with "homemade sausages and mash" a popular option. / www.rsoe.co.uk; Mon-Sat 10 pm, Sun 9 pm; No Amex.

BEAMINSTER, DORSET   2–4B

THE OLLEROD £77 4|2|2

3 PROUT HILL   DT8 3AY   01308 862200

"A hidden gem in Beaminster", this "atmospheric" fourteenth-century stone house is now a restaurant-with-rooms ('ollerod' being an old Dorset name for cowslip) serving "outstanding food" from Chris Staines, former head chef at Bath Priory and the Mandarin Oriental hotel in Knightsbridge ("there are clear but subtle oriental touches throughout the tasty menu"). The "charming front of house" is run by owner Silvana Bandini, formerly of Pig hotels. / theollerod.co.uk; theollerod; Mon & Tue, Thu-Sat 9 pm, Sun 7 pm; closed Wed.

BEARSTED, KENT   3–3C

FISH ON THE GREEN £78 3|3|2

CHURCH LN   ME14 4EJ   01622 738 300

A "great selection of well-presented fish" is the reason to visit this seafood restaurant on the village green (originally part of the neighbouring inn, which houses their sister restaurant, Oak on the Green). / www.fishonthegreen.com; Wed-Fri, Tue 11 pm, Sun 5 pm, Sat 11.30 pm; closed Tue L closed Sun D, closed Mon; No Amex.

BEAULIEU, HAMPSHIRE   2–4D

THE TERRACE, MONTAGU ARMS HOTEL £92 3|3|3

SO42 7ZL   01590 612324

"Exquisite food is served by charming and attentive staff in an atmospheric Arts & Crafts building" at this popular New Forest hotel, consistently well rated for its focus on local produce in its 4-course or 6-course menus. We've maintained the rating from our annual diners' poll unchanged, but it's worth noting that mid-survey, in May 2022, Nathan Eades took over the stoves here. / www.montaguarmshotel.co.uk; montaguarms; Wed-Sun 8 pm; closed Mon & Tue; Cash & all usual cards; children: 11+ D.

BECKENHAM, GREATER LONDON   3–3B

CHAI NAASTO £50 3|3|3

2 - 4 FAIRFIELD ROAD   BR3 3LD
020 3750 0888

This "quirky Indian restaurant" was set up by three brothers inspired by the cooking of their peripatetic grandmother, whose recipes contain traces of Somalia, Saudi Arabia and Britain as well as the street food of India. / www.chai-naasto.co.uk; chai_naasto; Wed-Sat 11 pm, Sun 8 pm; closed Wed-Fri L, closed Mon & Tue.

BELFAST, COUNTY ANTRIM   10–1D

DEANES EIPIC £110 3|4|3

28-40 HOWARD STREET   BT1 6PF
028 9033 1134

The flagship destination in the city-centre restaurant complex opened by pioneering Belfast chef Michael Deane 25 years ago, Eipic now has rising head chef Alex Greene at the helm, turning out "exceptional" and stylish cuisine – "I've eaten half a dozen Michelin star meals this year and Eipic edges it for me – better value for money, and you can dip in and out of the matching wines rather than having £90 added to the bill for taking all the pairings". Sceptics can find it "a bit uptight and textbook, even if the food is well-cooked" – "you get into Eipic (and indeed go to the toilet) by walking through another Deanes restaurant, and each time I did so I wanted to stay there instead!" / www.deaneseipic.com; DEANES_EIPIC; Thu-Sat 9 pm; closed Mon-Wed & Sun.

MOURNE SEAFOOD BAR £55 443

34 - 36 BANK STREET BT1 1HL
028 9024 8544

"Having helped create Belfast's vibrant foodie vibe", this well-known venue is still "a must-visit in the city". "Small and cosy, with wooden tables and a great atmosphere", it serves a "varied menu in generous portions, with interesting specials alongside staples". A newly extended beer garden with gazebos and heaters also offers street-food-style menu from 'The Shack'. Top Menu Tip – "the mussels are always superb". / www.mourneseafood.com; Mourne Seafood Bar; Wed & Thu 9.30 pm, Fri & Sat 10 pm, Sun 9 pm; closed Wed L, closed Mon & Tue; Cash & all usual cards; no bookings at lunch.

THE MUDDLERS CLUB £98 544

1 WAREHOUSE LANE BT1 2DX
028 9031 3199

"A Michelin starred restaurant tucked away in Belfast's Cathedral Quarter and deservedly so with exceptional food, wine and service" – that's still our take on Gareth McCaughey's ambitious but hard-to-pigeon-hole operation, with an open kitchen. It first opened in 2015, and has since established itself as one of the top destinations in Northern Ireland. / www.themuddlersclubbelfast.com; themuddlersclubbelfast; Wed-Sat 9.30 pm; closed Wed & Thu L, closed Mon & Tue & Sun.

OX £96 453

1 OXFORD ST BT1 3LA 028 9031 4121

"A great vibe makes up for the ordinary-looking space" at Stephen Toman's waterside venue, whose "fun" style is fueled by "lots of staff milling about to help you have a good time"; and the "exciting wine list from his attached wine bar" (OxCave). But it's far more than just a good-time place – renowned as one of the island of Ireland's top kitchens – and it serves an "exceptional", "well thought-out" and "good value" tasting menu (10 courses for £75). / www.oxbelfast.com; oxbelfast; Wed-Sat 9.30 pm; closed Wed L, closed Mon & Tue & Sun; Cash & all usual cards.

THE CRAB AND LOBSTER INN £63 333

32 FORELANDS FIELD RD PO35 5TR
01983 872244

This "excellent" seaside gastropub-with-rooms on the eastern tip of the Isle of Wight has stunning views to Hayling Island and Selsey on the mainland. Opinions divide slightly on the cooking: a couple of disappointed diners thought it's "no longer what it once was", but a majority recommend very good fish cooking here. / www.crabandlobsterinn.co.uk; Mon-Sun 8.30 pm; No Amex.

CERUTTI '2' £33 333

STATION SQUARE HU17 0AS
01482 866700

This "very good fish restaurant backing on Beverley railway station" (it occupies the old waiting room) was opened by chef-owner Tina Cerutti in 1989; she still runs it with her brother Tony, who closed the Hull branch in 2019. With roots in southern Italy, the family have been a fixture of the Yorkshire dining scene for 65 years. / www.ceruttis.co.uk; Wed-Sat 8.30 pm, Sun 2 pm; closed Sun D, closed Mon & Tue.

THE PIPE & GLASS £74 444

WEST END HU17 7PN 01430 810246

James and Kate Mackenzie imbue this "warm and professional" gastropub with personality and – notwithstanding an out-of-the-way location in East Yorkshire – it continues to be one of the most highly commented-on in the country. Despite its plaudits from Michelin, it has remained "realistically priced" and the menu steers a clever line between options that are ambitious enough to lift them well above the ordinary, but grounded enough not to seem fancy-schmancy: "superb dishes, all with a local accent". In summer, "a lovely evening is boosted by the beautiful garden and terrace for drinks". Fans say it's "well worth the 100 mile round trip!" although there are also "delightful rooms in the gardens" where you can stay. / www.pipeandglass.co.uk; pipeandglass; Tue-Sat 11 pm, Sun 4 pm; closed Sun D, closed Mon; Cash & all usual cards.

THE WESTWOOD RESTAURANT £78 433

NEW WALK HU17 7AE 01482 881999

"Excellent food, attentive service and reasonable prices" – this 15-year-old venue in a converted Georgian courthouse "never fails" to please under its "lovely owner-hosts", twins Michelle & chef Matt Barker, and their "friendly, welcoming team". Top Tip – "the local Leven duck crispy salad is delicious". / www.thewestwood.co.uk; the_westwood_restaurant; Wed-Sat 9.30 pm, Sun 3 pm; closed Sun D, closed Mon & Tue; Cash & all usual cards.

MILLER & CARTER BEXLEY £52 222

BOURNE RD DA5 1PQ 01322 552748

"Very busy steak-centric restaurant" (part of a chain owned by pub giant Mitchells & Butlers) that is one of the more commented-on destinations in our annual diners' poll in the poorly served 'burbs to the south east of the metropolis. The food is "reliable", "without being exceptional" and – notwithstanding some blips regarding service and management generally – this can be a "reasonable" destination in the locale. / www.millerandcarter.co.uk/restaurants/london/millerandcarterbexley ; millerandcarter;

Mon-Sat 11 pm, Sun 10.30 pm; Cash & all usual cards; No trainers.

KENTISH HARE £70 342

95 BIDBOROUGH RIDGE TN3 0XB
01892 525709

"Imaginative cooking, blending tastes and textures very well indeed", makes for "elevated pub food" at Chris & James Tanners' smart and "enjoyable" gastroboozer. It is delivered with "cheerful service" and at "decent prices". Top Tip – "fantastic Sunday lunch". / www.thekentishhare.com; Wed-Sat 9.30 pm, Sun 3.30 pm; closed Sun D, closed Mon & Tue.

THE THREE CHIMNEYS £54 444

HAREPLAIN RD TN27 8LW
01580 291472

This "lovely traditional Kentish pub" – timber-framed and full of nooks and crannies that include five dining areas – offers "imaginative dishes together with classics" on a menu that's "a cut above good pub food". "We love taking visitors there to impress". / www.thethreechimneys.co.uk; Mon-Sat 11 pm, Sun 10.30 pm; No Amex.

THE WEST HOUSE RESTAURANT WITH ROOMS £90 333

28 HIGH ST TN27 8AH 01580 291341

A happy crowd of regulars have beaten a path to the "delicious, inventive food and wine" served by rock drummer-turned-chef Graham Garrett at his sixteenth-century village weaver's cottage for 21 years now. Returnees are "not disappointed" – "the tasting menu took us on a wonderful journey with excellent stop-off points to taste the marvellous and beautifully presented food en route". / www.thewesthouserestaurant.co.uk; thewesthouserestaurant; Thu-Sat 9.30 pm, Sun 2.30 pm; closed Sat L closed Sun D, closed Mon & Tue & Wed; No Amex; booking max 8 may apply.

THE OYSTER SHACK £69 434

MILLBURN ORCHARD FARM, STAKES HILLS TQ7 4BE 01548 810876

"A lovely spot to eat fantastic fresh Devon seafood, simply served and tasty every time" – this informal operation was an oyster farm where guests picnicked beside the Avon estuary. These days there's a bar, but it's still pretty basic. / www.oystershack.co.uk; theoystershack; Mon-Sun 7.30 pm; Cash & all usual cards.

THE BILDESTON CROWN   £63   333

104 HIGH ST   IP7 7EB   01449 740510

This half-timbered fifteenth-century former coaching inn is a "reliable venue for good food", with a menu that ticks boxes all the way from basic cheeseburger or beer-battered hake 'n' chips to more original offerings such as goat cheese doughnut with beetroot sugar and a flexible selection of dishes available in two sizes – as either starters or mains. Top Tip – "the great lobster Caesar salad". / www.thebildestoncrown.com; bildestoncrown; Mon-Sun 8.30 pm; Cash & all usual cards.

ADAM'S   £127   553

16 WATERLOO ST   B2 5UG
0121 643 3745

"Easily Birmingham's top dining destination" (of the modern European variety), say fans of Adam & Natasha Stokes's local luminary, which is entering its tenth year of operation. Its "exquisite and inventive food has evolved and reinvented itself over the years and just keeps amazing with new creations and combinations of flavours". "Impeccable service" is "that lovely combination of being professional but also engaging" and "the general feel of the restaurant is classy with Art Deco influences". All this plus the "comprehensive wine list" you would expect. Top Tip – "the kitchen table experience is a well-designed and great experience". / www.adamsrestaurant.co.uk; RestaurantAdams; Tue-Sat 9 pm; closed Sun & Mon; Cash & all usual cards; booking max 8 may apply.

ALBERT'S SCHLOSS   £50

1 CHAMBERLAIN SQUARE   B3 3AX
0121 314 8858

Sibling to the well-known Manchester original – this Bavarian beer hall landed in Brum in December 2021. It didn't inspire any feedback in our annual diners' poll, but in an early review the BirminghamLive website declared that – on the strength of not one but four visits – it is "the best thing to happen to Birmingham in a very, very long time. If the owners could bottle the atmosphere of this venue and sell it, they would be millionaires thousands of times over", apparently. / www.albertsschloss.co.uk/birmingham; albertsschloss; Mon-Sun 2 am.

ASHA'S INDIAN BAR AND RESTAURANT   £60   333

12-22 NEWHALL ST   B3 3LX
0121 200 2767

This city-centre venue wins consistently strong ratings – if not much feedback this year – for its classic "rich" cuisine from India's northwest. It is part of an international group (with UK branches in Manchester and Solihull) owned by the prolific Bollywood singer Asha Bhosle and run by her son Anand; now 88, she is best-known in Britain from Cornershop's 1997 hit single 'Brimful of Asha', which punned on her name, meaning 'hope' in Hindi. / ashasbirmingham.co.uk; ashasuk; Mon-Wed 10.30 pm, Thu-Sat 11 pm, Sun 10 pm; closed Mon & Tue L; Cash & all usual cards.

@PIZZA   £24   333

UNIT 33 GRAND CENTRAL   B2 4BF
0121 274 2836

Rectangular pizza cooked in 90 seconds is the draw at this top local pizza pit-stop, which is consistently well-rated: choose a base sauce and cheese and then zhoosh it up with various toppings. / www.atpizza.com/birmingham; at.pizza; Mon-Thu 9 pm, Fri & Sat 10 pm, Sun 7 pm.

CARTERS OF MOSELEY   £165   454

2C WAKE GREEN RD   B13 9EZ
0121 449 8885

"The Chef's Table experience is one of the best dining experiences ever", according to fans of Brad Carter's fine-dining fixture in Moseley, which – since its opening in 2010 – "has developed over time into a fine modern restaurant". Early week, there's a slightly slimmed-down 6-course option available, but over the weekends the choice is between a 9-course or 11-course tasting menu. / www.cartersofmoseley.co.uk; cartersofmoseley; Fri & Sat, Wed & Thu midnight; closed Wed & Thu L, closed Mon & Tue & Sun; children: 8+.

CHAKANA   £53   334

140 ALCESTER ROAD   B13 8HS
0121 448 9880

A converted bank in Moseley Village plays host to Birmingham's first Peruvian restaurant, offering a range of dishes unfamiliar to the city. Limited feedback rates it good all-round and in his September 2021 visit, Jay Rayner of The Observer gave it the thumbs-up, saying that his discovering it in Brum was "like finding a gorgeous tropical flower at the base of a glowering mighty oak". / www.chakana-restaurant.co.uk; chakana.restaurant; Wed & Thu 10 pm, Fri & Sat 11 pm, Sun 4 pm; closed Wed-Fri L closed Sun D, closed Mon & Tue.

CRAFT   £74

THE TERRACE, UNIT 10-11 THE ICC, CENTENARY SQUARE   B1 2EA
0121 655 5550

Funky outside dining 'igloos' are a key attraction of this city-centre destination – a well-known venue locally which makes for a fun outing if not an especially foodie one. / www.weare-craft.co.uk; thecraft_experience; Wed-Sat midnight; closed Mon & Tue & Sun; Cash & all usual cards.

DISHOOM   £38   444

PARADISE, ONE CHAMBERLAIN SQUARE B3 3AX

The deservedly popular retro Bombay-themed chain has made itself thoroughly at home in Brum with this "busy, buzzy venue in the city centre" – "a very slick operation" serving "authentic and tasty" food with a "good variety of tapas-style small dishes and sharing plates". Much is made of Birmingham and Mumbai's shared histories of manufacture, commerce and craftsmanship. / www.dishoom.com/birmingham; dishoom; Sun-Thu 11 pm, Fri & Sat midnight; payment – credit card only.

8   £97

UNIT 8, 8 CENTENARY SQUARE   B1 2EA
0333 772 9329

'One of the UK's most progressive dining experiences' is promised by Andrew Sheridan and his brigade – to the backdrop of a resident DJ – at his year-old and extremely ambitious city-centre venture which aims to allow you to 'embrace an experience brought together by an immersive sensory and nostalgic story focused around food'. More prosaically, this centres around a 10-course tasting menu for £100. Initial reports are limited, but the AA awarded it a respectable three rosettes in their Autumn 2022 awards. More feedback please! / www.about8.co.uk; about8ight; Wed-Sat midnight; closed Mon & Tue & Sun.

HARBORNE KITCHEN   £99   433

B17 9QE   01214399150

This cleverly converted and relaxed former butcher's shop showcases a range of "exceptional" tasting menus from Kidderminster-born chef-patron Jamie Desogus, who worked at Gordon Ramsay's Pétrus before returning to the Midlands in 2016. Not a huge volume of feedback this year, but ratings remain strong across the board. / www.harbornekitchen.com; harbornekitchen; Tue-Sat 7.45 pm; closed Tue-Thu L, closed Sun & Mon; Cash & all usual cards.

LASAN   £68   443

3-4 DAKOTA BUILDINGS, JAMES STREET B3 1SD   0121 212 3664

Now in its 21st year, this "superior" Jewellery Quarter fixture has led the way in modernising British Indian cuisine, presented for "degustation" in a sophisticated setting. Ratings have remained very steady despite the travails of recent times – and the departure of high-profile chef-director Aktar Islam (see Opheem). / www.lasan.co.uk; lasan_restaurant; Tue-Fri 10 pm, Sat 11 pm, Sun 9 pm; closed Mon; Cash & all usual cards; No trainers.

OPHEEM   £73   544

65 SUMMER ROW   B3 1JJ   0121 201 3377

"The tasting menu is an exciting journey" at Aktar Islam's increasingly famous dining room a little out of the city centre, which is "going from strength to strength" as Brum's most commented-on destination; one of the top-10 most mentioned outside London in our annual diners' poll; and with some claim on being "the best Indian restaurant outside of London". The "elegantly presented" cuisine is rooted in the subcontinent, but might equally be described as "European with Indian flavours and spices". However you define the kitchen, it provides "a great experience with subtle spicing and some unique touches and flavours" complemented by "outstanding wine matches". The main dining room is a dim-lit, modern and stylish space and among improvements in recent times "the new lounge in particular is a fabulous addition". / www.opheem.com; opheemrestaurant; Wed-Sat 9 pm; closed Wed & Thu L, closed Mon & Tue & Sun; payment – credit card only; credit card deposit required to book; children: 12.

ORELLE

103 COLMORE ROW   B3 3AG

On the 24th floor of Brum's tallest office building – this new D&D London venue opened in mid-October 2022, with what is said to be a breathtaking 360-degree panorama of the city. Chris Emery provides a modern French menu from noon till past midnight. / Tue-Thu 9 pm, Fri & Sat 9.30 pm.

THE OYSTER CLUB   £187   3 2 3

43 TEMPLE STREET   B2 5DP
0121 643 6070

"The food is always great" – especially the oysters – at this "reliable" seafood outlet which is the more relaxed option from chef Adam Stokes, whose high-flying flagship Adam's is nearby. But diners expecting the same standards as his main gaff might be in for a "disappointment": ratings here are more generally good rather than outstanding and service has its ups and downs. / www.the-oyster-club.co.uk; the_oysterclub; Tue-Sun 11 pm; closed Mon.

PURNELLS   £109   4 4 4

55 CORNWALL ST   B3 2DH
0121 212 9799

A gastronomic "tour de force", this "fun and playful" Business Quarter flagship from exuberant locally born chef Glynn Purnell – aka 'the yummy Brummie' – continues to thrill both regulars and first-timers with food "so good we went back 3 times in 6 months!". "Being served by the man himself (twice) brought my wife to tears" – "the tasting menu was a revelation, from the showmanship of the mint choc chip dried ice to the intensity of the flavours throughout". / www.purnellsrestaurant.com; purnellsrestaurant; Mon & Tue 10.30 am, Wed-Sun 8.30 pm; Cash & all usual cards; children: 6+.

SABAI SABAI   3 3 3

25 WOODBRIDGE ROAD   B13 8EH
0121 449 4498

'A True Taste of Thailand' is the promise at the original Mosely branch of this small local Thai chain (nowadays also with branches in the city centre, Harborne and Stratford-Upon-Avon). Feedback remains relatively limited, but is enthusiastic all-round. / sabaisabai-restaurant. co.uk; sabaisabai_restaurant; Wed-Sat 10 pm, Sun 9 pm; Cash & all usual cards.

THE WILDERNESS   £102   5 4 3

27 WARSTONE LANE   B18 6JQ
0121 233 9425

"Edgy cuisine and environment, backed by friendly service and a rock 'n' roll playlist" (played loud!) is the distinctive formula of Alex Claridge's 'full-on' Jewellery Quarter venture, with black walls and black-leather furniture, and an open kitchen on display. As with some previous years, it doesn't generate a huge volume of feedback in our annual diners' poll, but fans say it's "outstanding". There are two tasting menus offered, a £70 version and more extensive and longer £130 option. Typical dish? – 'Childhood Reflections in the Shape of a Banana'. / wearethewilderness.co.uk; thewildernessrestaurant; Wed & Thu 8 pm, Fri & Sat 9 pm; closed Wed & Thu L, closed Mon & Tue & Sun; Cash & all usual cards; credit card deposit required to book; children: 12.

BLAIRGOWRIE, PERTH AND KINROSS   9–3C

KINLOCH HOUSE   £93   3 3 3

PH10 6SG   01250 884 732

"A very pleasant experience with beautifully cooked food (perhaps a little less fussy than it was previously) and discreet service that doesn't miss a trick" – this comfortable Relais & Château property is the epitome of a plush Scottish country retreat, and well rated by all who report on it. / www.kinlochhouse.com; kinlochhouse; Mon-Sun 8.30 pm; Cash & all usual cards; No shorts; children: 8 for dinner.

BLAKENEY, NORFOLK   6–3C

THE MOORINGS   £64   3 3 2

HIGH STREET   NR25 7NA   01263 740 054

This family-run north Norfolk restaurant "does what it does very well", and that's mainly fresh fish, along with local game – a formula that has served it well for more than 20 years. Sadly, co-chef/proprietor Richard Long died last year. "He will be sadly missed, but the good news is that his wife and co-chef/ proprietor, Angela, is carrying on with the business". / www.blakeney-moorings.co.uk; themooringsblakeney; Tue-Sat 9 pm; closed Tue-Sat L, closed Sun & Mon; No Amex.

BODIAM, EAST SUSSEX   3–4C

THE CURLEW   £68   4 4 3

JUNCTION RD   TN32 5UY   01580 861394

"If you fancy a change from normal dining", you should "save up and go" to chef Will Devlin's Grade II-listed clapboard former coaching inn, to sample his "extraordinary food and charming hosting all round" – it's a "wonderful little restaurant that cooks locally sourced ingredients and mixes them up in interesting and innovative flavour combinations". Will took the place over in 2020, and grows much of the produce himself on the grounds of his other highly rated restaurant, the Small Holding at nearby Kilndown. / www.thecurlew.restaurant; the_ curlew; Wed-Sat 11.30 pm, Sun 2.30 pm; closed Wed L closed Sun D, closed Mon & Tue; Cash & all usual cards; booking max 4 may apply.

BOLNHURST, BEDFORDSHIRE   3–1A

THE PLOUGH AT BOLNHURST   £73   3 4 3

MK44 2EX   01234 376274

This "gem in the Bedfordshire countryside" – a whitewashed gastropub with sixteenth-century origins – is "an oasis of consistency in a sea of mediocrity" under "brilliant" owners Martin & Jayne Lee. "We've been going regularly for over 15 years and have yet to eat a meal that was below their high standards". Top Tip – "always leave room for the soufflé". / www.bolnhurst.com; ploughatbolnhurst; Wed-Fri 11 pm, Sat 11.30 pm, Sun 4.30 pm; closed Sun D, closed Mon & Tue; No Amex.

BOREHAMWOOD, HERTFORDSHIRE 3–2A

KIYOTO   £30   3 4 2

31 SHENLEY ROAD   WD6 1AE
0203 489 6800

"Very reliable for sushi" – this Japanese operation is noted in a number of reports for its superior performance for somewhere out in the 'burbs. It's part of a small chain, with siblings in West Hampstead, Mill Hill and Cockfosters. / www.kiyotosushi.co.uk; kiyotosushi; Mon-Sun 9.30 pm.

BOSTON SPA, WEST YORKSHIRE   5–1C

CORA   £36   3 3 2

162 HIGH STREET   LS23 6BW
0333 090 3518

"Such an amazing new arrival to Boston Spa", say fans of local star chef and Great British Menu's Elizabeth Cottam's year-old venture – "part bakehouse part fine dining" – which opened in June 2021. "They offer brunch, lunch and dinner" – in the evening choose from a 3, 6 or 9-course menu of small plates (only the last option is available on Saturday night). It can, though, seem "expensive… these are extra-small plates". / www.coraleeds.co.uk; cora_bostonspa; Wed & Thu 5 pm, Fri & Sat 10 pm, Sun 3 pm; closed Wed & Thu, Sun D, closed Mon & Tue.

BOURNEMOUTH, DORSET　　2–4C

CHEZ FRED　£33　3 4 2

10 SEAMOOR RD　BH4 9AN
01202 761023

"Worth the very long queues for the best fish 'n' chips", according to fans of the Capel family's locally famous chippy (est. 1989), where "the staff are friendly and great with kids". / www.chezfred.co.uk; chezfredcafe; Mon-Thu 8.30 pm, Fri & Sat 9 pm, Sun 8 pm; closed Sun L; No Amex; no bookings.

LOLAS　£46　4 3 3

95 COMMERCIAL ROAD　BH2 5RT
07588 065360

"Big flavours on small plates" encapsulates the appeal of this "fabulous little tapas spot", whose popularity means you "need to book ahead". It feels "generous, atmospheric and family-friendly – can't wait to return". Top Tip – "the aubergine in honey is worth the trip alone". / www.lolasrestaurant.co.uk; lolashomemadetapas; Mon-Wed 11 pm, Fri & Sat 12.30 am, Thu midnight, Sun 10.30 pm; closed Mon-Thu L.

BOWDON, GREATER MANCHESTER 5–2B

BORAGE　£56　3 4 3

7 VALE VIEW, VICARAGE LANE
WA14 3BD　0161 929 4775

"Just don't let them grow out of their premises!" – this small neighbourhood spot inspires limited but very enthusiastic feedback for its excellent cooking. Miarisuz Dobies is the chef (with his wife front of house) and – though the cooking is somewhat Frenchified – some dishes come with an interesting central European spin reflecting his heritage. / www.boragebowdon.co.uk; boragerestaurant; Thu-Sat 9 pm, Sun 5 pm; closed Thu-Sat L closed Sun D, closed Mon & Tue & Wed.

BRACKLESHAM, WEST SUSSEX　3–4A

BILLYS ON THE BEACH　£51　3 3 3

BRACKLESHAM LANE　PO20 8JH
01243 670373

This "tight-for-space all-day beachside café gets it right for its market, so is usually full of contented customers" consuming "massive portions of fish 'n' chips" and other "really good simple food". It's a "lovely location, with lovely atmosphere" and views across to the Isle of Wight – and "the prices are great". / www.billysonthebeach.co.uk; billysonthebeach; Sun-Wed 5 pm, Thu-Sat 9 pm; closed Sun-Wed D; Cash & all usual cards.

BRADFORD, WEST YORKSHIRE　5–1C

AKBAR'S　£39　3 3 2

1276 LEEDS RD　BD3 8LF　01274 773311

Shabir Hussain's "fantastic" curry house prepares "Indian, Asian, Balti, Pakistani dishes to sort everyone's taste buds". Over three decades it has grown from a 28-seater in Bradford city centre into a national chain with spin-offs from Birmingham to Glasgow.

The menu features two 'challenges' for the greedy or brave – on quantity and heat. / www.akbars.co.uk; akbars.restaurants; Mon-Thu 11.30 pm, Fri & Sat midnight, Sun 11 pm; closed Mon-Sun L; Cash & all usual cards.

MUMTAZ　£38　3 4 2

386-410 GREAT HORTON RD　BD7 3HS
01274 571861

This 500-seat mega-restaurant is "still immensely popular with the Asian community", having started out more than 40 years ago as a tiny Kashmiri shop on the same street it now dominates. It's "maybe too big these days" to hit the highest culinary ratings, but remains a "great place for a family get-together". There's now a spin-off in Leeds and a national brand of ready meals. Mumtaz banned alcohol on the premises in 2019, 'to uphold the memory of our late Mother', founder Farzand Begum. / www.mumtaz.com; mumtazbradford; Sun-Thu midnight, Fri & Sat 1 am; Cash & all usual cards.

BRAEMAR, ABERDEENSHIRE　9–3C

THE CLUNIE DINING ROOM, THE FIFE ARMS　£94　3 3 3

MAR ROAD　AB35 5YN　01339 720200

This "lovely hotel" a few minutes' drive from Balmoral was opened in 2019 by King Charles III (back then merely the Duke of Rothesay when in Scotland), and was one of the first properties in Swiss art dealership Hauser + Wirth's fast-growing hospitality wing, Artfarm. Its restaurant, named after the river that flows past, specialises in "smoky food", with prime Scottish produce cooked over wood fire, but also serves "weird old-fashioned puddings like baked Alaska". The dining room walls are decorated by an abstract mural created in situ by Argentinian artist-in-residence Guillermo Kuitca. Other notable art is scattered through the property – but "a lot which was there originally has moved on, gone and not replaced. The Louise Bourgeois spider from the yard. Gone!" / thefifearms.com; thefifearms; Tue-Sat 9.30 pm, Sun & Mon 10.30 am; closed Sun & Mon D.

BRANCASTER STAITHE, NORFOLK 6–3B

THE WHITE HORSE £63　3 4 3

MAIN RD　PE31 8BY　01485 210262

"Stunning tidal-marsh views of the dunes and sea" from the dining room are just one of the attractions at this well-known coastal pub: "a beacon on the north Norfolk coast", where, in summer, "there is also outdoor dining on the terrace". Diners like its "lack of fuss and good quality cooking" too; and also its "really friendly style". "A fabulous seafood platter, a good Sauvignon blanc and a picture perfect sunset!" – what else do you need? / www.whitehorsebrancaster.co.uk; whitehorsebranc; Mon-Sat 9 pm, Sun 8 pm; Cash & all usual cards.

BRANSCOMBE, DEVON　2–4A

MASONS ARMS　£42　3 3 4

MAIN ST　EX12 3DJ　01297 680300

Pub classics jostle with more bistro-eseque fare on the menu of this recently refitted St Austell Brewery pub, about 10 minutes walk from Branscombe Beach. It's well-rated in reports and you get "lovely views over the countryside". / www.masonsarms.co.uk; masonsarmsinn; Mon-Sun 9 pm; No Amex; children: 14+ in restaurant.

BRAY, BERKSHIRE　3–3A

CALDESI IN CAMPAGNA　£86　3 4 3

OLD MILL LN　SL6 2BG　01628 788500

"Within walking distance of the Monkey Island and Bray high street" – Giancarlo & Katie Caldesi's "relaxed sister establishment to Caldesi in Marylebone" occupies a converted house complete with "a great bar and attractive glasshouse-type" addition. The dishes from its "excellent, typically Italian menu" are, say fans, "fantastic" and "the cost is rather like loose change compared to the nearby Fat Duck". / www.caldesi.com; caldesi_in_campagna; Wed-Sat 9.30 pm, Sun 2.30 pm; closed Sun D, closed Mon & Tue; Cash & all usual cards; No trainers.

THE CROWN AT BRAY　3 3 4

HIGH STREET　SL6 2AH　01628 621936

"Still going strong" – this comparatively un-foodie pub has thrived in this gourmet village by offering an attractive and traditional backdrop for easygoing British cuisine, realised with wit: fish finger sandwich, steak, top burgers and so on. / www.thecrownatbray.com; TheCrownatBray; Mon-Sat 11 pm, Sun 6.30 pm.

THE FAT DUCK　£353　3 2 2

HIGH ST　SL6 2AQ　01628 580333

"Was it a great meal? Yes it was. Was it a great meal for the price? I'm not so sure!" – In a nutshell, that's the major conundrum nowadays at this world-renowned destination which coined the term 'molecular gastronomy' two decades ago. A converted pub in this most bijou of Thames Valley villages, it is still fronted by über-chef Heston Blumenthal, although nowadays owned by a relative. "Expensive (obviously!), idiosyncratic, much hyped and copied…" – devotees say it's "an innovative assault on the senses and gastronomy that must be experienced at least once by any discerning gourmet". "Currently celebrating 25 years, they have created four different tasting menus showcasing the greatest dishes of the last quarter century (… I just wish I could go back another three times to have tried them all!)". But despite its golden oldie dishes ("excellent snail porridge of course, as was 'The Sound of the Sea'") some lucky enough to be regulars feel "the menu needs a refresh". And any doubts that it deserves its top billing from Michelin are sharpened by the vertiginous pricing. A number of reporters feel that "there's inventiveness throughout, lots of little tricks, but it feels like a place only to do once (if you strip aside the frippery I have to say I've eaten in two star places for half the price where the food was probably more consistently delicious)". A similar less wowed report is also revealing on the same topic: "It is so unbelievably overpriced. For two with wine matching, it cost us around £1,200 all together. Results were really hit and miss – the courses were either great or disgusting (and not really any in between). I can't say it's a bad restaurant as there were some great courses. The key issue for me is that we ate at a number of Michelin one stars at a similar time, which we enjoyed far more, and you could have had almost four meals at those restaurants for the price of just one at the Fat Duck!!! We will not be returning. All brand name and the Michelin men are crazy to give it 3 stars". / www.thefatduck.co.uk; theheatonblumenthalteam; Tue-Sat 8.30 pm; closed Sun & Mon; Cash & all usual cards; booking is online only.

THE HIND'S HEAD £97 334

HIGH STREET SL6 2AB 01628 626151

There's "always-great food and a wonderful atmosphere" at Heston Blumenthal's fifteenth-century gastropub, a short walk from his Fat Duck HQ "So good to be back after various lockdowns and find it as good as always" – a view endorsed by several long-time regulars this year. On the downside, there is an ongoing concern that its prices need reining in. / www.hindsheadbray.com; thehindsheadbray; Wed-Sat 9 pm, Sun 4 pm; closed Wed L closed Sun D, closed Mon & Tue; Cash & all usual cards.

WATERSIDE INN £226 555

FERRY RD SL6 2AT 01628 620691

"Perfection… and in a perfect waterside location" – Alain Roux's famous Thames-side bastion of haute cuisine (founded by his late father, Michel, in 1972) is "stunning in every sense" and above all for "a long summertime lunch". Sit on the terrace or hop in the electric launch for your aperitif, before progressing to the comfy if old-fashioned Thames-side dining room, whose romance is enhanced by the "amazing view". (It is one of the few in the UK to have publicly hosted her late majesty, Queen Elizabeth II). "Sophisticated, classical and luxurious French cuisine" is delivered by "incredibly attentive staff" who "make you feel like it's their privilege to have you there (as opposed to some other places, where you're made to feel the privilege is all yours)" – all part of an experience often described as "flawless". "It is, of course, insanely expensive, so it very much helps if someone else is paying". But, on practically all accounts, it's worth the hit to your mortgage: "I just want to eat here again before I die!" / www.waterside-inn.co.uk; rouxwatersideinnbray; Wed-Sat 10 pm, Sun 2.30 pm; closed Sun D, closed Mon & Tue; Cash & all usual cards; No jeans; booking max 6 may apply; children: 9.

BRECON, POWYS 2–1A

THE FELIN FACH
GRIFFIN £58 433

FELIN FACH LD3 0UB 01874 620111

Long-established gastropub (one of the first to be so-named) in a former cider mill on the edge of the Brecon Beacons National Park that's renowned as a "reliable" bet for good food, and is currently on top form with "absolutely delicious" cooking from chef Nick Evans (ex-Northcote and Tom Kerridge's Bull & Bear). His menu of seven starters and seven mains changes almost every day; ingredients are mostly local and the fish, from Cornwall, "is always perfectly cooked". / www.eatdrinksleep.ltd.uk; thefelinfachgriffin; Mon-Sun 11 pm; Cash & all usual cards.

BRENTWOOD, ESSEX 3–2B

ALEC'S £73 333

NAVESTOCK SIDE CM14 5SD 01277 375 696

"Come for the food, savour the view" from the airy conservatory in this well-known converted pub which specialises in seafood – everything from jellied eels to whole lobster – and is "excellent for every occasion". / www.alecsrestaurant.co.uk; alecsrestaurant; Tue-Sat

midnight, Sun 7 pm; closed Mon; No Amex; credit card deposit required to book; children: 12+.

BRIDGE OF ALLAN, STIRLING 9–4C

NICK'S ON HENDERSON
STREET

HENDERSON STREET FK9 4HR 01786 831616

Celeb chef Nick Nairn and wife Julia had only been open for a year or so at this all-day bistro/café before, in August 2021, it was struck by fire in the middle of Saturday evening's service and staff had to evacuate diners before it was engulfed by flames. It is due to re-open towards the end of 2022 or the beginning of 2023, with a new chef (Stephen Crawford); new kitchen; and new look ("light, airy and bright – contemporary Scottish"). / nicksonhendersonst. com; chefnicknairn; Wed-Sat 10 pm, Sun 6 pm; closed Sun D, closed Mon & Tue.

BRIDGE, KENT 3–3D

THE BRIDGE ARMS £82 534

53 HIGH STREET CT4 5LA 07818 567671

"Top-quality Kentish ingredients prepared inventively and with great skill" are served in this "wonderful gastropub in a pretty village a couple of miles from Canterbury". Launched in 2021 in their adopted home village by ambitious chef couple Daniel & Tasha Smith, of nearby big-hitter the Fordwich Arms, it focuses on cooking over locally produced charcoal on a Josper Grill – and is already "among the finest gastropubs anywhere". / www.bridgearms.co.uk; thebridgearms; Wed-Sat 9 pm, Sun 4.30 pm; closed Sun D, closed Mon & Tue.

THE PIG AT BRIDGE
PLACE £78 344

BREWERY LANE CT4 5LF 0345 225 9494

This Queen Anne manor house near Canterbury makes for a "lovely venue" in the eight-strong litter of Pig hotels, with some really "wonderful food and service". It's in a prime site on the South Downs, surrounded by vines that ultimately will be used to produce vintages for diners. / www.thepighotel.com/at-bridge-place; thepig_hotel; Mon-Sun 6.30 pm.

BRIGHOUSE, WEST YORKSHIRE 5–1C

BROOK'S £43 333

6 BRADFORD RD HD6 1RW 01484 715284

"Refreshing to have a place of this quality in the vicinity!" say local fans of this modern operation opposite the civic hall, which has been in new ownership since 2019 and where "really good food is served by a young and enthusiastic team" from breakfast onwards (for which it receives nominations). In late 2021, The Observer's Jay Rayner pronounced himself a fan: "powerless in the face of good bread… flavours are reliably big and self-assured… with nods towards the Middle East", while "the value is obvious" in a restaurant that "hums with a comfortable contentment". / www.brooks-restaurant.co.uk; brooksrestaurant;

The Coal Shed, Brighton

Wed & Thu 9 pm, Fri & Sat 9.30 pm, Sun 5 pm; closed Wed L closed Sun D, closed Mon & Tue; No Amex.

BASKETMAKERS ARMS   £45 3 3 2

**12 GLOUCESTER RD   BN1 4AD
01273 689 006**

This "little" Victorian boozer on a North Laine corner is "a bit away from the centre but not far from the station, so perfect when arriving at lunchtime" – "the menu's not massive, which is usually a good sign, and you'll find Sunday roast, fish 'n' chips, and classic pub dishes". / www.basket-makers-brighton.co.uk; Mon-Sun 11 pm; Cash & all usual cards; no bookings.

BINCHO YAKITORI   £40   4 3 3

**63 PRESTON STREET   BN1 2HE
01273 779021**

With its "brilliant small plates of sublime food and great atmosphere", this "welcoming" Japanese-style grill is "one of the best restaurants in Brighton". Founder David Miney picked up the skills – and a taste for relaxed izakaya dining – while working for three years as a chef in Japan. / www.binchoyakitori.com; binchoyakitori; Tue-Thu 10 pm, Fri & Sat 10.30 pm, Sun 9.30 pm; closed Tue-Sun L, closed Mon.

BURGER BROTHERS   £17   5 3 2

97 NORTH RD   BN1 1YE   01273 706980

"Not a restaurant… rather a tiny room with some bar stools along the wall". Fans say "it's a 'must-try' experience for all lovers of honest, tasty cuisine! The burgers are juicy, and full of flavour from the quality of the meat to the seasonings". / www.burgerbrothersbrighton.co.uk/?l=en; burgerbrothersbrighton; Tue-Sat 8.45 pm; closed Sun & Mon; Cash & all usual cards; no bookings.

BURNT ORANGE   £33   2 3 4

59 MIDDLE STREET   BN1 1AL

"Currently the 'in' place in town" – Razak Helalat (founder of Coal Shed and Salt room) has another hit on his hands with this sophisticated-looking yearling, which fans say is "deservedly popular, thanks to its exciting and seriously good Middle Eastern-inflected small plates", "very imaginative cocktails, and a 70s-but-cool aesthetic". Boosted by Giles Coren's upbeat review in The Times, it is the most commented-on venue in town in our latest annual diners' poll and "there's a great buzz around the place". The overall rating is dented though, by an unusual number of mixed or disappointing reports. The sceptics say "there are good flavours, but just too many of them, nor are they as good as the hype suggests". / www.burnt-orange.co.uk; burntorangeuk; Mon-Wed midnight, Thu-Sat 1 am, Sun 11 pm.

THE CHILLI PICKLE £42   3 3 3

17 JUBILEE ST   BN1 1GE   01273 900 383

"Vibrant, fresh and well-balanced flavours" make this "very reliable" Arts Quarter outfit "the best Indian restaurant in the area" for a huge army of locals, who reckon it's "now back to its best, after a dip in form". / www.thechillipickle.com; thechillipickle; Wed-Sat 9.30 pm, Sun 9 pm; closed Mon & Tue; Cash & all usual cards.

CHINA GARDEN   £39   3 4 3

**88-91 PRESTON ST   BN1 2HG
01273 325124**

This "long-established, proper Chinese restaurant" (est. 1980), "right near the Brighton seafront", features "highly attentive service" and is "routinely full of people of Chinese heritage". "Go for the dim sum – and stay for the kung pao prawns". / www.chinagarden.name; Mon-Sun 10 pm; Cash & all usual cards.

LA CHOZA   £37

**36 GLOUCESTER RD   BN1 4AQ
01273 945 926**

Decked out with neon lights, graffiti, sugar skulls and vivid flowers, this ten-year-old cantina has also spawned a (larger) Hove spin-off. Such feedback as we have says its "great value, with really enjoyable food" – more reports please! / www.lachoza.co.uk; lachozamexican; Mon-Sat 9 pm, Sun 7.30 pm; Cash & all usual cards; may need 10+ to book.

CIN CIN HOVE   £59   4 4 3

**60 WESTERN ROAD   BN3 1JD
01273 726 047**

"Love this relaxed and cool Italian place", declare fans of Italian-Australian former lawyer David Toscano's "simple and tasty" operation that started out in Vine Street (RIP) but is "really hitting form" in Hove (and now London's Fitzrovia). There's a "very short menu, so some diners worry they won't find anything they want – but there's no need to worry, as it's all delicious" – and even more "fun sitting at the counter". / www.cincin.co.uk; cincinuk; Wed-Sat 11.30 pm; closed Mon & Tue & Sun; No shorts.

THE COAL SHED   £68   3 2 3

8 BOYCES ST   BN1 1AN   01273 322998

"High-quality meat" – and "with a variety on the menu if you fancy a change from beef" – has helped win a significant fan club for Razak Helalat's well-known destination (which has a spin-off near Tower Bridge, in London). Reports remain generally upbeat, although a number of them note service can be "variable", especially when they are busy. / www.coalshed-restaurant.co.uk; thecoalshed; Mon-Sat 11 pm, Sun 9 pm; Cash & all usual cards.

CONSTANTINOPLE   £27   3 3 3

**51 NORFOLK SQUARE   BN1 2PA
01273 777355**

"Cosy Turkish-run restaurant on the border of Brighton and Hove" that aims to fuse the tastes of the Middle East, the Balkans, Greece, the Caucasus and central Anatolia. In particular, it's "busy at lunchtime, testament to good value and good food!" / //theconstantinople.co.uk; constantinoplebistro; Mon-Sun 11 pm.

CURRY LEAF CAFE £49   3 3 2

60 SHIP ST   BN1 1AE   01273 207070

This "nice, relaxed, simple South Indian street-food café" is "clearly part of the community in the Lanes" – the beating heart of Brighton. It "continues to offer good food and generous portions at reasonable prices", alongside a "great range of local beers". / www.curryleafcafe.com; curry_leaf_cafe; Mon-Thu 10 pm, Fri & Sat 10.30 pm, Sun 9 pm; Cash & all usual cards.

DONATELLO   £35   3 3 3

**1-3 BRIGHTON PL   BN1 1HJ
01273 775477**

"A bustling Italian pizzeria with huge helpings of food like Mama makes" in the heart of the Lanes. "Comforting and joyous" – it provides "value-for-money pastas and pizzas and is ideal for outings with young family members". / www.donatello.co.uk; donatello_brighton; Mon-Sun 10.30 pm; Cash & all usual cards.

DUE SOUTH   3 3 4

**139 KINGS ROAD ARCHES   BN1 2FN
01273 721667**

It has a "lovely setting" on the front, but Rob Shenton's well-known venue has yet to reestablish itself fully since he decided last year to restore its branding of ten years ago (and to move Riddle & Finns On the Beach – his operation here since 2011 – to a new site). On limited feedback, some locals do rave all-round: others say "it's not what it used to be – the food's nicely cooked, but not good value for money". / www.duesouthrestaurant.co.uk; duesouthrestaurant; Mon-Sat 10 pm, Sun 6 pm; closed Sun D.

ENGLISH'S   £72   3 3 4

29-31 EAST ST   BN1 1HL   01273 327980

"Great seafood" has long made this Lanes institution – one of the UK's truly venerable restaurants, dating from the 1890s and run by the Leigh-Jones family since 1945 – something of a "Brighton favourite". "If you can bag a table outside in the sun on the Lanes, with the hustle and bustle of the town around you and your partner opposite, the world will be good". / www.englishs.co.uk; englishsofbrighton; Mon-Sun 10 pm; Cash & all usual cards.

ETCH £112 **4 4 4**

216 CHURCH RD   BN3 2DJ   01273 227485

"The remodelling of the restaurant has made it even better", say fans, and with expansion Steven Edwards's "high quality dining experience" in Hove (which occupies a converted bank near the seafront, complete with basement bar) is reaching an expanded audience. Serving the now typical 8-9 small course tasting menus, with chefs delivering dishes to the table, all reports speak of a "stylish, fun and friendly" venue "with a very professional front of house team" and "great focus on local produce, letting great ingredients sing". The Indie's Kate Ng is a fan of the new look too and her April 2022 review described "a glimpse into the future of modern British cuisine!" / www.etchfood.co.uk; etchfood; Fri & Sat, Wed & Thu 8 pm, Sun 2 pm; closed Wed & Thu L closed Sun D, closed Mon & Tue; Cash & all usual cards.

FATTO A MANO £25 **3 2 3**

25 GLOUCESTER ROAD   BN1 4AQ   01273 693221

"Authentic Neapolitan-style pizzas cooked in a proper wood-fired oven" have proved a hit for this operation with three outlets in Brighton & Hove. (Their appeal extends further than the city limits, with a new branch at King's Cross in London). / www.fattoamanopizza.com; fattoamanopizza; Mon-Thu 10 pm, Fri & Sat 10.30 pm, Sun 9.30 pm.

FLINT HOUSE £52 **4 4 4**

13 HANNINGTON'S LANE   BN1 1GS   01273 916333

"A massive cult favourite among people in the know in Brighton", this Lanes outfit from Pamela & Ben McKellar's Gingerman group is "now almost impossible to get into", due to the fame of its small plates with "really interesting flavour combinations and seasoning". It's also "extremely good value", thanks to "incredibly good use of cheap ingredients". "Wish this was in London – but it's a good reason to go to Brighton!" / www.flinthousebrighton.com; theflinthouse; Mon-Sun 10 pm.

FOOD FOR FRIENDS £52 **3 3 2**

17-18 PRINCE ALBERT ST   BN1 1HF   01273 202310

"Lovely tasty veggie" cooking has drawn plaudits for this Lanes veteran for more than 40 years, which these days takes inspiration from global cuisines, including Chinese, Sicilian, Sri Lankan and Vietnamese. Botanique, its younger sibling, is in nearby Hove. Top Menu Tip – "I hope the sweetcorn is on the menu forever". / foodforfriends.com; FoodforFriendsBrighton; Mon-Sun 10 pm; Cash & all usual cards; no booking, Sat L & Sun L.

FOURTH AND CHURCH £40 **3 4 4**

84 CHURCH ROAD   BN3 2EB   01273 724709

A "great neighbourhood choice" – this restaurant/bar/wine shop in Hove serves "excellent small plates" plus a "delicious menu of dishes which is kept small enough to ensure freshness and innovation". It's a "warm and intimate" place which is now offering "one of the best tasting menus in town". / www.fourthandchurch.co.uk; fourthandchurch; Wed-Sat 9 pm; closed Mon & Tue & Sun.

THE GINGER PIG £68 **3 3 3**

3 HOVE ST   BN3 2TR   01273 736123

A "classy member" of a well-known local group, this "great gastropub a few yards from Hove seafront" "serves Paris bistro-style food, with a few innovative touches such as rabbit Scotch egg". "A lovely place for any meal, with an always-tempting menu: it never disappoints". / www.thegingerpigpub.com; gingerpighove; Mon-Sat midnight; closed Sun; Cash & all usual cards.

GINGERMAN £79 **4 3 2**

21A NORFOLK SQ   BN1 2PD   01273 326688

"This small and intimate backstreet gem remains deservedly popular with regulars" – and was the original in Ben & Pamela McKellar's successful local group, opening 25 years ago. It's gone "ever so slightly more 'haute' recently (fancy canapés), so some people might think it's on the dear side", but on most accounts, it isn't! – it's "not cheap, but fantastic". / www.gingermanrestaurant.com; Tue-Thu, Sun 8.30 pm, Fri & Sat 9 pm; closed Mon; Cash & all usual cards.

ISAAC@ £65 **3 3 3**

2 GLOUCESTER STREET   BN1 4EW   07765 934740

Isaac Bartlett-Copeland's ambitious and ultra-local operation in Brighton's boho North Laine is "so original and never the same twice", with its 'taste of Sussex' menus and an all-English list of wines. The "NYC vibe" goes too far for some tastes ("well-meaning front of house told us everything, and I mean absolutely everything, about every dish…") / www.isaac-at.com; isaac_at_; Wed-Sat 10.30 pm; closed Mon & Tue & Sun; Cash & all usual cards.

THE LITTLE FISH MARKET £112 **5 4 3**

10 UPPER MARKET ST   BN3 1AS   01273 722213

"For an exceptional foodie experience", this "absolute gem of a restaurant tucked away in a residential area of Hove" is "hard to beat". Chef Duncan Ray (part of Heston B's original launch team at the Fat Duck) is "fêted among restaurant owners and foodies" for his "fish-based 8-course menu, which invariably delights" – and has earned increasing recognition in his 10 years here. There are just 20 guests per sitting, and "everyone eats at the same time – like being at a dinner party". The "good wine list" is from the people behind Noble Rot. / www.thelittlefishmarket.co.uk; littlefishhove; Tue-Sat 10.30 pm, closed Tue-Sat L, closed Sun & Mon; booking is online only; children: 12.

MURMUR £55 **3 3 3**

91-96 KINGS ROAD ARCHES   BN1 1NB   01273 711 900

"Blessed with a sensational location" – under the arches on the seafront – Great British Menu winner Michael Bremner's casual venue makes a "lovely" spot for "reliable food, particularly the fish". But it is "much less adventurous than 64 Degrees" (his acclaimed Lanes flagship). / murmur-restaurant.co.uk; murmur_restaurant; Mon-Thu 9 pm, Fri & Sat 11 pm, Sun 6 pm; No Amex.

NANNINELLA PIZZERIA NAPOLETANA £39 **3 3 3**

26 PRESTON STREET   BN1 2HN   01273 325500

"Authentic Neapolitan pizzas" emerge from the imported oven at this independent pizzeria near the seafront. Owner Sergio grew up on his grandparents' farm outside Naples, and was inspired to open his business by memories of his Nonna's cooking. / www.nanninellapizzeria.co.uk; 26nanninella26; Wed & Thu, Sun 9.30 pm, Fri & Sat 10 pm; closed Wed & Thu L, closed Mon & Tue.

PETIT POIS £43 **3 4 2**

70 SHIP STREET   BN1 1AE   01273 911211

This "sound French bistro" in Brighton's Lanes serves "lovely food", although the "closely packed tables" can leave you vulnerable to "loud neighbours". / petitpoisbrighton.co.uk; petitpoisbrighton; Mon, Thu-Sun 10 pm; closed Tue & Wed.

THE REGENCY RESTAURANT £54 **3 3 2**

131 KINGS RD   BN1 2HH   01273 325014

"An old favourite for traditional fish 'n' chips", this "vibrant and very lively restaurant" has been a fixture of the Brighton seafront for 90 odd years. It remains "consistent", "excellent value", and is "great for families". / www.theregencyrestaurant.co.uk; The-Regency-Restaurant; Mon-Sun 10.30 pm; Cash & all usual cards.

RIDDLE & FINNS £66 **4 3 4**

12B MEETING HOUSE LN   BN1 1HB   01273 721667

This "wonderful little venue" in Brighton's Lanes (with an offshoot near the seafront) scores highly for its "incredibly fresh fish and seafood". There's a "real buzzy atmosphere", too, that sometimes makes it "a bit of a madhouse" – a small price to pay for somewhere that "performs this well in a tourist hot-spot". / www.riddleandfinns.co.uk; riddlesandfinnsBN1;

Sun-Fri 10 pm, Sat 11 pm; Cash & all usual cards; no bookings.

RIDDLE & FINNS ON THE BEACH £62 4️⃣3️⃣5️⃣

65 KINGS ROAD   BN1 1NA   01273 721667

"A palpable hit" – "now in its new home with glorious sea views", this "buzzy" spin-off from a well-established Lanes oyster bar (relocated to this new site in 2021) "continues to set the standard for seafood", while "staff add a warm and professional vibe". Top Menu Tip – "Malaysian crab and any of the mussel dishes are highlights". / www.riddleandfinns.co.uk; RiddleandfinnsBN1; Sun-Fri 10 pm, Sat 11 pm; Cash & all usual cards; no bookings.

THE SALT ROOM £71 3️⃣2️⃣3️⃣

106 KINGS ROAD   BN1 2FA   01273 929 488

"A window table gives a good view of the sunset on a sunny evening" at this "excellent seafront restaurant": a seafood brasserie near the old West Pier that's again one of the city's commented-on destinations in town in our annual diners' poll. Fans say it's "hard to get into, and not cheap, but everything about it's good" in particular its "great fish-based menu" ("it's a great place to share a whole fish at market price"). "The scale of the restaurant can make the service a little frenetic" though and the food can "try too hard to be interesting and only sometimes succeed". On most accounts, though, it's "still knocking it out of the park and a great place for a treat". / www.saltroom-restaurant.co.uk; thesaltroombrighton; Mon-Sat 11 pm, Sun 9 pm; Cash & all usual cards.

SHELTER HALL £42 3️⃣4️⃣4️⃣

KINGS ROAD ARCHES   BN1 2LN

"If you are happy with a food hall for your meal, then this is a good (but very popular) option" – this year-old venue has a "great location" on the seafront and features seven street-food concepts at a time. In her July 2022 visit, The Guardian's Grace Dent was also wowed: "The food, with each delivery by a chipper server, continued to be far better than a food hall ever tends to be… we left Shelter Hall jubilant, £60 down for lunch for three people with drinks". / www.shelterhall.co.uk; shelterhallmarket; Mon-Thu 11 pm, Fri & Sat midnight, Sun 8 pm; booking is online only.

64 DEGREES £113 4️⃣3️⃣2️⃣

53 MEETING HOUSE LANE   BN1 1HB   01273 770 115

Celebrating its 10th anniversary this year, Great British Menu winner Michael Bremner's Lanes 20-seater is still one of Brighton's more interesting culinary destinations. For "committed foodies", it provides an "amazing experience", with "sensational dishes of seasonal food – I even tried squirrel!". "Presentation is beautiful and sitting at the pass just adds to the experience". / www.64degrees.co.uk; chef64degrees; Sat, Mon, Thu & Fri, Sun 11.30 pm; closed Mon, Thu & Fri,

Sun L, closed Tue & Wed; No shorts; booking is online only.

TERRE À TERRE £70 5️⃣3️⃣3️⃣

71 EAST ST   BN1 1HQ   01273 729051

"Flavours bursting out everywhere" characterise the "great range of veggie food" ("Wow! I didn't know meat-free food could taste this great!") at this "very-Brighton-in-ambience" legend in The Lanes – according to many, "still the best vegetarian in the UK". Quibbles this year included "a menu that seemed less extensive than it used to be and service that was a little erratic". On most accounts, though, it's "simply the best" and "a must on any trip to Brighton (and we are not vegetarians… we just love the high quality and imaginative food!)". Top Menu Tip – "afternoon tea here is different and delicious, with a great variety of vegetarian savoury and sweet items". / www.terreaterre.co.uk; terreaterrebrighton; Wed-Sun 10 pm; closed Mon & Tue; Cash & all usual cards; booking max 10 may apply.

TUTTO

20-22 MARLBOROUGH PLACE   BN1 1UB

Raz Helalat has a strong track record in these parts (The Salt Room, Burnt Orange in Brighton, Coal Shed) so this new 80-cover Italian in a restored 1930s bank near the Pavilion is worth watching. The kitchen is to be run by Sardinian-born Mirella Pau, formerly of London's Café Murano and Padella. Originally slated for mid 2022, by autumn a final opening date is still awaited. / tutto-restaurant.co.uk; tutto.uk; Tue-Sat 10 pm, Sun 3 pm.

URCHIN £51 3️⃣4️⃣3️⃣

15-17 BELFAST ST   BN3 3YS   01273 241881

"Great seafood at reasonable prices", washed down by craft beer brewed on site, makes this corner venue one of Brighton's best-known pubs. "Perhaps the menu could change more frequently, but what the Urchin does, it does very well": "mainly shellfish" , some of it "wonderfully spicy". Top Menu Tip – "the mussels are delicious". / www.urchinpub.co.uk; urchinpub; Wed-Sat 9.30 pm, Sun 8 pm; closed Mon & Tue; Cash & all usual cards.

WILD FLOR £79 4️⃣4️⃣4️⃣

42 CHURCH ROAD   BN3 2FN   01273 329111

This three-year-old bistro "has made a huge impression on the Hove scene" with the "quality and inventiveness of its food", an "excellent and surprising wine list" and "impeccable service" led by founders James & Faye Thomson and Rob Maynard. "Proud to have Wild Flor in our 'hood!". / wildflor.com; wildflorhove; Thu-Sat, Wed 9 pm; closed Wed L, closed Mon & Tue & Sun.

ADELINA YARD £97 3️⃣3️⃣2️⃣

QUEEN QUAY, WELSH BACK   BS1 4SL   0117 925 6682

"A small restaurant serving glorious tasting menus" from chefs Jamie Randall and Olivia Barry, who set up shop in Bristol in this "pretty simple" venue near the Docks eight years ago after stints in some of London's top kitchens (Galvin Brothers, Angela Hartnett). They work hard to keep things interesting, and a number of reports note the "top-notch wine flights". / www.adelinayard.com; adelinayard; Wed-Sat 8 pm; closed Mon & Tue & Sun.

BOKMAN 4️⃣4️⃣3️⃣

3 NINE TREE HILL   BS1 3SB

"Some of the most exciting food I have eaten in ages" has made this two-year-old Korean with a "short but tasty menu" a big hit in Bristol and beyond. Chef Duncan Roberts, who has worked for Joel Robuchon in Paris, and his wife Kyu Jeong Jeon moved to Stokes Croft from South Korea, and their fans include Hugh Fearnley-Whittingstall. Top Tip – tongdak – whole chicken stuffed with sticky rice and grilled over charcoal. / bokmanbristol; Tue-Sat 11 pm; closed Tue-Sat L, closed Sun & Mon.

BOSCO PIZZERIA £48 3️⃣3️⃣3️⃣

96 WHITELADIES RD   BS8 2QX   01179 737 978

"Well-executed takes on classic pizza and pasta" show that "someone has thought about flavour combinations and what works" at this Bristol pizza joint. "In the summer when the front windows are open it has a European feel, while in winter it's nice to sit by the window people-watching on Whiteladies Road". There are now branches in Bath and Cheltenham. / www.boscopizzeria.co.uk; whiteladies-road; Mon-Sun 10 pm; Cash & all usual cards.

BOX-E £49 4️⃣4️⃣3️⃣

UNIT 10, CARGO 1, WAPPING WHARF   BS1 6WP

"Tiny restaurant but amazing food!". Elliott Lidstone (ex-Ortolan and Hackney's The Empress head chef) and his wife Tess opened their 14-seater spot "in two shipping containers at Bristol harbour's Cargo development" in 2016, and it has become one of the city's gastronomic highlights, earning national fame. Their 45-bin seasonal wine list is also a winner (with bottles available on a retail basis). / www.boxebristol.com; boxebristol; Wed-Sat 11 pm; closed Wed L, closed Mon & Tue & Sun; Cash & all usual cards.

BRAVAS £41 3️⃣3️⃣3️⃣

7 COTHAM HILL   BS6 6LD   0117 329 6887

Well known down Brizzle way, this small (16 seats) tapas haunt has an outsized reputation for its authentic approach. Our feedback is limited, but it's a favourite for one or two of our reporters who award it very high marks. It's part of a local group, and its siblings include Cargo Cantina and Gambas. / www.bravas.co.uk; bravasbristol; Mon-Wed 11 pm, Thu-Sat midnight; closed Sun; Cash & all usual cards.

BULRUSH £98 433

21 COTHAM ROAD SOUTH   BS6 5TZ
0117 329 0990

"Simply outstanding cooking, the menu beautifully balanced and the overall presentation stunning" is typical of the accolades heaped on chef-owner George Livesey (ex-St John and Club Gascon), whose former grocer's shop is now a star of the Bristol gastronomic scene. / www.bulrushrestaurant.co.uk; bulrushrestaurant; Fri & Sat, Wed & Thu 7.30 pm, Sun 2.30 pm; closed Wed & Thu L closed Sun D, closed Mon & Tue; Cash & all usual cards; credit card deposit required to book.

CLIFTON SAUSAGE £50 333

7 PORTLAND ST   BS8 4JA   0117 9731192

"As good a range of sausages as you could ask for, and the ones we had were very good!" – it does what it says on the tin at this descriptively named café; "cheerful service and a nice atmosphere" too. / www.cliftonsausage.co.uk; cliftonsausage; Mon-Sun 11 pm; Cash & all usual cards.

GAMBAS £46 322

UNIT 15 CARGO 2, WAPPING WHARF
BS1 6DP   0117 329 6887

"Sister restaurant to Bravas, with similar inventiveness" – "you get brilliant tapas, in a noisy, converted shipping container in the dock area" at Kieran & Imogen Waite's "very buzzy" operation. Fans feel it's "perhaps not quite cheap and cheerful, but incredible value, with excellent seafood options". "The shipping container environment is not a constraint and its first floor location gives good views over harbour" (and is "great outside on a warm day"). / www.gambasbristol.co.uk; gambastapasbar; Mon-Sat 10 pm, Sun 4.30 pm; closed Sun D; booking is online only.

THE IVY CLIFTON BRASSERIE £77 234

42-44 CALEDONIA PLACE   BS8 4DN
0117 203 4555

"Everything here is what one would expect of The Ivy"; so say fans of its popular Clifton offshoot. "It plays it posh, in a posh part of town, and attracts a devoted clientele", with its "lovely interior". "The menu is standard and uninspiring, but the dishes are tasty: best for breakfast, with a good range of dishes and drinks". / theivycliftonbrasserie.com; theivyclifton; Sun-Thu 10 pm, Fri & Sat 11 pm.

THE KENSINGTON ARMS £57 334

35-37 STANLEY RD   BS6 6NP
0117 944 6444

A smart Redland gastroboozer, the Kenny is known across town for the "always excellent food, service, convivial atmosphere and great wine list" that make it "a total gem!". / www.thekensingtonarms.co.uk; thekensingtonarms; closed Mon-Sat & Sun; Cash & all usual cards.

KLOSTERHAUS £69 344

CABOT CIRCUS   BS1 3DF   0117 452 3111

Maybe D&D London's operations in the capital could take a leaf out of their two-year-old Bristol cousin: a 'modern take on a Grand Café' which occupies the Grade I listed Quakers Friars building. All reports are upbeat: "I was very pleasantly surprised…" – an "excellent German-themed restaurant with super schnitzels and decent wine" and with "very efficient service" too. / klosterhaus.co.uk; klosterhaus_bristol; Mon-Thu 10.30 pm, Fri & Sat 11.30 pm, Sun 5 pm; closed Sun D; No shorts.

LIDO £65 334

OAKFIELD PLACE   BS8 2BJ
0117 933 9533

"A hidden gem" "in the heart of Bristol's university quarter" – this "balcony restaurant overlooks a secluded mid-Victorian lido", now restored and once again full of swimmers. It's a "well-designed, light-filled space with large windows", and a "menu that offers imaginative combinations, including vegetarian options". There was also the odd critical report this year, saying that standards had "deteriorated" of late, but even that said "the tapas served downstairs are still OK" (in the separate café area). / www.lidobristol.com; lidobristol; Mon-Sat 9.30 pm, Sun 4 pm; closed Sun D; No Amex.

LITTLE FRENCH £65 342

2B NORTH VIEW, WESTBURY PARK
BS6 7QB   01179 706276

This "great local bistro" from Bristolian chef Freddy Bird (ex-Bristol Lido) and his wife Nessy is "a dream to have on your doorstep" – although it's "really popular now, so you need to book ahead". It offers "fantastic French-inspired cooking, quite rich and in generous portions" – "the côte de beouf was mighty and certainly required a lie down afterwards!". / littlefrench.co.uk; littlefrench_bristol; Mon-Sat 9.30 pm, Sun 4 pm; closed Sun D.

MAGARI £15

CARGO 2, WAPPING WHARF, MUSEUM STREET   BS1 6ZA   0117 929 2865

'Authentically Italian, sustainably British' says the tagline of this new Wapping Wharf container restaurant, run by friends Gilda Lombardi and Delphi Ross, which specialises in numerous varieties of pasta made on-site daily. It opened in May 2022 – too late to generate feedback in our annual diners' poll – but the Bristol press says it's proving a big hit locally. /

magaripasta.co.uk; Tue-Sat 9.30 pm, Sun 4.30 pm; closed Sun D, closed Mon.

MARMO £53 443

31 BALDWIN STREET   BS1 1RG
0117 316 4987

"Beautifully cooked, simple yet imaginative dishes" have helped raise the profile of former St John and Brawn chef Cosmo Sterck and his wife Lily's first venture, and brought critics panting to the door, with Tim Hayward of the FT and Tom Parker Bowles of the Mail leading the charge. Top Tip – the weekday lunch menu is steal at £19 for 2 courses, £23 for 3 as we went to press. / www.marmo.restaurant; marmo.restaurant; Tue-Sat 9.45 pm; closed Sun & Mon; payment – credit card only.

THE MINT ROOM £57 433

12-16 CLIFTON RD   BS8 1AF
01173 291 300

The "well-cooked and interesting" "Moghul-style cuisine" at this slick Clifton outfit (and its Bath spin-off) is "a big change from usual Indian restaurants", with "incredible spice balances". Top Tip – "the monkfish starter is tops!" / www.themintroom.co.uk; themintroom; Mon-Sun 10 pm; closed Mon-Sun L.

PACO TAPAS, THE GENERAL £58 443

LOWER GUINEA ST   BS1 6SY
0117 925 7021

Newly expanded and now sole occupant of the Sanchez Group's harbourside HQ following last year's surprise closure of the all-conquering Casamia, this "lively" and "enjoyable" tapas bar (named after patron Peter Sanchez-Iglesias's father) is "well worth a visit". Nobody doubts the quality of the "great tapas" and accompanying Spanish wines and sherries, but there are persistent grumbles about the "expense" and the "extremely loud music" that can make conversation difficult for some. / www.pacotapas.co.uk; pacotapas_; Tue-Thu 10 pm, Fri & Sat 10.30 pm, Sun 4.30 pm; closed Tue-Thu L closed Sun D, closed Mon; Cash & all usual cards.

PASTA LOCO £65 443

37A COTHAM HILL   BS6 6JY
0117 973 3000

"Outstanding fresh pasta and sauces" are behind the enormous success of this Redland legend, which "looks very unassuming from outside" but is "always booked up ages ahead". There's "always something interesting and different" on the menu, which can change twice a day, and it's "always so fresh and appetising". Cousins Ben Harvey & Dominic Borel launched Pasta Loco in 2016, and have followed it up with a handful of other ventures in their group Bianchis. / www.pastaloco.co.uk; pastaloco; Tue-Sat 9 pm; closed Sun & Mon; Cash & all usual cards.

The Salt Room, Brighton

ROOT £61 443

WAPPING WHARF BS1 6WP
0117 930 0260

"The inventive food is amazing" at this dockside container venue, which flips the usual omnivore convention and casts vegetables as the stars of the show, with meat or fish in supporting roles. Part of Josh Eggleston's Eat Drink Bristol Fashion operation, the venue is run by chef Rob Howell and his partner Megan Oakley (both ex-Pony & Trap). Reporters say they're "made to feel welcome – nothing is too much trouble". / www.rootbristol.co.uk; RootBristol; Mon-Sat 10.30 pm; closed Mon & Tue L, closed Sun; No Amex; booking is online only.

SAN CARLO £67 344

44 CORN STREET BS1 1HQ
0117 922 6586

"You can always be sure of a good cheery welcome at this upmarket Italian" which is a longstanding stalwart both of the city and also of Carlo Distefano's smart national chain. "Perhaps it's slightly overpriced", but "the fish is always good as is the pasta" and service is "very efficient and well-trained". / www.sancarlo.co.uk; sancarlorestaurants; Mon-Sun 11 pm; Cash & all usual cards.

SONNY STORES £47 543

47 RALEIGH ROAD BS3 1QS
01179 028 326

"This is how you treat great produce with care and respect and create beautiful things!" – so say fans of Mary Glynn and Pegs Quinn's Italian-influenced two-year-old in Southville, whose "excellent" cuisine is informed by Pegs's 18-year stint at the Hammersmith's famous River Café. "Service is good and the place is lively and noisy (but some softening of the acoustics might help)". / www.sonnystores.com; sonnystores; Tue-Sat 10 pm; closed Sun & Mon.

SPINY LOBSTER £69 343

128-130 WHITELADIES ROAD BS8 2RS
0117 9737384

"Boy is the fish good" at Mitch Tonks's Bristol outpost – "shipped in daily from Cornwall, it couldn't be fresher". "Still a classic but perhaps getting a bit old-fashioned" after more than 15 years (it used to be called the Rockfish Grill) – it's perfect "if you like white linen tablecloths in a 'proper' restaurant". There are "some inventive flourishes mixed in with the standard fare", and overall it's "such a joy to eat there". / www.thespinylobster.co.uk; thespinylobster; Tue-Sat 10 pm; closed Sun & Mon; Cash & all usual cards.

WILSON'S £87 542

24 CHANDOS RD BS6 6PF
0117 973 4157

"Unpretentious, daring, and exceptional value" – Jan Ostle & Mary Wilson's "accomplished" Redland bistro is widely acclaimed for its "fresh and interesting" take on "fabulous, locally sourced food", most of which they grow on their own smallholding. "You could be forgiven for missing this small establishment in a residential street – we did! Tables are very close together, but this all adds to the atmosphere – it's not a restaurant you'd expect to be tasting menu only". / www.wilsonsbristol.co.uk; wilsonsbristol; closed Mon-Sat & Sun.

BRITWELL SALOME, OXFORDSHIRE 2-2D

OLIVIER AT THE RED LION £52

OX49 5LG 01491 613140

Chef-patron Olivier Bouet, who had presented "excellent rustic French cuisine" at this Chilterns village gastropub for five years, recently moved on, and the new owners reopened in July 2022, announcing their plans for an 'eclectic modern British menu with South African influence and popular grill favourites. Every item on the menu will be made on the premises'. It's a big change of style, hence for the time being we've left it unrated. / www.olivieratthelionbritwellsalome.co.uk; olivieratthelion; Wed-Sat 8.30 pm, Sun 2.30 pm; closed Sun D, closed Mon & Tue; Cash & all usual cards.

BRIXHAM, DEVON 1-3D

SHOALS £50 433

10 SOUTH WEST COAST PATH TQ5 9AF
01803 854874

"Best, freshest fish I have tasted for years – right off the Brixham fishing boats, served down by the sea". This "affordable and fun" venture looks like a beach shack. "It's in a strange location", above the seawater lido – on the coast path leading away from Brixham to Berry Head – but worth hunting out (and there is a car park at the back if you are driving). Only a few covers, so you need to book. Ask for the table by the window, and you have glorious views in the evening of the sun setting over Tor Bay. But what you come for is the fish. Not a sophisticated menu, but the fish doesn't need anything other than very simple cooking. The owner is one of the wholesalers at the Brixham fish market, so the fish will come from that morning's auction and is as fresh as it can get. One of the South West's best-kept secrets (well, it was…) / shoalsbrixham.co.uk; shoals_brixham; Mon-Sat 10 pm, Sun 3 pm; closed Sun D.

BROADSTAIRS, KENT 3-3D

KEBBELLS £56 343

8 VICTORIA PARADE CT10 1QS
01843 319002

This "terrific seafood" bistro with a full-length bar for informal eating makes a "great addition to Broadstairs". It has views over Viking Bay, Charles Dickens's favourite holiday spot (Betsey Trotwood's cottage from 'Great Expectations' just around the corner is now a museum). / www.kebbells.com; kebbells_broadstairs; Wed-Sat, Tue 9 pm, Sun 3 pm; closed Sun D, closed Mon.

POSILLIPO £35 343

14 ALBION STREET CT10 1LU
01843 601133

"A great neighbourhood Italian with a great view of the sea". The pizzas are "delectable" (handmade in the Neapolitan pizza oven) and there's also a focus on seafood and pasta dishes, plus regular daily specials. / posillipo.squarespace.com; posillipo.restaurant; Mon-Sun midnight.

STARK £89 544

15 OSCAR ROAD CT10 1QJ
01843 579786

"Not your usual restaurant but a labour of love" – Ben & Sophie Crittenden opened their minuscule 10-seater venue in a former sandwich shop in 2016, achieving rave reviews for Ben's seasonal 6-course tasting menus of "truly wonderful food, cooked in a tiny open-plan kitchen". / www.starkfood.co.uk; Wed-Sat 11 pm; closed Wed-Sat L, closed Mon & Tue & Sun; No shorts; booking is online only.

WYATT & JONES £63 333

23-27 HARBOUR ST CT10 1EU
01843 865126

"Spanish-influenced small plates" – "especially delicious fish dishes" – dominate at this well-established venue under the historic York Gate, while "in winter, their Sunday lunch is epic". "The outlook over Broadstairs beach to the sea is spectacular and sitting at the bar is simply divine". Next door, the new Flotsam & Jetsam has been split off from the original site, serving "super-creative fish 'n' chips". / www.wyattandjones.co.uk; Fri & Sat 9.30 pm, Thu 9 pm, Sun 5 pm; closed Thu L closed Sun D, closed Mon & Tue & Wed; Cash & all usual cards.

BROADWAY, WORCESTERSHIRE 2-1C

THE LYGON ARMS £73

HIGH ST WR12 7DU 01386 852255

It seems wrong to exclude this famous Tudor coaching inn (which accommodated both Charles I and Oliver Cromwell in different phases of the Civil War) although it inspired no feedback in our annual diners' poll this year. Nowadays run by the 'Iconic' Luxury Hotels Group (who run Cliveden and Chewton Glen), its magnificent barrel-vaulted dining room currently serves rather incongruously as a 'Bar & Grill', with steaks, burgers or the likes of butternut squash salad the orders of the day. / www.lygonarmshotel.co.uk; lygoncotswolds; Mon-Sun 9.30 pm; Cash & all usual cards; No jeans; booking max 8 may apply.

RUSSELL'S OF BROADWAY £72 343

20 HIGH STREET WR12 7DT
01386 853555

"Excellent and innovative cooking" contributes to a "really lovely meal" at this "reliable" restaurant-with-rooms named after furniture designer Gordon Russell, a former occupant of the property whose father owned the Lygon Arms. The chippie next door is under the same ownership, and offers "wonderful fresh fish 'n' chips – not all greasy, and cooked to order". / russellsofbroadway.co.uk; russellsofbroadway; Wed-Sat 9 pm, Sun 6.15 pm; closed Mon & Tue; No Amex.

BROCKENHURST, HAMPSHIRE 2–4D

CAMBIUM, CAREYS MANOR £76 3 3 3

LYNDHURST RD   SO42 7RH
01590 623551

'Alistair Craig's dishes pay homage to the British countryside, and embrace the nature of the seasons' – well that's what the website says! – at this "lovely restaurant in a beautiful hotel": a New Forest destination that started life as a royal hunting lodge and is nowadays a luxurious spa complex. Reports in our annual diners' poll agree, all of them applauding its attractive, light interior and brasserie food from an all-day menu that's "carefully cooked, and good value". / www.careysmanor.com; careysmanor_senspa; Mon-Sat 9.30 pm, Sun 12 pm; closed Sun D; Cash & all usual cards; children: 8.

THE PIG £81 2 2 3

BEAULIEU ROAD   SO42 7QL
01590 622354

"Quite possibly my favourite spot in England!" (and "kids love it, too") – Robin Hutson's original Pig on the edge of the New Forest is an immediate hit, setting the template for the litter of shabby-chic country-house hotels that has followed. The trademark "25-mile menu is a game-changer", guaranteeing locally sourced ingredients including vegetables from the kitchen garden. For all the good vibes, though, a minority of reporters are "disappointed" to find that the food is "pretty average". / www.thepighotel.com; thepig_hotel; Mon-Sun 9.30 pm; Cash & all usual cards.

BROMESWELL, SUFFOLK 3–1D

THE UNRULY PIG £83 2 3 3

ORFORD RD   IP12 2PU   01394 460 310

"In the Suffolk countryside near Woodbridge" (and handy for the A12), this rural gastropub "looks a bit unprepossessing from the road but is well worth a detour" and – having won just about every 'Top Pub' award around in recent years – is one of the most commented-on destinations outside of London in our annual diners' poll. Braised rabbit, venison saddle or gnocchi are typical main courses from the à la carte menu, and there is also a 'Be Unruly' tasting option (for £70). Its army of fans say it "hits all the right notes", providing "truly original cooking but without losing sight of the fact that this is a pub", alongside "a fantastic selection of wines by the glass". Ratings are dragged down, though, by a sizable minority who view it as "very expensive" for food that's "good-to-average" ("if there were more local alternatives, I suspect we would be diverted"). / www.theunrulypig.co.uk; unrulypig; Mon-Thu 9 pm, Fri & Sat 9.15 pm, Sun 8 pm; No Amex.

BROMLEY, KENT 3–3B

OCEAN BASKET £68

12-13 MARKET SQUARE   BR1 1NA
020 3370 6065

A South African-based affordable seafood brand has opened its first UK branch in a former Café Rouge on the market square; Peter 'Fats' Lazarides and his brother George opened their first restaurant in Pretoria – more than 300 miles from the nearest coast – in 1995, and there are now more than 215 Ocean Baskets in 19 countries – many of them in sub-Saharan Africa. We expect a roll-out to commence any day. / uk.oceanbasket.com; Mon-Sun 10 pm.

BROUGHTON, LANCASHIRE 5–1A

ITALIAN ORCHARD, SAN MARCO GROUP £52 3 4 3

96 WHITTINGHAM LANE   PR3 5DB
01772 861240

"Completely consistent… they still do the best ever Pizza Napoletana" – this huge Italian 'Ristorante & Pizzeria' just outside Preston was opened in 1985 and has grown over the years to house 300 guests in one sitting, of whom about a third are in a striking glazed extension, complete with al fresco terrace. / www.italianorchard.com; theitalianorchard; Mon-Thu 9.30 pm, Fri & Sat 10.30 pm, Sun 9 pm; Cash & all usual cards.

BRUNTINGTHORPE, LEICESTERSHIRE 5–4D

THE JOINERS £58 4 3 3

CHURCH WALK   LE17 5QH
0116 247 8258

"Amazing food in a lovely old pub with a pretty village setting" – this beamed rural gastroboozer has ticked the boxes for the best part of two decades with its "simple (seasonally changing) menu of flavoursome dishes using good-quality produce". Top Tip – the 'Auberge suppers' – three set courses for under £20 on midweek evenings. / www.thejoinersarms.co.uk; Tue-Sat 9 pm, Sun 3 pm; closed Sun D, closed Mon.

BRUTON, SOMERSET 2–3B

AT THE CHAPEL £59 3 3 3

28 HIGH ST   BA10 0AE   01749 814070

This "beautiful" eighteenth-century chapel was converted 15 years ago into an all-day restaurant-with-rooms, artisan bakery and wine shop, centred around a "fantastic" modern dining room. (In August 2022, after our annual diners' poll concluded, founder Catherine Butler sold the business to the Stay Original Company, which has five other boutique hotels and pubs in the southwest, and pledged to carry on without major changes). / www.atthechapel.co.uk; atthechapel; Mon-Sun 5 pm; closed Mon-Sun D; Cash & all usual cards.

THE BOTANICAL ROOMS AT THE NEWT £100 4 4 4

THE NEWT IN SOMERSET   BA7 7NG
01963 577777

"Love this place" – set in historic Hadspen House and its famous gardens (operated since 2019 as a luxury hotel, shop and restaurant by South African billionaire Koos Bekker and his wife Karen Roos, an ex-editor of Elle Decoration). It's "beautifully done", and the "wood-panelled restaurant in the old house, with its candlelit atmosphere", makes an ideal setting for "a wonderful, surprising tasting menu", which is "certainly not your usual country house hotel food" – and which includes pairings with cider produced on the estate. ("Perfect on a late summer evening as the sun finally sets after some great pre-dinner cocktails"). / thenewtinsomerset.com; thenewtinsomerset; Mon-Sun 9 pm.

OSIP £101 5 3 3

1 HIGH STREET   BA10 0AB
01749 813322

"Every mouthful is divine" at ex-Portland and Clipston chef Merlin Labron-Johnson's "tiny restaurant in rural Somerset" that "dares to be different" – serving a set meal with no menu, "so you just sit back and await the surprises (you receive a menu sheet at the end of the meal)". "I was absolutely stunned by the intensity of flavours, the simple presentation and responsible sourcing of ingredients". "Some ingredients I had never tasted before, and the flavour pairings were creative and so exciting" – "what an incredible surprise, superb from start to finish". / osiprestaurant.com; osiprestaurant; Thu-Sun 9.30 pm; closed Mon & Tue & Wed; payment – credit card only; booking is online only; children: 12.

ROTH BAR & GRILL £68 2 2 3

DURSLADE FARM, DROPPING LN
BA10 0NL   01749 814060

This "canteen in a converted barn" with "one or two more upscale menu items – for example, smoked local trout and excellent Devon scallops, with very good chips" – is attached to the rural gallery of Swiss contemporary art dealers Hauser & Wirth, and is named after Dieter Roth: one of the artists they represent. The venue kick-started their Artfarm hospitality spin-off, which has spawned rather grander projects in Mayfair and Los Angeles, and last year snapped up London's Groucho Club. / www.rothbarandgrill.co.uk; rothbarandgrill; Tue, Wed, Sun 5 pm, Thu-Sat 11 pm; closed Tue, Wed, Sun D, closed Mon; Cash & all usual cards.

BUCKFASTLEIGH, DEVON 1–3D

RIVERFORD FIELD KITCHEN £52 4 3 4

WASH BARN   TQ11 0JU   01803 762074

"A vegetal cornucopia delight!" – this canteen at an organic veg box company's HQ "oozes with enough excitement and deliciousness to make even the most hardened of meat-eaters squirm with pleasure". They do serve some meat, but "vegetables are always the star" – "though the puds are pretty tasty too" – "all homemade of course and quite delicious". / www.fieldkitchen.riverford.co.uk; riverford; Wed-Sat 10 pm, Sun 7 pm; closed Mon & Tue; Cash & all usual cards; booking lunch only.

BUCKLAND MANOR   £111   2 2 3

WR12 7LY   01386 852626

A "country house atmosphere", "excellent service" and "delicious food" win praise from fans of this "beautiful" Cotswolds hotel – owned by greetings card mogul Andrew Brownsword – and it "should please every romantic". Ratings were dragged down, though, by other reporters who feel that the house is "lovely but tired", while "the food is good-ish, but certainly could be better". / www.bucklandmanor.co.uk; brownswordhotels; Mon-Sun 9 pm; Cash & all usual cards; Jacket required; booking max 8 may apply.

TEMPLE   £54   3 4 3

10 GRANVILLE TERRACE   EX23 8JZ
01288 354739

"Impressive ambition" and a hospitable style ("they made us feel so welcome") endear people to this modern bistro, serving funky small plates alongside low-intervention wines. This year they added an upstairs bar and roof terrace with views over Bude. / www.templecornwall.com; Mon-Sun 11 pm; closed Mon-Sun L.

THE SWAN INN   £64   3 3 3

SWINBROOK   OX18 4DY   01993 823339

"High-quality pub food" and a "lovely setting by the river" earn high ratings across the board for this traditional Cotswolds inn. "On a brilliant sunny bank holiday Saturday, The Swan was rammed but the amazing staff never missed a beat – the chef & kitchen churned out really delicious food, and nobody was less than delighted with their choices". Top Tip – "the sticky toffee reaches new heights of orgasmic satisfaction". / www.theswanswinbrook.co.uk; swaninnswinbrook; Mon-Sat 11 pm, Sun 10 pm; No Amex.

THE BOTHY BISTRO   £58   4 3 3

16 GRANT STREET   IV30 5UE
01343 830006

"If you find yourself in Moray and want great seafood/fish at OK prices this is the place for you!" – so say fans of this family-friendly independent bistro. William Sitwell of The Telegraph paid a visit in October 2021, and awarded it five stars for its "fresh and exciting" menu of seafood and "not posh" dining room, painted in azure blues – he called it "utterly

charming and beautifully simple… a glorious, sensational discovery". / thebothy.co.uk; bootleggersbothy; Fri & Sat 12 pm, Sun 6 pm; closed Fri-Sun D, closed Mon-Wed & Thu.

SOCIUS   £48   4 4 3

11 FOUNDRY PLACE   PE31 8LG
01328 738307

In its four years since opening, this "delicious fusion-style small-plates" venue in the "sophisticated village of Burnham Market" has earned itself a reputation as one of the better culinary bets near the north Norfolk coast – and in September 2022 it was crowned the AA's 'Restaurant of the Year'. Self-taught chef-patron Dan Lawrence and his partner Natalie Stuhler "manage a food service that is innovative, tasty and full of surprises", in a "fresh, modern purpose-built setting that feels as though it should be a fifteenth-century barn". / sociusnorfolk.co.uk; sociusnorfolk; Wed-Sat 9 pm, Sun 2.30 pm; closed Sun D, closed Mon & Tue.

STAG & HOUNDS   £67   3 3 3

4 MAIN STREET   LE14 2JQ   01664 454250

"Old-fashioned and quirky pub" near Melton Mowbray "run by a charming couple" – chef Dom Clarke (ex-Barn at Moor Hall and Isle of Eriska) and Antonia Nelmes. "The menus are based on what is good and fresh (often local) and are very compact – just three mains and three starters", and fans say "the cooking is always exciting and a pleasure to eat". There was the odd reporter, though, who said "it's hyped up to be amazing, but we were disappointed". / www.stagnhoundspub.co.uk; stag_n_hounds; Tue-Thu 10 pm, Fri & Sat 11 pm, Sun 9 pm; closed Mon.

HIVE BEACH CAFE   £59   3 3 4

BEACH ROAD   DT6 4RF   01308 897 070

With its "superb seafood in a wonderful beach location", this daytime venue has been a fixture since 1991 and "is still as good as ever" – "perfect after a walk along the beach or cliffs". "Despite being very busy, they have an efficient system" – "and they now take bookings". / www.hivebeachcafe.co.uk; hivebeachcafe; Mon & Tue, Sun 5 pm, Wed-Sat 7 pm; closed Mon & Tue, Sun D; Cash & all usual cards; no bookings.

THE PARLOUR   £65   3 4 3

BREDY FARM, BREDY LANE   DT6 4ND
01308 897899

"Genuinely spectacular pizzas and gorgeous Italian food in the middle of a farmyard" in the picturesque Bride Valley may be "very off-road for many" – but this "interesting restaurant" with "friendly staff" is by all accounts well worth the trip. Brede Farm also hosts a cider press, micro brewery, campsite and live music. / www.theparlour-bredyfarm.com;

theparlourbredyfarm; Wed-Sat 10 pm, Sun 4 pm; closed Sun D, closed Mon & Tue.

CLIFF ROAD   DT6 4RB   01308 897 205

"An amazing location overlooking the sea" is the 'crown jewel' feature of this "delightful" hotel dining room on the Jurassic Coast, which has a "wonderful position" on Lyme Bay. All aspects of the operation are well-rated, not least its "imaginative cooking" (fish the highlight) and "friendly and efficient" service. / www.theseasideboardinghouse.com; theseasideboardinghouse; Mon-Sun 9 pm; Cash & all usual cards.

MAISON BLEUE   £68   5 4 4

30-31 CHURCHGATE ST   IP33 1RG
01284 760 623

"Very French… very well executed" – Pascal & Karine Canavet's converted old townhouse is "so slick" and "a big favourite" for its legions of fans for whom it is "simply the best restaurant in Suffolk" (to the extent that it's one of the more commented-on destinations in our annual national diners' poll). The ambience has a "genuine" quality and the kitchen produces "fabulous modern French cooking" pitched below 'haute cuisine' but well above the mundane "at what are – by comparison with many comparable places – bargain prices". Recently the couple launched neighbouring 'Léa' (Pascal's mother's name) – a high street and neighbourhood traiteur selling "artisan ready meals of the same outstanding gastronomic quality as dining in". / www.maisonbleue.co.uk; maisonbleuesuffolk; Tue-Sat 8.30 pm; closed Sun & Mon; Cash & all usual cards; children: 10.

1921 ANGEL HILL   £78   4 3 3

19-21 ANGEL HILL   IP33 1UZ
01284 704870

"Adventurous and beautiful food" featuring "really interesting combinations" and served in a "well-spaced" setting by "discreet staff" add up to a "delightful" combination for all who comment on Zack Deakins's "very welcoming" townhouse, off Angel Hill: the most commented-on eatery in the locality. / nineteen-twentyone.co.uk; 1921_angel_hill; Tue, Thu-Sat 9 pm; closed Mon, Wed & Sun; Cash & all usual cards.

THE ONE BULL   £53   3 3 3

25 ANGEL HILL   IP33 1UZ   01284 848220

"Dependably interesting food" continues to carve a strong local reputation for this bright, "high quality" gastropub – part of the local Gusto Pronto group which links into the town's Brewshed brewery. / www.theonebull.co.uk; theonebullbury; Tue-Thu 11 pm, Fri & Sat midnight, Sun 10 pm; closed Mon; Cash & all usual cards.

Wilson's, Bristol

PEA PORRIDGE £63 4 5 4

28-29 CANNON ST   IP33 1JR
01284 700200

"Allow your eyes to feast on the gorgeous colours and your nose to savour the rich perfume of the dishes" at this "small restaurant run by a husband (chef) and wife (front of house) team", which is "tucked a bit away from the town centre". One of the more commented-on restaurants outside London in our annual diners' poll, it has won its more-than-local following with Justin's "richly styled" Moorish/Iberian food, "cooked with real flair and passion": "big flavours, with interesting combinations from top-quality ingredients". There's a "very interesting wine list" too – "a real eye-opener" – and "Jurga is always very happy to suggest which wines will go well with the food you've ordered". "You never leave hungry!". It's Suffolk's only Michelin-starred restaurant, but not especially 'haute' in its approach: it's closer to "a proper neighbourhood place, serving top-notch food". / www.peaporridge.co.uk; peaporridge; Mon & Tue, Thu-Sat 9.30 pm; closed Wed & Sun; No Amex; booking is online only; children: 10.

ST JAMES £59 3 2 2

30 HIGH ST   WD23 3HL   020 8950 2480

"This stalwart carries on doing good food well" after 25 years in Bushey village, and is "an oasis in the culinary wilderness of West Herts". "Under the benevolent guidance of Alfonso La Cava", it "offers the best dining experience in the area. Lunches and early-evening table d'hôte meals are particularly good value". Afternoon tea is served in its Betsy's Tearoom. / www.stjamesrestaurant.co.uk; stjamesbushey; Tue-Sat 9 pm, Sun 2 pm; closed Sun D, closed Mon; No Amex.

THE GALLIVANT £81 3 3 3

NEW LYDD RD   TN31 7RB   01797 225 057

An "unprepossessing exterior" – the legacy of its 1960s origins as a motel – "belies a great experience" at this beachside venue, where you can feast on chef Jamie Guy's "delicious, perfectly cooked, fresh, locally sourced fish and seafood" and other regional produce. / www.thegallivant.co.uk; thegallivant; Mon & Tue 9 pm, Wed-Sun 9.30 pm; No Amex; children: 16.

THE CAMBRIDGE CHOP HOUSE £55 3 2 3

1 KINGS PARADE   CB2 1SJ
01223 359506

"Despite its tourist-trap location" on the Cambridge main drag, this steakhouse excels – for its "enormous slabs of decent meat, which has been properly cooked", "fair prices" and a "good-value lunch menu". It's "essential" to eat in the "lovely atmosphere downstairs", with "street-level views of King's College Chapel". / www.cambscuisine.com/cambridge-chop-house; cambscuisine; Mon-Thu 8.30 pm, Fri 9 pm, Sat 9.30 pm, Sun 5 pm; closed Sun D; Cash & all usual cards.

FANCETT'S £55 4 4 3

MILL ROAD   CB1 2BD   01223 354093

"A brilliant new restaurant in Cambridge" – Holly & Dan Fancett upped sticks from North Street in Burnham Market to launch this outlying yearling on Mill Road in late 2021. "The food from the small but perfectly formed menu gets better each time", according to fans. It's not a case of bewildering tasting menus with dazzling small plates, but very yummy, deftly realised bistro fare at un-scary prices and "wonderful" service. / www.fancetts.com; fancettsbistro; Wed-Sat 9 pm; closed Wed L, closed Mon & Tue & Sun.

FIN BOYS £47 4 4 3

2 MILL ROAD   CB1 2AD   01223 354045

"An outstanding newish restaurant in Mill Road" – this restaurant, deli and 'fish butchery' opened in mid 2021, further bolstering the ever-more thriving local scene. Fish and seafood is right, left and centre to the offering with an eclectic and inviting mashup of Asian curries, pho, pasta and funky small plates. Earlier in the week is à la carte – weekend evenings are a tasting menu format. / www.fin-boys.com; thefinboys; Tue-Sat midnight; closed Sun & Mon.

GARDEN HOUSE £69

GRANTA PLACE   CB2 1RT   01223 259988

"Focused on simple dishes, with excellent ingredients, all elevated by sharp cooking" – the year-old grill at this new Graduate Hotel (named for the previous hotel on this site) has positive feedback in our annual diners' poll (but too limited for a rating). / www.gardenhousecambridge.co.uk; gardenhousecambridge; Mon & Tue 10 am, Wed-Sat 9 pm, Sun 6 pm; closed Mon & Tue D.

HOT NUMBERS £27 3 3 3

4 TRUMPINGTON STREET   CB2 1QA
01223 612207

"Great coffee, great brunch sandwiches and great jazz music" are the name of the game at this coffee shop trio with venues in Gwydir Street (music), Trumpington Street and in the village of Shepreth south of Cambridge, where the in-house roastery and bakery are based – along with a pizza oven. Founder Simon Fraser fell for the Antipodean coffee culture while living in Melbourne, and returned to his home town to launch Hot Numbers in 2011. / hotnumberscoffee.co.uk; hotnumberscoffee; Mon-Sun 5 pm; closed Mon-Sun D.

THE IVY CAMBRIDGE BRASSERIE £68 2 2 4

16 TRINITY STREET   CB2 1TB
01223 344044

"A lovely bright and cheerful room, with good food and special touches" make this glossy British brasserie from Richard Caring's chain a useful option for many in the Varsity town – although, like its many siblings around the country, it "lacks the glitter of the London original". / www.theivycambridgebrasserie.com; theivycambridge; Mon-Thu 10.30 pm, Fri & Sat 11 pm, Sun 10 pm.

MIDSUMMER HOUSE £321 4 4 3

MIDSUMMER COMMON   CB4 1HA
01223 369299

"What an experience: from the brimming tray of Champagne choices and canapés to great coffee at the end and a parting gift", this Victorian villa delivers an experience that's "very special". It helps that it has an idyllic location, on the banks of The Cam opposite the college boathouses and surrounded by the greenery of Midsummer Common. In 2023, Daniel Clifford celebrates his 25th year at the stoves here. "There is alchemy at work with his magical combinations, creativity and attention to detail at every stage" – some very fine food, which helps make this one of the most commented-on destinations in the UK. Dishes are "prepared with wit and incredible to look at". But they are also "phenomenally expensive, particularly if you also have the wine flight" and the level of value remains the main issue when considering a meal here, with almost one in five diners feeling the place is too "overpriced". Still, "it always impresses even if it is somewhat pricey even when compared to London". ("There will be moans about the bill, but, as I was hosted by my children for a big birthday, that was not my problem. What an experience it was. I am not sure I like being this age, but the celebration was second to none!") / www.midsummerhouse.co.uk; midsummer_house; Wed-Sat 8 pm; closed Mon & Tue & Sun; Cash & all usual cards; No shorts; credit card deposit required to book; children: 10.

PARKER'S TAVERN £61 ☑34

1 PARK TERRACE CB1 1JH
01223 606266

"A proper brasserie in a lovely refurbished hotel in the middle of Cambridge" – "who would have guessed that the once-dismal University Arms would house such a charmer?". Ex-Launceston Place chef Tristan Welch champions local East Anglian produce on a menu that provides comfort rather than foodie fireworks. Rebuilt several years ago, this long-established hotel has a fantastic position, overlooking Parker's Piece. / www.parkerstavern.com; parkers_tavern; Sun-Fri 9.30 pm, Sat 10 pm.

PINT SHOP £54 323

10 PEAS HILL CB2 3PN 01223 352 293

This "useful stopping place in the centre of Cambridge" serves "solid pub food" and a "good selection" of craft beers. A boozer for only 10 years, it was once the home of E.M. Forster. / www.pintshop.co.uk; pint_shop; Sun-Thu 11 pm, Fri & Sat midnight; Cash & all usual cards; no bookings.

RESTAURANT TWENTY TWO £96 543

22 CHESTERTON ROAD CB4 3AX
01223 351880

"Much better value than its main local competitor Midsummer House" – you will need to book two months ahead if you want to visit Sam Carter and Alexandra Oliver's "very enjoyable" venue, "located in a Victorian terraced house with small cosy rooms" a short walk from the city centre (near the Cam and Jesus Green). One central London reporter acclaimed it as "worth the trip to Cambridge" thanks to its "very enjoyable" combination of personable service and very accomplished cuisine (all served – except at lunch and on certain evenings – via the now-obligatory tasting menu format). / www.restaurant22.co.uk; restaurant22_cambridge; Thu-Sat, Wed 8 pm; closed Wed L, closed Mon & Tue & Sun; Cash & all usual cards; children: 12.

SCOTT'S ALL DAY £41 333

MILL ROAD CB1 2AZ 01223 311105

On happening Mill Road, a "newish pizza eat-in and take-away with prompt service and great pizza". "Other food options are available" – a small selection of pasta, and dedicated weekday breakfast and weekend brunch menus. / www.scottsallday.com; scottsallday; Tue-Sat 9.30 pm, Sun 3 pm; closed Sun D, closed Mon.

STEM & GLORY £46 332

50-60 STATION ROAD CB1 2JH
01223 757150

Limited but positive feedback on this successful vegan, which shifted to this new location in a new development near the station in 2021. Worth remembering if you are catching a train and a place of pilgrimage for those who eat meat-free. It's a rare Cambridge eatery that has

spawned openings in the capital (see also). / www.stemandglory.uk; stemandglory; Mon-Sat 10 pm; closed Sun.

TRINITY £70 333

15 TRINITY STREET CB2 1TB
01223 322130

This "good (mainly) seafood restaurant – always with good oysters" – is a decent option for a meal on a prime tourist site, directly opposite the Great Gate of the college of the same name. "Service is lovely", and the "creative menu" is "now slightly SE Asian (coconut and/or curry with everything)". / www.trinitycambridge.co.uk; restauranttrinity; Thu & Fri 10 pm, Sat 10.30 pm, Sun 9.30 pm; closed Mon & Tue & Wed.

VANDERLYLE £92 543

38 MILL ROAD CB1 2AD

"So stunningly good" – there's "no need for meat or fish" at Alex Rushmer's "innovative and exciting" venture: "who cares if it's vegan/veggie or not? This is simply outstanding tasty food which will totally blow you away". The former MasterChef finalist ran the Hole in the Wall in nearby Little Wilbraham before launching here with Lawrence Butler in 2019. Top Tip – "the focaccia and yeast butter is a revelation". / www.vanderlyle-restaurant.com; vanderlylerestaurant; Tue-Sat 11 pm; closed Tue-Fri L, closed Sun & Mon; booking is online only.

CAFÉ DES AMIS £50 334

95 ST DUNSTAN'S ST CT2 8AA
01227 464390

A fixture of the Westgate for 35 years, this "colourful and very popular" spot serves "good portions of fairly priced and fresh-tasting Mexican food", "with lots of choices for non-meat eaters". The "good staff" ensure a "fun, buzzing atmosphere", and it "always seems to be busy, so best to book". Well-travelled owners Bill & Emmanuelle Betham have another Café des Amis in Hawaii, and a Café du Soleil serving Mediterranean food in Canterbury. / www.cafedez.com; Mon-Thu 10 pm, Fri & Sat 10.30 pm, Sun 9.30 pm; Cash & all usual cards; booking max 6 may apply.

THE COOK'S TALE (FKA THE AMBRETTE CANTERBURY) £55 432

14 - 15 BEER CART LANE CT1 2NY
01227 200 777

Well-known Kent restaurateur, Dev Biswal has refocused his local business empire on this converted backstreet pub which he renamed from 'The Ambrette' in mid 2022. All ingredients are now sourced within 30 minutes of the restaurant and he has put curry on the menu (always previously excluded). The move continues a direction of travel begun under his business's former brand, and we have rated it as for the Ambrette, and assumed a continuing of his "delicious cuisine that isn't from your run-of-the-mill Indian menu" – a "fantastic

combination of English and Indian food". / www.thecookstale.co.uk; Fri & Sat 11 pm, Sun-Thu 10.30 pm.

THE GOODS SHED £58 333

STATION ROAD WEST CT2 8AN
01227 459153

"Standards are high" at this "in-house restaurant in Canterbury's permanent Farmers' Market". "Quality ingredients are sourced from the stalls", and "the dishes have recently been more imaginative" – even if "prices have crept up". / www.thegoodsshed.co.uk; thegoodsshed_; Tue-Sat 9 pm, Sun 3 pm; closed Sun D, closed Mon; Cash & all usual cards.

ASADOR 44 £69 333

14-15 QUAY STREET CF10 1EA
029 2002 0039

Whole legs of lamb and great ribs of beef roasted Spanish-style on the parilla are the star turns at this spacious venue from Tom & Owen Morgan – and even the bread arrives charred. With its "great food and service", the outfit celebrates the Hispanic cuisine the brothers have championed in the 21 years since founding their Bar 44 group. / asador44.co.uk; asador44; Fri & Sat 11.30 pm, Thu 11 pm, Sun 6 pm, Wed 11 pm; closed Wed L closed Sun D, closed Mon & Tue; Cash & all usual cards; credit card deposit required to book.

BAR 44 CARDIFF £55 333

15-23 WESTGATE STREET CF10 1DD
03333 44 40 49

Hispanophile foodies Tom & Owen Morgan's city centre tapas bar, in the shadow of the Principality Stadium, serves an "interesting range of wines and sherries" and an "amazing Spanish Sunday lunch" (among other meals). The brothers launched their business two decades ago in Cowbridge, and now have venues in Penarth and Bristol. / www.bar44.co.uk; bar44tapas; Thu-Sat midnight, Wed 11 pm, Sun 6 pm; closed Wed L closed Sun D, closed Mon & Tue; Cash & all usual cards.

CASANOVA £64 333

13 QUAY ST CF10 1EA 029 2034 4044

This "little gem" of an Italian restaurant – "close to the Millennium stadium, so perfect to help you celebrate or forget" – has a "pleasingly old-fashioned and independent atmosphere", created by the three friends who have run it together for nearly two decades – Antonio, Selim and Luca. The small menu of "superb, authentic dishes" is not reliant on pasta and pizza, which makes a welcome change. / www.casanovacardiff.co.uk; casanovacardiff; Mon-Sat 10 pm; closed Sun; Cash & all usual cards.

CORA £83 332

83 PONTCANNA STREET (ABOVE MILKWOOD) CF11 9HS 07840 244060

"Tiny! Difficult to get a table but worth it" – ex-Hedone-chef Lee Skeet's 12-seater above

Pontcanna's Milkwood opened in January 2022 following the success of his 40 Days, 40 Nights pop-up, and he serves a seasonal tasting menu, majoring in fish and seafood. Limited early feedback all says the food is good, although one reporter felt "I really wanted it to be great, but thought the food was a little muted". / bones-entertainment.com/collections/cora; cora. restauran; Mon-Fri 9 pm; closed Sat & Sun.

HEANEY'S £91 5️⃣4️⃣3️⃣

6-10 ROMILLY CRESCENT   CF11 9NR
029 2034 1264?

Tommy Heaney's "fantastic food that challenges the taste buds" has wowed diners at the "atmospheric" venue he opened in a leafy suburb of Cardiff four years ago, after a stint at the Great House hotel in Bridgend. The self-taught Northern Irish chef has worked around the world, gathering influences in the US, Australia, Thailand and London that show up on his "great taster menu". Appearances on the Great British Menu brought him to a wider audience, and he has also opened an oyster and wine bar, Uisce, next door. / heaneyscardiff. co.uk; heaneyscardiff; Wed-Sat midnight, Sun 6 pm; closed Mon & Tue.

MATSUDAI RAMEN AT THE BANK

185 CLARE ROAD   CF11 6QD

Welsh ramen wizard James Chant, whose start-up became a lockdown meal-kit hit and a pop-up phenomenon touring Manchester, Bristol and London, opened his first bricks-and-mortar restaurant in the old NatWest bank in Grangetown in August 2022. This was after our annual diners' poll had concluded, but an early take from WalesOnline reports a packed and happy local scene (headline: "we can't tell you just how good it is"). / matsudai.co.uk; matsudairamen.

PURPLE POPPADOM £56 4️⃣3️⃣3️⃣

185A, COWBRIDGE ROAD EAST
CF11 9AJ   029 2022 0026

"Extremely popular and rightly so" – Anand George's Keralan specialist in the Cardiff 'burbs offers "classy cooking with subtle flavours". / purplepoppadom.com; purple_poppadom; Tue-Sat 11 pm, Sun 9 pm; closed Tue-Sat L, closed Mon; Cash & all usual cards.

THOMAS BY TOM SIMMONS £66 4️⃣3️⃣3️⃣

3-5 PONTCANNA STREET   CF11 9HQ

Pembrokeshire-born chef Tom Simmons's debut Welsh restaurant offers an "ambitious and very successful menu of fresh local produce, expertly and accurately cooked in interesting ways". His London restaurant near Tower Bridge did not reopen after the pandemic. / thomas-pontcanna.co.uk; thomasbytomsimmons; Wed-Sat midnight; closed Mon & Tue & Sun.

CARLISLE, CUMBRIA   7–2D

ALEXANDROS GREEK RESTAURANT AND DELI £49 3️⃣4️⃣3️⃣

68 WARWICK ROAD   CA1 1DR
01228 592227

"You are always assured a great welcome at this family-run Greek restaurant, where nothing is too much trouble. Aris, supported by his wife, two sons and brother-in-law chef, really cares about his food and how much you enjoy it". / www.thegreek.co.uk; alexandros-greek-restaurant-deli; Mon-Sat 9.30 pm; closed Sun; Cash & all usual cards.

CARTMEL, CUMBRIA   7–4D

AULIS AT L'ENCLUME £275 5️⃣5️⃣4️⃣

CAVENDISH ST   LA11 6QA

"The best way to do L'Enclume – same food as the restaurant but only 6 of you", providing "a stunning theatrical experience that takes gastronomic perfection to another level". It takes place at "a small counter beside the experimental kitchen, with Simon Rogan's classic seasonal dishes served alongside some ideas they're still perfecting (oyster custard), with food prepared in front of you by a chatty chef" so "all your questions are answered". Top Culinary Tip – "and it seems the answer is butter – lots of it!". / www.lenclume.co.uk/aulis; lenclume; Thu-Sun 9 pm; closed Mon & Tue & Wed; No Amex; booking is online only.

L'ENCLUME £296 5️⃣5️⃣5️⃣

CAVENDISH STREET   LA11 6QA
01539 536362

"Well deserving of its third Michelin star" – Simon Rogan's culinary mecca in the Lakes celebrated its 20th year by becoming the first restaurant north of Watford Gap to achieve the Tyre Men's top gong (and was the second-most commented-on destination in our survey after the somewhat more accessibly located Manoir aux Quat' Saisons). "17 courses of stunning food might seem somewhat excessive, but this remote and unique destination is certainly 'vaut le detour'" and few top establishments in our annual diners' poll achieve such consistent support from diners. "There seems to be no end to Simon Rogan's creativity" and – with head chef Paul Burgalieres – the kitchen delivers "unmatched seasonal food with true integrity" and "exceptionally beautiful" flavours, using produce from Rogan's own farm. ("Not a single bite is not surprising and delicious"; "as quite a picky eater I was amazed as I ate course after course containing items I usually wouldn't eat and yet they were all simply out of this world!"). "The team is so well drilled that it's like watching a ballet" and while the overall effect can seem "formal", the "staff obviously enjoy working there". "One of our most memorable experiences ever!" / www.lenclume.co.uk; lenclume; Tue-Sun midnight; closed Mon; No Amex; children: 12.

ROGAN & CO £79 3️⃣3️⃣3️⃣

DEVONSHIRE SQUARE   LA11 6QD
01539 535917

"This sibling to L'Enclume is much more relaxed than its big sister around the corner" (much "more chance of getting a reservation too!) with "a wonderful buzzy atmosphere" and the option to stay the night. In all respects, "it's more conventional in style" and not aiming for pyrotechnics like Simon Rogan's nearby mothership. "You still get the same attentiveness to detail" and "precise preparation" but the "cuisine is more traditional (if usually with a twist)" from an "interesting seasonal menu". Feedback was a little uneven this year, though, with ratings dragged down by a small number of "hit and miss" meals, particularly regarding service. Top Tip – "great home delivery food" too from an "ever-changing selection". / www.roganandcompany.co.uk; rogan_and_co; Mon, Wed-Sun 9 pm; closed Tue; No Amex; credit card deposit required to book.

CASTOR, PETERBOROUGH   6–4A

THE CHUBBY CASTOR £96 3️⃣3️⃣3️⃣

34 PETERBOROUGH ROAD   PE5 7AX
01733380801

Gordon Ramsay and Philip Howard-trained Adebola Adeshina's "beautifully presented tasting menu" wins praise for this "nicely decorated old thatched inn in a lovely village" outside Peterborough, which receives all-round good ratings from reporters. / www.thechubbycastor.com; chubbycastor; Wed-Sat 10.30 pm, Sun 3 pm; closed Sun D, closed Mon & Tue; No Amex.

CATTERLINE, ABERDEENSHIRE   9–3D

CREEL INN £35 3️⃣4️⃣3️⃣

AB39 2UL   01569 750254

"With outside seats looking over the coast or sitting inside looking through the windows, you get fabulous views" at this well-known inn, perched on the cliffs. "The food is generous and generally good" (for example "delicious Cullen skink, fabulous mussels, crab rolls and generous fish 'n' chips with perfect hake"). / www.thecreelinn.co.uk; Wed & Thu 11 pm, Fri & Sat midnight, Sun 10 pm; closed Mon & Tue; Cash & all usual cards.

CAVENDISH, SUFFOLK   3–1C

THE GEORGE £52 3️⃣3️⃣2️⃣

THE GREEN   CO10 8BA   01787 280248

This "delightful old village pub/restaurant" earns consistently strong ratings for its locally sourced and well cooked meals, which appeal to "locals and walkers alike". / www.thecavendishgeorge.co.uk; thegeorgecavendish; Wed-Sat 9 pm, Sun 3 pm; closed Sun D, closed Mon & Tue; Cash & all usual cards.

THE FARRIER £61 343

89 MAIN STREET YO11 3RP
01723 861432

"Smart and friendly" coastal gastropub and B&B that also incorporates a restaurant and coffee house. There's a wide range of food, including a menu of bistro-ish fare: all well-rated. / www.the-farrier.co.uk/restaurant; thefarrier_cayton; Sun-Thu 11 pm, Fri & Sat midnight.

BROCKENCOTE HALL £97 333

DY10 4PY 01562 777876

This grand Victorian manor house hotel on a 70-acre estate offers both tasting menus and a conventional 3-course format in its elegant Chaddesley Restaurant – "have eaten there several times in the past few months and the food never disappoints". / www.brockencotehall.com; brockencotehall; Wed-Sun 8.30 pm, Mon 12 pm; closed Wed L closed Mon D, closed Tue; Cash & all usual cards; No trainers.

GIDLEIGH PARK £160 445

TQ13 8HH 01647 432367

"Set majestically on the upper reaches of the River Teign, on the very edge of Dartmoor", Andrew Brownsword's luxurious if remote Tudorbethan pile has set the standard for British country-house dining over four decades (initially under Paul & Kay Henderson, who sold up in 2005). "Service and ambience are, as always, unsurpassed" and "Chris Eden's menu is superb" – even if he is yet to fully match the level of esteem achieved by some of his illustrious predecessors as chef, among them Shaun Hill, Michael Caines and Michael Wignall. / www.gidleigh.co.uk; brownswordhotels; Tue-Sat 9 pm; closed Sun & Mon; Cash & all usual cards; No jeans.

THE JOLLY FARMER £98 332

GOLD HILL WEST SL9 9HH
01753 887 596

Part of the White Brasserie Group, this popular gastropub is a cut-above in keeping with the rest of the group. There are no stand-out features noted in reports, but if you want a classic pub experience, it's one of the better options in this prosperous corner of Bucks. / www.jollyfarmerchalfont.com; closed Mon-Sat & Sun.

PRIME STEAK & GRILL, THE CLARENDON £77 243

REDHALL LANE WD3 4LU
01923 264 580

"Lovely steaks and Sunday roasts" plus "lots of fresh vegetables and salads" tick the boxes at this local trio (branches in St Albans and Beaconsfield), specialising in British grass-fed beef, dry-aged on the bone. The banquette seating and kids' activity sheets and menu make them good "family-friendly" eating options. / www.primesteakandgrill.com/chandlers-cross; primesteak; Mon-Sat 11 pm, Sun 10 pm.

THE CANDLELIGHT INN £54 333

BISHOPSWOOD TA20 3RS 01460 234476

This "nicely renovated" seventeenth-century inn, "nestled in a tiny hamlet on the outskirts of Chard", delivers some "exceptional cooking – focused, precise and tasty". Staff are "friendly and attentive", and "the surroundings clean, smart and relaxing". / www.candlelight-inn.co.uk; candlelightinnsomerset; Mon-Thu, Sat, Fri 11 pm, Sun 6 pm; closed Sun D.

PUMPROOM RESTAURANT AT COPPER RIVET DISTILLERY £50 334

ME4 4LP

A "huge" Victorian pumphouse that pumped water in and out of the dry dock at Chatham dockyard, with "views across the Medway to Upnor Castle", hosts this impressive yearling, which is praised for its "amazing food from a very talented young chef", Will Freeman, who is creating "ambitious menus in this stunning venue". Owners Bob Russell and his sons Matthew and Stephen opened their Copper River distillery here six years ago. / crdpumproom.com; copperrivetdistillery; Thu-Sat 8.30 pm, Wed 2.30 pm, Sun 3.45 pm; closed Wed & Sun D, closed Mon & Tue.

INDIAN TIFFIN ROOM £44 333

2 CHAPEL STREET SK8 1BR
0161 491 2020

"Quality gorgeous food" inspired by street stalls across India ("none of your generic bland rubbish") is on the colourful menu at this Cheadle outfit that has spawned spin-offs in Manchester and Leeds. It's the "extensive selection of delicious dosas that really marks this out from most other Indian restaurants" – and they're "ideal for vegetarians". / www.indiantiffinroom.com; indiantiffinroom; Tue-Sat 10.30 pm, Sun 9.30 pm; closed Tue-Fri L, closed Mon; Cash & all usual cards.

MOTO PIZZA £27 333

24 BADDOW ROAD CM2 0DG
01245 257819

"Cracking all-you-can-eat fresh Neapolitan pizzas" is the USP at this fun venue, which celebrates its fifth year in 2023. "Pizza is brought round to you and you can choose whether to try a slice or not. You keep eating until you switch your light off! There are fabulous and unusual flavours". "It's good value and with great quality ingredients". Also in Colchester. / www.motopizza.co.uk; motopizzauk; Tue-Sat 10 pm, Sun 8 pm; closed Mon.

L'ARTISAN £64 333

30 CLARENCE ST GL50 3NX
01242 571257

This warmly authentic Gallic spot from chef Yves and his wife Elisabeth Ogrodzki, veteran restaurateurs who have cooked their way to Cheltenham from Paris, Provence and rural Leicestershire, wins consistent high ratings – and thrilled Jay Rayner of The Observer for channelling another age (the '80s) "and beautifully so". / www.lartisan-restaurant.com; lartisanchelt; Tue-Thu 9 pm, Fri & Sat 9.30 pm; closed Sun & Mon.

BHOOMI £48 343

52 SUFFOLK RD GL50 2AQ
01242 222 010

"Reliably enjoyable and interesting" Keralan dishes are the attraction at this crowd-pleasing outfit from prolific local restaurateur Michael Raphel (Prithvi, Holee Cow), who was inspired by the flavours his chef grandfather brought from South India as an immigrant 50 years ago. A switch from fine-dining to a more casual approach a few years back has paid dividends, and now there is a spin-off in Oxford. Top Menu Tip – "the thali are particularly wonderful". / www.bhoomikitchen.co.uk; bhoomikitchen_; Tue-Sun 9.30 pm; closed Tue-Thu, Sun L, closed Mon.

LE CHAMPIGNON SAUVAGE £103 452

24-28 SUFFOLK RD GL50 2AQ
01242 573449

"A place to eat for people who prefer food to Instagram…" – "No visit to Cheltenham is complete without a meal at the delightful Champignon Sauvage" according to the many fans of David & Helen Everitt-Matthias's long-established foodie temple, which remains one of the more commented-on rural restaurants in the UK. For its many long-term devotees, "this is the yardstick used to judge everywhere else as its combination of skill, service and value is so hard to beat". Famously the kitchen is never open when David isn't in it to cook, and the result is "innovative, often-foraged seasonal dishes" – "precise, original and beautiful cooking that never strains for effect" and "whose flavours sing on the plate". "Friendly and professional service to match is provided by Helen", who also presides over the "super wine list with a great selection of half bottles". No-one has ever pretended the rather sedate room is a riot, but fans say "its serenity encourages conversation" and "still don't understand why this outstanding restaurant lost its second Michelin star a couple of years ago". Ratings here dipped a little this year, however, on one or two mixed (if far-from-damning) reports. Typical would be "our favourite last year was somewhat off its game this time and lacked a little sparkle"; or "the food was great as ever but the room felt dead… the wrong sort of hushed". Perhaps the strains of these pandemic times? Or "maybe it's just that everywhere else has upped its game?" Still, for the majority, "it's wonderful and creates some of the best things ever eaten". / www.lechampignonsauvage.co.uk; lechampsauvage; Wed-Sat 8.30 pm; closed Mon & Tue & Sun; Cash & all usual cards.

GL50 £60 3 3 4

8 NORFOLK HOUSE, CHESTER WALK GL50 3JX 01242 228555

'Informal fine dining' is the mantra at Jonas Lodge's three-year-old, where a zero-waste ethos informs the cooking style, and where dishes are often zhooshed up with funky ingredients, pickling and fermenting. The majority of reports are upbeat, but there is the occasional caution of "some odd dishes, so choose carefully" (and sceptics feel that "the chef is aiming for shock value: I go out to enjoy myself, not to be challenged!"). / www.restaurantgl50.com; restaurantgl50; Tue-Thu 9 pm, Fri & Sat 9.30 pm; closed Tue-Thu L, closed Sun & Mon; Cash & all usual cards.

THE IVY MONTPELLIER BRASSERIE £77 2 2 3

ROTUNDA TERRACE, MONTPELLIER STREET GL50 1SH 01242 894 200

"Do ask to sit under the rotunda" – which makes this spin-off from the national chain "a memorable place to eat". "The food is not memorable, but overall it is fine and predictable, one can rely on getting a decent meal". / www.theivycheltenhambrasserie.com; ivycheltenham; Mon-Sun 11 pm.

KIBOU CHELTENHAM £45 3 4 3

REGENT ARCADE, REGENT STREET GL50 1JZ 01242 507984

"What a wonderful experience" – this original of what is now a national chain (branches in Bristol, London and Solihull) serves "wonderful sushi" and other Japanese dishes that are "as good if not better since it moved to larger premises" – "the most stressful part of visiting is choosing from the menu!". Top Tip – "the aptly named volcano roll". / kibou.co.uk; kiboucheltenham; Sun-Thu 11 pm, Fri & Sat midnight.

LUMIÈRE £96 5 5 3

CLARENCE PARADE GL50 3PA 01242 222200

"Our best meal of the year!" – "we benchmark all fine dining experiences against Lumière and nobody beats them", say fans of chef Jon Howe and his front-of-house wife Helen's small restaurant, whose "unassuming exterior camouflages" a "gastronomic delight". "Sophisticated, balanced dishes with exquisite flavour" are "served with skill and passion" – and it's "come through lockdown even better than before". / www.lumiererestaurant.co.uk; lumiererestaurantcheltenham; Fri & Sat, Wed & Thu 8.30 pm; closed Wed & Thu L, closed Mon & Tue & Sun; Cash & all usual cards; children: 8.

MUSE BRASSERIE £35 4 3 3

60 ST GEORGE'S PLACE GL50 3PN 01242 239447

"Fabulous cooking, mixing Indian and French cuisines to offer unusual, superbly flavoured dishes" is the USP of this three-year-old collaboration, bringing together two chefs from very different culinary traditions – Franck Grillet and Pramod Tirunagari – and "it works!", producing meals of "fine-dining quality in a relaxed bistro atmosphere, and at bistro prices". The pair opened a spin-off in Bristol late last year. / www.musebrasserie.com; musebrasserie; Mon-Thu 10 pm, Fri & Sat 11 pm; closed Mon L, closed Sun; No shorts.

PRITHVI £70 5 4 3

37 BATH ROAD GL53 7HG 01242 226229

"Classy in every sense", this elegant 11-year-old shows "attention to detail in every department" resulting in "excellently executed takes on classic Indian dishes", underpinned by "exemplary service". It moved a few years ago to elegant Pittville Park premises. / www.prithvirestaurant.com; prithvirestaurant; Tue-Sat 9.30 pm; closed Tue-Thu L, closed Sun & Mon; Cash & all usual cards; No shorts; children: 12.

PURSLANE £66 4 3 3

16 RODNEY RD GL50 1JJ 01242 321639

Chef-patron Gareth Fulford's "intimate restaurant with great food and wine" is "a long way from the sea, but the fish is always beautifully cooked and so tasty". It's also "fantastic value", offering a range of options from 2 to 5 courses. "This is up there with my favourites – I just wished we lived nearer". / www.purslane-restaurant.co.uk; purslane_restaurant; Thu-Sat 12.30 am; closed Mon-Wed & Sun; No Amex.

SAFFRON SUMMER £53 4 3 2

4 ACE PARADE KT9 1DR 020 8391 4477

"A must visit" – this "high-end Indian restaurant" in the Surrey suburbs (with a sibling in Reigate) from ex-Oberoi and Cinnamon Club chef-patron Awanish Roy creates "very different" flavours that are "innovative, delicate and amazing". "The courteous staff are fabulous, and the prices are actually very reasonable for this quality of food" – in what is emphatically "not your typical curry house". / www.saffronsummer.co.uk; Tue-Sun 10.30 pm; closed Tue, Wed L, closed Mon.

ARCHITECT £44 3 4 4

54 NICHOLAS STREET CH1 2NX 01244 353070

With a "good location near the racecourse", this Georgian pub from Brunning & Price is "divided into cosy rooms and alcoves", and excels for its "traditional pub food" including "fabulous fish 'n' chips", "good pies and specials" – "but the key is in the sides: excellent samphire, sauces, creamy mash and more". The name honours prominent local architect Thomas Harrison, who designed the building as his own home. / architectchester; Mon-Thu 11 pm, Fri & Sat 11.30 pm, Sun 10.30 pm; No Amex.

THE ARKLE, THE CHESTER GROSVENOR £151

56-58 EASTGATE STREET CH1 1LT 01244 324 024

Owned by the Duke of Westminster, and sitting right next to the iconic Eastgate Clock, the city's flagship hotel has a plush (if windowless) main dining room, which in March 2022 was relaunched after a £250,000 refit. The change was to mark a turning of the page from its time under Simon Radley, who held one of the North West's more enduring Michelin stars here from 1998 till his retirement in mid 2021. So his replacement, Elliot Hill (arriving from Liverpool's Panoramic 34) has big shoes to fill. He made a start in November 2022, winning three rosettes at the AA Awards… although under Simon, the hotel held four. Our limited initial feedback on his start here is all positive (if too limited for a rating), including for afternoon tea in the adjoining lounges – "attentive staff and excellent sandwiches and pastries… they also serve a Gentleman's afternoon tea, with crispy haddock bloomers, and coronation chicken on spiced curry bread". / www.chestergrosvenor.com; chestergrosvenor; Tue-Sat 9 pm; closed Tue-Sat L, closed Sun & Mon; No trainers; children: 12+.

LA BRASSERIE, CHESTER GROSVENOR, CHESTER GROSVENOR £78 3 3 4

EASTGATE CH1 1LT 01244 324024

It's "always a pleasure" to visit this plush hotel, where the more relaxed, pavement-side Brasserie is "great for lunch" in "beautiful surroundings"; and where you'll be looked after by "attentive staff with an eye for detail" – whether you're after "casual dining (homemade soup and roll are delicious)" or an "à la carte menu (fish dishes are good)". For the Grosvenor's famous afternoon tea, head to the plush Arkle Bar & Lounge. / www.chestergrosvenor.com; chestergrosvenor; Mon-Sat 9 pm, Sun 8.30 pm; Cash & all usual cards.

THE FORGE

HOTEL INDIGO, GROSVENOR PARK ROAD CH1 1QQ

No reports as yet on this boutique hotel dining room run by game expert Mike Robinson. Dry-aged beef and venison are brought from maturation cabinets to be cooked over a flame grill and, on paper at least, this is one of the city's more interesting dining options. / theforgechester.co.uk; the_forge_restaurant_chester; Mon-Thu 9.30 pm, Fri & Sat 9.45 pm, Sun 8.30 pm; closed Mon & Tue L.

HYPHA £83 443

5 CITY WALLS CH1 2JG 01244 312490

"What a superb experience!" – chef Nicholas Friar's "innovative" experimental cuisine ('closed-loop' system, fermentation lab, ultra-seasonal and sustainable), presented in a reclaimed-wood-panelled dining room on the medieval city wall, is "a delight and a surprise – you wouldn't guess it was a vegan restaurant". "We sat at the Chef's Counter – I'd highly recommend it. Food was beautifully presented and delicious, wine pairings worked perfectly, chef and staff were friendly and helpful". In September 2022, Nicholas announced the temporary closure of the restaurant, and at the end of the month posted a Facebook message saying: "we have decided to close our doors for the current time… we will take this time to work on new projects and to develop a way to reimagine HYPHA in a different time, location and execution… this is not a goodbye but a see you later". / www.hypha.uk; H_Y_P_H_A; Wed-Sat 11 pm; closed Wed & Thu L, closed Mon & Tue & Sun.

PARS KAHVE 343

5 - 7 WATERGATE STREET SOUTH CH1 2LE 01244 327117

Situated on the ancient, picturesque top tier of 'The Rows' on Watergate Street, this August 2021 yearling from Adem & Holly Yilmaz (their first venture) is proving an excellent addition to the city. The Turkish cooking is "simple but there's a great choice of really good dishes" and the welcome is "warm and friendly". / parskahve; Mon-Sun 9 pm.

PORTA £69 323

140 NORTHGATE STREET CH1 2HT 01244 344295

"Great Spanish food" – including plenty of "tasty fresh seafood" – has made such a success of Joe & Ben Wright's ten-year-old wine-and-tapas spot that they closed Joseph Benjamin, their original bistro next door, to concentrate their resources on it in 2021. It's a "small (and you can't book), but lively place with attentive service and a great atmosphere". The brothers now have spin-offs in Altrincham and Salford. / www.portatapas.co.uk; porta_chester; Tue-Sat 10.30 pm, Sun 9 pm; closed Mon; Cash & all usual cards; no bookings.

STICKY WALNUT £65 444

11 CHARLES ST CH2 3AZ 01244 400400

"A very special place indeed" – this modest-looking backstreet bistro that chef Gary Usher opened 13 years ago in the Chester suburb of Hoole has achieved cult status and set the template for his crowdfunded Elite Bistros group, which now has six venues across the North West. "Always our choice for celebrations, delicious meals and superb service", it's "guaranteed to give you a great time". / www.stickywalnut.net; Sticky_Walnut; Mon-Thu 9 pm, Fri & Sat 10 pm, Sun 5 pm; closed Sun D; Cash & all usual cards; credit card deposit required to book.

X BY HARRY GUY

WILDES CHESTER, 10 BRIDGE STREET CH1 1NQ 01244 667550

Chef Harry Guy (ex-Savoy Grill and Mallory Court Hotel) will open his debut restaurant in Wildes Group's new Chester boutique hotel in 2023 (originally scheduled for mid 2022), by 'The Cross' at the ancient heart of this picturesque town. The venue itself sounds quite a 'do': with 18 bedrooms, rooftop pool, amphitheatre sauna and terrace with views overlooking the city. An "invitingly dark" dining room is promised, and setting its sights on becoming "one of the finest restaurants in the country". / www.xbyharryguy.com; xbyharryguy; Mon-Sun 9.15 pm; closed Mon-Sun L.

CHICHESTER, WEST SUSSEX 3–4A

CASSONS RESTAURANT & BAR £58 333

ARUNDEL ROAD, TANGMERE PO18 0DU 01243 773294

"A visit to this delightful restaurant is an event, not just an opportunity to eat", agree the many fans of Viv Cassons's "very good" cooking – who snap up bookings for the regular themed diners. Her husband, known simply as 'Cass', looks after the wine list and front of house. Even those who find it "a bit dated" say the food is "very good", and its "traditional" qualities include the fact that it's "well priced". / www.cassonsrestaurant.co.uk; Thu-Sat 11 pm, Sun 3 pm; closed Thu-Sat L closed Sun D, closed Mon & Tue & Wed; No Amex.

THE HORSE & GROOM £65 333

PO18 9AX 01243 575339

A short drive from Chichester (in the direction of Goodwood), this 200-year-old converted barn is nowadays "a proper boozer at the front and full of local village characters". "But at the back, in its art-filled restaurant, it serves pub classics like fish 'n' chips and a proper pie of the day alongside more ambitious fare". / thehorseandgroom.pub; horseandgroompubeastashling; Mon-Sat 9 pm, Sun 4 pm; closed Sun D.

PALLANT RESTAURANT AND CAFE £53 223

EAST PALLANT PO19 1TJ 01243 770827

The café at this art gallery is "above average for a museum" and is certainly a very pleasant place to grab a coffee or refuel over lunch. That said, the sentiment in reports is that the food's only "OK… used to be better". / www.pallantrestaurantandcafe.co.uk; Tue-Sun 3 pm; closed Tue-Sun D, closed Mon; Cash & all usual cards.

PURCHASES RESTAURANT 333

31 NORTH STREET PO19 1LX 01243 771444

Nick Sutherland's bar/restaurant-with-rooms in a bow-fronted Georgian house close to the cathedral offers a "great pre-theatre menu, just right for Chichester", and a "beautiful garden and terrace". The name was retained in reference to the premises' well-known previous occupant, the oldest wine merchant in Sussex. / www.purchasesrestaurant.co.uk; purchases_chichester; Mon-Sun 11 pm.

THYME & CHILLIES INDIAN KITCHEN £51 433

149 SAINT PANCRAS PO19 7SH 01243 778881

"Fresh, traditional Indian food" – "not your typical Bangladeshi-style 'Indian'" – is the USP at this "high-quality" curry house set up by a couple of medics (orthopaedic surgeon Mayank Gupta and his dentist wife Nita) who wanted to showcase 'food as it tastes in India'. There's a second branch along the harbour in Apuldram. / www.thymeandchillies.co.uk; thymechilli; Sun-Thu 10.30 pm, Fri & Sat 11 pm.

CHINNOR, OXFORDSHIRE 2–2D

THE SIR CHARLES NAPIER £76 434

SPRIGGS ALLEY OX39 4BX 01494 483011

"Quality you wouldn't expect deep in the countryside" means Julie Griffith's "charming, but off-the-beaten-track country pub/restaurant in the Chilterns" (impossible to find before the advent of satnav) is "a real treat" that's "worth a detour" and has a big, long-term fan club extending all the way into London (from which it's a welcome weekend 'run out'). It's "such a lovely building" always with "a warm and welcoming atmosphere", bolstered by "beautiful gardens from spring to autumn; and with cosy log fires in the winter". There's the odd background quibble of food that "sounds great on paper but falls short at the price" or a slight feeling of "complacency". These are drowned out for the most part though by more typical reports of "consistently good and excellent food" and a feeling that "Julie runs the place superbly". "Never fails to impress…" – "never a disappointment here in over 27 years and possibly 60 occasions!" / www.sircharlesnapier.co.uk; sircharlesnapier;

Paco Tapas, The General, Bristol

Tue-Sat 9 pm, Sun 3.30 pm; closed Sun D, closed Mon; Cash & all usual cards; children: Over 8yr for dinner.

CHISLEHURST, KENT — 3-3B

CINNAMON CULTURE £55 432

97 HIGH ST   BR7 5AG   020 8289 0322

With its "fabulous menu" and "buzzy atmosphere", this family-run contemporary Indian makes "a great addition to Chislehurst's culinary choices". The 10-year-old business moved last year from its former location in Plaistow Lane, Bromley. / www.cinnamonculture.com; cinnamonculture; Tue-Sat 11 pm, Sun 10 pm; closed Mon; No Amex.

CHRISTCHURCH, DORSET — 2-4C

CAPTAIN'S CLUB HOTEL & SPA £61 333

WICK FERRY, WICK LANE   BH23 1HU 01202 475111

"A wonderful waterside location" is the crown jewel feature of this "relaxed and unhurried" modern hotel dining room – the location overlooking boats on the Stour "makes the restaurant a romantic venue and if weather permits being seated outside is a bonus". "Lovely food" too – "well presented and reasonably priced". / www.captainsclubhotel.com; captainsclubhotel; Mon-Sun 9 pm.

THE JETTY, CHRISTCHURCH HARBOUR HOTEL & SPA £82 345

95 MUDEFORD   BH23 3NT   01202 400950

"Perched on the water's edge of Mudeford Quay", Alex Aitken's "stunning" destination, in the grounds of the Harbour Hotel, is one of the most commented-on destinations on the South Coast. The "idyllic harbour-side setting" ("with views of Christchurch Harbour") contributes to the "lovely and quite intimate atmosphere", and the culinary attraction is "impeccable" fish and seafood that's "allowed to be the star on the plate, without undue messing about": "local-caught oysters, lobster and shrimps, as well as a superb fresh fish choice, are married beautifully with seasonal produce, alongside some exceptional wines". "Staff are dynamic and knowledgeable" too. "I always take visitors here and they always love it". / www.thejetty.co.uk; Mon-Sat 10 pm, Sun 8 pm; Cash & all usual cards.

THE KINGS ARMS HOTEL 344

18 CASTLE STREET   BH23 1DT 01202 588933

By the ruins of Christchurch Castle, this stately hotel occupies a Georgian-style building on the River Avon, and is well-reviewed food-wise for its quality cooking. There's a wide variety of affordable menus featuring bistro/brasserie-style dishes. / www.thekings-christchurch.co.uk; harbour_hotels; Tue-Sun 3 pm; Cash & all usual cards.

CIRENCESTER, GLOUCESTERSHIRE — 2-2C

MBB BRASSERIE, THE CORNHALL £56 333

THE CORNHALL 26 MARKET PL   GL7 2NY 01285 641818

"Excellent food" and a "lively atmosphere" can be found at this brasserie set in the Corn Hall covered market in the centre of town, that has developed over 15 years from a deli and was formerly known as Made by Bob... although the founder is James Parkinson. / www.mbbbrasserie.co.uk/contact; foodmadebybob; Mon-Sun 9 pm; Cash & all usual cards.

TIERRA & MAR £52 333

29 SHEEP STREET   GL7 1QW 01285 642777

"The traditional Spanish tapas with an English twist are much better than average", say fans of this "tucked-away spot on the outskirts of a town surprisingly short of decent restaurants" – a big local favourite. It's owned and run by Spanish-born Silvia and her husband, chef Brett Russell, who uses produce from his parents' nearby smallholding; they added a bar for lighter bites last year. Top Tip – "lunch is a steal". / www.tierraandmar.co.uk; tierraandmar; Tue-Sat 8.30 pm; closed Sun & Mon; Cash & all usual cards.

CLANFIELD, OXFORDSHIRE — 2-2C

THE DOUBLE RED DUKE 333

BOURTON ROAD   OX18 2RB 03339 398875

"There are a lot of spaces to explore" at this ambitious two-year-old: a picturesque seventeenth-century coaching inn that was recently converted with little expense spared into a 19-bedroom hotel and restaurant. Fans say it's "a great Cotswolds lunch venue" ("I noted many locals settling in for a 2+ bottle old-style blowout!"). Others are more cautious: "wasn't as good as I expected, but we might give it another go". / www.countrycreatures.com/double-red-duke; doubleredduke; closed Mon-Sat & Sun.

CLAUGHTON, LANCASHIRE — 5-1B

THE FENWICK ARMS £63 332

LANCASTER RD   LA2 9LA   01524 221250

This "buzzy and busy but welcoming" old Lune Valley inn focuses on "excellent locally sourced fish from Morecambe Bay or the Irish Sea" – including a "good but enormous seafood platter to share, which you need to book in advance". Now part of Oakman Inns, it's a "convenient and comfortable place to stay near Lancaster and the M6", en route to the Lake District or Scotland. / fenwickarms.co.uk; fenwickarms; Sun-Fri 11 pm, Sat midnight; Cash & all usual cards.

CLIFTON, CUMBRIA — 8-3A

GEORGE & DRAGON £64 223

CA10 2ER   01768 865381

A fire in June 2022 closed this "very relaxed and charming" pub, just off the M6 (a "good staging post when travelling between North and South") and it remains 'Temporarily Closed' as of October 2022. One of the most commented-on destinations in Cumbria, it received a more mixed billing this year with the typical upbeat accounts counterbalanced by a few reports finding it "good but not as good as previously". / www.georgeanddragonclifton.co.uk; georgeanddragonclifton; Mon-Sun ; closed Mon-Sun L closed Mon-Sun D; Cash & all usual cards.

CLIMPING, WEST SUSSEX — 3-4A

BAILIFFSCOURT HOTEL £84 323

CLIMPING ST   BN17 5RW   01903 723511

This "beautiful" hotel a few minutes' walk from the sea is "very popular and it's not hard to understand why" – "the Guinness family's impressive recreation of a medieval settlement", built 100 years ago, is "like a film set". Its dining room is very much "a hotel restaurant", though a decent one", with "traditional and well-prepared food". / www.hshotels.co.uk; hshotels; Mon-Sun 10 pm; Cash & all usual cards; Jacket required; booking max 6 may apply.

CLIPSHAM, RUTLAND — 6-4A

THE OLIVE BRANCH £74 433

MAIN ST   LE15 7SH   01780 410355

A "delightful pub" with a "proper bar and superbly cooked dishes" – from both standard and more elevated tasting menus – that has long played an integral role in the thriving Rutland food scene, and is, for many, an "absolute favourite". "Sometimes standards slip", but "when it's good (which is most of the time), it's very good" with "high-quality ingredients and careful, imaginative cooking". / www.theolivebranchpub.com; olivebranchclipsham; Wed-Sat 9.30 pm, Sun 9 pm; closed Mon & Tue; No Amex.

CLITHEROE, LANCASHIRE — 5-1B

THE INN AT WHITEWELL £70 335

FOREST OF BOWLAND   BB7 3AT 01200 448222

"Just a fabulous timeless spot that does exactly what is expected and pretends be nothing but itself" – this celebrated country inn is scenically situated by the River Hodder in the Forest of Bowland, and its hallmarks are "old-fashioned good service", "an exceptional atmosphere with open fires in the winter", "great wine" (which it sells also at retail onsite, trading as 'Bowland Forest Vintners') plus "consistently good food", "simply done". Top Menu Tip – "the fish pie is an excellent choice". / www.innatwhitewell.com;

inn_at_whitewell; Mon-Sun 9.30 pm; Cash & all usual cards.

THE FIVE BELLS INN £55 3|3|3

EX15 2NT 01884 277288

Landlord James Garnham took over this lovely thatched pub in his boyhood village with his wife Charlie five years ago, building an excellent reputation for its food and hospitality. "We have now visited 3 times in as many weeks – which says it all!". / www.fivebells.uk.com; fivebellsdevon; Wed-Sat 9 pm, Sun 3.30 pm; closed Wed L closed Sun D, closed Mon & Tue; Cash & all usual cards.

COPPA CLUB COBHAM £50 2|2|4

13-15 BETWEEN STREETS KT11 1AA 01932 500608

This "light, bright and airy" 'clubhouse' incorporates a bar, lounge, orangery and terrace with "strategically placed roof lanterns" – and "igloos which are great fun". The food is "fine" – if a little "average" – leaving some to conclude: "I can't quite put my finger on it, but I always come away feeling underwhelmed". For others, though, its flexible style and attractive interior make it "great for occasions". / coppaclub.co.uk; coppaclub; Mon-Thu 11 pm, Fri & Sat 11.30 pm, Sun 10 pm.

THE CRICKETERS £60 3|3|3

DOWNSIDE COMMON KT11 3NX 01932 862 105

"A favourite because it's so consistently good", this spacious old pub in a beautiful setting on Downside Common is part of Raymond Blanc's White Brasserie chain, and has a menu that runs from baguette with dips to (royal butcher) Aubrey Allen steak and chips. A recent makeover has spruced things up a bit. / www.cricketerscobham.com; whitebrasseriecompany; Mon-Fri 9.15 pm, Sat 9.45pm, Sun 7.30 pm; Cash & all usual cards.

THE IVY COBHAM BRASSERIE £77 2|3|4

48 HIGH ST KT11 3EF 01932 901777

"A fantastic space" – "buzzing, colourful and friendly" – this Surrey branch of Richard Caring's national outfit is "still a cut above most chains", according to fans. But "it's a shame they've become so ubiquitous" – and a bigger shame that "the usual Ivy fare" is too often such a "disappointment". Top Tip – "ask for a table in the conservatory". / theivycobhambrasserie.com; theivycobham; Sun-Thu midnight, Fri & Sat 12.30 am.

THE PLOUGH INN £82 3|3|3

PLOUGH LANE KT11 3LT 01932 589790

This smartly turned-out steakhouse pub on the edge of Cobham from the Rare Breed Dining group specialises in "great meats on the grill" – and has its own in-house butchery and smokery to prepare the choicest cuts. / www.theploughinncobham.co.uk; theploughinncobham; Mon-Fri 11 pm, Sat midnight, Sun 10 pm.

KIRKSTILE INN £41 3|3|3

LOWESWATER CA13 0RU 01900 85219

Glorious Lakeland scenery surrounds this rural inn at the foot of Melbreak. The classic pub grub doesn't aim for fireworks but is well-realised and supplemented at lunch by handmade sarnies. / www.kirkstile.com; thekirkstileinn; Mon-Sat 11 pm, Sun 10.30 pm; No Amex.

KINTSU £128 4|4|3

11A NORTH HILL CO1 1DZ 01206 570005

"Gourmet tapas served at an open counter" from a "wonderful and very flexible choice of small plates" win praise for Paul Wendholt's "accomplished and adventurous" venue, which occupies a "small and intimate dining room". / kintsu.co.uk; kintsu_colchester; Wed-Sat 9.30 pm; closed Mon & Tue & Sun.

RESTAURANT HYWEL JONES BY LUCKNAM PARK, LUCKHAM PARK HOTEL £156 4|4|4

SN14 8AZ 01225 742777

"Wonderful, precise modern British fine dining" is presented with "impeccable service" in the "beautiful surroundings" of this privately owned luxury spa hotel, built in a mish-mash of historical architectural styles. Hywel Jones, who has presided over the signature restaurant since 2006, "is undoubtably one of this country's very best chefs, known for his tireless mentoring of up-and-coming talent". / www.lucknampark.co.uk; lucknam_park; Thu-Sun 9 pm; closed Thu-Sun L, closed Mon & Tue & Wed; Cash & all usual cards; Jacket required; children: 5+.

THE HUT £77 4|4|4

COLWELL CHINE ROAD PO40 9NP 01983 898 637

It's "like being in Ibiza" at this "really cool", "super-place right on the beach promenade", established 10 years ago Matt & George Adams – "now with a huge opening roof" and a "DJ who plays her various mixes at a modest volume all night". "As the night draws in and you've taken in the glorious sunset views", "the roof is closed and it becomes more intimate". The "really decent food" from Catalan chef Lucian Romocea has a suitable Med seafood vibe, and earns a general thumbs-up. / www.thehutcolwell.co.uk; thehutcolwell; Mon-Sun midnight; Cash & all usual cards.

BRYN WILLIAMS AT PORTH EIRIAS £58 3|3|3

THE PROMENADE, LL29 8HH 01492 577 525

"Excellent views" are a highlight at this beachside unit, with outside tables for good weather: part of a modern development created in a spirit of regeneration by the local council. All reports applaud the "great meals" to be had here, but don't go expecting the culinary pyrotechnics Bryn W is known for: it serves relatively simple fare (daily catch fish fingers, steak, risotto…) / www.portheirias.com; brynportheirias; Sun-Thu 4 pm, Fri & Sat 8.30 pm.

PECKS £69 3|2|3

NEWCASTLE RD CW12 4SB 01260 275 161

"Theatrical presentation" is a longstanding feature of the Pear family's stalwart fixture of four decades' standing, whose 'Dinner at 8' package was an early adopter of the tasting menu format, with a 7-course menu delivered in a single sitting (you arrive at 7.30 pm). Fans say "Covid hasn't affected the consistent high quality of this unique dining venue. And to the famous 'Dinner at 8', can be added the growing popularity of their afternoon tea": "a choice of gentleman's or lady's gives a useful mix of sweet and savoury, including the legendary homemade desserts. Ample portions (take-home boxes cheerfully provided), well served and a good range of teas". / www.pecksrest.co.uk; pecksrestaurant; Tue-Sat 11 pm, Sun 4 pm; closed Sun D, closed Mon; Cash & all usual cards.

THE JACKDAW

HIGH STREET LL32 8DB 01492 596922

No reports yet on this ambitious 30-seater, which opened in autumn 2021 run by ex-Fat Duck chef Nick Rudge. In May 2022, though, Marina O'Loughlin from The Sunday Times made the trip to this "small room in a curiously gothic building (that was formerly Conwy's cinema and bingo hall)", finding a "scene of buzz and busyness, full and welcoming" and food that "elicits a great sigh of relief". Local ingredients make up dishes full of flourishes – not everything works, but she was "mollified by a riot of Welsh cheeses". She concludes: "there's no doubt that Rudge can cook. If he concentrated more on showcasing the innate quality of the spectacular Welsh produce he's using and less on the likes of Great British Menu, he'd be unstoppable". / www.thejackdawconwy.co.uk; thejackdawconwy; closed Mon-Sat & Sun; booking is online only.

MALIKS £51 4|3|3

HIGH ST SL6 9SF 01628 520085

"Every dish is fresh and authentic" at this comfortable curry house which occupies a half-timbered building on the high street, and which has become well-known over many years for its superior Indian cuisine. Heston is a fan. / www.maliks.co.uk; maliksgroup; Mon-Sat 11 pm, Sun 10.30 pm; Cash & all usual cards.

THE WHITE OAK £61 3 3 2

THE POUND SL6 9QE 01628 523043

"Good food at a fair price" was reported again this year at this well-regarded pub: part of a local group with siblings in Gerrards Cross and Beaconsfield. In good weather you can eat on the terrace, or book an 'Oak Pod' which seats up to 6 people, and incorporate a heater. / www.thewhiteoak.co.uk; thewhiteoakcoo; Wed-Sat 11 pm, Sun 6 pm; closed Mon & Tue; No Amex.

YU £65 4 4 3

**500 LONGSIGHT RD BB1 9EU
01254 240665**

"Victor Yu has a quite brilliant menu and wine list", say fans of his roadside Chinese, "stylishly" converted from a former boozer on the A59. "Folk travel from all over" – "there's a party atmosphere in the bar and the fact it's packed every service means they are doing something very right". / www.yucopstergreen.co.uk; yu_copstergreen; Tue-Thu, Sun 10 pm, Fri & Sat midnight; closed Tue-Sun L, closed Mon; Cash & all usual cards.

THE VALLEY £50 4 4 3

**OLD STATION HS NE45 5AY
01434 633434**

"Located in an old railway station" – this quirky curry house is well-known in these parts for its "quality Indian food". From Newcastle, book their 'Passage to India' package, which includes your meal, plus travel by train! / www.valleyrestaurants.co.uk; thevalleycorbridge; Mon-Sat 10 pm; closed Mon-Sat L, closed Sun; Cash & all usual cards.

CORSE LAWN HOTEL £57

GL19 4LZ 01452 780771

In July 2022, Baba Hine put this long-established hotel (which she started with her late husband 40 years ago, and ran by herself for 17 years) on the market, having decided it's time to retire. Incorporating a 40-cover restaurant and similar-sized bistro, it's too soon as yet to predict the next chapter for this well-known establishment, hence for the time being it's unrated. / www.corselawn.com; corselawn; Wed-Sun 8.30 pm; closed Mon & Tue; Cash & all usual cards.

HARE AND HOUNDS £55 3 4 3

ABERTHIN CF71 7LG 01446 774892

"Always excellent food" has built a strong reputation for local lad Tom Watts-Jones's well-regarded pub in the Vale of Glamorgan. Chef's CV includes stints at London's St John and also The Anchor & Hope. There are numerous menus here, including an à la carte or nine-course tasting option. / www.hareandhoundsaberthin.com; hareandhounds_aberthin; Wed-Sat 9 pm, Sun 4 pm; closed Wed L closed Sun D, closed Mon & Tue; Cash & all usual cards.

NORTH HOUSE

30 SUN HILL PO31 7HY 01983 209453

In April 2022, Robert Thompson called time on his 'You Be Chef' delivery business and former venture, Thompson's (seemingly RIP) and started this new establishment: a 14-bedroom restaurant-with-rooms in the heart of Cowes. It opened too late for any survey feedback, but his track record as the island's leading culinary light suggests this will be one to watch. The brasserie serves à la carte meals with a fine-dining, tasting-menu-only, evening option up to five nights a week depending on the season. / northhouseiow.com; northhouseiow; Mon-Sun midnight.

SMOKING LOBSTER £57 3 4 3

**127 HIGH STREET PO31 7AY
01983 240916**

In July 2021, GC Giancovich – with the help of family and friends – opened this sibling to his Ventor original, with a similar pan-Asian, fish-heavy menu, plus sushi and cocktails. Fans say it's "not perfect yet but well on the way to being a must-go place". / www.smokinglobsterventnor.co.uk; Tue-Sat 10.15 pm, Sun 4 pm; closed Sun D, closed Mon.

THE MILK HOUSE £43 3 2 2

THE STREET TN17 2JG 01580 720200

This former coaching inn "offers a good range of well-cooked dishes in its small dining room" – "pre-booking is advisable as it's close to Sissinghurst Castle and Gardens". In the summer, "a pop-up pizza hut is open in the garden for a more casual dining experience". / www.themilkhouse.co.uk; tmh_tn17; Mon-Thu 10.30 pm, Fri & Sat 11 pm, Sun 10 pm.

JOLLY FISHERMAN £54 3 3 5

HAVEN HILL NE66 3TR 01665 576461

"Lovely, relaxed pub with adjoining restaurant" in a "wonderful setting" on the Northumberland coast that's welcomed visitors for 175 years. These days, it serves "imaginative fish and seafood at good prices" – local treats include Craster-landed lobster and Lindisfarne oysters. / www.thejollyfishermancraster.co.uk; thejollyfisherman; Mon-Sat 8.30 pm, Sun 5 pm; closed Sun D; No Amex; no bookings.

BULLS HEAD £53 3 4 3

HR2 0PN 01981 510616

This "landmark pub" – an unspoilt old drovers' inn in a remote spot in the Black Mountains, close to the Welsh border – has reopened after seven years, during which locals feared it would be turned into a private residence. New owner, Jon Stead of Longtown-based Wild By Nature has introduced a gastropub menu that has won excellent ratings. / www.wildbynaturellp.com/the-bulls-head-inn; wildbynaturellp; Thu-Sat 11 pm, Sun 6 pm; closed Mon & Tue & Wed; No Amex.

CRATHORNE ARMS £58 3 4 4

TS15 0BA 01642 961402

"It's still as good as ever at Eugene and Barbara McCoy's country pub" say fans of this destination, ten minutes from Middlesbrough. "It's one of the few places that still hold a traditional Beaujolais Day in November and has a waiting list of people wanting to come!" / thecrathornearms.co.uk; thecrathornearms; Tue-Thu 9 pm, Fri & Sat 3.30 pm; closed Fri & Sat D, closed Sun & Mon; Cash & all usual cards; no bookings.

THE FOX £68 3 3 3

**PEACH HILL LANE SO21 2PR
01962 461302**

This "lovely pub with great rooms" just outside Winchester was transformed five years ago, giving the Georgian building a smart contemporary look with a solidly rated menu to match – plus a pizza option that operates through the summer months. / the-fox.pub; the_fox_crawley; Wed-Sat 11 pm; closed Mon & Tue & Sun.

THE RING OF BELLS £50 3 4 3

**THE HAYES, CHERITON FITAPAINE
EX17 4JG 01363 860111**

"A real gem": this "lovely country pub with fab affordable food and a great atmosphere" is "greatly appreciated by locals and visitors alike". To its credit, it "constantly invests to improve its offer", most recently adding a "new barn and patio that have increased capacity". / www.theringofbells.com; the_ring_of_bells; Wed-Sat 9 pm, Sun 7 pm; closed Mon & Tue; No Amex.

THE GLENTURRET LALIQUE RESTAURANT £110 444

THE GLENTURRET DISTILLERY, THE HOSH PH7 4HA

One or two amazing meals are reported at this intriguing Lalique-branded venture, within Scotland's oldest working distillery, which opened its doors in summer 2021 with chef Mark Donald at the stoves: an 'Exclusive Jewel Box Dining Room' providing a 'Cosmopolitan Multi-course Tasting Menu' for £150 per head. We've rated it relatively conservatively on limited feedback ("wonderful", "best meal ever") – more reports please! / www.theglenturretrestaurant.com; TheGlenturretLalique; Tue-Sat 11 pm; closed Tue-Sat L, closed Sun & Mon.

THE BATH ARMS

CLAY ST BA12 8AJ 01985 212262

Rescued after lying derelict for four years and rebuilt last year by local entrepreneur Paul Gardner, who made a substantial amount of money selling hand sanitiser during the pandemic, this historic village pub has high gastronomic ambitions, with Ryan McCartney, former head chef at Jason Atherton's Social Eating House, heading the kitchen team ahead of a launch scheduled for the first half of 2023. The two men relaunched the George & Dragon at Erlestoke on the edge of Salisbury Plain last year. / www.batharmscrockerton.co.uk; Mon-Sat 11.30 pm; No Amex.

SUTOR CREEK £51 332

21 BANK ST IV11 8YE 01381 600855

Phoebe & Graham Fox's tiny waterside café has long been known for its "lovely food", which these days is "concentrated on their superb pizzas". There are "a few outside tables but lots of seats along the harbour with great views". / www.sutorcreek.co.uk; sutor_creek; Wed-Sun 8 pm; closed Mon & Tue; No Amex.

NO. 1 £36 433

1 NEW ST NR27 9HP 01263 515983

"Stunning fish 'n' chips", with a "great variety of fresh fish and gorgeously light batter", make this "excellently located" chippie from Galston Blackiston of Morston Hall fame "well worth the queue" – although you can sidestep that issue by making a "reservation in the upstairs restaurant, with sea views from its commanding hill-top position". "'Normal for Norfolk' does not apply here, it's far better than that!". / www.no1cromer.com; no1cromer; Wed-Sat 9 pm, Sun 8 pm; closed Mon & Tue; Cash & all usual cards; booking is online only.

THE PUNCH BOWL INN £67 343

LA8 8HR 01539 568237

"Terrific service, even during winter storms" is typical of this very scenically located pub in a small village a quarter of an hour's drive from Windermere and overlooking the Lyth Valley. It is the most commented-on pub in The Lakes in our annual diners' poll. Owner Richard Rose has built its renown as a generally well-run operation, which of course also includes "quality locally sourced food". Top Menu Tip – twice-baked Lancashire cheese soufflé. / www.the-punchbowl.co.uk; punchbowlinncr; Mon-Sun 9 pm; Cash & all usual cards; credit card deposit required to book.

MCDERMOTTS FISH & CHIPS £35 442

5-7 THE FORESTDALE SHOPPING CENTRE FEATHERBED LN CR0 9AS 020 8651 1440

"Great fish 'n' chips in a fairly dull area of Croydon" wins ongoing praise for Tony McDermott's local stalwart, which opened in 1987. "The restaurant has won many awards over the years and is well worth a visit". / www.mcdermottsfishandchips.co.uk; Tue-Thu, Sat 8 pm, Fri 9 pm; closed Tue, Wed L, closed Sun & Mon; Cash & all usual cards.

THE POTTING SHED £58 333

THE ST SN16 9EW 01666 577833

"Very good chateaubriand…", "one of the best chicken supreme dishes ever…", "outstanding cheese soufflé…" – all dishes that have reportedly been enjoyed this year at this cosy beamed pub in north Wiltshire. / www.thepottingshedpub.com; thepottingshedpub; Mon-Sun 9 pm; Cash & all usual cards.

THE PEAT INN £99 543

KY15 5LH 01334 840206

Geoffrey and Katherine Smeddle are "still on top of their game" at the eighteenth-century rural inn a short drive from St Andrews which they have run in golfing country for 16 years; and where "standards have remained so high", keeping it "up there with the best in Scotland". Geoffrey's "sound" modern Scottish cooking "hits all the right notes – not too fancy, but also not too casual" – while there's also "great people-watching on your visit". A single complaint this year: "miss their lunch openings". / www.thepeatinn.co.uk; ThePeatInn; Tue-Sat 9 pm; closed Tue-Sat L, closed Sun & Mon; Cash & all usual cards.

THE ORANGERY, ROCKLIFFE HALL £95 334

DL2 2DU 01325 729999

The striking interior is a talking-point at this five-star retreat, near the North Yorks border, set in over 365 acres: a very airy, glass-ceilinged conservatory with leafy views. Our annual diners' poll also acclaims the "excellent tasting menu" (there is also an à la carte option) and "friendly service"; and there's an impressive 400-bin wine list. / www.rockliffehall.com; RockliffeLife; Mon-Sun 9 pm; closed Mon-Sun L; payment – credit card only; No trainers; children: 12.

STABLE HEARTH NEAPOLITAN PIZZERIA & ENOTECA £34 333

DUKE STREET DL3 7RX 01325 730400

"Great pizza menu served by lovely people" remains the verdict on this award-winning pizza-stop, whose numerous accolades and certifications promise a Neapolitan experience through and through: your selection is cooked at 400 degrees and will be ready in 90 seconds! / www.stablehearth.com; Stable_hearth_pizzeria; Thu & Fri, Sun, Sat 10 pm; closed Thu & Fri, Sun, Sat L, closed Mon & Tue & Wed.

ROCKFISH £52 332

8 SOUTH EMBANKMENT TQ6 9BH 01803 832800

"A menu with a huge range of fish might suggest a serious fish place" but the original Rockfish (opened in 2010) overlooking the River Dart "feels more like a fish 'n' chip restaurant with less-than-smart tables, chips with everything and the usual few leaves for salad. People seem mostly to eat the fried food. That said, you could have whitebait, a huge crab at a huge price and juicy gurnard not fried. Service is fast and cheerful". / www.therockfish.co.uk; therockfishuk; Mon-Sun 9 pm; Cash & all usual cards.

THE SEAHORSE £83 333

5 SOUTH EMBANKMENT TQ6 9BH 01803 835147

Mitch Tonks's Mediterranean-inspired harbourside HQ "always hits the spot" and is run "with charm and polish" – "the anchoiade and focaccia alone is worth a trip from the northern Highlands!". / www.seahorserestaurant.co.uk; Tue-Sat 9 pm; closed Sun & Mon; Cash & all usual cards.

THE TILBURY £62 333

WATTON RD SG3 6TB 01438 815 550

"This lovely country pub" run by brothers Tom (a self-taught cook) and James Bainbridge

The Forge, Chester

(a former Fat Duck manager) wins consistent ratings for its high-quality cooking using "good-quality meat and fresh, tasty ingredients". There's a "lovely ambience and service to match", all at "amazing value-for-money prices". / www.thetilbury.co.uk; the_tilbury; Wed, Tue, Thu-Sat 8.30 pm, Sun 4 pm; closed Wed L closed Sun D, closed Mon; Cash & all usual cards; no bookings.

DAYLESFORD, GLOUCESTERSHIRE 2–1C

DAYLESFORD ORGANIC FARM, TROUGH CAFÉ £57 233

DAYLESFORD NEAR KINGHAM GL56 NEW08/2389 01608 731700

Lady Bamford (wife of JCB heir, Anthony Bamford) opened this chic farm shop and café near the family's 1,500 acre Cotswold estate about twenty years ago (and later on, spin offs in London). Fans love it, declaring: "it may have a reputation for being pricey, but the interiors are great and the food is just not as expensive as you might expect, given the exquisite perfection of the place". Critics can't get over the lack of value though: "the popularity is undeserved: it is just an out-and-out very expensive tourist trap". / www.daylesford.com; Mon-Sat 11 pm, Sun 4 pm; closed Sun D; 8am â€" 8pm SUN\; 1.

DEAL, KENT 3–3D

FROG & SCOT £70 323

86 HIGH STREET CT14 6EG 01304 379444

This "fantastic little bistro hidden away in Deal" is "well worth trying" for the "very high standard of its classic French cooking" – although there is some pushback against its "London prices". Owner-operators Benoit & Sarah (respectively the Frog and the Scot) also run Le Pinardier wine shop and bar a few doors away. / www.frogandscot.co.uk; Frog and Scot; closed Mon-Sat & Sun; Cash & all usual cards; children: 8.

THE ROSE £67 344

91 HIGH STREET CT14 6ED 01304 389127

The dining room of this "charming contemporary" hotel serves an "innovative and evolving menu", along with highly rated Scandi-style breakfasts. The 200-year-old venue has been revived by Christopher Hicks, whose great-grandfather once owned it as part of his Thompson & Son brewery business, and with art by Tracey Emin among others on the walls, it's very much in the spirit of the new Margate, just up the coast. / therosedeal.com; therosedeal; Wed-Sun 10.30 pm; closed Mon & Tue.

DEDHAM, ESSEX 3–2C

THE SUN INN £54 334

HIGH ST CO7 6DF 01206 564325

"A real find" – this "beautiful old coach-house pub with rooms", "bang opposite the church" in gorgeous Constable country, offers a delightful "casual ambience of sofas, log fires, magazines and top service" – backed up by a "short menu that changes frequently" and an "eclectic wine list developed by the owner". / www.thesuninndedham.com; suninndedham; Mon-Sat 9.30 pm, Sun 4 pm; closed Sun D; Cash & all usual cards.

LE TALBOOTH £91 235

GUN HILL CO7 6HP 01206 323150

This "beautiful location in the heart of Constable country" (indeed it was painted by the great man) with a terrace next to the River Stour, has hosted a restaurant for 70 years, with "food that has returned to form after a few years of not quite living up to the hype". There's a minority view, however, that they still need to "up the food quality" to match the location and prices. / www.milsomhotels.com; milsomhotels; Mon-Sat 9 pm, Sun 3 pm; closed Sun D; Cash & all usual cards.

DELL QUAY, WEST SUSSEX 3–4A

CROWN & ANCHOR £81 322

DELL QUAY RD PO20 7EE 01243 781712

This "beautiful pub overlooking Chichester harbour" has a "kitchen that takes pride in its work" – "with simply cooked and locally sourced fish and shellfish the bedrock of the menu". "There is a large outside terrace but even on colder days harbour views aplenty through many of the inside tables". / www.crownandanchorchichester.com; crowndellquay; Mon-Sat 11 pm, Sun 10 pm.

DERBY, DERBYSHIRE 5–3C

ANOKI £44 343

OLD PICTURE HALL, 129 LONDON ROAD DE1 2QN 01332 292 888

Naveed Khaliq's 20-year-old flagship provides "everything you could want from an Indian restaurant" – and most importantly "delicious curries at great prices". Meaning 'unique' in Urdu, Anoki now has spin-offs in Nottingham and Burton. / www.anoki.co.uk/derby; anokirestaurant; Mon-Sat 10.30 pm; closed Mon-Sat L, closed Sun; Cash & all usual cards.

EBI SUSHI £49 542

59 ABBEY ST DE22 3SJ 01332 265656

"Such delicate flavours… sushi is to die for… and reasonably priced!". This north-Midlands curiosity is "fairly basic and café-like in ambience" but delivers Japanese dishes of a very high quality. "The reason it's so good? The Toyota factory five miles down the road! Try the sake if you have deep pockets". / Tue, Wed, Fri & Sat 10 pm; closed Tue, Wed, Fri & Sat L, closed Mon, Thu & Sun; No Amex.

DEVIZES, WILTSHIRE 2–2C

THE BLACK SWAN INN £50 343

25 - 26 THE MARKET PLACE SN10 1JQ 01380 727777

This "traditional market town coaching inn" is a "real delight" – offering "great service" and "tasty, inventive food" which makes good use of "excellent locally sourced meat and exceptional vegetables". Top Tip – "top Sunday lunch". / www.blackswandevizes.co.uk; theblackswaninndevizes; Mon-Thu 9 pm, Fri & Sat 10 pm, Sun 8 pm.

DINTON, BUCKINGHAMSHIRE 2–3C

LA CHOUETTE £84 443

WESTLINGTON GRN HP17 8UW 01296 747422

"A joy to eat there and service is lovely!" – Frederic Desmette's cosy, beamed house on the village green only attracts a small volume of feedback this year, but it remains positive for his Belgian cuisine and well-kept cellar. / www.lachouette.co.uk; Wed-Sat 9 pm; closed Mon & Tue & Sun; No Amex.

DONCASTER, SOUTH YORKSHIRE 5–2D

CLAM & CORK £37 442

2 FISH MARKET DN1 1NJ 07912 687581

This "quirky market stall" in the fishmarket is the place to go in Doncaster if you're looking for fresh seafood, raw or cooked to order, and accompanied by a glass of champagne. There's a chalked-up menu but, beyond the "excellent" food and drink, not much in the way of creature comforts. Top Tip – "try the fish curry". / clam-cork.business.site; clam_and_cork; Fri & Sat 4 pm, Thu 3.30 pm; closed Thu-Sat D, closed Mon-Wed & Sun.

DORCHESTER, DORSET 2–4B

THE CLUB HOUSE £56 3 3 4
BEACH ROAD DT2 9DG 01308 898302
This "delightful and relaxing café/restaurant" in an "attractive" 90-year-old venue has "spectacular views" over pebbled Chesil Beach. "Informed and attentive staff" ensure there's a "good atmosphere", and the "interesting menu" offers "good value" for its "tasty fish choices". / www.theclubhousewestbexington.co.uk; theclubhouse2017; Wed, Sun 5 pm, Thu-Sat 7.30 pm; closed Wed & Sun D, closed Mon & Tue.

DORKING, SURREY 3–3A

SORREL £163 5 4 4
77 SOUTH STREET RH4 2JU
01306 889 414
Steven Drake's "formal, well-spaced but welcoming and comfortable Surrey Hills venue in the centre of Dorking" is "a great bonus to the Surrey dining scene" and one of the most commented-on non-metropolitan restaurants in our annual diners' poll. "It has really bounced back well post-lockdown – service is discrete and knowledgeable" and the "always exciting" cuisine "remains of the highest quality". It focuses on a tasting menu format: 9 courses for £125, and all of the many reports suggest results are "special in every way". / www.sorrelrestaurant.co.uk; sorrel_restaurant_dorking; Wed-Sat 8.30 pm; closed Mon & Tue & Sun; payment – credit card only; credit card deposit required to book.

DOUGLAS, ISLE OF MAN 7–4B

ENZO'S £24 3 4 3
52 BUCKS ROAD IM1 3AD 01624 622653
"Ever the best gastronomic experience in the Isle of Man" – "a classic-looking Italian restaurant" that's "quite formal in presentation" and serving a "modern interpretation of Italian dishes". / Mon-Sat 9.30 pm; closed Sat L, closed Sun.

WINE DOWN £32 3 3 3
24 DUKE STREET IM1 2AY 01624 624777
This "wine bar/shop in the oldest part of Douglas" offers "excellent and interesting dishes" with a focus on "local seafood", backed up by "exceptional wines, with expertise on hand". "The restaurant has a wine list but you can also pick any bottle from the shop for a small corkage charge". Formerly known as Macfarlane's restaurant, the business was relaunched under its new identity in 2018. / www.winedown.im; Mon & Tue 8.30 pm, Wed & Thu 9 pm, Fri & Sat 9.30 pm; closed Sun.

DREWSTEIGNTON, DEVON 1–3D

THE OLD INN £90 4 3 3
EX6 6QR 01647 281 276
"The cooking is all reliably performed by chef/owner Duncan" (Walker) at this well-established and descriptively named establishment, on the edge of Dartmoor, which he runs with his partner Anthea Christmas. Duncan used to be in charge of the stoves at Gidleigh Park, whose long drive starts just down the lane from the property. / www.old-inn.co.uk; duncansoldinn; Wed-Sat 8.45 pm; closed Mon & Tue & Sun; No Amex; children: 12.

DRONFIELD, DERBYSHIRE 5–2C

THE TICKLED TROUT £52
33 VALLEY ROAD S18 7SL
01142 89 1111
'Deliciously Derbyshire' is the motto at this Peak District gastropub – feedback is too limited for a rating, but such as we have gives the thumbs-up to high-quality pub grub, which includes a wide variety of sourdough pizzas. / www.tickledtroutbarlow.com; tickledtroutbarlow; Tue-Sat 9 pm, Sun 4 pm; closed Sun D, closed Mon.

DUMFRIES, DUMFRIES AND GALLOWAY 7–2C

THE AULDGIRTH INN £72 4 4 3
AULDGIRTH DG2 0XG 01387 740250
This "really excellent and ambitious gastropub" (which, legend has it, once gave shelter to Robbie Burns) wins high praise for the "clever" realisation of its restaurant-style menu, where a variety of quality, dry-aged steaks sits alongside a number of more "complex" options. / www.auldgirthinn.co.uk; auldgirthinn; Wed, Fri 9 pm, Thu, Sat 10 pm, Sun 8 pm; closed Wed, Fri, Thu L, closed Mon & Tue.

DUNMOW, ESSEX 3–2C

THE FLITCH OF BACON £92 3 3 2
THE ST CM6 3HT 01371 821 660
"You would pay double for this offering anywhere else", say fans of this upscale former pub – under the same ownership as Midsummer House in Cambridge – where "chef-patron Paul Croasdale (ex-Alyn Williams at the Westbury in Mayfair) had a tough act to follow after Tim Allen's departure". "He now seems to have hit his stride and his emphasis and enthusiasm for local ingredients is excellent. Perhaps for a while he was trying too hard, but that's no longer the case". By ancient tradition (mentioned by Chaucer), a 'flitch of bacon' was awarded in Dunmow to couples who had no regrets after a year and a day of marriage. / www.flitchofbacon.co.uk; flitchofbaconld; Wed-Sat 9.30 pm, Sun 6 pm; closed Mon & Tue; Cash & all usual cards; credit card deposit required to book.

DUNVEGAN, HIGHLAND 9–2A

THE THREE CHIMNEYS £92 4 3 3
COLBOST IV55 8ZT 01470 511258
With its "excellent food" matched by a "superb location", this former crofter's cottage has drawn foodies to the Isle of Skye for almost 40 years. A meal here remains a "great experience", despite the retirement of longtime owners Shirley & Eddie Spear in 2019; head chef Scott Davies remains at the helm, and the business is now part of the Wee Hotel Company, run by high-profile Scottish hotelier Gordon Campbell Grey. / www.threechimneys.co.uk; thethreechimneysskye; Mon-Sun 9.30 pm; Cash & all usual cards.

DURHAM, COUNTY DURHAM 8–3B

BARRIO COMIDA £41 3 2 3
34 CHURCH STREET DH1 3DG
01913709688
"Permanent home for the excellent Newcastle Quayside pop-up of a few years ago" – this lively taqueria moved into Durham in 2020 and occupies "large premises near a bridge over the river", with a patio area and fine views. It's "still delivering high-quality tacos and other Mexican fare". Top Menu Tip – "special mention to their homemade ice cream". / www.barriocomida.com; barriocomida; Wed-Sat 10 pm, Sun 8 pm; closed Mon & Tue.

COARSE
REFORM PLACE, NORTH ROAD DH1 3NB
0191 374 1123
Chef Ruari Mackay (who worked with Terry Laybourne at Jesmond Dene), along with Gemma Robinson and Craig Lappin-Smith, launched a £100,000 crowdfunding bid in order to open this mid 2022 newcomer, billed as 'Durham's first tasting menu restaurant'. It offers a 6-course tasting menu (also with a vegetarian alternative). Reports please! / www.coarse.restaurant; coarsedurham; Mon-Thu 9 pm, Fri & Sat 9.30 pm, Sun 7 pm.

DYFED, PEMBROKESHIRE 4–4B

THE FERNERY, GROVE OF NARBERTH £125 4 4 3
MOLLESTON SA67 8BX 01834 860915
"Outstanding" and refined dining in the Fernery, from highly rated chef Douglas Balish (ex-Bohemia, Whatley Manor and the Quay, Sydney) is a highlight of any stay at the modern luxury hotel Neil & Zoe Kedward have created, hidden away in the Narberth Hills. The Artisan Rooms provides a more casual dining alternative. / www.thegrove-narberth.co.uk; thegrovenarberth; Tue-Sat 9 pm; closed Tue-Sat L, closed Sun & Mon; Cash & all usual cards.

EAST CHISENBURY, WILTSHIRE 2–3C

RED LION FREEHOUSE £83 4 4 3
SN9 6AQ 01980 671124
"A seriously fabulous al- rounder that's so much more than a village pub" – Guy & Brittany Manning's "lovely hidden-away thatched gastropub" is north of Stonehenge, and its convenience to the A303 helps make it one of the most commented-on rural pubs in our annual diners' poll. "It's such a great place: the food is terrific, the people are great, and the rooms at the guest house a few steps down the road are idyllic". / www.redlionfreehouse.com;

redlionfreehouse; Wed-Sat, Tue 9 pm, Sun 12 pm; closed Tue L closed Sun D, closed Mon; No Amex; credit card deposit required to book.

THE STAR & GARTER   £61 3 3 3
PO18 0JG   01243 811318

In the heart of the Goodwood Estate, this attractive looking inn benefits from a "large garden" and serves an menu of "imaginative" pub grub (although the "menu descriptions tend to the obscure!"). / www.thestarandgarter.co.uk; star_garter; Sun & Mon 2.30 pm, Tue-Sat 9.30 pm; closed Sun & Mon D; No Amex.

GRAVETYE MANOR   £117 3 4 5
VOWELS LANE   RH19 4LJ   01342 810567

"A garden tour before summer lunch is just the most uplifting experience" at this "beautiful Elizabethan country house in the Sussex countryside" (whose grounds were laid out in the 1880s by its then-owner, a famous landscape gardener). Three years ago, a modernisation saw the opening of a new "airy, conservatory-style dining room" with "a picture window showing the garden to full effect": "a fantastic masterpiece where you feel as though you are within the beautiful gardens". It was a successful relaunch that has established the dining room as one of the most commented-on in our annual diners' poll. Elsewhere within the property, the scene is of "old-school lounges to relax in and classic hotel accommodation". Chef George Blogg's cuisine is "classical" in style, with "consistently delicious" flavours and "exceptional attention to detail in terms of presentation". / www.gravetyemanor.co.uk; gravetyemanor; Mon-Sun 9.30 pm; Cash & all usual cards; booking max 8 may apply; children: 7+.

THE ROYAL OAK   £62 3 4 3
POOK LN   PO18 0AX   01243 527 434

North of Chichester and at the foot of the South Downs, this rural pub (with two letting cottages) is consistently well-rated for "fantastic local food cooked perfectly". You can choose pub classics like fish 'n' chips or burgers, but the majority of the menu is too ambitious to qualify as 'pub grub'. / www.royaloakeastlavant.co.uk; Mon-Fri 9 pm, Sat 9.30 pm, Sun 7 pm; Cash & all usual cards; No shorts.

PINE   £151 5 4 4
VALLUM FARM, MILITARY ROAD NE18 0LL   01434 671202

"Sixteen courses of jewel-like complexity, with inventive (and delicious) combinations of flavours" helps win adulatory reviews for this Northumberland two-year-old from Cal

Byerley and partner Siân Buchan. Set in an old cow barn near Hadrian's Wall (part of the Vallum Farm complex of gym, shop, café, etc), some ingredients come from the kitchen garden as part of its "focus on locally sourced ingredients" and – with "the passion of the team coming through in abundance – there is a strong sense of 'terroir' with their approach". "Clearly able to hold its own against its garlanded nearish neighbour Hyem, it's another fantastic Nordic/Northumbrian-style restaurant along the Tyne valley" and in January 2022 received an ultra rave from Marina O'Loughlin in The Sunday Times, declaring it "one of the UK's most exciting new restaurants… to find something so life-affirming… is simply joyful". / www.restaurantpine.co.uk; Wed-Sat midnight; closed Wed & Thu L, closed Mon & Tue & Sun; booking is online only; children: 12.

THE BLUE LION   £79 3 3 3
DL8 4SN   01969 624273

This eighteenth-century Wensleydale inn has been "a favourite for years", and "has retained all the previous standards" with its "very good food". It's "well worth a trip to sit outside in the sun" in good weather, and a "joy to huddle round the roaring fires on cold evenings". / www.thebluelion.co.uk; bluelioneastwitton; Mon-Sat 9 pm, Sun 6 pm; closed Sun D.

CRU   3 3 4
8 HYDE GARDENS   BN21 4PN 01323 646494

"An enthusiasts' wine list does full justice to the very much above average bistro food" at this "restaurant, wine bar and wine shop offering small and large plates accompanied by your selection from the 200 vintages". "There's always a real buzz about the place and the owner's infectious sense of fun guarantees you have a great night out". Beers and coffees are on hand if you don't wish to partake of the grape. / www.cruwine.co.uk; crueastbourne; Thu-Sat 9.30 pm, Sun 5.45 pm; closed Sun D, closed Mon & Tue & Wed.

THE MIRABELLE, THE GRAND HOTEL   £83 2 3 3
KING EDWARDS PARADE   BN21 4EQ 01323 412345

"Still the grand doyen of the Eastbourne eating scene", this "delightful" and "slightly theatrical" traditional chamber inspires affection amongst everyone commenting on it, including its critics. There has been a concerted attempt in recent years to modernise the approach, which leads to some regrets – "there used to be a piano player in the old days, a touch which seems to have been dispensed with". New (he's been here three years) chef, Michael Sutherland "appears to be finding his feet" and a fair middle view is that "whilst in no way spectacular, the kitchen's output is at least now consistent (an improvement to before)". But "given the prices, there is substantial room, indeed need, for the kitchen to further improve". Still, some diners

report a "fantastic variety of dishes from the tasting menu, with lots of unusual aspects that make talking points with the serving staff". Top Tip – No complaints at all about the hotel's "gorgeous" and "good value" afternoon teas. / www.grandeastbourne.com; grandhoteleastbourne; Tue-Sat 9 pm; closed Sun & Mon; Cash & all usual cards; Jacket required.

209 TERMINUS ROAD   BN21 3DH 01323 301400

"Great attention to detail is the hallmark of this Italian restaurant close to the seafront in Eastbourne". Run by chef/patron, hospitality veteran Lorenzo Cinalli, it's in a traditional mould and – according to a recent review from the Mail on Sunday's Tom Parker Bowles "is one of those rare places that manages to combine the old school with the resolutely regional" including "spanking fresh turbot... up there with Scott's, Wiltons or Bentley's". / www.rostick.uk; Mon, Thu, Sun 9.30 pm, Fri & Sat 10 pm; closed Tue & Wed.

THE DINING ROOM, WHATLEY MANOR   £217 3 2 3
SN16 0RB   01666 822888

The "perfect place for a special celebratory meal" in a "lovely setting", this Cotswold manor house hotel has been one of the country's leading gastronomic destinations over the past two decades. Executive chef Ricki Weston (ex-Sat Bains) was promoted to his first lead role last year, and has yet to match the high ratings achieved by his two predecessors, Martin Burge and Niall Keating, although his commitment to sustainability has won 'green star' recognition from Michelin. / www.whatleymanor.com; whatleymanor; Thu-Sun 9.15 pm; closed Thu L, closed Mon & Tue & Wed; Cash & all usual cards; No jeans; children: 12+.

SIMPSONS   £108 4 4 4
20 HIGHFIELD ROAD   B15 3DU 0121 454 3434

Andreas Antona's attractive Edwardian villa in posh Edgbaston remains one of the city's most commented-on dining destinations, and all accounts are upbeat, with numerous reporters having their "best meal of the year here" and declaring it "a real experience". A 10-course tasting menu is available for £130, but they haven't ditched à la carte here, sometimes enhanced with competitive wine-inclusive deals. Chef Luke Tipping's cuisine is "top class" , service is "particularly impressive" and there's "a lovely atmosphere". / www.simpsonsrestaurant.co.uk; simpsons_restaurant; Wed & Thu, Sun 9 pm, Fri & Sat 9.30 pm; closed Mon & Tue; Cash & all usual cards.

EDINBANE LODGE £66 544

OLD DUNVEGAN ROAD IV51 9PW
01470 582217

"Really outstanding… and so surprising to find in such a location" – Calum Montgomery's converted hunting lodge (built in 1543 and extensively refurbed in 2018) is "so much better than so many acclaimed restaurants" (and invites comparisons with the much more established nearby Three Chimneys, which it narrowly edges with its food rating). The focus is on his 'Taste of Skye' ten-course tasting menu showcasing local produce and delivered by "friendly and attentive" staff. Ratings this year and last suggest it's "worthy of a Michelin star" but no sign yet: "maybe they're too modest". Perhaps the Tyre Men will finally catch on in their 2023 awards as in late 2022 the AA promoted him from 3 to 4 rosettes. / www.edinbanelodge.com; skyechefmonty; Wed-Sun 9 pm; closed Wed-Sun L, closed Mon & Tue.

AIZLE £85 543

THE GARDEN ROOM IN THE KIMPTON HOTEL, 38 CHARLOTTE SQUARE EH2 4HQ 0131 662 9349

"A lovely setting in the atrium that's not too formal and with a pleasant buzz" sets the scene at Stuart Ralston's bright, glass-roofed hotel dining room (he and his team moved on from a previous venture of the same name in Newington a couple of years ago). All reports acclaim "outstandingly good and inventive cooking" from the six-course menu (going up to £105 per person in 2023 from £85) and "friendly service". / www.aizle.co.uk; aizle_edinburgh; Wed-Sun 8.30 pm; closed Wed-Sun L, closed Mon & Tue; children: 3.

CAFÉ MARLAYNE £42 343

1 THISTLE STREET EH2 1EN
0131 226 2230

"A lovely little place" – "the sort of bistro you would like to have in your neighbourhood", with "a very nice menu of French dishes and excellent service". It's also "very cheap at lunchtime and reasonable in the evening, especially for central Edinburgh". / www.cafemarlayne.com/thistle-street; cafemarlayne; Tue-Sat 10 pm; closed Tue L, closed Sun & Mon; No Amex.

THE CAFÉ ROYAL BAR £74 334

19 WEST REGISTER STREET EH2 2AA
0131 556 1884

"The finest selection of oysters and mussels", "exquisite seafood platters", "Scottish game", "champagne and whisky", "a cracking wine selection with some big hitters" – all of it served in the "beautiful setting" of an ornate Victorian bar. No wonder that "it's a busy place", so you "need to book ahead". / www.caferoyaledinburgh.com; caferoyaledn; Mon-Sun 10 pm; Cash & all usual cards; children: 5.

CAFÉ ST-HONORÉ £61 334

34 NW THISTLE STREET LN EH2 1EA
0131 226 2211

"Tucked away in a back street off George Street" you'll find a little corner of "Left Bank Paris preserved en gelée" – serving "divine French bistro food" that's "just right for a romantic tryst". "This long standing restaurant continues to show others that great ingredients well prepared shine through", while demonstrating "outstanding commitment to local small suppliers". / www.cafesthonore.com; Mon, Thu-Sun 9 pm; closed Tue & Wed; Cash & all usual cards.

CIVERINO'S SLICE £5 333

49 FORREST ROAD EH1 2QP
0131 225 4026

This "buzzing and reliable" home-grown homage to New York-style pizza sells its "great" versions by the slice – "the slices are enormous and one will suffice most people" – in four outlets with a "quirky vibe and music (American rock and hip-hop)". "Their motto is branded on every cup and menu: 'Death Before Dominos'!" / www.civerinosslice.com; civerinos_slice; Sun-Thu 11 pm, Fri & Sat midnight.

CONDITA £159 544

15 SALISBURY PLACE EH9 1SL
0131 667 5777

"Amazing – a faultless, fixed tasting menu, and the best wine pairings ever" – so say fans of Conor Toomey's small venue a short taxi ride from the city centre. "I hate choice, so I love that there is none!" – the surprise multi-course meal takes about three hours and in 2023 prices will rise to £140 per person. / www.condita.co.uk; condita_restaurant; Tue-Sat 10.30 pm; closed Tue-Sat L, closed Sun & Mon.

CONTINI GEORGE STREET £74 334

103 GEORGE STREET EH2 3ES
0131 225 1550

This "busy and atmospheric" restaurant with "reliably excellent pasta dishes" (plus, unusually, 'full Scottish breakfasts') was opened almost 20 years ago in a former banking hall by Victor Contini, whose family has brought their Italian heritage to bear on the Scottish food scene for more than a century. The venue's success has led to further openings, at the Scottish National Gallery and in Cannonball House, next door to Edinburgh Castle. / www.contini.com/contini-george-street; continibites; Mon-Sat 10 pm, Sun 8 pm; Cash & all usual cards; booking weekends only.

DAVID BANN £44 433

56-58 ST MARYS ST EH1 1SX
0131 556 5888

David Bann's "top-notch" and "creative" meat-free cooking produces "beautifully presented dishes, often of complex structure and ingredients". Now in its 21st year, his Canongate venue is, fans insist, "not to be missed when in Edinburgh!". / www.davidbann.com; davidbannrestaurant; Mon-Sun midnight; Cash & all usual cards.

DEAN BANKS AT THE POMPADOUR, THE CALEDONIAN £105 444

WALDORF ASTORIA EDINBURGH - THE CALEDONIAN, PRINCES STREET EH1 2AB 07770 451668

"A superb location, where the chef's culinary skills are effectively displayed" – Dean Banks is succeeding where others have failed in this plush and "romantic" dining room, dating from 1925. Culinarily speaking, it's in a similar ambitious vein to his St Andrews venture, Haar, and even a reporter who thought it is "maybe a bit pricey" concludes that "the quality of food and the high standards effectively make this a no-brainer to visit". / www.deanbanks.co.uk; deanbankspompadour; Wed-Sun midnight; closed Wed-Sun L, closed Mon & Tue.

DISHOOM EDINBURGH £36 443

3A ST ANDREW SQUARE EH2 2BD
01312 026 406

"Top-quality food a country mile from your average curry house", inspired by the Parsi cafes of Mumbai, keeps the sole Scottish link in this nine-branch chain extremely busy. "I usually go for independent restaurants but Dishoom has been consistently excellent and maintained lovely service over various dinners this year". The only real problem is a veto on evening bookings, which makes it "difficult to get into – in four attempted visits I have only been able to get in once! The queues are half-way down the street. Worth it, though!" / www.dishoom.com; dishoom; Sun-Wed 11 pm, Thu-Sat midnight; payment – credit card only.

DUSIT £53 343

49A THISTLE ST EH2 1DY
0131 220 6846

"A stand-out for Thai food in Edinburgh", this well-run operation has now clocked up two decades serving "absolutely delicious food with some more adventurous choices than in your standard Thai". The "very efficient service" shines in the "cosy modern dining room". / www.dusit.co.uk; Mon-Sun 10 pm; Cash & all usual cards.

ELEANORE £33 543

30-31 ALBERT PLACE EH7 5HN

This "outstanding sharing plates restaurant" is "baby sister to the Little Chartroom", and occupies the site it vacated when founders Roberta Hall & Shaun McCarron needed bigger premises for their main operation. But there's no suggestion that Eleanore is a secondary consideration, and its "tasty changing menu" wows all who are lucky enough to bag a table. / www.eleanore.uk; eleanore_leithwalk; Fri & Sat-Mon 11 pm; closed Fri L, closed Tue, Wed & Thu.

L'ESCARGOT BLEU £53 ③④④

56 BROUGHTON ST   EH1 3SA
0131 557 1600

"Like a Gallic hug", chef-patron Fred Berkmiller's "properly sourced old-school French cuisine" comes packaged with "Gallic good humour, impeccable service and quirky decoration in this wonderfully authentic restaurant", "now with new wine bar underneath". Sadly, its nearby sibling L'Escargot Blanc closed down last year after 18 years. / www.lescargotbleu.co.uk; lescargot_edin; Wed-Sat 10.30 pm; closed Wed & Thu L, closed Mon & Tue & Sun; No Amex.

FARIN ROAD £47

103A HANOVER STREET   EH2 1DJ
07510 663835

The pop-up African supper club from chef Tunde Abifarin has found a permanent home in the city's New Town in May 2022 – too late to generate feedback in our annual diners' poll – taking a residency at the cafe Tani Modi on Friday and Saturday nights. In practice, the menu is quite a mash-up, and not as unfamiliar as you might expect with olives, confit garlic hummus and burgers (oxtail or plantain) served alongside goat haggis and more intriguing creations such as poached cod with yam brandade, mussels and okra. / www.farinroad.co.uk; farin.road; Fri & Sat 11 pm; closed Fri & Sat L, closed Mon-Thu & Sun.

FHIOR £111 ⑤④③

36 BROUGHTON STREET   EH1 3SB
0131 477 5000

This "fun, stylish and super-friendly restaurant" from chef Scott Smith and his wife Laura has a very serious mission – to showcase ultra-seasonal Scottish ingredients, many of them grown in their own kitchen garden. The cooking is of "superb quality", and "the tasting menu beautifully thought through, so each course feels as though it belongs after the previous one". Fhior, meaning 'true' in Gaelic, is the Smiths' follow-up to their highly regarded debut Norn, in Leith. / www.fhior.com; fhiorrestaurant; Thu-Sun midnight; closed Thu L, closed Mon & Tue & Wed; payment – credit card only.

FISHERS IN THE CITY £63 ③③③

58 THISTLE ST   EH2 1EN   0131 225 5109

An "excellent choice of fish and shellfish" again wins applause for this long standing sibling to the original, near the Leith shore, which occupies a converted warehouse handy for the National Gallery. / www.fishersrestaurants.co.uk; fishersinthecity; Mon-Sun midnight; Cash & all usual cards.

FISHERS LEITH £63 ④③③

1 THE SHORE   EH6 6QW   0131 554 5666

"If you want to eat fish in Edinburgh, this is the place to go" – "a great spot at a lovely quiet location down on the dockside in Leith, and just delicious". Set in a seventeenth-century watchtower, the "characterful restaurant" serves "really good fresh fish, simply and yet imaginatively". The owners also run The Shore next door, and Fishers in the City. / www.fishersrestaurants.co.uk; fishersleith; Mon-Sun midnight; Cash & all usual cards.

FISHMARKET £64 ④③②

23A PIER PLACE   EH6 4LP
0131 552 8262

Akin to a posh chippy, this tiled, two-year-old collab between the same backers as Ondine and fish suppliers Welche's again gets the thumbs-up – "a fab place at Newhaven Harbour that's busy and exciting, with great fresh Scottish seafood". / www.thefishmarketnewhaven.co.uk; thefishmarketnewhaven; Mon-Sun 10 pm.

LA GARRIGUE £66 ③③③

31 JEFFREY ST   EH1 1DH   0131 557 3032

Since 2001, Jean-Michel Gauffre's bistro has been a "friendly and welcoming" feature of the Old Town, serving a "delightful southern French/Mediterranean menu, and in particular the authentic cuisine of Languedoc" with "regional wines" to match. / www.lagarrigue.co.uk; la_garrigue; Mon-Sat 9 pm; closed Sun; Cash & all usual cards.

HAWKSMOOR £64 ③④④

23 WEST REGISTER STREET   EH2 2AA
0131 526 4790

"Mouth-watering steaks" from both sides of the border and seafood from the Scottish coasts are the draws to the northern capital's outpost of this powerhouse carnivorous chain, and the grand hall of the former Bank of Scotland HQ makes a "magnificent setting for top-notch food". While the feedback is positive, there is less of it than we might have anticipated this year. / thehawksmoor.com; hawksmoorrestaurants; Mon-Sat 10 pm, Sun 8.30 pm; closed Mon & Tue L.

HENDERSONS £46 ③②②

7-13 BARCLAY PLACE   EH10 4HW
0131 202 1635

This "reliable and good-quality" Bruntsfield restaurant was opened in 2021 by Barrie Henderson, reviving and modernising the 58-year-old vegetarian institution – said to be Britain's oldest veggie restaurant – which his grandmother Janet ran in the city centre, and which closed down during the pandemic. / www.hendersonsrestaurant.com; hendersonseatbetter; Mon-Sun 10 pm.

HERON ④④③

87-91 HENDERSON STREET   EH6 6ED
0131 554 1242

This "smart little place with elegant food and bespoke cocktails" overlooking the Water of Leith is a year-old continuation of a lockdown project from two twentysomething chefs, Tomas Gormley (ex-Andrew Fairlie) and Sam Yorke (ex-Dominic Jack's Castle Terrace). Their "lovely food" "lives up to (high) expectations" – "the whipped miso/crab butter which comes with the bread sets the tone". Top Menu Tip – "excellent venison and guinea fowl mains are high spots". / www.heron.scot; heron.scot; Wed-Sun 9 pm; closed Wed & Thu L, closed Mon & Tue.

THE IVY ON THE SQUARE £68 ②③④

6 ST ANDREW SQUARE   EH2 2BD
0131 526 4777

With its attractive and convenient setting overlooking St Andrew's Square, this iteration of the Ivy generates a reasonable number of reports but somewhat limited enthusiasm – "fairly average food which tends to be expensive for what is now a chain restaurant". / theivyedinburgh; theivyedinburgh; Sun-Thu 11 pm, Fri & Sat 10.30 pm.

KA PAO £38

UNIT 420, ST JAMES QUARTER   EH1 3AE
0131 385 1040

A second branch of Glasgow's South East Asian restaurant in the swanky new St James Quarter development, which opened in March 2022. It opened too late in the year to generate any feedback in our annual diners' poll but in April 2022 The Scotsman's Gaby Soutar declared herself "very happy that Edinburgh has its own Ka Pao", finding it "one of my favourite food premises in the building". / www.ka-pao.com; kapaofeeds; Mon-Sun midnight.

THE KITCHIN £149 ⑤④④

78 COMMERCIAL STREET   EH6 6LX
0131 555 1755

"A truly a fantastic experience from start to finish" – Tom & Michaela's flagship venue occupies a "buzzy" warehouse in Leith and was again Edinburgh's most commented-on destination in our annual diners' poll. Criticism is impressively absent: there is nothing but reams of praise for "excellent fine dining", produced from a glass-walled kitchen whose chefs create an "amazing food journey" (with "Tom and his senior team also coming out into the dining room to talk about the dishes"). There are tasting menus for either £130 or £180, with a more conventional evening à la carte menu priced at £110 (the best bargain being the set lunch, which is half this price). "An expensive experience, but well worth it and a real treat". "Despite a lot of competition in Edinburgh now, Kitchin holds its head up high". / www.thekitchin.com; thekitchin; Tue-Sat 10 pm; closed Sun & Mon; Cash & all usual cards; booking max 9 may apply; children: 5+.

KORA

14-17 BRUNTSFIELD PLACE   EH10 4HN
0131 342 3333

Tom Kitchen created this new gastropub to replace his bistro Southside Scran, which closed down in 2020 after barely a year's operation: a victim of both flooding and the pandemic. It opened in August 2022, too late for our annual diners' poll – reports please! / korabytk.com; korabytk; Fri & Sat 11 pm.

THE LITTLE CHARTROOM   £81   543

14 BONNINGTON ROAD   EH6 5JD
0131 556 6600

Roberta Hall-McCarron's Leith operation opened in 2018 and relocated to this larger location in late 2021 (the original premises now housing her other venture, Eleanore, see also) and its style is "much more 'grown-up' in its new home". It delivers "amazing food and great value" from a short and enticing menu. Locals note it's "bonkers popular… admittedly, it's exactly the kind of restaurant you want near your house…". (To reserve, you must leave credit card details with a £45 cancellation fee if you cancel within 24 hours of the booking). / www.thelittlechartroom.com; thelittlechartroom; Thu-Sun 8.30 pm; closed Thu & Fri L, closed Mon & Tue & Wed; payment – credit card only.

THE LOOKOUT BY GARDENER'S COTTAGE   £97   335

CALTON HILL   EH7 5AA   0131 322 1246

"Is this the most amazing restaurant space in Edinburgh, if not Scotland?" – "perched high up on Calton Hill and looking down on the city" from a striking cantilevered structure – "who could resist the irresistible view of the Rose of the North?". The bistro-style food is "thoroughly excellent" in some accounts – in others it's "great... but not as good as you want it to be, when you really want it to match the amazing setting". / www.thelookoutedinburgh.co; thelookoutbygc; closed Mon-Sat & Sun; booking is online only.

MOTHER INDIA'S CAFE   £36   433

3-5 INFIRMARY ST   EH1 1LT
0131 524 9801

"Wonderful Indian-style tapas" – "well cooked, well served and always worth booking when in Edinburgh". This spin-off in the Scottish capital's Old Town lives up to the reputation established by the iconic Glasgow original. / www.motherindia.co.uk/restaurant/mother-india-edinburgh; officialmotherindia; Sun-Thu 9.30 pm, Fri & Sat 10 pm; No Amex.

NEW CHAPTER   £68   333

18 EYRE PL.   EH3 5EP   0131 556 0006

This "popular" local from chef Maciej Szymik gives seasonal Scottish produce a modern European twist, earning general all-round approval. There's also a spin-off brasserie in the West End: Otro. / www.newchapterrestaurant.co.uk; newchapterrestaurant; Wed-Fri 9 pm, Sat 10 pm, Sun 9.30 pm; closed Mon & Tue; Cash & all usual cards.

NOK'S KITCHEN   432

8 GLOUCESTER STREET   EH3 6EG
0131 225 4804

"Beautiful Thai food just off the main Stockbridge thoroughfare is well worth a detour", according to fans of this "friendly and professional" operation in a seventeenth-century townhouse. Since late 2020, it has also had a sibling near the castle. / www.nokskitchen.co.uk; nokskitchen; Mon-Sun 11 pm; Cash & all usual cards.

NOON   £29   333

1 WATERLOO PLACE   EH1 3BG
0131 259 8294

"Very good food and friendly staff" inspire early applause for this two-storey opening, bang slap opposite the huge new St James Quarter. In a March 2022 review, The Scotsman's Gaby Soutar declared herself a fan too – the "casual menu is quite large, and healthy-ish, with all-day breakfast and brunch dishes": "Noon does the casual dining thing pretty well, and is exerting its own small, but efficient, gravitational pull" as "a good alternative for those who don't want to find themselves in the St James Quarter again". / www.atnoon.co.uk; withnoon; Tue-Thu 4 pm, Fri & Sat 5 pm; closed Tue-Sat D, closed Sun & Mon; payment – credit card only.

NOTO   £40   443

47A THISTLE STREET   EH2 1DY
0131 241 8518

"Excellent food and service" win all-round approval for this chic New Town venue from chef-owner Stuart Ralston: a follow-up to his Aizle which is inspired by his time in NYC (and named after his roomate there). There are strong Asian influences in the cooking, and a "front-of-house bar for a pre-dinner drink, sadly are rarity these days". Top Menu Tip – "the sesame prawn toast is a favourite (as is the North Sea crab!)". / notoedinburgh.co.uk; notoedinburgh; Mon-Sun 9 pm.

NUMBER ONE, BALMORAL HOTEL   £156   444

1 PRINCES STREET   EH2 2EQ
0131 557 6727

Chef Matthew Sherry has now had a year at the flagship dining room of this Edinburgh landmark, which manages to be "incredibly grand and imposing" for somewhere in a windowless basement ("the tables are all so far away from each other!"). Long known as one of Scotland's foremost restaurants, ratings here haven't skipped a beat despite Michelin having removed its star on the retirement of Jeff Bland. Service still "runs like clockwork"; and on the basis of the high-quality reports we receive (one such: "we have been for dinner twice in the last six months and had the seven-course set menu with matched wines both times… expensive but worth it") the Tyre Man owes them their star back some time soon. / www.roccofortehotels.com/hotels-and-resorts/the-balmoral-hotel/dining/number-one; numberoneindin; Mon, Thu-Sun 9.30 pm; closed Mon, Thu-Sun L, closed Tue & Wed; Cash & all usual cards; No trainers; booking evening only; children: 5.

ONDINE   £68   444

2 GEORGE IV BRIDGE   EH1 1AD
0131 2261888

"Top-notch oysters, shellfish and fish" make Roy Brett's "superb restaurant" a "must-visit when in Edinburgh" – and a more frequent "treat" for those lucky enough to live nearby. In a new departure last year, selected cuts of British meat were added to the menu, 'simply grilled to perfection'. / www.ondinerestaurant.co.uk; ondine_edinburgh; Tue-Sat 10 pm; closed Sun & Mon; Cash & all usual cards; booking max 6 may apply.

THE PALMERSTON   343

1 PALMERSTON PLACE   EH12 5AL
0131 220 1794

This year-old venture in a converted bank – restaurant, bar, bakery, coffee shop and butchery – "has taken Edinburgh by storm" with its "very unfussy and robust cooking, relaxed atmosphere" – and its excellent in-house baked goods. The "shabby-chic premises belie stunning prep and cooking" from ex-Spring chef Lloyd Morse, who has teamed up with ex-Harwood Arms GM James Snowdon. Top Tip – "on no account depart without buying one of their loaves". / www.thepalmerstonedinburgh.co.uk; the_palmerston; Tue-Sat 9.30 pm, Sun 3.30 pm; closed Sun D, closed Mon.

PURSLANE   £79   433

33A ST STEPHEN STREET   EH3 5AH
01312 263500

"Every course is delicious and made with meticulous care" at Paul Gunning's small venue in a Stockbridge basement. In the evening the choice is between a 5-course and 7-course tasting menu, and it provides "excellent value (especially at lunchtime with the set 2-course and 3-course menus)". / www.purslanerestaurant.co.uk; purslane1; Wed-Sun 9.30 pm; closed Mon & Tue; Cash & all usual cards; children: 6+.

RESTAURANT MARTIN WISHART   £125   553

54 THE SHORE   EH6 6RA   0131 553 3557

"Loved it! Everything is just right" at Martin Wishart's harbourside flagship: one of the city's most accoladed culinary destinations, where his menus of "Frenchified Scottish ingredients" offer "decadent luxury" in "the cool, gentrified environs" of the Leith waterfront. "Every bit as good as the first time I came nearly 20 years ago", it's held a "Michelin star for 20 years for a reason". It might be "slightly hushed and reverential for my (London!) tastes, but it totally deserves its accolades!" / www.martin-wishart.co.uk; martin_wishart; Wed-Sat 10 pm; closed Mon & Tue & Sun; Cash & all usual cards; No trainers.

RHUBARB, PRESTONFIELD HOTEL £76 [3][3][4]

PRIESTFIELD RD EH16 5UT
0131 225 1333

In the same stable as Edinburgh's famous Witchery, James Thomson's lavishly decorated hotel sits in 20 acres near Arthur's Seat and its rococo interior "never fails to please for a romantic occasion". The food is not centre stage, but is consistently well-rated too, with menu options including an à la carte menu, three-course 'fine dining' option and afternoon tea. / www.prestonfield.com; prestonfieldhouseedinburg; Mon-Sun 10 pm; Cash & all usual cards; booking max 8 may apply; children: 12+ at D, none after 7pm.

RICO'S £69 [4][4][4]

58A CASTLE STREET EH2 3LU
0131 322 6750

"Amazing Italian cooking using Scottish produce – impeccable – and with outstanding service" inspires excellent feedback on this stylish and moodily decorated New Town site. It was opened in mid 2021 by Stefano Pieraccini of the Rocca Group in premises vacated by Martin Wishart's The Honour (RIP). / www.ricosristorante.co.uk; ricosristorante; Tue-Sat 9 pm; closed Sun & Mon.

SCRAN & SCALLIE £78 [4][4][3]

1 COMELY BANK RD EH4 1DR 0131 332 6281

"Everything is spot-on" at this "lively" and "inventive" gastropub from a top-class chef – "we love it, and it's great to take international visitors as it showcases Scottish produce". With its "good pies and loads of local beers", the place "doesn't forget it's a pub" – but the "wonderful, skilled cooking" makes it "more than just that". He might not like to hear this, but "we enjoyed this far more than Tom Kitchin's main restaurant". / scranandscallie. com; scranandscallie; Mon-Sun 10 pm; Cash & all usual cards.

THE SPENCE AT GLENEAGLES TOWNHOUSE

39 ST ANDREW SQUARE EH2 1AF
0800 917 4655

With 33 bedrooms, the first-ever spin-off from the world famous sporting estate finally opened in June 2022 (it was originally scheduled for 2021) in the former HQ of the Bank of Scotland, complete with an all-day restaurant under the cupola of the former banking hall that's relatively casual for this grand address. In July 2022, Gaby Soutar of the Scotsman paid it a visit, declaring the food offering as "casual, but with luxurious tweaks. Birthday food". All seemed generally very satisfactory, although the review stops short of being an out-and-out rave. / gleneagles.com/the-gleneagle-blog/gleneagles-townhouse; Mon-Sun 10 pm.

THE STOCKBRIDGE [3][4][3]

54 ST STEPHEN'S ST EH3 5AL
0131 226 6766

Jane Walker & chef Jason Gallagher run this traditional venue in Stockbridge, which is praised as an "intimate and special" place with "well-prepared food, plus efficient and professional service". The only gripe this year? "some dishes seemed a bit too experimental". / www.thestockbridgerestaurant.co.uk; the_stockbridge_restaurant; Tue-Thu 9 pm, Fri & Sat 9.30 pm; closed Tue-Sat L, closed Sun & Mon; Cash & all usual cards; children: 18+ after 8 pm.

SUSHISAMBA

W HOTEL EDINBURGH, ST JAMES'S QUARTER EH1 3JD

As of October 2022, the UK's third branch of this luxurious and expensive wagyu-to-sushi brand is still 'Coming Soon' on the website of the vast St James Quarter development, whose rooftop it is to inhabit… as it has been for ages now. / www.sushisamba.com; sushisamba; Mon-Sat 9.45 pm, Sun 8 pm.

TIMBERYARD £97 [3][3][4]

10 LADY LAWSON ST EH3 9DS
01312 211222

The Radford family's Victorian warehouse conversion remains "relentlessly inventive and delicious", a decade after they were among the first to bring the lessons of 'new Nordic' cuisine to Scotland, with foraged or pickled ingredients presented in industrial-style premises. Head chef James Murray (ex-Lyles, Le Manoir & Nur in Hong Kong) joined the team last year. Natural and low-intervention wines are also an important part of the experience. Even a diner who felt "the food is overhyped" said "what an amazing place!" / www.timberyard.co; timberyard10; Thu-Sun 11 pm; closed Thu L, closed Mon & Tue & Wed; Cash & all usual cards.

21212 £112 [4][5][4]

3 ROYAL TER EH7 5AB 0345 22 21212

Paul Kitching's "wonderfully exciting food" has been a highlight of Edinburgh's dining scene for almost 15 years, served in the signature 'formation' of his restaurant's name: a choice of 2 starters followed by 1 soup, a choice of 2 mains, 1 cheese and 2 desserts, the line-up changing every week. There's a "beautifully decorated and elegant drawing room for pre- and post-dinner drinks". / www.21212restaurant.co.uk; 21212edinburgh; Wed-Sat 8.30 pm; closed Mon & Tue & Sun; Cash & all usual cards; children: 5+.

VALVONA & CROLLA £52 [3][3][3]

19 ELM ROW EH7 4AA 0131 556 6066

"A good choice of light dishes and excellent wine list" are key features of this straightforward café. It's famous in Auld Reekie due to the esteemed and marvellously stocked deli and wine merchants (est. 1934) that it's part of, and which provide the victuals for a meal, served from breakfast onwards. Wine lovers: you can choose any of the hundreds of retail wines for only £6 corkage… "from super value to super Tuscans". / www.valvonacrolla.com; valvonacrolla; Mon-Sat 6 pm; closed Mon-Sat D, closed Sun; Cash & all usual cards.

WEDGWOOD £70 [4][3][3]

267 CANONGATE EH8 8BQ
0131 558 8737

Celebrating its fifteenth year, Paul & Lisa Wedgwood's basement restaurant is on (and partly under) the Royal Mile. Tastefully decorated, it wins strong all-round praise, especially for its competitively priced cuisine (there is a tasting menu, but also a seasonally changing à la carte option with a fair amount of choice). / www.wedgwoodtherestaurant.co.uk; wedgwoodtherestaurant; Sun-Thu 9 pm, Fri & Sat 10 pm; Cash & all usual cards.

THE WITCHERY BY THE CASTLE £91 [2][3][5]

CASTLEHILL, THE ROYAL MILE EH1 2NF
0131 225 5613

"Definitely an experience" – James Thomson's "glorious" 40-year restoration of a 1595 merchant's house next to the castle makes a "totally unique and intimate location" for a candle-lit meal, either in the wood-panelled dining room, filled with leather furnishings and hung with tapestries, or in the 'Secret Garden'. The "atmospheric setting" is "perfect for a romantic dinner" so long as you "don't expect too much gastronomically" from the traditional menu – and there is a "killer wine list – sorry, Wine Bible". / www.thewitchery.com; the.witchery; Mon-Sun 10.30 pm; Cash & all usual cards.

THE TUDOR ROOM, GREAT FOSTERS HOTEL £86

STROUDE RD TW20 9UR 01784 433822

The "beautiful dining room" at this seventeenth-century manor-house hotel near Windsor, strikingly hung with tapestries, was relaunched as the Tudor Pass late last year following the recruitment of chef Alex Payne, formerly of the Thames Table at Crockers in Henley. His predecessor, Tony Parkin, won widespread acclaim for his "excellent" and luxurious modern cooking in his three years at what was then called the Tudor Room and our ratings have even improved since then. The venue is also noted for its afternoon teas – and "wonderful gardens to explore". / www.alexanderhotels.co.uk/great-fosters/food-drink/the-tudor-room; greatfosters; Wed-Sat 9 pm; closed Mon & Tue & Sun.

YNYSHIR RESTAURANT AND ROOMS, YNYSHIR HALL   £410   4 3 3

SY20 8TA   01654 781 209

"There's nowhere quite like it!". – A middle-of-nowhere mid-Wales location only adds to the mystique surrounding Gareth Ward's renowned country house hotel, whose (as predicted in our last guide) promotion to two Michelin stars reflects its current position as a major 'darling' of the UK fooderati. It's hard not to be impressed by such a rapid rise to fame while charging £350 per head in the heart of the distant countryside. 'Ingredient-led, flavour-driven, fat-fuelled, meat-obsessed' is its motto and many diners remain "absolutely blown away by a meal here" and the 20–30 courses of "mind bending flavours" created by "a fantastic team performance" that provides "pure theatre". Even fans, though, are starting to feel that "success has slightly gone to their heads" and even many who feel the food is "really good" think it risks becoming "ridiculously overpriced" (with almost 1 in 3 reporters now nominating the place as their most overpriced experience of the year). And while it's not like the place hides its maximalist, macho tendencies, these can also be a mixed blessing. ("Yes the food is amazing, flavours just jump out at you. But it is all so intense, dish after dish, 32 in all. The atmosphere is like a live performance and by the end you can't cope and sit in a dazed stupor. It's fun, but too intense and too alpha male"). / ynyshir.co.uk; ynyshirrestaurant; Tue-Fri 11 pm; closed Tue-Fri L, closed Mon, Sat & Sun; Cash & all usual cards; credit card deposit required to book; children: 9+.

THE DUNCOMBE ARMS   4 3 3

MAIN RD   DE6 2GZ   01335 324 275

"High-quality cooking in a 'done-up' pub setting" is acclaimed in all feedback on this "beautiful pub", near the Peak District. There is a fairly classic bar menu, but the restaurant menu is in a more bistro/brasserie mould. / www.duncombearms.co.uk; duncombe_arms; Wed & Thu 6 pm, Fri & Sat 9.30 pm, Sun 5 pm; closed Sun D, closed Mon & Tue; Cash & all usual cards.

THE BAY HORSE   £69   4 3 3

BAY HORSE LN   LA2 0HR   01524 791204

"Hardly any further from Junction 33 of the M6 than Forton Services": Craig Wilkinson's "always popular", "railway-side pub" has, say fans, "always unjustly sailed a little below the radar, while food and cooking continue in their accomplished, classically inspired, utterly satisfying way". "In a time when so many places turn out Identikit dishes from the same playbook, it's somehow refreshing to get a really good terrine, confit duck legs etc". Top Menu Tip – "Meat is first class, the Sunday roast beef is the best ever: pink and melting in the mouth". / www.bayhorseinn.com; Wed-Sat 9 pm, Sun 8 pm; closed Mon & Tue; No Amex.

OLD FIRE ENGINE HOUSE   £53   3 4 2

25 ST MARY'S ST   CB7 4ER   01353 662582

"Great food and service" have been the order of the day since 1968 at the restaurant and art gallery Ann Jarman founded in 1968 in a Georgian house near the cathedral (her husband Michael passed away two years ago). More like a private home than a commercial business, it is "very old-fashioned – but that's its charm". "First visit for over 40 (yes, over 40) and still doing proper home cooking so well. And our server was working there when I last went!" / www.theoldfireenginehouse.co.uk; Mon-Sun 8.30 pm; No Amex.

FAT OLIVES   £62   4 5 3

30 SOUTH ST   PO10 7EH   01243 377914

This "lovely little restaurant tucked away in Emsworth" – "just a stone's throw from the water's edge" and run by a "husband and wife team" – is "exactly what a local restaurant should aim to be", serving "excellently prepared fish and meat dishes with great attention to flavour and detail". Lawrence & Julia Murphy have built a loyal following over 23 years, so it's "best to book a few weeks in advance". / www.fatolives.co.uk; fatolives1; Wed-Sat 10.30 pm; closed Mon & Tue & Sun; No Amex; children: 8+, except Sat L.

36 ON THE QUAY   £78   4 4 3

47 SOUTH ST   PO10 7EG   01243 375592

This "reliably good restaurant" with "excellent seafood" overlooking Emsworth harbour has undergone something of a renaissance in recent years. Long one of the top spots on the South Coast, it is now owned and run by chef Gary Pearce and his wife Martyna. Gary trained here under former owners Ramon & Karen Farthing, and took over 20 years later in 2019 when the Farthings retired, having honed his skills at Cheltenham's Le Champignon Sauvage and at Belgium's famous De Wulf. / www.36onthequay.com; 36onthequay; Tue-Sat 8.30 pm; closed Sun & Mon; Cash & all usual cards.

THE BAILIWICK   £84   5 4 3

WICK ROAD   TW20 0HN   01784 682888

This "lovely little country pub" tucked away on the edge of Windsor Great Park "fits into almost any category – including bar, romantic, spectacular-fine-dining-at-pub-prices, elegant-and-extravagant in display". Launched in summer 2021 by ex-Core chef Steven Ellis and his pastry chef wife Ami, it mixes well-turned pub classics at lunchtime with more refined, often game-based dishes in the evening – "when you have amazing produce from Windsor Great Park and put it in the hands of fantastic chefs, the result is nothing short of perfection". Top Tip – "doughnut heaven: the

pheasant doughnut with truffle and parmesan custard blows you away!" / thebailiwick.co.uk; thebailiwickfreehouse; Wed-Sat 9.30 pm, Sun 4 pm; closed Sun D, closed Mon & Tue.

HAYWARDS RESTAURANT   £78   4 4 2

111 BELL COMMON   CM16 4DZ   01992 577350

"Love this restaurant with a very skilled chef and great, professional staff!". – Jahdre & Amanda Hayward's renovated coach house and skittle alley sits adjacent to the Forest Gate Inn (owned by Amanda's family), where they are celebrating their first decade of business this year and all reports on it continue to acclaim it as an "Epping Forest favourite". In February 2022, The Guardian's Grace Dent declared herself a fan too: "Haywards wasn't the coolest, newest or the most experimental place I ate at during that week, but it lives on in my memory as fantastic, and that makes all the difference". / www.haywardsrestaurant.co.uk; haywardsrestaurant; Thu-Sat 11.30 pm, Sun 6 pm; closed Thu L closed Sun D, closed Mon & Tue & Wed; Cash & all usual cards; credit card deposit required to book; children: 10.

GOOD EARTH   £66   3 3 2

14 - 18 HIGH STREET   KT10 9RT   01372 462489

This "very popular" and "upmarket Chinese" is "several clicks above your average" and "well worth the extra cost", with numerous regulars noting they have "never had a bad dish". A fixture "in the heart of Esher" for four decades now, one issue does inspires gripes – "the menu is unchanged for years". Top Menu Tip – "superb sea bass". / www.goodearthgroup.co.uk; goodearthgroup; Tue-Sat 10.30 pm, Sun 10.45 pm; closed Mon; Cash & all usual cards; booking max 12 may apply.

JOSÉ PIZARRO AT THE SWAN INN ESHER   £59   4 3 2

2 HARE LANE   KT10 9BS   01372 462 582

Tapas supremo José Pizarro's first foray outside the Big Smoke brings his "lovely Spanish fare" to this "relaxed former pub" in the Surrey suburbs near Esher Common. "The food seems to get better every time we visit"; and is equally suited to "bringing the whole family" or a "romantic tête-à-tête". / josepizarro.com/venues/jose-pizarro-swan-inn-esher; josepizarrorestaurants; Mon-Thu 11 pm, Fri & Sat 11.30 pm, Sun 8 pm; Cash & all usual cards.

GILBEY'S   £68   2 2 3

82 - 83 HIGH STREET   SL4 6AF   01753 854921

A "gorgeous cosy restaurant" (owned by the eponymous gin dynasty) near the bridge to Windsor, with a "lovely and romantic" front room and larger dining space to the rear.

It's "very traditional" in style and serves a menu of "solid if unspectacular, reliable, competitively priced modern British cooking". / www.gilbeygroup.com; gilbeys_eton; Sun-Thu 9.30 pm, Fri & Sat 10 pm; Cash & all usual cards.

THE ACORN INN   £64   3|3|4

28 FORE ST   DT2 0JW   01935 83228

This "quaint pub in the tiny village of Evershot" – immortalised as the 'Sow and Acorn' in Thomas Hardy's 'Tess of the d'Urbervilles' – offers "beautifully presented, consistently good and interesting" food from Kenyan-born chef Robert Ndungu. It is the more informal sibling of Summer Lodge on the other side of the village, from the Red Carnation hotel group. / www.acorn-inn.co.uk; acorn_inn; Mon-Sun 9 pm; closed Mon-Sun L; Cash & all usual cards.

SUMMER LODGE, SUMMER LODGE COUNTRY HOUSE   £123   3|4|3

DT2 0JR   01935 482000

This "very traditional and comfortable country hotel" from the Red Carnation group is one of the few left that still practise "silver service – the plates are placed in front of guests in synchronisation, and the staff are fabulous", while "the food is absolutely delicious (dinner is definitely better than afternoon tea in my opinion)". Deep in Thomas Hardy's Wessex, the village of Evershot appears disguised as the fictional Eversheaad, and the novelist even designed part of what is now the hotel in his days as an architect. / www.summerlodgehotel.co.uk; summer_lodge; Mon-Sun 9 pm; Cash & all usual cards.

THE WHITE DOG INN   £51   3|4|3

VILLAGE STREET   TN32 5TD
01580 830264

This "brilliant country gastropub" (with rooms) offers a "wide range of modern-British style food" – with many dishes making reference to local provenance. "Views of Bodiam Castle" and the option of glamping in a 5-person teepee on the grounds add to the considerable appeal. / www.thewhitedogwhurst.co.uk; thewhitedoginn; Mon-Thu 9 pm, Fri & Sat 9.30 pm, Sun 5 pm; closed Sun D.

GOTO   £17   3|3|2

38 NEW BRIDGE STREET   EX4 3AH
01392 437734

"There's not really much choice for Japanese cuisine in Exeter, but this recent opening (during lockdown) has really good sushi and sashimi as well as other traditional Japanese dishes". "It's slightly away from the city centre, but worth the walk down Fore Street" because "the food is authentic and the staff extremely nice". Top Menu Tips – "some really delicious

Lympstone Manor, Exmouth

vegan options – the agedashi tofu was delicious, as was the tempura. The 'carnists' enjoyed their sashimi and nigiri and the wine was pretty good too". / Mon-Sat 9 pm; closed Sun.

RENDEZVOUS WINE BAR   £61   3|4|4

38-40 SOUTHERNHAY EAST   EX1 1PE
01392 270 222

"A go-to place for dining in Exeter", this basement wine bar/restaurant with a walled garden near Cathedral Yard is "one of very few places in town where you can confidently go for a business lunch/dinner – no muzak, well-spaced tables". "The menu is always filled with interesting things and sourced locally – meat and fish always of the highest quality". / www.rendezvouswinebar.co.uk; rendezvouswinebar; Mon-Sat 9 pm; closed Sun; Cash & all usual cards.

LYMPSTONE MANOR   £201   5|4|4

COURTLANDS LANE   EX8 3NZ
01395 202040

"Beautiful food, served in a perfect location" makes Michael Caines's "very special" Georgian mansion and vineyard – overlooking the Exe estuary – nowadays one of the Top-5 most commented-on restaurants outside London in our annual diners' poll, and one of the country's foremost luxury destinations (with 21 bedrooms). "Great views out of the lounge and bar windows" contribute to an overall experience that's "truly a wow". "Impeccable" staff ("immensely efficient but low key") deliver "exceptional" modern cuisine, with the highlight being the 'Taste of the Estuary' tasting menu, supplemented by "a great variety of wines" (including, of course, those from the surrounding vines). There are three dining rooms: the Berry Head (with the best views), Powderham and Mamhead. On the downside, "prices are way off scale"… but hardly anyone seems to mind! / www.lympstonemanor.co.uk; lympstone_manor; Wed & Thu 9 pm, Fri-Sun 9.30 pm; closed Mon & Tue; Cash & all usual cards; No shorts; children; 5.

THE POOL HOUSE, LYMPSTONE MANOR £85

COURTLANDS LANE   EX8 3NZ
01395 202040

A new addition to Michael Caines's luxurious destination, this relatively relaxed 40-seat operation (with another 60 alfresco) overlooks the hotel's new outdoor pool and offers a casual menu of salads, seafood and BBQ from brunch time till mid afternoon and then again in the early evening. / lympstonemanor.co.uk; Mon-Thu 9 pm, Fri-Sun 9.30 pm; closed Mon & Tue L.

ROCKFISH EXMOUTH   £54   3|3|3

PIER HEAD   EX8 1DU   01395 272100

"We love the Rockfish chain" – and "Exmouth is our favourite", say fans of Mitch Tonks's West Country seafood group, which had eight branches as we went to press, with two more (Salcombe and Topsham) about to open, along with an online seafood market and a pioneering canned-fish operation. Despite being a multiple, it offers "top seafood, and the staff seem really passionate about the subject". / www.therockfish.co.uk/restaurants/exmouth; therockfishuk; Mon-Sun 9 pm; Cash & all usual cards.

THE SQUARE AND COMPASSES   £49   3|2|3

FULLER STREET   CM3 2BB
01245 361477

"A fantastic pub in the Essex countryside" say fans of this quietly situated old boozer north of Chelmsford, dating from 1652: "the food never disappoints and the portions are super generous". Game in season is a speciality. / www.thesquareandcompasses.co.uk; squareandcompasses; Wed-Sat 8.30 pm, Sun 4 pm; closed Mon & Tue; Cash & all usual cards.

SCULTHORPE MILL £54   3|3|3

LYNN ROAD   NR21 9QG   01328 633001

"A magical waterside setting, simple-but-good food and delightful service" have won praise for this "recently refurbished pub" in a converted watermill dating from 1757. Opened in summer 2021 by Siobhan and Caitriona Peyton, sisters of catering big-wig Oliver, its high-profile launch garnered national press attention, and the restaurant pleased most comers in its first year. On the other hand, even fans have found it "occasionally missing a beat" and some diners are cynical: "if a PR campaign could win an award this pub would have a display case full… lovely riverside premises, reasonable pub menu, but all fur coat and no knickers". / www.sculthorpemill.uk; sculthorpemillnorfolk; Mon-Sat 8.30 pm, Sun 8 pm.

FALMOUTH, CORNWALL   1–4B

THE COVE RESTAURANT & BAR   £82   223

MAENPORTH BEACH   TR11 5HN 01326 251136

This "glorious spot" by the sea, close to the SW coastal path and with a front-conservatory to take advantage of sea views, was taken over by high-profile chef Michael Caines of Lympstone Manor in 2020. Quell hopes of any culinary fireworks, though – reports here didn't hit the heights this year, with the experience too often "let down by chaotic service and pedestrian food". / www.thecovemaenporth.co.uk; the_cove_maenporth; Wed-Sun 11 pm; closed Mon & Tue; Cash & all usual cards; children: None.

CULTURE   £88

CUSTOM HOUSE QUAY, 38B ARWENACK STREET   TR11 3JF   01326 313001

South African chef Hylton Espey (formerly at Merchants Manor hotel) with his wife Petronella opened this July 2022 newcomer on Custom House Quay, just by the sea, with a hyper-seasonal approach including many foraged ingredients. His 'Journey Menu' provides seven courses for £65 per person and is served from an open kitchen, and design-wise the 30-cover room adopts a pared-back approach featuring bare brick-work, wood and steel. / www.culturerestaurant.co.uk; culture.restaurant; Mon-Wed, Fri & Sat 3 pm, Sun 2 pm.

HOOKED ON THE ROCKS   £57   433

SWANPOOL ROAD, SWANPOOL COURT TR11 5BG   01326 311886

"Great shellfish", eaten at a "nice location on the edge of the cliff" with views over Swanpool beach and nature reserve, makes this comfortable spot an attractive option in all seasons. There's a strong sustainability ethos, and the cooking is accurate. Worst comment? – The "brilliant scallops were slightly overpowered by the equally delicious sauce". / www.hookedontherocksfalmouth.com; Mon-Sun 9 pm.

THE VERDANT SEAFOOD BAR   £9   433

QUAY STREET   TR11 3HH

"Great food, great beer, great staff – what's not to like?" – Penryn-based Verdant craft brewery

opened this tiny taproom just off the Falmouth seafront four years ago, matching their brews with a small-plates menu of French, Italian and more locally inspired seafood, ranging from fish balls and fish-finger butties to pan-fried gurnard with mussels and crab sauce. / verdantbrewing.co/pages/seafoodbar; verdant_seafood_bar; Tue-Sat 10 pm; closed Sun & Mon; no bookings.

FARNHAM, DORSET   2–3C

THE MUSEUM INN   £64   334

DT11 8DE   01725 516261

This "brilliant thatched country pub" has "lots of game dishes" on its menu – appropriately enough for a traditional establishment in the historical hunting landscape of Cranborne Chase. "Vegetarians and vegans are well provided for" too, while there's also a "well-stocked bar with local ales and a reasonably priced wine list". / www.museuminn.co.uk; themuseuminn; Mon-Sat 9.30 pm, Sun 4 pm; closed Sun D; No Amex.

FAVERSHAM, KENT   3–3C

READ'S   £92   444

MACKNADE MANOR, CANTERBURY RD ME13 8XE   01795 535344

This "fine-dining manor house" in north Kent, run by chef-patron David Pitchford and his wife Rona as a "family business for 40 years plus", is "consistently wonderful in all aspects" and "always a real treat". "Although the food may be considered a little safe, its quality does not drop", while the "range of smaller dining rooms" makes it "the go-to restaurant for special family occasions" – "even teenage grandchildren love the style and ambience". Top Tip – "amazing soufflés". / www.reads.com; reads_restaurant; Tue-Sat 9 pm; closed Sun & Mon; No Amex.

YARD   £41   333

10 JACOB YD, PRESTON ST   ME13 8NY 01795 538265

This low-key daytime-only wholefood eco-store and café (with Thursday evening 'supperclub socials') started out 10 years ago as a pop-up street stall and now occupies a century-old joinery workshop in a mews. The "hearty" breakfasts, light bites and lunches win consistently good ratings. / www.yardfaversham.co.uk ; YardFaversham; Tue-Sat 4 pm; closed Tue-Sat D, closed Sun & Mon; Cash & all usual cards.

FENCE, LANCASHIRE   5–1B

WHITE SWAN AT FENCE   £97   543

300 WHEATLEY LANE RD   BB12 9QA 01282 611773

"Every dish is sublime" – "a real joy" – at this "unpretentious pub" near Burnley with "fantastic cooking" from "brilliant" chef Tom Parker, who "learned his craft at local Northcote and now has a diary released three months at a time". "It's a one-hit menu each day depending on seasonality and his mood"

– "not exclusively fish but the fish dishes are superb". The whole operation, including co-owners Gareth & Laura Ostick, is "very clever" and represents "excellent value" – "it's not really cheap, but much much cheaper than similar establishments of this class". / www.whiteswanatfence.co.uk; Tue-Sat 8.40 pm; closed Fri & Sat L, closed Sun & Mon; Cash & all usual cards.

FERRENSBY, NORTH YORKSHIRE   8–4B

GENERAL TARLETON   £61   333

BOROUGHBRIDGE RD   HG5 0PZ 01423 340284

"New management are making an impact" according to reports on this well-known coaching inn, not far from the A1, which was taken over in January 2021 by father-and-daughter owners, Jonathan & Sarah Morris. The food from 2018 MasterChef: The Professionals competitor, Chris McPhee, is consistently well-rated: "if you missed the old 'GT' in its heyday, make a return visit: you will not be disappointed!" / www.the-gt.co.uk; generaltarleton; Mon-Sat 9 pm, Sun 3 pm; closed Mon-Thu L closed Sun D; Cash & all usual cards.

FLAUNDEN, HERTFORDSHIRE   3–2A

THE BRICKLAYERS ARMS   £68   343

HOGPITS BOTTOM   HP3 0PH 01442 833322

Emphatically "not your most ordinary pub" – this ivy-clad Georgian boozer in a "lovely countryside setting" has been well run by Sally & Alvin Michaels for twenty-odd years, and boasts a "good menu of delicious food". / www.bricklayersarms.com; Mon-Sat 9.30 pm, Sun 7 pm; Cash & all usual cards.

FLETCHING, EAST SUSSEX   3–4B

THE GRIFFIN INN   £72   323

TN22 3SS   01825 722890

This "lovely, buzzing old pub" in the Sussex Weald has all the ingredients required for a "perfect country inn": "a lovely old bar", "great food from an interesting menu", and "a brilliant garden that's even more beautiful in the sun". Piers Morgan grew up on site – but don't worry, he's long gone! / www.thegriffininn.co.uk; thegriffininn; Mon-Fri 11.30 pm, Sat & Sun midnight; Cash & all usual cards.

FOLKESTONE, KENT   3–4D

LITTLE ROCK   £54   333

FOLKSTONE HARBOUR   CT20 1QH 01303 762565

This "very buzzy spot in a pink container on the harbour arm" serves "very fresh fish and seafood", and is the "sister restaurant to Rocksalt". "Spilling out onto a terrace, it makes a delightful spot for lunch in the sun, with engaging service and all that one wants from a decent fish restaurant". / www.littlerockfolkestone.co.uk; littlerockfolkestone;

Wed & Thu 9 pm, Fri & Sat 8 pm, Sun 5 pm; closed Sun D, closed Mon & Tue.

ROCKSALT £63 324

4-5 FISHMARKET CT19 6AA
01303 212 070

"A fabulous seaside site by the harbour" helps guarantee custom as this well-known fish restaurant, which opened in June 2011, and is one of the more commented-on restaurants in Kent. It continues to spark a large volume of interest and praise for its "beautifully presented and well-executed seafood dishes" ("the fish is caught locally, so super fresh and tasty"). Since founding chef Mark Sargeant left the business last year, however, it's taken slightly more flak generally: nothing grievous, but reports of service that "can be a little hit and miss", or food that's "edible but instantly forgettable" and "on the pricey side". / www.rocksaltfolkestone.co.uk; rocksaltfolkestone; Mon-Thu 10 pm, Fri & Sat 10.30 pm, Sun 5 pm; closed Sun D; Cash & all usual cards.

STEEP STREET COFFEE HOUSE £20 333

18-24 THE OLD HIGH STREET CT20 1RL
01303 247819

"A lovely little place on Old Folkestone High Street situated in the middle of the Creative Quarter". "It's created its own library as the setting" and serves "great coffee, cakes and brunch". / www.steepstreet.co.uk; steep_street; Mon-Sat 6 pm, Sun 5 pm; closed Mon-Sun D.

FONTHILL GIFFORD, WILTSHIRE 2–3C

BECKFORD ARMS £61 333

SP3 6PX 01747 870 385

A traditional, ivy-clad inn dating from 1740, smartly modernised while retaining an "old country-house ambience and service" and remaining "popular with locals". It's the sort of place "happy to provide a breakfast sharpener", where nothing is too much trouble: "my sister asked for an omelette and something amazing simply appeared – not on the menu, not a problem". / www.beckfordarms.com; thebeckfordarms; Mon-Sun 9.30 pm; No Amex.

FORDWICH, KENT 3–3D

THE FORDWICH ARMS £79 543

KING STREET CT2 0DB 01227 710444

"Lovely old pub, serving brilliant modern cooking" from chef-patron Dan Smith (ex-Clove Club) and his pastry chef wife, Tash, that "gets better with each visit", and the "imaginatively presented and delicious" dishes now make it "one of the best restaurant experiences in the Southeast" – "worth travelling to enjoy". The highest accolade of all? – "enjoyed it even more than the Sportsman!" (just up the road in Whitstable). / www.fordwicharms.co.uk; thefordwicharms; Wed-Sat 9.30 pm, Sun 5 pm; closed Sun D, closed Mon & Tue.

FORT WILLIAM, HIGHLAND 9–3B

CRANNOG £57 323

TOWN CENTRE PIER PH33 6DB
01397 705589

A "lovely position on the water" overlooking Loch Linnhe makes Finlay & Lorna Finlayson's distinctive red and white painted pierside venue the ideal place to sample fresh-caught West Coast fish and shellfish. / www.crannog.net; crannoghighland; Wed-Sun 9.30 pm; closed Mon & Tue; No Amex.

FOWEY, CORNWALL 1–4D

FITZROY £75 333

2 FORE STREET PL23 1AD
01726 932934

Associated with London foodie hits Primeur and Westerns Laundry, this three-year-old favourite, which occupies a former bank, continues to inspire high ratings for its food. It's a seasonal operation, which closes each year between late Autumn and mid Spring. / www.fitzroycornwall.com; fitzroyoffowey; Tue-Sun 10 pm; closed Tue-Sun L, closed Mon.

THE Q RESTAURANT, THE OLD QUAY HOUSE £62 334

28 FORE STREET PL23 1AQ
01726 833302

"Reliably good food for a meal that feels special, with estuary views" – the backdrop of the water defines the experience at this Victorian hotel with 13 bedrooms, and where there's no better location than the deck on a sunny day. / theoldquayhouse.com; oldquayhouse; Mon-Sun 9 pm; closed Mon-Sun L; Cash & all usual cards; children: 8+ at D.

FRAMLINGHAM, SUFFOLK 3–1D

WATSON & WALPOLE £65 443

3 CHURCH STREET IP13 9BQ
01728 666556

"The epitome of a neighbourhood restaurant", this "lovely" two-year-old trattoria from TV's 'Hotel Inspector' Ruth Watson, her husband Dave and Rob Walpole have made it "a great addition to Framlingham" – "the inventive menu offers authentic Italian dishes which reflect the skill, knowledge and enthusiasm of all involved", and "the standard of cooking and service is remarkably consistent, with prices that are genuinely reasonable". / watsonandwalpole. com; watsonandwalpole; Tue-Sat 9.30 pm; closed Sun & Mon; payment – credit card only; booking is online only; children: Lunch any age but 10 years old at dinner.

FRAMPTON MANSELL, GLOUCESTERSHIRE 2–2B

JOLLY NICE FARM SHOP £16 343

THE OLD WHITE HORSE FILLING STATION, CIRENCESTER ROAD GL6 8HZ
01285 760868

This "innovative rustic drive-through" in a converted country petrol station offers "brilliant fresh food that packs flavour" – and boasts impeccable provenance: where else could you feast on burgers from shorthorn cattle or sausage rolls from rare-breed pigs reared and butchered on the property? There's a meadow for picnics, a shop stuffed with produce from the farm, whose third-generation owners made the switch to sustainable regenerative agriculture 10 years ago – and "friendly service from enthusiastic young staff who are always smiling!" jollynicefarmshop.com; jollynicefarmshop; Mon-Sun 7 pm; payment – credit card only; no bookings.

FRESSINGFIELD, SUFFOLK 3–1D

THE FOX & GOOSE £57 334

CHURCH RD IP21 5PB 01379 586247

This "lovely old building" – a beamed former guildhall – is "as reliable as ever" under longtime owners Paul & Sarah Yaxley, who deliver modern European cuisine "at very reasonable prices for the quality". / www.foxandgoose.net; Tue-Sat 11 pm, Sun 3.30 pm; closed Sun D, closed Mon; No Amex; children: 6+ at D.

FRILSHAM, BERKSHIRE 2–2D

THE POT KILN £78 444

YATTENDON ESTATE RG18 0XX
01635 201366

This "lovely country pub in the middle of nowhere" (deep in the Berkshire countryside, where it's easy to ignore the nearby M4) hits all targets with "big portions of delicious, gamey, meat dishes, friendly knowledgeable service and a relaxed atmosphere". Owner Kate Robinson made a few changes when she took over from her former husband, the well-known shooting chef Mike Robinson, and now runs it with her partner, musician Rocky Rockliff. Top Tip – the snacks in the bar and huge garden are high quality, and considerably cheaper than eating a full meal inside. / www.potkiln.org; thepotkiln; Mon-Sat 8.30 pm, Sun 3 pm; closed Sun D; Cash & all usual cards.

FRITHSDEN, HERTFORDSHIRE 3–2A

THE ALFORD ARMS £60 234

HP1 3DD 01442 864480

An "absolute favourite pub" – this "lovely spot" in a wooded valley just north of London is a "good local standby" that "is very popular at weekends, when booking is advisable". "We would go back, less for the food perhaps, but certainly for the location and ambience". / www.alfordarms.co.uk; alfordarms; closed Mon-Sat

& Sun; Cash & all usual cards; booking max 12 may apply.

WHITE HART   £65   3 4 5

MAIN ROAD   OX13 5LW   01865 390585

The "lovely location and atmospheric building" justify a visit to this fifteenth-century inn with a stunning high-beamed dining room. The setting is "well matched" by "imaginative" modern British food from self-taught chef Mark Chandler, who has run the pub for 18 years with his wife Kay. Top Tip – "the signature pork belly is excellent". / www.whitehart-fyfield.com; Tue-Sat 9 pm, Sun 4 pm; closed Sun D, closed Mon; Cash & all usual cards.

TRAKOL   £67   4 3 3

HILLGATE QUAYS   NE8 2BH

"Wood-fired wonders from one of Newcastle's best!" – a "tremendous menu" of "raw-in-tooth-and-claw meat cooking over open flame" draws aficionados to this "wonderful location, right under the Tyne Bridge". There's "nothing here I could cook at home – many things I couldn't even imagine. Risky, but it works!" / www.bytheriverbrew.co/trakol; bytheriverbrewco; Wed-Sat 10 pm, Sun 6 pm; closed Wed-Fri L, closed Mon & Tue.

THE HOEBRIDGE   £69   3 4 3

**HOEBRIDGE ROAD WEST   TD6 9LZ
01896 823082**

"A top find with delicious food and great service" – ex-New Yorker Kyle Tidd and his husband, chef Hamish Carruthers run this elegant restaurant in the Borders, focused on seasonal small plates. In August 2022, The Scotsman's Catriona Thomson paid it a visit and was wowed: "calm… understated elegance… extensive and impressive wine list… even the most demanding diva… would not be able to fault the service or the delicious food". / www.thehoebridge.com; thehoebridge; Thu-Sat 8 pm, Sun 5 pm; closed Thu-Sat L closed Sun D, closed Mon & Tue & Wed.

MALIKS   £53   4 3 3

**14 OAK END WAY   SL9 8BR
01753 889634**

"Amazing food" (including a "great duck curry") has earned this classy curry house a chorus-line of local celeb cheer-leaders, including Heston Blumenthal and Sir Ben Kingsley (of Gandhi fame). It has sister venues in Cookham and Marlow. / www.maliks.co.uk; maliksgroup; Fri-Sun 10.30 pm; closed Mon-Wed & Thu; Cash & all usual cards.

THREE OAKS   £60   4 4 3

**AUSTENWOOD LN   SL9 8NL
01753 899 016**

With its "beautifully presented, delicious food", this "better-than-standard gastropub justifiably attracts custom from a wide area" – and its heated 'Oak pods' are popular for outdoor eating in all seasons. It's run by Harry Cripps and his wife Katherine, daughter of the late broadcaster Terry Wogan – whose brothers run the London pizza specialist Homeslice. / www.thethreeoaksgx.co.uk; thethreeoaksgx; Wed-Sat 11 pm, Sun 6 pm; closed Mon & Tue; Cash & all usual cards.

LA LOCANDA   £55   4 4 3

MAIN STREET   BB7 4HH   01200 445303

"Think of La Locanda as small agriturismo restaurant somewhere rural in the northern half of Italy, but which has somehow materialised in a weaver's cottage in the Ribble Valley, on the main E-W route of the A59, and you'll get an idea of what the Bocchis are about. Maurizio cooks; Cinzia serves (loudly). Fresh produce in virtually all dishes is locally sourced, the meats usually from a local organic farm a couple of miles away. Drinks are resolutely Italian. Don't ask for Coke: they don't have it, but they have a couple of Italian colas, among the intriguing soft drinks list. The same goes for the lengthy beer list, and the oenophiliac delight that is the wine list. What a wine list. Wines I have never seen anywhere else in this country, and in all the years I've been going to La Locanda, not a single disappointing wine. While the wine list explores every corner of Italy, the food, or at least the cooking, tends to focus more on the rustic styles of the north, particularly Lombardy and Piedmont. It's important to note that there is no pizza and there is definitely no garlic bread: this is an Italian Italian, not a Britalian. Cinzia runs front of house: some find her a bit abrupt, but she really isn't: the problem is that she speaks Italian using English words". / www.lalocanda.co.uk; lalocandagisburn; Tue-Thu 9.30 pm, Fri 10 pm, Sat 10.30 pm, Sun 8 pm; closed Tue-Fri L, closed Mon; Cash & all usual cards.

BATTLEFIELD REST   £42   3 3 3

**55 BATTLEFIELD ROAD   G42 9JL
0141 636 6955**

A 1914 landmark (a scenic-looking former tram stop) houses this "homely Italian" on the Southside. That it's "a bit cramped when busy" is the worst anyone has to say of it – it's consistently praised as a "cheap 'n' cheerful" local favourite. On the menu, pizza, pasta and gelati alongside a few nourishing mains (pork Milano, beef cheek pie, risotto…) / www.battlefieldrest.co.uk; restbattlefield; Mon-Sat 8.45 pm; closed Sun; Cash & all usual cards.

CAFÉ GANDOLFI   £55   3 3 4

64 ALBION ST   G1 1NY   0141 552 6813

Original hand-made furniture (by Tim Stead) and a characterful, panelled interior add to the enduring appeal of this 40-year-old favourite in the Merchant City – one of Glasgow's stalwart culinary institutions. The food (served from breakfast) is wholesome, but un-fancy: burger, risotto, rarebit, Arbroath Smokies and so on. / www.cafegandolfi.com; cafegandolfi; Sun & Mon 5 pm, Tue-Sat 10.30 pm; closed Sun & Mon D; Cash & all usual cards; booking weekdays only.

CAIL BRUICH   £153   5 4 3

**725 GREAT WESTERN RD   G12 8QX
01413 346265**

"The passion and intelligence in linking the food and wine is impressive" at this increasingly renowned destination in the West End. Founded in 2008 (and entering our guide in 2018), it won Glasgow's first Michelin star for 18 years in 2021 shortly after the appointment as chef of Lorna McGee (an Andrew Fairlie protégée). All reports acknowledge its "exceptional" cuisine, served from an eight-course tasting menu, and feel it's "fully deserving of its awards". "It's becoming more pricey", though, to the extent some fans "fear it's now becoming inaccessible even for those very special occasions". / www.cailbruich.co.uk; cailbruich; Tue-Sat midnight; closed Tue-Thu L, closed Sun & Mon; Cash & all usual cards; children: N/A.

CRABSHAKK   £57   4 3 4

**1114 ARGYLE ST, FINNIESTON   G3 8TD
0141 334 6127**

This intriguing and cramped venue (no surprise its owner is an architect) is "full of fun and just the freshest, simplest food – whole crabs and great fish" – a formula that has carried the Finnieston original since 2009 (it added a sibling this year, see also). "Be prepared to be very close to fellow diners, but it's so worth it for the totally awesome food". / www.crabshakk.com; crabshakkfinnieston; Mon, Wed-Sun midnight; closed Tue; No Amex.

CRABSHAKK BOTANICS   £64

**18 VINICOMBE STREET   G12 8BE
0141 530 4407**

John Macleod's late April 2022 newcomer – sibling to his popular Finnieston original – occupies the same beautiful, art deco Botanics garage building as Ka Pao (see also). It opened too late for feedback in our annual diners' poll, but in a June 2022 visit, Rosalind Erskine for The Scotsman declared: "what made the first Crabshakk stand the test of time can be found here too – quality food, cooked well and served with a smile – making it easy to imagine it soon being as big a Glasgow institution as the original". / www.crabshakk.co.uk/botanics-crabshakk; crabshakkbotanics; Tue-Sun midnight; closed Mon.

DAKHIN £33

89 CANDLERIGGS G1 1NP
0141 553 2585

Well-established (est. 2004) venue in the Merchant City that's mentioned in a (limited) number of reports as an exceptional all-rounder for its affordable and interesting introduction to the cuisine of south India. / www.dakhin.com; dakhinglasgow; Mon-Sun 10.30 pm; Cash & all usual cards.

EIGHTY EIGHT £41 3|3|3

88 DUMBARTON ROAD G11 6NX

Just along the road from Kelvingrove Museum, it's worth remembering this small-plates restaurant: the menu is inventive and all reports rate the results well. / 88glasgow.co.uk; 88glasgow; Mon & Tue 11 pm, Wed-Sun midnight; closed Mon & Tue L.

EUSEBI DELI £60 5|3|3

152 PARK ROAD G4 9HB 0141 648 9999

"Outstanding Italian cooking and pasticceria" plus some "very interesting wines" ("mainly Italian but the selection is a bit 'different" and includes a good variety by the glass) have won renown for this long-established (40 years plus) family-run deli/café near Kelvinbridge subway station. "There are great outdoor tables as well as on the ground floor… avoid the basement!" / eusebideli.com; eusebi_deli; Mon, Wed-Sun midnight; closed Tue; Cash & all usual cards.

GAGA £35 4|3|3

566 DUMBARTON ROAD G11 6RH
0141 334 9407

"The pan-Asian menu is limited but it's good stuff" at this collaboration between Julie Lin, owner of Julie's Kopitiam, and Marc Ferrier and Ken Hamilton of The Thornwood; originally a pop-up street-food stall during the summer of 2020. It serves small and larger sharing plates, plus a wide variety of cocktails. / www.gagaglasgow.com; gaga.glasgow; Mon-Sun midnight.

GAMBA £79 3|3|2

225A WEST GEORGE ST G2 2ND
0141 572 0899

Derek Marshall's "always excellent" – "if slightly difficult to find" – basement seafood spot celebrates its 25th anniversary this year. It's particularly noted for its "interesting good-value lunch". / www.gamba.co.uk; gambaglasgow; Wed-Fri 9 pm, Sat 10 pm; closed Mon & Tue & Sun; Cash & all usual cards; booking max 6 may apply.

THE GANNET £57 4|4|3

1155 ARGYLE ST G3 8TB 0141 2042081

"Good cooking and fair pricing… one of Glasgow's best!" – this casual Finnieston haunt celebrates its tenth year of operation in 2023. Chef Peter Mckenna aims to deliver a 'modern Scottish fine dining experience' via a multi-course tasting menu (or, if you go for lunch, there are two-course and three-course options).

"Staff are pleasant too… always love stopping here". / www.thegannetgla.com; thegannetgla; Wed, Fri-Sun, Thu 10.30 pm; closed Wed & Thu L, closed Mon & Tue; Cash & all usual cards.

HANOI BIKE SHOP £37 3|4|3

8 RUTHVEN LN G12 9BG 0141 334 7165

"A cheerful, inventive place" in the West End, "offering small dishes of Vietnamese street food: yummy!" – "an authentic-ish taste of 'Nam with student babble to make it more fun". / www.hanoibikeshop.co.uk; hanoibikeshop; Fri-Sun 11 pm; closed Mon-Wed & Thu.

HOOLIGAN £42

UPSTAIRS AT 1 LYNEDOCH STREET
G3 6EF 0141 352 9841

Open in autumn 2021, this quirkily named, natural-wine-focussed, sharing-plate restaurant occupies an old tenement flat, and its website promises a menu that "champions bright, bold flavours with a Mediterranean influence, using seasonal produce". No feedback yet, but in an early review, Rosalind Erskine of The Scotsman noted its "beautiful high ceilings, parquet floors, cornicing and large windows"; and said a visit was akin to "a very grown-up house party". She feels: "I bet it's here to stay". / www.hooliganwine.co.uk; Mon-Thu midnight, Fri & Sat 1 am, Sun 10 pm; closed Mon & Tue L.

KA PAO £25 4|3|3

BOTANIC GARDENS GARAGE, 26
VINICOMBE STREET G12 8BE
0141 483 6990

The "fresh, vibrant, exciting" flavours of Southeast Asia, using mainly Scottish produce, attract custom to this "superb venue" in the Botanical Gardens . Guests are "well looked after by staff", and the prices are attractive. A second branch opened last year in the St James Quarter of Edinburgh. / www.ka-pao.com; kapaofeeds; Mon-Sun midnight.

LOBO GLASGOW £26

758 POLLOKSHAWS ROAD G41 2AE
0141 423 5828

This Southside newcomer opened in late 2021 on the site of Gnom (RIP) and serves up Mediterranean small plates (as well as a dedicated vegan menu) inspired by the cuisines of Spain, Italy and France. No feedback as yet in our annual diners' poll, but in an August 2022 review, Rob Mackenna of The Herald hailed its "delicious small plates": "short, sharp flavour bombs exploding all over the palate". / www.loboglasgow.co.uk; loboglasgow; Wed-Sun 10 pm; closed Mon & Tue.

MOTHER INDIA £47 4|3|3

28 WESTMINSTER TER G3 8AD
0141 339 9145

"What a gem!" – "a must if you are in Glasgow". Monir & Smeena Mohammed opened their three-floor West End institution in 1990, scoring a hit with their "brilliant authentic Indian food", based on home-

cooked Punjabi dishes and all served at a notably "reasonable price". Top Tip – "the fantastic naan". / www.motherindiaglasgow.co.uk; officialmotherindia; Thu, Sun 9.45 pm, Fri & Sat 10 pm; closed Thu L, closed Mon & Tue & Wed; Cash & all usual cards.

111 BY MODOU £39 4|4|3

111 CLEVEDEN ROAD G12 0JU
0141 334 0111

"If you had a category for the 'best gastronomic value for money', then the 10-course tasting menu available at Modou on Mondays would really be hard to beat!" – Modou Diagne worked his way up through the ranks under Nico Simeone (of Six by Nico) and handed management of this former branch to Modou for him to run it. "His set course menu is exquisite and the competitive price means a fabulous atmosphere: young and old, filling the restaurant in a suburb. Some might feel that the food, and the cocktails, sometimes lack edge in terms of flavour, but this is a great place to spend an evening". And "he and his staff work exceptionally hard and always deliver". / 111bymodou.co.uk; 111bymodou; Mon, Thu-Sun 11 pm; closed Mon, Thu L, closed Tue & Wed.

OX AND FINCH £56 4|3|4

920 SAUCIEHALL ST G3 7TF
0141 339 8627

"Gutsy flavours" from an "eclectic, ever-changing and high-quality" menu of "varied and creative" dishes "never fail to impress" at Jonathan MacDonald's Kelvingrove gastropub, which regularly hits the heights. Its chilled and lively atmosphere is "brilliant" too. / www.oxandfinch.com; oxandfinch; Tue-Sun 1 am, Mon midnight; Cash & all usual cards.

PAESANO PIZZA £34 5|4|3

94 MILLER STREET G1 1DT
0141 258 5565

"You don't have to go to Naples" to find "great, reasonably priced pizza and excellent ice cream". This "very buzzy place in the centre of Glasgow" is "setting the standard for great, no-frills pizza". There is a second branch also in the city's West End, and owner Paul Stevenson also runs pasta specialist Sugo. / paesanopizza.co.uk; paesanopizzaglasgow; Sun-Thu 10.30 pm, Fri & Sat 11 pm; Cash & all usual cards.

ROGANO £67

11 EXCHANGE PLACE G1 3AN
0141 248 4055

Shuttered in September 2020 and marked as 'Permanently Closed' on Google, this city-centre fish and seafood institution is one of the city's best-known restaurants thanks in large part to its Art Deco interior, created in 1935 by the same craftsmen who fitted out the Queen Mary. According to an August 2022 report in the Glasgow Evening Times, it will re-open… but no-one seems to know when. / www.roganoglasgow.com; roganoglasgow; Mon-Sun 10 pm.

SHUCKS £54

168 HYNDLAND ROAD   G12 9HZ
0141 473 0080

The team behind Cail Bruich opened a seafood restaurant in Hyndland in March 2022 – their fourth site overall – serving up fresh Scottish produce with Champagne and cocktails. No reports as yet in our late spring annual diners' poll, but in The Scotsman, Gaby Soutar reviewed it as an "excellently-named" newcomer, praising its rather lovely interior, with a smallish bar downstairs and a smart mezzanine level, where you can see their coppery fish scale wall art. On-the-bone Shetland plaice was "downy and perfect, like eating oceanic candyfloss". / www.shucksglasgow.com; shucks_glasgow; Mon-Sat midnight, Sun 10 pm; closed Mon-Thu L.

STRAVAIGIN £58 3 3 2

28 GIBSON ST   G12 8NX   0141 334 2665

As it approaches its 30th anniversary, Colin Clydesdale and Carol Wright's bar/restaurant remains a well-known local icon for Glasgow foodies, but has never inspired matching interest in our annual diners' poll. Its motto of 'Think Global, Eat Local' has held up very well over the years, with its eclectic mixture of 'world food' from Scottish ingredients having proved well ahead of its time. / www.stravaigin.co.uk; stravaigin_g12; Tue, Fri-Sun midnight; closed Tue L, closed Mon, Wed & Thu; No Amex.

TWO FAT LADIES AT THE BUTTERY £67 3 4 5

652 ARGYLE ST   G3 8UF   0141 221 8188

This "superb" Glasgow institution from Ryan James makes brilliant use of a classic Victorian interior (one of the city's more historic interiors). "The only criticism is that the menu is on the 'traditional' side" – although that might seem appropriate to the site – "but you cannot fault the execution and the attention to detail". / twofatladiesrestaurant.com/buttery; twofatladiesatthebuttery; Tue-Sat 10.30 pm, Sun 10 pm; closed Mon; Cash & all usual cards.

UBIQUITOUS CHIP £68 3 3 5

12 ASHTON LN   G12 8SJ   0141 334 5007

A "Glasgow institution" in the city's West End, established in 1971 by Ronnie Clydesdale and now run by his son Colin. It is "still a great place for food, atmosphere and good company", whether in the main restaurant, the brasserie or one of its four bars. "Hadn't been back for ages until this month – excellent" – although naturally there have been changes over the years, such as "the new tasting menu" showcasing top-class Scottish ingredients. / www.ubiquitouschip.co.uk; ubiquitous_chip; Mon-Sun 1 am; Cash & all usual cards; children: No restrictions in dining areas..

UNALOME BY GRAEME CHEEVERS £123 5 4 3

36 KELVINGROVE STREET   G3 7RZ
0141 564 1157

"A really wonderful dining experience" – ex-Isle of Eriska chef Graeme Cheevers's ambitious Finnieston yearling was "well deserving of its Michelin star" within eight months of opening, for its "immaculate dishes, beautifully served", "exceptional service" and "great and highly accessible wine list": "Glasgow needed a lunch like this". The name? – apparently it's a Buddhist symbol representing the path to enlightenment. / www.unalomebygc.com; unalomebygc; Wed-Sun 10.30 pm; closed Mon & Tue.

GLINTON, RUTLAND   6–4A

THE BLUE BELL £53 3 3 3

10 HIGH STREET   PE6 7LS   01733 252285

Will and Kelly Frankgate celebrate their tenth year at this attractively located and extended village gastropub in 2023. It only induced limited feedback again this year, but once again of the good all-round variety. / www.thebluebellglinton.co.uk; Wed-Sat 8.45 pm; closed Mon & Tue & Sun; Cash & all usual cards.

GLOSSOP, GREATER MANCHESTER 5–2C

HYSSOP

54 HIGH STREET WEST   SK13 8BH
01457 861054

Fooderati insider Thom Hetherington was amongst those sending out an SOS on behalf of this well-regarded neighbourhood restaurant in his hometown, which was gutted by fire in September 2022. By the end of the month it had crowdfunded the money to re-open and restore its mix of funky small plates (typically you would order 7-8 in a meal), plus gins, cocktails and a thoughtful small selection of wines. / hyssopglossop; Mon-Sun 10 pm.

GOATHLAND, NORTH YORKSHIRE   8–4C

THE HOMESTEAD KITCHEN £50 4 3 3

PRUDOM HOUSE   YO22 5AN
01947 896191

"A great addition to the North Yorkshire Moors dining scene", this yearling from well-known local chef Peter Foster (latterly co-owner of The Pheasant in Harome), occupies a site in his partner Cecily Fearnley's home village ("beautiful journey over the moors to get there"), and it's already "getting increasingly difficult to book a table". Even a reporter who feels that it's "not quite firing on all cylinders yet", thought it's "already producing great food to a high standard, with lots of potential". / www.thehomesteadgoathland.com; homestead_goathland; Wed-Sat 8.30 pm; closed Mon & Tue & Sun.

GORING-ON-THAMES, OXFORDSHIRE   2–2D

DON GIOVANNI AT THE LEATHERNE BOTTEL £81

BRIDLE WAY   RG8 0HS   01491 872667

"A brilliant location" – on a picture-perfect stretch of lush Thames riverbank – is the justification for maintaining the listing of this Thames Valley veteran, on the fringe of Goring. On a sunny day, there are few nicer places to be. Its "classic Italian menu"? Not much commented on (nor, to be fair, criticised) and not the main point. / www.leathernebottel.co.uk; don_giovanni_goring; Mon-Sat 10.30 pm, Sun 3 pm; closed Sun D; Cash & all usual cards; children: 10+ for D.

GOUDHURST, KENT   3–4C

THE SMALL HOLDING £104 5 4 4

RANTERS LANE, KILNDOWN   TN17 2SG
01892 890105

Widely acclaimed for its hyper-localism since opening in 2018 – this "fabulous little restaurant serves imaginative small plates of very locally sourced ingredients", many of them grown on the smallholding after which it was named, or foraged nearby. Kent-born chef, Will Devlin qualified as a mechanic before switching to the kitchen, and trained at Gordon Ramsay's Petrus. He also runs The Curlew (see also), eight miles away in Bodiam. / thesmallholding. restaurant; the_small_holding_; Thu-Sat, Wed 11.30 pm, Sun 4 pm; closed Wed L closed Sun D, closed Mon & Tue; children: 12.

GRANDTULLY, PERTH AND KINROSS   9–3C

THE GRANDTULLY HOTEL BY BALLINTAGGART £45 3 3 3

PH9 0PX   01887 447000

This rejuvenated Victorian railway hotel 10 miles south of Pitlochry now serves "tasty and imaginative food, with good wine choices to match", since being taken over by the team behind the nearby Ballintaggart Farm cookery school. / www.ballintaggart.com/grandtully-hotel; ballintaggart; closed Mon-Sat & Sun.

GRANTLEY, YORKSHIRE   8–4B

FLETCHERS AT GRANTLEY HALL £64 3 4 4

HG4 3ET   01765 620070

"A special place surrounded by manicured lawns and with a helicopter pad for departure" – this very plush Yorkshire five star also has a brasserie option to Shaun Rankin at Grantley Hall (see also), that is uniformly well-rated in reports. (It almost didn't pass the Jay Rayner test though, as – in February 2022 – he declared it "confused and asphyxiatingly expensive" for what it is, with "exhaustingly fussy presentation"; he did, though, admit to encountering "some of the very best examples

Sorrel, Dorking

of detailed patisserie work it has been my pleasure to experience in a long time"). / www.grantleyhall.co.uk; grantley_; Wed-Sat 8.30 pm, Sun 8 pm; closed Wed-Sat L, closed Mon & Tue.

SHAUN RANKIN AT GRANTLEY HALL £171 4 4 5

HG4 3ET   01765 620070

"Great for a romantic meal or a special occasion" – Valeria Sykes's "gorgeous" country-house hotel, opened three years ago after a £70 million makeover, showcases the skills of chef Shaun Rankin, returning to his native Yorkshire after making his name with Ormer in the Channel Islands and London. The food is "second to none" – "thoroughly enjoyable!". Top Tip – "they mix their own tea and I haven't been able to match the taste of their oolong blend – the best tea I have ever had!". / www.grantleyhall.co.uk; grantley_; Mon-Fri 7.30 pm, Sat & Sun 5.30 pm; closed Sat & Sun D.

GRASMERE, CUMBRIA   7–3D

THE FOREST SIDE £158 5 5 4

LA22 9RN   01539 435 250

Especially when viewed as an all-round experience, Andrew Wildsmith's luxurious hotel is one of the highlights of Lakeland and indeed UK gastronomy – "the food rates mention next to that of L'Enclume, but the beautiful surroundings raise it even higher as an experience" for some fans and "all aspects are balanced perfectly with a relaxed atmosphere". "Top-quality ingredients are cooked superbly" by chef Paul Leonard and his team, who "continue to impress with excellent food that's not too foamy, and matched with top-notch wine pairings". And the option of a 4-course menu alongside the 8-course one frees you from the tyranny of the tasting menu format; although the latter inspired the odd gripe this year of portions that were "too minimal". Quibbles overall were few, though, and for most diners here "the ideal number of times to visit is the current number of times you have visited… plus one!" / www.theforestside.com; the_forest_side; Wed-Sun 9 pm; closed Mon & Tue; children: Any Age for Lunch & 8Yrs for Dinner.

THE JUMBLE ROOM £70 3 3 3

LANGDALE ROAD   LA22 9SU
01539 435 188

Over a quarter of a century old, Chrissy & Andy Hill's village restaurant continues to inspire approving reviews: "service is very good and friendly and the food is good middle-of-the-road fare: perfect for when you need to eat on holiday". As their website confirms, they are "feeling the staffing pressures with more limited opening times" of late. / www.thejumbleroom.co.uk; thejumbleroom; Thu-Sat 11 pm; closed Thu-Sat L, closed Mon-Wed & Sun; Cash & all usual cards.

THE YAN £40 3 3 3

BROADRAYNE FARM   LA22 9RU
015394 35055

"Well-cooked food", most notably the Grasmere Herdwick lamb that appears in various guises – the signature shepherds' pie, a slider in a brioche bun, a Greek-style roast shoulder – is par for the course at this family-run restaurant-with-rooms. Breakfast is a particular hit, too. / www.theyan.co.uk; yanatbroadrayne; Mon-Sun 8.45 pm.

GREAT GONERBY, LINCOLNSHIRE 5–3D

HARRY'S PLACE £104 5 5 2

17 HIGH STREET   NG31 8JS
01476 561780

This "unique and magical" venture sees Harry & Caroline Hallam welcoming a maximum of 10 guests into the front room of their elegant townhouse for a "beautifully cooked" meal, chosen from a small handwritten menu – as they've done now for more than 30 years (long before the term 'pop-up' was invented). Harry's pitch-perfect cuisine follows the Anglo-European tradition established by writers such as Elizabeth David and Jane Grigson – a style that never really goes out of fashion. Reporters were thrilled at the resumption of service following the pandemic: "it's great to have you back, Harry!" / Tue-Sat 9.30 pm; closed Sun & Mon; No Amex; children: 5.

GREAT HASELEY, OXFORDSHIRE 2–2D

LA TABLE D'ALIX AT THE PLOUGH 4 4 4

RECTORY ROAD   OX44 7JQ
01844 279283

Antoine & Camille Chretien have created a "wonderful French atmosphere" at their "excellent and genuine" bistro-pub (named after their son) in an Oxfordshire village – "a wonderful place to take your loved ones and be spoilt by a well-chosen menu and wine list, and great hosts, away from all the hustle and bustle". It's a "very welcome – and "good value" – addition to this part of the world" – and exactly a mile away from Raymond Blanc's Le Manoir Aux Quat'Saisons (Antoine once worked for his 'old friend' Raymond at Brasserie Blanc in Oxford). / latabledalix.co.uk; Thu-Sat 11 pm, Sun 6 pm; closed Sun D, closed Mon & Tue & Wed.

GREAT MILTON, OXFORDSHIRE 2–2D

BELMOND LE MANOIR AUX QUAT' SAISONS, BELMOND £269 5 5 5

CHURCH ROAD   OX44 7PD   01844 278881

"Go on, spoil yourself!". This "fabulous" fifteenth-century manor house is regularly the most commented-on destination outside London in our annual diners' poll, and consistently one of the highest rated. Founded by Raymond Blanc in 1984, he remains its public face, although ownership nowadays is in the hands of LVMH and the executive head chef is Gary Jones. A visit here often starts with a tour ("so interesting!") around the "spectacular and peaceful" grounds and kitchen gardens: TV star Blanc helped pioneer the current vogue for sustainable produce grown on-site, and herbs and veg from the gardens regularly feature in the dishes. Gradual expansion has created over 23 bedrooms and suites, and "for a special occasion, especially a romantic one", a night away here is many couples' first choice ("words cannot describe the joy this place brings to my wife and me"… "It's an annual pilgrimage just to reset the benchmark of what dining perfection should be"). As an all-round experience, it's hard to match. "You are made to feel special the second you set foot inside"; a spell in the "cosy" lounges bookends a meal with aperitifs and coffee; and "the finishing touches are what makes dining here such a pleasure". Since Covid, the only option now is a tasting menu format. Some long-time guests miss the à la carte, although the classical-ish modern French cuisine is almost invariably still applauded for its "complete culinary precision" and "exceptional" flavours ("one of the best meals we have ever eaten… we ran out of superlatives!"). Opinions vary on whether the best tables are those in the dining conservatory, or elsewhere in the body of the house and extensions. Even fans caution: "be in no doubt that the trip is very, very expensive" (in particular, there are "enormous mark-ups on the wine list", which is as heavyweight as you might expect). But they still recommend a trip "goes on the bucket list"… "Yes! you are worth it!!". (Watch this space, as some change is afoot. In July 2022 the local council approved a plan for a £36m expansion at the property, to lead ultimately to a bistro, spa and new garden suites – the aim being to encourage guests to extend their stay). / www.manoir.com; belmondlemanoir; Mon-Sun 9.30 pm; closed Mon L; Cash & all usual cards; booking max 12 may apply.

GREAT OXENDON, NORTHUMBERLAND 5–4D

THE GEORGE £56 3 3 3

HARBOROUGH ROAD   LE16 8NA
01858 465205

"Very consistent, high-quality pub food" is on the menu at this sixteenth-century village inn-with-rooms south of Market Harborough that was modernised in a two-year refurbishment a few years back. Owners Stephen and Tracy Fitzpatrick also run the Joiners Arms at Bruntingthorpe (see also). / www.thegeorgegreatoxendon.co.uk; thegeorgegreatoxendon; Mon-Fri 8.30 pm, Sat 9 pm, Sun 3 pm; closed Sun D.

GREAT SHEFFORD, BERKSHIRE 2–2C

THE GREAT SHEFFORD £85 3 3 3

NEWBURY ROAD   RG17 7DS
01488 648462

Complete with a riverside terrace, this privately owned pub near Newbury receives a good rep in our annual diners' poll for its 40-seat dining room overlooking the river Lambourn, where chef Sam Cary aims to deliver 'refined modern

British pub food'. In an April 2022 visit, Tatler's Fay Maschler declared it "a rare jewel of a country pub" offering "everything you want a welcome to be". / www.thegreatshefford.com; thegreatsheffordpub; Mon-Thu 9 pm, Fri & Sat 9.30 pm, Sun 7 pm.

GREAT WALTHAM, ESSEX   3–2C

GALVIN GREEN MAN   £58   3 3 3

HOWE ST   CM3 1BG   01245 408 820

"Highly recommend for a slice of London in the heart of Essex" – the Galvin brothers' "large gastropub" (dating from the 14th century) "in a lovely Essex village" is one of the most commented-on destinations in our annual diners' poll. And it draws fans from across the county as well as from 'The Smoke' for a run-out. One "splendid lunch" included "torched mackerel fillet, a top burger, lovely wood-roasted skate wing in beurre noisette, lemon posset", typifying the kind of superior "everyday" food that secures its fanbase, and staff who are "always friendly and helpful" is another recurring theme. Top Tip – for parents, there's a big garden with a play area. / www.galvingreenman.com; galvingreenman; Thu, Wed 8 pm, Fri & Sat 10 pm, Sun 5 pm; closed Wed L closed Sun D, closed Mon & Tue; Cash & all usual cards.

GREEN QUARTER, GREATER MANCHESTER   5–2B

THE SPÄRROWS CONTINENTAL PASTA & SPÄTZLE   £49   4 4 3

16 RED BANK   M4 4HF   0161 302 6267

This "unusual and unique find" – "hidden away in a railway arch near Manchester's Victoria Station" – offers "a wide selection of pasta and dumplings from south Germany, Switzerland, Alsace, Austria and the German-speaking parts of northern Italy", washed down with an interesting variety of beers, wines and Japanese alcoholic drinks. Even the occasional critic who finds it "not entirely to my liking" concedes that "the very interesting menu has good and unusual food". The same team is scheduled to open a sake bar and shop called Suzume. / www.thesparrows.me; sparrows_mcr; Tue-Sat 11 pm, Sun 10 pm; closed Tue-Fri L, closed Mon.

GREETHAM, RUTLAND   5–3D

THE WHEATSHEAF   £56   3 3 2

STRETTON RD   LE15 7NP   01572 812325

"The Wheatsheaf is almost a Rutland institution now", after 15 years under Carol & Scott Craddock. The Grade II-listed village pub is "a byword for quality cooking" – "the smell of freshly baked bread and the buzz of happy, smiling customers tells you that this is a fine local restaurant". "Lockdown provided an opportunity for some interior redecoration and tasteful additions, resulting in an interior almost as fine as the welcome". / www.wheatsheaf-greetham.co.uk; wheatsheafgreetham; Wed-Sat 11 pm, Sun 7 pm; closed Mon & Tue; Cash & all usual cards.

GRESFORD, WREXHAM   5–3A

PANT-YR-OCHAIN   £53   3 4 4

OLD WREXHAM ROAD   LL12 8TY   01978 853525

This "cracking pub" – a spacious and rambling sixteenth-century inn from the Brunning & Price group – feels "like having your own country club!". It's "very comfortable, with good beers" and "excellent ever-changing food served in generally substantial portions", plus "warm service and a big garden for the kids to run around in". / www.brunningandprice.co.uk/pantyrochain; pantyrochain; Mon-Sat 11 pm, Sun 10.30 pm; Cash & all usual cards.

GUERNSEY, CHANNEL ISLANDS   –

CHINA RED   £52   3 3 2

34 SAINT GEORGE'S ESPLANADE   GY1 2BG   01481 723888

A "very good" Chinese spot on the esplanade that wins solid ratings and is particularly strong on its fish and seafood options. There's also a "rare-to-find" selection of "authentic and delicious Sichuan dishes", including spicy hotpots. / www.chinared.gg; china_red_gsy; Tue-Sun 11 pm; closed Tue-Fri L, closed Mon.

DA NELLO   £53   3 3 4

46 LE POLLET   GY1 1WF   01481 721 552

In the heart of the town, this traditional Italian stalwart (est. 1978) comprises a small dining room, with glass atrium. It doesn't generate a huge volume of feedback, but such as there is continues to praise its good cooking (fish in particular) and inviting style. / www.danello.gg; Mon-Sun 10 pm; Cash & all usual cards.

THE HOOK   £66   3 3 3

N PLANTATION   GY1 2QL   01481 701373

"An excellent selection of Japanese sushi" is served alongside "very good steak and always fresh fish" at this two-floor operation, where "the main restaurant is on the first floor" (with ace views of the harbour) and "with a bar serving lighter dishes on the ground floor". It's a stylish, casual operation, with good cocktails too. / www.thehook.gg; Tue-Sat 10 pm; closed Sun & Mon.

GUILDFORD, SURREY   3–3A

THE IVY ASIA GUILDFORD   £85   3 2 4

UNIT 23 TUNSGATE QUARTER   GU1 3QT   01483 958880

Its "enviable position" in the Tunsgate Quarter, a stone's throw from Guildford cathedral, and the "lack of other decent options locally" helped generate a "stampede" amongst locals to visit this glossy new venue (with trademark illuminated floors) from Richard Caring's slick pan-Asian spin-off brand when it opened last year. The "fabulously presented sushi" and "lovely atmosphere" won early praise, but there is the odd query regarding the "chunky" prices.

/ www.theivyasiaguildford.com; theivyasiaguildford; Sun-Fri 12.30 am; closed Sat.

THE IVY CASTLE VIEW   £77   3 3 4

TUNSGATE SQUARE, 98-100 HIGH STREET GU1 3HE   01483920100

By most accounts "one of the better Ivy Cafés" – there are "no real surprises", "but it's well executed and a fun place in a nice location"; "if the weather's pleasant you can sit on the balcony". / www.theivyguildford.com; theivyguildford; Sun-Thu midnight, Fri & Sat 12.30 am.

RUMWONG   £36   3 4 4

18-20 LONDON RD   GU1 2AF   01483 536092

"Always reliable and hard to beat" for its "wonderful food", this "bustling and enjoyable" Thai has been a local hotspot for four decades. "If you're looking for a different experience, sit on cushions at the low-level table in the separate 'Khan Tok' dining room". / www.rumwong.co.uk; Mon-Sun 11 pm; Cash & all usual cards.

THE THAI TERRACE   £55   3 3 3

CASTLE CAR PK, SYDENHAM RD GU1 3RW   01483 503350

A "stunning location… from a car park rooftop!" provides "amazing views over Guildford and the hills beyond" at this long-established fixture, known for its "wide selection of quality Thai dishes". / thaiterrace.co.uk; crgthaiterrace; Mon-Sat 10.30 pm; closed Sun; No Amex.

GULLANE, EAST LOTHIAN   9–4D

THE BONNIE BADGER   £78   3 3 4

MAIN STREET   EH31 2AB   01626 21111

"A very stylish pub/restaurant with rooms" run by Edinburgh restaurant royalty, Tom & Michaela Kitchin, where the "food comes with a distinctly Scottish bias and the atmosphere and service are friendly". "Very nice outside area with a BBQ for those days in Scotland when the weather permits". / bonniebadger.com; bonniebadgergullane; Mon-Sun 10 pm.

GULWORTHY, DEVON   1–3C

THE HORN OF PLENTY, COUNTRY HOUSE HOTEL & RESTAURANT   £88   3 2 3

COUNTRY HOUSE HOTEL & RESTAURANT PL19 8JD   01822 832528

This "long established hideaway on the Devon/Cornwall border" offers "modern British cooking using local ingredients with flair and imagination". There are "fabulous views of Tamar Valley from the dining room", and service is "enthusiastic, if sometimes a little untrained". / www.thehornofplenty.co.uk; Mon-Sun 9 pm; Cash & all usual cards; No jeans.

HAIGHTON MANOR £34 3 2 3

**HAIGHTON GREEN LANE   PR2 5SQ
01772 706350**

"Popular pub restaurant in a lovely rural setting that serves quality pub meals, both in its traditional dining areas and outside in the large conservatory and garden area". "The food's always good, and it's a relaxing place to meet up and enjoy a meal in the countryside, not too far from the centre of Preston". / www.brunningandprice.co.uk/haightonmanor; haightonmanor; Mon-Thu 10.30 pm, Fri & Sat 11 pm, Sun 10 pm.

SIGIRIYA £61 3 3 2

**173 ASHLEY ROAD   WA15 9SD
0161 941 3025**

"My Sri Lankan colleague rates it as the closest thing he's found to his mum's cooking!" – Don Buddhika's local restaurant has brought some unusually authentic cooking to this chichi Manchester 'burb. / sigiriya.co.uk; sigiriyahale; Tue, Sun 10 pm, Wed & Thu 10.30 pm, Fri & Sat 11 pm; closed Tue L, closed Mon.

SHIBDEN MILL INN £61 4 3 4

**SHIBDEN MILL FOLD   HX3 7UL
01422 365840**

"Beautiful old Yorkshire inn" – originally an eighteenth-century corn and spinning mill – that hosts "some seriously excellent cooking" from chef Will Webster. It's a "fabulous and cosy spot" – in a place made famous by TV's 'Gentleman Jack' – "and best of all there's no mobile phone reception, so you can escape the world for a couple of hours of peace!". Top Menu Tip – "breaded lamb spam and lamb-fat peas". / www.shibdenmillinn.com; shibdenmillinn; Mon-Fri 11 pm, Sat 11.30 pm, Sun 10.30 pm; Cash & all usual cards.

FINCH'S ARMS £50 2 2 3

OAKHAM RD   LE15 8TL   01572 756575

A "lovely old pub" in scenic Hambleton near Rutland Water that's "at its best if one eats in the bar and older part of the building, in front of a log fire (the newer additions seem less appealing)". Over many years, it's provided "a classic 'curate's egg' experience. It has a great location and if all goes well it's a great experience. But sadly service and quality can vary quite a lot. And, as is the case for many establishments today, they no longer wish to offer a simple single lunch dish – good for their profitability but less good for the casual diner". At best, the food's "interesting". At worst "service is awful, and as to the view from the dining room… well, there is no view!". Whatever your experience, "there are lovely walks from the pub to walk it off!" / www.finchsarms.co.uk; thefinchsarms; Mon-Sat 9 pm, Sun 8 pm; Cash & all usual cards.

HAMBLETON HALL £129 5 5 5

LE15 8TH   01572 756991

"On a hot day there is the terrace with its glorious views over the water. On a cooler day, it's time for the comfy seats by the log fire. Whatever the weather, there is always a top quality meal to be had" at this "stunning" country house hotel (back in the day, owned by the Hoare banking family, and which actually pre-dates the surrounding reservoir, created in 1975, by many decades). Its "opulent" lounges and dining room epitomise "old-fashioned elegance" and provide "the quietest and most relaxing environment". Staff are "professional but very friendly" and "go above and beyond to provide a memorable and enjoyable experience". Chef Aaron Patterson has been at the stoves for a remarkable three decades and his cuisine "tends towards the traditional but is none the worse for that". It's superb quality but not showy food – "his deft touch lets the locally sourced, seasonal, food sing, rather than the chef!". Owner Tim Hart (whose sons run Quo Vadis, Barrafina, El Pastor, etc in the capital) has amassed a fine wine list and "they have started providing some of their brilliant

cellar wines by the glass, a great opportunity to experiment". For a romantic stay in particular, it's "truly wonderful and well worth the cost". / www.hambletonhall.com; hambleton_hall; Mon-Sun 8.45 pm; Cash & all usual cards; children: 5.

SMOKE AT HAMPTON MANOR 3 4 4

**SHADOWBROOK LANE   B92 0EN
01675 446080**

Launched in late 2021, an old Victorian furnace house on the edge of the Manor's walled garden provides the venue for this relatively informal operation, where MasterChef: The Professionals winner, Stuart Deeley, cooks over coals. It was the most popular option at the property this year, although one report felt that "while the BBQ was perfectly good, it needed elevating to meet its aspirations". / hamptonmanor.com/smoke; hamptonmanor; Wed-Sat 8.30 pm; closed Wed-Sat L, closed Mon & Tue & Sun.

GRACE & SAVOUR £149

**HAMPTON MANOR, SHADOWBROOK LANE
B92 0EN   01675 446080**

Launched in early 2022, this very 'now' operation is built into the walls of Hampton Manor's Victorian Garden and promises an immersive sustainable dining experience built around a fifteen-course tasting menu served from an open kitchen, where (according to the website) 'every choice is a commitment to soil health, biodiversity, ethics and sustainability'. At the stoves, your hosts for the evening chef David Taylor with his wife Anette on FOH. There's also the option for an overnight stay in the Walled Garden, incorporating a kitchen garden tour, a 'bedroom lounge' with views of the open kitchen and 'bath time ritual that celebrates the scent of the garden designed by local organic apothecarists'. Limited feedback so far, but it's an instant favourite for one early reporter who thought it "outstanding all-round" (and in Autumn 2022, the AA awarded it a rare four rosettes). / hamptonmanor.com; hamptonmanor; Thu-Sat midnight; closed Thu-Sat L, closed Mon-Wed & Sun.

PEEL'S, HAMPTON MANOR £146

**HAMPTON MANOR, SHADOWBROOK LANE
B92 0EN   01675 446080**

Too limited feedback this year for a rating of this flagship dining room, whose many accolades have established it as a bastion of the Midlands hospitality scene. The property is currently emerging from major investment under long-term owners, the Hills, who have recently added 'Smoke' and 'Grace & Savour' – see also. / www.hamptonmanor.com; hamptonmanor; Tue-Sat 9 pm; closed Tue-Sat L, closed Sun & Mon; children: 12.

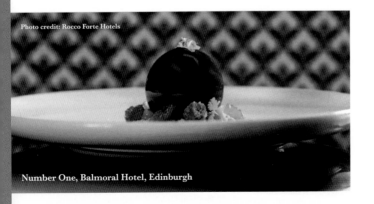

Photo credit: Rocco Forte Hotels

Number One, Balmoral Hotel, Edinburgh

THE PIG AT HARLYN BAY £79 **4**|**4**|**5**

PL28 8SQ 01841 550240

"Just excellent" – "laid-back yet friendly service combined with good ticks all the boxes" at this "buzzy" Cornish operation, this year's highest-scoring member of Robin Hutson's shabby-chic Pig hotel group. Chef Adam Bristow's "delicious, locally sourced menu at a great price" avoids some of the inconsistencies that mar the food offering at sister Pigs, while the "great old building" – a substantial fifteenth-century house with decor inspired by Wolf Hall – and "great surroundings" with Padstow and Rock close by, complete the appeal. / www.thepighotel.com/at-harlyn-bay; thepig_hotel; Sun-Fri 6 pm, Sat 7.30 pm.

THE PHEASANT HOTEL £88 **3**|**4**|**3**

YO62 5JG 01439 771241

"A superb country restaurant with rooms", "very well run" by Jacquie Pern, whose former husband Andrew runs the neighbouring Star Inn in the same small North Yorkshire village. / www.thepheasanthotel.com; thepheasant_hotel; Mon-Sun 9 pm; No Amex.

THE STAR INN £93

HAROME YO62 5JE 01439 770397

Reopened in late 2022 after being gutted by a disastrous fire that swept through its ancient thatch a year earlier, this 14th-century inn is, for many people, "one of my favourite places to eat in the UK" – "the staff ooze Northern charm and make you feel very welcome", while "patron Andrew Pern and his incredible team, including head chef Steve Smith and restaurant manager Eve Cullen, ensure a wonderful experience every time". "Love how they offer 'Michelin' cuisine but also a locals' menu which is accessible to a wider audience" – "love it so much, we got married here!". Top Tip – "the black pudding and foie gras is a best-ever dish". / www.thestaratharome.co.uk; Mon-Fri 8.30 pm, Sat 9 pm, Sun 6 pm; closed Mon L closed Sun D; No Amex.

LUSSMANNS £53 **2**|**2**|**3**

20A LEYTON ROAD AL5 2HU 01582 965393

"Very good all round at this price" and now "back on form after an inconsistent couple of years", Andrei Lussmann's converted eighteenth-century coach house is "a reliable choice for a decent meal out in an otherwise unexceptional culinary town". It is part of a five-strong Herts-based group (Berkhamsted the most recently opened) with a strong emphasis on sustainable fish. / www.lussmanns.com/restaurants/harpenden-restaurants; andrei_lussmann; Tue-Thu

9 pm, Fri & Sat 10 pm, Sun 7 pm; closed Mon; Cash & all usual cards.

THE SILVER CUP £95 **4**|**4**|**3**

5 ST ALBANS ROAD AL5 2JF 01582 713095

It looks like a fairly typical roadside pub (with rooms), but this two-year-old venue beside Harpenden Common from local lads Matthew Reader (chef) and Michael Singleton is a distinct cut above. You get "very good cooking from a local team who are serious about delivering a quality experience in an area not known for the quality of its eateries". / www.thesilvercup.co.uk; thesilvercup; Wed-Sat 11 pm, Sun 9 pm; closed Mon & Tue.

BALTZERSENS £18 **3**|**3**|**2**

HG1 1PU 01423 202363

This "quirky café with wonderful cinnamon buns and waffles" offers a "real taste of Scandinavia in Harrogate". It's "very popular with yummy-mummies in the morning so can get a little loud, but you can buy all the baked goods from their shop just by the theatre". Owner Paul Rawlinson's Scandi restaurant Norse is still missed, five years after its closure. / www.baltzersens.co.uk; baltzersens; Mon-Sun 4 pm; closed Mon-Sun D; no bookings; children: N/A.

BETTYS £43 **3**|**4**|**5**

1 PARLIAMENT STREET HG1 2QU 01423 814070

"Betty's is a real institution in Harrogate" of over a century's standing, and as the home of "traditional afternoon tea at its best" these "quintessential" tea rooms are peerless (they are "masters of the art of making a visit memorable"). "Amazing cakes and pastries are made on the premises and served alongside a wonderful selection of teas", in a "stunning" setting enlivened by a pianist tinkling away on the ivories in the background. "Thoughtful, delicious and with no unnecessary frills: this is Yorkshire through and through". "You cannot book so turn up early". / www.bettys.co.uk/cafe-tea-rooms/our-locations/bettys-harrogate; bettys; Mon-Sun 5 pm; closed Mon-Sun D; No Amex; no bookings.

BETTYS GARDEN CAFÉ, RHS GARDENS HARLOW CARR £39 **4**|**4**|**4**

CRAG LANE, BECKWITHSHAW HG3 1QB 01423 505604

"The view out over the RHS gardens is especially pretty in the spring and makes a lovely backdrop to the central European savouries and expertly rendered pastries and cakes" at this outpost of the well-known local group. "Bettys is a Yorkshire tradition for a reason!"… it's "just lovely" for a fancy tea (or breakfast). / www.bettys.co.uk; bettys; Mon-Sun 5 pm; closed Mon-Sun D; Cash & all usual cards.

CLOCKTOWER RESTAURANT, RUDDING PARK HOTEL **3**|**3**|**3**

RUDDING PK, FOLLIFOOT HG3 1JH 01423 871350

Open from an early breakfast to dinner, the modern brasserie at this Georgian stately home near Harrogate wins solid ratings across the board. Afternoon tea can be taken in the Conservatory, while Horto restaurant next door provides the destination's fine-dining option. / www.ruddingpark.co.uk/clocktower-restaurant; ruddingparkhotel; Tue-Sun 9 pm, Mon 10 pm; closed Mon L; Cash & all usual cards.

DRUM & MONKEY £59 **4**|**4**|**3**

5 MONTPELLIER GDNS HG1 2TF 01423 502650

This "wonderful stalwart of Yorkshire dining" is, to its many fans, "a mainstay of any visit to Harrogate" for its fabulous fish and "attentive service". Founded in 1971, it has been run for the past 10 years by Ray & June Carter of the Sportsman's Arms in Wath-in-Nidderdale – under whose ownership it "never disappoints". / www.drumandmonkey.co.uk; drumandmonkeyhgte; Mon-Fri 9 pm, Sat 9.30 pm; closed Sun; No Amex; booking max 10 may apply.

ORCHID £56 **3**|**3**|**2**

28 SWAN ROAD HG1 2SE 01423 560 425

The "amazing pan-Asian food" has been a crowd-pleaser at this venue under the Studley Hotel for more than twenty years. "The room itself is perhaps a little drab, but boy the food is good" – "we've been coming for years and it still has the best Weeping Tiger we've ever eaten!". "Pity the Sunday buffet has gone", though. / www.orchidrestaurant.co.uk; studleyandorchid; Sun-Thu 8.30 pm, Fri & Sat 9.30 pm; closed Mon-Thu, Sat L; Cash & all usual cards.

SASSO £55 **3**|**4**|**4**

8-10 PRINCES SQUARE HG1 1LX 01423 508 838

Chef-owner Stefano Lancellotti and his wife Sara Ferguson celebrate the 25th anniversary of their highly rated restaurant this year. Named after his home town in Emilia Romagna, it brings an authentic taste of the region to Yorkshire – even the eggs are imported to create pasta as it should be. / www.sassorestaurant.co.uk; Mon-Thu 9 pm, Sat, Fri 10 pm; closed Sun.

STARLING £21 **3**|**3**|**3**

47 OXFORD STREET HG1 1PW 01423 531310

"Terrific breakfast and brunch", "excellent coffee", "brilliant beers and pizzas, plus more healthy fare" – all win high praise for this "independent bar, café, kitchen", which opened in 2016. "It's a flexible haunt, and a great place to work too, with fab music!" / www.murmurationbars.co.uk; StarlingHgte; Mon-Wed 10 pm, Thu, Sun 11 pm; closed Fri & Sat.

STUZZI £53 433

46B KINGS ROAD   HG1 5JW
01423 705852

Named after the 'stuzzichini' or snacks served in Venetian osterias, this "fantastic but quirky" spot serves an "ever-changing menu of authentic Italian" small plates. "The place is often buzzing", with a "friendly and casual atmosphere", "fabulous pasta", and a "very well selected, reasonably priced wine list". / stuzzi. co.uk; stuzziharrogate; Wed-Sat 11 pm, Sun 8 pm; closed Mon & Tue; Cash & all usual cards.

SUKHOTHAI 333

17-19 CHELTENHAM PDE   HG1 1DD
01423 500 869

"Always a vibrant dining experience!" – Ban Kaewkraikhot's outpost of her Yorkshire group of traditional Thai venues (which started in Chapel Allerton in 2002) continues to draw a regular fan club for its comprehensive menu of authentic-tasting dishes. / sukhothai.co.uk; sukhothai_; Sun-Thu 10 pm, Fri & Sat 11 pm; closed Sun-Thu-Sat L; Cash & all usual cards.

THE TANNIN LEVEL £60 333

5 RAGLAN ST   HG1 1LE   01423 560595

Founded in 1985, this local stalwart wins praise for its "sympathetically prepared local ingredients" (realised in fairly conventional style) and "clearly competent staff". Top Tip – "great value early-bird dinner". / www.tanninlevel.co.uk; tanninlevel; Mon-Fri 9 pm, Sat 9.30 pm, Sun 4 pm; closed Sun D; Cash & all usual cards.

THE CROWN HASTINGS £46 334

64 - 66   ALL SAINTS STREET   TN34 3BN
01424 465100

"Popular pub in the old town of Hastings", very close to the beach. The menu mixes some gentle invention into a fairly classical gastropub selection of dishes and reports praise "great food and vibe". / www.thecrownhastings.co.uk; thecrownhastings; Mon-Sat 11 pm, Sun 10.30 pm; Cash & all usual cards.

MAGGIE'S £30 343

ROCK-A-NORE ROAD   TN34 3DW
01424 430205

"A go-to place for fresh fish" – "right on the beach amongst the fishing boats" in "one of the most attractive parts of the Hastings shoreline" – this weather-beaten wooden shack offers "great value" with its "huge portions", and is "very popular with both visitors and locals". / www.maggiesfishandchips.co.uk; maggiesfishandchipshastings; Tue-Sat 8 pm, Sun & Mon 4 pm; closed Sun & Mon D; Cash only.

ROCK A NORE KITCHEN £41 433

23A ROCK-A-NORE RD   TN34 3DW
01424 433764

"A real must-visit" – this "tiny converted fisherman's hut by the harbour" serves "the freshest fish from local boats". It's a "real favourite" for both locals and visitors, which makes it "essential to book". / rockanorekitchen. com; Fri & Sat 9 pm, Sun 3.30 pm; closed Sun D, closed Mon-Wed & Thu; Cash & all usual cards; no bookings.

WEBBE'S ROCK-A-NORE £54 333

1 ROCK-A-NORE ROAD   TN34 3DW
01424 721650

"You can see where your food comes from through the restaurant windows" at Paul Webbe's seafood spot by the traditional fishing harbour. His team are "extremely knowledgeable and passionate about local fish and fisheries" – and that enthusiasm is passed on to guests. A prominent East Sussex chef, Paul has two other restaurants and a cookery school in the area. / www.webbesrestaurants.co.uk; rockanorewebbes; Tue-Thu 9 pm, Fri & Sat 9.30 pm, Sun 8.30 pm; closed Mon; Cash & all usual cards.

THE BLUE STRAWBERRY £60 334

THE STREET   CM3 2DW   01245 381333

This "gorgeous restaurant" has "delivered style and taste" for almost 30 years, and wins high praise for the unerring consistency of its traditional service and cuisine: "never had a bad experience – always look forward to return visits". Top Menu Tip – "individual beef Wellingtons to die for!". / bluestrawberrybistro. co.uk; bluestrawberrybistrot; Mon-Sat midnight; closed Sun; No Amex.

WATER LANE £58 345

WATER LANE   TN18 5DH

"A super-charming setting for some imaginative cooking" – this funky project on the Kent/Sussex borders combines the restoration of a bucolic walled garden with vinery, Victorian glasshouses, restaurant and shop. Eat from breakfast onwards, either outside in summer or under the tented awning, or in the glasshouses during the winter. / www.waterlane.net; water. lane; Wed-Fri 5 pm, Sat & Sun 4.30 pm; closed Wed-Sun D, closed Mon & Tue; payment – credit card only; booking is online only.

THE OWL AT HAWNBY £42 334

HILLTOP   YO62 5QS   01904 208000

"A superb find" in North Yorkshire, the former Inn at Hawnby has been smartly refurbed by Coastal & Country Inns as a luxury pub/restaurant with rooms. Meals are "well presented and taste superb", while "nothing is too much trouble" for the friendly staff. / www.theowlhawnby.co.uk; coastalandcountryinns; Mon-Sat 9 pm, Sun 6 pm; closed Sun D.

CHAPTERS £67 444

LION STREET   HR3 5AA   07855 783799

"Beautiful food is produced by a small team showcasing local produce" at this small venture, known for its thoughtful, sustainable ethos (for which it won one of Michelin's green gongs) and which is entering its fifth year of operation. The atmosphere is relaxed and it's not a super-pricey experience: chef Mark McHugo provides five courses for £52 per person. / www.chaptershayonwye.co.uk; chapters_hayonwye; Wed-Sat 9 pm; closed Wed-Sat L, closed Mon & Tue & Sun; booking evening only; children: 12.

THE PACK HORSE £71 543

3-5 MARKET STREET   SK22 2EP
01663 749126

This "local village pub in the shadow of Kinder Scout" "does astonishing food", and "seems to be going from strength to strength in the wise hands of Luke Payne, who is entirely self-taught". Marina O'Loughlin of the Sunday Times and Tim Hayward of the FT are among its many fans, the former declaring her meal "divine" and "unimprovable". Top Menu Tip – "the knock-out dish was a beef curry pie with a gravy that most of our great Indian restaurants would be hard-put to match!" / www.thepackhorsehayfield.uk; thepackhorsehayfield; Wed-Sat 9 pm, Sun 7 pm; closed Wed L, closed Mon & Tue.

COIN HEBDEN 433

ALBERT STREET   HX7 8AH
01422 847707

"A fabulous new addition to the valley" – this "lovely new bar" occupies a "fantastically converted former bank which is bright, airy and lots of fun". It has a "great wine list with some really interesting orange and natural wines" and a "great selection of beers". "Plates of well-sourced charcuterie and top-notch cheeses feature alongside a smattering of oysters mignonette, a potato fondue or a pork katsu to flesh out the small but precise menu". / www.coinhebden.co.uk; coinhebden; Wed-Sat 11 pm, Sun 6 pm; closed Wed & Thu L closed Sun D, closed Mon & Tue.

HECKFIELD, HAMPSHIRE 2–3D

MARLE, HECKFIELD PLACE £58 4|3|4

HECKFIELD PLACE RG27 0LD
0118 932 6868

"Skye Gyngell's country outpost" occupies the dining room of a Georgian house – nowadays a luxurious hotel and spa. It doesn't inspire a huge volume of feedback, but such as we have says its a "lovely venue with a beautifully executed menu relying heavily on local produce". / www.heckfieldplace.com; heckfield_place; Mon-Sun 10 pm.

HEDLEY ON THE HILL, NORTHUMBERLAND 8–2B

THE FEATHERS INN £54 5|4|3

NE43 7SW 01661 843 607

Chef-owner Rhian Cradock, who took over the 200-year-old drovers' inn 15 years ago, has long been ahead of the curve as a champion of "locally sourced quality food", sustainability and ethical practices – and his prices are generous, too. A "fantastic village pub – it serves the locals well while consistently turning out high-quality dishes": "the produce and the care that goes into their production is amazing". / www.thefeathers.net; Thu-Sat 11 pm, Sun 7 pm; closed Mon & Tue & Wed; No Amex.

HELFORD PASSAGE, CORNWALL 1–4B

THE FERRYBOAT INN £52 2|3|4

TR11 5LB 01326 250625

"Nice views over Helford estuary" from this atmospheric 300-year-old inn and some decent food makes it "well worth trying to get a parking space" for a meal here. The menu may be "limited, but there's something for everyone", ranging from a "huge chicken schnitzel" to "seafood chowder with a great depth of flavour" and "top fish 'n' chips". / ferryboatcornwall.co.uk; theferryboathelford; Mon-Sun 10 pm.

HENLEY IN ARDEN, WARWICKSHIRE 5–4C

CHEAL'S OF HENLEY £67 3|3|3

64 HIGH ST B95 5BX 01564 793 856

Ex-Simpson's head chef, Matt Cheal's "smart but comfortable" venue occupies "a timbered building on Henley in Arden's picturesque high street". The six-course tasting menu offers a succession of dishes described in reports as "delightful" and "accurately cooked". / www.chealsofhenley.co.uk; chealsofhenley; Wed & Thu 9 pm, Fri & Sat 9.30 pm, Sun 3 pm; closed Sun D, closed Mon & Tue; Cash & all usual cards.

THE MOUNT BY GLYNN PURNELL £61

97 HIGH STREET B95 5AT 01564 792135

Celeb chef Glynn Purnell opened in this 200-year-old building on the High Street at the end of May 2022, aiming for a simpler formula than his 'fine dining' HQ. It was too late to generate feedback in our annual diners' poll, but we'd love some feedback so please give it a whirl! / themountpub.co.uk; themountpubhenley; Wed-Fri 8.30 pm, Sat 9 pm, Sun 4 pm; closed Sun D, closed Mon & Tue.

HENLEY-ON-THAMES, OXFORDSHIRE 3–3A

BISTRO AT THE BOATHOUSE, THE BOATHOUSE £61 3|4|3

THE BOATHOUSE RG9 1AZ
01491 577937

"On a summer's day the Thames-side terrace is a paradise" at this riverside venue. In 2019, Shaun changed tack here, adopting a more bistro style in contrast to the fine dining approach it had previously adopted. Long-term regulars say: "it's cheaper than it used to be, but never disappoints". / www.bistroattheboathouse.co.uk; bistroattheboathouse; Wed-Sat 8.30 pm, Sun 3 pm, Mon 2.30 pm; closed Sun & Mon D, closed Tue; Cash & all usual cards.

THE GREYHOUND £67 3|3|3

GALLOWSTREE RD, PEPPARD COMMON RG9 5HT 0118 972 2227

Antony Worral Thompson's spacious and quirky country spread is, for fans, "a go-to choice for any special occasion" – "the pub and garden are beautiful, the service professional and discrete, and most often AWT himself is a visible presence ensuring the highest standards". The globally inspired menu features "high-quality ingredients, well combined and perfectly cooked". Top Tip – "good steaks – try the wagyu". / www.awtgreyhound.com; thegreyhoundawt; Wed & Thu 9.30 pm, Fri & Sat 10 pm, Sun 5 pm; closed Sun D, closed Mon & Tue; Cash & all usual cards.

HENSOL, RHONDDA CYNON TAF 1–1D

LLANERCH VINEYARD £42 3|3|3

CF72 8GG 01443 222716

This "buzzy hotel restaurant" in a "lovely sunny setting overlooking its vineyard" is "great to know about if you're in the area". Chef Andy Aston wins good ratings for cooking that is notably "good-value" for its quality. / www.llanerch-vineyard.co.uk; llanerchhotel; Mon-Sat 11 pm, Sun 8 pm.

HEREFORD, HEREFORDSHIRE 2–1B

BEEFY BOYS £30 5|3|3

HR4 9HU 01432 359209

The "fabulous, high-quality burgers" at this local independent in the Old Market are "a real highlight of Hereford". It was opened by a quartet of competitive burger fanatics on the back of winning the UK's biggest competition, Grillstock, in 2014 and coming second in the world championship in Las Vegas the next year. Their mobile truck can be seen at various events around the country, and they now have a second site in Shrewsbury. / www.thebeefyboys.com; thebeefyboys; Mon-Sun 9.30 pm; booking is online only.

THE BURGER SHOP (A RULE OF TUM) £38 3|3|3

32 AUBREY STREET HR4 0BU
01432 351764

The first bricks-and-mortar venture from Hereford's 10 year-old 'A Rule of Tum' hospitality group, this local hit serves "top burgers in a great atmosphere", with a focus on locally produced beef and other produce. A branch in Worcester has followed. / www.burgershop.restaurant; _burgershop; Mon-Thu 9 pm, Fri & Sat 10 pm, Sun 8 pm.

CASTLE HOUSE RESTAURANT, CASTLE HOUSE HOTEL £70 3|3|3

CASTLE ST HR1 2NW 01432 356321

Owned and run by the Watkins family, this hotel is a Hereford fixture and its highly rated restaurant showcases "very good cooking" from Hungarian-born chef Gabor Katona – much of it using produce from Ballingham Hall farm eight miles away, which is also owned by the Watkinses. / www.castlehse.co.uk; castlehousehotel; Wed-Sat 9 pm, Sun 3 pm; closed Sun D, closed Mon & Tue; Cash & all usual cards.

HESWALL, MERSEYSIDE 5–2A

BURNT TRUFFLE £59 4|4|3

104-106 TELEGRAPH ROAD CH60 0AQ
0151 342 1111

"Described as a 'small, local bistro'… what an example of British understatement!" – Gary Usher's Wirral outpost (his initial follow-up to Sticky Walnut) continues to win a thumbs-up in feedback. "The friendly, cheerful and very knowledgeable staff make you feel at home instantly, and the food? Novel, inventive, well prepared and VERY tasty!" / www.burnttruffle.net; burnt_truffle; Tue-Thu 9 pm, Fri & Sat 10 pm, Sun 5 pm; closed Sun D, closed Mon.

HETTON, NORTH YORKSHIRE 5–1B

THE ANGEL £104 5|4|3

BD23 6LT 01756 730263

"A stark – and welcome – makeover from the Angel in its previous very traditional guise" has helped Michael Wignall put his stamp on this famous northern inn: often cited as the UK's original country gastropub, which he purchased in 2018. "Having enjoyed Michael Wignall's cooking at his former outpost, The Latymer, we were interested to see how it might translate to North Yorkshire: very well, we thought, with no lack of sophistication and ambition, but losing any of the possible pretension expected in a Surrey hotel". "Thank heavens! He's a great chef who does not insist you eat what he chooses, but who offers a choice of dishes, all of which tempt and intrigue": "really exceptional food". If you stay over, "the breakfast is a joyous surprise" too. / www.angelhetton.co.uk; angelathetton; Mon, Fri-Sun 8.30 pm, Thu 8 pm; closed Thu L, closed Tue & Wed.

HEXHAM, NORTHUMBERLAND   8–2A

THE BEAUMONT   £47   2 3 2

**BEAUMONT STREET   NE46 3LT
01434 602331**

This "traditional hotel" has undergone "amazing change" through a rolling modernisation programme in recent years, and its kitchen sends out some "very good" dishes of "locally sourced produce". But ratings were undercut by a number of reporters who "expected more" after a rave review from The Guardian's Grace Dent, and were "disappointed" by their meal. / www.thebeaumonthexham.co.uk; thebeaumonthexham; Mon-Sun 9 pm.

BOUCHON BISTROT   £53   3 4 3

4-6 GILESGATE   NE46 3NJ   01434 609943

With its "superb classic bistro dishes" – "probably the best French cuisine in the area" – Loire Valley-born Greg Bureau's long-standing venue "feels like stepping into France". It's a "brilliant-value, ideal neighbourhood restaurant", and a "recent makeover is a bonus", adding a "fabulous glass balcony". / www.bouchonbistrot.co.uk; Bouchonbistrot; Tue-Sat 9 pm; closed Sun & Mon; Cash & all usual cards.

LANGLEY CASTLE HOTEL   £59   3 4 5

LANGLEY   NE47 5LU   01434 688888

"Suits of armour, spiral staircases, gigantic fireplaces" – this "stunning, preserved medieval castle turned into a country-house hotel" makes a "wonderfully romantic destination", just "two minutes off the A69 between Carlisle & Newcastle" – "you'd rave about it if you found its like abroad, yet here it is". "Service is attentive, friendly and professional", while "the food is extremely good, if not top fine dining". / www.langleycastle.co.uk; langleycastle; Mon-Sun midnight.

THE RAT INN   £61   4 3 5

ANICK   NE46 4LN   014 3460 2814

This "picture-perfect pub overlooking the Tyne Valley", an old drovers' inn outside Hexham, specialises in "local beef – choose your size and enjoy it on a platter with cress and chips". There's also a dynamic blackboard menu of "amazing" daily specials that reflect the "fine dining" background of chef Phil Mason, who won a Michelin star at the nearby Green Room before taking over the Rat with his partner Karen Errington 15 years ago. Children are well catered for, as well. / www.theratinn.com;

theratinn; Tue-Sat 8 pm, Sun 3 pm; closed Sun D, closed Mon; Cash & all usual cards.

HINTLESHAM, SUFFOLK   3–1D

HINTLESHAM HALL £69   3 3 4

HINTLESHAM   IP8 3NS   01473 652334

"A beautiful adaptation of a lovely house" – this gorgeous Grade I listed Georgian pile in Suffolk dating from the reign of Henry IV and most famous to oldies for its associations with 1970s TV-chef Robert Carrier (for which the dining room is named) – is a ten-minute drive from Ipswich. It's praised all-round in reports this year, not least for its "splendid afternoon tea". / www.hintleshamhall.co.uk; hintleshamhall; Mon-Sun 9 pm; Cash & all usual cards; Jacket required; children: 12+.

HITCHIN, HERTFORDSHIRE   3–2A

THE FARMHOUSE AT REDCOATS   £53   3 2 2

**REDCOATS GREEN   SG4 7JR
01438 729500**

"Great food" from "an imaginative menu" makes this "delightful traditional farmhouse hotel" a real "local favourite" – and a useful bolthole just 25 minutes from London. But service, particularly from junior staff, "can be hit and miss", and some find the new conservatory (opened February 2022) to be "very noisy with sound bouncing off the hard surfaces". / www.farmhouseatredcoats.co.uk ; farmhouse redcoats; Mon-Sat 9 pm, Sun 4 pm; closed Sun D; Cash & all usual cards.

HOLKHAM, NORFOLK   6–3C

THE VICTORIA AT HOLKHAM, HOLKHAM HALL   £63   2 2 4

.   NR23 1RG   01328 711008

This ivy-clad pub-hotel by the gates of Holkham Hall makes a perfect destination after "a gorgeous walk on Holkham beach" – although its dining room can be "a bit hit-and-miss" – "when it's good it is very, very good, but it can have some really poor days" (fluctuating standards that have bedevilled reports for "over 20 years"). / www.holkham.co.uk; holkhamestate; Mon-Sun 10.30 pm; Cash & all usual cards.

HOLT, NORFOLK   6–3C

MEADOWSWEET   £92   5 4 3

**37 NORWICH ROAD   NR25 6SA
01263 586954**

"Truly world-class cookery… what an achievement to get a Michelin star after such a short time being open" – Greg Anderson and Rebecca Williams's summer 2021 launch (given top marks in Harden's several months before the Tyre Men's accolades!) is one of the more exciting rural openings of recent times, certainly up Norfolk way. "Greg's cooking is deft, refined, exquisite and packed with beautiful flavours, while Rebecca's service is thoughtful, considerate, knowledgeable and warm. When the chefs bring the dishes to the table they comment on the food with humility

and charm. Not a false note or a jarring element in numerous courses." One ardent fan finds the rise in price of the tasting menu since it opened (from £85 to £130 per person) "alarming" (although you do get more courses now). The most representative view though? – "Just completely stunning in every sense of the word. We were blown away by every aspect of our meal. Can't wait to dine again!" / www.meadowsweetholt.com; meadowsweetholt; Wed-Sat 8 pm; closed Wed-Sat L, closed Mon & Tue & Sun.

HOLYMOORSIDE, DERBYSHIRE   5–2C

THE BULLS HEAD   £69   3 2 3

NEW ROAD   S42 7EW   01246 569999

Chef/Patron Mark Aisthorpe personally hunts for some of the ingredients served at his "lovely Peak District pub", which features game alongside "a nice line in local steaks" as part of his "wonderful" cooking – "high-end cuisine that deserves wider recognition" according to fans, with the option of a tasting menu alongside the à la carte and bar menu. One repeated gripe, though – the "front of house needs the same amount of attention as the food". / www.bullsheadholymoorside.co.uk; bullsheadholymoorside; Fri & Sat 9 pm, Wed 10 pm, Thu 8.30 pm, Sun 5 pm; closed Wed L closed Sun D, closed Mon & Tue; No Amex; No shorts.

HOLYWOOD, COUNTY DOWN   10–1D

NOBLE   £63   4 5 4

**27A CHURCH RD   BT18 9BU
028 9042 5655**

"Ticking all the boxes, with modern but unpretentious food of fine quality in decent portion sizes" – including "some top seafood". It's a "small, intimate" place with a "buzzy atmosphere and friendly service" from 'butler' Saul McConnell and "fantastic quality food" from cook Pearson Morris. "I stumbled on it by chance, but will return for sure!" / nobleholywood.com; nobleholywood; Thu-Sat 9.30 pm, Sun 6.30 pm; closed Mon & Tue & Wed.

HONITON, DEVON   2–4A

THE PIG AT COMBE £74   3 4 4

**COMBE HOUSE, GITTISHAM   EX14 3AD
01404 540400**

"Great food, lovely location, a dream of a kitchen garden" is the generally agreed verdict on this Otter Valley outpost of the boho-styled Pig hotel group, in a handsome Elizabethan mansion with a panelled dining room. There's an "interesting focus on local produce", including "lots of nicely cooked veg" from the kitchen garden. / www.thepighotel.com/at-combe; the_pig_hotels; Mon-Sun 9.30 pm; No Amex.

HOPE COVE, DEVON   1–4D

HOPE COVE HOUSE   3 3 4

INNER HOPE   TQ7 3HH   01548 561371

"Worth a detour. Have been coming since they opened under new ownership in 2019 and it's only grown in strength despite the pandemic. Absolute gem!" – limited but very enthusiastic feedback on this 14-bedroom hotel on the South West Coast path, with commanding views of the sea and looking over Hope Cove beach (which is yards away). The food is brasserie-style fare (sirloin, red mullet, confit duck…) and good value. / hopecovehouse.co; househopecove; Mon-Sun 8.30 pm.

HOPE VALLEY, SOUTH YORKSHIRE 5–2C

LOSEHILL HOUSE HOTEL & SPA £80 344

LOSEHILL LANE, EDALE ROAD S33 6AF
01433 621 219

"From the homemade bread and the hors d'oeuvres to the dessert course everything is just perfect", say fans of this characterful hotel, which has a "wonderful setting" in the Peak District National Park, and is praised for its "professional and friendly" staff and "fantastic food" (from an à la carte three-course menu). / www.losehillhouse.co.uk; losehillhouse; Mon-Sun 8.30 pm.

HORNDON ON THE HILL, ESSEX 3–3C

THE BELL INN £62 334

HIGH RD SS17 8LD 01375 642463

"One of the original gastropubs still going strong" – this long-established destination is "a family favourite" for its sizable fanclub: a fifteenth-century picturesquely located inn, which has been owned and run by John and Christine Vereker's family for over 75 years. "The food is excellent and service is energetic and welcoming". / www.bell-inn.co.uk; bellhorndon; Mon-Sat 9 pm, Sun 6 pm; closed Sun D; Cash & all usual cards.

HOUGH ON THE HILL, LINCOLNSHIRE 6–3A

BROWNLOW ARMS £66 333

NG32 2AZ 01400 250234

A "great local for all the family" in a pretty village in the Lincolnshire flatlands, where Paul & Lorraine Willoughby look after their guests well in this classic seventeenth-century inn. / www.brownlowarms.co.uk; Tue-Sat 9 pm, Sun 3 pm; closed Tue-Sat L closed Sun D, closed Mon; No Amex; no bookings at lunch; children: 10+.

HUDDERSFIELD, WEST YORKSHIRE 5–1C

ERIC'S £69 333

73-75 LIDGET ST HD3 3JP 01484 646416

"Excellent seasonal menus and a bargain early-bird" – not to mention "a top brunch locally" and "the best Sunday lunch" – all fuel satisfaction with Eric Paxman's well-established local destination. / www.ericsrestaurant.co.uk; erics_restaurant; Tue-Sat 10 pm, Sun 6 pm; closed Sun D, closed Mon; No Amex.

HULL, EAST YORKSHIRE 6–2A

TAPASYA @ MARINA £51 332

HUMBER DOCK STREET, MARINA, HU1 1TB 01482 242607

"Good food overlooking the marina" is reported in all accounts of this swish contemporary Indian. Even someone who feels its expensive-looking styling is "all a bit too grand for its own good" says "the food is well cooked and comes in generous portions". / www.tapasyarestaurants.co.uk/marina; tapasyahull_; Mon-Sat 10 pm; closed Sun; Cash & all usual cards.

HUNSDON, HERTFORDSHIRE 3–2B

THE FOX AND HOUNDS RESTAURANT & BAR £56 333

2 HIGH STREET SG12 8NH
01279 843 999

This "lovely old gastropub with way above average cooking" "keeps up the standard year on year" – chef-patron James Wix and his wife Bianca have run it for almost 20 years. There's a "lovely atmosphere and friendly staff", and James's "first-class cooking" has plenty of European influences. / www.foxandhounds-hunsdon.co.uk; thefoxandhoundshunsdon; Wed-Sat 10 pm, Sun 5 pm; closed Sun D, closed Mon & Tue; Cash & all usual cards.

HUNTINGDON, CAMBRIDGESHIRE 3–1B

OLD BRIDGE HOTEL £61 233

1 HIGH ST PE29 3TQ 01480 424300

"This institution has been a feature of Cambridgeshire life for 50 years" – an ivy-clad Georgian hotel in a "lovely location" overlooking the Great Ouse, owned for almost 30 years by Master of Wine John Hoskins, whose expertise is reflected in the "exceptional wine list" and on-site shop. Some diners feel the food is "pretty average" by comparison, but others feel it is "imaginative" enough and with "top-quality local ingredients". For wine buffs, though, the cellar is sufficient attraction, as "the hotel has an excellent wine shop with two Enomatic wine dispensers, allowing for a great wine tasting experience as well as underpinning an exceptionally large by-the-glass selection". / ///www.oldbridgehuntingdon.co.uk; oldbridgehuntingdon; Mon-Sun 9 pm; Cash & all usual cards.

HURWORTH, COUNTY DURHAM 8–3B

THE BAY HORSE £73 433

45 THE GRN DL2 2AA 01325 720 663

One of the most commented-on pubs in the North of England – few are as consistently highly rated this year as chef-patron Marcus Bennett's "excellent gastropub", which he has run since 2008. The cooking is "very enjoyable, especially in the game season – for example, partridge beautifully presented". /

www.thebayhorsehurworth.com; bayhorsehurworth; Mon-Sat 11 pm, Sun 10.30 pm; Cash & all usual cards.

ICKHAM, KENT 3–3D

THE DUKE WILLIAM £58 333

THE ST CT3 1QP 01227 721308

This "lovely gastropub in a pretty Kent village" maintains a "good standard of food" – and has a "beautiful log fire to keep you warm on chilly nights". It is "part of the Rocksalt group", which means there's a focus on local seasonal ingredients. / www.thedukewilliamickham.com; dukewilliamkent; Mon-Fri 9 pm, Sat 9.30 pm, Sun 5 pm; closed Sun D.

ILKLEY, WEST YORKSHIRE 5–1C

BETTYS £40 345

32 THE GROVE LS29 9EE 01943 608029

"Afternoon tea IS Bettys!". This old-fashioned tearoom is "always worth the queue" for its epic teas and fine spreads of pastries and sarnies. It's also "a great place to meet over a very good breakfast. Coffee, understandably, is excellent!" / www.bettys.co.uk/tea-rooms/locations/ilkle; Bettys; Mon-Sun 5 pm; closed Mon-Sun D; No Amex; no bookings.

BISTROT PIERRE £45 343

THE CRESCENT, BROOK STREET
LS29 8DG 01943 811250

"Always reliable for tasty and reasonably priced French food", this handy venue is one of twenty remaining branches of a national chain launched 29 years ago (six more closed down in 2020). / www.bistrotpierre.co.uk/locations/ilkley; bistrotpierre; Sun-Thu 9 pm, Fri & Sat 10 pm.

THE BOX TREE £116 444

35-37 CHURCH ST LS29 9DR
01943 608484

"Well worth the trek while on a trip 'up North'", noted a Wimbledon-based reporter on this esteemed and "always enjoyable" foodie destination. Set in one of the town's oldest buildings, it first became a restaurant in 1962 and was cradle to the talents of the young Marco Pierre White prior to its last 19 years of ownership by chef Simon Gueller and his wife Rena. There's a three-course menu at lunch – dinner is 6 courses plus canapés, amuse-bouche and bread – and fans say the kitchen "absolutely nails it". / www.theboxtree.co.uk; boxtreerestaurant; Wed-Sat 8 pm, Sun 2.30 pm; closed Wed & Thu L closed Sun D, closed Mon & Tue; Cash & all usual cards; No jeans; children: 10+.

ILMINGTON, WARWICKSHIRE 2–1C

THE HOWARD ARMS £70 334

LOWER GREEN CV36 4LT 01608 682226

"Reliable old-school inn", "in a charming if chilly corner of the Cotswolds", that "still feels like you're in the country and not a London trattoria!". The food may not offer "fireworks", but it excels for dishes such as "asparagus bang in season with egg and hollandaise", complemented by "lovely service". / www.howardarms.com; thehowardarms; Tue-Sat 9 pm, Sun 8 pm; closed Mon; No Amex.

ILMINSTER, SOMERSET   2–3A

THE BARRINGTON BOAR £50 **4 4 4**

MAIN STREET   TA19 0JB   01460 259 281

"Everything that a gastropub should be" – this eighteenth-century inn in a "charming Somerset village" was relaunched in 2021 after extensive renovations as a restaurant-with-rooms, by husband-and-wife team Alasdair Clifford (ex-Chez Bruce & Harwood Arms) and Victoria Collins. "Al's menu is first-class and delivers close to Michelin star standard, while Victoria marshals the front of house". / www.thebarringtonboar.co.uk; the_barrington_boar; Thu-Sat, Wed 9 pm, Sun 3 pm; closed Wed L closed Sun D, closed Mon & Tue.

INGHAM, NORFOLK   6–4D

THE INGHAM SWAN £95 **4 3 4**

SEA PALLING ROAD   NR12 9AB
01692 581099

This "exceptional" restaurant-with-rooms showcases chef-patron Daniel Smith's "adventurous and imaginative menus", ranging from two to eight courses and built around "superb locally sourced produce". "Having visited over the years, I feel it's getting better and better". / www.theinghamswan.co.uk; theinghamswan; Wed-Sun, Tue 9 pm; closed Tue L, closed Mon.

INVERNESS, HIGHLAND   9–2C

NESS WALK £79 **3 4 3**

12 NESS WALK   IV3 5SQ   01463 215215

In "a great location right beside the River Ness", this smart hotel was cited this year as being "ideal for business, with staff who are so obliging and attentive". On the dining room's menu "there's not a huge choice", but all reports say "the cuisine is also very good". / www.nesswalk.com/dining; ness_walk; Mon-Sun midnight.

IPSWICH, SUFFOLK   3–1D

TRONGS **4 3 3**

23 ST NICHOLAS ST   IP1 1TW
01473 256833

This "very popular" Chinese has built a loyal local following over 25 years for its "great food" and "brilliant staff" – most of them from founder Foo Trong's family, including his wife Michala, brother and head chef Viet Hoa, sister Lucy and parents – all of whom "really care". "Trongs never disappoints – nothing is too much trouble. We've been going for 15 years and just ask them to bring us what they think is good!" / www.trongschineserestaurant.com; Mon-

Sat 10 pm; closed Mon-Sat L, closed Sun; Cash & all usual cards.

JERSEY, CHANNEL ISLANDS   –

BISTRO ROSA **4 3 3**

BERESFORD STREET FISH MARKET
JE2 4WX   01534 729559

This "tiny" "Portuguese-run" restaurant with a blackboard menu in the St Helier fish market is well worth tracking down if you're looking for flavour rather than luxury on Jersey. Top Tip – "the best lobster Thermidor". / Mon-Sat 9.30 pm; closed Sun.

BOHEMIA, THE CLUB HOTEL & SPA £100 **4 5 4**

GREEN ST, ST HELIER   JE2 4UH
01534 876500

"Out-of-this-world" food and "interesting wine pairings" help make it "an absolute pleasure to dine" at this renowned dining room, which has long been the best-known gastronomic destination on the island. Callum Graham has been at the stoves since early 2020, and regulars feel "he has raised the bar again, with simply stunning tasting menus combining sublime flavours and textures and featuring amazing local ingredients including, of course, locally caught fish and shellfish" ("the Pescatarian tasting menu is from another dimension"). "Impeccable" service and the cosseting setting helps it "tick all the boxes" for a luxurious treat. / www.bohemiajersey.com; bohemiajersey; Mon-Sat 1 am, Sun 10.30 pm; Cash & all usual cards; No trainers.

LONGUEVILLE MANOR £113 **4 4 4**

LONGUEVILLE RD, ST SAVIOUR   JE2 7WF
01534 725501

"An excellent traditional hotel with a first-class restaurant and extensive wine list" – this well-established Relais & Châteaux property occupies a fourteenth-century major house and has been run by the Lewis family since 1949. Its traditional dining room, The 'Oak Room', is presided over by chef Andrew Baird, whose cuisine is complemented by the 600-bin cellar. / www.longuevillemanor.com; longuevillemanor; Mon-Sun 9 pm; closed Mon-Wed L; No Amex.

KENILWORTH, WARWICKSHIRE   5–4C

THE CROSS AT KENILWORTH £70 **4 4 3**

16 NEW ST   CV8 2EZ   01926 853840

"Adam Bennett produces dishes of supreme quality, prepared with flair and skill" according to all reports on this "lovely" Grade II listed inn, which – aided by the profile of Andreas Antona of Birmingham star Simpson's – has become one of the most commented-on destinations in the Midlands. All accounts say a meal here is "absolutely stunning" and "it is also very refreshing to be able to order à la carte at a Michelin-starred restaurant, rather than being forced to order a tasting menu" (although one local "would eat here more often

if there were a greater variation of dishes on offer"). Service is "always friendly, attentive and competent" and "it maintains a brilliant experience". Top Menu Tip – "the most extravagant chicken liver parfait imaginable, top venison, and a wonderful variation on ile flottante". / www.thecrosskenilworth.co.uk; thecrossatkenilworth; Wed-Sat 9 pm, Sun 3 pm; closed Sun D, closed Mon & Tue.

KESWICK, CUMBRIA   7–3D

THE COTTAGE IN THE WOOD £79 **4 5 4**

WHINLATTER FOREST   CA12 5TW
01768 778409

A "gem in the Lakes" with "superb views" from its dramatic location – this seventeenth-century former coaching inn above Keswick in the Whinlatter Forest earned a stellar dining reputation in recent years under chef Ben Wilkinson, who left last summer. His successor, Yorkshire-born Sam Miller, has worked in senior roles at Noma in Copenhagen and Faviken in Sweden, and has done a good job of maintaining a high rating this year. (Owners Kath and Liam Berney have said they would like to sell up and retire if they can find a buyer to take the Cottage forward.) / www.thecottageinthewood.co.uk; thecottageinthewoodkeswick; Wed-Sat 11 pm; closed Mon & Tue & Sun; No Amex.

FELLPACK £53 **4 4 3**

19 LAKE ROAD   CA12 5BS   01768 771177

"Fab pub with a great choice of local foods": the ideal spot to recover from a yomp across the surrounding fells, with a bistro-style menu that "delivers every time". It is part of a hybrid hospitality and outdoor adventure brand that escorts guests on fell-running excursions, then feeds them. The business also incorporates the Fellshack, a vintage Airstream trailer parked next door and selling burritos, and the Darkroom, a coffee shop around the corner. Note: more sedentary types are quite welcome to eat without running. / fellpack.co.uk/venue/the-fellpack-28883; theroundkeswick; Tue-Sat 9 pm; closed Tue-Sat L, closed Sun & Mon.

LYZZICK HALL COUNTRY HOUSE HOTEL £58 **4 3 4**

UNDERSKIDDAW   CA12 4PY
017687 72277

"The excellent standard of the last few years is being maintained" at this mid-Victorian gentleman's residence below Skiddaw, which has been a family-run hotel since 1986. The building has seen "big changes, which include moving the restaurant to the front, with wonderful views over the northern lakes". "A table in the bay window, with views over the fells, then lazing over coffee followed by a walk around the small grounds and a photo session with the alpacas… Oh, and the food is also extremely good!" / www.lyzzickhall.co.uk; lyzzickhall; Mon-Sat 2 pm; closed Mon-Sat D, closed Sun; No Amex.

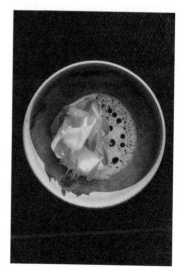

Peel's, Hampton Manor, Hampton-in-Arden

THE PHEASANT AT KEYSTON £62 3|3|3

LOOP RD   PE28 0RE   01832 710241

"Great pub dishes executed well above the norm and a very decent wine list" are on the menu at this "lovely old thatched inn on a village green", re-launched in 2021 by chef Martin Russell and his partner Zoe. "How can you not highly rate any pub that has a traditional suet pudding stuffed with beef bourguignon on the menu?" / thepheasantatkeyston.co.uk; thepheasantatkeyston; Wed-Sat 9 pm, Sun 4 pm; closed Sun D, closed Mon & Tue; No Amex; booking is online only.

KINNEUCHAR INN 3|3|3

9-11 MAIN STREET   KY9 1LF
01333 340377

Part of the Balcaskie Estate – which provides much of the produce for the menu – this seventeenth-century pub is run by chef James Ferguson and front-of-house Alethea Palmer, and continues to be highly rated for its short-but-impactful menu that would look just as at home in Shoreditch as it is in the middle of Fife. / kinneucharinn.com; kinneucharinn; Wed-Sat 8 pm, Sun 3 pm; closed Sun D, closed Mon & Tue; payment – credit card only; booking is online only.

PARADISE CAFÉ AT DALESIDE NURSERIES £36 4|3|3

RIPON ROAD   HG3 2AY   01423 755196

"Finally, Frances Atkins has opened a place to sample her exemplary cooking after the sad ending of the Yorke Arms as a 'go-to' destination". Her legion of fans will be relieved to know it's "an easy place to visit", in a garden centre close to Harrogate. The first woman in the UK to earn a Michelin star, Frances has revived her Yorke Arms team of more than 20 years for the new project – chef Roger Olive and front-of-house manager John Tullett. / www.paradisewithfrj.co.uk; paradise_foods_; Tue-Sun 4 pm; closed Tue-Sun D, closed Mon.

THE KINGHAM PLOUGH £67 3|3|3

THE GREEN   OX7 6YD   01608 658327

This "great Cotswolds gastropub" is a well-known watering-hole near Chipping Norton, with "excellent, hearty and delicious cooking", "majoring in wood-fired dishes" including scallops in the half shell, iceberg lettuce, giant tiger prawns, gurnard fillets and Barnsley chop. Matt & Katie Beamish took over from GBM winner Emily Watkins a couple of years ago. / www.thekinghamplough.co.uk; kinghamplough; Tue-Sat 9 pm, Sun 8 pm; closed Mon; No Amex.

THE WILD RABBIT £88 3|3|4

CHURCH ST   OX7 6YA   01608 658 389

The "great food and amazing service" are everything you would expect at this deluxe Cotswolds gastropub handy for the Chipping Norton set and owned by Lady Bamford, chatelaine of Daylesford Organic (which supplies much of the produce) and hostess of BoJo's post-prime ministerial wedding bash. It all comes, of course, "at a fairly significant price". Sam Bowser, the latest chef to head the kitchen, did a stint as the Bamfords' private chef a few years back. / www.thewildrabbit.co.uk; thewildrabbitkingham; Wed-Sun 9 pm; closed Mon & Tue; Cash & all usual cards.

ROZ ANA £47 4|3|2

4-8 KINGSTON HILL   KT2 7NH
020 8546 6388

"This great local up-market Indian" from chef and co-owner Deepinder Sondhi has earned a strong following in London's southwest suburbs over 15 years for "great specials" and "interesting regional dishes", which avoid the cliché of serving "protein added to standard sauces". It also has a "top-class cocktail bar". / www.roz-ana.com; therozana; Sun-Thu 10 pm, Fri & Sat 10.30 pm; Cash & all usual cards.

HIPPING HALL £100 3|4|4

COWAN BRIDGE   LA6 2JJ   01524 271187

"Really inventive food that reflects the area" is a major attraction at this handsome venue on the edge of the Yorkshire Dales from hotelier Andrew Wildsmith. There's "lots of foraging", and "chefs come to the table to chat about it and explain their food" – which goes down well with reporters. Head chef Peter Howarth has worked in some of the country's best kitchens including The Latymer, Gidleigh Park and the Devonshire Arms. / www.hippinghall.com; Wed-Sun 10.30 pm; closed Mon & Tue; No Amex; No trainers; children: 12+.

THE RISING SUN £55 4|4|4

KNAPP ROAD   TA3 6BG   01823 491027

This 500-year-old building in a "beautiful part of Somerset" now houses an "excellent dining pub" that "serves up top-class modern British dishes using brilliant local ingredients". Chef Olly Jackson and his manager wife Rebecca "used to run the nearby and sadly missed Langford Fivehead hotel". / www.therisingsunknapp.co.uk; therisingsunknapp; Wed-Sat 10 pm, Sun 4 pm; closed Sun D, closed Mon & Tue.

APRIL'S KITCHEN £28 3|3|3

37 REGENT STREET   WA16 6GR
01565 651111

This "glitzy shed" has a strong reputation locally for its "great breakfasts": "excellent omelettes and light dishes or more substantial fare, if that's what is needed to set you up for the day. Good coffee is served with iced water – a simple touch but so rare!". Later on, it's "bistro in style with service all day" – there's "reduced tapas-type options since Covid but still a choice of well prepared specials if you want more than a salad or sandwich", plus "a carefully chosen selection of wines and beers or a fun choice of cocktails". / www.aprils-kitchen.co.uk; aprilskitchenknutsford; Mon-Wed 4 pm, Thu-Sun 9 pm; closed Mon-Wed D.

KYLESKU HOTEL £62 3|3|4

IV27 4HW   01971 502231

"Fantastic views over sea lochs and mountains from the dining room" greet visitors to this distant hotel in the boonies of northwest Scotland, overlooking Loch Glendhu, known for its "good, locally sourced food" (particularly seafood). Since April 2021 it's been run by new owners, Highland Coast Hotels. / www.kyleskuhotel.co.uk; kylesku_hotel; Mon-Sun 10 pm; Cash & all usual cards.

THREE HORSEHOES £58 3|3|3

25 SHEPPERTON ST   TW18 1SE
01784 455014

"The best by far in the locality" – with "upmarket pub food that puts many expensive restaurants to shame" – this "buzzing" gastroboozer is "always excellent, whether you want a quick lunch or are celebrating a special occasion". Top Tip – "walk there along the towpath on a sunny summer evening". / www.3horseshoeslaleham.co.uk; Mon-Sat 9 pm, Sun 7 pm; Cash & all usual cards.

LANGAR HALL £80 3|3|4

CHURCH LN   NG13 9HG   01949 860559

"Outstanding cooking" – "impressive yet comforting" – is on the menu at this "well-loved country house – not too formal but everything just so" in a "beautiful rural setting" in the Belvoir Valley, with local produce including game from the nearby Belvoir estate well to the fore. Opened 40 years ago by the late Imogen Skirving in her family home, the hall's regulars have ranged from Barbara Cartland to Jools Holland – and it's "still quirky after Imogen's passing (RIP)", under her granddaughter Lila. / www.langarhall.com; langarhall; Thu-Sat 8.30 pm, Sun 7.30 pm; closed Mon & Tue & Wed; No Amex; No trainers.

NORTHCOTE £92 554

NORTHCOTE RD   BB6 8BE   01254 240555

"Lancashire hospitality at its best" but in a thoroughly forward-looking vein has won rightful acclaim for this much-extended manor house, in the Ribble Valley (which stands immediately off the A59). "The team of chef Lisa Goodwin-Allen and MD and cellarmaster Craig Bancroft are paired like the best food and wine" and staff "remain fun, focused and dedicated". Lisa manages to juggle her increasing TV fame with delivering "really elegant and fabulously balanced menus" ("always enhanced with fabulous wine pairings" overseen by Craig); and "despite running an exceptional kitchen, she still finds time to pop out to chat to dinner guests". Grievous complaints are notable by their absence, although the niggle that "portions are definitely on the ungenerous side" surfaced in a couple of reports this year, as did the notion that the overall style "seems just a little more 'corporate' since it has joined ownership with The Stafford in London". But "for a special occasion, it's hard to beat" and "divine bedrooms add to the fabulous experience". A highpoint of the year is the international gastronomic festival called Obsession which they run annually in January and February, which "has grown over 20 years from them chasing chefs to attend, to restaurants now asking how they can be considered for one of the nights". "We try to go here at least once a year... well worth the 3-hour drive!" / www.northcote.com; northcoteuk; Wed-Sun 8.30 pm; closed Mon & Tue; payment – credit card only; No trainers.

THE BLACKSMITHS ARMS £48 333

FRONT ST   YO62 6TN   01751 417247

"Assured cooking from an interesting menu means you could do a lot worse in the area" than this seventeenth-century village pub. Young chef-patron Ali Moran, who took over a year ago, grew up in the neighbouring hamlet of Hartoft, and serves game from his parents' farm. / blacksmithslastingham.com; blacksmiths_lastingham; Mon-Sat 8.30 pm, Sun 4.30 pm; closed Sun D; No Amex.

THE EARL OF MARCH

LAVANT RD   P018 0BQ   01243 533993

The view (towards Goodwood) from the window is said to have inspired William Blake's anthem, Jerusalem, in 1803, but the current future is uncertain at this eighteenth-century coaching inn, which shut its doors in early October 2022. We await news of the new incarnation of this vantagepoint over 'England's green and pleasant land'. / www.theearlofmarch.com; theearlofmarch; Mon-Sat 9 pm, Sun 3 pm; closed Sun D.

ANNWN £150

SA68 0PW

Matt Powell's mission is to create 'Wild food experiences in the heart of Pembrokeshire' at this spring 2022 newcomer: a converted potting shed near the Cleddau estuary, which seats only ten. Early feedback awards it full marks all-round for his ten-course menu (at £120 per person) delivered over 3-4 hours; but is too limited to earn a rating. (In October 2022, it made it to the list of The Good Food Guide's Top 20 UK restaurants). / Mon & Tue, Thu-Sun 10 pm.

LA COPPOLA £51 343

**14 THE PARADE   CV32 4DW
01926 888 873**

"A great surprise! An authentic Italian restaurant with a broad menu of very good food and wine" – "delivered with panache and generosity". The "beautiful and romantic decor, with cherry trees garlanded with tiny lights" only adds to the appeal. / www.lacoppola.co.uk; lacoppolaleam; Mon-Sun 10 pm; No Amex.

OSCARS FRENCH BISTRO £59 343

**39 CHANDOS STREET   CV32 4RL
01926 452807**

"The epitome of the proper French bistro as you would have found in France 25 years ago", owned by acclaimed butchers, Aubrey Allen. "Pascal the patron excels at providing excellent meat and fish dishes that are always reliable, and service is friendly even when they are packed!" / www.oscarsfrenchbistro.co.uk; oscarsfrenchbistro; Tue-Sat 11 pm; closed Tue L, closed Sun & Mon; Cash & all usual cards; No trainers.

THE DINING ROOM, BEAVERBROOK £96 445

REIGATE ROAD   KT22 8QX   01372 571300

"We keep going back for the top-notch Japanese dishes in sumptuous surroundings", enjoyed in the surprising venue of press baron Lord Beaverbrook's palatial mansion in the Surrey Hills. The "super-high-end sushi" and "tasty" Japanese grilled dishes are prepared by Wojciech Popow, founder of the Polish Association of Sushi Chefs, formerly of Noma in Copenhagen and Japanese specialist Yashin in London. / beaverbrook.co.uk; beaverbrook; Mon-Sun 9 pm; closed Mon L; Cash & all usual cards.

BOMBA PAELLA & TAPAS BAR £47

1 SAWMILL YARD   LS11 5WH

In April 2022, Leeds restaurateur Joe McDermott opened this paella and tapas specialist at Saw Mill Yard in Holbeck Urban Village, on the city's South Bank. Named after a variety of rice from eastern Spain, Bomba started off as a paella delivery service during lockdown, operating from Kirkgate Market. McDermott originally made his mark on the Leeds dining scene almost 30 years ago, launching the Arts Café in Call Lane in 1994. / www.bombapaella.uk; bombapaella; Wed-Sat 11.30 pm; closed Mon & Tue & Sun; payment – credit card only.

BUNDOBUST £31 433

6 MILL HILL   LS1 5DQ   0113 243 1248

"Very tasty authentic Indian vegan and vegetarian street food" is paired with a "great beer selection" at the Leeds branch of the Manchester-based winner. "Could just as easily be in the 'best Indian' or 'best cheap eats' category". Top Tip – "you have to try the okra fries!". / www.bundobust.com; bundobust; Mon-Thu 9.30 pm, Fri & Sat 10 pm, Sun 8 pm; payment – credit card only.

CHEF JONO AT V&V £96 443

**68 NEW BRIGGATE   LS1 6NU
0113 345 0202**

"A fabulous evening out" – "Chef Jono's cooking is so different: outstanding, creative and beautifully presented". Yorkshire-born Jono Hawthorne has worked in leading kitchens including the Box Tree in Ilkley, Noma in Copenhagen and the Quay in Sydney – and is now making a real name for himself in Leeds. / www.chefjonoatvandv.co.uk; vandvleeds; Wed-Sat 9.30 pm, Sun 3 pm; closed Wed-Sat L closed Sun D, closed Mon & Tue.

DASTAAN LEEDS £47

473 OTLEY ROAD   LS16 7NR

Ex-Gymkhana chefs, Nand Kishor and Sanjay Gour have stormed London's outer burbs with their outstanding Ewell-based Indian restaurant and now, in July 2022 have opened 'up north' in Adel – one of Leeds's northerly burbs. Judging from the pics, the decor in this newcomer is a tad more upmarket than in Ewell, but admittedly that's not setting the bar super-high. Many dishes are shared between the two menus – if they can replicate their success in Surrey this could be one of the more exciting openings in the city in recent years. / www.dastaan.co.uk/leeds; Tue-Sun 11 pm.

HANAMATSURI £170

580 MEANWOOD ROAD   LS6 4AZ

In January 2020, chef/patron Kaoru Nakamura changed direction at his small Japanese venture in Meanwood to adopt an omakase-style format. Feedback so far is too limited for a rating, but the odd report we receive tips this as a contender as Leeds's foremost dining experience. For £135 per person, you receive a selection of nigiri, sushi rolls and small plates with miso soup, tea and homemade ice cream. Other dishes (A5 grade Wagyu beef sashimi or spider roll) can also be pre-ordered as supplementary dishes. More reports please! / Mon & Tue, Thu-Sun 10 pm.

HOME £105 433

3 BREWERY PLACE LS10 1NE
0113 430 0161

"The new venue" and "absolutely brilliant menu" have "really taken things up a level" at Elizabeth Cottam's five-year-old venture, now in the city centre at Brewery Wharf on the River Aire. "The interior is very sexy and intimate, while the food has just gone up a notch", with "an astonishing set of dishes". / www.homeleeds.co.uk; home_leeds; Wed, Fri & Sat 8.30 pm, Sun 3.30 pm; closed Wed L closed Sun D, closed Mon & Tue & Thu; Cash only; booking is online only; children: 14.

THE IVY ASIA £85

55 VICAR LANE LS1 6BA

Richard Caring's swanky, spin-off Asian brand opened in Leeds in mid October 2022, complete with signature green onyx flooring, two large cherry blossom trees and the brand's customary culinary mishmash of sushi and sashimi, plus a hodge-podge of 'pan-Asian classics with a twist'. (The Man Behind the Curtain's Michael O'Hare was amongst local c'lebs Instagramming its launch party). / www.theivyasia.com; Sun-Thu 9 pm, Fri 4.30 pm.

KENDELLS BISTRO £57 333

ST PETERS SQUARE LS9 8AH
0113 2436553

"A warm and intimate" little bistro of over 15 years' standing near the Leeds Playhouse in traditional French style, with a blackboard menu. "It's even better value if you take advantage of the early-bird deals". / www.kendellsbistro.co.uk; kendellsbistro; Tue-Thu 9 pm, Fri & Sat 10 pm; closed Tue-Sat L, closed Sun & Mon; No Amex.

THE MAN BEHIND THE CURTAIN £63 444

TOP FLOOR FLANNELS, 68-78 VICAR LN LS1 7JH 0113 2432376

"Pure gastronomic theatre and drama" has won national fame for Michael O'Hare and – after some ups and downs in feedback over recent years – his moody and "romantic" basement in the city centre reestablished itself this year as the most commented-on venue in Leeds in our annual diners' poll. From a 10-14-course tasting menu, "the food pushes the limits of taste like at the Fat Duck and some dishes go a little far (oyster in a dessert?)". Not everyone's super-impressed, with the odd reporter feeling that "while the food's good, it's clear that everyone involved fancies themselves

too much". Significant disappointments are notable by their absence, though, with most diners feeling the place is on dazzling form. / www.themanbehindthecurtain.co.uk; ohare.michael; Tue-Sat 8.30 pm; closed Tue, Wed L, closed Sun & Mon; booking is online only.

THE OWL £68 433

LOCKSIDE. MUSTARD APPROACH, MUSTARD WHARF LS1 4EY
0113 5316621

"Recently moved from the market, but still with a down-to-earth feel" – this Leeds gastropub moved in early 2022 from Kirkgate market to Lockside, in the Mustard Wharf development, complete with a covered canalside terrace. It is run by a MasterChef semi-finalist (Liz Cottam) and a former head chef of Ilkley's Box Tree (Mark Owens), who also run Home. "The food is what every gastropub should be: delicious and always seasonal with their catch of the day". / www.theowlleeds.co.uk; theowlleeds; Wed-Sat 11 pm, Sun 5 pm; closed Wed L closed Sun D, Mon & Tue.

OX CLUB £68 332

19A THE HEADROW LS1 6PU
07470 359961

A contemporary café in a former textile mill, which sources its meat, fish and produce locally and serves them alongside "interesting and diverse wines". "Take your date for oysters, steak and woodfired burnt Basque cheesecake". / www.oxclub.co.uk; oxclubleeds; Wed-Sat 10 pm, Sun 5 pm; closed Wed-Fri L closed Sun D, closed Mon & Tue; Cash & all usual cards.

PRASHAD £52 433

137 WHITEHALL RD BD11 1AT
0113 285 2037

"They could convince me to go vegetarian" – so good is the "well-prepared and authentic" Gujarati food at this West Yorkshire legend (est. 1992). First timers say "everything is delicious, slightly novel without being scary": "it opened my eyes to several new Indian dishes I hadn't tried before". And "you just don't notice there's no meat or fish… impressive!" / www.prashad.co.uk; prashad_veggie; Tue-Thu 10.30 pm, Fri & Sat 11 pm, Sun 10 pm; closed Tue-Fri L, closed Mon; Cash & all usual cards.

THE RELIANCE £48 343

76-78 NORTH ST LS2 7PN
0113 295 6060

Tom Hunter's bar & dining room is "worth the walk beyond the centre of Leeds" for "food of a much higher standard than you would expect for the area, with a consistently interesting, changing menu of specials" which "often surprise and delight". There are both small and large plates, which makes it "a good option at any time of day", and "everything is very reasonably priced for the quality". / www.the-reliance.co.uk; the_reliance; Wed & Thu 11 pm, Fri & Sat midnight, Sun 9.30 pm; closed Wed & Thu L, closed Mon & Tue; payment – credit card only.

SALVO'S £62 343

115 & 107 OTLEY ROAD LS6 3PX
0113 275 2752

"I've been going to Salvo's for almost 40 years… it's still great" – this well-known Italian restaurant has been run by the Dammone family since 1976, providing pizza and pasta alongside more substantial dishes (including such Italian specials as 'hand-cut chips'!). / www.salvos.co.uk; salvosleeds; Sun-Thu 9 pm, Fri 9.30 pm, Sat 10 pm; No Amex.

SOUS LE NEZ EN VILLE £64 333

QUEBEC HS, QUEBEC ST LS1 2HA
0113 244 0108

For its many regulars, a meal at this "always-consistent French bistro" with a "great wine list of interesting bottles, including aged classics" is "the highlight of any trip to Leeds". The large basement venue has hosted business lunches and evening celebrations for more than 30 years. / www.souslenez.com; kitchensouslenez; Tue-Sat 11 pm; closed Sun & Mon; Cash & all usual cards.

THE SWINE THAT DINES £57 343

58 NORTH STREET LS2 7PN
0113 244 0387

"Perfectly executed and well-priced" dishes, including some "great puddings", win the seal of approval for this sharing-plates venue. "Mabgate is starting to become a very cool neighbourhood – due in no small part to the Swine". Top Tip – "those beef-fat buns!" / swinethatdines.co.uk; Thu-Sat 10.30 pm, Sun 5 pm; closed Thu & Fri L closed Sun D, closed Mon & Tue & Wed.

TATTU £76 233

29 EAST PARADE, MINERVA HOUSE LS1 5PS 0113 245 1080

Rooftop blossom and dark clubby decor help create a scene-y atmosphere at this popular branch of the upmarket national Chinese chain, which expanded to include a London outlet this year. One or two reports accuse it of "style over substance" but ratings overall are decent for its dim-sum and small plates selection. / www.tattu.co.uk; tatturestaurant; Mon-Sun midnight; closed Mon-Wed L; Cash & all usual cards; No shorts.

THARAVADU £46 443

7- 8 MILL HILL LS1 5DQ 0113 244 0500

"You would walk past it if you didn't know how good the food was inside" at this "buzzing" curry house (one of the city's most commented-on destinations) not far from the railway station (a favourite, it is claimed, of former India cricket captain Virat Kohli). The "slightly chaotic vibe is part of the charm" and it delivers "authentic south Indian tastes" with "absolutely delicious Keralan flavours" ("had probably the best dosa ever and an amazing range of fish curries dominate the menu"). /

www.tharavadurestaurants.com; tharavadu; Mon-Sat 9.30 pm; closed Sun; Cash & all usual cards.

WEN'S £37 3 3 2

72-74 NORTH STREET LS2 7PN
0113 244 4408

This family-run spot delivers "beautifully cooked" home-style dishes from Shandong, including their signature "lovely crispy dumplings for starters" and dan dan noodles. "We used to go here when it was Hansas (RIP), so it's great to find that Wen's Chinese restaurant also produces good-quality, authentic dishes". / wensrestaurant.co.uk; wensrestaurantleeds; Tue-Sat 9.30 pm; closed Tue-Fri L, closed Sun & Mon.

ZAAP £39 3 3 3

16 GRAND ARCADE LS1 6PG
0113 243 2586

"Delicious and fresh-tasting" grub served in a space "decorated like a Bangkok street market – there are even a couple of tuk tuks you can eat in" – adds up to a "cheap 'n' cheerful, tasty Thai street-food experience in the centre of Leeds". "Although it often looks packed, it's not difficult to get a place straight away – service is prompt and efficient". Launched in 2015, it now has spin-offs in Headingley, York, Newcastle, Nottingham and most recently Sheffield. / www.zaapthai.co.uk/zaap-leeds; zaap_thai_streetfood; Sun-Thu 10 pm, Fri & Sat 11 pm; no bookings.

ZUCCO £42 4 3 3

603 MEANWOOD ROAD LS6 4AY
01132 249679

"Arguably the best Italian restaurant in Leeds", according to fans of this "stylish and warm" fixture in slightly "out of town" Meanwood. It serves a "really outstanding menu with many small plates to satisfy everyone, including a wide variety of vegetarian dishes, plus a great selection of wines and cocktails too". / zucco. co.uk; zucco_meanwood; Tue-Thu 9.30 pm, Fri & Sat 10.30 pm, Sun 8.30 pm; closed Mon.

BOBBY'S £25 2 2 2

154-156 BELGRAVE RD LE4 5AT
0116 266 0106

This "longstanding vegetarian" was one of the first Gujarati canteens on Leicester's 'Golden Mile', founded by the late couple Bhagwanjibhai and Manglaben Lakhani in 1976 and named after a hit Bollywood film of the era (and is still family-run). It's always been a bit of an uneven performer, regularly inspiring dud reports, but equally consistently pleasing fans who feel "it always delivers great-tasting food". / www.eatatbobbys.com; eatatbobbys; Mon, Wed-Sun 8 pm; closed Tue; No Amex.

KAYAL £45 3 3 2

153 GRANBY ST LE1 6FE 0116 255 4667

A "fantastic, authentic-tasting southern Indian restaurant" close to the station. It is "very popular for visitors to the rugby" at Leicester Tigers' nearby Welford Road stadium. / www.kayalrestaurant.com; kayal_restaurants; Mon-Sat 11 pm, Sun 10 pm; Cash & all usual cards.

COOMBESHEAD FARM £109 5 3 4

COOMBESHEAD FARM PL15 7QQ
01566 782 009

"I just can't get over what a magical place this is" – chefs April Bloomfield (ex-Spotted Pig, NY) and Tom Adams (Pitt Cue, London) have combined to create a secluded guesthouse with a "farm-to-fork operation as it should be", with a "lovely relaxed atmosphere and friendly passionate staff". "The food is just fantastic, with amazing flavours and mostly vegetables, although items like pork and duck are wonderful too. And the bread is the best ever…" / www.coombesheadfarm.co.uk; ccoombesheadfarm; Thu-Sun 11 pm; closed Thu-Sun L, closed Mon & Tue & Wed; Cash & all usual cards.

FORK £62 3 3 3

14 STATION STREET BN7 2DA
01273 809445

"A great small restaurant with very creditable cooking and friendly engaged service". Chef Adam Paice's "good small menu focuses on well realised, straightforward food". / www.fork-lewes.co.uk; forklewes; Tue-Sat 9.30 pm; closed Tue-Thu L, closed Sun & Mon.

THE SANDPIPER INN £61 3 4 3

MARKET PLACE DL8 5AT 01969 622206

This stone-built, oak-floored eighteenth-century inn in a Wensleydale market town rates well for its "first-class cooking" and "staff who genuinely care about high standards". / www.sandpiperinn.co.uk; thesandpiperinn; Wed-Sat 8.30 pm; closed Mon & Tue & Sun.

THE BOAT INN £111 3 3 3

WALSALL ROAD WS14 0BU
01543361692

You're "always guaranteed a superb meal" from "a favourite top chef" – Liam Dillon (who has worked for the likes of Marcus Wareing and Tom Sellers) – at the "great pub" he has converted into an ambitious restaurant, with 4- and 6-course tasting menus in the evening and a chef's table option. / www.theboatinnlichfield.com; theboatinn_; Thu-Sun 9 pm; closed Thu L, closed Mon & Tue & Wed.

UPSTAIRS BY TOM SHEPHERD £99 5 4 4

25 BORE STREET WS13 6NA
01543 268877

"Already outstanding", this 2021 debut from a well-qualified chef hit the ground running, nabbing rave reviews within months of opening. The accolades are "thoroughly deserved" – "food and service are brilliantly executed" and there's a "nice relaxed vibe" in the 28-cover restaurant with a chef's table and roof terrace. Previously head chef at Adam's in Birmingham and development chef for Sat Bains, Tom Shepherd opened quite literally upstairs from his father's jewellery shop. / www.upstairs.restaurant; rest_upstairs; Wed-Sat 9 pm; closed Mon & Tue & Sun.

JEW'S HOUSE RESTAURANT £78 4 4 3

15 THE STRAIT LN2 1JD 01522 524851

"The amazing old building" adds to the appeal of this modern British stalwart, which (despite a fairly modern interior) occupies a twelfth-century building in the heart of this historic city. It's a good all-rounder though, which provided some reporters with their top gastronomic experience of the year, thanks to the "delicious cuisine" created by Gavin Aitkenhead and delivered seamlessly by staff overseen by FOH Samantha Tomkins. / www.jewshouserestaurant.co.uk; thejewshouserestaurant; Thu-Sat 9.30 pm, Sun 3 pm; closed Thu-Sat L closed Sun D, closed Mon & Tue & Wed; No Amex; booking is online only.

CHAMPANY INN £79 3 4 4

EH49 7LU 01506 834532

"The best steaks we have ever eaten!" – the Davidson family's roadside inn near Linlithgow has built its renown over four decades in operation, for the quality of its meat; and there's also a selection of prime-quality burgers. Reflecting their heritage, South African wines are the backbone of what's a high-quality list to bolster the generally red-blooded vibe. / www.champany.com; champanyinn; Wed-Sun 10 pm; closed Mon & Tue; Cash & all usual cards; No jeans; children: 8+.

NATHAN MARSHALL PRESTOR HOUSE £79 4 4 3

FARNHAM ROAD GU33 6JQ
01730 779360

"A husband and wife team run this small restaurant and run it well, with exceptional food and charming front of house service". Reports are few, but that's the low-down on this converted rural courthouse, now run by Nathan and Evi Marshall. The cuisine steers a line between being complex yet down-to-earth: for example your banoffee pie pudding is here presented as a soufflé! /

nathanmarshallsrestaurant.co.uk; n.marshall_chef; Thu-Sat 11 pm; closed Mon-Wed & Sun.

LITTLE ECCLESTON, LANCASHIRE 5–1A

THE CARTFORD INN £64 4|3|3

CARTFORD LANE   PR3 0YP
01995 670 166

"The indefatigable Beaume family put heart and art" into this "quirkily decorated boutique hotel and restaurant next to the toll bridge over the River Wyre". It's a "true gastropub" – "I've lunched in my jeans, I've dined in a dress, I've had beers at the bar and the welcome is the same" – and the "daily specials continue to be very reliable, while regular items like the oxtail pudding and French onion soup are things of hearty beauty". / www.thecartfordinn.co.uk; cartfordinn; Wed-Sat 9 pm, Sun 6 pm; closed Sun D, closed Mon & Tue; Cash & all usual cards; No shorts.

LITTLE HUCKLOW, DERBYSHIRE   5–2C

THE BLIND BULL £46 4|4|4

SK17 8RT   01298 211949

"Great renovation of an ancient inn, successfully brought back from dereliction" – this twelfth-century Peak District building is said to be the fifth-oldest pub in the country. It's "excellent at every level", serving "really good food" mostly sourced from within 10 miles, while the "newly added rooms look fantastic and will undoubtedly make this a destination". / theblindbull.co.uk; theblind_bull; Thu-Sat 9 pm, Sun 5 pm; closed Thu L closed Sun D, closed Mon & Tue & Wed.

LIVERPOOL, MERSEYSIDE   5–2A

ALBERT'S SCHLOSS

BOLD STREET   L1 4DG

This Manchester-based mock-Bavarian concept already has a small Liverpool outpost (Albert's Schenke), but a full-sized 'Schloss' is set to open in late 2022; Roy Ellis of Mission Mars says he plans to spend £3m on a complete

Bohemia, The Club Hotel & Spa, Jersey

refurbishment of a former food market at Radiant House. The art-deco building was formerly home to The Liverpool Gas Company and has been empty since 2019. / www.albertsschloss.co.uk; albertsschloss; Mon-Thu 9 pm, Fri & Sat 10 pm, Sun 7 pm.

THE ART SCHOOL £78 5|4|4

SUGNALL ST   L7 7EB   0151 230 8600

Paul Askew's "high-class" venue ("next door to the Philharmonic") is the most commented-on in 'The Pool' in our annual national diners' poll and wins extremely high scores for all aspects of the operation. "Brilliant" cooking is the main talking point, providing "very subtle flavours and textures from a varied and ambitious menu". But service too "is like a well-oiled machine" ("so slick!"), but with a touch of "Liverpool friendliness and good humour") and the venue itself is a "bright and airy space, complete with white linen and shining cutlery and tableware". Celebrating its eighth year: "this is a place to savour and it is a mystery as to why Paul does not get recognition from the Michelin guide". / www.theartschoolrestaurant.co.uk; theartschoolrestaurant; Tue-Sat 9.15 pm; closed Sun & Mon; Cash & all usual cards; No trainers.

BARNACLE £61

MEZZANINE, DUKE STREET MARKET, 46 DUKE STREET   L1 5AQ   0151 245 5113

Open in December 2021 – no feedback as yet on this new venture, which has a bird's eye view over the very good-looking Duke Street food market from its mezzanine. A number of local food glitterati are involved (including The Art School's Paul Askew and Bone & Block's Harry Marquart). The menu's local sourcing is evident, with the aim of creating an 'intimate Scouse brasserie'. / barnacleliverpool.co.uk; barnacleliverpool; Wed-Sat 9 pm, Sun 6 pm; closed Wed & Thu L closed Sun D, closed Mon & Tue.

BELZAN £52 4|4|3

371 SMITHDOWN ROAD   L15 3JJ
0151 733 8595

"Fantastic and friendly service", "amazing food" and a "lovely wine list" is the winning combination at this modest but high-achieving local bistro launched five years ago in a row of shops by owners Chris Edwards & Owain Williams with chef Sam Grainger. / belzan.co.uk; belzan_lpl; Wed-Sat 11 pm, Sun 6 pm; closed Wed-Sat L closed Sun D, closed Mon & Tue.

GAUCHO £87

7 WATER STREET   L2 0RD

While the upper floors of this former bank are turned into a ten-suite aparthotel, the ground floor will – in November 2022 – become the 18th member of this long-established chain, which majors in fine Latino steaks and one of the UK's best selections of South American wines. With Hawksmoor arriving in the city at a similar time, Liverpudlians have never had more ways of blowing their cash on a big old meat-fest! / Mon & Tue, Thu-Sun 10 pm.

HAWKSMOOR £94

INDIA BUILDINGS, 31 WATER STREET L2 0RD

In the Grade II-listed India Buildings, on the corner of Brunswick Street and Fenwick Street, Will Beckett and Huw Gott's steak (and nowadays seafood) phenomenon will add the city to its list of outposts, with an opening towards the end of 2022. If it can replicate the success of the Manchester debut a few years ago, this will be one of the most exciting things to happen to 'The Pool' in years. / hawksmoorrestaurants; closed Mon-Sat & Sun.

LERPWL £106 4|3|4

ALBERT DOCK   L3 4AD

Ellis & Liam Barrie's two-year-old Albert Dock venue is a tribute to Welsh produce – they made their name with Marram Grass on Anglesey – and showcases some of the "best seafood ever". It makes for a "fantastic meal out", with "excellent food, well-cooked and served" – whether you opt for tapas-style small plates or the full 8-course tasting menu. Top Tip – "ask to sit where you can watch the kitchen". / www.lerpwl.com; lerpwl; Fri & Sat 9.30 pm, Wed & Thu 9 pm, Sun 6 pm; closed Mon & Tue.

LUNYA £48 3|2|2

55 HANOVER STREET   L1 3DN
0151 706 9770

"This Liverpool tapas institution continues to go from strength to strength", with a "menu heavy on Spanish classics but with a Scouse twist" – "you do feel you're getting a genuine taste of Spain, with the fabulous paella and a great Spanish vermouth to kick things off". It was launched in 2010 by Peter & Elaine Kinsella, who followed up with Lunyalita in the Albert Dock. Top Tip – "don't miss the excellent Catalonian deli as well". / www.lunya.co.uk; lunyadeli; Mon & Tue 9 pm, Wed-Fri 9.30 pm, Sat 10 pm, Sun 8.30 pm; payment – credit card only.

LUNYALITA £46 3|3|4

UNIT 5, BRITANNIA PAVILION, ROYAL ALBERT DOCK   L3 4AD   0151 317 7199

Outdoor tables near the water are an option during good weather at Lunya's little sister – a two floor operation, with terrace and upstairs bar in a fabulous setting by Albert Dock. It serves an impressive range of tapas and sharing deli platters. / lunya.co.uk/lunyalita; lunyadeli; Mon-Wed 8.30 pm, Fri & Sat 9.30 pm, Thu 9 pm, Sun 8 pm.

MARAY £45 3|4|4

91 BOLD STREET   L1 4HF   0151 709 5820

"Levantine fusion small plates" are served "to a high standard in a bustling dockside location" at this busy venue inspired by the melting-pot cuisine of Le Marais in Paris. There's a "small but varied selection of dishes cooked really well, and a great choice of vegetable dishes". The 2014 Albert Dock original has been followed by branches in Bolod Street, Allerton and most recently Manchester. / www.maray.co.uk; marayrestaurants; Sun-Thu 10 pm, Fri & Sat 11 pm; Cash & all usual cards.

MOWGLI £42 3 4 4

69 BOLD ST   L1 4EZ   0151 708 9356

Former barrister Nisha Katona established the template for what is now an 18-strong (and counting) Indian street food chain with the 2014 launch of this "amazing conversion of an old bank", serving "fabulous dishes" in a "vibrant atmosphere, full of hustle and bustle". The "excellent value tiffin boxes" and "delicious yoghurt chaat bombs" are singled out for particular praise. Top Tip – "avoid sitting on one of the gimmicky swings, which prevent you from raising your elbows to eat!". / www.mowglistreetfood.com; mowglistreetfood; Sun-Thu 9.30 pm, Fri & Sat 10.30 pm.

PANORAMIC 34, WEST TOWER £69 3 4 5

BROOK STREET   L3 9PJ   0151 236 5534

"Magnificent distant views of Snowdonia are the highlight of this establishment" on the 34th floor of the West Tower – although the "great modern food and service make for a lovely dining experience" that is "definitely one for romantics watching the city views at night". Chef Elliot Hill left in June 2022 (after our annual diners' poll concluded) to head up the kitchens of the Chester Grosvenor, but we've held the ratings as the food here historically has always been surprisingly good for a 'room with a view'. / www.panoramic34.com; panoramic34liverpool; Tue-Sat 9.30 pm, Sun 8 pm; closed Mon; No Amex; No trainers.

PEN FACTORY £41 3 3 3

13 HOPE ST   L1 9BQ   0151 709 7887

This "buzzy bar-cum-diner" next door to the Everyman Theatre is Paddy Byrne's reincarnation of the original Everyman Bistro, serving "small plates of simple but delicious food" and "slightly quirky specials for a quick dinner". It has a "great atmosphere", and "although the acoustics aren't great it's a lot of fun". / www.pen-factory.co.uk; the_pen_factory; Tue, Wed 11 pm, Thu-Sat midnight; closed Sun & Mon; No Amex.

ROSKI £111 5 4 3

**16 RODNEY STREET   L1 2TE
0151 708 8698**

"Amazing food and good value compared to equivalent standards elsewhere" help inspire ongoing high ratings for MasterChef: The Professionals winner, Anton Piotrowski's stylishly sparse venue. Its 8-course tasting menu for £85 wins it very high ratings from fans. The only gripe? – "wish they had smaller menus in the evening: by the final courses I am just too full!" / www.roskirestaurant.com; roskirestaurant; Thu-Sat, Wed 9.30 pm; closed Wed L, closed Mon & Tue & Sun; No Amex; children: 8.

SALT HOUSE £59 3 3 3

**1 HANOVER STREET   L1 3DW
0151 706 0092**

Two-level tapas haunt opposite John Lewis that's "still a big favourite" thanks to its "interesting" selection of dishes. "The only drawback can be the noise – it's a high space with a mezzanine level and lots of hard surfaces, so it is difficult to talk when it's busy". / www.salthousetapas.co.uk; salthousetapas?ref=badge; Mon-Sun 10.30 pm; Cash & all usual cards.

SPIRE £53 4 4 3

**1 CHURCH ROAD   L15 9EA
0151 734 5040**

"The Locke boys are still 'smashing it' in south Liverpool with fresh seasonal dishes..." say fans of Adam and Matt's "top-notch local", a short stroll from Penny Lane. "It's a little crushed when it's full, but worth accepting that for what you get": "the food is always excellent and served by friendly staff". / www.spirerestaurant.co.uk; Wed-Fri 9 pm, Sat 9.30 pm, Sun 5.30 pm; closed Sat L closed Sun D, closed Mon & Tue; Cash & all usual cards.

WRECKFISH £53 3 3 2

60 SEEL STREET   L1 4BE   0151 707 1960

"Good quality cooking and ingredients" and "wonderful helpful staff who never intrude" keep everything ticking over nicely at the Liverpool outpost of chef-entrepreneur Gary Usher's Elite Bistros operation, which opened five years ago on the strength of a £200,000 crowdfunding drive. It has a "limited menu, but done well", which helps keep costs from spiralling. / wreckfish.co; wreckfish_bistro; Mon-Sat 10 pm, Sun 5 pm; closed Sun D.

LLANDAFF, CARDIFF   2–2A

HEATHCOCK £42 3 3 3

**58 - 60 BRIDGE STREET   CF5 2EN
029 2115 2290**

In one of Cardiff's leafy 'burbs, this large pub (sibling to the Hare & Hounds at Aberthin) has acquired something of a foodie reputation with a listing from Michelin and a visit this year from the Observer's Jay Rayner, who discerned a "pleasingly straightforward approach to the business of feeding people well" with "a touch of St John about it" too ("white, utilitarian spaces", offal, ox heart, pickled walnuts, duck fat, etc). Our feedback remains quite limited, but very upbeat all-round. / www.heathcockcardiff.com; heathcock_cardiff; Wed-Sat 9.30 pm, Sun 4 pm; closed Wed L closed Sun D, closed Mon & Tue; Cash & all usual cards.

LLANDEWI SKIRRID, MONMOUTHSHIRE   2–1A

THE WALNUT TREE £95 4 3 3

**LLANDDEWI SKIRRID   NP7 8AW
01873 852797**

"Our favourite restaurant when in Wales" – this "treasure" of a gastropub was made famous

in the 1970s (by Ann and Franco Taruschio) and under Shaun Hill (at the stoves since 2008) "maintains an enviable reputation" for "dizzyingly good food in the absolute middle of nowhere". Regulars say it's "like going to dine with an old friend in complete relaxation", but with "top-flight" cuisine that's also grounded and "making extensive use of excellent local produce" ("the best ever lamb…", "unbelievable cheese soufflé…", "great value lunch with pork rillettes with pickles and toast"). And it's quite "reasonably priced" too. Aged 74, Shaun has been threatening to step back for years: "make sure you get there before he retires!" / www.thewalnuttreeinn.com; lovethewalnuttree; Wed-Sat 9.30 pm; closed Mon & Tue & Sun; Cash & all usual cards.

LLANDRILLO, DENBIGHSHIRE   4–2D

TYDDYN LLAN £94 4 4 4

LL21 0ST   01490 440264

"You have to go a long way to find better food and surroundings" than Bryan & Susan Webb's comfortable former hunting lodge, where "great produce is cooked to perfection, service is always just right", and the wine list is superb. You may have to be quick to book a meal, though: the couple put the place on the market last summer and have their eyes on retirement. Bryan has been a chef for more than 45 years, and they opened here 21 years ago. / www.tyddynllan.co.uk; Wed-Sun 9 pm; closed Mon & Tue; Cash & all usual cards; credit card deposit required to book.

LLANDUDNO, CONWY   4–1D

BODYSGALLEN HALL, DINING ROOM £95 3 3 3

**THE ROYAL WELSH WAY   LL30 1RS
01492 584466**

In the "stylish National Trust-owned surroundings" of this Grade I-listed seventeenth-century manor house on the outskirts of town – run these days as a spa hotel – this dining room is notable for its reliable standards, although it is "not adventurous in any way", and the formality can make for a "slightly stuffy atmosphere" for some tastes. Unless you have a major appetite, you do "need to decide between afternoon tea and dinner" – both would be a stretch! / www.bodysgallen.com; bodysgallenhallspa; Mon-Sun 9 pm; Cash & all usual cards; No trainers; children: 6+.

TOPS 3 3 2

**43 MOSTYN AVENUE   LL30 1YY
01492 876729**

"Best Chinese in Llandudno" is arguably a double-edged compliment to this well-established fixture, which occupies an old ice cream factory in this characterful Victorian seaside resort. But local reporters say its cooking is "consistently good" – "vegetables and fish dishes always seem particularly fresh and tasty". / Mon-Sun 10.30 pm; closed Mon-Sun L.

THE CORN MILL   £51   334

DEE LN   LL20 8PN   01978 869555

"In a beautiful setting adjacent to the River Dee and with decking overhanging the river, this former watermill with wheel could not be better located with stunning views from all windows". The "food is of a high standard", but it is the backdrop of the racing water of the River Dee that creates a memorable experience at this Brunning & Price operation. "Get a table outside for an unforgettable meal". / www.brunningandprice.co.uk/cornmill; cornmillpub; Mon-Sat 11.30 pm, Sun 11 pm; Cash & all usual cards.

LLANGOED HALL   £92   334

LD3 0YP   01874 754525

This "fab former stately home" set in "beautiful grounds" in the Welsh countryside was restored by Laura Ashley co-founder Sir Bernard Ashley. Known for its "exceptional food", it has lost two highly regarded head chefs in recent years, Nick Brodie and Sam Bowser, but still achieves strong ratings across the board. / www.llangoedhall.com; llangoedhall; Thu-Sun midnight; closed Mon & Tue & Wed; No Amex; No trainers; children: 12.

CHAPTER ONE   £78   433

**FARNBOROUGH COMMON   BR6 8NF
01689 854848**

This big-hitter on London's southeastern fringe has established an enviable reputation for its "excellent food" under long-time chef Andy McLeish, who now owns it alongside a business partner – "have been dining here some 25 years and never been disappointed". Following a refurb a couple of years back, it is, by all accounts, better than ever – "fell out of love with this restaurant, but am delighted to report that it's back on top form". / www.chaptersrestaurants.com; chapteronekent; Wed & Thu 9 pm, Fri & Sat 9.30 pm, Sun 3 pm; closed Sun D, closed Mon & Tue; Cash & all usual cards; No trainers; booking max 10 may apply; children: 5.

THE HOLLIST ARMS   £39   433

GU28 9BZ   01798 861310

This "excellent South Downs destination in a picture-perfect village" – "with fine, restaurant-quality cooking" from chef Jesse Bryson (ex-Noble Rot and Leroy) – "is flourishing for good reason". The stone-built seventeenth-century pub was taken over in 2020 by Angus Davies, a former manager at Chez Bruce and Lorne. / www.thehollistarms.com; thehollistarms; Wed-Sat 9 pm, Sun 3 pm; closed Sun D, closed Mon & Tue.

OXHEART   £86

**50 MAIN STREET   CV36 5JJ
01608 684505**

Opened in June 2021, this 'micro-restaurant in the Cotswolds' offers an ambitious tasting experience to no more than 11 people at a time. No feedback as yet in our annual diners' poll, but Marina O'Loughlin of the Sunday Times paid an early visit saying: "I can't remember the last time I had such an assured ten-course tasting menu with wines – even a martini each – where the bill didn't cost north of a ton a head". / www.oxheart.co.uk; restaurant.oxheart; Fri & Sat 10 pm; closed Fri & Sat L, closed Mon-Thu & Sun; booking is online only; children: 14.

THE MOLE & CHICKEN   £58   334

**EASINGTON LANE   HP18 9EY
01844 208387**

"A delightful find" – this "exceptionally welcoming" village pub with five rooms and an attractive garden just off the M40 has "excellent food" and "spectacular views" over countryside on the Oxfordshire-Buckinghamshire border. / www.themoleandchicken.co.uk; themoleandchicken; Mon-Sat 8.45 pm, Sun 4.30 pm; closed Sun D; Cash & all usual cards.

ASQUITHS   £54   443

**19 NORTH STREET   PL22 0EF
01208 871714**

"A small and intimate restaurant" – opposite an old church in Cornwall's antiques capital – Graham Cuthbertson's wood-panelled spot "serves great modern European and local dishes and the dining room is really comfortable". "I went there with all my family and they were really accommodating with young children". / asquithsrestaurant.co.uk; Wed-Sat 8.30; closed Wed-Sat L, closed Mon & Tue & Sun.

THE HAMMER & PINCERS   £74   443

5 EAST RD   LE12 6ST   01509 880735

"High standards and consistently delicious, creative food" have been the hallmarks of Savoy-trained chef-patron Danny Jimminson and his wife Sandra's former village forge for two decades. With its ambitious 8-course tasting menus, it is very much a "gastropub pressing towards purely restaurant status" and provided some local reporters' best meal of the year. / www.hammerandpincers.co.uk; thehammerandpincers; Tue-Sat 9 pm; closed Sun & Mon; No Amex.

THE PASS RESTAURANT, SOUTH LODGE HOTEL   £107

**BRIGHTON ROAD   RH13 6PS
01403 891711**

In the second half of 2022 (well after our annual diners' poll had concluded), Ben Wilkinson (formerly of The Cottage in the Woods) was named as chef to relaunch the open kitchen, chef's counter operation at this foodie hotel. It hit fame when it first launched in 2008, quickly winning a Michelin star, when it was one of the early adopters of the now-ubiquitous open dining-as-theatre approach. In recent years it has struggled to hit an even keel seeing a number of chefs come and go for different reasons. His eight-course menu is £120 per person. / www.exclusive.co.uk/south-lodge/ restaurants-bars/the-pass; exclusive_uk; Thu-Sun 8.30 pm; closed Thu & Fri L, closed Mon & Tue & Wed; Cash & all usual cards; children: 12+.

YALBURY COTTAGE   £78   343

DT2 8PZ   01305 262382

This "lovely cottage" in the heart of Thomas Hardy country serves "very good British food with interesting twists" from owner Jamie Jones, a former exec chef with Four Seasons hotels who settled here with his wife Ariane in 2007. The novelist would have known the 300-year-old thatched shepherd's cottage well – he was born a mile away and grew up in the village. The Joneses also run the Yalbury Café in nearby Dorchester. / www.yalburycottage.com; Tue-Sat 8.30 pm, Sun 2 pm; closed Sun D, closed Mon; No Amex; practically no walk-ins – you must book.

THE COMPASSES INN   £58   333

SP3 6NB   01722 714318

"Always worth the journey (although it can be impossible to find a space in the car park!)" – this characterful thatched pub with four bedrooms, a self-catering cottage and beer garden) is owned by fooderati royalty (Fay Maschler's son, Ben Maschler). The menu divides between 'Pub' (burger, fish 'n' chips) and much more interesting and hardly more costly 'Mains', of a more bistro-style variety. / thecompassesinn.com; thecompasses; Mon-Sun 11 pm.

THE SLAUGHTERS MANOR HOUSE   £122   333

COPSEHILL RD   GL54 2HP   01451 820456

"The dining room is a lovely room… the service is attentive… the food is interesting and very good" – this gorgeously located manor house hotel (part of the Brownsword group) receives nothing but praise in our annual diners' poll, including for Nick Chappell's accomplished three-course menu. / www.slaughtersmanor.co.uk; slaughtersmanor; Tue-Thu 9 pm, Fri & Sat 9.30 pm; closed Sun & Mon; Cash & all usual cards; No jeans; children: 8.

THE CHARLTON ARMS, CHARLTON ARMS HOTEL   £59 343

LUDFORD BRIDGE   SY8 1PJ
01584 872813

"The views from the window tables overlooking the river are stunning" at Cedric (brother of Claude) Bosi and his wife Amy's well-established inn, on the Ludford Bridge (and with outdoor seating). Its gastrofare provides "a high standard of preparation and presentation" and "is reasonably priced, as are the wines". "Well-kept real ales" too. / www.thecharltonarms.co.uk; charltonarmsludlow; Mon-Sun 8.15 pm; closed Mon & Tue L; Cash & all usual cards.

THE CLIVE RESTAURANT WITH ROOMS   £55

BROMFIELD   SY8 2JR   01584 856565

This comfy B&B in a Georgian House (with 17 bedrooms) is one of the better places to stay in this foodie corner of Shropshire, a short drive from Ludlow. Limited feedback on the seasonal cuisine served in its dining room, but such as there is says it's good all-round. / www.theclive.co.uk; theclivearms; Mon & Tue 7.30 pm, Wed-Sat 10.30 pm, Sun 5 pm; closed Mon-Sat L closed Sun D; Cash & all usual cards.

CSONS AT THE GREEN CAFE   £45 334

DINHAM MILLENNIUM GREEN   SY8 1EG
01584 879872

Maybe avoid the culinary fireworks for which this foodie town is known, and head to this gorgeously situated café, with a "really nice outdoor space" near the River Teme and beneath the walls of Ludlow Castle. Run by local food heroes, the Crouch brothers (who also operate in Shrewsbury) it provides tea, coffee, cakes, breakfast, lunch and dinner on Friday night. / thegreencafe.co.uk; csons_food; profile picture csons_food; Mon-Thu, Sat & Sun 4 pm, Fri 10 pm; closed Mon-Thu, Sat & Sun D; Cash & all usual cards.

GOLDEN MOMENTS £39   443

50 BROAD STREET   SY8 1NH
01584 878 488

"For 20 years this restaurant has shown what good Indian food should be", with its "great, freshly cooked" meals that include "the usual favourites as well as more interesting dishes". Prominent former Ludlow chefs including Shaun Hill and Claude Bosi count themselves fans, but sadly "it seems this could be its last year before the building reverts to housing", following a change-of-use application from the landlord. / www.goldenmomentsofludlow.co.uk;

Mon, Wed-Sun 10 pm; closed Mon, Wed-Sun L, closed Tue; Cash & all usual cards.

MORTIMERS   £81   343

17 CORVE ST   SY8 1DA   01584 872 325

"The food can be exceptional", while "service is spot-on without being overbearing and condescending" in chef Wayne Smith's oak-panelled dining room – a lingering taste of Ludlow's former heyday as a gastronomic destination. The cuisine may not quite match the heights of Claude Bosi's late, lamented Hibiscus, which used to occupy the same premises – but "it is certainly value for money". / www.mortimersludlow.co.uk; mortimersludlow; Thu-Sat, Wed 8 pm; closed Wed L, closed Mon & Tue & Sun; Cash & all usual cards; credit card deposit required to book.

OLD DOWNTON LODGE   £81   444

DOWNTON ON THE ROCK   SY8 2HU
01568 771826

"Absolutely lovely surroundings, worth a 6/5 for ambience!" – this medieval-to-Georgian country house with its own cider press, just outside Ludlow, is a "glorious" setting for newly installed chef Nick Bennett's "tip-top", "creative, inventive and delicious" cooking; and his "set menus offer just enough choice over a 3-night stay". Pippa & Willem Vlok are "such friendly owners". / www.olddowntonlodge.com; olddowntonlodge; Mon-Sun 8.30 pm; closed Mon-Sun L; Cash & all usual cards; children: 13.

HIX OYSTER & FISH HOUSE   £66   333

COBB RD   DT7 3JP   01297 446910

Mark Hix's primely positioned and well-known seafood spot in Lister Gardens (with outside decking, although this is currently a source of local dispute with The Lyme Regis Society) is known for its "good relaxed vibe" and views over Lyme Bay. It is still mostly applauded for some "excellent dishes", but ratings dipped this year with a number of reporters clearly expecting a little more from such a high-profile chef: "it's a nice but not a wow restaurant" – "food was fine but hardly mind-blowing". / theoysterandfishhouse.co.uk; theoysterandfishhouse; Mon-Sat 9.15 pm, Sun 3 pm; closed Sun D; Cash & all usual cards.

LILAC   £35   333

CELLAR 57-58 BROAD STREET   DT7 3QD
07308 079427

This 400-year cellar serves "tasty small plates of interesting food and a good wine list, featuring lots of natural wines". It's the little sister of Harriet Mansell's nearby restaurant Robin Wylde, operated with the same local and sustainable ethos. / www.lilacwine.co.uk; lilacfoodandwine; Wed-Sun 9 pm; closed Wed-Sun L, closed Mon & Tue.

ROBIN WYLDE   £80   554

63 SILVER STREET   DT7 3QE
07717 227094

"We've dined in numerous Michelin-starred restaurants through the last year but none have come close to this" – chef Harriet Mansell's "fabulous" debut (following a series of successful pop-ups), which has earned a unanimous string of accolades. There's "a real sense of ownership here. The tasting menu (which seems to depend partly on what has been foraged that day) is creative and exceptionally good. The accompanying wine flight is well chosen (partly English) and balanced, staff informative and helpful and the owner/chef very chatty and open. A superb evening". The sister wine cellar Lilac nearby is run with the same ethos, serving snacks and casual meals. / www.robinwylde.com; robinwyldedining; Mon-Sun 6 am.

TOM'S LYME REGIS   £80   334

MARINE PARADE   DT7 3JQ
01297 816018

"Overlooking the sea in the best spot in Lyme Regis!" – this attractive establishment wins consistently good ratings for its short, fish-focused menu. "Get a window seat or sit outside on the terrace for a top view of the bay". / www.tomslymeregis.com; toms_lymeregis; Thu-Sat 8.30 pm; closed Mon L closed Sun D.

ELDERFLOWER   £101   543

QUAY ST   SO41 3AS   01590 676908

"Seemingly booked up months in advance following a TV appearance but definitely worth the wait if you like high-end food" – Andrew & Marjolaine du Bourg's "sophisticated little restaurant, set in the pretty town of Lymington" is firmly establishing itself on the foodie map (having also had a recent rave from the FT Magazine). "It serves up a delicious 'surprise' tasting experience, using local, seasonal ingredients. Full of little flavour bombs... this is impeccable cookery at its best. Service is highly professional, explaining each dish as it is served". "Exceptional!" / www.elderflowerrestaurant.co.uk; Wed-Fri 8.30 pm, Sat 08.30 pm, Sun 2 pm; closed Sun D, closed Mon & Tue; Cash & all usual cards.

RIVAAZ   £35   443

7 SAINT THOMAS STREET   SO41 9NA
01590 679999

This "exceptional, well-run Indian restaurant", a fixture in the town for 15 years, wins high ratings across the board for its "great menu, good staff, and well-priced dishes". Reporters are lavish in their praise of what one described as "among the very best meals I have ever eaten – every dish was perfection". / www.rivaazdining.com; rivaazlymington; closed Mon-Sat & Sun.

LYMM, CHESHIRE — 5–2B

THE CHURCH GREEN   £73   3 3 4

HIGHER LANE   WA13 0AP   01925 752068

Ex-Manchester House chef, Aiden Byrne's attractive pub is cutely situated opposite said St Mary's Church in one of the scenic commuter towns on the Cheshire/Greater Manchester borders. Steaks, burgers, pies and the likes of lobster and chips typify its quality gastrofare; and they also serve pizza and snacks from their garden 'shack'. / www.aidenbyrne.co.uk; thechurchgreen; Mon-Fri 9 pm, Sat 10 pm, Sun 7 pm; No Amex.

LA BOHEME   £57   4 4 3

3 MILL LANE   WA13 9SD   01925 753657

"French cuisine at its best!" – "the eclectic menu leaves you spoiled for choice" at this "comfortable restaurant (ideal for romance)" opened in 2000 by chef-patron Olivier Troalen, who arrived in England to work at the French Embassy in London before heading north, where he hopes to be acknowledged as 'the Cantona of cooking'. "Service is speedy and you certainly won't feel disappointed with either the standard or size of the dishes". / laboheme. co.uk; oliviertroalen_laboheme; Wed-Sat 8.30 pm, Sun 7.30 pm; closed Sat L, closed Mon & Tue; Cash & all usual cards.

LYNDHURST, HAMPSHIRE — 2–4C

HARTNETT HOLDER & CO, LIME WOOD HOTEL   £100   3 3 4

BEAULIEU RD   SO43 7FZ   02380 287177

"A beautiful restaurant in a stunning hotel" in the New Forest – this co-production from Anglo-Italian celeb chef Angela Hartnett and Luke Holder achieves good ratings for its "delicious, excellently presented food and charming service". Most reports here are unreserved rave reviews, and even the odd diner who finds the offering overpriced concedes "at least cooking and service have risen to the challenge: a bowl of lobster spaghetti cost an arm and a leg, but it was a faultless dish". / www.limewoodhotel.co.uk/food/hh-and-co; limewoodhotel; Mon-Sun 9 pm; booking max 4 may apply.

MAIDEN BRADLEY, SOMERSET — 2–3B

THE BRADLEY HARE   £52   3 2 2

CHURCH STREET   BA12 7HW   01985 801018

This plush June 2021 launch from an ex-Soho House team on the Duke of Somerset's estate (it used to be named after him) offers a "brilliantly executed dining experience plus fantastic rooms to stay in". FOH Ben Jones and chef Nye Smith "are an emerging force in great destination hospitality" – although they have yet to fully persuade reporters that they have achieved their stated aim of creating the 'best pub in the South West of England'. /

www.thebradleyhare.co.uk; thebradleyhare; Tue-Sat 9 pm, Sun 8.30 pm; closed Tue L, closed Mon.

MAIDENHEAD, BERKSHIRE — 3–3A

THE CROWN AT BURCHETTS GREEN   £58

BURCHETTS GREEN   SL6 6QZ   01628 824079

In June 202, Dom Chapman took on this well-known Thames-valley pub (he also owns The Beehive in White Waltham, see also), which had been run by the Bonwick family for the previous nine years. It opened too late for feedback in our annual diners' poll, but an early report from fooderati insider, Andy Hayler, suggested that Champan will be continuing the high quality of The Beehive and also the Bonwicks' former regime here: "service… was excellent. Overall, this was a very enjoyable evening, The Crown offering a very appealing menu and generally well-made food. … this is already shaping up to be a charming restaurant, and based on the chef's track record I expect the food to progress further from this solid start". / crownburchettsgreen.com; Tue-Sat 9 pm; closed Sun & Mon.

MANCHESTER, GREATER MANCHESTER — 5–2B

ADAM REID AT THE FRENCH, MIDLAND HOTEL   £138   5 4 4

PETER ST   M60 2DS   01612354780

"Located in a grande dame of a Manchester hotel" – don't let the fact that this bastion of the city (where Mr Rolls first met Mr Royce) is situated in the heart of a classic traditional hotel gull you into thinking that its glory days (it held the city's first Michelin star until losing it in 1975) are behind it. "Once you walk through the doors of the restaurant, you do feel removed from the hotel" – a "delightful" setting – and 'The French' is "worthy of a visit for Adam Reid's tasting menu food that fully delivers on the hit to the tastebuds". "It's not all serious plates, with some playful dishes offering something a little different and intriguing" and – though not as commented-on as Mana nowadays – some diners still hail it as "the best culinary experience in Manchester". / www.themidlandhotel.co.uk; thefrenchmcr; Wed-Sat 8.30 pm; closed Wed-Sat L, closed Mon & Tue & Sun; Cash & all usual cards; No trainers; children: 8.

THE ALAN   £61

18 PRINCESS STREET   M1 4LG   0161 236 8999

Very promising but limited (too much so for a rating) feedback on the food at this funky new boutique hotel, which opened shortly before our annual diners' poll concluded and inhabits a six-storey building near Chinatown. The Observer's Jay Rayner was an early fan too, declaring in a May 2022 review that – "the kitchen… led by chef Iain Thomas, is cooking a truly delightful and admirably tight menu of diverting dishes, which reveal their joys a little at a time… and all at a price positioned to

comfort rather than terrorise". / thealanhotel. com; Mon-Sun 9.45 pm.

ALMOST FAMOUS   3 3 2

49-51 EDGE STREET   M4 1H2   0161 244 9424

Manchester's own dirty burger brand (it now has branches in Liverpool and Leeds) is – its loyal fans insist – "the best in the UK, by a mile". They have partnered with Aubrey Allen – 'literally the best butcher in the country: they deliver to Buckingham Palace ffs' – to develop an ultra-juicy and tender burger with flavour to match. There are now four in town, although the original on High Street closed this year, moving to the nearby site vacated by Home Sweet Home (RIP). / www.almostfamousburgers.com; almostfamous; Mon & Tue, Thu-Sun 10 pm; no bookings.

THE BLACK FRIAR   £64   3 3 3

13 KING STREET   M3 7DB   0161 667 9555

Closed for 15 year following fire damage, this handsome late-Victorian tavern in Salford was transformed for its 2021 reopening, and now "feels like a country pub when you walk in but then morphs into a very smart restaurant at the back". Chef Ben Chaplin (ex-20 Stories in Spinningfields) has put together a menu that addresses both sides of the equation – winning plaudits for some 'serious cookery' from the Observer's Jay Rayner, among others. / www.theblackfriarsalford.co.uk; theblackfriarsalford; Tue-Thu, Sun 10 pm, Fri & Sat 11 pm; closed Mon.

BUNDOBUST   £33   3 2 3

61 PICCADILLY   M1 2AG   0161 359 6757

"Terrific vegetarian Indian street food" specialist that "wears its shabby-chic location with style" – it's also "great value", and the craft beer "isn't too bad, either". "Don't be put off by the service rating as it's largely self-service – which is part of its charm". The hit formula has led to branches in Leeds and Liverpool, and most recently a cavernous brewery-restaurant across town in Oxford Street. It's the "best casual dining space for a single diner" while also catering well for groups through its (almost) everything-on-the-menu-for-£100 deal, that should feed 6. / www.bundobust.com; bundobust; Mon-Thu 9.30 pm, Fri & Sat 10 pm, Sun 8 pm; payment – credit card only.

CANTO   3 3 4

CUTTING ROOM SQUARE, BLOSSOM STREET   M4 5DH   0161 870 5904

This "buzzing place with a fine selection of Mediterranean tapas" is Simon Shaw's follow-up to El Gato Negro, where he pioneered Hispanic cuisine in Manchester. The "laid-back atmosphere", "authentic food" and "great wine list" all impress, while head chef Carlos Gomes adds a taste of his native Portugal to the mix. / www.cantorestaurant.com; cantomcr; Mon-Sun midnight; closed Mon-Thu L; Cash & all usual cards.

Woven, Coworth Park, Ascot

CROMA £32 3|3|3

500 WILBRAHAM RD M21 9AP
0161 881 1117

"Always buzzing, with very helpful staff" – this "busy but reliable" pizza-stop in Chorlton is now – since the demise of its much-missed city-centre counterpart – the most commented-on branch of this small Mancunian pizza chain. It's most often nominated for being "excellent with children". / www.cromapizza.co.uk; cromapizza; Mon-Thu 9 pm, Fri & Sat 9.30 pm, Sun 8.30 pm; closed Mon-Fri L; Cash & all usual cards; may need 6+ to book.

DAKOTA GRILL £112

DAKOTA HOTEL, 29 DUCIE STREET
M1 2JL 0161 674 9180

Stylishly decorated, comfortable and good value hotel dining room which didn't attract feedback in our annual diners' poll, but which in March 2022 Giles Coren of the Times complimented – in between lots of gauche commentary on the nature of Manchester women – for its excellent steaks, grills and fish. An even better read is the riposte a week later from Ben Arnold in The Manchester Evening News – similarly upbeat on the "wildly reasonable" pricing of the restaurant along with its steaks and wines, but about Giles… not so much. / www.dakotahotels.co.uk/manchester/grill; dakotahotel_mcr; Mon-Sat 9.30 pm, Sun 9 pm.

DISHOOM £48 4|4|5

32 BRIDGE STREET M3 3BT
AWAITING TEL

The all-conquering chain brings its "fabulous menu" of "inventive Indian dishes", "full of really great surprises", to a "stunning, evocative room" in a former Freemasons' lodge. "I haven't missed a meal here in my last 15 trips to Manchester and for a good reason!". "The millennial metropolitans (my daughters) may have decided that it is over-rated, but for me it's a wonderful experience". Top Tip – "the lamb shank biryani, which is unique to Manchester, is always top-notch". / www.dishoom.com; dishoommcr; Sun-Thu 11 pm, Fri & Sat midnight.

THE EDINBURGH CASTLE £53 3|3|3

BLOSSOM STREET M4 5AN

"Awesome gastropub" on a prominent corner in Ancoats dating from 1811, but which was abandoned as the industrial suburb around it declined. It was restored from dereliction and reopened three years ago with a restaurant upstairs, as the locality has redeveloped around it. It serves "a good choice of reasonably priced dishes", including "decent roasts on a Sunday". / www.ec-ancoats.com; ec_ancoats; Sun-Thu 11 pm, Fri & Sat midnight; payment – credit card only.

ERST £25 5|4|4

9 MURRAY STREET M4 6HS
0161 826 3008

The "incredible tastes" created by chef Patrick Withington make this "unpretentious place with a modern interior", "a wonderful find in a rejuvenated and restored Victorian street in Ancoats" – "I could eat here every day". The "light dishes designed for sharing" are "served by enthusiastic staff who clearly love the food", while the "interesting" list of natural wines is "curated by people who really have a passion for their work and know what they are doing". / www.erst-mcr.co.uk; erst_mcr; Tue-Sat 10.30 pm; closed Sun & Mon; booking is online only.

ESCAPE TO FREIGHT ISLAND £54 3|3|4

BARING STREET M1 2PY 0161 806 0078

This vast street-food and entertainment concept accommodating up 1,000 visitors in an old freight depot by Piccadilly station is simply "another world" – "a mind-blowing-sized venue and organisation" where "the food is not really the main attraction" – although there is plenty of sufficient quality to earn high ratings, from 15 different restaurants and bars in an "eclectic mix" that ranges from Voodoo Rays pizza, Brad Carter's One Stop Döner Bar and asador grills from Baratxuri to tacos from Madre. / www.escapetofreightisland.com; escapetofreightisland; Mon-Thu 11 pm, Fri & Sat 1 am, Sun 10 pm; closed Mon-Fri L.

EVUNA £52 3|2|3

277 - 279 DEANSGATE M3 4EW
0161 819 2752

This Deansgate-based quartet offers a "great selection of tapas", after two decades at the forefront of Hispanic cuisine in Manchester. The excitement level has fallen off a little in recent years, but there's little to suggest that standards have greatly declined. The original is now joined by branches in the Northern Quarter, Knutsford and Altrincham. / evuna. com; evunarestaurants; Mon-Sat 11 pm, Sun 9 pm; Cash & all usual cards.

EL GATO NEGRO £69 4|3|4

52 KING STREET M2 4LY 0161 694 8585

"Wherever you sit – the downstairs bar, the rooftop terrace (lovely on the top floor in summer), one of the booths – you can hardly go wrong and the tapas remain excellent" at Simon Shaw's happening multi-level townhouse, which remains one of the more high-profile locations in the city. "It's hard to criticise anything, everything is just done really well", and it helps that "staff are well informed". / www.elgatonegrotapas.com; elgatonegromanc; Mon-Sun 10 pm.

GREENS £47 4|4|3

43 LAPWING LN M20 2NT 0161 434 4259

A Didsbury institution for its "creative vegan and vegetarian" cooking for more than 30 years, Simon Rimmer's "excellent little restaurant" is surfing the wave of plant-based dining, and opened its first spin-off last year, in Stanley Square, Sale, last summer. "Dishes are divine and you're always spoilt for choice on all courses", with "lots of seasonal produce". "Simon is often seen in his chef's apron and is always happy to say hello – long may that continue!". / www.greensdidsbury.co.uk; greensdidsbury; Mon-Sat 9.30 pm, Sun 8.30 pm; closed Mon L; No Amex.

HABESHA £23 4|2|1

29-31 SACKVILLE STREET M1 3LZ
0161 228 7396

"The food is the star here – super-tasty and in large portions, served in a very basic setting on Canal Street": that's the deal at this long-serving Ethiopian destination above a kebab shop, where – as is typical for the cuisine – many of the stews and stir fries are served on an injera (a large circular bread). Giles Coren of The Times visited in 2022, finding you "can eat for a tenner with very little trouble". / www.habesharestaurant.co.uk; Mon-Sun 11 pm; closed Sun-Fri L.

HAWKSMOOR £68 4|4|4

184-186 DEANSGATE M3 3WB
0161 836 6980

Quickly established as a "Manchester institution" since its 2015 opening, this Deansgate branch of the hit London chain offers "quite simply the best steak and accompaniments around" – it's "difficult to find fault as everything is top notch: the quality and cookery of the beef; the exemplary seafood, be it Salcombe crab on toast or lobster; even down to their sides of mac'n'cheese, bone marrow or Caesar salad". That said, as with its cousins down south, it's "best if someone else pays!". / www.thehawksmoor.com; hawksmoorrestaurants; Sun-Thu 9 pm, Fri & Sat 10 pm; Cash & all usual cards.

HISPI BISTRO £67 4|4|3

1C SCHOOL LANE M20 6RD
0161 445 3996

"Bistro food at its best – well cooked and well presented by knowledgeable staff" – wins all-round applause for this "reliable and accommodating" venue in Cheshire-based chef-restaurateur Gary Usher's Elite Bistros group, built on a series of successful crowdfunding campaigns. / www.hispi.net; hispi_bistro; Mon-Thu 9 pm, Fri & Sat 10 pm, Sun 5 pm; closed Sun D; Cash & all usual cards.

INDIQUE £47 3|3|3

110-112 BURTON ROAD M20 1LP
0161 438 0241

A plush curry house in posh West Didsbury that's both 'Indian' and 'Unique' (geddit?). It only attracted limited feedback this year but such as we have continues to declare it as outstanding all-round. / www.indiquerestaurant.co.uk; indique_manchester; Sun-Thu 10.30 pm, Fri & Sat 11 pm; closed Mon-Fri L.

THE IVY ASIA £78 **344**

THE PAVILION, BYROM STREET **M3 3HG**
0161 5033222

The Spinningfields launch-site for Richard Caring's Asian-themed Ivy spin-off provides a "stunning setting" for a celebration, and staff "cannot do enough to ensure an enjoyable time has been had". The glossily OTT interior is a real feast for the eyes, with a floor of green semi-precious stone and a (slightly cheesy) pagoda roof across the bar – and if some feel "the food is average", most reporets seem happy enough with the pan-Asianish menu. / theivymanchester.com; theivymanchester; Mon-Sun 11 pm; closed Mon-Wed L.

JAJOO STREET FOOD DIDSBURY **333**

846 WILMSLOW ROAD **M20 2SG**
0161 434 5151

There are "no duds" on the menu at this south Manchester duo (with branches in Hale and Didsbury), which champions street foods from India's regions – Calcutta kathi rolls, momo dumplings from the north, Kerala-style prawns. "Starters are fantastic – subtle, light, layered. Mains are again good – fresh and subtle, not overly heavy and cloying". / www.jajoostreetfood.co.uk/didsbury; jajooindianstreetfood; Tue-Sat 10 pm.

KALA £58 **433**

KING STREET **M2 7AT** **0800 160 1811**

"Outstanding food" at sensible prices hits the sweet spot at this "really enjoyable" three-year-old, the sixth venue in Gary Usher's crowd-funded Elite Bistros group. "The service was excellent and the standards really high" – "I loved being able to watch what was going on in the kitchen". / www.kalabistro.co.uk; kala_bistro_manchester; Mon-Thu 8.30 pm, Fri & Sat 9.30 pm, Sun 5 pm; closed Sun D.

THE LIME TREE £54 **444**

8 LAPWING LN **M20 2WS** **0161 445 1217**

Patrick Hannity's "charming old restaurant" in posh West Didsbury has hosted a steady stream of satisfied diners for 35 years, achieving "the highest standards" across the board. "Consistency with enthusiasm is still the hallmark of this much loved venue"; "the food is always good but unfussy – hence the loyal following over so many years". Ahead of the curve on provenance, Patrick established his own 20-acre smallholding in Macclesfield Forest 15 years ago to provide vegetables, eggs and meat for the kitchen. / www.thelimetreerestaurant.co.uk; thelimetreeres; Tue-Sat 9.30 pm, Sun 5.45 pm; closed Sun D, closed Mon; Cash & all usual cards.

LITTLE YANG SING £43 **322**

17 GEORGE ST **M1 4HE** **0161 228 7722**

This "reliable old standby" is "a definite cut above a regular Chinese restaurant, with good dim sum" and remains a "solid enough option now that its big brother remains closed" (the original Yang Sing, which opened on this site in 1977, is still closed as of our annual data refresh – see also). It has plenty of devotees – "we've been coming here for over 20 years" – but there are some who grumble that it's "now very expensive and generally devoid of Chinese custom". Top Tip… "the 'C'weeds' special dim sum platter is still a highlight". / www.facebook.com/littyangsing; littleyangsing; Mon-Thu 11 pm, Fri & Sat 11.30 pm, Sun 10.30 pm; Cash & all usual cards.

MACKIE MAYOR £41 **335**

1 EAGLE STREET **M4 5BU** **NO TEL**

"A great street food experience, with wines and beers to match" – Smithfield's Grade II Listed 1858 market has been refurbished and reimagined as a food hall by the folk behind Altrincham Market; ten food and drink stalls serve up a range of interesting fare, and there are over 500 seats. / mackiemayor; Tue-Sat 10 pm, Sun 6 pm; closed Sun D, closed Mon.

MANA £203 **444**

SAWMILL COURT **M4 6BF** **01613927294**

"Undeniably one of the UK's top tables" – Simon Martin's "fabulous airy space within the foodie hotspot that is Ancoats" shot to national fame in 2019 when it secured Manchester's first Michelin star since 1977. On practically all accounts, "exemplary cooking" with an emphasis on fire and fermentation and British ingredients "comes out of that entirely open kitchen, and the team work methodically alongside each other to produce it". "Flavours are knock-out and every dish is evocative of place and origin, with evident care and attention to detail. This level of refinement usually knocks all the oomph out of the produce (ahem, France, ahem) but here it only adds to it. Who on earth would carefully fillet and re-stuff a mussel. The result, in its bath of smoky butter, is amazing". And "wine pairings are interesting and varied" too. "Being seated adjacent to the open kitchen and able to view the focused choreography of the chefs adds to the delight" – "there's such a great theatre and occasion". With stardom has come higher prices, however, and doubts are creeping in about the ultimate level of value it delivers. One in six now consider it notably overpriced. The remainder that "it's not cheap, but you pay for what you get". / www.manarestaurant.co.uk; restaurant.mana; Wed-Sat midnight; closed Wed L, closed Mon & Tue & Sun; booking is online only; children: 6.

MARAY £35

14 BRAZENNOSE STREET **M2 6LW**
0151 347 0214

In summer 2022, this successful Liverpool mini-group opened its largest restaurant to-date… in Manchester. James Bates, Tom White and Dom Jones were inspired by Le Marais district of Paris to start in business and the menu here as back in the Pool is full of Middle Eastern influences. They also serve an authentic Med'-inspired Sunday Lunch. / maray.co.uk; marayrestaurants; Mon-Sat 10 pm, Sun 8 pm.

MUSU

64 BRIDGE STREET **M3 3BN**

Open from November 2022, this exciting-sounding arrival occupies the site that was previously Randall & Aubin (RIP), now transformed into a very ambitious Japanese restaurant, under chef-patron Michael Shaw. Musu translates as 'infinite possibilities' – here that's translated as an à la carte, 7-course or 11-course kaiseki menu; or an omakase experience delivered at a special six-seater counter, looked after by head sushi chef, Andre Aquiar. Delicacies will include A5 grade wagyu beef and wild, certified bluefin tuna. At the weekends a more drinks-led operation is planned. / Mon, Thu-Sun 11 pm.

NOI QUATTRO £39 **343**

120 HIGH STREET **M4 1HQ**
0161 834 9032

"Italian passion for authentic Neapolitan pizza" shows in this "industrial-style" Northern Quarter venue from a quartet of Italian friends (who also run the nearby Pasta Factory). "Pizzas range from the traditional to the hip", and there's also an interesting range of 'cuoppi' and 'stuzzichini' – savoury nibbles to munch while your pizza cooks. / www.noiquattro.co.uk; Noiquattrouk; Tue-Sat 10 pm, Sun 9.30 pm; closed Mon.

THE OYSTERCATCHER £47 **333**

123 MANCHESTER ROAD **M21 9PG**
0161 637 5890

"This friendly, well-run Chorlton" five-year-old delivers "brilliant seafood", with an emphasis on the bivalves of its name along with dishes cooked over coals. A second branch is slated to open in Sale's new Stanley Square development. / www.theoystercatcher.org; theoystercatcherchorlton; Mon-Sat 10 pm, Sun 8 pm; closed Mon-Thu L.

ROSSO £83 **334**

43 SPRING GARDENS **M2 2BG**
0161 8321400

This celeb-favoured Italian in a listed Victorian building was founded 12 years ago by former United captain Rio Ferdinand – and fans reckon it is a "stunning restaurant", serving "superb Sunday lunch" and "amazing cocktails". Despite the ownership, no shorts or football tops are permitted – the dress code is rigorously enforced! / www.rossorestaurants.com; rossorestaurant; Sun-Thu 10 pm, Fri & Sat 11 pm; closed Mon-Thu L; Cash & all usual cards.

RUDY'S £42 **444**

9 COTTON STREET, ANCOATS **M4 5BF**
0161 660 8040

The "busy and thriving original venue" in Ancoats is still a byword for "atmospheric, authentic Neapolitan pizza" – "the best ever eaten", fans insist – as the template it established spreads around the country, with 14 spin-off branches to date. Jim Morgan

& Kati Wilson launched the original in 2015, and two years later Mission Mars, the operator of Albert's Schloss, took up the challenge of funding the national rollout. / www.rudyspizza.co.uk/peter-st; wearerudyspizza; Sun-Thu 10 pm, Fri & Sat 11 pm; Cash & all usual cards; no bookings.

SAM'S CHOP HOUSE £51 333

BACK POOL FOLD OFF CROSS STREET M2 1HN 0161 834 3210

"Now reopened and feels like it has never been away" – this local landmark (LS Lowry's favourite, dating from 1872) has emerged unchanged in its essentials from a recent refurb which included the addition of some outside tables. "Pubby in the bar, and comfortable in the restaurant, with pleasant service, the traditional northern English food (such as Corned Beef Hash) is well cooked and very enjoyable, though not something to eat every day if you're planning to live long and prosper!" / www.samschophouse.com; samschophouse_; Tue-Thu 11 pm, Fri & Sat midnight, Sun 10 pm; closed Mon; Cash & all usual cards.

SAN CARLO £67 334

40 KING STREET WEST M3 2WY 0161 834 6226

"An Italian classic where lots of local celebs go, especially the footballers" – this Italian stalwart (opened in 2004) is nowadays something of a local stalwart, and is one of the city's better traditional eateries. "Never letting you down, it is generally packed to the brim with rather inebriated people and decked in fairy lights providing a great atmosphere and where the dress code is 'dressy'. Food is always of high quality ingredients, many of which are flown in from Italy. There are authentic, typical Italian dishes including pasta, pizza and seafood. All the waiters and staff are Italian and the food comes rapidly. It's a bit pricey, but you have to pay for quality!" / www.sancarlo.co.uk; sancarlorestaurants; Mon-Sun 10 pm; Cash & all usual cards.

SEXY FISH

UNIT 1 & 2 SPINNINGFIELDS SQUARE M3 3AE

London, Miami… Manchester… is to be the third location for Richard Caring/Caprice Holding's ostentatious ultra-luxe fish and seafood brand. Mancunians have never exactly been averse to a bit of bling, so it may have found its spiritual home here, at the gateway to Spinningfields where the Armani Emporium used to be. On the menu, its mix of sashimi, wagyu and 'Sexy fruit de mer'. Mad fer it! / sexyfish.com.

STREET URCHIN £47 444

72 GREAT ANCOATS STREET M4 5BG 07470 804979

"A hidden gem on the fringe of the Northern Quarter and Ancoats", Kevin & Rachel Choudhary's 'English market diner' is "driven by seasonal produce", with "a constantly changing menu of adventurous and innovative dishes". There's "serious culinary ambition here and the reach mostly falls within their grasp – rabbit and pistachio cigars, smoked aubergine, tempura crab in green curry, venison, mackerel, 'Manchester moneybags' to finish – this is contemporary, international cuisine with a confident touch". / street-urchin.co.uk; st_urchin; Tue-Sun 11 pm; closed Tue-Thu L, closed Mon.

SUGO £58 432

46 BLOSSOM STREET M4 6BF 0161 236 5264

"Simply stunning pasta" heads a menu of "absolutely delicious southern Italian food" at this Ancoats spin-off from a smaller Altrincham original – and makes "a perfect antidote to winter blues, if needed!". Top Menu Tip – "the house sugo is to die for" (orecchiette with 8-hour beef shin, pork shoulder and nduja ragu). / www.sugopastakitchen.co.uk/manchester; sugopastakitchen; Tue-Sat 10 pm, Sun 8.30 pm; closed Tue-Thu L, closed Mon.

TAMPOPO £43 332

16 ALBERT SQ M2 5PF 0161 819 1966

This "family fave" has assembled a greatest hits of East Asian cuisine, from satay skewers, spring rolls and gyoza dumplings to nasi goreng, pad Thai, ramen and laksa. They're "geared up for a great family experience with a top attitude towards children" – who will always find something to eat on the menu. There are now three branches in Manchester and one in London. Top Tip – "love the secret off-menu chicken options!". / www.tampopo.co.uk; tampopoeats; Sun-Thu 9 pm, Fri & Sat 10 pm; Cash & all usual cards; may need 7+ to book.

TATTU £73 234

3 HARDMAN SQ, GARTSIDE ST M3 3EB 0161 819 2060

"A great-looking restaurant" – this glossy Chinese was the first outpost of a glam-looking national chain that hit central London this year occupying a striking building on Oxford Street. One or two reports suggest it can "fall short on food and service" but others acclaim it all-round. / www.tattu.co.uk; tatturestaurant; Mon-Sun midnight; closed Mon-Wed L; Cash & all usual cards; No shorts.

THAIKHUN £47 333

UNIT 17, 3 HARDMEN ST M3 3HF 01618 192 065

This "big, fun, bustling Thai street food operation" serves "authentic and good-value food" in a "retro-feel" space with "decor like a typical marketplace". It is part of the Thai Leisure Group of restaurants, founded in Leeds almost 20 years ago by chef-entrepreneur Kim Kaewkraikhot. / www.thaikhun.co.uk; thaikhun; Mon-Sat 10 pm, Sun 9 pm; Cash & all usual cards.

THIS & THAT £16 422

3 SOAP ST M4 1EW 0161 832 4971

This legendary cheap 'n' cheerful Northern Quarter curry canteen is "still the best-value food in Manchester city centre" – as it has been for almost 40 years. "If you're a veggie you can choose rice and 3 curries for under a fiver: an absolute bargain". It even inspires poetry amongst some fans: "steaming-full plates of flavour-packed nosh, all of them served for v little dosh". / www.thisandthatcafe.co.uk; Sun-Thu 8 pm, Fri & Sat 9 pm; Cash only.

TNQ RESTAURANT & BAR £74 334

108 HIGH ST M4 1HQ 0161 832 7115

"What neighbourhood bistros should all be about!" say fans of this long-established venue, named for its location in The Northern Quarter, which on nearly all accounts "always delivers great food at reasonable prices". / www.tnq.co.uk; tnqrestaurant; Mon-Sat 10 pm, Sun 7 pm; Cash & all usual cards.

20 STORIES £93 234

NO 1 SPINNINGFIELDS, 1 HARDMAN SQUARE M3 3JE 0161 204 3333

It has the 360° vistas, it has the rooftop terrace planted with trees scaling two storeys, but whether it has top cuisine is more debatable at this D&D London operation, named for its position at the top of the Spinningfields Tower. Feedback remains limited and muted, but in early 2022, Daniel Scott (whose recent CV includes Mana) took over the stoves, so perhaps change is afoot. To dip a toe in the water, sample the view from the cocktail bar. / 20stories.co.uk; 20storiesmcr; Sun-Thu midnight, Fri & Sat 2 am.

WING'S £59 444

1 LINCOLN SQ M2 5LN 0161 834 9000

"A superior mainstream Chinese" – this large, modern Cantonese in the city centre is eighteen years old and fans say it "shows just how familiar dishes should be done", and with "excellent service" too. / www.wingsrestaurant.co.uk; Mon, Wed-Sun midnight; closed Mon, Sat L, closed Tue; Cash & all usual cards; children: 11+ after 8 pm Mon-Fri.

WOOD RESTAURANT £142 333

JACK ROSENTHAL STREET M15 4RA 0161 236 5211

"The food is quite stunning and the wines… wow!" – Simon Wood's "impressive" three-year-old is a "special" venue for all who comment on it, some of whom had their best meal of the year here. "The tasting menu is exceptional" and "most times you go it changes, which is fantastic". "You can also go upstairs afterwards to Homage where they do matching cheese and wine, which again has an extensive menu". / www.woodmanchester.com; WoodRestaurants; Fri & Sat, Wed & Thu 9.30 pm; closed Wed & Thu

L, closed Mon & Tue & Sun; credit card deposit required to book; children: 8.

YANG SING £54

34 PRINCESS STREET   M1 4JY
0161 236 2200

"Still the best after all these years"… with "the finest most elegant dim sum in the city", say fans of this famous Chinatown destination, which in days of yore was Manchester's main contribution to UK gastronomy. Somewhat eclipsed in recent years, even fans may note that "the Manchester Chinese community seem to have found other places to go for lunch" and a regular noted an off-kilter experience in a late 2021 visit. Since early 2022 it has closed its doors, is shown as 'Temporarily Closed' on Google and its website – while wishing everyone 'Happy New Year' – says 'Our restaurant is currently closed for refurbishment'. We have contacted the establishment for an update, and will post news as we have it. / www.yang-sing.com; yangsingmcr; Mon-Sun 9.30 pm; Cash & all usual cards.

YUZU £34 **4 4 2**

39 FAULKNER STREET   M1 4EE
0161 236 4159

"This tiny place on the edge of Chinatown is a knockout", with its "calming atmosphere and very, very good Japanese food". It has built an enthusiastic following over the past decade for a good range of dishes, from yakitori and kara-age chicken to gyoza, udon noodles and tempura – but not sushi, which requires special training. There's also a "good sake selection, at fair prices too". Top Menu Tip – "salmon to die for". / yuzumanchester.co.uk; yuzumanchester; Tue-Sat 10 pm; closed Sun & Mon; Cash & all usual cards; credit card deposit required to book.

ANGELA'S £52 **5 4 3**

21 THE PARADE   CT9 1EX   01843 319978

"Margate's tiny but mighty gem". "I have never tasted seafood quite like this", say admirers of Lee Coad & Charlotte Forsdike's "charming café-like" spot, where "local fish and seafood are the keynotes, beautifully cooked, often with an unusual aspect, plus modern-style wines and local beers". It "prides itself on being sustainable and using local suppliers where possible", and is "well worth the trip if you don't live nearby" or are visiting the nearby Turner Contemporary. / angelasofmargate.com; angelas_of_margate; Tue-Sat 9 pm; closed Sun & Mon; booking is online only.

BOTTEGA CARUSO £55 **4 4 3**

BROAD STREET   CT9 1EW   01843 297142

"Authentic Italian grub" – much of it imported from co-owner Simona Di Dio's family farm in Campania, or hand-made on-site – is the draw at the "cosy but rather basic" operation she runs with partner Harry Ryder, with a cookery school next door. Set in the Old Town, close to Turner Contemporary, it is very much a part of Margate's booming gastronomic scene. /

www.bottegacaruso.com; bottegacaruso; Wed & Thu 3 pm, Fri & Sat 9 pm; closed Wed & Thu D, closed Mon & Tue & Sun.

BUOY & OYSTER £64 **4 4 2**

44 HIGH STREET   CT9 1DS   01843 446631

"Perfect seaside dining experience" – a family-run seafood bistro on the beach. "It's a great find in Margate with a really interesting menu with spanking fresh seafood, and really friendly service". / www.buoyandoyster.com; buoyandoyster; Mon-Sun 9 pm.

DORY'S £41 **4 3 3**

24 HIGH STREET   CT9 1DS
01843 520 391

An "exceptional range of creative small-plate, tapas-style fish dishes" – many of them raw, cured or smoked – win acclaim for this walk-ins-only seafood bar (little sister to Angela's around the corner): an "informal" set-up with "friendly and helpful staff", providing "excellent value for money", plus "views of the sea… and the main road". / dorysofmargate.com; dorys_of_margate; Mon, Thu-Sun 10.30 pm; closed Tue & Wed.

SARGASSO **4 3 3**

MARGATE HARBOUR ARM, STONE PIER CT9 1AP

"A beautiful spot on the harbour arm in Margate" where Ed Wilson and Josie Stead (of London's Brawn fame) opened in July 2021 and produce "simple dishes with an emphasis on good sourcing in a very friendly and laid-back atmosphere". In February 2022, the Sunday Times's Marina O'Loughlin paid a visit, declaring it "as invigorating as the sea air" with "a mix of serious intent on the menu and a breezy, ad hoc environment", not to mention "insanely light Parmesan fritters". / www.sargasso.bar; sargasso.bar; Wed-Sat 9 pm, Sun 4 pm; closed Sun D, closed Mon & Tue.

ASCOUGH'S BISTRO £46 **3 2 3**

24 ST MARY'S ROAD   LE16 7DU
01858 466 966

Chris & Abby Ascough's town-centre bistro has earned a solid local following over almost two decades for its "artistic presentation" of "high-quality cooking" from a "monthly changing menu". It's "reasonably priced", too, with a 6-course tasting menu at under £50 with matching wine flight at £20. / www.ascoughsbistro.co.uk; Tue-Sat 9 pm; closed Sun & Mon; practically no walk-ins – you must book.

DAN'S AT THE CROWN £53 **3 4 3**

6-7 THE PARADE   SN8 1NE
01672 512112

"Going from strength to strength" – Australian Dan Bond runs this "delightful" restaurant, which serves an "interesting and excellently prepared" menu. "The entire staff work hard to give customers a great experience and this is one of those thoroughly well-run spots where the whole is more than the sum of the parts!" / dansrestaurant.co.uk; dans_restaurant; Tue-Sat 9 pm, Sun 3 pm; closed Tue L closed Sun D, closed Mon.

RICK STEIN £68 **2 3 3**

LLORAN HOUSE, 42A HIGH STREET SN8 1HQ   01672 233333

"Good ol' fish 'n' chips" is the strong suit at Rick Stein's smart venue in a fine period building on Marlborough High Street, where "the cooking is steady rather than inspired" – fancier fare is available, but some regulars feel it's best to settle for "the simple things done well here". / www.rickstein.com/eat-with-us/marlborough; rick-stein-marlborough; Mon-Sun 9 pm; Cash & all usual cards.

THE COACH £83 **4 4 4**

3 WEST STREET   SL7 2LS   01628 483013

"Better IMHO than the Hand & Flowers up the road" – Tom Kerridge's lower-profile, no-bookings, local's favourite is "a great alternative to the nearby H&F" and "hits the mark where others from TK continue to disappoint". It provides "lovely tapas-style plates" (although these "smaller plates" are "not that small") with a number of options cooked rotisserie style and chips that are "some of the best ever". "Fantastic service and ambience" too. / www.thecoachmarlow.co.uk; thecoachmarlow; Wed-Sun 8.45 pm; closed Mon & Tue; Cash & all usual cards; no bookings.

THE HAND & FLOWERS £131 **3 3 2**

126 WEST STREET   SL7 2BP
01628 482277

"The food is good, but it just feels like he overcharges because he can…" – that's a middleground opinion on TV-star Tom Kerridge's Thames Valley phenomenon: a fairly ordinary-feeling old inn on the edge of the town, which catapulted him to fame in 2012 after Michelin (slightly bizarrely) awarded the place not just one but two of its stars (and – partly as a result – it remains in the top-10 most mentioned venues in our annual diners' poll outside the capital). Supporting the lack-of-value theme, the Hand & Flowers created national tabloid headlines in August 2022 for its highly priced grills (The Sun thundered: 'TV chef Tom Kerridge defends charging £87 for a steak — by comparing it to a Bentley'). Views have been divided on the virtues of the cooking for years and when you even out the 'ayes' and 'nayes' it earned slightly better ratings again this year for food that fans say is "brilliant" ("the original Tom Kerridge and the best!"). For a significant majority, though, "it doesn't seem much different from average pub food" and is "horribly overhyped" and "overpriced beyond anything ever previously experienced". "Two Michelin stars??? It's a boozer for heavens' sake!". / www.thehandandflowers.co.uk; handfmarlow; Mon-Sat 9.15 pm, Sun 5 pm; closed Sun D; Cash & all usual cards.

THE IVY MARLOW GARDEN £77 222

66-68 HIGH ST SL7 1AH 01628 902777

As the name suggests, this outpost of Richard Caring's Ivy empire is at its best for "summer dining in the lovely garden, with beautiful plants". The food, though, is generally felt to be rather "underwhelming" for the price – a common complaint with this chain – but, nevertheless, as a venue, it serves a purpose. / www.theivymarlowgarden.com; theivymarlowgarden; Mon-Thu 10.30 pm, Fri & Sat 11 pm, Sun 10 pm.

LEIVITI £20 333

13 SPITTAL STREET SL7 3HJ 01628337377

"A wonderful new addition to Marlow's restaurant scene", this year-old indie from the team behind the nearby Satollo Deli has made its mark with "incredible pizza made with top-notch ingredients" (mostly organic or with Italian DOP/IGP certification). "The atmosphere is pretty buzzy, too". / www.lieviti.co.uk; lievitimarlow; Tue-Sun 10 pm; closed Tue-Thu L, closed Mon.

THE OARSMAN £55 332

46 SPITTAL STREET SL7 1DB 01628 617755

"A pub which is going upmarket in stages", with an attractive menu of "good (but expensive) brasserie cooking". Operated by Nigel Sutcliffe, who helped Heston B set up The Fat Duck, and chef James McLean, the venture remains "very popular" with its audience. / www.theoarsman.co.uk; theoarsmanmarlow; Mon-Sat 9.45 pm, Sun 5.30 pm; closed Sun D.

SINDHU, MACDONALD COMPLEAT ANGLER HOTEL £83 433

THE COMPLEAT ANGLER SL7 1RG 01628 405 405

"Incredibly original Indian cuisine served gracefully in a wonderful location" makes this well-commented-on Marlow destination one of the country's top grand Indians outside the capital. "A beautiful dining room overlooking the Thames" and with a "fabulous view of Marlow Weir" (gorgeous in daytime, perhaps less impactful at night) is the venue for "an enormously enjoyable, fine-dining take on Indian cuisine that's beautifully presented,:

"with lovely spicing, but never being overwhelmed by too much heat". It's "one of those experiences where practically everything is spot on". / www.sindhurestaurant.co.uk; sindhumarlow; Sun-Thu 9.30 pm, Fri & Sat 10 pm.

VAASU BY ATUL KOCHHAR £84 533

2 CHAPEL STREET SL7 1DD 01628 362274

This two-year-old from prolific celeb-chef-restaurateur Atul Kocchar (who runs Sindhu at The Compleat Angler and Hawkyns in Amersham) is thought by some reporters to be his best in the area, with a "stunning tasting menu" that "gets the quantities just right". Top Menu Tip – "perfect venison". / vaasurestaurant.co.uk; vaasumarlow; Wed-Sun 9.30 pm; closed Mon & Tue.

THE VANILLA POD £71 433

31 WEST ST SL7 2LS 01628 898101

Michael Mcdonald's well-established favourite occupies an intimate room that's part of a house that was, in days gone by, owned by TS Eliot. Fans continue to say its performance is "consistently excellent in all areas and amazing value". As well as the à la carte menu, there is also now a five-course tasting option – at £60 per head for seven courses, it's not punishingly priced by the standards of such offerings and fans say "it's absolutely brilliant. You've got to go for it!". / www.thevanillapod.co.uk; Tue-Sat 9 pm; closed Sun & Mon; Cash & all usual cards.

MARTON, CHESHIRE 5–2B

LA POPOTE £74 443

CHURCH FARM, MANCHESTER ROAD SK11 9HF 01260 224785

'Casual fine dining' is the promise at chef Joseph Rawlins and Gaëlle Radigon's "contemporary"-feeling establishment – a converted farmhouse, next to a fine, very ancient church (Europe's oldest with a timber frame) not far from Alderley Edge. Wilmslow-born and Paris-trained Joseph produces a modern French menu, and fans say dishes can be "inspired". / la-popote.co.uk; lapopoteuk; Thu-Sat 11 pm, Sun 6 pm; closed Sun D, closed Mon & Tue & Wed.

MASHAM, NORTH YORKSHIRE 8–4B

SAMUEL'S, SWINTON PARK HOTEL & SPA £97 334

SWINTON PARK HG4 4JH 01765 680900

Occupying a small corner of a "fabulous old-school country pile" – itself set in 20,000 acres of ground – this "smart restaurant in a very smart hotel" makes use of game and fish from the estate, as well as produce from the very large kitchen garden, to provide "good cooking that's well presented". Afternoon tea in the splendid adjacent lounges is also a feature worth discovering. / www.swintonestate.com/eating; swintonestate; Mon-Sun 9 pm; closed Mon-Sat L; Cash & all usual cards; No jeans; children: 8+ at D.

THE POET £65 543

MAIDSTONE RD TN12 7JH 01892 722416

"Ambitious, top-class cooking with real panache, from fresh high-quality ingredients and with haute-cuisine touches (such as crispy arancini amuse-bouches)" provides a real "gastronomic surprise" in this "lovely former village pub" where South African chef-patron Petrus Madutlela showcases his "amazing food in an old-world pub environment". It's "imaginative and uplifting, not the usual hum-drum run-of-the-mill selection" – "you could easily slog up to town and pay double the money and still not eat as well". BTW, the name honours World War I poet Siegfried Sassoon, who lived in the village. / thepoetatmatfield.co.uk; poetatmatfield; Tue-Sat 9 pm, Sun 6 pm; closed Mon; Cash & all usual cards.

MATLOCK, DERBYSHIRE 5–3C

STONES £64 444

1C DALE RD DE4 3LT 01629 56061

"A treat of a place, both in terms of tastes and in terms of being looked after" – Kevin Stone's converted pub sits overlooking the River Derwent and is often noted for its "good value": be it from its à la carte or tasting menu. / www.stones-restaurant.co.uk; stonesmatlock; Tue-Sat 8.30 pm; closed Sun & Mon; Cash & all usual cards.

MAWGAN PORTH, CORNWALL 1–3B

THE SCARLET HOTEL £83 324

TREDRAGON RD TR8 4DQ 01637 861800

This "modern spa hotel with views out to sea" from its clifftop vantage point is fully geared-up for the eco tourist, with a solidly rated kitchen serving up sustainable meals from breakfast via lunch and afternoon tea to dinner, when there is a choice of tasting menus including vegetarian and vegan. Non-residents are now welcome to book, but it remains child-free. / www.scarlethotel.co.uk; scarlethotel; Mon-Sat 9 pm, Sun 4 pm; closed Sun D.

MAWGAN, CORNWALL 1–4B

NEW YARD RESTAURANT £43 434

STABLEYARD, TRELOWARREN TR12 6AF 01326 221595

"A deservedly popular 'find' with innovative and exciting cooking, which has in fact been going for years but has recently reached new heights" (and won a Michelin green star last year). "Chef-owner Jeffery Robinson grows and cooks with local produce", cooking "memorable" meals eaten in an old coach house or outside in its yard – a venue "perfectly situated to serve the Trelowarren estate's luxury timeshare properties". / newyardrestaurant.co.uk; newyardrestaurant; Wed-Sun 3 pm; closed Wed-Sun D, closed Mon & Tue; No Amex.

Noto, Edinburgh

THE DRUMMING SNIPE   £60   3|3|2

GUILDFORD ROAD   GU22 9QT
07849 088460

This "very tasty gastropub" (fka The Mayford Arms) from former Ivy staffers James Lyon Shaw and Jamie Dobbin "makes the most of its building", and offers a "great set lunch menu". Its 2020 opening was the second from the pair's Brucan Pubs group following the Greene Oak in Windsor; there are now four. / thedrummingsnipe.co.uk; thedrummingsnipe; Mon-Sat 9.30 pm, Sun 9 pm.

CHEFSTABLE AT TRUEFOODS   £165   5|5|3

9 HALLIKELD CLOSE   HG4 5GZ
01765 640927

"Utterly outstanding" – "My best meal of 2022… I cannot believe that the chef runs this restaurant almost as a 'hobby'". Chef-owner Mitch Mitchell presides over this unusual venture: a professional kitchen within a small factory unit on an industrial estate whose main purpose is the manufacture of stocks and sauces for top retailers and the restaurant trade. The website promises that its 14-course tasting menu is 'an up close and personal dining event like no other' and our reports would concur with Giles Coren's adulatory 2020 review in which he compared results to Noma and El Bulli. / www.truefoodsltd.com/chefstable; truefoodsltd; Mon-Fri 5 pm; closed Mon-Fri D, closed Sat & Sun.

DYLAN'S RESTAURANT   £55   2|2|3

ST GEORGE'S ROAD   LL59 5EY
01248 716 714

All reports acknowledge the "great building and position" – a stylish modern structure with "terrific views over the Menai Straits" – at this waterside venue (with branches now in Criccieth and Llandudno) and there's always a decent crowd here. But some diners feel there's "always a slight disappointment" about the "very average" nosh: "I felt the accountants are in charge, not the chefs". /

www.dylansrestaurant.co.uk; dylansrestaurants; Mon-Sun 10 pm; Cash & all usual cards.

SOSBAN & THE OLD BUTCHER'S   £193   4|3|2

1 HIGH ST, MENAI BRIDGE   LL59 5EE
01248 208 131

"Outstanding" or "good but overly pricey"? Both strands of thought are still evident in diner feedback on Stephen & Bethan Stevens' ambitious venue, in a converted butcher's just over the Menai Bridge. Its renown has been boosted in recent times both by a Michelin star and four hard-to-win rosettes from the AA. It's only open three nights per week, offering a 'unique culinary journey' for £175 per person. / www.sosbanandtheoldbutchers.com; Thu-Sat 11 pm; closed Thu & Fri L, closed Mon-Wed & Sun; Cash & all usual cards; children: 12.

THE CLOCKSPIRE   £80   5|3|3

GAINSBOROUGH   DT9 5BA
01963 251458

Chef Luke Sutton's "consistently excellent and interesting" cooking, from a "delicious locally sourced menu", is served in the "beautiful setting" of a high-ceilinged hall with exposed wood beams – a "fantastic conversion of an old school building" from the 1860s. The set lunch and early evening menu is particularly "great value". / www.theclockspire.com; theclockspire; Wed-Sat 9.30 pm, Sun 4.30 pm; closed Sun D, closed Mon & Tue.

DULSE   £55

TY MILFORD WATERFRONT HOTEL, NELSON QUAY   SA73 3AF

Named for an edible variety of seaweed, this spring 2022 newcomer is connected to a large (100 bedroom), new contemporary hotel on the coast – part of a waterside development which provides views from the dining room of Milford Marina. Chef Simon Crockford provides a brasserie-style menu (with dishes such as steak, salmon wellington, pork belly with celeriac and apple). / www.ty-hotels.com/destinations/milford-waterfront/dining; tyhotels; Mon-Sun 11 pm.

BRITANNIA THAI   £22   4|4|3

1 HIGH STREET   SO41 0QF
01590 642226

"Amazing food, speedy and accurate service, with no frills": this family-run Thai (with a second branch in Brockenhurst) is "exactly what you'd want from a mid-week outing" – "even our Thai friends think it's exceptional". Top Tip – "the fish dishes are fabulous". / www.britanniathai.com; Tue-Sun 10 pm; closed Tue L, closed Mon.

VERVEINE FISHMARKET RESTAURANT   £81   5|4|3

98 HIGH ST   SO41 0QE   01590 642 176

David Wykes has carved out a unique niche over a dozen years with his "intimate and innovative seafood restaurant", "almost hidden behind the fish-shop in front" – the source of its "delicious fresh fish". It's an "interesting concept", too: "you choose the number of courses (2, 3 or 6 at lunch; 4, 6 or 8 at dinner) and are then served whatever the chef is cooking that day". "Staff clearly love the place and not only announce the food but can talk to you about how it is cooked". / www.verveine.co.uk; Tue-Sat 9.30 pm; closed Sun & Mon; No Amex.

HOTEL ENDSLEIGH £71   4|3|3

PL19 0PQ   01822 870 000

The "stunning" combination of "really good, classic food" and the "lovely setting" of "Humphry Repton's last garden, overlooking the Tamar", makes a meal in the original wood-panelled dining room here a real pleasure. There's also a notable cream tea in the afternoon. Sibling to Hotel Tresanton in the Polizzi Collection, Endsleigh was originally the Duke of Bedford's private lodge for hunting and fishing. / www.hotelendsleigh.com; hotelendsleigh; Mon-Sun 9.30 pm; Cash & all usual cards.

MINSTER MILL   £60

OLD MINSTER   OX29 0RN   01993 774 441

Limited but good all-round feedback on this handsome hotel on the fringe of the Cotswolds and a short drive from Oxford (part of Andrew Brownsword's luxurious group), whose beautiful terrace borders the banks of the River Windrush. In the beamed, pitched-roof dining room, chef Joshua Brimmell holds a hard-to-win three AA rosettes. / www.minstermill.co.uk; brownswordhotels; Wed-Sun 9.30 pm; closed Mon & Tue; Cash & all usual cards.

THE CHURCH INN   £61   3|3|3

CHURCH LANE   WA16 7RD   01565 873178

"A cut above the average pub" – this popular old village boozer occupies an "attractive location" opposite twelfth-century St Wilfrid's

Church. Everything is "cooked superbly accurately and well seasoned, with delicious layers of flavour". It's "not cheap", but nobody is complaining. / churchinnmobberley.co.uk; churchinnmobb; Mon & Tue, Sun 10.30 pm, Wed-Sat 11 pm.

MONTGOMERY, POWYS   5-4A

CHECKERS PANTRY £88

BROAD ST, POWYS   SY15 6PN
01686 669 822

In Spring 2022, Andrew Birch (erstwhile head chef of London's Savoy Grill) and his wife Rachel relaunched this well-known coaching inn, part of a small scenic town in rural Powys. The main option is a seven-course tasting menu (with a vegetarian alternative), but there's also a simpler lunch. No feedback as yet in our annual diners' poll. / www.checkerswales.co.uk; Wed-Sat 8.30 pm, Sun 2.30 pm; closed Wed L closed Sun D, closed Mon & Tue; No Amex; children: 8+ at D.

MORECAMBE, LANCASHIRE   5-1A

MIDLAND HOTEL   £61   3 4 4

MARINE ROAD WEST   LA4 4BU
01524 424000

"The best afternoon tea ever, with beautiful views over Morecambe Bay to the Lake District plus delicious sandwiches, scones and cakes, and a choice of teas and more if needed" – this well-known hotel is an Art Deco masterpiece (dating from 1933) and most recommended for its "first-class afternoon tea". Its "lovely dining room" – the aptly named 'Sun Terrace' – also receives enthusiastic support, though: "good food with local choices and the sunsets are truly amazing". / www.englishlakes.co.uk; englishlakes; Mon-Sat 9 pm, Sun 2 pm; closed Sun D; Cash & all usual cards.

MORETON, ESSEX   3-2B

THE DOG & PICKLE   £60   3 3 3

CHURCH ROAD   CM5 0LF   01277 600 501

"Off-the-chart pub food" – ranging from standard classics and "excellent roasts" to "fantastic, restaurant-style" European dishes – makes this 500-year-old Essex village boozer an appealing option for both locals and visitors. / www.dogandpickle.com; dogandpickle; Wed-Sat 11 pm, Sun 10 pm; closed Mon & Tue.

MORSTON, NORFOLK   6-3C

MORSTON HALL   £132   5 4 5

MAIN COAST RD   NR25 7AA
01263 741041

"Making the drive to north Norfolk worthwhile!" – "Galton Blackiston (with wife Tracy) are nearing their thirtieth year at their acclaimed country house hotel, near the coast, and support in our annual diners' poll (in which it's one of the most commented-on destinations) shows no signs of diminishing. Thanks to "personable and efficient" staff, you "feel you are in very capable hands throughout" and "cooking of the daily-changing 7-course tasting menu is assured and simply stunning every

night". "An ideal place for a romantic break staying in their accommodation and enjoying great food." Top Top – "the wine flight seemed expensive and a better option looked like the limited but imaginative selection of wines by the glass" ("a broad, judiciously chosen variety, at reasonable price"). / www.morstonhall.com; morstonhallhotel; Tue-Sun 11.30 pm, Mon 12 pm; closed Mon D; Cash & all usual cards.

MOULSFORD, OXFORDSHIRE   2-2D

THE BEETLE & WEDGE BOATHOUSE   £55   3 3 4

FERRY LN   OX10 9JF   01491 651381

"Loved it!" – with its "unexpectedly high-quality food", this "somewhat out-of-the-way" boathouse/restaurant at a "gorgeous riverside location" makes a "delightful" spot for a meal with a slightly Edwardian, Three Men in a Boat/Wind in the Willows ambience (this is one of the stretches of water immortalised in both books). Improvements are promised following a refurb late last year. / www.beetleandwedge.co.uk; beetleandwedgeboathouse; Mon-Sun 11 pm; Cash & all usual cards.

MOULTON, CAMBRIDGESHIRE   3-1C

THE PACKHORSE INN   £68   3 3 3

BRIDGE ST   CB8 8SP   01638 751818

"A warm pub setting, solid food and great service" help establish this first member of the local Chestnut Collection of pubs as "just a really top place to dine". "My happy place!". / www.thepackhorseinn.com; thepackhorseinn; Wed-Sat 8.30 pm, Sun 7.45 pm; closed Mon & Tue; Cash & all usual cards.

MOUNTSORREL, LEICESTERSHIRE 5-4D

JOHN'S HOUSE   £94   5 4 3

139-141 LOUGHBOROUGH ROAD LE12 7AR   01509 415569

John Duffin was born on the farm where he now cooks (as part of the family business incorporating a petting farm and motor museum), and which provides some of the produce for its farm-to-plate ethos. All reports applaud its "superb" cooking and declare a visit "a wonderful experience" that's "exceptional value for money". / www.johnshouse.co.uk; johnshouserest; Tue-Sat 7.30 pm; closed Sun & Mon; No Amex; children: 10.

MOUSEHOLE, CORNWALL   1-4A

THE OLD COASTGUARD   £57   3 3 4

THE PARADE   TR19 6PR   01736 731222

"Friendly staff" and a "fabulous location, with a great sea view from the large garden", are the main attractions of this small seaside hotel, which offers guests a well-rated menu with plenty of fish and seafood. It's from the same ownership as The Gurnard's Head and, further afield, The Felin Fach Griffin in Wales. / www.oldcoastguardhotel.co.uk; theoldcoastguard; Mon-Sun 11 pm; Cash & all usual cards.

2 FORE STREET

2 FORE STREET RESTAURANT   £48   4 3 3

2 FORE ST   TR19 6PF   01736 731164

"A busy restaurant full of happy people" – Joe Wardell's unassuming bistro a short walk from the harbour is a mainstay of the village and its ongoing popularity is "a testament to the food offering and service". It serves "great food with daily specials at a reasonable price" – "good local fish (e.g. sardines) is very good value for money". / www.2forestreet.co.uk; 2Forestreet; Mon-Sun 9.30 pm; Cash & all usual cards.

MUDEFORD, CORNWALL   2-4C

NOISY LOBSTER   £56   3 4 4

BH23 4AN   01425 272162

"Fish served as caught daily" and served up in "creative and tasty dishes" by "excellent staff" ensure there's "often a queue" at this beachfront diner at a "great location" – so "grab a window seat if you can". Top Tip – "the lobster is amazing". / avon-beach.noisylobster.co.uk; thenoisylobster; Mon-Sun 11 pm; Cash & all usual cards.

MURCOTT, OXFORDSHIRE   2-1D

THE NUT TREE INN £95   3 3 3

MAIN STREET   OX5 2RE   01865 331253

"Lovely historic pub" that "never fails to delight" having "maintained an extremely high level of food and service" for more than 15 years under Mike & Imogen North, respectively chef and front of house. Even one diner who "doesn't really like gastropubs as they seem to occupy a peculiar no-man's-land that is neither one thing nor the other" says "this is an exception that delivers on all levels!". Top Tip – "exceptional soufflés to die for!". / www.nuttreeinn.co.uk; Nuttreeinn; Tue-Sat 7.30 pm; closed Sun & Mon; Cash & all usual cards; booking max 20 may apply.

NAILSWORTH, GLOUCESTERSHIRE 2-2B

WILLIAM'S   £62   3 3 3

3 FOUNTAIN STREET   GL6 0BL
01453 832240

"Excellent fish, in generous portions, and cooked really well" is the highlight you'd hope for at this Cotswolds fishmonger/deli/restaurant – an institution of over forty-five years' standing, which was given an attractive refit in recent years. / www.williamsfoodhall.co.uk; williamsfoodhall; Tue-Thu 4 pm, Fri & Sat 11 pm; closed Tue-Thu D, closed Sun & Mon.

NAIRN, HIGHLAND   9-2C

BOATH HOUSE HOTEL £99

IV12 5TE   01667 454896

Set in 20 acres of manicured gardens and woodland, this fine Georgian property is nowadays a retreat with 10 bedrooms. As part of the set-up, there's a 400-year-old walled garden, with a cafe. In mid-2022, the team behind this year's London smash hit, Sessions Art Club (chef Florence Knight, the artist and restaurateur Jonny Gent, and architect Russell Potter) became involved, with a new small-plates format. There are loud echoes of their earlier project – the quirky corner of a historic site – but it opened after our annual diners' poll concluded so a rating will have to wait for next year. / www.boath-house.com; Wed-Sun 9 pm; closed Mon & Tue; Cash & all usual cards; No jeans.

NANTGAREDIG, CARMARTHENSHIRE 4–4C

Y POLYN £69 4 3 4

CAPEL DEWI SA32 7LH 01267 290000

Mark & Sue Manson's "bistro-style restaurant uses very local fresh ingredients" to cook accomplished meals that have earned it consistently high ratings. It combines perfectly with a visit to Wales's National Botanic Garden two miles away. Top Menu Tip – "try the sewin (Welsh sea trout) if available". / www.ypolyn.co.uk; polyncarmarthen; Tue-Sat 9 pm, Sun 2.30 pm; closed Sun D, closed Mon; Cash & all usual cards.

NARBERTH, PEMBROKESHIRE 4–4B

ULTRACOMIDA 3 3 3

7 HIGH ST SA67 7AR 01834 861491

This daytime-only restaurant serves a "wonderful array of tapas in a vibrant atmosphere", along with an "excellent range of Spanish food and wine" to take home. Paul & Shumana Grimwood's family-run operation has grown gradually over the two decades since they launched their first deli in Aberystwyth, and now includes the night-time bar Curado in Cardiff. Fans say the "invariably delicious, relaxed food and service keeps drawing us back". / www.ultracomida.co.uk; Mon-Sat 4 pm; closed Mon-Sat D, closed Sun.

NEEPSEND, SOUTH YORKSHIRE 5–2C

NATIVE £60 4 3 3

169 GIBRALTAR STREET S3 8UA 0114 2682225

This "excellent seafood restaurant" was opened in 2021 by "top Sheffield fishmonger J H Mann" – an institution that opened a century earlier in Hillsborough. "Being run by a fishmonger means they have varieties way more exciting that the usual offerings, including lobster, oysters and scallops" – which means it's "a wonderful place for fish lovers". The retail part of the business is now based in Sharrow Vale, with a second shop in Bakewell. / www.nativejhmann.co.uk; nativejhmann; Wed-Sat 11 pm, Sun 5.30 pm; closed Sun D, closed Mon & Tue.

NETHER BURROW, CUMBRIA 7–4D

THE HIGHWAYMAN £55 3 3 3

BURROW LA6 2RJ 01524 273338

"This pub goes from strength to strength" – "the people of Nether Burrow are lucky to have it as their local". An eighteenth-century former coaching inn now run by Brunning &

Price, and notably family-friendly, it offers "food that's well presented by extremely efficient and welcoming staff" and at "reasonable prices". / www.brunningandprice.co.uk/highwayman/homepage; highwaymanpub; Sun-Thu 10 pm, Fri & Sat 11 pm; Cash & all usual cards.

NETHER EDGE, SOUTH YORKSHIRE 5–2C

BENCH £25 3 3 3

7B NETHER EDGE ROAD S7 1RU

"Nice, if somewhat out-of-the-way, neighbourhood-style spot serving small plates and good wine", outside Sheffield – a bar / kitchen and shop that started life with sell-out pop-up dinners. Its cuisine was given a strong plug by The FT in early 2022. / www.benchsheffield.co.uk; benchsheffield; Wed-Sat 11 pm, Sun 3 pm; closed Wed-Fri L closed Sun D, closed Mon & Tue.

NETHER WESTCOTE, OXFORDSHIRE 2–1C

THE FEATHERED NEST INN £97 3 3 3

OX7 6SD 01993 833 030

This 350-year-old, Cotswold-stone former malthouse makes a "great setting" for a "smallish but very enjoyable menu". These days it's "more of an upmarket restaurant than a pub" under chef Matt Weedon (ex-Lords of the Manor and Glenapp Castle) – "and the prices reflect this", starting at £29 for the wagyu burger, with a 6-course tasting menu at £80. / www.thefeatherednestinn.co.uk; thefeatherednestinn; Mon, Thu-Sun 9.30 pm; closed Tue & Wed; Cash & all usual cards.

NETTLEBED, BERKSHIRE 2–2D

THE CHEESE SHED 3 3 3

HIGH STREET RG9 5DA 01491 642127

"Lovely cheese toasties served out of a barn, with nice coffee and cakes" might not sound all that wonderful, but they're "Instagram ready" and dripping with just-melted cheese, served in a modern agricultural building strewn with straw and with hay bales for seats, on a 120-year-old family dairy farm (now organic) near Henley. You can also buy cheeses made on the farm to take home. / www.nettlebedcreamery.com; nettlebedcheese; Mon-Sun 3 pm; closed Mon-Sun D.

NEW MILTON, HAMPSHIRE 2–4C

CHEWTON GLEN £107 3 3 3

CHEWTON GLEN RD BH23 5QL 01425 282212

This famous Relais & Châteaux hotel and spa set in gorgeous grounds on the edge of the New Forest is a byword for luxury and provides a splurgy, "romantic" getaway for its regular guests. Even some who find its style too "glitzy" for their personal taste, acknowledge that "it's hugely popular with a large audience who obviously enjoy the style". Chef Luke Matthews is entering his twentieth year at the stoves here,

and while a meal here is an arm-and-a-leg job, even cynical reporters feel that "it is heartening that the kitchen standards are (nearly) as high as the prices". / www.chewtonglen.com; chewtonglen; Mon-Sun 9.30 pm; Cash & all usual cards; No trainers.

THE KITCHEN AT CHEWTON GLEN £87 3 4 3

CHEWTON FARM ROAD BH23 5QL 01425 275341

"A great fun restaurant for indoor and outdoor dining" – this is the dressed down (a bit) option at this luxurious country house hotel, complete with plush banquettes, a swish outdoor terrace, cookery school and greenery-filled views over the kitchen gardens. Not all reviews are perfect, but the lowest food rating it receives is "good". / www.chewtonglen.com/thekitchen; TheKitchenatCG; Mon-Sat 9.30 pm; closed Sun.

NEWBURY, BERKSHIRE 2–2D

THE HARE & HOUNDS £63

BATH ROAD, SPEEN RG14 1QY 01635 521152

After months of restoration, this 17th century Georgian building near Newbury re-opened in January 2022 and now boasts a traditional pub, very attractive pitched-roof dining room in contemporary style and 30-bed coaching inn, as well as a covered garden terrace. No feedback as yet in our annual diners' poll – reports please! / www.hareandhoundsnewbury.co.uk; hareandhounds_newbury; Mon-Sun 9 pm.

THE WOODSPEEN £84 4 3 4

LAMBOURN RD RG20 8BN 01635 265 070

"A most sophisticated dining experience in charming surroundings" has established this "barn-like" eatery, converted from a restored seventeenth century farm and former pub in West Berkshire, as one of the most commented-on restaurants in our annual diners' poll. And – unusually for a rural spot – the professionalism of its approach (the owner is top catering CEO, Alastair Storey) means it's often tipped for business meetings as well as being "an ideal place for meeting friends". Chef Peter Eaton's cuisine makes "excellent use of native ingredients" with "confident" cooking that's "always beautifully presented and full of flavour", while "service is always attentive and interested in you". "Always charming, and deservedly always full!". Top Tip – "set lunch menu is very good value but rather limited in choice". / www.thewoodspeen.com; thewoodspeen; Mon-Sat 9.30 pm, Sun 4.30 pm; closed Sun D.

NEWCASTLE UPON TYNE, TYNE AND WEAR 8–2B

BLACKFRIARS RESTAURANT £58 3 3 4

FRIARS ST NE1 4XN 0191 261 5945

"An old building, with lots of candles and nooks and crannies" – "this beautiful 13th century former Dominican friary" is particularly "atmospheric in winter" (but it also has "a lovely courtyard area for summer dining"). From its bistro/brasserie-style menu, there's "always a good choice of dishes based on good local produce" and its standards are "accomplished and reliable". / www.blackfriarsrestaurant.co.uk; BlackfriarsRestaurant; Mon-Sat 9.30 pm, Sun 4 pm; closed Sun D; Cash & all usual cards.

THE BROAD CHARE £66 3|4|4

25 BROAD CHARE NE1 3DQ
019 1211 2144

"Quality locally sourced food" "in an excellent refurbished pub close to the Quayside" wins consistently high ratings across the board for this long-running collaboration (12 years and counting) between Terry Laybourne's 21 Hospitality Group and the neighbouring Live Theatre, a theatre for new writing. / www.thebroadchare.co.uk; _thebroadchare; Mon-Sat 10 pm, Sun 5 pm; closed Sun D; No Amex.

COOK HOUSE £49 4|4|4

FOUNDRY LANE NE6 1LH **0191 276 1093**

A "really excellent find in a charming location", "Anna Hedworth's flagship restaurant in the Ouseburn serves an unusual and interesting menu" in "a quirky building just away from the city centre". The former Quo Vadis and Rochelle Canteen chef started out here in a shipping container, before graduating to this upstairs, open-kitchen venue. ("Flawless… high praise from a veggie going to a 'normal' restaurant!") / cookhouse.org; cookhouse_anna; Wed-Sat 11 pm, Sun 4 pm; closed Sun D, closed Mon & Tue.

DABBAWAL £40 4|3|3

69-75 HIGH BRIDGE NE1 6BX
0191 232 5133

"A full menu with lots of variety, and super staff" underpin the appeal of this street food pioneer, which opened in 2008, near the Theatre Royal. "The only downer is that it is sooooo popular now, it is hard to get a table!". / www.dabbawal.com; dabbawal; Sun-Thu 10.30 pm, Fri & Sat 11 pm; Cash & all usual cards.

DOBSON AND PARNELL £44 3|3|4

21 QUEEN ST NE1 3UG **0191 221 0904**

Casual fine dining is the style nowadays at this buzzy Quayside destination, which occupies an address made famous in its days as '21 Queen Street' (long RIP). There is a conventional two-course/three-course menu, but also competitively priced 5-course and 7-courses options featuring more "unusual taste combinations". All are well-reviewed as "always reliable" and "delicious" as is the "friendly and attentive service". See also its siblings: Blackfriars Restaurant in Newcastle and Hinnies in Whitley Bay. / www.dobsonandparnell.co.uk; dobsonandparnell; Thu-Sat, Wed 9.30 pm, Sun 4 pm; closed Wed L

---

closed Sun D, closed Mon & Tue; Cash & all usual cards.

DOSA KITCHEN £42 3|3|3

7 OSBORNE ROAD (REAR) NE2 2AE

"A very pleasant change from some of the run-of-the-mill Asian offerings elsewhere in Newcastle" – this "very nice South Indian restaurant" which doesn't have the greatest entrance ("entry is via a door on a different street and up a flight of stairs"). "An excellent range of dosas" is the highlight of its "excellent value and very consistent food". Top Tip – "Sunday buffet is especially good value and a great introduction to South Indian cuisine for those unfamiliar and/or unsure what to order". / www.dosakitchen.co.uk; dosakitchenuk; Tue-Fri 9.30 pm, Sat 10.30 pm, Sun 8.30 pm; closed Tue-Fri L, closed Mon.

FRANCESCA'S £36 3|3|4

134 MANOR HOUSE RD NE2 2NA
0191 281 6586

"Queues seem to be longer than ever" at this "well-established, great-value Italian institution" in Jesmond – "a testament to the popularity" of its generous servings of pizza, pasta and much else on a long menu that "continues to provide VFM". / www.francescasjesmond.co.uk; Mon-Sat 9.30 pm; closed Sun; No Amex; no bookings.

HOUSE OF TIDES £128 5|3|4

28-30 THE CLOSE NE1 3RN
0191 2303720

Kenny & Abbie Atkinson's Grade I-listed sixteenth-century merchant's house on the old Quayside is frequently hailed as Newcastle's best restaurant, and it's historically the most renowned of the city's more ambitious culinary destinations. And its "lovely, informal, friendly atmosphere makes this haute cuisine dining experience an all-round joy". The worst thing anyone said about the food this year? "The caviar was a bit soft and non-descript" [first world problems! Ed]. / www.houseoftides.co.uk; houseoftides; Wed-Fri 8.30 pm, Sat 9 pm; closed Wed & Thu L, closed Mon & Tue & Sun; Cash & all usual cards; credit card deposit required to book; children: 12.

JESMOND DENE HOUSE £81 3|3|4

JESMOND DENE RD NE2 2EY
0191 212 6066

"A great escape in the centre of Newcastle", the "excellent" dining room in this Arts & Crafts boutique hotel serves "reliably decent food in a very nice setting". Coffee and tea are served in the "beautiful lounges or garden" – and it's all "reasonable value". / www.jesmonddenehouse.co.uk; jesmonddenehouse; Wed-Sat 9.30 pm; closed Wed-Sat L, closed Mon & Tue & Sun; Cash & all usual cards; booking max 7 may apply.

KALTUR £157 3|4|4

19 DEAN STREET NE1 1PQ
0191 447 1180

"Chic Spanish restaurant, with a varied menu of creative tapas plus good sherries" and an "excellent and extensive range of Spanish wines", where "a perch at the bar is a front-row seat for watching the cooking". It opened in 2019, and is a large spin-off from an older wine bar and tapas stop at 8 High Bridge Street. / www.kalturrestaurant.co.uk; kalturfood; Fri & Sat 11 pm, Sun-Thu 10 pm.

KHAI KHAI £35 4|4|3

29 QUEEN STREET NE1 3UG
0191 261 4277

This 2020 newcomer in a Victorian building just off the Quayside creates "unusual twists on Indian cuisine" by using a modern Josper grill to recreate the 'primal' smoky flavours of the subcontinent's traditional regional cuisines. Top Tip – "wonderful cocktails". / khaikhai.co.uk; khaikhaincl; Mon-Thu 10.30 pm, Fri & Sat 11 pm, Sun 9.30 pm.

MANTRA £41 3|4|3

29 FORTH BANKS NE1 3SG
0191 232 6080

This "authentic Thai" venture – run by a "family passionate about their food" – occupies a prominent Quayside building "built in traditional Asian style" (formerly the Waterside Palace Chinese restaurant). It has a "calm and relaxing atmosphere, with staff who are helpful and have good knowledge of the food". / www.mantra-thai.co.uk; mantrathai; Tue-Sun 11 pm; closed Mon.

PANI'S £44 3|4|4

61-65 HIGH BRIDGE NE1 6BX
0191 232 4366

Roberto & Walter Pani's Tyneside fixture (est. 1995) is "still a very reliable venue after all these years", serving an Italian menu with "interesting Sardinian specialities" – and there's "always a great vibe both lunchtime and evenings". / www.paniscafe.co.uk; panisitalian; Mon-Thu 9 pm, Fri & Sat 10 pm; closed Sun; Cash & all usual cards.

PEACE & LOAF £78 5|4|4

217 JESMOND ROAD NE2 1LA
0191 281 5222

"I've never had a bad meal here". Local chef Dave Coulson trained at Le Gavroche in London, and returned to open his "outstanding" Jesmond restaurant 10 years ago, steadily building its reputation ever since for "adventurous and delicious" cuisine from its seasonal tasting menus. "Dave is renowned locally and deserves national recognition". Top Tip – lunchtime and early evening, try it out more inexpensively with the '2, 1, 2, 1' menu for £35 per person. / www.peaceandloaf.co.uk; peaceandloafjes; Wed-Sat 9 pm; closed Mon & Tue & Sun; Cash & all usual cards.

ROUTE £54 [4][4][4]

35 SIDE   NE1 3JE   0191 222 0973

The route in question is that from castle to Quayside – the street where John Calton's "lovely and intimate" modern bistro is located. There's nothing but praise for the "exceedingly creative and imaginative menu, featuring original combinations and matched with a good value wine list". Top Menu Tip – "Oh, the treacle bread…" / routenewcastle.co.uk; routenewcastle; Wed-Sat 9 pm; closed Wed-Fri L, closed Mon & Tue & Sun.

SIMLA £37 [4][4][3]

39 SIDE   NE1 3JE   07917391319

"One of the best fine-dining Indian restaurants in the region", with "fantastic food and service", this family-run Quayside fixture opened 42 years ago and was transformed with the modernisation of both premises and menu in 2016. / www.simlarestaurant.net; simlanewcastle; Tue-Thu, Sun 11 pm, Fri & Sat 11.30 pm; closed Tue-Thu, Sun, Fri & Sat L, closed Mon.

SOLSTICE

5 - 7 SIDE   NE1 3JE   0191 222 1722

Kenny Atkinson's follow-up to House of Tides next door (and replacement for Violets Café) offers a tasting menu for just 14 guests. It opened in summer 2022, too late for feedback in our annual diners' poll, but a September 2022 review from Grace Dent of The Guardian suggests it's a 'must-visit': "For every Ynyshir, Moor Hall or Ikoyi – and Solstice is easily as impressive as those three – there are others that keep you hostage for hours, offering endless edible gold leaf and interminable pauses, and leaving you hungrier when you leave than you were when you arrived. That's why I appreciate the theatre, the pacing and the exquisite attention to detail of the likes of Solstice." / www.solsticencl.com; solstice_ncl; Tue-Fri 8.30 pm; closed Tue, Wed L, closed Mon, Sat & Sun.

21 £75 [4][3][3]

TRINITY GARDENS, QUAYSIDE   NE1 2HH   0191 222 0755

Terry Laybourne's "buzzy Quayside fixture" is "clearly the place to be in the Toon" – "reliably pleasing and deservedly popular" after providing "top-quality dining at surprisingly affordable prices" for 35 years. Top Tip – "great pre-theatre prix-fixe menu" ahead of a visit to the Sage, just across the Millennium Bridge. / 21newcastle.com; 21Newcastle; Mon-Sat 10.30 pm; closed Sun; Cash & all usual cards.

NEWCASTLE, COUNTY DOWN   10–1D

MOURNE SEAFOOD BAR £35 [3][3][3]

10 MAIN ST   BT33 0LU   028 4375 1377

In an attractive coastal town, this breezily themed offshoot from the Belfast original has been a local feature for over ten years. Though decently rated, it's said that "the food is not as good as in the city branch", but its "lively" atmosphere is sometimes cited as compensation. / www.mourneseafood.com; mourneseafooddundrum; Wed & Thu 9 pm, Sat, Fri 9.30 pm, Sun 6 pm; closed Mon & Tue; Cash & all usual cards.

NEWLYN, CORNWALL   1–4A

MACKEREL SKY [4][4][3]

NEW ROAD   TR18 5PZ   01736 448982

"Jump on the sleeper to Penzance and make a B-line for this gem", to feast on "the freshest catch of the day delivered from Newlyn harbour opposite", at this "tiny seafood bistro" with "reasonable prices for the best and freshest seafood". Founders Nina & Jamie MacLean used to run the Mackerel Sky restaurant in Penzance, before moving to start a family. The no-bookings seafood bar has been so successful they decided to open a seafood shack two doors down for the 2023 season. Top Tip – "crab nachos are absolutely divine". / www.mackerelskycafe.co.uk; mackerelskyseafoodbar; Mon-Sun 9 pm.

NEWPORT ON TAY, FIFE   9–3D

THE NEWPORT £92 [5][4][3]

1 HIGH STREET   DD6 8AA   01382 541 449

"Jamie Scott is a genius! – He and his team produce remarkable combinations of flavour and inventive dishes" at his modern restaurant-with-rooms, "with great views across the Tay to Dundee", which he opened with his wife Kelly in 2016, two years after winning MasterChef: The Professionals. "Having dined in many Michelin-starred restaurants, The Newport is still my favourite". / www.thenewportrestaurant.co.uk; thenewportrestaurant; Thu-Sat 9 pm, Sun 8.30 pm; closed Mon & Tue & Wed; Cash & all usual cards.

NEWPORT, GWENT   2–2A

GEM 42 £69 [4][3][3]

42 BRIDGE STREET   NP20 4NY   01633 287591

"Very pleasantly surprised!" – brothers Sergio (chef) and Pasquale (pastry chef) Cinotti are carving a strong reputation out of nowhere at this fairly humble-looking destination, which they opened in un-lovely Newport in 2018. "Having been around for some time, they have reinvented themselves". First listed in Harden's last year, in September 2022 they were awarded 'Wales Restaurant of the Year' by the AA, alongside an impressive three rosettes. It's "expensive for Newport!" but well worth a try for its highly ambitious cuisine: the blow-out ten-course option is £180, but there is a much more accessible 4-course option. Expect luxury ingredients a-go-go: foie gras, truffle, venison, lobster, black cod… / www.gem42.co.uk; gem42newport; Mon-Sat 10.30 pm; closed Mon-Sat L, closed Sun; No shorts; booking evening only; children: 12.

NEWQUAY, CORNWALL   1–3B

FISH HOUSE [4][3][4]

UNIT 5 INTERNATIONAL SURF CENTRE, HEADLAND ROAD   TR7 1HY   01637 872085

"Never fails to bring joy to my heart" – Paul Harwood's "lovely, intimate, high-quality seafood restaurant" right "by the sea" on Fistral Beach again wins a big thumbs-up in reports: "super fresh fish" is the big deal you'd hope, for somewhere with top views of the surf and sands. / www.thefishhousefistral.com; thefishhousefistral; Mon-Sun 11 pm.

NEWTON ABBOT, DEVON   1–3C

THE ROCK INN £46 [3][3][3]

HAYTOR VALE, DARTMOOR NATIONAL PK   TQ13 9XP   01364 661305

Beautifully situated on Dartmoor, this rural pub was consistently well-reviewed this year for its hearty and enjoyable bistro-style menu (it's not a pub grub kind of place). There are nine bedrooms, too, and – if you stay – there's the additional option of a lighter early bird supper. / www.rock-inn.co.uk; Wed-Sat 8.30 pm, Sun 2.30 pm; closed Sun D, closed Mon & Tue.

NEWTON IN CARTMEL, CUMBRIA   7–4D

HEFT £87 [4][4][3]

LA11 6JH

"Exceptional food created by chef Kevin Tickle" (formerly of Forest Side Hotel) underpinned all reports on his July 2021 newcomer, opened with wife Nicola after a successful crowdfund in a "lovely" and historic-looking 17th century inn. As with Sunday Times critic Marina O'Loughlin's early critique, however, there's the odd caveat in reports concerning the tasting-only formula (although lunches are much simpler). For the odd reporter it seems "tasty but with value verging on daylight robbery". For Marina, "godlike" but with umami tastes "blared through a loudspeaker… a bit of light and shade wouldn't go amiss". / hefthighnewton.co.uk; heft_high_newton; Thu-Sat 7 pm, Sun 6 pm; closed Sun D, closed Mon & Tue & Wed; booking is online only.

NEWTON ON OUSE, NORTH YORKSHIRE   8–4C

THE DAWNAY ARMS £62 [3][4][2]

YO30 2BR   01347 848345

"Whilst walking in the area, dropped in for lunch without prior knowledge – what a gem!". Kerry & Martel Smith's rustic gastropub by the River Ouse, is consistently well rated. "The ambience and friendly welcome make it immediately a winner and that's cemented with the tremendous cuisine". / www.thedawnayatnewton.co.uk; Tue-Sat 9 pm, Sun 4 pm; closed Sun D, closed Mon; Cash & all usual cards.

THE PARKERS ARMS £67 543

HALL GATE HILL   BB7 3DY
01200 446236

"Stosie Madi and her team draw folk for many miles to remote Newton-in-Bowland for some of the best and freshest dishes ever" note fans of this ever-more famous pub, in the Forest of Bowland: one of the most commented-on country destinations in our annual diners' poll. "Even as a regular, it's getting hard to get a table given her seasonal and fabulous cooking: a combination of sheer simplicity, classic technique, and (if you're lucky) flavours from Madi's Lebanese (etc) heritage". "Her understanding of flavours is sublime… no wonder she's knocking awards out like a fast lunch service!" "AJ runs the bar with a bewildered look of surprise and the punters love it." Top Menu Tip – the pies. / www.parkersarms.co.uk; theparkersarms; Thu & Fri 8.30 pm, Sat 9 pm, Sun 5.30 pm; closed Sun D, closed Mon & Tue & Wed; No Amex; credit card deposit required to book.

LES MIRABELLES £59 444

FOREST EDGE RD   SP5 2BN
01794 390205

"A great place at top of its game" – "this very French establishment" on the edge of the New Forest "works hard under patron Claude Laage and has a loyal following". There's now "an extremely good-value set menu with a wide range of choices" branded as 'Le Frog Bistro' – which operates "rather confusingly in the same space"; "the food is all good". / www.lesmirabelles.co.uk; Wed-Sat 9.30 pm; closed Mon & Tue & Sun; No Amex.

OSTERIA £60 343

71 HIGH STREET   EH39 4HQ
01620 890589

"A gem in East Lothian" – "Angelo Cocchia and his discreet but warm team" have provided a "calm and sophisticated setting for delicious Italian food" for 16 years. The cooking is "consistent" but "the menu evolves", while "the fish is especially noteworthy". / www.osteria-no1.co.uk; osterianb; Mon-Sun 11 pm.

BETTYS £43 333

189A HIGH ST   DL7 8LF   01609 775154

"Sometimes the queues are horrendous, but it is worth the wait (well, perhaps not if it's raining!)" at this "absolutely dependable and traditional" representative of the legendary Yorkshire tearoom chain. "Service is sometimes a bit slow but that is part of the old world charm. This is NOT Costa Coffee!". Just the job for tea and a bun. / www.bettys.co.uk; bettys;

Sun-Fri 4.30 pm, Sat 5 pm; closed Sun-Fri & Sat D; No Amex.

ORIGIN SOCIAL £20 332

2 FRIARAGE STREET   DL6 1DP
01609 775900

"A very welcome addition to Northallerton" – this December 2021 newcomer has become a favourite with its "interesting and varied food". / www.originsocial.co.uk; originssocial; Tue-Thu 11 pm, Fri & Sat midnight; closed Tue L, closed Sun & Mon.

BENEDICTS £82 333

9 ST BENEDICTS ST   NR2 4PE
01603 926 080

Entering its eighth year, Richard & Katja Bainbridge's "relaxing" operation remains the most commented-on option in town in our annual diners' poll and also the highest rated. Fans say it's their "go-to" option, thanks to its "incredible" menus ("catering to all tastes") and staff who are "attentive without being overly ever present". However, ratings were dragged down by a few "disappointing" reports of the "might-have-been-a-bad-day-but…" variety. / www.restaurantbenedicts.com; restbenedicts; Tue-Sat 10 pm; closed Tue-Thu L, closed Sun & Mon; Cash & all usual cards.

BENOLI £59 433

5 ORFORD STREET   NR1 3LE
01603 633056

This central Norwich newcomer (est. 2019) from ex-Roux at the Landau head chef Oliver Boon and his brother Ben (the Ben & Oli of its name) "always offers tasty pasta-based and Italian-styled treats, in a modern setting". The commendably short menu "changes regularly", revolving around a handful of handmade pastas, one main meat and one fish dish, and vegan options. / benolirestaurant.com; benoli_restaurant_norwich; Mon-Sat 10 pm, Sun 9 pm.

FARMYARD RESTAURANT £44 333

23 SAINT BENEDICTS STREET   NR2 4PF
01603 733 188

This "vibrant" operation from chef-patron Andrew Jones, who worked for Richard Corrigan and Claude Bosi before returning to his native Norfolk, majors on "interesting, well-executed dishes" using "locally sourced ingredients". He and his partner, Hannah, also run The Dial House restaurant-with-rooms in Reepham. / www.farmyardrestaurant.com; farmyard_frozen; Wed-Fri 9 pm, Sat 9.30 pm; closed Mon & Tue & Sun; Cash & all usual cards.

THE GUNTON ARMS £64 335

CROMER RD   NR11 8TZ   01263 832010

"Love the vibe and art" at this "exciting" restaurant-with-rooms, opened in 2011 by Chelsea art dealer Ivor Braka on his country estate, with paintings and sculpture by luminaries from Lucian Freud, Paula Rego and Damien Hirst to Anthony Caro and Sol Le Witt on the walls and in the grounds outside. It's "definitely a meat-eater's heaven", with "superb food" from ex-Mark Hix chef Stuart Tattersall – "most locally sourced, including their own stunning venison from the estate", and some "cooked over the dining-room fire". / www.theguntonarms.co.uk; guntonarms; Mon-Sat 9.30 pm, Sun 9 pm; Cash & all usual cards.

ROGER HICKMAN'S £84 333

79 UPPER ST. GILES ST   NR2 1AB
01603 633522

"A long-term destination in the culinary wastelands of Norfolk, but so good it is worth a trip", say fans of Roger Hickman's "lovely" culinary beacon (which dates from 1990 under former owner David Adlard). Reports often compare it favourably with nearby Benedicts, although the latter outscored it by a whisker again this year. Whatever the ranking, all reports rate it well, lauding "superbly executed food, with touches of inventiveness which all hit the spot". Such gripes as featured in feedback are that it's pricey or "a bit OTT" in its approach. / www.rogerhickmansrestaurant.com; rogerhickmans; Tue-Sat 10 pm; closed Sun & Mon; Cash & all usual cards.

ALCHEMILLA £122 544

192 DERBY ROAD   NG7 1NF
0115 941 3515

"Mind-blowing experimental food and interesting wine pairings" continues the acclaim for Alex Bond's "totally unique" five-year-old, which deserves the comparisons it sometimes attracts with that of his former employer, Sat Bains. It helps that it occupies an attractively converted former Victorian coach house on the Park Estate (just outside the city centre) with very atmospheric, brick-lined vaulted rooms. Tasting menus start at £95 for five courses, and there are also options for seven courses (£130) and 10 courses (£160 pairings). "Very friendly staff, who are very knowledgeable about the offering" complete the rosy picture painted in reports. / alchemillarestaurant.uk; alchemillarestaurant; Wed-Fri 7.30 pm, Sat 8 pm; closed Wed-Fri L, closed Mon & Tue & Sun.

ANNIE'S BURGER SHACK £28 333

5 BROADWAY   NG1 1PR   01156849920

With "a truly dizzying number of very satisfying burgers to choose from" (more than 30 at a recent count), this Lace Market operation has become hugely popular: "the place is always packed". Success has led to a branch in Derby. Founder Anmarie Spaziano grew up in Rhode Island, where the American diner apparently originated. / www.anniesburgershack.com; anniesburgershacknotts; Mon-Sun 10.30 pm; Cash & all usual cards.

The Loch & The Tyne, Old Windsor

CAFE ROYA £49 **443**

130 WOLLATON RD NG9 2PE
0115 922 1902

This "brilliant vegetarian place" from ex-Sat Bains chef Roya Bishop is "always popular, so book in advance". "Every dish is exotic and exciting" as she looks to cuisines around the world for ideas. "A committed carnivore, I'm always heartily impressed by the vegetarian cooking here. Deciding what to order can be rather like Sophie's Choice!". / www.caferoya.com; caferoya130; Tue-Sat 10 pm; closed Tue L, closed Sun & Mon; Cash & all usual cards.

CALCUTTA CLUB £48 **443**

8-10 MAID MARIAN WAY NG1 6HS
0115 941 4441

This "simply amazing" and decidedly upmarket Indian (which opened in 2014) recreates the atmosphere of polo clubs under the Raj, with "delicious food" that is "not overpowering", and "friendly, knowledgeable staff". / www.calcutta-club.co.uk; calcuttaclub; Mon-Thu 10.30 pm, Fri & Sat 11 pm; closed Mon-Sat L, closed Sun.

THE CUMIN £41 **542**

62-64 MAID MARIAN WAY NG1 6BJ
0115 941 9941

The Anand's "family-run restaurant serving utterly delicious food" has stood out on the Nottingham curry scene for 15 years. "The chutneys and sauces with poppadoms set the scene for a faultless performance both with food and level of service". "The whole place has a real buzz – forget quiet conversation." Top Tip – "the prawn Manchurian appetiser is absolutely spot-on". / www.thecumin.co.uk; the_cumin_indian_restaraunt; Mon-Thu 11 pm, Fri & Sat 11.30 pm; closed Mon-Sat L, closed Sun; Cash & all usual cards.

EVERYDAY PEOPLE £45 **333**

12 BYARD LANE NG1 2GJ
0115 958 2445

"Top ramen" scores solid marks for this popular yearling which opened in August 2022, and which serves a few other options like corn dogs or Thai chicken larb alongside the noodle dishes. We expect another location will be coming soon. / www.theeverydaypeople.co.uk; homeboysuk; Thu-Sat, Wed 11 pm, Sun 6 pm; closed Wed L closed Sun D, closed Mon & Tue.

FRENCH LIVING £53 **334**

27 KING ST NG1 2AY **0115 958 5885**

"A stalwart of the Nottingham restaurant scene" for almost 30 years, "it can feel like you are eating in France" at this city-centre outfit with a "constantly changing menu, strong on unfamiliar but interesting dishes". It's still run by its founders, Corsican Stéphane Luiggi and his Notts-born wife, Louise. / www.frenchliving.co.uk; frenchlivinguk; Tue-Sat midnight; closed Sun & Mon; No Amex.

HART'S KITCHEN £70 **342**

STANDARD HILL, PARK ROW NG1 6GN
0115 988 1900

"A very apt restaurant for business meetings" – Tim Hart's (of Rutland's Hambleton Hall) "smart and modern" brasserie has long been known for its professional standards, and this has remained the case since 2019, when he moved it from its location of two decades' standing into his boutique hotel in the city. Its hallmarks are "top-class food and drinks", "slick and friendly service" and "the added bonus of an outside area in summer". / www.hartsnottingham.co.uk; hartsnotts; Mon-Sun 8.30 pm; Cash & all usual cards.

IBERICO £56 **343**

THE SHIRE HALL, HIGH PAVEMENT
NG1 1HN **01159 410410**

This "buzzy tapas bar", in a "lovely vaulted-ceiling basement" in the Lace Market, serves "a tremendous variety" of "authentic Spanish dishes". A "cheerful" fixture for more than 15 years, it's "probably the first choice for tapas in the area" – and "you can have the menú del día for not much more than a tenner". There is also a spin-off in Hockley. / www.ibericotapas.com; iberico_tapas; Tue-Thu 9 pm, Fri & Sat 10 pm; closed Tue-Fri L, closed Sun & Mon; Cash & all usual cards; children: 12+ D.

KUSHI-YA £39 **533**

1A CANNON COURT, LONG ROW WEST
NG1 6JE **0115 9411369**

"Amazing Japanese tapas, packed full of flavour" are served at this "unique and creative" five-year-old which started out as a supper club. These days it "rivals places charging twice the amount" – and it's "where all the top chefs go on their day off". Jay Rayner of The Observer visited in October 2022 after a tip-off from a Nottingham-based pal, and declared it "a restaurant of the year". / www.kushi-ya.co.uk; kushi_ya; Wed-Sat 10 pm; closed Mon & Tue & Sun.

MEMSAAB £46 **443**

12-14 MAID MARIAN WAY NG1 6HS
0115 957 0009

Amita Sawhney's "fantastic Indian restaurant has been around for ages, but doesn't disappoint". It's "not the cheapest, but friendly service and fantastic food" have earned it a stellar reputation. Top Tip – "try the tandoori ostrich" (free-range, locally farmed, infused with garlic and red chilli". / www.mem-saab.co.uk; memsaabnottingham; Mon-Thu 10.30 pm, Fri & Sat 11 pm, Sun 10 pm; closed Mon-Sun L; Cash & all usual cards; No shorts.

NO.TWELVE £45 **332**

2 - 3 ELDON CHAMBERS NG1 2NS

"An award-winning vegan restaurant in the city centre of Nottingham" whose website says it's "changing the stigma of plant-based cuisine" [hopefully removing rather than just changing it? Ed]. Five years old now, it's hosted in a brick-walled converted mill and offers a lunchtime 'Classics' menu of sharing plates, while in the evening there's a 7-course tasting menu for £55 per person. / www.no12nottingham.co.uk; no12nottingham; Thu-Sat 10 pm, Sun 5 pm; closed Sun D, closed Mon & Tue & Wed.

RESTAURANT SAT BAINS £199 **443**

LENTON LANE NG7 2SA **0115 986 6566**

"Having wanted to visit for a long time, I was not disappointed despite the strange location!". – Amidst motorway flyovers, industrial estates, electricity pylons and the concrete banks of the River Trent, Sat & Amanda Bains's converted motel remains one of the UK's more offbeat gastronomic adventures and is entering its twentieth year as a flagship of Nottingham dining. Here, one of the most expensive and ambitious tasting menus is served in a "high-class" if low-key setting: "a stunning 10-course extravaganza" where regulars note "increasing use of subtle spice" and the continual introduction of "many new dishes". For those who stay, there are "great rooms and a lovely breakfast too". Having topped our Top 100 UK Restaurants last year, ratings slipped a fraction this year: some regulars noted (as they have at some other top places this year) both pressures on service ("I felt standards had dropped since pre-pandemic days"); and concerns over value ("I have been eating at Restaurant Sat Bains since 2006… prices nowadays are becoming astronomical"). / www.restaurantsatbains.com; restaurant_sat_bains; Wed-Fri 7 pm, Sat 7.45; closed Wed-Sat L, closed Mon & Tue & Sun; No Amex; children: 8+.

SEXY MAMMA LOVE SPAGHETTI £29 **333**

3 HEATHCOAT STREET NG1 3AF
0115 948 4610

"If you want pasta come here" – this "tiny local restaurant" is "good value and worth a visit". Owner Edin Gondzic is a veteran of the Hockley food scene with a knack for memorable restaurant names: his stable includes Botti di Mamma and the now-closed Crazy Fish My Love. / sexymammalovespag; Mon-Sun 9 pm.

SHANGHAI SHANGHAI £47 **332**

15 GOOSE GATE NG1 1FE
0115 958 4688

"High-quality and authentic" cuisine has earned regular inclusion in our guide for this Cantonese venue within walking distance of the Lace Market. There is the odd less-wowed report though: "I was expecting something special, but only just rated the food as good. The ambience only just got average…" / www.shanghai-shanghai.co.uk; Sun-Thu 10 pm, Fri & Sat 11 pm.

200 DEGREES `3` `4` `3`

HESTON HS, MEADOW LANE `NG2 3HE`
0115 837 4849

"Great freshly ground coffee" at this hipster indie coffee shop has proved the foundation for a national chain. Founded in 2012, they now have branches in 17 locations around the country, although the flagship venue in a panelled 17th Century coaching inn off the city centre's Market Square receives the most attention. / www.200degs.com; 200degs; Mon-Fri 5 pm; closed Mon-Fri D, closed Sat & Sun; Cash & all usual cards; no bookings.

WORLD SERVICE £79 `3` `3` `4`

NEWDIGATE HS, CASTLEGATE `NG1 6AF`
0115 847 5587

Near the castle, this long-serving stalwart occupies "comfortingly clubby surroundings" (seventeenth-century Newdigate House also hosts the Nottingham Club for the city's business and professional community) and remains "a definite favourite" that "sometimes hits five stars". Following the trend of over a decade, the kitchen is "wildly variable: some dishes can be wonderful, others poorly conceived and lacking in flavour". / www.worldservicerestaurant.com; Wed & Thu 9 pm, Fri & Sat 9.30 pm, Sun 3.30 pm; closed Wed L closed Sun D, closed Mon & Tue; Cash & all usual cards; children: 10+ at D.

ZAAP £37 `4` `4` `4`

UNIT B, BROMLEY PLACE `NG1 6JG`
0115 947 0204

"Fantastic Thai food, Thai people and decor give it the authentic feel of being down a side street in a city in Thailand" at this street-food offshoot from Ban Kaewkraikhot's Sukhothai brand – "great value and super tasty, with a great atmosphere". / www.zaapthai.co.uk; zaap_thai_streetfood; Sun-Thu 10 pm, Fri & Sat 11 pm; Cash & all usual cards; no bookings.

NUN MONKTON, NORTH YORKSHIRE `5–1D`

THE ALICE HAWTHORN £68 `4` `4` `4`

THE GREEN `YO26 8EW` 01423 330 303

"From a humble inn to an outstanding eatery in a very short time" – this "lovely pub in the delightful village of Nun Monkton" has been turbocharged in recent years by investment from millionaire plumber Richard Harpin and is run by Claire & John Topham. The latest investment has been a new block adding 12 bedrooms, which opened in early 2022. Practically all reports acclaim "a well-balanced menu providing relaxed, comfortable dining with first-class service". (The name, by the way, is that of a famous racehorse, and another reason to visit is England's tallest maypole, on the village green). / www.thealicehawthorn.com; thealicehawthorn; Wed-Sat 8.30 pm, Sun 2.30 pm; closed Wed L closed Sun D, closed Mon & Tue; No Amex.

OAKHAM, RUTLAND `5–4D`

HITCHEN'S BARN £65 `4` `4` `3`

12 BURLEY ROAD `LE15 6DH`
01572 722255

A "little gem" with a "quirky interior" in the town centre that offers "wonderful service" and "amazing seasonal local food". Owners Neal & Louise Hitchens met working up the road at swanky Hambleton Hall and cooked at luxury destinations around the world before taking on the Berkeley Arms at Wymondham, switching to the Barn in 2019. "Hambleton may be more impressive, but Hitchen's knocks it out of the park on value!". / www.hitchensbarn.co.uk; hitchensbarnoakham; Tue-Sat 11 pm; closed Sun & Mon.

OARE, KENT `3–3C`

THE THREE MARINERS £53 `3` `3` `3`

2 CHURCH RD `ME13 0QA` 01795 533633

"Fantastic fresh daily fish, well-cooked, no-nonsense food and the best pint of Shepherd Neame ever" sums up the appeal of this classic boozer near Faversham, dating from 1787. / www.thethreemarinersoare.co.uk; thethreemarinersoare; Tue-Sat 9 pm, Sun 5 pm; closed Sun D, closed Mon; No Amex.

OBAN, ARGYLL AND BUTE `9–3B`

COAST £63 `4` `4` `3`

104 GEORGE STREET `PA34 5NT`
01631 569900

"Lovely small restaurant" in an old bank building that's carved a niche for itself over the past two decades with "great cooking" that makes good use of Argyll's "local and seasonal produce" – with seafood, meat and game all featured. Chef-patron Richard Fowler and his wife Nicola are "lovely people" and offer "great service" – "we dropped in for an impromptu lunch and it massively exceeded our expectations". It's "good value too". / www.coastoban.co.uk; coastrestaurantbar; Tue-Sun 9.30 pm; closed Sun L, closed Mon.

EE-USK (SEAFOOD RESTAURANT) £63 `3` `3` `3`

NORTH PIER `PA34 5QD` 01631 565666

"Great local seafood" is the USP of the MacLeod family's operation, perched in a "lovely position" on a pier overlooking the waters which provide all their shellfish. By most accounts everything is "well cooked", although some reporters feel the "large modern restaurant lacks a bit of atmosphere". / www.eeusk.com; eeusk; Mon-Sun 9.30 pm; No Amex; children: 12+ at D.

ETIVE £94 `5` `4` `3`

43 STEVENSON STREET `PA34 5NA`
01631 564899

"Everything here blew me away" – John McNutty & David Lapsley's relaxed venue provides "an excellent tasting menu showcasing

ingredients from Argyll's 'Land and Sea'" and inspires a hymn of praise in reports: it "was not the main restaurant we booked on our trip but is the main reason we will return: absolutely loved it and definitely worth a detour!" / www.etiverestaurant.co.uk; etiverestaurant; Wed-Sun 9 pm; closed Wed-Sun L, closed Mon & Tue; Cash & all usual cards; booking evening only.

ISLE OF ERISKA HOTEL

BENDERLOCH `PA37 1SD` 01631 720371

"A beautiful and romantic setting" – this small hotel and golf resort has an idyllic, away-from-it-all location on a small tidal island at the entrance to Loch Creran. Still too few reports for a rating, although such feedback as we have on Ernst Van Zyl's cuisine is upbeat. / eriska-hotel.co.uk; Isleoferiska; Mon-Sun midnight.

OCKHAM, SURREY `3–3A`

THE BLACK SWAN £63 `3` `3` `3`

OLD LN `KT11 1NG` 01932 862364

"Good solid food" and a "large outdoor space for eating" makes this country pub a handy refuelling spot for visitors to the RHS gardens at nearby Wisley. / www.blackswanockham.com; blackswanockham; Mon-Sat 11 pm, Sun 10 pm; Cash & all usual cards.

OLD HUNSTANTON, NORFOLK `6–3B`

THE NEPTUNE £96 `5` `4` `3`

85 OLD HUNSTANTON RD `PE36 6HZ`
01485 532122

"Sublime food, always expertly executed" ensures this former coaching inn on the north Norfolk coast "is a place to return to time and time again". Hosts Kevin & Jackie Mangeolles "are so special and their welcome is always the warmest", while "lots of local food/suppliers" benefit from "the owner's obvious skills". Top Tip – "the rooms (both upstairs and in the Cottage next door) are a cut above most r-with-r establishments". / www.theneptune.co.uk; theneptuneoldhunstanton; Tue-Sat 9 pm; closed Tue-Sat L, closed Sun & Mon; children: 10+.

OLD WINDSOR, BERKSHIRE `3–3A`

THE LOCH & THE TYNE £85 `3` `3` `3`

10 CRIMP HILL `SL4 2QY` 07722 293359

"Adam Handling's menu is high on big flavours and very satisfying", according to fans of his superior gastropub yearling, who leave "stuffed and happy". In style, "this is at the very posh end of pub dining (though to be fair there are still stools at the bar for Old Windsor locals wanting a drink)". "Some interesting signature courses include 'The Mother' with apple, dates and truffle and a supplementary course of lobster cooked in wagyu fat – it tastes decadent" and exemplifies Handling's maximalist and luxurious culinary MO: "full of flavour, imaginative and beautifully presented". But while nearly all reports rate the food well, ratings were not as high as last year. One or two reports jibe that "the food is not as good as the chef thinks it is" or feel that its style "sits slightly uncomfortably between high-end pub food and good restaurant standards, with rather greedy prices". Top Tip – "the outside terrace is fun in winter or summer". / www.lochandtyne.com; lochandtyne; Thu-Sat, Wed 10 pm, Sun 7 pm; closed Wed L closed Sun D, closed Mon & Tue; children: No minimum age.

OLDSTEAD, NORTH YORKSHIRE   5–1D

THE BLACK SWAN £196 [4][3][3]

YO61 4BL   01347 868 387

"A bucket-list place so we had high expectations… did not disappoint in any area!". Tommy Banks and his family's out-of-the-way pub in North Yorks is one of the most commented-on destinations in our annual diners' poll and inspires high hopes – inflamed in large part by TripAdvisor declaring it the #1 restaurant in the world some years ago – which it arguably does a surprisingly good job of living up to. New chef Callum Leslie was appointed in November 2021, and wins consistent praise for his "out-of-this-world tasting menu with outstanding wine pairings" all delivered by "very knowledgeable" staff. / www.blackswanoldstead.co.uk; blackswan_oldstead; Sat, Wed-Fri, Sun 8 pm; closed Wed-Fri, Sun L, closed Mon & Tue; No Amex; booking is online only; children: 10.

ONGAR, ESSEX   3–2B

SMITH'S BRASSERIE   £71 [3][3][2]

FYFIELD RD   CM5 0AL   01277 365578

"We've visited here and in Wapping many times and we've never had less than a hugely enjoyable experience!" – this big seafood brasserie (est. 1958, with its London spin-off of about a decade's standing) is one of Essex's brightest culinary features and as such "a regular haunt for TOWIE and other local stars!". "Wonderful fish" is the main feature of a menu of "always first-class food". The worst comment? "It can be a bit cramped and noisy!". / www.smithsrestaurants.com; Tue, Wed 11.30 pm, Fri & Sat 12.30 am, Thu midnight, Sun 8 pm; closed Mon; Cash & all usual cards; No trainers; children: 10+.

ONICH, HIGHLAND   9–3B

LOCH LEVEN SEAFOOD CAFÉ   £56 [5][4][3]

PH33 6SA   01855 821 048

"Lovely seafood and with a nice terrace area overlooking the loch" – this scenically located eatery near the water sprung out of a sister business, Lochleven Shellfish (and you can buy retail on-site). Stop off if you can, if you are in the locale and fancy a meal of oysters, scallops, crab, lobster, langoustine… / www.lochlevenseafoodcafe.co.uk; lochlevenseafoodcafe; Wed-Sun ; closed Wed-Sun L closed Wed-Sun D, closed Mon & Tue; No Amex.

ORFORD, SUFFOLK   3–1D

BUTLEY ORFORD OYSTERAGE   £67 [4][2][2]

MARKET HILL   IP12 2LH   01394 450277

"I could eat anything on the menu and be satisfied" at the Pinney family's "not-to-be-missed" Suffolk institution. It "never changes: why fiddle with perfection" when "for beautiful fresh or smoked local seafood in a simple rustic restaurant there's hardly anywhere better" – "even if there's a distinct lack of vegetables". Top Tip – "griddled squid is a must". / www.butleyorfordoysterage.co.uk; Mon-Sun 9 pm; No Amex.

ORPINGTON, KENT   3–3B

XIAN   £48 [3][3][2]

324 HIGH ST   BR6 0NG   01689 871881

"A very good standard for a local Chinese" – this family-run Cantonese was famously the late Gary Rhodes's favourite. It doesn't attract quite the volume of support it did in yesteryear, though, and some diners feel "it's decent enough, but not as special as I'd expected". / Tue-Sun 10 pm; closed Sun L, closed Mon; Cash & all usual cards.

OSWESTRY, SHROPSHIRE   5–3A

SEBASTIAN'S   £77 [3][4][3]

45 WILLOW STREET   SY11 1AQ   01691 655 444

Chef-patron Mark Sebastian & Michelle Fisher's "newly decorated restaurant-with-rooms only gets better" – after more than three decades – "and is always full", a tribute to the "high standard of its French-influenced food". Set in three seventeenth-century cottages knocked together, it's a "quiet place to satisfy the foodie in you". / www.sebastians-hotel.com; Fri, Thu, Sat 9 pm, Wed, Tue 9.30 am, Sun 10 am; closed Sun, Wed, Tue D, closed Mon; No Amex; children: 10.

OTLEY, WEST YORKSHIRE   5–1C

BUON APPS   £60 [3][3][4]

HARTLEY HOUSE, 50 MILL WAY   LS21 1FE   01943 468 458

"With its attentive staff and lovely setting by the river", Alessandro & Sofia Elena Tocca's "wonderful Italian restaurant" draws an appreciative crowd and is "a favourite of many locals". One of Wharfedale's most consistent performers for two decades, it has blossomed since moving into an old weir-side mill five years ago. / www.buonappsotley.co.uk; buonapps; Wed & Thu, Sun 8.30 pm, Fri & Sat 9.30 pm; closed Mon & Tue.

OUNDLE, RUTLAND   6–4A

TAP & KITCHEN   £52 [3][3][3]

STATION ROAD   PE8 4DE   01832 275069

An "ever-changing menu keeps things fresh and interesting" at this "reliable" modern warehouse venue with "lovely outdoor seating" on a wharf – "and the Nene Valley beers are superb". / www.tapandkitchen.com; tapandkitchen; Mon-Sat 11 pm, Sun 9 pm.

OXFORD, OXFORDSHIRE   2–2D

ARBEQUINA   £53 [4][4][3]

74 COWLEY RD   OX4 1JB   01865 792777

"The best tapas ever" insist aficionados of the "short and interesting menu" at this "exceptional" former chemist's shop. "Yes, it's a little pricier than average, but let's face it – this is by no means run-of-the-mill tapas!". Top Menu Tips – "stunning aubergine, crispy chickpea and the baked cauliflower dishes". / arbequina.co.uk; arbequinaoxford; Thu & Fri 10.30 pm, Sat 10 pm; closed Thu & Fri L, closed Mon-Wed & Sun; Cash & all usual cards; children: 12.

ASHMOLEAN DINING ROOM   £56 [2][2][4]

BEAUMONT ST   OX1 2PH   01865 553 823

"The beautiful roof terrace of the Ashmolean Museum" makes a "great location" for an "excellent afternoon tea" – with a glass-fronted indoor area for winter use and an open-air lounging space and bar in the summer. More generally though, it's "a pity the food is overpriced and doesn't live up to the setting". / www.ashmolean.org/cafe-and-restaurant; ashmoleanmuseum; Mon-Sun 4.30 pm; closed Mon-Sun D; Cash & all usual cards.

BHOOMI KITCHEN   £53 [3][3][3]

70 LONDON ROAD   OX3 7PD   01865 762696

This "new kid on the block blows others away", say fans of this Headington offshoot of a popular Cheltenham Indian restaurant. Founder Michael's grandfather came to Oxfordshire from Kerala 50 years ago, to work as a private chef to a farmer near Burford. / www.bhoomikitchen.co.uk; bhoomikitchen_; Tue-Sun 9.45 pm; closed Tue-Thu L, closed Mon.

BRANCA   £52 [3][3][3]

111 WALTON ST   OX2 6AJ   01865 556111

"You really feel like you're in a continental bistro" at this "good-value and ever-reliable venue" in Jericho which has been popular for two decades. There is extra outdoor seating nowadays, which adds further to the Mediterranean atmosphere, and this year will see the opening of five bedrooms. / www.branca.co.uk; branca_oxford; Wed-Sat 9 pm, Sun 7 pm; closed Wed-Fri L, closed Mon & Tue; No Amex.

BRASSERIE BLANC £59 [2][2][3]

71-72 WALTON ST   OX2 6AG   01865 510999

Raymond Blanc's "reliable" local brasserie has shown good longevity and, according to fans, "manages to hold off much of the competition In busy Jericho, thanks to its varied menu", "excellent Sunday lunch" and "good wine list". Sceptics, though, are disappointed by "food that's OK but below what I had expected" for a location that sparked the national brand, and which was, back in the day, the warm-up act for what's now Le Manoir aux Quat' Saisons. / www.brasserieblanc.com; brasserieblanc; Mon-Sat 11 pm, Sun 9.30 pm; Cash & all usual cards.

CHERWELL BOATHOUSE £55 2|3|4

BARDWELL ROAD OX2 6ST
01865 552746

"An idyllic setting on the River Cherwell" – "right on the water, watching comings and goings and the odd person going overboard on their rowing boats" – guarantees a memorable occasion at this "beautiful Oxford institution", incorporated into a boathouse (run by the Verdin family since 1968). The food has always risked playing second fiddle here, and even though fans praise its "simple but perfect cooking", there were a number of "very average" reports this year ("I have had worse, but prefer better") or gripes about an excessive level of pricing. Some compensation can be found in "the best wine list in Oxford"… or "you can always hire a punt". / www.cherwellboathouse.co.uk; cherwellboathouse; Mon, Wed & Thu 9 pm, Fri & Sat 9.15 pm, Sun 8.45 pm; closed Tue; Cash & all usual cards.

CHIANG MAI £48 3|3|4

KEMP HALL PASSAGE, 130A HIGH STREET OX1 4DH 01865 202233

Bang in the middle of Oxford – occupying an early seventeenth-century building where Raymond Blanc cut his teeth as a chef in the 70s – this solidly rated Thai outfit celebrates its 30th anniversary this year. "Very much eclipsed in the last decade by Oli's Thai, but the latter's closure leaves a gap which this old favourite partially fills". / www.chiangmaikitchen.co.uk; chiangmaikitchenoxford; Mon-Sat 10 pm; closed Sun; No Amex.

THE COCONUT TREE £47 3|3|2

76 SAINT CLEMENT'S STREET OX4 1AH
01865 421865

"The food is exceptional and very different to what you'll find elsewhere" at this fast-growing chain (nine and counting) of "cheerful" Sri Lankan venues – whose "absolute bargain prices (£35 for the three of us)", "fantastic vegan options" and gluggable cocktails make it a particular "hit with students". Top Tip – "sri-tato is genuinely wonderful". / www.thecoconut-tree.com; thecoconuttreeuk; Sun & Mon 11 pm, Tue-Thu 11.30 pm, Fri & Sat 1 am.

CUTTLEFISH 3|4|3

36 ST CLEMENT'S STREET OX4 1AB
01865 243003

"Fresh fish cooked simply to perfection" is the siren call to this "great seafood spot on St Clement's, in the heart of the city". The menu runs the gamut from burgers and 'posh fish fingers' through to fresh Devon oysters, Canadian lobsters and seafood paella with

black venus rice. / www.cuttlefishoxford.co.uk; cuttlefishoxford; Mon-Sat 10.30 pm, Sun 9.30 pm.

GEE'S £54 2|3|4

61 BANBURY RD OX2 6PE 01865 553540

The "wonderful greenhouse setting" of this romantic and long-established north Oxford fixture was revamped and extended to the tune of £1.5 million during a three-month closure last year, giving it an appropriate leafy atmosphere. Originally a late-Victorian florist's, the Grade II-listed building was converted into a restaurant almost 40 years ago. There's a "nice buzz" to the place, and a "reliably good European menu" from new chef Matt Smith, but the feeling persists that – if you take into account the prices – the food is somewhat "run of the mill". / www.gees-restaurant.co.uk; geesrestaurant; Mon-Sun 10.30 pm; Cash & all usual cards.

THE IVY OXFORD BRASSERIE £96 2|2|3

120 - 121 HIGH STREET OX1 4DF

Bang in the centre of town, the Oxford branch of Richard Caring's tentacular national operation struggles to generate even the mixed praise it achieves elsewhere. "Perfectly adequate – but now The Ivy is a chain, it's missing the magic" is about as good as it gets. Other reporters are less kind: "overpriced sub-standard food with service to match" being about par for the course. / www.theivyoxford.com; theivyoxford; closed Mon-Sat & Sun.

THE MAGDALEN ARMS £58 3|3|3

243 IFFLEY ROAD OX4 1SJ
01865 243159

From the illustrious stable of London's Anchor & Hope and Canton Arms, this "cosy", high-quality gastropub exploded onto the Oxford dining scene in 2010. It keeps a much lower profile nowadays, notwithstanding its "friendly" style and "fantastic" cooking. / www.magdalenarms.co.uk; magdalenarms; Wed & Thu, Tue 9 pm, Fri & Sat 10 pm, Sun 8 pm; closed Tue L, closed Mon; No Amex; no bookings.

NO.1 SHIP STREET £61 4|3|3

1 SHIP STREET OX1 3DA 01865 806637

"Classic bistro food" – "delicious and beautifully presented, amid a good ambience" – makes this a handy venue for a meal, an easy walk from the Ashmolean Museum in the city centre; the set lunch is particularly good value. / www.no1shipstreet.com; no1shipstreet; Mon-Sat 10 pm; closed Sun.

THE OLD PARSONAGE £79 2|4|4

1 BANBURY RD OX2 6NN 01865 292305

This very "attractive hotel" just north of the city centre makes good use of a "lovely" seventeenth-century building with an ambience redolent of "Oxford academic

power and money". Foodwise, the ratings are dragged down by the odd reporter who feels its "bog-standard brasserie food needs more competition". The best bet might be its "very nice traditional tea – especially when served in the courtyard garden". / www.oldparsonage-hotel.co.uk; oldparsonagehotel; Mon-Sun 11 pm; Cash & all usual cards.

THE PERCH £59 3|3|4

BINSEY LN OX2 0NG 01865 728891

"Close to the centre of Oxford but a million miles away in atmosphere, at the end of the rural Binsey Lane", this "delightful riverside gastropub" surrounded by Port Meadow is "a very special place", complete "with elegant indoor dining and outdoor terrace, and also pub benches in the large garden with simpler food served from the 'shed'". "A lovely place for special celebrations and an excellent choice of dishes to suit all tastes." / www.the-perch.co.uk; theperchoxford; Mon-Sun 10 pm; Cash & all usual cards.

PIERRE VICTOIRE £49 3|2|3

LITTLE CLARENDON ST OX1 2HP
01865 316616

This "old-school" Gallic bistro is "consistently good in every way, and still probably the best-value food within walking distance of the city centre". It's also "much better than the chain used to be" (having split off when that company went spectacularly bust 25 years ago). / www.pierrevictoire.co.uk; Mon-Sat 11 pm, Sun 10 pm; closed Mon-Thu L; No Amex.

POMPETTE £68 4|3|3

7 SOUTH PARADE OX2 7JL
01865 311166

The "consistently high standard of cooking" at this French wine bar and bistro from Laura & Pascal Wiedermann (ex-Terroirs) in the north Oxford suburb of Summertown make it a valued favourite for numerous reporters, some of whom had their best meal of the year here. The "professional team makes us very welcome", and the "set meals are really good value". / www.pompetterestaurant.co.uk; pompetterestaurant; Tue-Sat 10 pm, Sun 3 pm, Mon ; closed Mon L closed Sun & Mon D.

THE PUNTER £48 3|4|3

7 SOUTH ST OX2 0BE 01865 248832

This "picturesque riverside venue" on Oxford's Osney Island (which opened in 1871 as The Waterman) is notable for its "laid-back but beautifully presented vegetarian food, full of flavours from a varied and interesting menu". "I'm not a vegetarian myself but most definitely hope to be back". Top Tip – "the whipped goats' cheese". / www.thepunteroxford.co.uk; Mon-Sun 9 pm; Cash & all usual cards.

Hide & Fox, Saltwood

QUOD, OLD BANK HOTEL £61 233

92-94 HIGH ST   OX1 4BJ   01865 202505

The "modern brasserie" in the central Old Bank Hotel serves "interesting, well thought-out dishes with a bit of pizzazz" in a "nice room – not too formal but equally quite smart". It's "such a pleasant place to eat: the food is not fancy and overworked but properly and consistently cooked", and "the prices are very reasonable". "Service is pleasant and efficient without being particularly friendly – like the food, they get the job done." / www.quod.co.uk; quodrestaurant; Mon-Sun 11 pm; Cash & all usual cards; booking max 10 may apply.

SICHUAN GRAND £56 322

THE OLD SCHOOL, GLOUCESTER GRN OX1 2DF   01865 236 899

"Brilliant cooking and a very buzzy atmosphere" attract a "significant Chinese clientele" to this "big restaurant in the lovely Old School on Gloucester Green", in the middle of Oxford. It has a sister restaurant at Westfield Stratford in east London. / sichuangrand.com; sichuan_grand; Mon-Sun 5 pm; closed Mon-Sun D.

TASTE TIBET £18 432

109 MAGDALEN ROAD   OX4 1RQ 01865 499318

"Very friendly and informal" – Yeshi Jampa opened this small restaurant in November 2020 after several years of serving up 'Himalayan soul food" at fairs and festivals. His dumplings, curries, noodles and bowls provide "great food with good vegan options. / www.tastetibet.com; tastetibet; Thu-Sat 9.30 pm, Wed 3 pm; closed Wed D, closed Mon & Tue & Sun; no bookings.

THE VAULTS AND GARDEN CAFE £32 334

UNIVERSITY CHURCH OF ST MARY THE VIRGIN, RADCLIFFE SQ   OX1 4AH 01865 279112

"In the medieval vaults of the University Church, in the centre of Oxford and the university" – this sweet but also "busy and vibrant" self-service café serves "large portions of freshly-cooked daily specials at very reasonable prices, as well as soups and salads". Great views of the Radcliffe Camera from the outside tables. / www.thevaultsandgarden.com; vaultsandgardencafe; Mon-Sun 5.30 pm; closed Mon-Sun D; Cash & all usual cards.

WILDING £57 343

11 LITTLE CLARENDON STREET OX1 2HP   01865 985630

This "independent & affordable" restaurant, wine bar and vintner in Jericho makes a "very welcome addition to the Oxford food & drink scene". With more than 400 vintages available, wine is very much the star of the show, backed up by "very knowledgeable staff" and a "friendly ambience". There are also branches in Salisbury and Frome. / www.wilding.wine; wilding_ox; Mon-Sun 11 pm.

OXSHOTT, SURREY   3–3A

THE VICTORIA OXSHOTT £78 332

HIGH STREET   KT22 0JR   01372 841900

"Superb food, beautifully presented, and really friendly service" win early plaudits for this yearling in an old pub in a London-fringe village, which has been thoroughly spruced up by a duo of Fat Duck alumni, chef Matt Larcombe and FoH Simon King. Common gripes – the menu can seem "limited" and prices "OTT". / thevictoriaoxshott.com; thevictoriaoxshott; Mon & Tue 10 pm, Wed-Sat 11.30 pm, Sun 9 pm.

OXTED, SURREY   3–3B

THE HAYCUTTER 333

TANHOUSE ROAD   RH8 9PE 01883 776955

This "lovely" mid-Victorian boozer (believed to be the only 'Haycutter' in the country) earns solid ratings for its "good old-fashioned pub grub" and "brilliant" all-round performance. It is now part of the Brunning & Price group. / www.brunningandprice.co.uk/haycutter; Mon-Sat 10 pm, Sun 9.30 pm.

OXTON, CHESHIRE   5–2A

FRAICHE £134 543

11 ROSE MOUNT   CH43 5SG 0151 652 2914

"Marc Willkinson is a genius" and "never fails to impress" at his "compact" venue – an unexpected find "off the beaten track" out on The Wirral, in a conservation village bordering Birkenhead. It has, on several occasions, topped our diners' poll as the UK's No. 1 destination. With just a dozen covers, it's very much one man's labour of love with its "imaginative visuals and playlist", not to mention his really "unusual" and distinctive cuisine, delivered as a six-course tasting menu. Save space for the end of the meal: chef really knows his way around pudding and chocolates. Early in 2022, there was news that the restaurant was to close, but this is not the case. Marc is hunting for new premises, though, and if he finds them change will be afoot. / restaurantfraiche.com; Marcatfraiche; Thu-Sat 9.30 pm, Sun 1.30 pm; closed Thu-Sat L closed Sun D, closed Mon & Tue & Wed; No Amex; children: -8.

OXWICH, SWANSEA   1–1C

BEACH HOUSE £87 434

OXWICH BEACH   SA3 1LS   01792 390965

"What a gorgeous place" – chef Hywell Griffith showcases his "just right, rather than over-processed" cuisine in a rugged ex-coalhouse with a "spectacular seafront setting" – "literally on the beach, with fabulous views over Oxwich Bay on the Gower Peninsula". Even when it's not sunny, "the cosy atmosphere looking out to grey skies and moody seas is almost as spectacular". While most of the ingredients are local, "it's not all fish by any means – but the fish dishes are exceptional". / www.beachhouseoxwich.co.uk; beachhouseoxwich; Wed-Sat 9 pm; closed Mon & Tue & Sun; Cash & all usual cards.

PADSTOW, CORNWALL   1–3B

CAFFÈ ROJANO £54 332

9 MILL SQUARE   PL28 8AE 01841 532093

"Paul Ainsworth's casual outpost", the long-established Rojano's, was relaunched in 2020 as a "relaxed bistro/café", with a "nice atmosphere and a generally high standard of food" – including "great pizzas", "very good pasta made in-house" and other Italian-inspired dishes. It wins praise for "not trying too hard". / www.paul-ainsworth.co.uk/rojanos; Mon-Sun 9.30 pm.

PAUL AINSWORTH AT NO6 £156 544

6 MIDDLE ST   PL28 8AP   01841 532093

"Face-slappingly good flavours" – "it often takes me by surprise with the amazing combinations of tastes" – have long established Paul Ainsworth's bijou Georgian townhouse as a less commented on but higher rated alternative to Rick Stein's nearby HQ. "It's not cheap but has to be on the list to eat if you are in Cornwall." Top Tip – you can book at a counter by the kitchen as well as in the dining room. / www.number6inpadstow.co.uk; no6padstow; Tue-Sat 8.30 pm; closed Sun & Mon; No Amex; credit card deposit required to book; children: 4+.

PRAWN ON THE LAWN
£62 4|4|3

11 DUKE STREET   PL28 8AB
01841 532223

Rick and Katie Toogood's sibling to their London operation is a "miniscule café" ("can you even call it a restaurant?") down near the harbour, which moved to this famous Cornish town from Islington in 2015. It's "very basic" and attracted much less attention in our survey compared to their summer pop-up, Prawn on the Farm, which occupies a big marquee on Trerethern farm a short drive outside Padstow, with fine views over the countryside to the sea. It "has real soul to it, shown by the young, enthusiastic service. The small fish plate menu is generally great and it's good fun as a concept". On the downside, "you need to go easy on the number of plates" and one or two reporters found results "insanely good, but incredibly salty and rich". The most common verdicts, though... "exceptional...", "incredible...", "superb..." / prawnonthelawn. com; prawnonthelawn; Tue-Thu, Sat 5 pm, Fri 9 pm; closed Tue-Thu, Sat D, closed Sun & Mon; Cash & all usual cards.

RICK STEIN'S CAFÉ
£59 2|3|2

10 MIDDLE STREET   PL28 8AP
01841 532700

"Great fresh seafood" is the draw you would hope for, according to fans of this casual joint run by the TV chef and his family – one of their four venues in Padstow. Overall ratings in our annual diners' poll are middling, though – it can just seem "overpriced". / www.rickstein.com; ricksteinrestaurants; Mon-Sun 10 pm; No Amex; booking evening only.

ST PETROC'S HOTEL & BISTRO
£81 3|4|3

4 NEW STREET   PL28 8EA   01841 532700

Part of the 'Padstein' empire of Rick, Jill and family, this hotel bistro a little away from the harbour is a simpler offering than their flagship. Its performance has sometimes been a little uneventful historically, but its "well-priced menu of great tasting fish and seafood" is well-rated by all who commented on it this year. / www.rickstein.com/eat-with-us/st-petrocs-bistro; theseafood; Mon-Sun 10 pm; No Amex.

SEAFOOD RESTAURANT
£96 4|3|4

RIVERSIDE   PL28 8BY   01841 532700

"Still amazing and it is over 25 years since we have last been!" – the harbourside HQ of the Stein family's national group was opened in 1975 by Jill and Rick Stein and remains one of the most commented-on destinations in our annual diners' poll. "It may be 47 years old, but the food is still amazing – the 'Fruits De Mer' is such a dreamy treat" and "so scrummy lobster" is another much-mentioned option amongst "the amazing fish choices that are so delicious and so fresh". There are quibbles – "some tables are exceptionally close!" – and

"service can struggle to attend to everyone". Still, "the busy-ness creates a buzz, somehow the venue still delivers a memorable occasion and a trip feels like a right of passage that everyone should experience at least once!". / www.rickstein.com/restaurants/ the-seafood-restaurant; ricksteinrestaurants; Sun-Thu 9 pm, Fri & Sat 9.30 pm; No Amex; booking max 14 may apply; children: 3+.

PATCHETTS GREEN, MIDDLESEX   3–2A

THE THREE COMPASSES
£55 3|4|2

PEGMIRE LANE   WD25 8DR
01923 857655

This "great gastropub" serves "consistently good food" with an Italian-influenced menu from chef James Harkin, whose parents owned the Alpine Restaurant in nearby Bushey for 48 years. His partner Magdalena, who runs the front of house, was previously at Locanda Locatelli in London. / thethreecompassesaldenham.co.uk; threecompasses; Tue-Thu 9 pm, Fri & Sat 9.30 pm, Sun 8.30 pm; closed Mon.

PEASMARSH, KENT   3–4C

TILLINGHAM
£68 3|3|4

DEW FARM, DEW LANE   TN31 6XD

"Excellent food" and staff who ensure you're "well looked after" justify a visit to former Gusbourne CEO Ben Walgate's farmhouse vineyard with "lovely views to the sea": it's "not easy to find, but well worth the effort". The project is "still in development", but "is a beautiful location with all the right intentions". / tillingham.com; tillinghamwines; Wed-Sat 8 pm, Sun 3 pm; closed Wed & Thu L closed Sun D, closed Mon & Tue; booking is online only; children: 10.

PENARTH, CARDIFF   1–1D

HOME
4|3|3

1 ROYAL BUILDINGS, STANWELL ROAD CF64 2AB

"Superb food, decor and service – an unbelievable experience!". "James Sommerin and family have created something exceptional that faithfully displays their outstanding food and service" – following the forced closure of his Michelin-starred venue on the Penarth seafront in 2020, James bounced back the following year with this 'immersive' venture behind blacked-out windows, bagging another star. This time, it's more than ever a family affair: James cooks alongside daughter Georgia (a rising chef in her own right), wife Louise takes care of the admin and second daughter Angharad works FoH. "It's not cheap (London prices), but it's very good." / homeatpenarth. co.uk; home.penarth; Wed & Thu midnight, Fri & Sat 12am; closed Wed & Thu L, closed Mon & Tue & Sun; No Amex; credit card deposit required to book.

PENRITH, CUMBRIA   7–3D

ALLIUM AT ASKHAM HALL
£139 4|3|4

ASKHAM   CA10 2PF   01931 712350

This Grade-I listed mansion (a restaurant-with-rooms since 2013) has associations with poet William Wordsworth (the aristocratic family who still own it first cheated, then supported the poet) and sits amidst fine Lakeland scenery on the Lowther Estate. RIchard Swale's well-regarded cuisine here is "superb" ("the individual flavours in every dish are just so perfect") but he has his work cut out eclipsing the "extraordinary wine list which is on every level like a connoisseur's emporium". It may be the "largest wine ledger you ever see", although part of the selection is "definitely unaffordable for most of us", with numerous vintages over £1,000 per bottle and some approaching £30,000. "There is, however, a reasonable choice for those who do not want to go to town" and "the sommelier is helpful and – given the amount of choice – definitely needed!". / www.askhamhall.co.uk; Askham_hall; Tue-Sat 9.30 pm; closed Tue-Sat L, closed Sun & Mon; Cash & all usual cards; children: 10.

FOUR & TWENTY
£50 4|3|3

42 KING ST   CA11 7AY   01768 210231

This "great quality local bistro in an old bank" in the centre of town near the market square "was historically the 'other' restaurant to Mrs Millers at Culgaith, but the garden centre housing the latter closed down a couple of years ago". "It's all bistro stuff, with a very firm grounding of classic technique, that's not going to set star chasers' chins wagging. But it's all very well done, and there's the same unbelievable value as there used to be at Culgaith. At these prices... rude not to". / www.fourandtwentypenrith.com; four_and_twenty_; Tue-Thu 11 pm, Fri & Sat 11.30 pm; closed Sun & Mon; Cash & all usual cards.

PENSFORD, SOMERSET   2–2B

THE PIG NEAR BATH
£74 2|2|4

HUNSTRETE HOUSE, HUNSTRETE BS39 4NS   01761 490 490

"Fantastic for a foodie weekend" – this comfortably boho country-house hotel in the Mendip Hills from the Pig group owes its vibe to the shabby-chic interior designed by Judy Hutson, wife of Robin Hutson (ex-Hotel du Vin and Soho House) who founded the chain a dozen years ago with backing from Ineos billionaire Jim Ratcliffe. The 25-mile kitchen sourcing regime results in some "amazing local ingredients" on the table. / www.thepighotel.com/near-bath; the_pig_hotels; Mon-Sun midnight; No Amex.

THE SHORE £98 5 3 4

13-14 ALVERTON STREET TR18 2QP
01736 362444

Bruce Rennie provides the one-man kitchen team at his very personal 14-seater, where you must book in advance, and a reservation is – according to his website – like "booking a ticket at a (very small and personal) theatre with a supper club vibe". All who comment "love the whole concept of this place": "Bruce is a wizard with fish which is landed just down the road in Newlyn – lots of Asian flavours make for really imaginative tasting menu offerings". / www.theshorerestaurant.uk; shore_pz; Tue-Sat 9 pm; closed Tue-Sat L, closed Sun & Mon; Cash & all usual cards; credit card deposit required to book.

TOLCARNE INN £73 4 4 3

TOLCARNE PL TR18 5PR 01736 363074

"Unrivalled access to the day's catch" – ("it is Newlyn after all") – is the secret to the "consistently amazing food" at chef-owner Ben Tunnicliffe's unspoilt 300-year-old pub by the sea wall. It's "perfect for alfresco dining on a summer's day" – and not so shabby whatever the weather. / www.tolcarneinn.co.uk; tolcarneinn; Mon-Sat 6 pm; closed Sun; Cash & all usual cards.

VICTORIA INN £64 3 3 4

TR20 9NP 01736 710309

"Simply all that you could desire of a gastropub" – this attractive twelfth-century inn welcomes everyone from walkers from the nearby SW Coast Path near St Michael's Mount to dog walkers with its enjoyable bistro-style food – "good Sunday lunch" in particular. / www.victoriainn-penzance.co.uk; vicinnperranuthnoe; Mon-Sat 11 pm; closed Sun.

INDIAN ESSENCE £64 4 3 3

176-178 PETTS WOOD RD BR5 1LG
01689 838 700

"Crisp, fresh flavours and excellent presentation… Atul Kocchar's signature is everywhere" according to the numerous fans of this popular operation, whose high quality might be unexpected on a typical shopping street in the 'burbs. One gripe, though: "please bring back the peppered crab!" / www.indianessence.co.uk; indianessenceak; Mon-Fri 10 pm, Sat 10.30 pm, Sun 9.30 pm; Cash & all usual cards; No trainers; children: 5 YEARS.

THE THIMBLE INN £57 3 3 3

14 HIGH STREET DT2 7TD 01300 348270

This thatched eighteenth-century Piddle Valley pub with an "enchanting garden" wins solid ratings across the board for its "great service and good food, whether you prefer pub grub or something more ambitious". Its popularity was sealed by a rave review from The FT's Tim Hayward a couple of years ago, and you need to book early to secure a table at busy times, especially Sunday lunch. / www.thimbleinn.co.uk; thimbleinn; Tue-Sat 8.30 pm, Sun 5 pm; closed Sun D, closed Mon.

HONKYTONK WINE LIBRARY £42 3 3 4

2 NORTH EAST QUAY, SUTTON HARBOUR PL4 0BN 01752 257968

"What an amazing place!" – a hybrid 250-bottle wine shop/deli where you can nibble on "sharing plates to die for" while relaxing in a "wonderful setting with views over Sutton Harbour, surrounded by wines". There's not much of a library hush, though, with a calendar of events including music and comedy nights. / honkytonkwinelibrary.com; honkytonkwinelibrary; Tue-Thu 10 pm, Fri & Sat 10.30 pm, Sun 6 pm; closed Mon.

ÀCLÈAF AT BORINGDON HALL £142 3 3 4

BORINGDON HALL PL7 4DP
01752 344455

A 40-seat raised gallery overlooking the Great Hall of this very impressive-looking (like a castle!) five star near Plymouth provides the venue for this ambitious dining space, which is entering its third year of operation. Feedback is not as plentiful as we'd like for Scott Paton's cuisine, showcased with a 4-course menu, but such as we have acclaims it as "amazing from start to finish!". / www.boringdonhall.co.uk/dining-drinks/acleaf-restaurant; acleafrestaurant; closed Mon-Sat & Sun.

SAM'S ON THE BEACH £55 3 3 4

PL24 2TL 01726 812255

"A gorgeous spot to eat tasty food while watching the sea", this former Victorian lifeboat station has been transformed under Sam Sixton, who launched his local dining empire at the age of 17, back in 1988 (his son Noah is now part of the team). The "casual" menu runs from "wonderful fresh fish and seafood" to "tasty pizzas with both traditional and unusual toppings". / www.samscornwall.co.uk; samscornwall; Mon-Sun 11 pm; No Amex.

THE BLUE PETER INN £58 3 3 3

QUAY ROAD PL13 2QZ 01503 272743

Down by the quayside, this cute pub is tipped for "fish that's obviously as fresh as you can get, and an excellent seafood platter" from amongst its other more typically pub grub offerings. / www.thebluepeterinn.com; thebluepeterinnpolperro; Mon-Sat 8 pm, Sun 4 pm; closed Sun D.

THE GUILDHALL TAVERN £74 4 3 4

15 MARKET STREET BH15 1NB
01202 671717

This gorgeous old tavern on a corner site near the harbour – newly spiffed-up last autumn and with the recent addition of a conservatory – specialises in "excellent-quality" local seafood, served in a warm atmosphere that is "like being in France". / www.guildhalltavern.co.uk; guildhalltavernpoole; Mon-Sun 9 pm, Sun 2.45 pm; closed Sun D; No Amex.

1863 BAR BISTRO ROOMS £79 3 3 3

ELM HOUSE, HIGH STREET CA10 2NH
017684 86334

Named for the date of its construction (as a blacksmith's), this restaurant with rooms (eight of them) in a scenic Lakeland village on Ullswater is consistently well rated for Phil Corrie's locally sourced and traditionally rooted cuisine, available both in an à la carte or tasting menu format. / www.1863ullswater.co.uk; 1863_restaurant; Mon, Thu-Sun 11 pm; closed Mon, Thu & Fri L, closed Tue & Wed; children: 12.

PIERHOUSE HOTEL £70 4 3 5

PA38 4DE 01631 730302

It's "worth the detour" to sample the "excellent fresh and simple seafood" at this former piermaster's house overlooking Loch Linnhe, noted for its "old-fashioned service and ambience". "Sister to the Three Chimneys on Skye, this hotel is more accessible and equally good". / www.pierhousehotel.co.uk; thepierhousehotel; Mon-Sun 9 pm; Cash & all usual cards.

OUTLAW'S FISH KITCHEN £111 5 4 3

1 MIDDLE ST PL29 3RH 01208 881138

"The little brother… but one which doesn't have to worry about its other sibling as it stands up as a very good restaurant in its own right" – Nathan Outlaw's small No 2. venue on the quayside of this picturebook Cornish fishing harbour provides "a wonderful experience from start to finish". "Decor is quirky" and there's "a delicious selection of small fish dishes", consistently rated as "outstanding". / www.nathan-outlaw.com/restaurants/outlaws-fish-kitchen; outlawsgrubclub; Mon-Sat 9 pm; closed Sun; Cash & all usual cards.

OUTLAW'S NEW ROAD £215 5 4 3

6 NEW RD PL29 3SB 01208 880896

"A view over the beach on one side and into the kitchen the other helps make for a wonderful atmosphere" at Nathan Outlaw's harbourside HQ, a short step from Outlaw's Guest House, which now allows his diners to stay and eat with a variety of accommodation and dinner deals. It's a case of 'Back to the Future' here – perhaps it should be called 'Outlaw's Old Road' – because, having renamed it from 'Restaurant Nathan Outlaw' and simplified the menu in mid-2020 in response to Covid (doing away with the previous posher format which won him two Michelin stars) he did a 180° U-turn in September 2022, reducing the number of covers to 28 and now offering the sole option of a £175 per head, seven-course tasting menu. According to the press release 'it's a natural progression… to use a better array of luxurious seafood' yada, yada, yada, but it looks for all the world like a reinstatement of a posher business as usual after the upheavals of the pandemic. We have maintained the (excellent) ratings of the previous regime, on the basis that they changed precious little after the first reformatting anyway. / outlaws.co.uk/restaurants/new-road; outlawsnewroad; Tue-Sat 9 pm; closed Sun & Mon; children: 10.

PORT GAVERNE HOTEL £65 343

PL29 3SQ   01208 880244

"A quirky hotel and restaurant serving excellent local fish" – this whitewashed, seventeenth-century hotel in a coastal bay is "always outstanding". Chef James Lean (appointed in 2015) oversees a menu that's naturally fish-focused. "Friendly service and great Cornish ales" complete the picture. / www.portgavernehotel.co.uk; port_gaverne_hotel; closed Mon-Sat & Sun; Cash & all usual cards; children: 7+.

TALLAND BAY HOTEL £81 343

PL13 2JB   01503 272667

'The best sea view in the West Country' is the proud boast on the website of this beautifully situated establishment, which for some nostalgics in our poll "is like hotels used to be, but with a quirky edge". There's a breakfast, afternoon tea and bar menu – the latter with "tasty fare" such as steak, fish 'n' chips and other brasserie-style dishes, as well as sharing platters. / www.tallandbayhotel.co.uk; tallandbayhotel; Mon-Sat 9 pm; closed Sun.

THE SHED AT PORTHGAIN £61 333

SA62 5BN   01348 831518

The "freshest of fish, plumpest of mackerel, stacks of hot chips and salad sides" make up the menu at this "simple, unpretentious and old-school" fish bistro, ideally placed as a pitstop on the coastal path, with "up to 7, 8 or 9 options on the choice of fish". Surrounded by ex-quarry machinery in a small harbour, it's in a "great stormy and dramatic location" – and is "always chilly, so dress up warmly". /

www.theshedporthgain.co.uk; theshedporthgain; Mon-Sun 8.45 pm; No Amex; no bookings.

THE HARBOURSIDE REFUGE £61 433

MOUNT PLEASANT ROAD   TR13 9JS   01326 331758

"Amazing food in a wonderful setting" say fans of Michael Caines's relatively new (summer 2020) casual bistro looking onto the harbour of this most southernmost of English ports. There's an à la carte menu, offering two or three courses served at lunch and dinner, and also a seven-course tasting option. / www.theharboursiderefuge.co.uk; closed Mon-Sat & Sun.

KOTA £65 534

HARBOUR HEAD   TR13 9JA   01326 562407

One of the "top gastronomic establishments in the southwest" – this harbourside restaurant from Maori/Chinese-Malay chef Jude Kereama thrills all comers with "a memorable marriage of local seafood and Asian influences". He opened the venture in 2006 with his late wife Jane, who sadly died of cancer in 2019; she was the driving force behind Porthleven's annual food festival, which now attracts up to 70,000 visitors. Top Tip – "the blue cheese ice cream is a revelation". / www.kotarestaurant.co.uk; Tue-Sat 9 pm; closed Tue-Sat L, closed Sun & Mon; No Amex.

KOTA KAI £53 444

CELTIC HOUSE, HARBOUR HEAD   TR13 9JY   01326 574411

"The more informal, café-style, sister to Kota" – the local star from chef Jude Kereama – "this place overlooking the harbour just hits the spot for a holiday lunch, with on-point sharing plates that have fantastic flavours", thanks to Jude's New Zealand and Asian heritage. "The menu is imaginative, innovative and a cut above the norm", and the "great-value food" comes in "generous portions". / www.kotakai.co.uk; kota_kai; Tue-Sat 9 pm; closed Sun & Mon; No Amex.

THE SQUARE AT PORTHLEVEN £67 333

7 FORE STREET   TR13 9HQ   01326 573 911

"Great cooking at very reasonable cost" is on offer at this family-run brasserie with deli and ice-cream parlour from Cornish-born chef Stew Eddy (who trained under both Raymond Blanc and Michael Caines) and his wife Anna, in a "lovely former fishing village that's fast becoming a foodie destination to rival Padstow". Top Tip – "the memorable Goan fish curry". / www.thesquareatporthleven.co.uk; thesquarepl; Tue-Sat 9 pm; closed Sun & Mon; No Amex.

PORTMEIRION HOTEL £79 335

LL48 6ER   01766 772440

"An incredible setting in the remarkable village of Portmeirion" (built, over five decades, in Mediterranean style by the late Clough William-Ellis) adds to the occasion at this "delightfully situated hotel", "with views across the estuary to the mountains". Ratings are not yet back to the stellar highs of ten-plus years ago, but the food is well received, with "exceptional presentation" in particular. "Sunday lunch is particularly good"… "with a window seat, or outside if sunny, followed by a stroll through the gardens: what could be nicer!". Top Tip – "Superb afternoon tea. You will not need to eat again that day. An inventive spread of sandwiches, cakes and scones are beautifully presented; and a wide range of teas too". / portmeirion.wales/eat/hotel-portmeirion/the-dining-room; visit_portmeirion; Mon-Sun 6.30 pm; Cash & all usual cards.

KNOCKINAAM LODGE £106 345

DG9 9AD   01776 810471

"Galloway's finest" – this boutique hotel in an "idyllic location" takes full advantage of "local ingredients, fine fish, beef and lamb", which are "sensitively and inventively prepared" by long-serving chef Tony Pierce, a pioneer of the now-commonplace tasting menu concept for almost 30 years. The Lodge has a secure place in both history (Churchill & Eisenhower planned D-Day here) and fiction (in John Buchan's 'The 39 Steps'). Top Tip: "stay over – breakfast is very good too". / www.knockinaamlodge.com; knockinaamlodge; Mon-Sun 10 pm; Cash & all usual cards; No jeans; children: 12+ after 7 pm.

ABARBISTRO £60 333

58 WHITE HART RD   PO1 2JA   02392 811585

In the old town, there has been a pub on this site for more than 200 years. Nowadays an indie bar serving pizza and a range of bistro fare, fans say it's "always good, especially with the additional option of choosing wine from their shop as well as from the list". / www.abarbistro.co.uk; abarbistro_; Mon-Sun 11 pm; Cash & all usual cards.

HARRY'S SHACK £52 334

118 STRAND ROAD   BT55 7PG   028 7083 1783

"Wonderful views out to the surfers' beach (and you park on the beach too)" accompany a trip to this large shack, owned by the National Trust. As you'd expect, fish and seafood are the main events on Donal Doherty's menu. (The eponymous Harry was Donal's father, who passed away a couple of years ago). / harrys_shack; Mon & Tue, Sun 10 pm, Wed-Sat 11 pm.

263 PRESTON   £97   3 4 3

10 CAMDEN PLACE   PR1 3JL
01772 252630

"Local ingredients but in more unusual combinations" than you might expect make it well worth knowing about this small 'aparthotel' dining room, where chefs Oli Martin and Rikki Hughes aim for more culinary ambition than typically expected of this 'rust-belt' town. / www.263preston.co.uk; 263preston; Thu-Sat, Wed 9.30 pm; closed Wed L, closed Mon & Tue & Sun; No shorts; booking is online only.

THE CUCKOO   £48   3 4 3

CM4 0LT   01245 248946

"A good-to-find culinary outpost in an area with few interesting eating spots" – this "welcoming" gastropub is well worth remembering: "a steady hand in the kitchen meets good ingredients, and if food and wine both tread a relatively safe path, it's no less enjoyable for that". / cuckooradleygreen.com; Tue-Sat 9 pm; closed Sun & Mon; No Amex.

MASH INN   £100   5 4 4

HORSESHOE RD, BENNETT END
HP14 4EB   01494 482 440

"Foraged food prepared over a fire: unbeatable?" – Nick Mash's higgledy-piggledy village inn is "an absolute treasure of a place", with "really interesting, special cooking" on a purpose-built wood-fired grill that helps achieve outstanding results. It's "well worth the trip" to the Chilterns, "(and the beautiful rooms mean it's worth the stay, too)". We've rated it in the hope that it can maintain the high standards set by former chef Jon Parry, who departed in mid-2022 after five years at the helm. / www.themashinn.com; themashinn; Thu-Sat 11 pm; closed Thu & Fri L, closed Mon-Wed & Sun.

LEVANTER   £53   4 3 3

10 SQUARE ST   BL0 9BE   01706 551530

Quite limited reports this year on Joe & Fiona Botham's offbeat find – a tiny Andalusian-style bar, on a terraced street in the town. Fans "return here again and again, as the service is always warm, friendly and sharp, and the food is exceptional". The focus is on wood-fire grilled and roasted dishes plus tapas and charcuteria. It does occasionally take flak, though, for "overhyped average dishes". / www.levanterfinefoods.co.uk; baratxuri; Wed-Sat 8.45 pm, Sun 6.45 pm; closed Sun D, closed Mon & Tue; booking is online only.

THE BLACK SWAN   £75   3 2 3

FELL ROAD   CA17 4NG   015396 23204

This "small, family-run hotel" in the idyllic Eden Valley has a "lovely restaurant" serving "good-quality locally sourced food" which includes "some very unusual dishes with lovely flavours". The "front-of-house staff are great", and you can make your stay more adventurous by glamping in a yurt in their private forest. / www.blackswanhotel.com; blackswanhotel; Mon, Thu-Sat 9 pm, Sun 8 pm; closed Tue & Wed.

CLAY'S HYDERABADI KITCHEN   £51   4 3 3

22-24 PROSPECT STREET   RG1 4PS
0118 959 6888

Nandana & Sharat Syamala are moving their Hyderabadi kitchen into new premises in Caversham after their "great eatery" and growing national delivery service outgrew its original London Street site on the back of rave reviews. The new, part-crowdfunded venue is a former Wetherpoons pub, the Baron Cadogan, is to give the couple sufficient space to run a 'fine-dining' restaurant as well as a separate open kitchen with bar counter for snacks, small plates and street food, plus eight beers from local brewers. As of October 2022, both the original address and national delivery are closed as they focus all their efforts on the move. / www.clayskitchen.co.uk; clayshyderabadi; Wed-Sat 10.30 pm; closed Wed-Sat L, closed Mon & Tue & Sun; children: 8.

THAMES LIDO   £60   3 3 4

NAPIER ROAD   RG1 8FR   0118 207 0640

"A shining light in the middle of Reading dining" – this glass-fronted dining room overlooking a Grade II listed Edwardian swimming pool serves a "frequently changing selection" of "very decent tapas". "The lovely space and atmosphere have made it a new favourite". It's from the team behind the similar Clifton Lido in Bristol and "the swimming makes a fun backdrop while you eat!" / www.thameslido.com; thameslido; Mon-Sun 9.30 pm.

MONTE FORTE   £19   3 3 2

12 WEST STREET   RH2 9BS
07584 833810

"Top-notch wood-fired pizza" wins praise for brothers Paolo and Luca's small debut restaurant, launched in 2019. They started out with a mobile food truck in Redhill market two years earlier, naming the business after their inspirational Neapolitan-born grandmother, Lucia Monteforte. There's now also a bigger branch in Horsham. / www.monteforte.co.uk; montefortepizza; Tue, Wed 9 pm, Thu-Sat 9.30 pm, Sun 8 pm; closed Tue L, closed Mon.

MARKHAM MOOR INN   £47   3 2 2

OLD GREAT NORTH ROAD   DN22 0QU
01777 838229

This "fantastic" Grade II-listed seventeenth-century inn, just off the A1, has been run by Stephen & Laura Heath as a "good-value restaurant-with-rooms" for almost 25 years. "You may drive past it thinking it's just a pub, but the food is excellent", with a "changing menu" and regular themed dinners. / www.markhammoorinn.co.uk; markhammoorinn; Wed-Sat 9 pm, Sun 4 pm; closed Sun D, closed Mon & Tue.

OYSTER CATCHER   £50   3 3 3

MAELOG LAKE   LL64 5JP   01407 812829

"An amazing location on the Isle of Anglesey" inspires nothing but good vibes at this striking looking, glass-walled destination, overlooking the dunes above Traeth Llydan beach, where "great seafood is served with panache". "The entertainment offered by Valley RAF can add to the experience!" (the nearby airfield being home to No 4 Flying Training School, the UK's centre for training fighter pilots). / www.oystercatcheranglesey.co.uk; Mon-Sun 9 pm.

CHEZ LINDSAY   £53   3 2 3

11 HILL RISE   TW10 6UQ   020 8948 7473

"Authentic Breton galettes and cider, and excellent seafood" are the USP at this "cheap 'n' cheerful" bistro near Richmond Bridge, which celebrates its 35th anniversary this year. As an independent, it stands out in an area increasingly dominated by chains. / www.chez-lindsay.co.uk; chez_lindsay; Mon-Sun 10 pm; Cash & all usual cards.

THE ANCHOR   £65   3 3 2

HIGH ST   GU23 6AE   01483 211866

This "welcoming and genuine gastropub" with an "interesting menu" "delivers what it promises", in the form of "creative cooking and good value". Hosts Mike Wall-Palmer and Dave Adams met 10 years ago working at nearby Drake's, and jumped at the opportunity to open their own place when this charming, wood-framed, red-brick old boozer came their way four years ago. / www.ripleyanchor.co.uk; ripleyanchor; Tue-Sat 9.30 pm; closed Sun & Mon; Cash & all usual cards.

THE CLOCK HOUSE   £153   4 4 4

THE CLOCK HOUSE, HIGH STREET
GU23 6AQ   01483 224777

A meal at Serina Drake's "relaxed and informal" Georgian house conversion is a "really special experience" – and "food is still the focus" under chef Paul

Nicholson, who joined the kitchen from Yorkshire's famous Yorke Arms two years ago and sends out meals that are "fresh, light, diligent and mouthwatering". Top Tip – "have a drink in the garden beforehand" to set up "the most amazing dinner". / www.theclockhouserestaurant.co.uk; theclockhouseripley; Wed-Sat 9 pm; closed Wed L, closed Mon & Tue & Sun; Cash & all usual cards.

ROCK, CORNWALL   1–3B

DINING ROOM   £81   4 4 3

PAVILION BUILDINGS, ROCK RD PL27 6JS   01208 862622

"Not been here for a few years… I had forgotten how exquisite the food was" – this "serene", long-established venue in a low-key parade of shops is one of the area's more enduring culinary destinations. Run by the Beedles – "Fred makes some incredibly inventive dishes and his cooking is as reliable as ever. Wife Donna keeps everything calm front-of-house. The wine list has some unusual entries and is well-priced". / www.thediningroomrock.co.uk; Thediningroomrock; Tue-Sat 8.30 pm; closed Tue-Sat L, closed Sun & Mon; No Amex; children: 10.

KARREK, ST ENODOC HOTEL   £127   5 4 4

ROCK ROAD   PL27 6LA   01208 863394

With its good views over the estuary, this 1920s hotel (owned since 2019 by Lucy & James Strachan and family) has a prime position in this chichi resort, and in former incarnations has provided a springboard for the likes of Nathan Outlaw. With its choice of 6-course and 9-course tasting menus, it inspires as yet limited feedback, but all of it rapturous. / enodoc-hotel.co.uk/fine-dining; Karrekrock; closed Mon-Sat & Sun.

THE MARINERS   £60   4 4 3

PL27 6LD   01841 532796

"Fantastic pub grub in great surroundings" is the crowd-pleasing combination at local champion Paul Ainsworth's venue with views across the Camel estuary. Classic dishes are given a tasty contemporary makeover, so the Cornish shepherd's pie contains slow-cooked lamb shoulder and seaweed ragu with mint salsa verde, while the prawn sandwich comes with sherry-cured tomato. / paul-ainsworth.co.uk/the-mariners/about; themarinersbeachclub; Mon-Sat 9.30 pm, Sun 9 pm; Cash & all usual cards.

ROSEVINE, CORNWALL   1–4B

DRIFTWOOD HOTEL   £92   3 3 5

TR2 5EW   01872 580644

On the Roseland Peninsula, this clifftop boutique hotel occupies a fine-looking Georgian building in a glorious position, a short walk from the beach. Aaron McNamara succeeded Olly Pierrepoint as head chef in May 2022, just as our survey was concluding. We have

rated the restaurant assuming a continuation of his predecessor's high standard of cooking, which fans say was "simply fabulous! The tasting menu with superbly chosen wine flight is a journey you just don't want to end!". / www.driftwoodhotel.co.uk; driftwood_hotel; Mon-Sun 9.30 pm; Cash & all usual cards; children: 7.

ROWSLEY, DERBYSHIRE   5–3C

THE PEACOCK AT ROWSLEY   £109   4 3 3

BAKEWELL RD   DE4 2EB   01629 733518

An "old manor house hotel with fabulous food", in the Peak District National Park close to Chatsworth, that has "a slightly old-fashioned feel – i.e. American tourists would love it". The dining room can seem on the "formal" side, but dishes are "really excellent". Top Menu Tip – "dessert, a raspberry financier with an apricot and cream, was bloody lovely – couldn't be improved". / www.thepeacockatrowsley.com; Mon-Sun 9 pm; Cash & all usual cards; booking max 8 may apply; children: 10+ at D.

RYDE, ISLE OF WIGHT   2–4D

THE DUCK   £51   3 2 3

APPLEY RISE   PO33 1LE   01983 613925

Chef-owner Charlie Bartlett's "little gem serving lovely food cooked with imagination" is "well worth a trip" – and by some accounts offers "close to the best cooking on the Island", although not everyone is convinced by "a mishmash of clashing influences in the dishes". / www.theduckiow.co.uk; duckiow; Tue-Sat 10.30 pm, Sun 4 pm; closed Sun D, closed Mon.

RYE, EAST SUSSEX   3–4C

THE GLOBE INN MARSH   £52   2 2 4

10 MILITARY ROAD   TN31 7NX 01797 225220

"If only every pub was like this!" – "a quirky place" a short walk from the town centre which makes the most of its olde-worlde decor. The food is "competent and innovative", and there's a "good range of drinks". / www.ramblinns.com; globeinnrye; Mon-Sat 9 pm, Sun 8 pm.

LANDGATE BISTRO   £61   4 3 2

5 - 6 LANDGATE   TN31 7LH 01797 222829

"Small and perfectly formed", with a "short, locally sourced and interesting menu, plus a reasonable wine list" – this "lovely little bistro" is "a must for visitors to Rye" and provided a number of reporters with their best meal of the year. Top Tip – "the local Romney Marsh lamb". / www.landgatebistro.co.uk; landgatebistro; Wed-Sat 9 pm; closed Wed-Sat L, closed Mon & Tue & Sun; No Amex.

TATNERS STREET KITCHEN   3 4 3

24 WISH STREET   TN31 7DA 01797724111

"The most intensely tasty, well executed and imaginative street food outside of Shoreditch", say fans of this new permanent home for a popular food truck familiar to visitors to Camber Sands: "great service and reasonable prices complete one of the best places for proper eats in this gorgeous little gem of a town". Top Menu Tip – "the chilli brisket or buttermilk chicken burger with maple bacon and satay mayo will transport you into raptures to say nothing of the spicy chips with scotch bonnet jam that always remain crispy no matter the additions piled on!". / www.tatnersstreetkitchen.com; Mon-Wed 10 pm, Thu, Sun 11 pm.

WEBBE'S AT THE FISH CAFE   £60   3 3 2

17 TOWER STREET   TN31 7AT 01797 222 226

"Our favourite restaurant in Rye", chorus the many fans of Paul Webbe's "busy" local spot, which is "always reliable" for "great cooking and ingredients (often fresh from Rye harbour)" and "service that feels personal and relaxed". "The one slight reservation is the ambience, which somewhat places function over comfort" thanks to the "bare interior". / www.webbesrestaurants.co.uk/the-fish-cafe; webbesrye; Sun-Thu 9 pm, Fri & Sat 9.30 pm; Cash & all usual cards.

SALCOMBE, DEVON   1–4C

CRAB SHED   £50   4 4 3

GOULD ROAD   TQ8 8DU   01548 844 280

This "tiny restaurant executing delicious fish" is "a real gem" and "hugely successful in expensive Salcombe" – no wonder it's "always fully booked". Experienced owners Nick & Nikki Horne took over from Rob & Anna Johnstone two years ago and it has been a seamless transition – they are "friendly, professional, not stuffy and know what they are doing". The menu is dominated by their own hand-picked local crab, but there's also "scallops to die for". / crabshed.com; crabshedsalcombe; Mon-Sun 8.30 pm; No Amex.

SALE, GREATER MANCHESTER   5–2B

CHEZ NOUS BISTRO £39

179 MARSLAND ROAD   M33 3ND 0161 969 1172

Needing to eat in Manchester's plush southern 'burbs? – this 'suburban bistro with urban attitude' (their words) doesn't generate huge feedback in our survey, but such as there is rates it as excellent value. / www.cheznousbistro.uk; cheznoussale; Tue-Sat 9.30 pm, Mon 9 pm, Sun 6 pm; closed Mon L; Cash & all usual cards; booking is online only.

THE PERFECT MATCH £68 333

103 CROSS STREET   M33 7JN
0161 204 3665

This "fantastic local restaurant" makes a "great new addition to south Manchester's restaurant scene". The husband-and-wife team of Italian-born sommelier Andrea and Manchester-born chef Jazz met while working at Gordon Ramsay's Savoy Grill and combined their talents to open their dream venue, with each dish listed alongside an appropriate wine. "The small menu is well thought out – all the dishes are simply delicious, with fantastic wines". "The ambience is romantic – the perfect setting to celebrate our anniversary!". / www.theperfectmatchsale.co.uk; closed Mon-Sat & Sun.

SALISBURY, WILTSHIRE   2–3C

ANOKAA £54 332

60 FISHERTON ST   SP2 7RB
01722 414142

"In a higher league than other Indian restaurants" nearby, this 20-year stalwart of Salisbury dining is "well worth a detour" for its contemporary menu with Persian influences. / www.anokaa.com; Mon-Sun 10 pm; Cash & all usual cards; No shorts.

SALTBURN, NORTH YORKSHIRE   8–3C

THE SEAVIEW RESTAURANT £70 433

THE FORESHORE BUILDING, LOWER PROMENADE   TS12 1HQ   01287 236015

"The name is quite right… the view of the sea, the pier and the cliffs make it a very calming place to enjoy some really good seafood" and it's "a great place to while away a summer evening". "As well as battered fish, there are also more adventurous dishes" – "you'd be a fool to miss the crab brioche" – although overall some reporters "would choose fish 'n' chips over the more 'restaurant-y' dishes". "Only walk-ins, during the day and not easy to book a table in the evening." / theseaviewrestaurant.co.uk; seaviewrestaurant; Mon-Sun 10.30 pm; no bookings at lunch.

SALTHOUSE, NORFOLK   6–3C

DUN COW £50 333

PURDY ST   NR25 7XA   01263 740467

A "great gastropub" in a "lovely location" with views over the salt marshes, which serves a "menu a notch above standard pub fare, with a good range of fish dishes accompanied by a good selection of local real ales". "Friendly and efficient staff" create "an excellent, relaxed atmosphere", while "bustling crowds for a late midweek lunch on a cold day in March are testament to the pub's well-deserved reputation". / www.salthouseduncow.com; theduncowsalthouse; Mon-Sun 9.30 pm; Cash & all usual cards.

SALTWOOD, KENT   3–4D

HIDE & FOX £96 543

THE GREEN   CT21 4PS   01303 260915

The impressive 2019 debut restaurant from Kent-born chef Allister Barsby (who was appointed head chef at Devon's Gidleigh Park at the age of 24), and Italian-born Alice Bussi (food & beverage manager of the year in the 2018 Catey awards). It helps that it's a "cosy" venue, but the focus is on the "excellent food" – with the choice of a 5-course or 8-course tasting menu – and accompanying wine matches ("a good choice of local vintages, as well as many from further afield"). / hideandfox.co.uk; hideandfox; Wed-Sat 8.30 pm, Tue 8 pm; closed Tue L, closed Sun & Mon.

SANCTON, EAST YORKSHIRE   6–2A

THE STAR INN £73 333

KING ST   YO43 4QP   01430 827269

A meal at this former coaching inn in the East Yorkshire Wolds is by most accounts "a delightful experience, with many firm pub grub favourites" on the menu. There are "frequently changing seasonal items and specials" and a "great-value Sunday lunch", all provided with "excellent service and good hospitality". / www.thestaratsancton.co.uk; thestaratsancton; Tue-Sat 11 pm, Sun 10 pm; closed Mon.

SANDBANKS, DORSET   2–4C

CLIFF POOLE £36 333

6 RAVINE ROAD   BH13 7HX
01202 492921

This "nice gastropub with large gardens" has undergone a dramatic £800,000 refurb since our annual diners' poll, to be reborn with cocktail bar-style décor replacing the traditional pub interior, and fitted seating with cushions in the 100-seater garden. The new menu replaces standard 3-course meals with a globally inspired selection of small plates. / www.thecliffcanfordcliffs.co.uk; Tue-Sat 11 pm, Sun 10.30 pm; closed Mon.

RICK STEIN £72 333

10-14 BANKS RD   BH13 7QB
01202 283 000

An "absolutely fantastic location by Poole Harbour" and "a large selection of fish dishes" keep the tills ringing at the TV chef's Dorset outpost. "The food is standard Stein fare" – which pleases most reporters ("gorgeous seafood"), if not quite all – and "prices are really going up". Top Tip – "get a table upstairs for lunch in the summer". / www.rickstein.com/eat-with-us/rick-stein-sandbanks; theseafood; Mon-Sun 10 pm; children: 3.

SANDIACRE, NOTTINGHAMSHIRE   5–3D

LA ROCK £102 333

4 BRIDGE STREET   NG10 5QT
0115 9399 833

With its untreated oak tables, black granite surfaces and antler candelabras, chef-patron Nick Gillespie's unusual and "very quiet" venue makes an appropriate showcase for his distinctive modern British cooking, which provided some reporters' best meal of the year. "Staff cannot do enough for you." / www.larockrestaurant.co.uk; Larock_ng10; closed Mon-Sat & Sun; No shorts; children: 8.

SANDSEND, NORTH YORKSHIRE   8–3D

THE FISH COTTAGE £67 333

FISH COTTAGE   YO21 3SU   01947 899342

This two-year-old just twenty yards from the beach at Sandsend serves highly rated fish 'n' chips plus some more elevated seafood dishes, to eat in or take away (which some reporters reckon is "the best option"). A second branch in York Market makes a "fabulous addition" to the city's food offering. / www.fishcottage.co.uk; Mon-Sun 11 pm.

SAUNDERSFOOT, PEMBROKESHIRE   4–4B

COAST £97 443

COPPET HALL BEACH   SA69 9AJ
01834 810800

This "lovely", modern wood-and-glass restaurant in a "brilliant location overlooking the sea" showcases the "excellent" skills of chef Fred Clapperton (ex-The Clockhouse, Surrey), with locally sourced ingredients ranging from line-caught sea bass from the bay and native oysters farmed with regenerative methods; through to Rhug Estate game and vegetables grown at sister hotel Grove of Narberth. / coastsaundersfoot.co.uk; coastsaundersfoot; Wed-Sat 8.30 pm; closed Mon & Tue & Sun; Cash & all usual cards.

SCARBOROUGH, NORTH YORKSHIRE   8–4D

LANTERNA £56 342

33 QUEEN STREET   YO11 1HQ
01723 363616

"A hidden gem with authentic Italian home cooking", this Yorkshire stalwart provides much better cooking than one might expect of this seaside town, thanks to its careful sourcing and preparation by chef-patron Giorgio Alessio (owner since 1997) who travels regularly to Italy to buy white truffles and other ingredients. "Since 1975 we have eaten here 2-3 times a year: it has never disappointed!". / www.lanterna-ristorante.co.uk; Thu-Sat 9.30 pm; closed Thu-Sat L, closed Mon-Wed & Sun; Cash & all usual cards.

Prawn on the Lawn, Padstow

SCAWTON, NORTH YORKSHIRE 8–4C

THE HARE INN RESTAURANT £125 443
YO7 2HG 01845 597769

Paul & Liz Jackson are celebrating their tenth year at this ancient pub, which has overlooked the North York Moors since the twelfth century. Its decor and culinary style are fully modernised though, and its small fan club says it's "a fabulous wee restaurant with lovely rooms". It's not a place to drop into though – it's a tasting-menu-only format for which you are advised to allow 3 hours. More reports please! / www.thehare-inn.com; Thu-Sat 9 pm; closed Thu-Sat L, closed Mon-Wed & Sun; Cash & all usual cards; booking evening only; children: -18.

SEASALTER, KENT 3–3C

THE SPORTSMAN £92 544
FAVERSHAM ROAD CT5 4BP
01227 273370

"Yes, it is a long drive and the surroundings are simple, but the food makes the journey worthwhile…" – Stephen Harris's "unpretentious and cherished" estuary-side destination set on the marshes near Whitstable "looks just like an old seaside pub from the outside" but is one of the most famous eateries in the country (and in the top-10 most commented-on destinations outside London in our annual diners' poll). It can seem "a bizarre location", but "the situation of the pub is very evocative which helps give the place its charm" and – however you view it – it's so popular "you must book way ahead to secure a table". "The decor may be 'old pub' but the food is fine dining" with "so much taste on the plate". Given the locale, "oysters are always a must!" and the signature slip soles are star features on an "interesting" menu whose "fabulous seafood" and salt-marsh lamb showcase the local larder: "excellent ingredients all served with integrity and expertise". "A superb, generously priced wine list completes a sublime gastronomic experience." To complete the trip, there's "nothing better than a good walk on the beach". Or, alternatively, you can now stay and many of the most enthusiastic reports this year are from those who "chose to stay in one of their wildflower meadow cabins – charming and very comfortable, with everything you need to make yourself a great breakfast (they have little kitchens). Highly recommended". / www.thesportsmanseasalter.co.uk; sportsmankent; Tue-Sat 8.30 pm, Sun 2.30 pm; closed Sun D, closed Mon; No Amex; children: 10+.

SEDBERGH, CUMBRIA 7–4D

THE BLACK BULL INN £61 433
44 MAIN STREET LA10 5BL
015396 20264

James Ratcliff and Nina Matsunaga's "lovely" little pub with rooms opened in 2018 and seems to have "really upped the ante post-lockdown", with growing acclaim for the quality of Nina's "brilliant Anglo-Asian fusion cuisine". Dishes are "surprisingly ambitious and successfully so", with those which have found favour including starter of pigeon, beetroot and blackberry; wild Lakeland rabbit; hand-dived scallop; and Skrie cod finished with a yoghurt mousse. "The locals are out in force" but reports on it originate from all over the country. / www.theblackbullsedbergh.co.uk; theblackbullsedbergh; Wed-Sun 9 pm; closed Mon & Tue.

SEER GREEN, BUCKINGHAMSHIRE 3–3A

THE JOLLY CRICKETERS £58 333
24 CHALFONT RD HP9 2YG
01494 676308

This "good village pub" excels for its "lovely grub" and "friendly staff". Landlord Chris Lillitou grew up in the village, and took over the pub with his wife, Tante-Claire-trained Amanda Baker, 15 years ago. / www.thejollycricketers.co.uk; thejollycricketers; Mon-Fri 9 pm; closed Sat & Sun.

SEVENOAKS, KENT 3–3B

NUMBER EIGHT £45 322
8 LONDON ROAD TN13 1AJ
01732 448088

"A much-needed independent in the heart of town serving delicious small plates (although the bill can add up)". It was launched in early 2022 by Stuart Gillies and his wife Cecilia and though feedback is limited, it's all upbeat. / / / no8sevenoaks.com; no8sevenoaks; Tue-Sat 11 pm, Sun 6 pm; closed Tue L closed Sun D, closed Mon.

SHEFFIELD, SOUTH YORKSHIRE 5–2C

JORO £93 544
294 SHALESMOOR S3 8US
0114 299 1539

"World-class cooking" – "a blisteringly good fusion of Nordic, Japanese and modern British ingredients and techniques" – continues to win ever-more renown for Luke & Stacey Sherwood-French's "brilliant and imaginative" venue, in a "slightly cramped" converted shipping container (but see note below) "with a great playlist of music that you wouldn't normally hear in a fine-dining restaurant!". "It's a travesty that this place hasn't been awarded a Michelin star, as it's definitely operating at that level and restaurants less deserving are awarded one (one guesses that the shipping container location has put off the traditionalist tyre men)". "A light touch and high-end technique in the kitchen make unusual combinations feel natural" – "every dish is a flavour bomb!" – while "inventive drinks flights showcase some bold pairings". Watch this space, as a move is afoot to a new location in late 2022/early 2023, and the couple are also expanding their local empire (which includes House of Jōro, see also) with a new deli concept: Grocerant. / www.jororestaurant.co.uk; restaurant_joro; Thu-Sat, Wed 11.30 pm; closed Wed L, closed Mon & Tue & Sun; credit card deposit required to book.

RAFTERS £124 443
220 OAKBROOK RD, NETHERGREEN
S11 7ED 0114 230 4819

"Still one of the best, with great service (and also good for special events)" – Tom Lawson & Alastair Myers's small (26-seater) dining room in Nethergreen is ever-more focused on its tasting menu format, delivering 6 courses for £95. There's also the option of eating at the 'Kitchen Bench'. / www.raftersrestaurant.co.uk; raftersrestaurant; Wed-Sat 8 pm; closed Wed-Fri L, closed Mon & Tue & Sun; Cash & all usual cards; credit card deposit required to book; children: 8.

STREET FOOD CHEF £19 333
90 ARUNDEL ST S1 4RE 0114 275 2390

Richard & Abi Golland's street-food operation wins high ratings for its tacos and other lively Latino dishes, available at its city-centre Burrito Bar or the fully licensed Mexican Canteen in Sharrow Vale Road. / www.streetfoodchef.co.uk; Wed-Sat 9 pm, Sun 7 pm; closed Mon & Tue; No Amex; no bookings.

TONCO £37
2 DYSON PLACE S11 8XX 0114 349 3996

Flo Hiller and Joe Shrewsbury opened this modern and minimalist small-plates restaurant in late 2019, since which time it's made waves locally in the local press (if not our annual diners' survey). In April 2022, it caught the eye of Marina O'Loughlin in The Sunday Times, who gives it a full-on rave: in the city's "coolest, restaurant-lined neighbourhood" she finds it "warmly ramshackle… as far from fancy as it's possible to get". The menu is a "box of delights" that "fairly jitters with promise" with a "maverick touch" that pairs mussels with rhubarb and "ajo blanco (Spanish-style almond and garlic 'soup')"… "sounds like madness, tastes like genius". / www.tonco.co.uk; toncosheffield; Wed-Sat 9.30 pm; closed Mon & Tue & Sun.

VERO GUSTO £81 444
12 NORFOLK ROW S1 2PA
0114 276 0004

A charming "family-run" operation, which after 16 years is "now a Sheffield institution". Neapolitan-born Ester's "delicious" dishes are backed up by Saverano's "mind-boggling wine listed topped by super-Tuscans", while "there's a small bar for pre-dinner drinks". Top Menu Tip – "sublime ravioli". / www.verogusto.com; verogusto; Wed-Sat 10.30 pm; closed Mon & Tue & Sun; Cash & all usual cards.

SHELLEY, WEST YORKSHIRE 5–2C

THREE ACRES £80 233
ROYDHOUSE HD8 8LR 01484 602606

"A popular local staple for many years", this posh and hugely successful pub has been run by the Truelove family since 1968 and – much extended over the years – is known for its "consistently good food and service, with a great atmosphere". Supporters reckon it is currently "back on form and, though expensive, a great meal is guaranteed (potted shrimps and shellfish superb!)". A contrary view is that "the dining room decor is in a time warp, with no hint of frivolity to brighten the dullness", while the "surprisingly long menu could do with being edited", and the dishes arrive in "generous portions, but lack finesse". / 3acres.com; 3acresinn; Wed-Sat 9.30 pm, Sun 6 pm; closed Mon & Tue; No Amex.

SHERBORNE, DORSET   2–3B

THE CROSS KEYS HOTEL   3|3|2

88 CHEAP STREET   DT9 3BJ 01935 812492

Well-located in the centre of the town on 'The Parade' – this old inn wins praise for "good pub food with some more adventurous items" and "community-minded owners who have become part of the town". The latter are Mo Gherras and his family, who put their savings into the place in 2019, the pub having lain vacant for a number of years. / www.thecrosskeyssherborne.com; crosskeyssherborne; Mon-Sat 11 pm, Sun 4 pm; closed Sun D.

THE GREEN   £58   3|3|2

3 THE GREEN   DT9 3HY   01935 813821

"Excellent food at very reasonable prices" is the proposition at this townhouse with a focus on local West Country produce. Chef-patron Sasha Matkevich, who has lived in England for almost 30 years, was inspired to cook by the food he ate as a child at his grandmother's house in the foothills of the Caucasus mountains in southern Russia. / www.greenrestaurant.co.uk; Thegreenrestaurant; Tue-Sat 9.30 pm; closed Sun & Mon; Cash & all usual cards.

THE PLUME OF FEATHERS   £42   4|4|4

HALF MOON STREET   DT9 3LN 01935 389709

"It looks and sounds like a pub", but this "lively and friendly" old inn opposite Sherborne Abbey "is actually an Italian restaurant providing small plates by the score". The menu includes a "stupendous choice" (including pizzette and pasta) "using local and Italian ingredients" and it's very easy to assemble an interesting and varied meal with "dishes to suit all tastes". "The main difficulty is limiting yourself as there's so much to tempt!". Top Tip – Rapido lunch for two at £14 per person, served weekdays. / www.theplumesherborne.co.uk; Tue-Thu 9 pm, Fri & Sat 9.30 pm; closed Sun & Mon.

SHERE, SURREY   3–3A

KINGHAMS   £56   3|3|3

GOMSHALL LN   GU5 9HE   01483 202168

Leafily located in the Surrey Hills, this cute-looking, converted red-brick cottage has been a restaurant since 1993, and has been run by Jack Forrest Foster since 2019. The odd

reporter sees its slightly old-school menu as "a last bastion of nouvelle cuisine" but feedback overall rates it decently well all-round. / www.kinghams-restaurant.co.uk; Tue-Sat 9 pm, Sun 2 pm; closed Sun D, closed Mon; Cash & all usual cards.

SHINFIELD, BERKSHIRE   2–2D

L'ORTOLAN   £111   4|4|3

CHURCH LN   RG2 9BY   0118 988 8500

A "consistent, high-level performer" – this Grade-II listed Victorian rectory near Reading became a restaurant in 1978 (as the 'Milton Sandford') and has held a Michelin star for much of the intervening time… until February 2022 that is. Despite the Tyre Men getting cold feet on the place, the feedback in our annual diners' poll has remained constant, if not perhaps being as plentiful as it was. "New young chef James Greatorex is innovative, offering very tasty dishes, using seasonal ingredients and a particularly good-value lunch menu". For some tastes though "the dining room could do with a makeover… it's starting to show its age a bit". / www.lortolan.com; lortolan; Tue-Sat midnight; closed Tue L, closed Sun & Mon; Cash & all usual cards; No shorts; children: 3.

SHIPLAKE, OXFORDSHIRE   2–2D

ORWELLS   £92   5|4|3

SHIPLAKE ROW   RG9 4DP   0118 940 3673

"Exquisite" cooking is commended by diners at Ryan & Liam Simpson-Trotman's well-rated venue, near Henley, where numerous reporters had their best meal of the year in our latest annual survey. There is a ten-course tasting menu for £130, but you don't have to go the whole hog: there's also a 'half menu' option (at £80) and an à la carte offering. / www.orwellsrestaurant.co.uk; orwells_rest; Wed-Sat 9 pm, Sun 3.30 pm; closed Sun D, closed Mon & Tue; Cash & all usual cards.

SHIPLEY, WEST YORKSHIRE   5–1C

AAGRAH   £39   3|3|2

4 SALTAIRE RD   BD18 3HN 01274 530880

Mohammed Sabir was still working as a bus driver in Shipley when he launched his Kashmiri curry business as a mobile takeaway from his Commer van, the 'Spice Box' in 1976. The next year he opened his first bricks-and-mortar restaurant Aagrah, which still wins consistently solid marks for its food and has nine branches across Yorkshire. / www.aagrah.com/find-a-restaurant/shipley; aagrah; Wed & Thu, Mon & Tue, Sun 11 pm, Fri & Sat 11.30 pm; closed Sat, Mon & Tue, Sun L; Cash & all usual cards.

WATERSIDE BISTRO   £72   4|3|3

UNIT B, 7 WHARF STREET   BD17 7DW 01274 594444

"Very good cooking at these prices" is the attraction at this "brilliant" venue, on the Leeds & Liverpool canal, which occupies part

of an old Victorian warehouse. Chef-partner Paul Huddleston has an impressive CV and fans say "a visit is a must when in the area". / www.watersideshipley.com; watersideshipley; Tue-Sat 9 pm; closed Sun & Mon.

SHOREHAM-BY-SEA, WEST SUSSEX   3–4B

INTO THE BLUE   £50   3|3|3

29-31 FERRY ROAD   BN43 5RA 01273 464768

"Never disappoints" say regulars at this popular destination, near Shoreham Beach, where "the menu is predominantly fish dishes". "It's our local. We love this place and highly recommend it. Choose the specials!". / www.intothebluerestaurant.com; Tue-Sat 10.30 pm; closed Sun & Mon.

SHREWSBURY, SHROPSHIRE   5–4A

RHUBARB   £45   3|3|4

10 SAINT MARY'S PLACE   SY1 1DZ 01743 341105

"An excellent addition to the town" – this year-old bistro occupies a "quirky and enchanting" sixteenth-century merchant's house (the old Drapers Guild Hall) that "is worth a visit in its own right" and was "once a setting for the TV film adaption of Charles Dickens' Christmas Carol". "The food is very good indeed, based on local ingredients and the menu changes regularly." "Wine is from the long-established local wine merchants Tanners." / Wed-Sat 9 pm, Sun 4 pm; closed Sun D, closed Mon & Tue.

THE WALRUS   £65   4|4|3

5 ROUSHILL   SY1 1PR   01743 240005

Ben Hall and Carla Cook have created a "super menu and the food delivered matches up… in fact exceeds expectations" at this four-year-old venture with an open kitchen. "It's small, so be sure to book in advance, especially for a special occasion." / www.the-walrus.co.uk; thewalrusrestaurant; Wed-Sat 9 pm; closed Wed-Sat L, closed Mon & Tue & Sun.

SKELTON, CUMBRIA   7–3D

THE DOG & GUN   £69   4|3|3

CA11 9SE   01768 484301

"Amazingly good cooking in a proper pub" makes Ben Queen-Fryer's five-year-old venture, "deep in the countryside near Penrith", a "rewarding detour" for anybody passing near the Lakes on the nearby M6. "Everything is cooked on the premises by one-man kitchen, chef Ben", and it's all "really interesting, very reasonably priced, and with a good selection of wine". / www.dogandgunskelton.co.uk; dog_and_gun_skelton; Wed-Sat 11 pm; closed Wed-Fri L, closed Mon & Tue & Sun.

THE BURLINGTON AT THE DEVONSHIRE ARMS HOTEL AND SPA   £68 3 4 4

BOLTON ABBEY   BD23 6AJ
01756 718100

The Duke of Devonshire's Bolton Abbey estate in Yorkshire provides a "stunning setting" for this "traditional, French-inspired" dining room, within a well-known luxury hotel. Ratings are very good all-round for Chris O'Callaghan's cuisine, which is bolstered by an "open-plan wine cellar the staff will be happy to show you round" (look out for some famous vintages). Top Tip – "one of Yorkshire's top afternoon teas". / devonshirehotels.co.uk/wine-dine; devarmsboltonabbey; Mon-Sun 9 pm; Cash & all usual cards; No trainers.

THE DEVONSHIRE FELL HOTEL, DEVONSHIRE HOTELS & RESTAURANTS   £70 3 3 4

BURNSALL VILLAGE   BD23 6BT
01756 729000

A "superb location" in the heart of the Dales is a key feature at this handsome-looking hotel, whose dining room has gorgeous views over the surrounding countryside. Limited but good feedback, too, on the affordable cuisine (two courses for £37.50, three courses for £45 as we went to press). / www.devonshirefell.co.uk/index.shtml; devonshirefell; Mon-Sun 8 pm; No shorts.

THE WOOLPACK INN   £66 4 4 3

SLAD ROAD   GL6 7QA   01452 813429

In Gloucestershire's lovely Slad valley, "Laurie Lee's local has just gone from strength to strength over the years – although it's not clear what Laurie Lee would think about it now, as while it's still all scrubbed tables and good cider, it now also has a talented chef producing high-end pub grub". "Sometimes the food is exceptional" (it was on Giles Coren's June 2022 visit) – "service has been varied, but everywhere is struggling with staff… but on the right day, a visit here is magical". / thewoolpackslad.com; woolpackslad; Sun & Mon 9 pm, Tue-Thu 11 pm, Fri & Sat midnight.

HERITAGE   £68 4 4 4

THE CHEQUERS INN   RH17 6AQ
01444 401102

"Still an all-round top-notch experience", chef Matt Gillan's "lovely restaurant with rooms" serves "exceptional food at very reasonable prices". His "Great British Menu 'extra course' of goat" (inspired by his mother, who is from St Helena) is also a "treat" – and it's "worth staying overnight for the breakfast", too. Top Tip – quirky wines are a feature, as are "cocktail pairings to die for, created for every dish". / heritage.restaurant; heritage_mattgillan;

Thu-Sat 8 pm, Sun 1.45 pm; closed Sun D, closed Mon & Tue & Wed.

KINLOCH LODGE   £118 3 3 4

SLEAT   IV43 8QY   01471 833333

In a "lovely setting" on Skye, the sixteenth-century former clan Macdonald hunting lodge has been run as a hotel for 50 years and is now under the direction of Isabella Macdonald – with meals bookended by "cocktails or Champagne in front of a roaring fire in the lounge before, and coffee and digestives after – WOW". "The restaurant is equally enticing", with "the best local ingredients, well cooked" – although "the choice on the menu is very limited for a 3-night stay". But it's fair to say that reactions can differ: what for most diners is "heritage dining" can for a minority seem like an "old-school restaurant that has been left behind". / www.kinloch-lodge.co.uk; kinloch_lodge; Mon-Sun 9 pm; No Amex.

THE OLD BANK BISTRO   4 4 3

10 LYNN ROAD   PE31 7LP   01485 544080

This "tiny dining room with absolutely fabulous food and service" – "from a superstar of a chef and his wife, managing front-of-house" – is "ideal for that very special occasion". Norfolk-born chef Lewis King and his wife Aga launched their 24-cover spot in a former coffee shop in 2016, on a budget of just £15,000. / www.theoldbankbistro.co.uk; theoldbankbistro; Wed-Sat 11.30 pm; closed Wed-Sat L, closed Mon & Tue & Sun.

TOFFS

16 DRURY LANE   B91 3BG

Local boy Rob Palmer, previously head chef at Hampton Manor – where he won the hotel's Peel's restaurant its first Michelin star in 2016 – opened this tasting-menu spot in a former computer game shop in Solihull in early 2022. No reports as yet, but this looks like one to watch in this plush Brum 'burb. / toffsbyrobpalmer.com; toffsbyrobpalmer; Tue-Sat 9 pm; closed Sun & Mon.

28 MARKET PLACE   4 4 3

28 MARKET PLACE   TA11 7NB

"This lovely, outstanding restaurant set in a beautiful historic market town" is "a wonderful find off the beaten track". The "remarkably good, modern English-style food" from Dan Fletcher – who has worked for uber-chefs Tommy Banks & Phil Howard – "is both delicious and beautifully presented", while "every component down to the glasses and plates is carefully chosen" by founders Vanessa & Ben Crofton (ex-Soho House & French Laundry director). With its in-house bakery, it's an "excellent addition to the West Country

restaurant scene". / 28marketplace.co.uk; 28marketplace; Wed-Sat 11.30 pm, Sun 5 pm; closed Wed-Sat L closed Sun D, closed Mon & Tue; booking is online only.

THE FRENCH HORN   £123 3 4 5

RG4 6TN   0118 969 2204

"The setting on the Thames at Sonning Eye is just fantastic, but better still, the quality of the food that comes out of the kitchen is always first class", according to fans of this long-established and well-known Thames-valley institution, which has been owned by the Emmanuel family since 1972. "If you like formal, this is the place to go", and while fans acknowledge that "it's a little pricey", they feel the investment is "well worth it for special occasions". As well as its signature duck, spit-roasted over an open fire, it's "very impressive wine list" is another feature ("we call it 'The Bible'"). / www.thefrenchhorn.co.uk; frenchhornsonning; Wed-Sat 9.30 pm, Sun 4.30 pm; closed Sun D, closed Mon & Tue; Cash & all usual cards; booking max 6 may apply.

THE HOPE & ANCHOR   £68 3 4 4

SLUICE ROAD   DN18 6JQ   01652 635334

"Thankful for it in a part of Lincolnshire that's something of a culinary desert" – this large boozer near the Humber Bridge is "so family friendly, with lovely views of the estuary" and is often tipped as a "first-class" stopping-off point. / www.thehopeandanchorpub.co.uk; thehopeandanchorpub; Tue-Sat 8.30 pm, Sun 5 pm; closed Sun D, closed Mon; Cash & all usual cards.

HOLM   4 4 4

28 ST JAMES STREET   TA13 5BT
01460 712470

"Excellent food in a converted former bank" is the 'elevator pitch' for this November 2021 newcomer from Nicholas Balfe, Mark Gurney and Matt Bushnell of south London's Levan and Larry's. Initial reports are upbeat all-round on all aspects of the 30-cover dining room in the original vault, complete with open kitchen and bookable diners' counter. Or you can now also eat on the newly added outside terrace (also available for drop-in coffee, drinks and snacks) and next year will see the opening of seven bedrooms. / holmsomerset.co.uk; holmsomerset; Thu-Sat 11 pm, Sun 6 pm; closed Mon & Tue & Wed.

Haar, St Andrews

SOUTH SHIELDS, TYNE AND WEAR 8–2B

COLMANS £35 [4][4][3]

182-186 OCEAN RD   NE33 2JQ
0191 456 1202

"The menu is simple but they know what they are doing… as you would expect now they're into their fourth generation running the place" at this Tyneside "local institution", which first started out as a hut on the foreshore in 1905 – a "fantastic traditional chippy with a good selection of other dishes too. Always busy, but they always find room for you!". / www.colmansfishandchips.co.uk; Mon-Sun 6 pm; Cash & all usual cards; no bookings.

COLMANS SEAFOOD TEMPLE £49 [4][3][3]

SEA ROAD   NE33 2LD   0191 511 1349

"A great choice of seafood and lovely sea view" accompany a trip to this beachfront landmark (dating from 1921 and known locally as Gandhi's Temple), which was relaunched as this descriptively-named spot in May 2017, by the family behind local well-known institution, Colmans (see also). "More up-market than their old established chippy in the town, this is a top venue with the same value for money combined with a great setting". Top Menu Tips – "fabulous Lindisfarne oysters, the best king scallops Thermidor and smoked haddock soufflé". / colmansseafoodtemple.co.uk; colmansseafoodtemple; Mon-Thu 7.30 pm, Fri & Sat 8.30 pm, Sun 6 pm.

SOUTHAMPTON, HAMPSHIRE 2–3D

BLUE JASMINE £54 [3][3][3]

UNIT 3-4 ALEXANDRA WHARF, MARITIME WALK, OCEAN WAY,   SO14 3QS
023 8063 6387

This relative newcomer (est. 2019) by the water at Southampton's Ocean Village Marina serves "excellent Southeast Asian fusion food, in a very nice atmosphere with excellent service". Executive chef Daren Liew (formerly of Hakkasan and Duddell's of Hong Kong) has created a range of signature dishes, led by his play on Peking duck flavoured with Sarawak black pepper from the forests of east Malaysia. / www.bluejasmine.co.uk; Tue-Sat midnight; closed Sun & Mon.

LAKAZ MAMAN £43 [4][3][3]

22 BEDFORD PLACE   SO15 2DB
023 8063 9217

"Didn't expect to find really good Mauritian food in Southampton… but it was!" – Shelina Permalloo's 'street kitchen' is "more like a fun cafe than a restaurant, with food that's different, interesting and beautifully cooked". / www.lakazmaman.com; lakazmaman; Mon-Sun 10 pm; Cash & all usual cards; booking is online only.

SOUTHBOROUGH, KENT 3–4B

TALLOW £65 [5][4][3]

15A CHURCH ROAD   TN4 0RX

Not only "an excellent new addition in Tunbridge Wells" ("a fine-dining desert for too long") – Rob & Donna Taylor's move in late 2021 from The Compasses Inn in Crundale to this "small and intimate" (26-cover) beamed venue has created the most commented-on newcomer outside London in our annual diners' poll. The menu can seem "limited" in scope but "changes monthly and every dish is put together with thought, care and obvious skill" delivering meals that are "full of flavour and beautifully presented". "Front of house really know their stuff too. Highly recommended". / tallowrestaurant.co.uk; tallow_restaurant; Tue-Sat 9.30 pm; closed Sun & Mon; booking is online only.

SOUTHBOURNE, DORSET 2–4C

RESTAURANT ROOTS £93 [5][4][3]

141 BELLE VUE ROAD   BH6 3EN
01202 430005

"Jan and Stacey are legends" according to fans of the Bretschneider's small, "friendly" and "relaxed" tasting menu restaurant. "The amazing food is even more impressive when you realise it is created and delivered by only 3 staff. If this was in London it would be hugely acclaimed!". The 9-course evening menu is £105 per head. / restaurantroots.co.uk; restaurant_roots; Wed-Sat midnight; closed Wed L, closed Mon & Tue & Sun.

SOUTHEND-ON-SEA, ESSEX 3–3C

THE PIPE OF PORT £60 [3][4][4]

84 HIGH ST   SS1 1JN   01702 614606

This delightfully Dickensian wine vault has lured knowing customers for more than 45 years, via an "almost anonymous door opening to a flight of stairs leading to an amazing basement eatery". "The specialities are pies, which are delicious, and the wine is good as well" – it's "well worth a visit". / www.pipeofport.co.uk; thepipeofport; Mon-Sat 11 pm; closed Sun; No Amex; children: 16+.

SOUTHLEIGH, DEVON 2–4A

GLEBE HOUSE £74 [5][3][3]

EX24 6SD   01404 871368

"A wonderful dining experience" – "not Michelin prices and just as good": this yearling from Hugo Guest (ex-Marksman and Sorella in London) has transformed the Georgian vicarage previously run by his parents as a B&B into a smart restaurant-with-rooms. Dinner (Thu-Sat and Sun lunch) is four no-choice courses with an Italian flavour, showcasing produce sourced locally or from the property's 15-acre smallholding – "exquisite food served simply and without pretension in a homely atmosphere". The kitchen also offers a casual supper every night. / www.glebehousedevon.co.uk; glebehousedevon; closed Mon-Sat & Sun.

SOUTHPORT, MERSEYSIDE 5–1A

BISTROT VÉRITÉ £49 [4][4][4]

7 LIVERPOOL ROAD   PR8 4AR
01704 564 199

"This great French bistro" with a "buzzy ambience" is, for fans, "a favourite place for a special occasion meal" – "there's always a great choice of imaginative seasonal dishes". It's very much a family business, with owners Marc & Michaela Vérité joined by their sons Jacques, the head chef who trained at the Chester Grosvenor, and Charlie, part of the FoH team. "The new bar area in the recently acquired adjacent premises is a welcome addition." / www.bistrotverite.co.uk; bistrotverite; Tue-Sat 10 pm; closed Tue L, closed Sun & Mon.

THE VINCENT HOTEL V-CAFE £70 [3][3][4]

98 LORD STREET   PR8 1JR
01704 883 800

Large, comfortable and stylish hotel brasserie with large windows looking onto Eastbank Street Square. Billing itself as 'the place for the first bite, the last cocktail and everything in between', it lives up to its billing with an extensive menu – from sushi to "delicious steaks" via "recommended fish 'n' chips" to bao buns and a variety of casual bites. It's "a great spot for people watching" too and "usually has a buzzy atmosphere". Top Tip – "good afternoon tea with dainty finger sandwiches and a great selection of pastries and cakes". / www.thevincenthotel.com; vincent.hotel.southport; Mon-Sun 11 pm; Cash & all usual cards.

SOUTHROP, GLOUCESTERSHIRE 2–2C

OX BARN AT THYME £75 [3][3][4]

SOUTHROP MANOR ESTATE   GL7 3NX
01367 850174

"What a room! – a delightful space – where everything is satisfyingly well thought out and pleasing to the eye" ("reflecting the large amounts of money spent on them!"), at Caryn & Jerry Hibbert's barn-conversion, which sits within a chocolate-box-pretty Cotswolds development, incorporating bar, pub, cookery school, spa and shopping. The food, in an easygoing vein, is "flavoursome" too – "we'd stay… if we didn't live around the corner". / www.thyme.co.uk; thyme.england; Mon-Sun 9 pm.

SOUTHSEA, HAMPSHIRE 2–4D

RESTAURANT 27 £72 343

27A SOUTHSEA PARADE PO5 2JF
023 9287 6272

Chef-patron Kevin Bingham has presented his "excellent" 'global French' cuisine at this consistent performer near the Southsea seafront for more than a decade – and at restaurant Montparnasse (RIP) before that. The tasting menu goes down well, "with a well-chosen wine flight to complement it". / www.restaurant27.com; Wed-Sat 8.30 pm, Sun 2.30 pm; closed Wed-Sat L closed Sun D, closed Mon & Tue; Cash & all usual cards.

SOUTHWOLD, SUFFOLK 3–1D

THE CROWN, ADNAMS HOTEL £76 223

90 HIGH ST IP18 6DP 01502 722275

This "homely" Georgian hotel restaurant "with great ambience" "continues to be the heart of Southwold" and "has usually been a reliably safe bet for an interesting menu and sound cooking". But eating here has been a losing bet too often in recent times – "making the right choice from the menu is essential, as not all dishes are good". "One change post-Brexit and Covid is that staff are mostly local, taking it back to what it was 30 years ago – which is fitting for such a retro location." / thecrownsouthwold.co.uk; crownsouthwold; Mon-Sun 9 pm; payment – credit card only; children: All welcome.

SOLE BAY FISH COMPANY £56 322

22E BLACKSHORE IP18 6ND
01502 724241

This "unpretentious and quirky clapperboard-style shack" on the Blyth estuary quayside excels for its "really fresh seafood, served simply". It's "difficult to get to without a car", but they also run the Little Fish & Chip Shop in the middle of town. Top Menu Tip – "wonderful oysters and superb grilled prawns". / www.solebayfishco.co.uk; solebayfishcompany; Mon-Sun 7 pm; Cash & all usual cards.

TWO MAGPIES £24 333

88 HIGH STREET IP18 6DP
01502 726120

"Not just a roadside caff, a destination in itself!" – this "brilliant, friendly and bustling café/bakery on the A12" is "full of life", with "excellent coffee", "freshly cooked breakfasts and lunches" and "dangerous cakes". There are another half-dozen branches of this artisan bakery scattered across East Anglia. / www.twomagpiesbakery.co.uk; Sun-Fri 5 pm, Sat 8.30 pm; closed Sun-Fri D.

SOWERBY BRIDGE, WEST YORKSHIRE 5–1C

ENGINE SOCIAL DINING £48 544

72 WHARF STREET HX6 2AF
01422 740123

"I'm struggling to find fault with this local gem as it goes from strength to strength" – chef Mark Kemp's team "turns out dish after dish of superbly presented, but more importantly delicious, food" at this pub-conversion in the Upper Calder Valley, while "Wil Akroyd is unflappable and assured as the FoH". With its dynamic mix of ingredients and flavours from all parts of the world, this "may not be a restaurant for someone with traditional English tastes" – but "news of its quality seems to be spreading, with national press reviewers at last paying a visit". "I think it's safe to say I utterly love this place!" / enginesocial.co.uk; enginesocialsb; Wed-Sat 9 pm; closed Mon & Tue & Sun; booking is online only.

THE MOORCOCK INN £61 543

MOORBOTTOM LANE HX6 3RP
01422 832103

In March 2022, Aimee Turford and chef Alisdair Brooke-Taylor called time on their tenure at (to use their words) "this little pub on this windy hill. With its wild weather, warm people and those sunsets". "Gutted" is the general sense amongst its numerous fans, who will miss the "virtuosic inventiveness" of Alisdair's "glorious cuisine" ("such an outstanding talent") and "Aimee's effortless front-of-house skills there for all to behold". "This place has become a draw for this part of West Yorkshire and it was with much sadness that we all learned that it will close in January 2023. Go quickly and before it's gone. I know that I will." Perhaps someone will step into their shoes, although "the pub itself is nothing to write home about". / www.themoorcock.co.uk; themoorcock; Thu-Sat 11 pm, Sun 6 pm; closed Thu & Fri L closed Sun D, closed Mon & Tue & Wed.

ST ALBANS, HERTFORDSHIRE 3–2A

DYLANS KINGS ARMS £56 343

7 GEORGE STREET AL3 4ER
01727530332

"Top grub, a cut above the local culinary landscape", has earned a devoted following for this fifteenth-century pub in the St Albans cathedral quarter, named after a dog belonging to landlord Sean Hughes – who "continues to be the host with the most". The menu changes monthly, but may include a smoked duck Caesar Scotch egg, or a spectacular prime rib of English dairy cow to share at £80. / www.dylanskingsarms.com; dylanskingsarms; Wed-Sat 11 pm, Sun 10 pm; closed Wed L, closed Mon & Tue; Cash & all usual cards; booking is online only.

LUSSMANNS £52 323

WAXHOUSE GATE, HIGH ST AL3 4EW
01727 851941

With its "tasty food" and "unusual setting" in a glass-roofed modern building next to the eleventh-century cathedral, this well-priced local bistro with an emphasis on sustainable cuisine makes "a good base for lunch or dinner". It is part of Andrei Lussmann's five-strong Hertfordshire-based group. / www.lussmanns.com/restaurants/ st-albans-restaurants; lussmanns; Tue-Thu 9 pm, Fri & Sat 10 pm, Sun 7 pm; closed Mon; Cash & all usual cards.

THOMPSON £96 333

2 HATFIELD RD AL1 3RP 01727 730 777

Chef-patron Phil Thompson's "lovely food continues to excite" at the restaurant he has owned for 10 years (formerly known as Darcy's) – which makes an "excellent place for a leisurely romantic evening". His classical style reflects his early years cooking for the Galvin brothers and Marco Pierre White. / www.thompsonstalbans.co.uk; thompsondining; Wed & Thu, Tue 9 pm, Fri & Sat 9.30 pm, Sun 3 pm; closed Tue L closed Sun D, closed Mon; Cash & all usual cards; booking is online only.

ST ANDREWS, FIFE 9–3D

HAAR £114 543

1 GOLF PLACE KY16 9JA 01334 473387

"Chef Dean Banks is very committed to his outstanding St Andrews restaurant, making the most of wonderful ingredients, and giving his customers a real experience" from a tasting menu, with various options priced from £82.50. That's the initial view on this Christmas 2021 newcomer, which Dean opened at the former 'Golf Inn' (by the 18th floor of the Old course) after a crowdfunding campaign to move from his former location, within a five-star hotel elsewhere in the town. The name means a cold sea fog on the east coast of Scotland. / www.haarrestaurant.com; haarrestaurant; Wed-Sun midnight; closed Mon & Tue.

JAHANGIR £27 333

116A SOUTH STREET KY16 9QD
01334 470300

"A wonderful selection of dishes, perfect for vegans and omnivores alike" wins a thumbs-up for this long-established curry house (est. 1998). "Knowledgeable staff talk about the food and recommend combinations for you." / jahangirstandrews.co.uk; Mon-Sun 11 pm; closed Sun L.

THE SEAFOOD RISTORANTE £86 435

THE SCORES, BRUCE EMBANKMENT
KY16 9AB 01334 479475

A long drive from the A&R clubhouse but just a short putt from the sea, this swanky modern seafood restaurant occupies a glass box perched dramatically on the shore, with "wonderful views" and a menu that takes full advantage of the "great fish" caught nearby. / www.theseafoodrestaurant.com; theseafoodsta; Tue-Sat 21.30 am; closed Sun & Mon; Cash & all usual cards; children: 12+ at D.

ST DAVIDS, PEMBROKESHIRE   4–4A

BLAS RESTAURANT, TWR Y FELIN HOTEL, TWR Y FELIN HOTEL   444

SA62 6QT   01437 725 555

Uniformly highly rated dining room that's been a feature of this modern boutique hotel since it opened in the heart of the town in 2015. The name means 'Taste' in Welsh, and under chef Sammy Owen it is winning increasing acclaim (having been promoted in 2022 to a hard-to-win three AA rosettes). / www.twryfelinhotel.com/dining; twryfelinhotel_ stdavids; Mon-Sun 9 pm; Cash & all usual cards; booking evening only; children: 12.

ST IVES, CORNWALL   1–4A

ONE FISH STREET   £91   543

1 FISH STREET   TR26 1LT

"The food is not only picture perfect but tastebud-wateringly delicious" at this "small and lively" owner-operated venue, which "has it all, not just for Instagram but for the discerning diner from age 4 to 100" (down to the "wonderful crockery, glassware and cutlery"). It serves an "excellent fish-based tasting menu" of "amazing quality and innovation, with pedigree and traceability on all food sourcing". / www.onefishstreet.net; onefishstreet_stives; Mon-Fri 11 pm; closed Mon-Fri L, closed Sat & Sun.

PORTHMINSTER CAFÉ   £67   335

PORTHMINSTER BEACH   TR26 2EB
01736 795352

"Great for lunch on a breezy summer's day" – this "special" venue in a "fabulous beach location" with a "beautiful view" has earned a reputation as one of the most notable in St Ives over more than 25 years. Its mainly seafood menu, with Asian and Mediterranean influences, is "well executed with some long-established favourites". The same team own the Porthmeor Beach Café, below Tate St Ives. / www.porthminstercafe.co.uk; porthminstercafe; Wed-Sat 9 pm, Mon & Tue, Sun 3 pm; closed Mon & Tue, Sun D; No Amex.

PORTHMINSTER KITCHEN   £51   343

WHARF RD   TR26 1LG   01736 799874

"It's slightly easier to get a table here than at its sibling, the Porthminster Cafe." But, nevertheless, this is a "nice little place in this tourist town" – "pleasant outside on a good day" and with "good basic food". / www.porthminster.kitchen; porthminster_kitchen; Mon-Sun 9.30 pm.

UGLY BUTTERFLY   £120   423

CARBIS BAY ESTATE   TR26 2NP

Celeb chef Adam Handling arrived in Cornwall in August 2021 with this 65-cover all-day dining experience set in a new, luxury beachside estate on the fringes of St Ives. Fans say it's a "simply stunning location" with ocean views through the floor-to-ceiling windows and an open kitchen (although the impression is a fraction modern and "soulless" to some tastes). Adam is known for his sustainable focus and this continues in the tasting-menu format (5-courses for £100, 7-courses for £125). Some reporters' best meals of the year won it generally high marks, but there were some more middling reports and complaints regarding pricing ("not a nightmare evening, but who has persuaded them they are special?"). Perhaps change will be afoot, as in July 2022 (post-survey) a new head chef, Connor Blades, was appointed.. / www.uglybutterfly.co.uk; uglybutterflybyah; Wed-Sat 10 pm, Sun 7pm; closed Sun D, closed Mon & Tue; children: No minimum age.

ST KEW, CORNWALL   1–3B

ST KEW INN   £57   333

PL30 3HB   01208 841259

"A lovely location (both inside and out)" – this fifteenth-century, stone-built inn with garden is one of the better hostelries for a meal near touristy Padstow. "An interesting menu is well cooked and the open-fire cooking of some dishes seems to work well". "Some tables are cramped, but it is an old pub…" / www.stkewinn.co.uk; STKEWINN; Mon-Sun 11 pm; No Amex; booking is online only; children: no children in bar.

ST LEONARDS-ON-SEA, EAST SUSSEX   3–4C

THE ROYAL   £54   343

1 SAINT JOHNS ROAD   TN37 6HP
01424 547797

"A welcome addition to the up-and-coming St Leonards area" – this "great little gastropub opposite Warrior Square station" was "a bit of a rough-and-ready pub" until it was taken over just before lockdown by a young team from London "who have changed it radically". "The food is consistently good, service is charming and ambience is old-fashioned pub chic" under chef Sam Coxhead and front-of-house James Hickson, whose "serious pedigrees" include St John, Moro, Great Queen Street and Stockwell's Canton Arms. / theroyalstleonards. co.uk; the_royal_st_leonards; Thu-Sat 11 pm, Wed 10 pm, Sun 5.30 pm; closed Wed L closed Sun D, closed Mon & Tue; No Amex.

ST MAWES, CORNWALL   1–4B

HOTEL TRESANTON   £79   335

27 LOWER CASTLE ROAD   TR2 5DR
01326 270055

The last word in calm elegance on Cornwall's south coast, Olga Polizzi's famous former yacht

club is "consistently classy", with "good food, fantastic service" – and, inevitably, "prices to match". The restaurant is open to non-residents but you need to book in the evening, while the Dogs' bar and Beach Club offer more casual eating options. / www.tresanton.com; hoteltresanton; Mon-Sun 9.30 pm; No Amex; booking max 8 may apply; children: 6+ at dinner.

THE IDLE ROCKS   £125   444

HARBOURSIDE   TR2 5AN   01326 270270

"A really special place to eat in summer or winter with views out over the bustling harbour of St Mawes" – this 18-bedroom Relais & Châteaux hotel is perched near the sea, and its restaurant occupies a "light and attractive dining room" that's warmly reviewed in all feedback. "A limited seasonal menu doesn't detract: each course is beautifully presented by cheerful staff; and the fish is fresh and guaranteed to make you want to come back time and again". If you want to push the boat out, there's also a seven-course 'signature' option. / www.idlerocks.co.uk; idlerocks; Wed-Sun, Mon & Tue 9 pm; closed Mon & Tue L.

ST MERRYN, CORNWALL   1–3B

THE CORNISH ARMS   £59   333

CHURCHTOWN   PL28 8ND   01841 520288

The Stein empire's village pub has been much-extended over the years and nowadays feels much more restauranty and professional than when the family first took it over in 2009. Results in prior years have been up-and-down, but ratings were good this year – "had mixed expectations for this, but the food was enjoyable, and pretty reasonably priced given its good execution". / www.rickstein.com/eat-with-us/the-cornish-arms; rycksteinrestaurants; Mon-Sun 11 pm; No Amex; booking is online only.

ST MONANS, FIFE   9–4D

CRAIG MILLAR @ 16 WEST END   £63   344

16 WEST END   KY10 2BX   01333 730327

"A lovely local restaurant with a high level of cookery" – Craig Millar's bright coastal dining room provides "a good choice, especially fish at reasonable prices, plus beautiful sea views". He follows a tasting menu format, offering 5-course and 6-course options. / www.16westend.com; craig_millar_16_west_end; Wed-Sat 9 pm, Sun 2 pm; closed Sun D, closed Mon & Tue; Cash & all usual cards; children: 5+.

ST-LEONARDS-ON-SEA, EAST SUSSEX   3–4C

GALLERIA   £55

39 NORMAN ROAD   TN38 0EG
07445 033561

No feedback as yet on this August 2020 arrival in this ever-more fashionable seaside town, but it's a July 2022 tip from Giles Coren writing in The Times and awarding it 23/30. "I probably shouldn't have been as surprised as I was by the low, low prices on the menu" achieved with "unfashionable fish – mussels, sea trout, plaice, mackerel – and plenty of pasta." / www.galleriabar.co.uk; galleriastleonards; closed Mon-Sat & Sun.

STAFFORD, STAFFORDSHIRE　　5–3B

MOAT HOUSE　　£62　333

LOWER PENKRIDGE RD, ACTON TRUSSELL　ST17 0RJ　01785 712217

A "smart hotel" with its own lake set in the Staffs countryside, where the "cosy restaurant serves good value food using local produce". Tuesday night is grill night – on other evenings steaks and pub classics feature on the menu alongside somewhat fancier fare. / www.moathouse.co.uk; themoathouse; Tue-Sat 9 pm, Sun 3 pm; closed Tue-Fri L closed Sun D, closed Mon; Cash & all usual cards.

STAMFORD, LINCOLNSHIRE　　6–4A

CLOISTERS　　£31　343

9 SAINT MARY'S STREET　PE9 2DE　01780 755162

"Should you be visiting Burghley House, make sure to take some time to stroll around one of England's most beautiful towns". To eat, consider this "lovely Italian" where the food is "quite traditional, but great quality ingredients elevate the overall platter". "After lunch, pop next door and shop for the same ingredients in their deli." Top Menu Tip – "the polpette made with pork and a smidge of 'nduja, which gives it a lovely scented and spicy undertone". / www.cloistersbistro.com; cloistersitalian; Tue-Thu 10 pm, Fri & Sat 10.30 pm; closed Sun & Mon.

THE GEORGE HOTEL　　£109　224

71 ST MARTINS　PE9 2LB　01780 750750

"This great institution carries on, as historic and handsome as ever" – a supremely grand old coaching inn on the Great North Road as it passes through this delightful Georgian town that in days gone by has hosted the great and the good including Charles I and Sir Walter Scott. It's "a place to be cherished", and any meal in the "fantastic old-school restaurant", with its wonderful oak panelling, heavyweight wine list and carving trolley, is a superb "treat". It is a "very expensive" occasion, though, and "the food can be a bit 'beige'" ("would be good value at half the price"). / www.georgehotelofstamford.com; Mon-Sun 9.30 pm; Cash & all usual cards; Jacket required; children: 8.

STANHOE, NORFOLK　　6–3B

THE DUCK INN　　£58　433

BURNHAM RD　PE31 8QD　01485 518 330

"It is great to see the ever-growing number of plaudits for this restaurant" – this family-run gastroboozer has an "ever-growing" army of fans (including Giles Coren of The Times). "Last visited in 2012" – a year before chef-landlord Ben Handley and his wife Sarah took over – "when we walked out after being

ignored by the staff. Wow, how it's changed! Buzzy atmosphere, friendly and helpful staff, food interesting, fresh and perfectly cooked". There's now a garden room annexe to the 300-year-old pub to accommodate demand. / www.duckinn.co.uk; duckinnstanhoe; Wed-Sat 9 pm, Sun 6 pm; closed Sun D, closed Mon & Tue; Cash & all usual cards.

STANTON, SUFFOLK　　3–1C

LEAPING HARE VINEYARD　　£60　435

WYKEN VINEYARDS　IP31 2DW　01359 250287

"Surrounded by the Wyken vineyards and the Suffolk countryside", this "bright and airy converted barn is warmed by a wood-burning stove that makes it cosy on colder days". A "wonderful" wood-framed building, with a soaring ceiling, it serves "surprisingly excellent cooking" – say, "beetroot soup and freshly baked focaccia, feta cheese salad with maple and blood orange salad" – "washed down by Moonshine, their vineyard's sparkling wine". A fixture for more than 25 years, its latest addition is an outdoor pizza oven in an outdoor setting heated by fire chimneys. / www.wykenvineyards.co.uk; wykenvineyards; Wed & Thu, Sun 5.30 pm, Fri & Sat 9 pm; closed Wed & Thu, Sun D, closed Mon & Tue; Cash & all usual cards.

STEIN, HIGHLAND　　9–2A

LOCH BAY RESTAURANT　　£154　543

1 MACLEODS TERRACE　IV55 8GA　01470 592235

"Wonderful seafood" is a highlight at Michael & Laurence Smith's 18-seater venue in an old fishing village at the north end of the island. It's presented via Michael's 'Skye Fruits de Mer' menu, which is served over an evening and must be pre-booked at £120 per person. / www.lochbay-restaurant.co.uk; lochbayskye; Tue-Sat 10.30 pm; closed Tue-Sat L, closed Sun & Mon; No Amex; credit card deposit required to book; children: 12+ at D.

STIRCHLEY, WEST MIDLANDS　　5–4C

YIKOUCHI AT CHANCER'S CAFÉ　　£18

1418 PERSHORE ROAD　B30 2PH

It looks unpromising – derelict even – on the outside, but this quirky venue from chef James Kirk-Gould and his partner Cassie caught attention in April 2022, when Jay Rayner of The Observer decided to give it a review. At the weekends, it's all about waffles and fudge sauce (Cassie has a fudge business), but Wednesday to Friday it serves up "thrilling dishes paying homage to their time together in China" making this, says Jay, a "brilliant-cut-gem of a place", with dishes rarely costing over £9. / chancers_cafe; Wed, Sat 2 pm, Thu & Fri 9 pm, Sun 1 pm; closed Wed, Sat & Sun D, closed Mon & Tue.

STOCK, ESSEX　　3–2B

THE HOOP　　£42　332

HIGH STREET　CM4 9BD　01277841137

This "lovely old pub" – a timber-fronted fifteenth-century building with brick fireplaces – has a "well deserved reputation as one of the best in Essex", with "reliable pub grub" and a new beer garden featuring an outdoor pizza oven. "Eat in the restaurant upstairs if you can". / www.thehoop.co.uk; thehoop; Tue-Sat 10 pm, Sun 8.30 pm; closed Mon.

STOCKBRIDGE, HAMPSHIRE　　2–3D

GREYHOUND　　£60　334

31 HIGH STREET　SO20 6EY　01264 810833

"Not just a pub!" – this "gorgeous spot by the Test, with great food and friendly staff" has been smartly run for 10 years by Lucy Townsend, and is "lovely inside, with a cute little courtyard and a very good atmosphere". Outside, it's in prime fly-fishing territory that used to be (as the name suggests) a centre for hare-coursing. / www.thegreyhoundonthetest.co.uk; ghstockbridge; Mon-Sat 9.30 pm, Sun 7 pm; Cash & all usual cards; booking max 12 may apply.

STOCKCROSS, BERKSHIRE　　2–2D

THE VINEYARD AT STOCKCROSS　　£97　333

RG20 8JU　01635 528770

"The wine list is immense, but good sommeliers are on hand to guide you through it" at Sir Peter Michael's modern, luxury country estate, whose "stunning, if challengingly extensive, cellar" features vintages from his family's Sonoma County and Napa Valley vineyards. So "do not be daunted, as there is plenty of advice from the wine team" and the selection is "deep, complex, and fascinating… if expensive" ("if you are seriously into Californian wines, this is the place", but "deep pockets are needed!"). Other aspects of the operation have a hard time living up to the main event and harsher reporters feel aspects of the place are "dull" or "nothing memorable by comparison to the wine". Others, though, are "surprised by the good food" with dishes noted in despatches including "very good crab tortellini and Berkshire trout with caviar" and "beautifully presented Berkshire game pie". / www.the-vineyard.co.uk; thevineyardhotel; Wed-Sun 9 pm; closed Mon & Tue; Cash & all usual cards.

STOCKPORT, GREATER MANCHESTER　　5–2B

BISTRO MARC AT WINTER'S　　£36

23-27 LITTLE UNDERBANK　SK1 1LA　0161 260 0207

Rachel Winter Jones and Marc Molé opened this new French spot in a fascinating historic building owned by the local council – built as a Victorian jewellers and clockmakers – in April

2022 (too late to inspire any feedback in our annual diners' poll). Marc, an architect from Paris, and Rachel, a lawyer with a 20-year career at the World Bank, met on a blind date in a bistro in Paris and here that's exactly the style of cuisine they are emulating. Open from the morning onwards for coffee and pastries. / bistromarc.co.uk; bistromarc; Wed-Sat 10 pm, Sun 4 pm; closed Sun D, closed Mon & Tue.

THE EASY FISH COMPANY £60 433

117 HEATON MOOR ROAD   SK4 4HY
0161 442 0823

"Fishmonger's with a restaurant at rear, where you're guaranteed a wide range of really tasty, always-fresh seafood". The family-owned fish business goes back four generations, stretching back 120 years to Smithfield Market in Manchester's Northern Quarter; they have a similar outlet in Wilmslow. / www.theeasyfishco.com; theeasyfishco; Tue-Sat 11.30 pm; closed Sun & Mon; Cash & all usual cards.

WHERE THE LIGHT GETS IN £121 444

7 ROSTRON ROW   SK1 1JY
016 1477 5744

"Rooftop views towards nearby Robinsons Brewery and dishes using plants grown on the local multi-story car park" both add to the epic street cred of Sam Buckley's famous hipster hotspot, housed within the vibey brick-lined first floor of an old Victorian warehouse, with huge windows. Feedback is very good all-round including when it comes to the sustainably sourced small plates that have earnt it such renown, but this is one of the few UK venues where a massive media profile is not reflected by a huge volume of feedback in our annual national diners' poll. / wtlgi.co; arestaurantwherethelightgetsin; Wed-Sat 10 pm; closed Wed-Sat L, closed Mon & Tue & Sun.

PENSONS AT NETHERWOOD ESTATE £70 544

NETHERWOOD ESTATE, PENSONS YARD
WR15 8RT   AWAITING TEL

A "delicious spot in the Herefordshire undergrowth" that's "well worth a detour" – Peta Darnley "has created something really special with innovative, seasonal, regional fare" served in a converted barn on her family's Netherwood Estate – earning a "very rare Michelin Green star for sustainability" – while head chef Chris Simpson (ex-Adam Outlaw and Gidleigh Park) "conjures delicate flavours from local ingredients, many grown in their own kitchen garden, that build in intensity throughout the meal". / www.pensons.co.uk; pensonsrestaurant; Mon-Fri 5 pm, Sat & Sun 4 pm; closed Mon-Sun D.

GRILL AT THE OLD PLOUGH £49 343

2 STATION ROAD   KT11 3BN
01932 862244

A "best-kept secret" – although enough locals know about it to ensure that it's "always busy" – this gastropub is "really consistent and thoroughly enjoyable": "I've never had a bad meal at the Old Plough." A 300-year-old listed building, it was formerly used as a courthouse. / www.oldploughcobham.co.uk; oldploughcobham; Mon-Thu 10.30 pm, Fri & Sat 11 pm, Sun 9 pm; Cash & all usual cards; no bookings.

STOKE MILL £73 333

MILL ROAD   NR14 8PA   01508 493 337

"A bit quirky, but it has a lot class as well" – this scenic, 700-year-old mill on the River Tas was once home to the business that became Colman's Mustard, and since 2013 under Ludo and Andy Rudd has been restored to be a restaurant of some ambition. There is an à la carte menu, or go the whole hog and have the 7-course tasting menu for £75. Top Menu Tip – "the best Sunday lunch for miles". / // www.stokemill.co.uk; stokemill; Wed-Sun 10 pm, Sun 2.30 pm; closed Sun D, closed Mon & Tue; Cash & all usual cards.

THE WILDEBEEST ARMS £90 334

82-86 NORWICH RD   NR14 8QJ
01508 492497

"Excellent food, beautifully prepared and presented from local produce", ticks the boxes at this village pub-restaurant just outside Norwich, which serves a modern British menu from Norfolk-born chef Daniel Smith (ex-Le Gavroche and Morston Hall), who also runs the Ingham Swan (his third venture, Warwick Street Social in Norwich, closed during the pandemic). The Wildebeest's name is a relic of its previous life as an African-themed gastropub. Top Tip – "the fixed-price lunch is a real bargain". / thewildebeest.co.uk; thewildebeestnorfolk; Mon-Sun 9 pm; Cash & all usual cards.

THE CROOKED BILLET £74 334

NEWLANDS LN   RG9 5PU   01491 681048

"Food is the star" at this country pub, owned since 1989 by former musician and self-taught cook Paul Clerehugh (ex-Sweet et al) – although the "outstanding roster of live music" runs a close second and "a handful of people still go there just for a drink outside". The "heavily carnivorous menu" features "well-cooked seasonal French and English food", "served in vast portions". / www.thecrookedbillet.co.uk; crookedbillet_stokerow; Mon-Sun midnight; Cash & all usual cards.

THE CROWN £64 333

PARK STREET   CO6 4SE   01206 262 001

In the heart of Constable Country, this gastropub with rooms is "a busy venue with a good atmosphere and friendly service". Foodwise, it's praised for cooking that's "outstanding" at the "very reasonable price"; and wine lovers are well-catered for too, with 250 bins (they also run their own merchants). / www.crowninn.net; thecrownstokebynayland; Mon-Sat 11.30 pm, Sun 10.30 pm; Cash & all usual cards.

THE OLD BUTCHERS £77 322

PARK ST   GL54 1AQ   01451 831700

"Excellent seafood in the unlikely named Old Butchers" is the calling card of Pete & Louise Robinson's long standing Stow venue, most of it delivered from Cornwall. "All the food served is of a very high standard" – even if arguably "the simple ambience doesn't match the cooking". / www.theoldbutchers.squarespace.com; the_old_butchers; Tue-Sat 9 pm; closed Sun & Mon; Cash & all usual cards.

THE OLD STOCKS INN 334

THE SQUARE   GL54 1AF   01451 830 666

"A fantastic option in this Cotswolds village" that's part of an old inn (with rooms) in the heart of the town that was given an attractive refit a couple of years ago. Despite some pub associations, the food is very much restaurant fare from a two-course or three-course menu. / www.oldstocksinn.com; oldstocksinn; Mon-Fri 9.30 pm, Sat & Sun 2.30 pm; closed Mon-Fri L closed Sat & Sun D.

INVER RESTAURANT £98 423

STRACHLACHLAN   PA27 8BU
01369 860 537

"Stunning local produce and foraged ingredients are cooked to perfection" at this "lovely" fisherman's croft with a "beautiful view over Loch Fyne", from chef Pam Brunton and her partner Rob Latimer (both ex-Noma). It's "not too remote but feels like you're in the wilderness", so is "highly recommended for a romantic overnight stay". Top Tip – "they also make great cocktails from interesting local and foraged ingredients". / www.inverrestaurant.co.uk; inverrestaurant; Fri-Sun, Thu 8.30 pm; closed Thu L, closed Mon & Tue & Wed; Cash & all usual cards.

LAMBS £55 3|3|4

12 SHEEP STREET CV37 6EF
01789 292554

One of the oldest buildings in Stratford – this beamed house in the town centre is convenient to the RSC, and one of the better options in town for a meal, with a competitively priced set menu. / www.lambsrestaurant.co.uk; lambsrestaurant; Mon-Sun 9 pm; closed Mon L; No Amex.

LOXLEYS £61 3|3|3

3 SHEEP ST CV37 6EF 01789 292128

"The limited but cracking value pre-theatre menu" is a particular feature at this two-floor operation in an historic building not far from the RSC. It's open from breakfast onwards, serving all day, seven days a week. / www.loxleysrestaurant.co.uk; loxleysrestaurantandwinebar; Mon-Sat 11 pm, Sun 10.30 pm; Cash & all usual cards.

THE OPPOSITION 3|3|2

13 SHEEP STREET CV37 6EF
01789 269980

"In a rather overcrowded but mediocre local food-scene", this "always dependable" bistro, near the RSC, stands out: "not quite as frantic as the others nearby" and praised in all reports for its "consistently good food" ("standard dishes but well done"). / www.theoppo.co.uk; theoppostratford; Tue-Sat 9 pm; closed Sun & Mon; No Amex; booking max 12 may apply.

ROOFTOP RESTAURANT, ROYAL SHAKESPEARE THEATRE £51 2|3|4

WATERSIDE CV37 6BB 01789 403449

"The ambience if you can get a window seat is excellent" in the top-floor restaurant of the RSC, whose rooftop position gives fine views of the river and swans below. It's not a foodie experience as such, but some regulars believe "standards have improved since their enforced Covid break". / www.rsc.org.uk/eat; thersc; Mon-Fri 9.30 pm; closed Sat & Sun; No Amex; booking is online only.

SALT £125 5|4|3

8 CHURCH ST CV37 6HB 01789 263566

"A treasure" – Paul Foster's "phenomenal, truly inspiring food", served in the "cosy rustic setting" of a timbered building in Shakespeare's hometown, "goes from strength to strength". The "whole team is engaging, knowledgeable and friendly", and it's "definitely the place to go for wine buffs – we tried several wines we'd never heard of and food pairings we thought we wouldn't like but were delighted with". / www.salt-restaurant.co.uk; salt_dining; Wed-Sat 8.30 pm; closed Mon & Tue & Sun; No Amex.

The Woodsman, Hotel Indigo, Stratford upon Avon

THE WOODSMAN, HOTEL INDIGO £77 3|3|3

CHAPEL STREET CV37 6HA
01789 331535

Expert game chef Mike Robinson's collaboration with the Indigo boutique hotel brand, in a timber-beamed dining room from the Shakespearean era, has made "a great addition to Stratford" over its first three years of operation. There's an "unpretentious" menu of tasty sustainable wild meat, and "if you sit around the small chefs' counter it gets a little warm from the wood-fired oven, but is a great spot from which to chat with the chefs". / www.thewoodsmanrestaurant.com; thewoodsmanrestaurant; Wed-Sun 9.30 pm; closed Mon & Tue.

COUL HOUSE HOTEL 4|4|4

CONTIN MAINS COTTAGES IV14 9ES
01997 421 487

This "beautiful hotel with gorgeous grounds", a 200-year-old country house in the Highlands, "family-run" for the past two decades, is a really "fabulous place to stay and eat", with "amazing food" served with a pleasing level of formality. The "delicious, inventive food is made from the best local ingredients", while "service is attentive but discreet". / www.coulhousehotel.com/delicious-dining; coul_house_hotel; Wed-Sat 11 pm, Sun 6 pm.

PIG ON THE BEACH £66 2|3|4

MANOR HOUSE, MANOR ROAD
BH19 3AU 01929 450 288

A "lovely setting" with views across Studland Bay and accommodation ranging from cute attic rooms to shepherds' huts and converted dovecotes are the big attractions at this branch of the shabby-chic Pig hotel group. "Food can be a bit hit or miss", although they mean well with a 25-mile limit for produce – "and braying London visitors can sometimes dominate the experience". / www.thepighotel.com/on-the-beach; the_pig_hotels; Mon-Sun 9.30 pm; Cash & all usual cards.

SHELL BAY £69 3|3|4

FERRY ROAD BH19 3BA 01929 450363

"Fresh, fresh fish", "roasted in their wood oven" is the straightforward but irresistible offer at this "perfect seafood restaurant right on Poole Harbour", with views from every table across to Brownsea Island. "What's not to like? There were no negatives". / www.shellbay.net; shellbayrestaurant; Mon-Sun 11 pm; Cash & all usual cards.

THE SECRET GARDEN CAFÉ & RESTAURANT £49 3|3|3

BUZZARDS HALL, 17 FRIARS STREET,
CO10 2AA 01787 372030

"A joy to eat in, whether for lunch or dinner" – this Gallic institution in a timber-framed old Sudbury property has been run for almost 20 years by Stéphane Chapotot and chef Alain Jacq, who took it over from the former's uncle. In fact you can eat here even earlier, since the café that used to be separate was combined into the same site to economise during the pandemic. "Although not strictly vegetarian or vegan, the Secret Garden always has absolutely delicious vegetarian choices". / www.tsg.uk.net; thesecretgardensudbury; Mon-Thu 5 pm, Fri & Sat 9.30 pm; closed Mon-Thu D, closed Sun; Cash & all usual cards.

RABY HUNT £277 4|3|2

DL2 3UD 01325 374 237

"An absolute 'tour de force'" – all reports acclaim James Close's luxurious and supremely accomplished cuisine at this converted Grade-II-listed old pub (with rooms), remotely located in the wilds of County Durham, and holder of two of the Tyre Men's gongs. Other aspects of the experience are a little more divisive. A minimalist interior that is, for fans, "all the things one would wish for: spacious, sophisticated, calming…" is to its critics "a little cold". And then there's the final bill, which can seem plain "exorbitant" and contributes to an overall impression that can appear "overcomplicated and too self conscious". The strongest overall sentiment, though? "Wow, wow and wow is all I can say!". / www.rabyhuntrestaurant.co.uk; rabyhunt; Fri & Sat, Wed & Thu 8 pm; closed Wed & Thu L, closed Mon & Tue & Sun; Cash & all usual cards; children: 12.

INDIAN ZEST   £45   443

21 THAMES STREET   TW16 5QF
01932 765 000

"A true gem in our neighbourhood" – Manoj Vaskaikar's colonial-style villa remains one of the top destinations in the outer 'burbs and is located in an attractive part of Sunbury. All reports applaud its "very good food". / www.indianzest.co.uk; indianzest; Mon-Sun 11 pm; Cash & all usual cards; No trainers; children: 6.

THE FRENCH TABLE   £78   543

85 MAPLE RD   KT6 4AW   020 8399 2365

"Consistently outstanding" – Eric & Sarah Guignard's "cosy" backstreet gem has provided Surbiton's contribution to London gastronomy for over two decades now. Their "professional and amiable" team deliver "confident", "high-end" Gallic cuisine in a low-key but "delightfully decorated" space. In the words of a diner, who crossed town (from Watford!): "worth the very long, 3-hour drive for us… great crispy pig's head and ham hock: excellent lamb assiette and the broccoli in a chickpea batter with pistou dressing was outstanding as part of a first-class culinary experience!". / www.thefrenchtable.co.uk; the_french_table_surrey; Thu-Sat 9.30 pm; closed Mon-Wed & Sun; Cash & all usual cards.

THE FRENCH TARTE   £10   343

83 MAPLE ROAD   KT6 4AW
020 8399 1123

This "lovely local friendly coffee shop" with a French accent and pastries is a spin-off from Eric and Sarah Guignard's French Table next door, and does a particularly good Gallic take on the English afternoon tea. / www.thefrenchtarte.co.uk; the_french_tarte_surbiton; Tue-Sun 4 pm; closed Tue-Sun D, closed Mon; no bookings.

NO 97   £56   444

97 MAPLE ROAD   KT6 4AW
020 3411 9797

Sam & Alex Berry's "small neighbourhood restaurant" is a real winner. It's a chic and vibey place that's "always a really special experience – I can't believe this is a suburban restaurant!" – and the "consistent" and imaginative cooking comes at "reasonable prices". The Berrys also run the Bone Idyll micro-distillery, pizzeria Cento Uno in Surbiton and One One Four restaurant in Teddington. / no-97.co.uk; numberninetyseven; Tue, Wed 9.30 pm, Thu-Sat 12.30 am, Sun 4 pm; closed Tue, Wed L closed Sun D, closed Mon; Cash & all usual cards.

THE BOXING HARE   £69   334

BANBURY ROAD   OX7 4AP   01608 683212

"Excellent pub food, ambience and service" are on offer at this elevated Cotswolds village boozer (fka The Mason's Arms) from the experienced team of owner Antony Griffith Harris and chef Nick Anderson, who first worked together 35 years ago. It's a handy watering and feeding hole for the Chipping Norton set, and for escapees from Soho Farmhouse, a couple of miles away. / theboxinghare.co.uk; hare_2017; Wed-Sat 9 pm, Sun 3.30 pm; closed Sun D, closed Mon & Tue.

THE ASTOR GRILL   333

CLIVEDON ROAD   SL6 0JF
01628 607 107

"A walk around the Cliveden estate afterwards is a bonus" if you visit this luxe brasserie in the stables of this famous Thames-side mansion, which is the property's 'affordable' option. "Nice seating in booths is very private" and regulars say it's "better out of doors in the summer". Its cooking is rated as "good, if not a bit expensive". / www.clivedenhouse.co.uk; clivedenhouse; Mon-Sun 10 pm; Cash & all usual cards.

THE DINING ROOM AT CLIVEDEN, CLIVEDEN HOUSE   £97   225

CLIVEDEN RD   SL6 0JF   01628 668561

The "spectacular drive up to the property" is all part of the experience at this majestic ancestral pile of the Astor family (host, in its day, to the events behind the Profumo scandal; where Meghan stayed before marrying Prince Harry; and nowadays owned by the National Trust). The dining room occupies a "gorgeous hall" primely located within the property and with "great views". As you might expect, a visit is an experience as much as it is a gourmet spectacular, and although cooking from chef Chris Hannon (replacing Paul O'Neill in October 2021) is generally well-received, feedback follows the up-and-down pattern established over many years here. A typical example: "lovely room, pretty good food actually but it isn't a restaurant that wows. Some dishes were very good but it was a case of hit-and-miss, especially for the high price, and service was good but not outstanding". Top Tip – "perfect afternoon tea for special occasions". / www.clivedenhouse.co.uk; clivedenhouse; Mon-Sun 10 pm; closed Mon-Sat L; Cash & all usual cards; No trainers.

ROUX AT SKINDLES   £83   444

TAPLOW RIVERSIDE, MILL LANE
SL6 0AF   01628 951100

"Roux family favourites in a superb setting by river – and at reasonable prices": no, we're not talking about the exalted Waterside Inn, but its casual spin-off a couple of miles along the Thames, created by Alain and his late father Michel Roux senior in 2017, on the site of a famous old hotel, recreating a neighbourhood family brasserie in France. The result is "very impressive" – and relatively speaking wallet-friendly. / www.rouxatskindles.co.uk; rouxatskindles; Tue-Sat 11.30 pm, Sun 5 pm; closed Sun D, closed Mon.

AUGUSTUS   £62   443

3 THE COURTYARD, ST JAMES ST
TA1 1JR   01823 324 354

"A local 'go-to' restaurant" where co-owner Richard Guest is at the stoves, and where "there are always some surprise choices on the excellent modern European/French menu". Co-owner Cedric Chirrosel runs the front of house, with dining in the courtyard in warmer months. / augustustaunton.co.uk; Tue-Sat 9.30 pm; closed Sun & Mon; No Amex.

BRAZZ, CASTLE HOTEL, CASTLE HOTEL   £39   342

CASTLE BOW   TA1 1NF   01823 252000

"Well-cooked and well-presented food" is served in this 70-cover brasserie at the Castle Hotel, a well-known and picturesque-looking local institution (complete with crenellations) run by three generations of the Chapman family for 72 years, although the modern decor of Brazz itself means those searching for period style should look elsewhere. "Service is charming and very helpful" and the overall package is "good value too". In April 2022, towards the end of our annual diners' poll, Andrew Swann took over the stoves here. One of his early innovations has been the introduction of an eye-catching £15 lunch deal. / www.brazz.co.uk; brazztaunton; Sun & Mon & Tue-Thu 9 pm, Fri & Sat 9.30 pm; closed Sun & Mon L; Cash & all usual cards.

THE CASTLE BOW RESTAURANT

CASTLE BOW   TA1 1NF   01823 328328

With its Art Deco-style interior, this local landmark's traditional dining room provides a heartily traditional environment. It has yet to reopen for lunch and dinner post-pandemic, but is currently dedicated to the service of afternoon tea, for which – on limited feedback – it comes recommended. / www.the-castle-hotel.com/castle-bow; Wed-Sat 6 pm; closed Wed-Sat L, closed Mon & Tue & Sun; Cash & all usual cards; children: 5.

CORNISH ARMS   £71   222

15 WEST STREET   PL19 8AN
01822 612145

Chef-patron John Hooker and his wife Emma celebrate their 10th anniversary this year at this old coaching inn on the road to Cornwall (hence the name). Marks are down this year, with a couple of disappointing reports. Perhaps it's just a blip because there is still plenty of enthusiasm for "John's delightful, unfussy cooking", which fans say "stays just on the right side of good value". / www.thecornisharmstavistock.co.uk; the_cornish_arms_tavistock; Mon-Thu 11 pm, Fri & Sat midnight, Sun 10.30 pm; No Amex.

CRAB SHACK   £63   2 2 3

3 QUEEN ST   TQ14 8BY   01626 777956

"Seafood platters on the back beach" are the big draw to this popular shack. All feedback this year was fundamentally positive, but sometimes with a catch. For example: "can't help feeling the magic has slipped a bit and prices seem to have gone up". But "the owners try hard, and it's still worth a visit when you're in the area, especially on a sunny afternoon". / www.crabshackonthebeach.co.uk; thecrabshackteignmouth; Mon-Sun 9 pm; No Amex.

ERIC'S FISH & CHIPS   £34   3 3 3

DROVE ORCHARD, THORNHAM RD PE36 6LS   01485 472 025

This "quintessential fish 'n' chip experience" – set in a working apple orchard with farm shop – was opened by Eric Snaith of nearby family-owned Titchwell Manor hotel in 2015, and has since been followed by branches in Holt and St Ives as well as a pizza yurt. The standard chippie offerings are all "excellent", but "it's well worth trying some of the more non-traditional options", such as crispy cod in chilli salt with black garlic mayo or spinach and halloumi arancini. / www.ericsfishandchips.com; ericsfandc; Mon-Sun 8.30 pm; Cash & all usual cards; no bookings.

LAWNS GRILL, THORNTON HALL HOTEL & SPA   3 4 3

NESTON RD   CH63 1JF   0151 336 3938

A lot of water has passed under the bridge since 2019 when Boris Johnson and former Irish Taoiseach, Leo Varadkar, met for crunch post-Brexit talks at this posh hotel & spa out on the Wirral. On limited feedback, ratings for its grill are good all-round, but more plaudits go to the rather dramatically named 'Great Wirral Afternoon Tea' – a "well thought-out offering with good choice of sweet or savoury options" that's "particularly nice on the terrace or lawn". / www.thorntonhallhotel.com; lawnsgrill; Mon-Sun 9.30 pm; Cash & all usual cards; No trainers.

THE RED FOX   £55   3 3 3

LIVERPOOL ROAD   CH64 7TL 0151 353 2920

This "crowd-pleasing gastropub" on the Wirral still luxuriates in the lawns and flower borders of the country club it once was – and its "lovely staff" ensure a "buzzy atmosphere" that make it "ideal for family groups, with something for everyone". The large Victorian

property is now part of the Brunning & Price group, and is "very good at what it does". / www.brunningandprice.co.uk/redfox; redfoxwirral; Sun-Thu 8.30 pm, Fri & Sat 9.30 pm; Cash & all usual cards.

BAKERS ARMS   £43   3 3 3

MAIN ST   LE16 7TS   01858 545201

Kate & Tim Hubbard have owned and run this "traditional thatched pub" for 21 years, ensuring it is "perfect for a cosy night out" – with "high-quality food" from chef Emilie Bull, an "amazing wine list" overseen by Tim, "friendly staff and a great ambience". / www.thebakersarms.co.uk; Wed-Sat 9 pm, Sun 2.30 pm; closed Wed-Fri L closed Sun D, closed Mon & Tue; No Amex; children: 12+.

THE DOLPHIN INN   £34   3 3 3

PEACE PLACE   IP16 4NA   01728 454994

This "jolly venue in a characterful seaside town" serves "excellent pub food, using top-quality ingredients and no silly gimmicks". There's something for everyone, ranging from a 'steak deal' to 'vegan night' and – given that it also functions as a B&B – breakfast is also catered for. / www.thorpenessdolphin.com; the_dolphin_thorpeness; Mon-Sat 10 pm, Sun 9 pm.

THE HORSE GUARDS INN   £78   4 4 4

UPPERTON RD   GU28 9AF   01798 342 332

"A proper gastropub in a bucolic setting" – this "cosy" tavern on the edge of the Petworth estates sits in a quintessential village setting (complete with neighbouring post office, red phone box, and little lane to the church) and a meal often starts with a drink in the "lovely, large garden". One of the most commented-on West Sussex destinations, it provides "a modern and eclectic menu" – "not the normal selection you see in most pubs" – which results in "really delicious food made with top-quality seasonal ingredients". (For example "hoglet stew in red wine sauce with feta cheese or superb salmon, cod and seafood with chorizo".) All this plus "great beers" and a thoughtful wine selection. / www.thehorseguardsinn.co.uk; horseguardsinn; Wed-Sat 9 pm, Sun 4 pm; closed Sun D, closed Mon & Tue; No Amex.

STAGG INN   £62   3 3 4

HR5 3RL   01544 230221

"Consistently good unpretentious food" has long been the hallmark of this country inn on an old drivers' route. Steve & Nicola Reynolds retired last year after more than two decades and it's now "settling down under the new ownership" of London-born hospitality veteran Muralidhar Shanmugam, known as 'Shan' – and "the food is still first class". Top Menu

Tip – "unbeatable bread and butter pudding". / www.thestagg.co.uk; the-stagg-inn; Wed-Sat 9.30 pm, Sun 4.30 pm; closed Sun D, closed Mon & Tue; Cash & all usual cards; credit card deposit required to book.

THE SLANTED DOOR   £55   3 3 3

43 SAINT MARY'S STREET   PE9 2DS 01780 757773

"A welcome new addition to Stamford, with a well-known local chef at the helm" in Dameon Clarke, formerly of the Wicked Witch in Rywell – this modern bar and restaurant in a sixteenth-century building was a 2020 opening from brothers Oliver & Joseph Regis. The "cosy" upstairs dining room has achieved solid ratings across the board in its first full year. The downstairs bar has a balcony overlooking Stamford Meadows. / www.theslanteddoor.co.uk; theslanteddoorstamford; Tue-Sat 9 pm, Sun 3.30 pm; closed Sun D, closed Mon.

THE POACHER   £61   3 3 3

HARTLAKE RD   TN11 0PH   01732 358934

This cavernous venue from the regional Elite Pubs group wins consistently solid ratings for its well-executed gastropub menu. Tudeley village's main attraction is All Saints' Church, where all 12 windows were designed by the artist Marc Chagall to commemorate local girl Sarah D'Avigdor-Goldsmid, who drowned in a sailing accident in 1963. / elitepubs.com/the-poacher-and-partridge-home; elite_pubs; Mon-Sat 11.30 pm, Sun 10.30 pm.

THE MOLE INN   £62   3 3 3

OX44 9NG   01865 340001

This "charming pub with delicious, imaginative food and a welcoming atmosphere" is "tucked away down a narrow road" in a village close to Oxford. "Fantastic garden" for dining in the summer. / www.themoleinn.com; moleinn; Mon-Thu 8.45 pm, Fri & Sat 9.15 pm, Sun 4.30 pm; closed Sun D; Cash & all usual cards.

THE GALLEY   £51   4 4 4

41 FORE ST, TOPSHAM   EX3 0HU 01392 876078

This well-known seafood spot was closed for several months last year but reopened in the autumn under new head chef James Checkley, who received a classical training under Michael Caines. He has quite a rep to live up to and so far he seems to be succeeding: fans hail "the best fish restaurant in an area where there are lots of good ones". / www.galleyrestaurant.co.uk; galleytopsham; Tue-Sat 9 pm; closed Sun & Mon; Cash & all usual cards; children: 12+.

Ugly Butterfly, St Ives

THE SALUTATION INN £73 343

68 FORE STREET   EX3 0HL
01392 873060

"An excellent, good value, buzzy and atmospheric choice in this patchy region" – this old coaching inn near the River Exe has "a dedicated glazed restaurant atrium so it doesn't look or feel like a pub". A wide variety of menus caters well to just about any eventuality. / www.salutationtopsham.co.uk; salutationinn; Wed-Sat, Tue 8 pm; closed Tue L, closed Sun & Mon; Cash & all usual cards.

ELEPHANT RESTAURANT & BRASSERIE £80 442

3-4 BEACON TER, HARBOURSIDE
TQ1 2BH   01803 200044

"Stunning food with excellent service" have earned plaudits for high-profile chef Simon Hulstone's "faultless" flagship, which he opened 20 years ago – in the town where he grew up, as the son of a chef. He now has a 100-acre farm in Brixham, to guarantee supplies of his favourite produce. / www.elephantrestaurant.co.uk; hulstone; Tue-Sat 9 pm; closed Sun & Mon; Cash & all usual cards; children: 14+ at bar.

NO 7 FISH BISTRO & WINE BAR £53 433

7 BEACON TERRACE   TQ1 2BH
01803 295055

The "best fish", landed across the harbour at Brixham, is what the Stacey family fixture, now 30 years old, is all about. Upstairs there's an evening wine (and oyster) bar with panoramic views, and both venues provide ever-changing blackboard menus. / www.no7-fish.com; No7fishbistro; closed Mon-Sat & Sun; Cash & all usual cards.

THE GURNARD'S HEAD £60 334

TR26 3DE   01736 796928

This "interesting old pub" is a well-known destination and offers a "warm welcome on a lonely part of the Cornish coast" – "you couldn't miss it even on a misty day, due to the bright mustard-yellow exterior". Inside, there's "excellent food and faultless service", with a "reasonably priced wine list" – "long may it continue". / www.gurnardshead.co.uk; gurnardshead; Mon-Sun 11 pm; Cash & all usual cards.

CROCKER'S TABLE £54 443

74 HIGH STREET   HP23 4AF
01442 828971

"Fabulous food" (including "outstanding vegetarian options") brings people together at chef Scott Barnard's sociable chef's table.

"Think of sitting round a table with your friends cooking in front of you, chatting and explaining what they're doing. When you've finished your 6 or 12 courses, you will have spoken to most of the guests at the same sitting as you (15 maximum)". There's a separate cellar bar and dining room. The spin-off restaurant-with-rooms in Henley opened just as we went to press. / www.tring.crockersuk.com; crockers_tring; Tue-Sat 11 pm; closed Tue L, closed Sun & Mon; Cash & all usual cards; credit card deposit required to book; children: 12.

BOWLEY'S AT THE PLOUGH £44 332

6 TAYLORS LANE   ME19 5DR
01732 822233

"It's going places!", according to fans of this village pub – originally two weather-boarded farm cottages from 1483 – which was saved from development six years ago when 120 villagers raised £450,000 to secure its future under community ownership. The Yates family now runs its 26-cover restaurant; David Yates is a wine merchant who worked in a senior role for Balls Brothers in London. But while fans trumpet "sensational" dishes from chef David's son, Alex (ex-Goring Hotel, London) and his young kitchen team, other reports are more nuanced: "has potential and I want it to succeed as a community venture but they really need to get some input if they aspire to convert the recent Michelin listing to a star, as they do". / www.theploughkent.com; bowleys_restaurant; Tue-Sat 10.30 pm, Sun 6 pm; closed Sun D, closed Mon.

HIDDEN HUT £20 425

PORTSCATHO BEACH   TR2 5EW

This "fabulous gem of a place" operates out of a shed reached via a footpath on the Roseland Peninsula, and offers an "amazing amount of yum" in the form of no-booking takeaway picnic lunches or ticketed evening feasts on selected summer evenings – the "long queues offset by the exceptional ambience of a beach to eat on". "You can't fault it – maybe the clientele of holidaying Londoners, desperate to Instagram that they've made it here, makes it less than great… but I can hardly complain when I'm one of them!". / www.hiddenhut.co.uk; hiddenhut; Mon-Sun 4 pm; closed Mon-Sun D; Cash only; no bookings.

PENROSE KITCHEN £70 444

PENROSE WATER GARDEN,
TREGAVETHAN, TR4 9ES   01872 225697

This "hidden gem just outside Truro" from husband-and-wife team Ben & Sam Harmer features "impressive" cooking, "exceptional service" and a "splendid outdoor eating area" for warmer weather. Ben's classical training took in the kitchens of The Savoy and Le Gavroche – hence "the soufflé is impressive". / www.penrosekitchen.co.uk; kitchenpenrose; Wed-Sat 9 pm, Sun 5 pm; closed Sun D, closed Mon & Tue; No Amex.

TUDDENHAM MILL, TUDDENHAM MILL HOTEL £74 333

HIGH ST   IP28 6SQ   01638 713 552

This "lovely renovated" watermill, in "pleasant grounds with a mill pond", makes a great setting for chef-patron Lee Bye's cooking, which is showcased in "two different restaurants" – the more formal "upstairs room, which is great for dinner", and the "Tipi on the Stream, a fantastic casual outdoor eatery" which wows all comers with its cocktails and seafood. Either way, "service is personal, friendly and attentive" and the food "excellent and reasonably priced". / www.tuddenhammill.co.uk; tuddenhammill; Mon-Sun 6.30 pm; Cash & all usual cards.

THE BEACON KITCHEN £90 334

TEA GARDEN LANE   TN3 9JH
01892 524252

"The food is always great, the room is lovely and the view unbeatable" at this "good brasserie-style restaurant" offering "great service and a cool vibe" in an Arts & Crafts house overlooking Happy Valley and popular as a wedding venue from the 'I'll Be Mother' group. / www.the-beacon.co.uk; thebeacon_tw; Mon-Wed 5 pm, Thu-Sat 10 pm, Sun 7 pm; closed Mon-Wed D; Cash & all usual cards.

THE BICYCLE BAKERY £7 422

118-120 CAMDEN ROAD   TN1 2QZ
01892 541541

"Absolutely delicious coffee and pastries" – all made in-house – are on offer at this "bakery with a couple of tables" – "and you can leave with a perfect sourdough loaf". Founder Jamie Tandoh was the first independent sourdough baker in Tunbridge Wells when he opened in 2014. Top Tip – "the best croissants". / www.bicycle-bakery.com; the_bicycle_bakery; Tue-Sat 4 pm; closed Tue-Sat D, closed Sun & Mon; payment – credit card only.

THE IVY ROYAL TUNBRIDGE WELLS £77 234

46-50 HIGH STREET   TN1 1XF
01892 240 700

A "family favourite" for its "lovely atmosphere and brasserie food" – and handily close to Tunbridge Wells station – this spin-off from the ever-expanding Ivy operation is well regarded by most reporters, but also suffers from the complaints commonly levelled against its Identikit siblings: most especially indifferent cooking that's "poor value for money". / www.theivytunbridgewells.com; theivytunbridgewells; Mon-Sun 12.30 am.

SANKEY'S THE OLD FISHMARKET £87 333

**19 THE UPPER PANTILES TN2 5TN
01892511422**

This smart oyster bar in the heart of the historic Pantiles serves up a wide range of British seafood, including crawfish – 'a native species of crustacean almost exclusively exported to mainland Europe until very recently'. "Loved the fact we could build our own seafood platter" and "enjoyed sitting at the kitchen bar and interacting with the chefs". Drinks include fizz from the Squerryes vineyard in nearby Westerham. / www.sankeys.co.uk; sankeysrtw; Tue-Sat midnight; closed Sun & Mon; Cash & all usual cards.

THE SQUARE PEG £91

**46 CAMDEN ROAD TN1 2QD
01892 514819**

This tiny Tunbridge Wells restaurant has just 5 tables, serving 12-14 covers, and offers a six-course menu. The work of a self-taught chef, Rob Marshall, it has yet to generate feedback in our annual diners' poll, but looks worth a go. / www.thesquarepegtw.co.uk; thesquarepegtw; Thu-Sat 11 pm; closed Thu-Sat L, closed Mon-Wed & Sun; children: 14*.

THACKERAY'S £93 344

85 LONDON RD TN1 1EA 01892 511921

The "beautifully cooked and presented" meals from chef Patrick Hill are a good match for their smart setting in this Regency villa, named after the Victorian novelist who once called it home. A "good wine list at reasonable prices" and "excellent service" complete the offer, ensuring a "lovely time" for all who eat here. / www.thackerays-restaurant.co.uk; thackeraysrestaurant; Wed-Sat 10.30 pm, Sun 3 pm; closed Sun D, closed Mon & Tue; Cash & all usual cards.

ONE ONE FOUR £57 333

**114-116 HIGH STREET TW11 9BB
020 3745 8114**

Sam & Alex Berry's "great local" "never fails to deliver", and provides a "very interesting take on classics". There's a very slick 15-seat bar counter which is equally suitable for taking cocktails, a snack or a full meal. The couple also own nearby Cento Uno, No 97 and gin bar/distillery The Good Life. / oneonefour.co.uk; numberoneonefour; Tue-Sat 9.30 pm, Sun 4 pm; closed Tue, Wed L closed Sun D, closed Mon.

TSARETTA SPICE 423

55 CHURCH STREET TW1 3NR

"Excellent and innovative tapas-style Indian food" from former Tamarind and Dishoom chef Yousuf Mohammed is served in a "nice location on popular, cobbled Church Street with a pleasant outdoor dining courtyard for the warmer months" (and specials laid on for big rugby days at nearby Twickers stadium).

One bugbear this year though – a couple of incidents of "diabolical service" (in terms of speed or misplaced dishes). / tsarettaspice.com; tsarettaspice; Tue-Sat 11 pm, Sun 9 pm; closed Mon.

UMI £43 542

**30 YORK STREET TW1 3LJ
020 8892 2976**

A "Twickenham institution", this "small and very basic" Japanese canteen "is an absolute gem, with food to rival the top London restaurants" and "unassuming, hard-working owners and staff". The "incredible service" is led by "the constantly friendly Bobby on front of house", while "the menu is unchanging but consistently delivers good-quality sushi and Japanese dishes". / umiedinburgh.com; closed Mon-Sat & Sun.

RILEY'S FISH SHACK £39 545

**KING EDWARD'S BAY NE30 4BY
0191 257 1371**

"Just unique. Love it, love it, love it!". "On a glorious sunny day this converted shipping container on Tynemouth Beach is the best eating option anywhere on the NE coast", say fans, and it has become the north east's most commented-on destination in our annual national diners' poll. "Sitting with your toes in the sand in a deckchair on the beach with a parasol, with a picture postcard day of blue sky, sun and warm breeze, while eating small mountains of delicious seafood that's just been cooked in 'the shack' is bliss." And "this is not your standard fish on the beach: they play with flavours and make sure the fish is super fresh". As an experience, it's "weather dependent unfortunately (freezing North Sea winds can spoil the ambience) but they do all they can to mitigate this with what is within their control – the food is outstanding". "One of the highlights of the year." / www.rileysfishshack.com; rileysfishshack; Mon-Sun 10 pm; Cash & all usual cards; no bookings.

RILEY'S FISH SHOP £55 543

3-5 PERCY PARK ROAD NE30 4LZ

This 2021 opening is "a brilliant restaurant innovation in Tynemouth village to add to Adam Riley's successful (and widely acclaimed) beach Fish Shack" – because "for all the hoo ha, who wants to sit on a beach with the wind whipping in from the North Sea? Better be tucked up inside, where you can have an excellent selection of small plates, often using parts of the fish (e.g. cod jaw) that are otherwise discarded". "Dishes range from simple small plates made to order at the ground floor wet fish counter, to an outstanding 5-course themed meal in the first-floor dining room, allowing chef to showcase his creative skills using the latest catch." / rileysfishshop.com; rileysfishshop; Thu-Sat midnight, Sun-Wed 11 pm.

TYTHERLEIGH ARMS £63 433

EX13 7BE 01460 220214

On the Devon-Dorset border, this popular old coaching inn (dating from the sixteenth century) is a "lovely local, providing seasonal food, cooked with care and great presentation" by chef Jack Cannell from an interesting menu; plus, there's "very professional and friendly service". / www.tytherleigharms.com; tytherleigharms; Wed & Thu 9 pm, Fri & Sat 9.30 pm, Sun 2.30 pm; closed Sun D, closed Mon & Tue; No Amex; children: 5.

SEAFOOD SHACK £47 542

**9 WEST ARGYLE STREET IV26 2TY
07596 722846**

"Outstanding!" – the name doesn't lie regarding Kirsty Scobie & Fenella Renwick's straightforward street-food style operation serving yummy crab claws, fish wraps and other simple bites from the daily catch, advertised via a blackboard menu. / seafoodshack.co.uk; theseafoodshackullapool; Mon-Sun 8 pm; Cash & all usual cards; no bookings.

NORTHCOTE MANOR £79 344

BURRINGTON EX37 9LZ 01769 560501

High ratings across the board for this "lovely old manor house" whose Georgian dining room (with contemporary murals) makes a "charming setting" for "food which never disappoints", and where you are well looked after by "enthusiastic staff who really care". / www.northcotemanor.co.uk; northcotemanor; Mon-Thu 9.30 pm, Fri & Sat 10 pm, Sun 9 pm; Cash & all usual cards; No jeans.

THE LAKE ISLE £74 334

**16 HIGH STREET EAST LE15 9PZ
01572 822951**

"An ideal neighbourhood restaurant" – this attractive fixture (with rooms), near the cute market square of this small Rutland town provides cooking that's "original without striving for effect" alongside "efficient, professional and pleasant service". "The room feels lively whilst being quiet enough for easy conversation." Top Tip – the 'dine for less' menu is terrific value". / www.lakeisle.co.uk; thelakeisle; Tue-Sun 9 pm; closed Mon; No Amex.

THE HODDINGTON ARMS 333

BIDDEN RD RG25 2RL 01256 862371

"A wonderful country experience" is reported at this rural inn ('The Hodd'), run by the Barnes family since 2015, whose concise menu aims for superior realisation of classic pub dishes. / www.hoddingtonarms.co.uk; Sun-Thu 11 pm, Fri & Sat midnight.

UPTON MAGNA, SHROPSHIRE   5–4A

THE HAUGHMOND   £53   343

SY4 4TZ   01743 709918

Self-taught chef Martin Board's "really tempting menu" of "beautifully presented dishes" wins consistent ratings at the seventeenth-century inn-with-rooms he runs with his wife Mel in a village outside Shrewsbury. / www.thehaughmond.co.uk; thehaughmond; Tue-Sat 8 pm; closed Tue, Wed L, closed Sun & Mon.

UPTON, WILTSHIRE   2–4C

THE CROWN INN   £51   333

SP11 0JS   01264 736044

"Always reliable, serving exceptional food for a village pub", say fans of Dave Watts's rural inn, where classic pub dishes jostle on the menu with somewhat more ambitious fare. Top Tip – "the plat du jour is unbelievable value!" / www.crownupton.co.uk; thecrowninnupton; Wed & Thu 9 pm, Fri & Sat 9.30 pm, Tue 8 pm, Sun 3 pm; closed Sun D, closed Mon.

USK, MONMOUTHSHIRE   2–2A

THE BLACK BEAR INN   £65   433

BETTWS NEWYDD   NP15 1JN
01873 880701

This "small, atmospheric gastropub in the back of the Welsh beyond" (closest town Usk), opened by Josh & Hannah Byrne four years ago, is "well worth seeking out for its innovative and well-priced food". A "short (three main courses) and frequently changing menu makes the best of local produce and the chef's inspiration", delivering "incredible flavours in deceptively simple dishes". / www.theblackbearinn.co.uk; theblackbearusk; Wed-Sat 10 pm, Sun 4 pm; closed Wed & Thu L closed Sun D, closed Mon & Tue.

VENTNOR, ISLE OF WIGHT   2–4D

DRUNKEN LOBSTER   343

2 PIER STREET   PO38 1ST   01983 852500

This "pleasurable small town-centre bar/ bistro" serves a "short but exceptional Asian-inspired menu" that "would put many well-known central London restaurants to shame". "The staff were welcoming and extremely knowledgeable about the food." / www.drunkenlobster.co.uk; drunkenlobsterbar; Thu-Sat midnight, Sun 8 pm; closed Thu & Fri L, closed Mon & Tue & Wed.

SMOKING LOBSTER   332

ESPLANADE   PO38 1JT

"A great location on the seafront at Ventnor" further boosts the appeal of GC Giancovich's "bustling" five-year-old venue, which – "in a town where the eating choices are distinctly limited – stands out for its interesting and well prepared food". On the menu, "fantastic, fresh and varied seafood" prepared in an "Asian-fusion" style, including some sushi, all washed down with cocktails. In September 2022, fire crews were called to the restaurant and it remains closed as of October 2022. / Mon & Tue, Thu-Sun 10 pm.

WADDINGTON, LANCASHIRE   5–1B

THE HIGHER BUCK   £50   333

THE SQUARE   BB7 3HZ   01200 423226

"In an area renowned for its pub food, this one stands out against more fancied opposition", say fans of this Ribble Valley hostelry. "Great food, friendly service, wonderful value. This is what pub food and hospitality is supposed to be about." / www.higherbuck.com; thehigherbuck; Mon-Thu 9 pm, Fri & Sat 9.30 pm, Sun 8 pm.

WALBERSWICK, SUFFOLK   3–1D

THE ANCHOR   £53   322

MAIN STREET   IP18 6UA   01502 722 112

This attractive Arts & Crafts pub-with-rooms and an acre of land is a "good place to stay on the Suffolk coast", with "friendly service" and "good pub grub" which puts an emphasis on local seafood and produce – including beers from champion local brewer Adnams. Mark & Sophie Dorber (formerly of the White Horse in Parsons Green, aka the Sloaney Pony) have owned and run it for 19 years. / www.anchoratwalberswick.com; Mon-Sun 20 pm; Cash & all usual cards.

WALL, NORTHUMBERLAND   8–2A

HJEM   £157   544

THE HADRIAN HOTEL   NE46 4EE
01434 681232

"Wow, just wow" – "gorgeous, delicious, astoundingly flavourful dishes" combine with "thoroughly individual service" to create "absolutely outstanding" meals at this Scandi-inspired three-year-old that "has not been resting on its laurels". Swedish chef Alex Nietosvuori and his Northumberland-born partner Ally Thompson "have created a laid-back foodie haven" tucked away inside a pub beside Hadrian's Wall – which this many fans regard as "our happy place". For some, it's "a huge trek to get there, but so worth it, what a treat!". "Shout out too to Anna (Frost), the sommelier, who has curated an unusual and largely biodynamic wine list." And for those who stay overnight, the breakfast spread in the morning simply prolongs the fun. / www.restauranthjem.co.uk; restauranthjem; Wed-Sat 11 pm; closed Wed-Sat L, closed Mon & Tue & Sun; booking is online only.

WALLINGFORD, OXFORDSHIRE   2–2D

FIVE LITTLE PIGS   £46

26 ST MARY'S STREET   OX10 0ET
01491 833999

Opened in May 2021, this high street venture has yet to inspire feedback in our annual diners' poll, but did provide the fodder for an April 2022 review from The Observer's Jay Rayner: a "well-dressed, smart little bistro", whose menu lists "interesting-sounding things" and dishes up "the best kind of nourishing, invalid food… supremely comforting even if you're not under the weather". / www.fivelittlepigs.co.uk; fivelittlepigs_wallingford; Tue-Thu 11.30 pm, Fri & Sat midnight, Sun 6 pm; closed Mon.

WANSFORD, CAMBRIDGESHIRE   6–4A

PRÉVOST AT HAYCOCK, HAYCOCK HOTEL   £65   543

HAYCOCK MANOR   PE8 6JA
01780 782223

"Worth a trip" – "Prevost has always been a destination stop in Peterborough but since its move to the Haycock it has surpassed even its own excellent offer" – so say fans of Lee Clarke's fine-dining restaurant which reopened in 2021 in the revamped Grade II-listed Haycock Manor Hotel in a cute village on the fringe of Peterborough. Perhaps "it deserves a star" – "the food is superb and interesting" and there's "a new repeated wine list". In February 2022, the FT declared the new launch "an amazing project" ("the Baron Bigod had been made into an ice cream, sandwiched between two oat crisps and dotted with gooseberry gel. I could easily have eaten four"). / haycock.co.uk/ dining; haycock_manor_wansford; Mon-Sun 8.30 pm; Cash & all usual cards.

WARWICK, WARWICKSHIRE   5–4C

LA MESA   333

5B OLD SQUARE   CV34 4RA
07528 080151

"Gerald never disappoints. No menu, just great food chosen and cooked the way he likes it and always fresh and filling". That's the surprise-menu formula at Gerald Maguire's small independent, whose menu is described on its website as follows: 'Some soup, Some Fish, Some Meat, Some Rice, Bread, Coffee… Something Sweet!' / www.lamesawarwick.co.uk; Mesa.la; Wed-Sat 9 pm; closed Wed-Sat L, closed Mon & Tue & Sun.

WASS, NORTH YORKSHIRE   5–1D

THE STAPYLTON ARMS   £56   343

YO61 4BE   01347 868280

"Good-value, flavoursome dishes made from excellent ingredients" constitute the menu selection of quality, traditional pub classics at Rob & Gill Thompson's well-rated whitewashed inn. / www.stapyltonarms.co.uk; Mon-Sun 9 pm.

WATERGATE BAY, CORNWALL   1–3B

EMILY SCOTT AT WATERGATE BAY   £65   324

TR8 4AA   01637 860543

With its "simple, top-quality seafood" combined with "one of the most romantic locations in Cornwall" – "who could fail to be impressed on a date at Emily Scott's new restaurant overlooking stunning Watergate Bay?". One of four restaurants in the Watergate Bay Hotel, it followed a 2020 beachside pop-up from the Cornwall-based chef whose profile has been on the rise. On the downside, there are those who feel the experience is "lovely, but overpriced". / www.emilyscottfood.com/reservations; emilyscottfood; Wed-Sat 9.30 pm; closed Mon & Tue & Sun.

WELLAND, WORCESTERSHIRE   2–1B

THE INN AT WELLAND   £63   4 3 3

**HOOK BANK, DRAKE STREET   WR13 6LN
01684 592317**

Terraced gardens and a glazed verandah help capitalise on the fine views of the Malvern Hills from this highly popular gastropub: "a class Worcestershire act" and the most commented-on venue in the county in our annual diners' poll. All reports say "you can't fault it" – "always great food" and "the team is very efficient" / www.theinnatwelland.co.uk; theinnatwelland; Wed-Sat 8.30 pm, Sun 3 pm; closed Sun D, closed Mon & Tue.

WELLS NEXT THE SEA, NORFOLK   6–3C

WELLS CRAB HOUSE   £59   3 4 3

**38 FREEMAN ST   NR23 1BA
013 2871 0456**

"A wide range of freshly caught fish, inventive dishes and their very own gin" underpin enthusiasm for this "bustling restaurant". Owners Kelly and Scott Dougal "never rest on their laurels and have constantly sought to improve their menus and service" over the past six years. The only problem is booking a table – we live 500 yards away and need to book months in advance". Top Menu Tip – "the crab platter with cockles, prawns, crayfish, smoked salmon and potato salad". / wellscrabhouse.co.uk; wellscrab; Tue-Sat 8.30 pm, Sun 3 pm; closed Sun D, closed Mon.

WELLS, SOMERSET   2–3B

GOODFELLOWS   £63   4 3 3

**5 - 5 B SADLER STREET   BA5 2RR
01749 673866**

Adam & Martin Fellows's "homely", "small bistro" continues to inspire nothing but good vibes. "Very friendly and competent staff" deliver "good quality", "expertly prepared" French food in "copious portions". In 2024 it will hit its twentieth anniversary. / www.goodfellowswells.co.uk; Wed, Fri & Sat 11 pm, Sun 3 pm; closed Sun D, closed Mon & Tue & Thu; Cash & all usual cards.

WELWYN, HERTFORDSHIRE   3–2B

AUBERGE DU LAC, BROCKET HALL   £96

AL8 7XG   01707 368888

By the lake of the Brocket Hall estate, this former hunting lodge achieved fame in the early noughties but hasn't since fully capitalised on its characterful style and beautiful location. Originally set to reopen after a major refurb in April 2022, it will now be 2023 before it is officially relaunched, although new chef John Barber will be organising pop-up events from October 2022 as an opportunity to try out some of his new dishes and entice diners to return once the Auberge re-opens. / www.brocket-hall.co.uk; brockethall; Wed-Sat 9.30 pm, Sun 3 pm; closed Sun D, closed Mon & Tue; Cash & all usual cards; No jeans; children: 12+.

WEST BAY, DORSET   2–4B

THE STATION KITCHEN   £43   2 2 4

OLD WEST BAY RAILWAY STATION, STATION ROAD   DT6 4EW   01308 422845

Two vintage railway carriages near the sea and harbour in the former West Bay station constitute this "delightful" venue. The cooking is sometimes seen as the weakest link ("they try hard, without really hitting the spot"), but most reports are upbeat, citing "above average food" in an "unusual and quirky setting". Since our annual diners' poll concluded, change is afoot with a new arrangement introduced in autumn 2022, which sees fine dining from chef Chris Chatfield's seasonal menu in the newer 'Beeching' carriage, and relaxed dining in 'Brunel', from the First World War, with both menus available in the dog-friendly 'Station House'. / www.thestationkitchen.co.uk; thestationkitchen; Thu-Sat, Wed midnight; closed Wed L, closed Mon & Tue & Sun.

WEST CLANDON, SURREY   3–3A

THE ONSLOW ARMS   £63   3 3 3

THE STREET   GU4 7TE   01483 222447

This "reliable and well-run pub-restaurant in a charming part of Surrey is a great place to meet friends, chat, relax and eat good classics". "There's also a good selection of local beers", "a lovely garden", and "friendly and efficient service". / onslowarmsclandon.co.uk; onslowarmsclandon; Mon-Sat 11 pm, Sun 10.30 pm; Cash & all usual cards; children: 18+ after 7.30pm.

WEST HATCH, WILTSHIRE   2–3C

PYTHOUSE KITCHEN GARDEN   £62   3 3 4

SP3 6PA   01747 870444

This "gorgeous gem of a place, set in beautiful Wiltshire countryside", serves "superb and creative vegetable dishes made from home-grown produce" by chef Darren Brown in the eighteenth-century walled garden of a property at lunch or (more occasionally) at communal 'long-table' suppers. Fans say it's a "must-visit if you are in the area" (it also hosts weddings and glamping). / www.pythousekitchengarden.co.uk; kitchengardenco; Wed-Sun 4.30 pm; closed Wed-Sun D, closed Mon & Tue.

WEST HOATHLY, WEST SUSSEX   3–4B

THE CAT INN   £67   3 3 3

NORTH LANE   RH19 4PP   01342 810369

This sixteenth-century inn is "a totally traditional country pub with open fires, nooks and crannies" and "a friendly owner and team", serving "decent portions of fantastic food, with no pretensions". Top Tip – "excellent Sunday lunch, with good roast potatoes". / www.catinn.co.uk; Wed & Thu, Sat, Fri 8.30 pm, Sun 5 pm; closed Sun D, closed Mon & Tue; Cash & all usual cards; children: 7.

WEST MALLING, KENT   3–3C

ST. LEONARD'S   £63   3 3 2

**47 SWAN STREET   ME19 6JU
01732 600128**

An "excellent find" – this "friendly and professional" yearling boutique hotel/restaurant serves a short menu of "delicious and well-presented food". There's good generosity of spirit here: "we were given turbot when they ran out of cod!" / www.stleonardskent.co.uk/restaurant; stleonardskent; Wed-Fri 9 pm, Sat 9.30 pm, Sun 3 pm; closed Sun D, closed Mon & Tue.

WEST MERSEA, ESSEX   3–2C

THE COMPANY SHED   £43   4 3 3

**129 COAST ROAD   CO5 8PA
01206 382700**

"Simple seafood at its best" – "straight from the sea", and sold without frills from a basic shack (so bring your own wine, bread and butter). Well known for many miles around: "it's on an island, 65 miles from London. They don't advertise as they don't need to!". Top Tip – "native oysters from September to April are extraordinary". / www.the-company-shed.com; the_company_shed; Wed-Sun 5 pm; closed Wed-Sun D, closed Mon & Tue; Cash & all usual cards; no bookings.

WEST RUNTON, NORFOLK   6–3C

ROCKY BOTTOMS   £22   4 3 3

**CROMER ROAD   NR27 9QA
07848 045607**

"Caught by dad, served by the family" – Richard & Alison Matthews serve seafood "fresh out of the sea" at their "fish restaurant located in an old brick kiln on the cliff top between East and West Runton". "He catches the fish, crabs and lobsters daily" – "simply the best offerings with excellent service and ambience". / www.rockybottoms.co.uk;

rockybottoms.uk; Sun-Thu 5 pm, Fri & Sat 8 pm; closed Sun-Thu D.

WEST WITTON, NORTH YORKSHIRE — 8–4B

THE WENSLEYDALE HEIFER — £82 · 333

MAIN ST   DL8 4LS   01969 622322

"Very good seafood" makes a somewhat surprising speciality for this gastropub/ hotel in the Yorkshire Dales – but there's "a lot else besides" ("vegetarian, meat, superb desserts") and it's "all excellent". "What a great place to dine and stay" – "welcomes kids and dogs, too, so a great holiday venue". / www.wensleydaleheifer.co.uk; thewensleydaleheiferofficial; Mon-Sun 9.15 pm; Cash & all usual cards; booking max 6 may apply.

WESTBURY-ON-SEVERN, GLOUCESTERSHIRE — 2–1B

SEVERN & WYE SMOKERY — £65 · 433

CHAXHILL   GL14 1QW   01452 760191

"Fabulous fish and seafood dishes" led by "smoked platters and whole fish of the day" are on the menu at this "small restaurant" in an "interesting setting" – above Richard & Shirley Cook's long-established smokery on the Severn estuary. "Everything is yummy – including the wonderful desserts." There's also a more conventional café in the yard, the Barn. / severnandwye.co.uk; severnandwyesmokery; Tue-Thu 4 pm, Fri & Sat 9 pm; closed Tue-Thu D, closed Sun & Mon.

WESTERHAM, KENT — 3–3B

THE OLD BANK — £86 · 433

8 MARKET SQUARE   TN16 1AW
01233 659890

"Lucky to have this place as a local!" – Adam Turley's "lovely" and descriptively named venture is complemented for its "friendly service" and his "absolutely delicious" cuisine, which can be enjoyed à la carte (two courses are £55 per person) or in an 8-course tasting menu format (for £90 per person). / www.oldbank-westerham.co.uk; theoldbankkent; Thu-Sat 11 pm, Sun 8 pm; closed Mon & Tue & Wed; Cash & all usual cards.

WESTFIELD, EAST SUSSEX — 3–4C

THE WILD MUSHROOM — £61 · 543

WOODGATE HOUSE, WESTFIELD LANE TN35 4SB   01424 751137

Paul Webbe's "well-established rural restaurant" celebrates its 25th anniversary this year, and is a "destination venue well worth travelling to" for its "wide but manageable choice of dishes and exceptionally good-value dining". Paul also has fish-focused restaurants in Hastings and Rye, but this more land-based venture was his first, and by many accounts, remains his best. / www.webbesrestaurants.co.uk; webbesrestaurants;

Wed-Fri 9 pm, Sun 2.30 pm, Sat 9.30 pm; closed Sun D, closed Mon & Tue; Cash & all usual cards.

WESTON TURVILLE, BUCKINGHAMSHIRE — 3–2A

THE CHEQUERS INN — 333

35 CHURCH LANE   HP22 5SJ
01296613298

"A lovely destination pub in the country with a high-end restaurant serving super food that's great value, making it a fantastic find!". Chef-owner Dritan and maître d' Ranka (husband and wife) took it over in 2010 and have turned it into something of a landmark locally. / www.thechequerswt.co.uk; thechequersinnwt; Wed-Sat 11 pm, Sun 5 pm; closed Sun D, closed Mon & Tue.

WEYMOUTH, DORSET — 2–4B

CATCH AT THE OLD FISH MARKET — £87 · 433

THE OLD FISH MARKET, CUSTOM HOUSE QUAY   DT4 8BE   01305 590555

This "interesting" yearling serves "fantastic seafood" in the "authentic surroundings" of the 1855 fish market, refurbished in minimalist style to host a restaurant serving fish landed directly from day boats based in the harbour. There's a heavy emphasis on sustainability, with the dishes complemented by English wines from the region. Top Tip – "wear a scarf – it's a tad chilly inside". / www.catchattheoldfishmarket.com; catchattheoldfishmarket; Fri & Sat, Tue-Thu 9.30 pm; closed Tue-Thu L, closed Sun & Mon; payment – credit card only.

CRAB HOUSE CAFE — £59 · 544

FERRYMANS WAY, PORTLAND ROAD DT4 9YU   01305 788 867

"Incredible seafood in season" is to be found at this "lovely little fish restaurant: the best place to eat in or near Weymouth". "Overlooking Chesil Beach, with a new heated marquee for cooler months, it provides a truly welcoming experience." Top Menu Tip – "fabulous lobster, perfectly cooked". / www.crabhousecafe.co.uk; thecrabhousecafe; Wed & Thu 9 pm, Fri & Sat 9.30 pm, Sun 3 pm; closed Sun D, closed Mon & Tue; No Amex; credit card deposit required to book.

AL MOLO — £53 · 444

PIER BANDSTAND, THE ESPLANADE DT4 7RN   01305 839 888

Chef Giuseppe Vannucci offers "lovely fresh seafood" at this smart outfit in the "interesting location" of an Art Deco bandstand on the pier overlooking Weymouth Bay, but there's also a full menu of classic Italian dishes. With seven years of success behind them, Giuseppe and co-founder Tim Newton opened a second branch in Dorchester last summer. / www.almolo.co.uk; al_molo_weymouth; Thu-Sun, Mon-Wed 9.15 pm; closed Mon-Wed L.

WHALLEY, LANCASHIRE — 5–1B

BREDA MURPHY RESTAURANT — £50 · 343

41 STATION RD   BB7 9RH   01254 823446

"Simplicity" combines with "top quality" at Carlow-born Breda Murphy's deli-restaurant, a popular destination in the Ribble Valley since 2006 for her Anglo-Irish home-style cooking. "At first it feels overly conservative, but every dish is perfectly cooked, often with a small and interesting twist such as thick-cut lime and soy-cured salmon." / www.bredamurphy.co.uk; foodbybredamurphy; closed Mon-Sat & Sun; Cash & all usual cards.

THE THREE FISHES — 333

MITTON RD   BB7 9PQ   01254 826888

"Hurrah! Nigel Haworth has come out of retirement, and he's also brought/bought the original pub of Northcote's former Ribble Valley Inns out of retirement" – which means that this long-time champion of Lancashire gastronomy is at the helm here for the second time in 20 years. He also "seems to have done the impossible: found some good front-of-house staff and trained them well". Most reports eulogise "spot-on meals" that are "so well thought out and good value for the quality" (although one or two dissenters dragged the ratings down.) Top Tip – "a big cheer for Lancashire cheese ice cream… it's fabulous!" / thethreefishes.co.uk; thethreefishesmitton; Wed-Sun 9 pm; closed Mon & Tue; Cash & all usual cards.

WHATCOTE, WARWICKSHIRE — 2–1D

THE ROYAL OAK — £94 · 443

2 UPPER FARM BARN   CV36 5EF
01295 688 100

With its "absolutely top-rate food" and "very attentive service", Solanche & Richard Craven's "friendly" operation on the northern edge of the Cotswolds "never fails to delight". "Richard's cookery is always spot on" and "his love of game always shines through in the dishes he serves up" in the "light, modern-built dining area attached to the ancient pub." Top Menu Tip – "ox tongue and doe steak just melt in the mouth". / www.theroyaloakwhatcote.co.uk; the_royal_oak_whatcote; Thu-Sat 11 pm, Sun 10 pm; closed Thu L, closed Mon & Tue & Wed.

WHITBY, NORTH YORKSHIRE — 8–3D

THE MAGPIE CAFE — £45 · 542

14 PIER RD   YO21 3PU   01947 602058

"The UK home of fish 'n' chips" – no rival inspires greater acclaim (or more reports in our annual diners' poll) than this "old-style café" on the harbour, where "the queues confirm the quality and value for money"; and which has earnt national renown for serving "simply the best fish 'n' chips anywhere!". "Thankfully the fire a while ago hasn't changed the experience" – "very steep steps lead up to the door", the inside is "squashed" and "sometimes very busy" but the payoff is "a varied menu of great seafood", plus all the treasured staples.

HOLM, South Petherton

"Stunning views of Whitby Abbey" too, or "just watch the kids with the seagulls". / www.magpiecafe.co.uk; magpiecafewhitby; Mon-Sun 9 pm; no bookings at lunch.

THE STAR INN THE HARBOUR £68 3|2|2

LANGBORNE ROAD YO21 1YN
01947 821 900

"I love this place!" – "it used to be the tourist information centre until local lad Andrew Pern tastefully converted the harbourside building into a destination restaurant", which "manages to walk the line between modern and traditional" with "wonderful food" including a "generous seafood platter". Pern made his name at The Star at Harome, the famous thatched pub which burnt to the ground in 2021 and rose from the ashes late last year. Amidst solidly good ratings this year, though, there is one recurrent gripe – it's pricey. BREAKING NEWS: In early November 2022 it was announced that the establishment is to close as of November 12 2022. / www.starinntheharbour.co.uk; starinntheharbour; Mon-Sat 9 pm, Sun 6 pm; closed Mon L closed Sun D; Cash & all usual cards.

TRENCHERS £53 4|4|3

NEW QUAY RD YO21 1DH 01947 603212

"Best crab sandwich with chips ever" typifies support for this Whitby fixture, which – though somewhat eclipsed by the renowned Magpie nearby – is, nevertheless, tipped by its fans as "the best chippy in town by far". / www.trenchersrestaurant.co.uk; Mon-Sun 8.30 pm; Cash & all usual cards; may need 7+ to book.

DOCKET NO.33 £90 5|4|3

33 HIGH STREET SY13 1AZ
01948 665553

New York, London, Doha… Whitchurch – that's been the progression for Stuart Collins and wife Frances, who started this slightly unlikely venue five years ago, bringing a level of culinary ambition that was previously unknown to this corner of the Shropshire/Cheshire borders. Helped by a star turn from Stuart on Great British Menu a couple of years ago, it continues to attract some "outstanding all round" reviews for its 9-course tasting menu

(at £85 per person). / docketrestaurant.com; docket_restaurant_whitchurch; Wed-Sat 11 pm; closed Wed-Fri L, closed Mon & Tue & Sun.

ETZIO £38 4|3|4

58 - 60 HIGH STREET SY13 1BB
01948 662248

"If only there were more locals like this" – so say fans of this "lovely" Italian. With a menu ranging from pizza and pasta to more ambitious dishes, "the food's amazing, with lots of menu options for all price brackets", it's "incredibly reasonably priced", plus "there's friendly service from Jo and her team". / www.etzio.co.uk; Tue-Sat midnight; closed Sun & Mon.

THE BEEHIVE £85 5|4|3

WALTHAM RD SL6 3SH 01628822877

"Just superb cooking" from chef-patron Dominic Chapman, whose skills were sharpened working for Rowley Leigh and Heston Blumenthal, lifts this "hidden village pub" overlooking a cricket pitch to a level above the competition – "it's just a shame they don't have beds". Top Tip – "you really should leave room for the signature freshly baked honey madeleines". / www.thebeehivewhitewaltham.com; thebeehivetweet; Tue-Thu 9.30 pm, Fri & Sat 10 pm, Sun 4 pm; closed Sun D, closed Mon; Cash & all usual cards.

THE WHITEBROOK, RESTAURANT WITH ROOMS £144 5|4|3

NP25 4TX 01600 860254

"Noma meets Wales" say fans of Chris & Kirsty Harrod's "lovely" restaurant, "tucked away in a wood in the Wye valley", whose "idiosyncratic tasting menus built around local and locally foraged ingredients" have made it one of Wales's most renowned culinary destinations, founded on its "unique" style of cooking. "The dining tables are well spaced in the attractively decorated interior, making it a cosy and relaxing environment" and there are "stylish bedrooms for an overnight stay". "There is nothing more romantic than sitting on the terrace on a warm day, sipping a sparkling wine and enjoying the solitude." / www.thewhitebrook.co.uk; thewhitebrook; Fri-Sun, Thu 8.30 pm; closed Thu L, closed Mon & Tue & Wed; children: 12+ for D.

HINNIES £46 4|4|3

10 EAST PARADE NE26 1AP
0191 447 0500

"Shabby chic on the seafront in what had become a very run-down area", this seafood café is "bustling, with good reason": "confident cooking including local ingredients and featuring some slightly gussied up traditional dishes". "Superb, and good value for money." / www.hinnies.co.uk; hinniesrestaurant; Tue-Fri 9 pm, Sat 9.30 pm, Sun 4 pm; closed Sun D, closed Mon.

JOJO'S £51 3|4|2

2 HERNE BAY RD CT5 2LQ
01227 274591

"Nothing changes here, but in a good way" at this "relaxed and relaxing" out-of-town spot with "wonderful views out to the sea", serving "lovely fresh fish and great tapas dishes" – "who could ask for more?". A 2021 crowdfunder to buy the freehold attracted support from a foodie A-list including chef Tom Kerridge, writers Nigella Lawson and Jay Rayner, and Madness frontman Suggs. / www.jojosrestaurant.co.uk; Thu-Sat, Wed 10.30 pm, Sun 5 pm; closed Wed L closed Sun D, closed Mon & Tue; Cash & all usual cards.

THE LOBSTER SHACK RESTAURANT £28 4|3|3

EAST QUAY CT5 1AB 01227 771923

"Amazingly priced lobsters" and other "beautifully cooked fresh seafood" are consumed in a "perfect setting" at this shack at the far end of the harbour, operated by the Whitstable Oyster Company, which farms oysters and catches native lobsters in season from its own boats in the waters in front of you. There's an "amazing atmosphere" – and a wood-burning stove for meals inside during colder months. / thelobstershack.co.uk; thelobstershackwhitstable; Mon-Sun 9 pm.

PEARSON'S ARMS £74 3|2|4

THE HORSEBRIDGE, SEA WALL CT5 1BT
01227 773133

The dining room "upstairs in a rickety old pub, with wonderful views over Whitstable Bay", offers a "good mix of innovative food" – including "beautifully cooked fish" – "and homemade pub classics, served by staff from the kitchen on the floor below". "Eaten there many times: the ambience is excellent and always found the food good". / www.pearsonsarmsbyrichardphillips.co.uk; pearsonsarms; Tue-Thu 9 pm, Fri & Sat 9.30 pm, Mon 2.30 pm, Sun 5.30 pm; closed Sun & Mon D; Cash & all usual cards.

SAMPHIRE £64 4|4|3

4 HIGH STREET CT5 1BQ 01227 770075

"Utterly delicious cooking, including the freshest fish and seafood" and other "interesting dishes from locally sourced products", plus a "friendly owner and staff" help ensure that this family-run indie is "always very busy". / www.samphirewhitstable.co.uk; samphire_whitstable; Sun-Thu 9.30 pm, Fri & Sat 10 pm; No Amex.

WHEELERS OYSTER BAR £59 3|3|3

8 HIGH STREET CT5 1BQ 01227 273311

"The best crab cakes in the UK and other great fresh seafood" – including oysters, obvs – win nothing but affection and acclaim for this "splendid" ancient venue (est. 1856): "a tiny back parlour that only seats 14-16". "There's no wine licence, but you can BYO", which "makes it a very-good-value experience". But despite consistently good feedback in recent times, the full-on raves of yesteryear were absent and a number of long-term fans now rate it as good rather than exceptional. Some regulars also suggest you "stick to the basic dishes: it doesn't work as well when they go more complicated or ambitious". / www.wheelersoysterbar.com; wheelersob; Mon & Tue, Thu, Sun 5 pm, Fri & Sat 8 pm; closed Mon & Tue, Thu, Sun D, closed Wed; Cash only.

WHITSTABLE OYSTER FISHERY CO. £70 323

ROYAL NATIVE OYSTER STORES, HORSEBRIDGE CT5 1BU 01227 276856

"Fresh seafood as it should be" (most notably "marvellous native oysters") served in a "fantastic location on the beach at Whitstable" make this "lively and atmospheric" venue "worth the slightly higher prices". "It's not inventive cooking", but it doesn't need to be. / www.whitstableoystercompany.com; whitstableoystercompany; Mon-Sat 9 pm, Sun 4 pm; closed Sun D; Cash & all usual cards.

WILLIAN, HERTFORDSHIRE	3–2B

THE FOX £61 322

SG6 2AE 01462 480233

This village pub-with-rooms just off the A1 offers "attractively presented food" on a menu which is "a cut above standard gastropub fare" – best enjoyed in the "new outside dining area, which in summer evokes a lovely Mediterranean feel". / www.foxatwillian.co.uk; foxatwillian; Mon-Sat 9 pm, Sun 4 pm; Cash & all usual cards.

WINCHCOMBE, GLOUCESTERSHIRE	2–1C

5 NORTH STREET £67 422

5 NORTH ST GL54 5LH 01242 604566

Chef-patron Gus Ashenford and his wife Kate this year celebrate the 20th anniversary of their "small restaurant – a bow-windowed former tea room – in a pretty little Cotswolds town", where they treat guests to consistently "amazing food", "full of flavour and providing excellent value". Gus trained under the late Michel Roux at the Waterside Inn, and his cuisine is underpinned by classical French techniques. / www.5northstreetrestaurant.co.uk; Wed-Sat, Tue 9 pm, Sun 1.30 pm; closed Tue L closed Sun D, closed Mon; No Amex.

WINCHESTER, HAMPSHIRE	2–3D

BANGKOK BISTRO 334

33 JEWRY ST SO23 8RY 01962 841811

With its "superb collection of regional Thai specials", this two-year-old venture is "a real find": it has "excellent service and fantastic set menus" (and a meat-free diner said "well done for having such a wide vegan menu, as Thai food is notorious for shrimp paste, fish sauce and oyster sauce in base preparations").

/ www.bangkok-bistro.co.uk; Wed & Thu, Mon & Tue, Sun 11 pm, Fri & Sat 11.30 pm; Cash & all usual cards; no bookings.

THE CHESIL RECTORY £69 334

1 CHESIL ST SO23 0HU 01962 851555

"Fabulous food in a wonderful setting" sums up the appeal of this "historic fifteenth-century building", five minutes' walk from the city centre. "There's an air of restrained cosy elegance about it", while "the food, too, is the epitome of good taste". The restaurant itself is pretty historic, having been open for more than 75 years; the current owners took over in 2008. / www.chesilrectory.co.uk; chesil_rectory; Wed & Thu 9 pm, Fri & Sat 9.30 pm, Sun 8.30 pm; closed Mon & Tue; Cash & all usual cards; children: 12+ at D.

GANDHI RESTAURANT £44 343

163-164 HIGH ST SO23 9BA 01962863940

A city fixture of 35 years' standing just a few minutes' walk from the cathedral, this well-run curry house enjoys high ratings across the board and has an "interesting menu with lots of unusual specialities, including particularly good fish and vegetable dishes". / www.gandhirestaurant.com; Wed & Thu, Sun, Tue 10.30 pm, Fri & Sat 11 pm; closed Tue L, closed Mon; Cash & all usual cards.

THE IVY WINCHESTER BRASSERIE £77 223

103-104 HIGH STREET SO23 9AH 01962 790700

"Busy and buzzing", this well commented-on branch of The Ivy's spin-off group takes full advantage of its High Street address. But "standards are getting too much like a chain outlet": "the food's fine, but doesn't justify its cost". / theivywinchester.com; theivywinchester; Sun-Thu midnight, Fri & Sat 12.30 am.

KYOTO KITCHEN £47 444

70 PARCHMENT STREET SO23 8AT 01962 890895

"The best restaurant in Winchester!" is our diners' poll's verdict on Miff Kayum's Japanese destination, which he opened in 2012 – "a lovely, friendly little place with fantastic sushi" and other "authentic Japanese cuisine, perfectly cooked and presented". "Excellent staff make it a real dining experience". Top Menu Tip – the 'Winchester Roll' – claiming to be the world's first sushi roll to use wasabi leaf instead of seaweed. / www.kyotokitchen.co.uk; kyotokitchen; Mon-Sun 9.45 pm; closed Mon L; Cash & all usual cards.

RICK STEIN £63 332

7 HIGH STREET SO23 9JX 01962 353535

Of Stein's national stable, this buzzy destination is the most-mentioned branch after the Padstow original and London spin-off. It scored slightly

less highly this year: although the general tenor of reports was of "well-cooked and presented" cuisine, there were also one or two more mixed experiences ("clunkier saucing than I remember"). Major disappointments are few, though, and the general theme is that "even if it can be a bit hit-and-miss, generally its fish is of good quality". / www.rickstein.com/book; steinwinchester; Mon-Fri 10 pm, Sat & Sun 9 pm; Cash & all usual cards.

SHOAL £34 333

GUILDHALL, THE BROADWAY, SO23 9GH 01962 861919

This "upmarket" fish 'n' chip venue makes a "very welcome addition to the Winchester restaurant scene" with "homemade sauces and comfortable seating right in the middle of town" – "on the ground floor of the Guildhall". "The fish, chips and scampi are delicious, really juicy and fresh, the chips beautifully crisp", and "there are pies, chicken and options for vegetarians too". Top Tip – "they'll take the skin off the haddock if you ask – very civilised!" / www.shoal.uk.net; shoalwinchester; Tue-Sat 8.30 pm, Sun 3.30 pm; closed Sun D, closed Mon.

WINDERMERE, CUMBRIA	7–3D

GILPIN SPICE, GILPIN LODGE £66 444

CROOK ROAD LA23 3NE 01539 488818

"Absolutely superb" "Asian-inspired dishes to savour" are enjoyed by all at this "relaxed and welcoming" venue from highly rated chef Hrishikesh Desai – his number two restaurant at the Gilpin Lodge. Some reporters quietly admit that they "actually preferred the food here to Hrishi" – supposedly his number one. / www.thegilpin.co.uk; gilpinhotel; Mon-Thu, Sat & Sun 9.30 pm, Fri 9 pm.

HENROCK £83 343

LINTHWAITE HOUSE, CROOK ROAD LA23 3JA 015394 88600

This more relaxed offshoot from maestro Simon Rogan of L'Enclume makes the most of a "delightful setting" at this Lakeland hotel dining room, with views over the outcrop that inspired its name. "A beautiful sunny evening sitting on a lovely terrace overlooking Windermere is followed up with a special meal." When it comes to the cuisine itself, though – which is in a slightly less ambitious mould than his most famous ventures – there's a slight divergence of opinion. For the majority, "the flavours are distinct and exciting, making this a memorable meal as one would expect of a Rogan restaurant". Others, though, caveat their reports as "disappointing" or "overpriced": "I know they say that less is more, but you also need to consider how much is enough!" / www.henrock.co.uk; henrocksimonrogan; Sat-Mon, Thu & Fri 9 pm; closed Thu & Fri L, closed Tue & Wed.

HOOKED £61 3|3|2

ELLERTHWAITE SQUARE LA23 1DP
015394 48443

This "tiny restaurant in Windermere
specialises in expertly cooked fish and
seafood". Established in 2010, it changed
hands three years ago and now shares
ownership with Bowness-on-Windermere's
Urban Food House. On the debit side, it
can be "a bit lacking in atmosphere" (one
reporter discerned a "retail shop feel") and
a couple of reports diagnose service issues
relating to "post-Brexit and pandemic staff
shortages". / www.hookedwindermere.co.uk;
Hookedwindermere; Mon-Sun 9 pm; closed Mon-
Thu L; Cash & all usual cards; booking max 6 may
apply.

HRISHI, GILPIN
LODGE £93 4|4|3

CROOK RD LA23 3NE
01539 488818

"A total wow all round" – "every time we visit,
chef Hrishikesh Desai delights with classic
cooking, delicately and cleverly spiced". The
more refined of his two restaurants at the
Cunliffe family's luxury hotel, "Hrishi is simply
perfection in every way", with its "innovative"
Asian-inflected modern British cuisine
adding spice to the "unimprovable" Lakeland
surroundings. / www.thegilpin.co.uk; gilpinhotel;
Mon-Sun 9 pm; closed Mon-Sun L; Cash & all
usual cards; No jeans; children: 7+.

THE SAMLING £150 4|4|5

AMBLESIDE ROAD LA23 1LR
01539 431922

Set in 27 acres, this country house hotel is one
of the better-known luxury destinations in the
Lakes and boasts a dining room whose floor-to-
ceiling windows provide magnificent views of
Windermere and the surrounding peaks, where
chef Robby Jenks presides over the kitchen.
It inspired very upbeat (but relatively little)
feedback again this year, with nominations as
an ideal romantic choice or for its impressive
afternoon teas. For a full meal in the dining
room, lunch is a four-course affair for £60 per
person, and in the evening the sole option is a
seven-course tasting menu at £115 per person.
/ www.thesamlinghotel.co.uk; thesamling; Mon-
Sun midnight; Cash & all usual cards; children:
eight years old.

WINDSOR, BERKSHIRE 3-3A

AL FASSIA £50 3|4|3

27 ST LEONARDS RD SL4 3BP
01753 855370

"Unexpected" it may be, but this restaurant has
provided the "royal town" with "very delicious
Moroccan food" – including "excellent filo
pastries with chicken and almonds, and
generous, authentic tagines" – for a quarter
of a century. Founder Mustapha Chab based
it on an original Al Fassia in Marrakech,
opened by his brother who had been a
director at the city's famed Mamounia hotel.
/ www.alfassiarestaurant.com; alfassiarestaurant;

Mon-Fri 10 pm, Sat 10.30 pm, Sun 9 pm; closed
Mon-Fri L; Cash & all usual cards.

THE GREENE OAK £46 3|4|3

DEADWORTH RD, OAKLEY GRN SL4 5UW
01753 864294

This "super gastropub" with an "imaginative
menu, sound cooking and very reasonable
prices" is a "notably better choice than the
more expensive pub-restaurants around
Windsor". It "feels like it's family-run", with
"excellent service with a smile" – although in
fact it was the first launch from former Ivy Club
head chef Jamie Dobbin and James Lyon-Shaw,
whose Brucan Pubs operation now has four
gastroboozers and aims to open another six in
the next five years. / www.thegreeneoak.co.uk;
thegreeneoak; Sun-Fri & Sat 11 pm; Cash & all
usual cards.

WINGHAM, KENT 3-3D

THE DOG AT
WINGHAM £77 3|3|3

CANTERBURY ROAD CT3 1BB
01227 720339

In a village just outside Canterbury, this "cheery
pub" is well supported by fans, who come
from postcodes across the South East; it wins
consistent praise for its "beautifully presented"
and delicious food ("perfect venison and the
blackberry soufflé was worth returning for!)" /
www.thedog.co.uk; dogwingham; Mon-Sat 9 pm,
Sun 6 pm; closed Sun D.

WINNALL, HAMPSHIRE 2-3D

GURKHA'S INN £25 3|3|2

17 CITY ROAD SO23 8SD 01962 842843

"A busy, excellent Indian restaurant worth
trying for both eat in and takeaway". It's a
plain and simple operation in Winnall on the
fringes of the town, where the inclusion of
Nepalese dishes adds interest to the menu. /
www.gurkhasinnwinchester.com; Mon-Sat 11 pm,
Sun 10 pm.

WINTERINGHAM, LINCOLNSHIRE 5-1D

WINTERINGHAM
FIELDS £155 4|4|3

1 SILVER ST DN15 9ND 01724 733096

"A little off the tracks but worth a visit" – this
converted sixteenth-century manor house near
the southern banks of the Humber has long
been a beacon in something of a gastronomic
wasteland (and boasts Lincolnshire's only
Michelin star). Its recherché location and
plush rooms lead many diners to plan dinner
as part of a "very relaxing" overnight stay
and a Manchester-based fan feels "the whole
experience is worth the journey from anywhere
in the UK" ("from arriving to leaving the whole
visit is unforgettable"). "There's an excellent
8-course tasting menu" and the "food, quality
of local produce, presentation and service are
fabulous". "Good wine flight selection too." /
www.winteringhamfields.co.uk; winteringham_
fields; Wed-Sat 9 pm; closed Mon & Tue & Sun;
Cash & all usual cards; No trainers.

WISLEY, SURREY 3-3A

THE TERRACE 3|3|4

RHS GARDEN WISLEY, WISLEY LANE
GU23 6QB 01483 668015

This "lovely, airy, half-conservatory-style
restaurant" makes "a nice treat when you
visit the RHS Garden". The "sensibly short
menu" is (as you might hope) "good on food
origins, and uses Wisley fruit and veg when
possible". It's also "good value" and – "even
on days when there's a long queue to get
into the gardens – calm and organised". /
www.rhs.org.uk/gardens/wisley/
Food-Drink/terrace-restaurant; The_RHS; Mon-
Sun 4.30 pm.

WISWELL, LANCASHIRE 5-1B

FREEMASONS AT
WISWELL £99 4|3|4

8 VICARAGE FOLD CLITHEROE BB7 9DF
01254 822218

"Set in a quaint Ribble Valley village", Steve
Smith's "delightful and traditional" destination
"provides a slice of country refinement in a real,
classic country pub" and holds its own against
much of the stiff culinary competition in the
area. His cuisine "continues to provide unusual
combinations of exceptionally prepared
dishes", crafted from "unfailingly good quality
ingredients". You can stay, too, which fans say
is "amazing" ("the breakfast is something else!")
/ freemasonsatwiswell.co.uk; freemasonsatwiswell;
Wed & Thu 8 pm, Fri & Sat 8.30 pm, Sun 5 pm;
closed Sun D, closed Mon & Tue; Cash & all usual
cards; booking max 6 may apply.

WITNEY, OXFORDSHIRE 2-1D

THE EDGE EATERY £14 3|4|3

62A HIGH STREET OX28 6HJ
07983 930662

"Very San Francisco vibes here... and
that's meant as a compliment!" – this
funky haunt has become "very popular",
especially for brunch. Top Tip – the "best
seats are in the corner at the back!" /
www.order.storekit.com/the-edge-eatery-lttd/menu;
Mon-Sun 3 pm; closed Mon-Sun D.

WIVETON, NORFOLK 6-3C

WIVETON BELL £60 3|3|3

BLAKENEY RD NR25 7TL 01263 740 101

This "very welcoming pub" is the most
commented-on of those on the north
Norfolk coast (perhaps due to its recent 'Bib
Gourmand') and though not super-foodie
"serves hearty meals and enjoys a buzzy
atmosphere". "The ingredients are selected
from local suppliers, cooked with skill, and
served by a young, efficient and enthusiastic
team." In June 2022, it was acquired by East
Anglian pub and restaurant company The
Chestnut Group. / www.wivetonbell.co.uk;
Mon-Sat 8 pm, Sun 7.30 pm; No Amex; booking
evening only.

Paris House, Woburn

PARIS HOUSE £114 5 4 5

WOBURN PARK MK17 9QP
01525 290692

"An incredible location, with a fabulous driveway through herds of deer" helps set an impressive tone at this striking mock-Tudor, timber building (originally built in France in 1878), which sits in the grounds of Woburn Abbey. It's long been known as a foodie destination, and on current form, reports acclaim "perfection in food and setting" with "slick service and food that's to die for". "Why that one Michelin star is so elusive to regain is a mystery. (We have been eating at Paris House since it very first opened in 1983! After the happy days of Peter Chandler it went through a difficult phase. But Phil Fanning the chef stayed with it and eventually acquired the business. He hasn't looked back. It remains a favourite and the food and wine are superb)". / www.parishouse.co.uk; parishousechef; Thu-Sat 8.30 pm, Sun 2 pm; closed Sun D, closed Mon & Tue & Wed; No Amex; No trainers.

THE COD'S SCALLOPS £41 5 3 2

170 BRAMCOTE LN NG8 2QP
0115 985 4107

John Molnar's "great fish restaurant and take-away in the hinterlands of Nottingham" wins our highest rating for "excellent quality food" – 20 varieties of fresh seafood, "all beautifully cooked before your eyes": it's "easy to see why it's won so many awards". And there's "more to it than just fish 'n' chips": Sat Bains, the maestro behind the city's world-famous fine-dining restaurant, has chipped in (with his mum) with recipes for a vegan samosa, chickpea curry and tamarind chutney that all appear on the menu under the 'Momma Bains' label. Launched in 2011, there are now four branches in the city and two more in Market Harborough and Birmingham. / www.codsscallops.com; Mon-Thu 9 pm, Fri & Sat 9.30 pm; closed Sun; No Amex; no bookings.

BILASH £64 4 4 3

2 CHEAPSIDE WV1 1TU 01902 427762

Often hailed as the "best curry house in Wolves", Sitab Khan's "special treat" destination has been "taking curries to the next level" for 41 years. "It's not cheap but then the best never is!" / www.thebilash.co.uk; the.bilash; Mon-Sun 9.30 pm; Cash & all usual cards.

MANJIT'S KITCHEN 3 3 3

333 KIRKSTALL ROAD LS2 7HY
07941 183132

Manjit's "fantastic and ever-reliable" Indian vegetarian street food – found at Kirkgate Market and the more recent restaurant on Kirkstall Road – "will always leave you wanting to come back for more". Unlike many veggie places, they keep things interesting with a "frequently changing menu, and collaboration brews too". / www.manjitskitchen.com; manjitskitchenuk; closed Mon-Sat & Sun.

ANDALUCIA £44 3 3 3

60 FERRING STREET BN12 5JP
01903 502605

"A gem in sleepy old Ferring", serving "great, good-value tapas" in a "delightfully unrushed" atmosphere – this "lovely" spot was founded in 1986 by Granada-born Manuel Quirosa and his wife Sue. They retired five years ago, passing the business on to sons Luis, the head chef, and Miguel, whose "much-needed revamp has turned it into a trendy local restaurant". / www.andaluciasussex.co.uk; andaluciasussex; Tue-Sat 11 pm, Sun 7.30 pm; closed Mon.

BAYSIDE SOCIAL £31 4 3 5

1 BEACH PARADE BN11 2FG
01903 867050

"Set within feet of the sea and feeling like Barcelona or Valencia on a sunny day" – MasterChef winner Kenny Tutt's "perfectly situated" beachside yearling (opened in September 2021) boasts "floor-to-ceiling glass walls" to capitalise on its 180-degree views of the Worthing coastline. Often tipped for breakfast, it serves all day and there's "a great

selection of food options" – small plates that are "all excellently cooked and presented". Jay Rayner raved on a January 2022 visit, comparing it to Kenny's first venture (Pitch, see also): "the confident, relaxed second child of a team that now knows what it's doing… God is in the detail and the detail has been fully attended to". / www.baysidesocial.co.uk; baysidesocial; Sun-Thu 10 pm, Fri & Sat 11 pm.

CRABSHACK £50 4 4 3

2 MARINE PARADE BN11 3PN
01903 215070

"Worthing's finest!" – this "funky, classy", family-run spot on the seafront excels for its "fresh seafood treated with care"; there's a "short menu that delivers on all fronts", "friendly service" and an "exceptional evening ambience". Top Tip – "best crab sandwiches around". / www.crabshackworthing.co.uk; crabshack_worthing; Tue, Wed, Sun 6 pm, Thu-Sat 10 pm; closed Tue, Wed, Sun D, closed Mon.

PITCH £64 3 3 2

16 WARWICK STREET BN11 3DF

MasterChef winner Kenny Tutt's first restaurant, in his hometown, "does not disappoint", with some "exceptional and excellent dishes" – "it's great to have a top-class place on the South Coast!". Top Tip – "the goat's cheese and honey doughnuts starter". / www.pitchrestaurant.co.uk; pitchrestaurant; Mon-Sun 9 pm.

THE ETHICUREAN £170 4 3 4

BARLEY WOOD WALLED GARDEN, LONG LANE BS40 5SA 01934 863713

"Kind of a romantic and fantastic Scandi-Bristolian take on dining!" – "You'd have to go a long way to replicate this really original experience", where you eat in the "special location of a marvellous Victorian walled garden with lovely views (of the Mendips)". There's a "very individual" menu prepared by head chef Mark McCabe with 14 courses for £150 per person: "just superbly executed, if expensive". / www.theethicurean.com; theethicurean; Wed-Sat 7.30 pm, Sun 3.30 pm; closed Wed-Fri L closed Sun D, closed Mon & Tue; payment – credit card only; booking is online only.

BILLY WINTERS BAR & DINER, CRAB HOUSE LTD 3 3 3

FERRY BRIDGE BOATYARD, PORTLAND ROAD, DT4 9JZ 01305 774954

"A lovely sunset evening and fish 'n' chips" – what could be better? This "great value" beach shack and café (named for the locally caught prawns) overlooking the bay is just the job for its "great value" fodder. As well as seafood staples, they serve a good variety of pizzas and burgers. / billywinters.co.uk; billywintersweymouth; Wed & Thu, Sun 7 pm, Fri & Sat 8 pm; closed Mon & Tue; no bookings.

WYTHAM, OXFORDSHIRE 2–2D

THE WHITE HART £57

OX2 8QA   01865 244372

"A foodie gem", this well-known eighteenth-century pub in a village on the outskirts of Oxford has been going through a period of flux, hence we've removed a rating for the time being. High-profile chef Jon Parry joined in summer 2022, after our annual diners' poll had concluded, having made a name for himself cooking over an open fire at The Mash Inn in Buckinghamshire, and declared his ambition to 'turn The White Hart into something really special'. Four months later, owner Baz Butcher announced his intention to sell up and retire to France. / whitehartwytham.com; Wed & Thu 8.30 pm, Fri & Sat 9 pm, Sun 4 pm; closed Sun D, closed Mon & Tue; No Amex.

YARMOUTH, ISLE OF WIGHT 2–4D

THE GEORGE HOTEL £72 334

QUAY STREET   PO41 0PE   01983 760331

A "glorious summer lunch spot" – "if the sun is shining you could be in the South of France drinking rosé and eating lovely – if somewhat pricey – seafood to the soundtrack of Dmitri from Paris". The seventeenth-century hotel is run by Prince Harry's pal Howard Spooner, who last year won a High Court battle against his former business partner Sally Johnson, following the pair's failed attempt to turn The George into a celebrity retreat for A-listers, including old rockers, yachtsmen, polo players and wealthy Americans. / www.thegeorge.co.uk; thegeorgehotelisleofwight; Mon-Sat 9 pm, Sun 5 pm; closed Sun D; Cash & all usual cards.

THE TERRACE £71 234

QUAY STREET   PO41 0NT   01983 303013

This "fab" harbourside wine bar-bistro "with gorgeous views across the Solent" has three glass shelters on its eponymous terrace, so you can eat outside in all seasons. The menu highlight is steaks from retired dairy cows from the island's Briddlesford Farm, hung for 40 days and cooked to medium for the 'tangy, rich and yellow fat to melt nicely'. / www.theterraceiow.co.uk; the_terrace_yarmouth; Mon-Sun 11 pm; payment – credit card only.

YORK, NORTH YORKSHIRE 5–1D

AMBIENTE £29 333

31 FOSSGATE   YO1 9TA   01904 638 252

A "popular and enjoyable" tapas bar with "helpful staff" and "great Spanish food" (including "very good paella") which has spin-off branches in York, Leeds and Hull. "What makes it special is the choice of sherries, with several tasting flights offered". / www.ambiente-tapas.co.uk; ambientetapas; Mon-Sun 10 pm.

ARRAS £80 443

THE OLD COACH HOUSE, PEASHOLME GREEN   YO1 7PW   01904 633 737

"So many things to like…" This "attentive small restaurant" is the work of Adam & Lovaine Humphrey, who cut their teeth 'down under' and moved to York after 17 years of running restaurants in Oz. Here, "there's a total of only 18-20 covers, so they have to make each person's experience a good one". "The interior is bright, stylish and elegant without being OTT… The same can be said of the staff, plus friendly and efficient". Foodwise, the culinary style is "interesting and appealing, without being too far out" delivering "a first-class meal at a reasonable price". "You must leave room for the cheese trolley, personally presented by the chef". Top Menu Tips – "Superb bread… outstanding rhubarb with the pigeon starter… beautiful venison". / www.arrasrestaurant.co.uk; arras_york; Wed-Sat 9.30 pm; closed Mon & Tue & Sun.

BETTYS £42 344

6-8 ST HELEN'S SQUARE   YO1 8QP   01904 659142

"An institution for a very good reason, so be prepared to queue" – this "absolute classic" tea shop is a "must-visit" that "always delivers great quality". The original Bettys was opened in Harrogate in 1919 by Swiss confectioner Frederick Belmont – an era that the group still embodies, and a nationality commemorated in the "really good rösti" still served. The brand has become thoroughly naturalised in Yorkshire over the ensuing century, and York is now its biggest branch – whose only fault is "that it's always crowded". / www.bettys.co.uk/tea-rooms/locations/york; bettys1919; Sun-Thu 5.30 pm, Fri 6 pm, Sat 7 pm; closed Sun-Thu & Fri D; No Amex; booking lunch only.

THE BLUE BARBAKAN £53 343

34 FOSSGATE   YO1 9TA   01904 672 474

This "cosy, traditionally decorated Polish restaurant in Fossgate" with "very friendly and helpful staff" serves "excellent, heart-warming Polish food" – pierogi dumplings, bigos stew and more – alongside a few excursions into east and western Europe and a classic range of proper breakfast dishes. / www.bluebarbakan.co.uk; bluebarbakanyork; Tue-Sat 10 pm, Sun & Mon 9 pm.

THE BOW ROOM RESTAURANT, GRAYS COURT £101 444

GRAYS COURT HOTEL, CHAPTER HOUSE STREET   YO1 7JH   01904 612613

"Quietly top class" – York's oldest inhabited house (and boasting a medieval walled garden) is the backdrop to a meal at this small hotel, some of whose rooms have unmatched views of York Minster. The dining room (holder of hard-to-win three AA rosettes) is looked after by chef Adam Jackson, and his tasting menus with matching wine flights offer "a very pleasant experience with some great flavours". / www.grayscourtyork.com/the-bow-room-restaurant-york; grayscourtyork; Wed & Thu 10.30 pm, Fri & Sat 11.30 pm; closed Mon & Tue, Sun D; credit card deposit required to book; children: 10.

CAVE DU COCHON £33 443

19 WALMGATE   YO1 9TX   01904 633669

One of the North's better wine bars – this small venue hosts an "amazing selection of wines," backed up by a "short menu full of really good ingredients and tasty non-standard pizzas". It's a spin-off from Le Cochon Aveugle just up the street, whose closure announced last year came at the height of its renown and came as a shock to many. Owner Josh Overington said the Cave would carry on as usual. / www.caveducochon.uk; cave_du_cochon; Wed-Sun 11 pm; closed Wed-Fri L, closed Mon & Tue.

FISH AND FOREST £67 443

110 MICKLEGATE   YO1 6JX   01904 220587

"An outstanding neighbourhood bistro that strives to produce and make sustainable food fresh from local produce, game shoots and day boats" – Stephen Andrews (supported by manager Yohan Barthelemy) delivers a "menu that's small but perfect" in this inviting industrial-style space, complete with lots of concrete and wood. He took on these premises in April 2020, after a succession of pop-ups in other venues. Top Menu Tip – "incredibly fresh fish, well executed". / www.fishandforestrestaurant.com; fishandforest_york; Wed-Sat 11 pm; closed Wed-Fri L, closed Mon & Tue & Sun.

IL PARADISO DEL CIBO £42 343

40 WALMGATE   YO1 9TJ   0190 461 1444

There are "no airs and graces in this homely little Italian" from Sardinian-born Paolo Silesu – just "great food, friendly service and a lively buzz". "If you just woke up here, you'd think you were in the back streets of Naples – it's mad and hectic, but brilliant" – and "totally authentic". / www.ilparadisodelciboyork.com; il_paradiso_del_cibo_in_york; Mon-Sun 10 pm; Cash & all usual cards.

MANNION & CO £49 333

1 BLAKE ST   YO1 8QJ   01904 631030

"A wonderful breakfast with local produce" is to be found at this popular and highly rated deli/café, with a restored Tudor frontage, which the Mannion family first opened as a grocer's over three decades ago. At other times, charcuterie boards and cheese slates come from the deli counter are the order of the day. / www.mannionandco.co.uk; mannionsofyork; Mon, Wed-Sat 5 pm, Sun 4.30 pm; closed Mon, Wed-Sun D, closed Tue; Cash & all usual cards; no bookings.

MELTON'S £83 444

7 SCARCROFT RD   YO23 1ND
01904 634 341

"Truly exceptional food" is often reported at this well-regarded bistro, founded in 1990 and still run by "caring owners" Michael Hjort (director of York Food Festival) and his wife Lucy, who manages the front of house. "No pretension and no distracting gloss" are a big plus for its fans. "There may be places that are considered 'smarter' and 'more fashionable', but none of them hold a candle to Melton's for a first-class meal." / www.meltonsrestaurant.co.uk; Wed-Sat, Tue 9.30 pm; closed Tue L, closed Sun & Mon; Cash & all usual cards.

LOS MOROS £48 433

15-17 GRAPE LANE   YO1 7HU
01904 636834

"North African-inspired deliciousness" wins universal acclaim for the market stall Tarik Abdeladim opened in 2015, and the restaurant that followed three years later in Grape Lane. Much of the produce is sourced from nearby Yorkshire farms, and Brew York has even produced branded Los Moros pale ale and lager to complement the flavours of its food. / www.losmorosyork.co.uk; losmorosyork; Fri & Sat 10 pm, Tue-Thu 9 pm; closed Sun & Mon.

THE PIG & PASTRY £86 444

35 BISHOPTHORPE ROAD   YO23 1NA
01904 675115

"Great home-baked products and scrumptious breakfast/brunch, all at very reasonable prices" have drawn a steady crowd to this neighbourhood café for 15 years. "There should be a place like this in every town, it's wonderful." Top Tip – "the shroomaloumi is a great veggie option". / thepigandpastry.com; thepigandpastry; Mon-Sat 3 am; closed Sun; Cash & all usual cards.

THE RATTLE OWL £93 433

104 MICKLEGATE   YO16 6JX
01904 658 658

"A great find in York with superb food paired expertly with wines for a great dining experience" – this Grade II-listed seventeenth-century building in York's historic centre took two years to renovate when it was opened eight years ago. Chef Tom Heywood provides a four-course and eight-course menu and his cooking is highly rated by reporters. One quibble though – "service is knowledgeable but can be terribly slow". / www.rattleowl.co.uk; therattleowl; Wed-Sat 9.30 pm, Sun 6 pm; closed Mon & Tue; Cash & all usual cards.

ROOTS £164 444

68 MARYGATE   YO30 7BH   NO TEL

"We went the day after having eaten at The Black Swan and all enjoyed this more!" – "Tommy Banks continues to surprise, amaze and delight in equal measure" at his family's converted pub in the city centre, which nowadays is the most talked-about place in town, and one of the most commented-on restaurants nationally in our annual diners' poll. Head chef, Will Lockwood, moved here from The Black Swan in late 2021 and his tasting menus showcase "the Banks ethos of local produce and sustainability". "Each course is a work of art starting with lots of foraged and locally sourced ingredients", all "served impeccably in a relaxed manner by knowledgeable and friendly staff" and "complemented by good wine pairings". "The location even allows a gentle post-prandial stroll along the river bank – assuming York's legendary floods are not present!". The experience is, however, decidedly "not cheap" and as a result even some who rate it as "exceptional" feel it's "a one-visit-only job". / www.rootsyork.com; rootsyork; Wed-Sat 8 pm; closed Wed & Thu L, closed Mon & Tue & Sun; No Amex; booking is online only; children: 10.

SKOSH £62 543

98 MICKLEGATE   YO1 6JX   01904 634849

"It's worth getting one of the counter tables so you can watch the chefs work" at Neil Bentinck's "go-to", small, city-centre destination – one of the top three most commented-on destinations in this decidedly foodie city. "It is a place people rave about and once you have been, you become part of a community where your mind is blown by the flavour combinations that Neil and his team bring together" – "amazing, amazing, amazing!". "You could describe it as British-Japanese fusion" ('Skosh' is Japanese for 'small amount') – "very inventive using local ingredients and exceptional for the price". "It's a convivial place with friendly staff" too ("walking in and sitting down for dinner is almost like being at a friend's house – relax and laugh out loud, like there are no strangers around"). Top Menu Tips – "the 'egg' is divine as a pre-starter and the buttermilk chicken is to die for (but the vegetables are also treated with care and respect to make excellent dishes in their own right)". (In late 2021 an application was put in to expand the restaurant, and Neil hinted in a May 2022 Yorkshire Post article that change is coming some time soon). / skoshyork.co.uk; skoshyork; Wed-Sat 10 pm; closed Mon & Tue & Sun; Cash & all usual cards; credit card deposit required to book.

STAR INN THE CITY £71 223

LENDAL ENGINE HOUSE, MUSEUM STREET   YO1 7DR   01904 619208

Acclaimed Yorkshire chef Andrew Pern's city version of his famous Star Inn at Harome (which he spent last year rebuilding after a disastrous fire) has a "lively atmosphere, excellent food, efficient service and good setting" on the River Ouse, making it "ideal for family celebrations". Its ratings are dragged down by a significant minority of reporters who feel it is "distinctly average in all respects, given the prices charged". / www.starinnthecity.co.uk; thestarinnthecityyork; Mon-Thu 11 pm, Fri & Sat midnight, Sun 10 pm; Cash & all usual cards.

31 CASTLEGATE RESTAURANT £53 333

31 CASTLEGATE   YO1 9RN
01904 621404

"Good value and relaxing" – Nick Julius's well-rated independent bar/restaurant occupies the erstwhile HQ of Georgian architect G.T. Andrews, in the shadow of the Clifford's Tower. "Friendly and helpful" staff deliver a very wide range of competitively priced menu options of a bistro/brasserie nature. / 31castlegate.com; 31castlegate; Sun-Thu 9.30 pm, Fri & Sat 10 pm; practically no walk-ins – you must book.

THE WHIPPET INN £65 333

15 NORTH ST   YO1 6JD   01904 500660

This "owner-operated pub that's now basically a restaurant" is noted for its "great steaks", with cuts sourced from ex-dairy cows in England, Finland and Galicia in Spain that are put out to pasture for two years after retiring – providing ethical beef with a fuller, more developed flavour. "Fantastic wines" complete the deal. / www.thewhippetinn.co.uk; thewhippetinn; Sun-Thu 11 pm, Fri & Sat midnight; credit card deposit required to book; children: 14.

Burnt Orange, Brighton

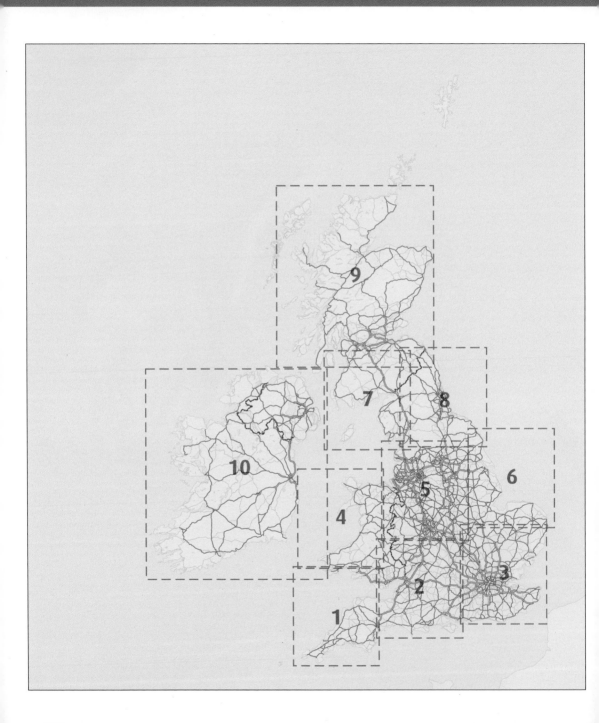

MAP 1

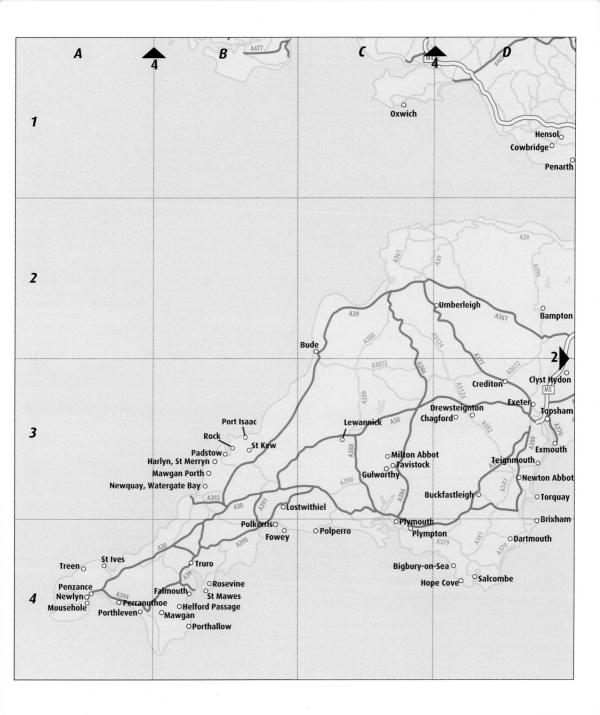

MAP 2

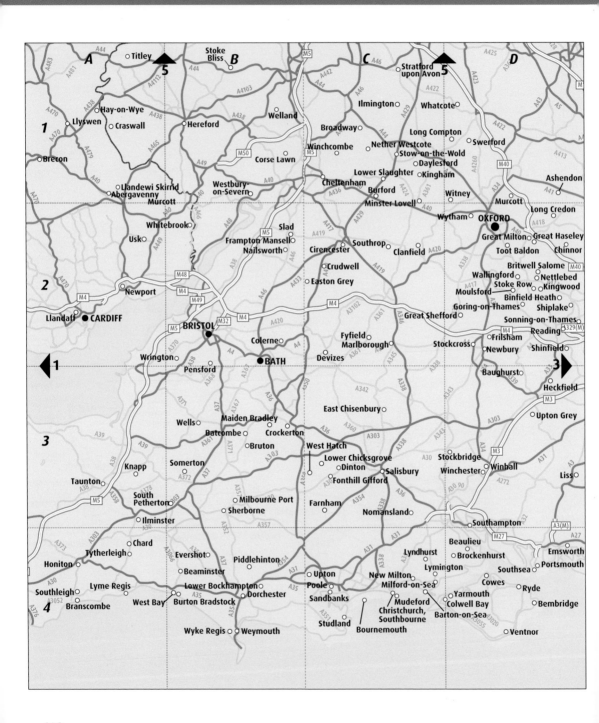

MAP 3

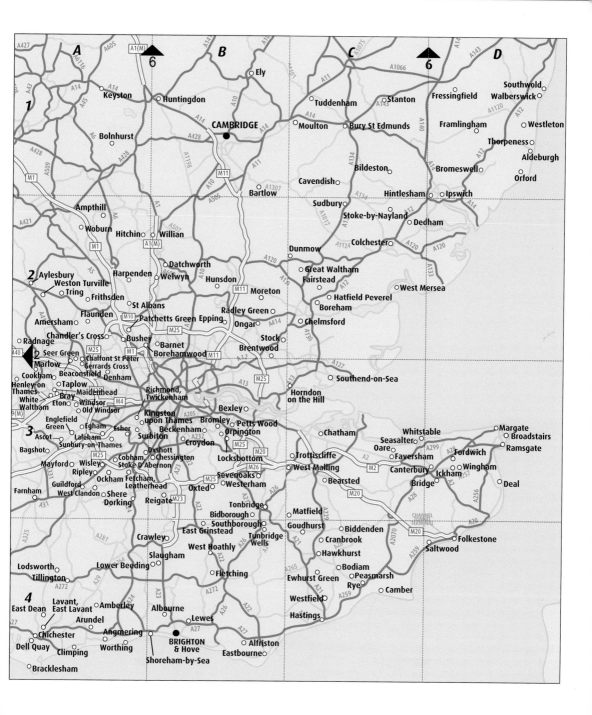

MAP 4

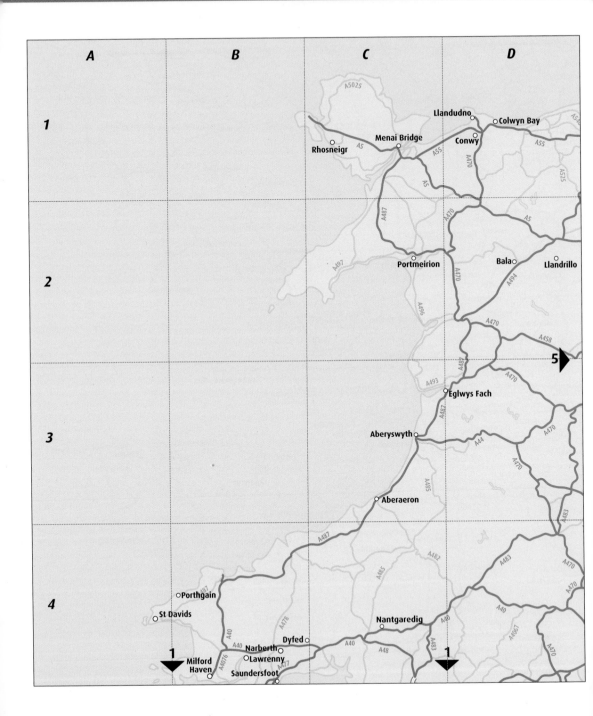

MAP 5

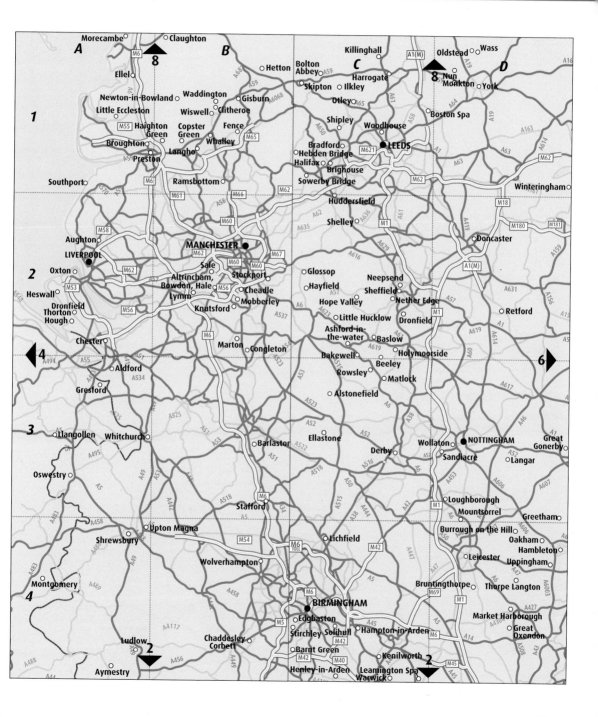

MAP 6

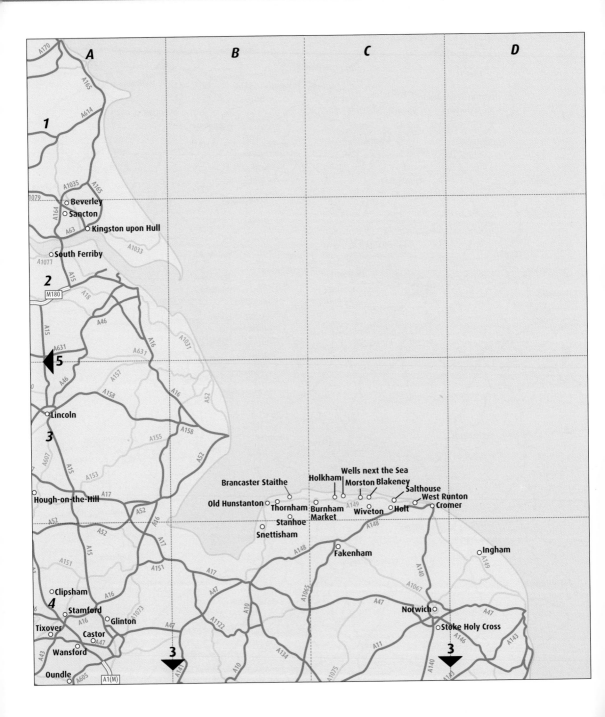

MAP 7

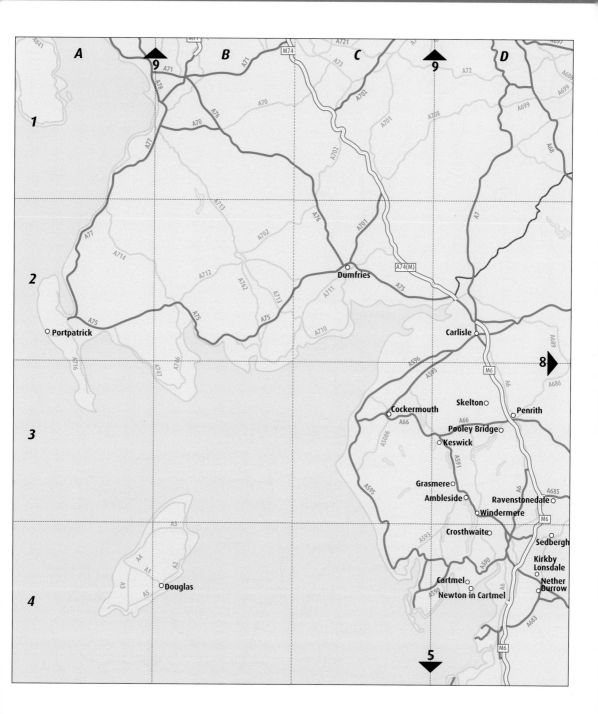

MAP 8

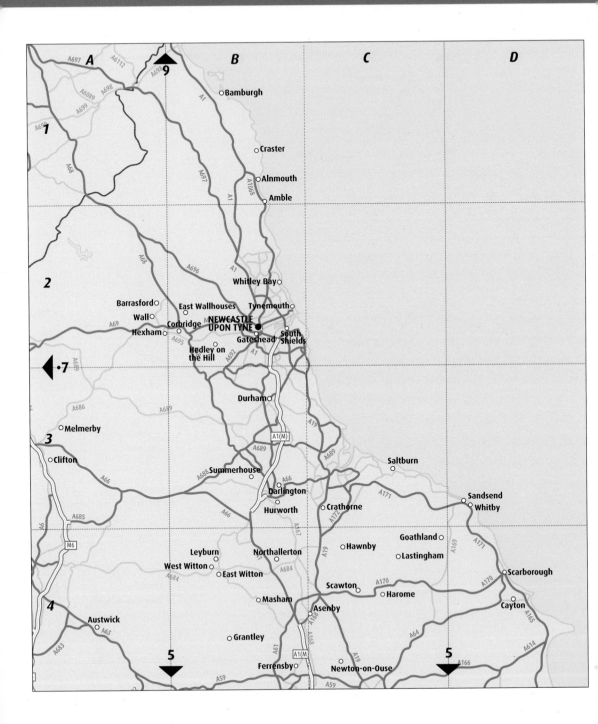

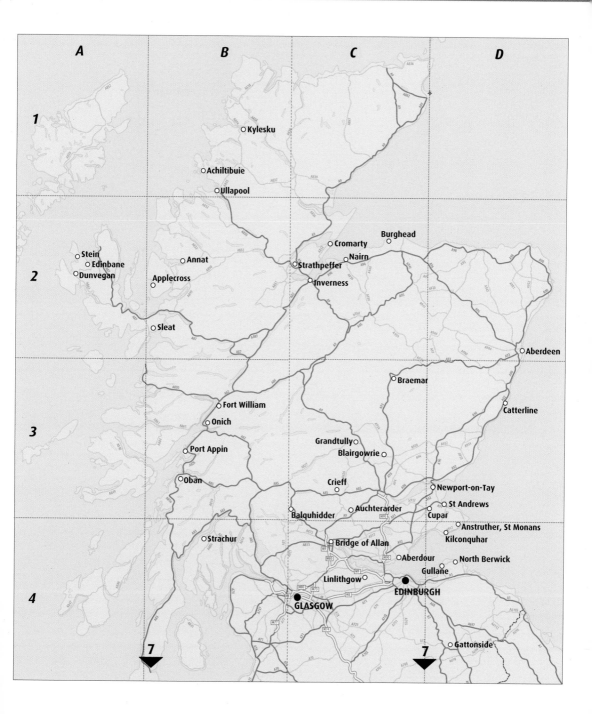

MAP 9

A B C D

1

○ Kylesku

○ Achiltibuie
○ Ullapool

Burghead
○
○ Cromarty
2 ○ Stein ○ Annat ○ Nairn
○ Edinbane ○ Strathpeffer
○ Dunvegan ○ Applecross ○ Inverness

○ Sleat

Aberdeen ○

○ Braemar
○ Fort William
Catterline ○
○ Onich

3 ○ Port Appin Grandtully ○
Blairgowrie ○

○ Oban Crieff ○ Newport-on-Tay ○
○ St Andrews
Balquhidder ○ Auchterarder ○ Cupar ○
○ Strachur ○ Anstruther, St Monans
○ Bridge of Allan Kilconquhar ○

○ Aberdour ○ North Berwick
Linlithgow ○ Gullane ○
GLASGOW ● EDINBURGH ●

4

▼7 ▼7 ○ Gattonside

MAP 10

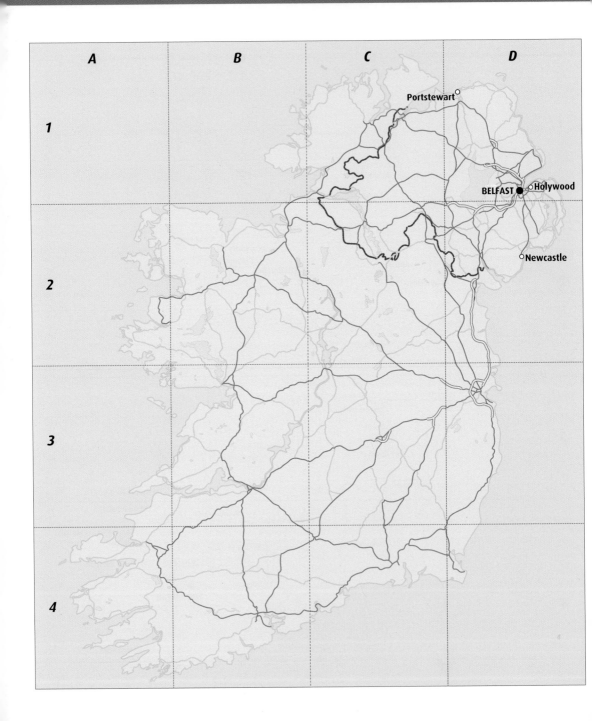

Portstewart

BELFAST ○Holywood

Newcastle

Bocca di Lupo, London

ALPHABETICAL INDEX

ALPHABETICAL INDEX

Mon Plaisir Restaurant
London 96

Monachyle Mhor
Balquhidder 187

Monmouth Coffee
Company London 96

Monte Forte
Reigate 272

Moor Hall Aughton 186

The Moorcock Inn
Sowerby Bridge 280

The Moorings
Blakeney 194

Morito London 96

Moro London 97

Los Moros York 298

Morso London 97

Morston Hall
Morston 258

Mortimers Ludlow 249

Motcombs London 97

Mother India
Glasgow 229

Mother India's Cafe
Edinburgh 222

Moto Pizza
Chelmsford 208

The Mount by Glynn
Purnell Henley in
Arden 237

Mourne Seafood Bar
Belfast 192

Mourne Seafood Bar
Newcastle 261

Mowgli Liverpool 247

Mr Bao London 97

Mr Falafel London 97

Mr Ji London 97

Mr Todiwala's Petiscos
London 97

The Muddlers Club
Belfast 192

Mumtaz Bradford 195

Munal Tandoori
London 97

Murano London 97

Murmur Brighton 198

Muse London 97

Muse Brasserie
Cheltenham 209

The Museum Inn
Farnham 226

MUSU Manchester 253

Myrtle London 98

Nandine London 98

Nanninella Pizzeria
Napoletana
Brighton 198

The Narrow London 98

Nathan Marshall
Prestor House
Liss 245

Native Neepsend 259

Native at Browns
London 98

Naughty Piglets
London 98

Nautilus London 98

The Neptune Old
Hunstanton 265

Ness Walk
Inverness 240

Nessa London 98

NEST London 98

New Chapter
Edinburgh 222

New Yard Restaurant
Mawgan 256

Newens: The Original
Maids of Honour
London 98

The Newport Newport
On Tay 261

Ngon London 98

Nick's on Henderson
Street Bridge of
Allan 196

1921 Angel Hill Bury St
Edmunds 204

The Ninth London
London 98

No 7 Fish Bistro &
Wine Bar Torquay 288

No 97 Surbiton 285

No. 1 Cromer 215

No. Fifty Cheyne
London 98

No.1 Ship Street
Oxford 267

No.Twelve
Nottingham 264

Noble Holywood 238

Noble Rot London 99

Noble Rot Soho
London 99

Nobu London 99

Nobu Portman Square
London 99

Nobu Shoreditch
London 99

Noci London 99

Noi Quattro
Manchester 253

Noisy Lobster
Mudeford 258

Noizé London 99

Nok's Kitchen
Edinburgh 222

NoMad London
London 99

Noon Edinburgh 222

Noor Jahan London 99

Nopi London 99

The Norfolk Arms
London 100

Norma London 100

Normah's London 100

Normans Cafe
London 100

El Norte London 100

North China London 100

North House Cowes 214

North Sea Fish
London 100

The Northall, Corinthia
Hotel London 100

Northcote Langho 243

Northcote Manor
Umberleigh 289

Noto Edinburgh 222

Novikov (Asian
restaurant)
London 100

Noya's Kitchen
Bath 189

Number Eight
Sevenoaks 276

Number One, Balmoral
Hotel Edinburgh 222

Numero Uno
London 100

Nuovi Sapori
London 100

Nusr-Et Steakhouse
London 100

The Nut Tree Inn
Murcott 258

Nutshell London 102

O'ver London 102

Oak 102

Oak Bath 189

The Oarsman
Marlow 256

Obicà Mozzarella
Bar, Pizza e Cucina
London 102

Oblix London 102

Ocean Basket
Bromley 203

Odette's London 102

Odos Barnet 187

Off the Hook
London 102

Ognisko Restaurant
London 102

Oka London 102

Oklava London 102

The Old Bank
Westerham 292

The Old Bank Bistro
Snettisham 278

The Old Boat House
Amble Amble 184

Old Bridge Hotel
Huntingdon 239

The Old Butchers Stow-
on-the-Wold 283

The Old Coastguard
Mousehole 258

Old Downton Lodge
Ludlow 249

Old Fire Engine House
Ely 224

The Old Inn
Drewsteignton 217

The Old Parsonage
Oxford 267

Old Stamp House
Ambleside 184

The Old Stocks Inn
Stow-on-the-Wold 283

The Olive Branch
Clipsham 212

The Olive Tree,
Queensberry Hotel
Bath 189

Oliveto London 102

Olivier at the Red Lion
Britwell Salome 202

Olivo London 102

Olivocarne London 103

Olivomare London 103

The Ollerod
Beaminster 190

Olley's London 103

Olympic Studios
London 103

Olympus Fish
London 103

Ombra London 103

Ondine Edinburgh 222

The One Bull Bury St
Edmunds 204

One Fish Street St
Ives 281

108 Brasserie
London 103

111 by Modou
Glasgow 229

104 Restaurant
London 103

101 Thai Kitchen
London 103

116 at the Athenaeum
London 103

1 Lombard Street
London 103

One One Four
Twickenham 289

123V London 103

Only Food and Courses
London 103

Les 110 de Taillevent
London 104

The Onslow Arms West
Clandon 291

Opera Tavern
London 104

Opheem
Birmingham 193

The Opposition
Stratford upon
Avon 284

Opso London 104

The Orange London 104

Orange Pekoe
London 104

The Orange Tree
London 104

The Orangery, Rockliffe
Hall Darlington 215

Orasay London 104

Orchid Harrogate 235

Orelle Birmingham 194

Oren London 104

Orient London
London 104

Origin Social
Northallerton 262

Ormer Mayfair by
Sofian, Flemings
Mayfair Hotel
London 104

Oro Di Napoli
London 105

Orrery London 105

L'Ortolan Shinfield 277

Orwells Shiplake 277

Oscar Wilde Lounge
at Cafe Royal
London 105

Oscars French Bistro
Leamington Spa 243

Osip Bruton 203

Oslo Court London 105

Osteria, Barbican
Centre London 105

Osteria North
Berwick 262

Osteria Antica Bologna
London 105

Osteria Basilico
London 105

Osteria Tufo
London 105

Otto's London 105

Ottolenghi London 105

Outlaw's Fish Kitchen
Port Isaac 270

Outlaw's New Road
Port Isaac 270

The Owl Leeds 244

The Owl at Hawnby
Hawnby 236

The OWO London 105

Ox Belfast 192

Ox and Finch
Glasgow 229

Ox Barn at Thyme
Southrop 279

Ox Club Leeds 244

Oxeye London 106

Oxheart Long
Compton 248

Oxo Tower, Restaurant
London 106

Oxo Tower, Brasserie
London 106

Oyster Catcher
Rhosneigr 272

The Oyster Club
Birmingham 194

Smokestak, London